# —THE—
# Good
# Guide 1994

O7903446890 - SUMIT.

# —THE—
# *Good Food Guide® 1994*

## Edited by Tom Jaine

Consumers' Association

*Which? Books* are commissioned and researched by
The Association for Consumer Research and published by
Consumers' Association,
2 Marylebone Road, London NW1 4DF

Copyright © 1993 Consumers' Association Ltd

*The Good Food Guide* is a registered trade mark of
Consumers' Association Ltd.

Cover photograph by John Parker
Cover design by Paul Saunders
Typographic design by Tim Higgins
Maps by Bartholomew, a division of
HarperCollins Publishers

**British Library Cataloguing-in-Publication Data**
A catalogue record for this book is available
from the British Library.

ISBN 0-340-59213-3

Photoset in Linotron Meridien Medium
by Tradespools Ltd, Frome, Somerset
Printed and bound in The Netherlands
by Rotatie Boekendruk B.V., Krommenie

# Contents

## *Restaurants*

## A service to keep readers up to date

From December 1993 *The Good Food Guide* will offer a recorded telephone message giving details of restaurant sales, closures, chef changes and so on, since this edition was published. Telephone 071-830 7607 to hear the latest information.

## To all readers

*The Good Food Guide* is your guide. It is independent, takes no free meals, inducements or advertising, and reflects the experience of thousands of consumers in restaurants throughout the land. Nor is it a self-appointed arbiter of hide-bound gastronomic taste. It reports on real experiences by real people in search of nourishment, pleasure or celebration.

As purchaser of this *Guide*, you are part of a huge network of correspondents, and you are a member of the Good Food Club. Please help other readers by recounting your own experiences to us.

There is a form at the back of this book; you can ask for more report forms from the *Guide* office; the address is FREEPOST, so you do not have to use a stamp. Every letter received is one more brick in the edifice of next year's *Guide*.

# How to use this *Guide*

All the entries in this year's *Guide* have been rewritten between April and August 1993. The information on which they are based is from reports sent in by readers over the last year and confirmed by anonymous inspection. No entry is based on a single nomination. In every case readers and inspectors have been prepared to endorse the quality of the cooking, the dining-room and the value for money.

The rating system grades restaurants, on the basis of their cooking, from 1 to 5. This takes less account of elegance, ambience, service and value than it does of food and cooking. The marks take into account the perception of the *Guide* and its reporters, and signify the following:

1 **Competent cooking** Restaurants that achieve a satisfactory standard, endorsed by readers as worthy of the *Guide*.

2 **Good cooking** Restaurants that produce good food in most departments, though some inconsistencies may have been noted. They please most readers much of the time.

3 **Very good cooking** The kitchen achieves consistent quality, rarely disappointing in any department. Seldom faulted by *Guide* reporters.

4 **Excellent cooking** Restaurants with a high level of ambition and achievement. Generally, they delight.

5 **The best** These may excite debate, not as to whether the cooking is good, but whether it is better than their peers'.

* An asterisk next to a mark signifies that the *Guide* and its readers are of the opinion that the restaurant is a particularly fine example within its numeric classification.

The *Guide* office is reliant on proprietors for price information. Each year owners are asked to mark on a questionnaire the cost, for autumn of that year, of any set meals, and also the lowest and highest à la carte prices for each course. We then calculate the lowest and highest prices for a three-course meal per person, including the cost of coffee, service (if any) and half a bottle of house wine. The lowest price forms the first figure that you see in the cost line above an entry. In practice, some people may have drinks before the meal and drink a more expensive wine; also, prices are likely to rise during the currency of the *Guide*. To reflect this, the second price in the cost line is the highest price we have calculated for a three-course meal (sometimes four or five courses if it is a set meal) inflated by 20 per cent to bring some realism to bear on the likely upper limit. In essence, the cost line shows the least and the most you are likely to pay, with most meals falling somewhere in between.

# How to read a *Guide* entry

CANTERBURY Kent [1]                                                      map 3 [2]

▲ *Mary's Kitchen* [3] ♟ ⧸ [4]   ✻ [5]   £ [6]          | NEW ENTRY | [7]

16 Elwood Avenue, Canterbury CT41 4RX [8]
CANTERBURY (0227) 7770666 [9]                              COOKING 2* [11]
on B2068, 2m S of Canterbury [10]                            COST £19–£24 [12]

(main text) [13]        CELLARMAN'S CHOICE [14]

CHEF: Mary Smith   PROPRIETORS: Mary and David Smith [15]   OPEN: Mon to Sat; 12 to 2, 7 to 9 [16]   CLOSED: Aug [17]   MEALS: alc (main courses £6 to £12). Set L £12, Set D £25. [18]   Cover £1. Minimum £5 L. Unlicensed, but bring your own: corkage £1 [19]   SERVICE: net prices, card slips closed [20]   CARDS: Access, Amex, Diners, Visa [21]   DETAILS: 72 seats. 4 tables outside. Private parties: 26 main room, 10 private room. [22]   Car park. Vegetarian meals. [23]   Healthy eating options. [24]   Children's helpings. No children under 10. [25]   Jacket and tie. [26]   No-smoking in dining-room. [27]   Wheelchair access (2 steps; also WC). [28]   No music. [29]   Air-conditioned   ACCOMMODATION: 14 rooms, all with bath/shower. B&B £20 to £40. [30]   Deposit: £50. [31]   Rooms for disabled. [32]   Children welcome. [33]   Baby facilities. [34]   Pets welcome. [35]   Afternoon teas. [36]   Garden. Swimming-pool. Sauna. Tennis. Air-conditioned. TV. Phone. Doors close at 11.30. Confirm by 6  (*The Which? Hotel Guide*) [37]

1   The town and county. The *Guide*'s main entries are divided into eight sections: London, England, Scotland, Wales, Isle of Man, Channel Islands, Northern Ireland and Republic of Ireland. In the London section, restaurants are listed alphabetically by name; in all other sections, they are listed under town. The maps (at the back of the book) can be used as a starting point to locate areas of interest; then look up the entries under the town name. The London maps locate restaurants by name.

2   The map number. The maps are at the end of the *Guide*.

3   The name of the restaurant. ▲ in front of the name denotes that it offers accommodation too.

4   ♟ denotes a wine list that is good, well above the ordinary. The symbol ⧸ indicates a truly outstanding wine list.

5 ✚ indicates that smoking (cigarettes, pipes and cigars) is either banned altogether or that one dining-room is maintained for non-smokers. The symbol does not appear if a restaurant simply has a no-smoking area, or bans smoking at one mealtime only, although these features will be mentioned in the details at the end of an entry. Establishments that do not allow smoking in a dining-room may allow it elsewhere on the premises, such as in the bar or lounge. If you are a smoker, it is always worth checking beforehand.

6 £ indicates that it is possible to have a three-course meal, including coffee, a half-bottle of house wine and service, at *any* time the restaurant is open (i.e. at dinner as well as at lunch, unless a place is only open for dinner), for £20 or less per person. Meals may often cost much more than this, but, by choosing carefully, £20 should be achievable.

7 If a restaurant is new to the *Guide* this year (did not appear as a main entry in the last edition) NEW ENTRY appears opposite its name.

8 The restaurant's address and post code.

9 The restaurant's telephone number, including its exchange name and STD code.

10 Any special directions in case the restaurant is difficult to find.

11 The *Guide*'s mark, out of five, for cooking quality, ranging from 1 for competent cooking to 5 for the best. See page 7 or the inside front cover for a full explanation.

12 This is the price range for three-course meals (lunch and/or dinner) for one person, including coffee, wine and service, according to minimum and maximum prices provided by the proprietor for set meals and à la carte dishes. The first figure shows what is probably the least you would have to pay for a three-course meal (often at lunch only), while the second figure indicates a likely maximum amount. The second figure has been inflated by 20 per cent to reflect (i) that some readers will order extra drinks and some top-range dishes, and (ii) likely price rises that will come into play during the life of the *Guide*.

13 The text is based on reports sent in by readers during the last *Guide* year, confirmed by commissioned, anonymous inspections.

14 Some entries conclude with a CELLARMAN'S CHOICE. These are wines, usually more expensive than the house wine, that the restaurant assures us will be in stock during 1994, and recommends as suitable for the kind of food served.

15 The names of the chef(s) and owner(s), so that any change in management will be instantly detectable.

16 The days of the week the restaurant is open, and the times of first and last orders for meals. It is always advisable to book before going to a restaurant. If you book and then cannot go, please remember to telephone the restaurant to cancel.

17 Annual closures.

18  The types of meals that are available, with any variations for lunch (L) or dinner (D). The letters alc denote an à la carte menu. This is followed by a range of main course prices (rounded up to the nearest 50p). Set L and/or Set D denote set lunches and set dinners, and include the basic charge for those meals. Set meals consist usually of three courses, but can cover anything from two to six courses. If a set meal has only two courses, this is stated. Coffee is often included, wine very occasionally. Special menus, such as a cheaper bar menu or vegetarian menu, may be mentioned in this line. The meal information will be followed by details of any cover charge and minimum charge.

19  A restaurant is unlicensed but customers may bring their own alcoholic drinks on to the premises. Any corkage charge is indicated.

20  Net prices indicates that the prices given on a menu and on a bill are inclusive of VAT and service charge, and that this practice is clearly stated on menu and bill. Card slips closed indicates that the total on the slips of credit cards is closed when handed over for signature. When a fixed service charge is added to the bill the percentage is specified. When not inc is stated, service is at the discretion of the customer.

21  The credit cards accepted by the restaurant.

22  Not all restaurants will take private parties. The maximum number of people in a party is given for both main and private rooms.

23  This means a vegetarian dish should always be available. Many restaurants claim to cater for vegetarians but do not include suitable dishes on their menus as a matter of course. It is always advisable to explain, when booking, if you do not eat meat or fish.

24  Healthy eating options indicates that a restaurant marks on its menu, in words and/or using symbols, low-fat dishes or other healthy eating choices.

25  Some restaurants and hotels are not keen on children in the dining-room. Where it says children welcome or children's helpings, this indicates that they don't mind, although children must be well behaved. Any limitations on age are specified.

26  Jackets and ties are compulsory in very few restaurants and this is specified; otherwise it is indicated if smart dress is preferred.

27  Any no-smoking arrangements as given to us by the restaurants. See also point 5.

28  Wheelchair access means that the proprietor has confirmed that the entrance is at least 80cm wide and passages at least 120cm across – The Royal Association for Disability and Rehabilitation (RADAR) recommendations. This does not guarantee access to all areas of an establishment. Where there are steps it will say so. If there are more than three steps, wheelchair access is not stated. If it says 'also WC', then the owner has told us that the toilet facilities are suitable for disabled people.

The *Guide* relies on proprietors giving accurate information on wheelchair access. If you find the details in the *Guide* are inaccurate, please tell us. It is always important to ring first and inform the restaurant of any special requirements.

29 Dining-rooms where live and recorded music will never be played. Where a restaurant has told us that music may be played we indicate this.

30 The price for rooms and breakfast as given to us by hotels. The first price is for one person in a single room or single occupancy of a double, the second is the upper price for two people in a double room or suite. When a price is for dinner, bed and breakfast it is indicated as D,B&B.

31 The deposit required to secure accommodation. It may also be expressed as a percentage.

32 There are rooms suitable for wheelchair users.

33 Children are welcome in the accommodation. Any age limitations are specified.

34 At least some facilities, such as cots and high chairs, are available for those guests with babies. It is important to inform the proprietors of any special requirements.

35 Pets are welcome in the hotel, although they may be restricted to certain rooms.

36 Teas are served to non-residents.

37 (*The Which? Hotel Guide*) denotes that this establishment is also listed in the 1994 edition of our sister guide to over 1,000 hotels in Britain.

# The top-rated restaurants

## Mark 5 for cooking

### London
Chez Nico at Ninety Park Lane, W1
Le Gavroche, W1
La Tante Claire, SW3

### England
Le Manoir aux Quat'Saisons,
    Great Milton
L'Ortolan, Shinfield

### Scotland
Altnaharrie Inn, Ullapool

## Mark 4* for cooking

### London
Alastair Little, W1
Bibendum, SW3
Four Seasons Hotel, W1
Inter-Continental Hotel,
    Le Soufflé, W1

### England
Waterside Inn, Bray
Gidleigh Park, Chagford
Carved Angel, Dartmouth

## Mark 4 for cooking

### London
The Capital, SW3
Clarke's, W8
Connaught, W1
Lanesborough, SW1
Le Meridien Hotel, Oak Room, W1

### England
Adlard's, Norwich
Castle Hotel, Taunton
Chester Grosvenor Hotel,
    Arkle, Chester
Croque-en-Bouche, Malvern Wells
Hambleton Hall, Hambleton
Heathcote's, Longridge
Lettonie, Bristol
Mr Underhill's, Stonham
Morels, Haslemere
Normandie, Birtle

Oakes, Stroud
Old Vicarage, Ridgeway
Le Poussin, Brockenhurst
Restaurant Nineteen, Bradford
Seafood Restaurant, Padstow
Sharrow Bay, Ullswater
Winteringham Fields,
    Winteringham

### Scotland
Airds Hotel, Port Appin
Braeval Old Mill, Aberfoyle
Kinnaird, Dunkeld
Peat Inn, Peat Inn
La Potinière, Gullane

### Wales
Plas Bodegroes, Pwllheli
Walnut Tree Inn, Llandewi Skirrid

# Restaurants with outstanding wine cellars

## marked in the text with a 🍾

### London

Au Jardin des Gourmets, W1
Bibendum, SW3
Boyd's, W8
Clarke's, W8
Gilbert's, SW7
Hilaire, SW7
Leith's, W11
Mijanou, SW1
Odette's, NW1
192, W11
Le Pont de la Tour, SE1
RSJ, SE1

### England

Adlard's, Norwich
Angel Inn, Hetton
Beetle & Wedge, Moulsford
Bell, Aston Clinton
Bridgefield House, Spark Bridge
Carved Angel, Dartmouth
Cherwell Boathouse, Oxford
Chewton Glen, Marryat Room,
    New Milton
Cobwebs, Leck
Corse Lawn House Hotel,
    Corse Lawn
Croque-en-Bouche, Malvern Wells
Crown, Southwold
Dundas Arms, Kintbury
Epworth Tap, Epworth
Fountain House, Dedham
Fox and Goose, Fressingfield
French Partridge, Horton
George Hotel, Stamford
Gidleigh Park, Chagford
Gravetye Manor, East Grinstead
Hambleton Hall, Hambleton
Hartwell House, Aylesbury
Harveys, Bristol
Le Manoir aux Quat'Saisons, Great
    Milton
Manor, Chadlington
Markwicks, Bristol
Morels, Haslemere
Normandie, Birtle
Old Beams, Waterhouses
Old Manor House, Romsey

Old Rectory, Campsea Ash
Old Vicarage, Ridgeway
Old Vicarage, Witherslack
Pool Court, Pool in Wharfedale
Porthole Eating House,
    Bowness-on-Windermere
Read's, Faversham
Redmond's, Cleeve Hill
Röser's, St Leonards
Seafood Restaurant, Padstow
Sir Charles Napier Inn, Chinnor
Sous le Nez en Ville, Leeds
Ston Easton Park, Ston Easton
Summer Lodge, Evershot
Le Talbooth, Dedham
Three Lions, Stuckton
Ramsbottom Victuallers Company
    Ltd/Village Restaurant,
    Ramsbottom
White Moss House, Grasmere
White Horse Inn, Chilgrove
White House Hotel, Williton

### Scotland

Airds Hotel, Port Appin
Altnaharrie Inn, Ullapool
Ard-Na-Coille, Newtonmore
Braeval Old Mill, Aberfoyle
Cellar, Anstruther
Champany Inn, Linlithgow
Clifton House, Nairn
The Cross, Kingussie
Knipoch Hotel, Oban
Peat Inn, Peat Inn
La Potinière, Gullane
Summer Isles Hotel, Achiltibuie
Ubiquitous Chip, Glasgow
Witchery by the Castle,
    Edinburgh

### Wales

Llangoed Hall, Llyswen
Old Rectory, Llansanffraid Glan
    Conwy
Penhelig Arms Hotel, Aberdovey
Plas Bodegroes, Pwllheli
Walnut Tree Inn, Llandewi Skirrid

13

# County restaurants of the year

This award does not necessarily go to the highest-rated restaurant in a county, but rather to one which has shown particular merit or achievement during the year. It may go to an old favourite or to a new entry to the *Guide*. In either case it means that all the places listed below are not only worth visiting in their own right, but also because they have enhanced the eating-out experience in their county. Unfortunately, not all counties are lucky enough to have such places.

## England
**Avon** Harveys, Bristol
**Berkshire** L'Ortolan, Shinfield
**Cheshire** Churche's Mansion, Nantwich
**Cornwall** Café Volnay, Porthoustock
**Cumbria** Swinside Lodge, Keswick
**Derbyshire** Waltzing Weasel, Birch Vale
**Devon** Carved Angel, Dartmouth
**Dorset** Riverside Restaurant and Café, West Bay
**East Sussex** Röser's, St Leonards
**Essex** Warehouse Brasserie, Colchester
**Gloucestershire** Lords of the Manor, Upper Slaughter
**Greater Manchester** Normandie, Birtle
**Hampshire** Rocher's, Milford on Sea
**Hereford & Worcester** Pheasants, Ross-on-Wye
**Humberside** Winteringham Fields, Winteringham
**Kent** Eastwell Manor, Boughton Lees
**Lancashire** Heathcote's, Longridge
**Norfolk** Adlard's, Norwich
**Northamptonshire** Bruerne's Lock, Stoke Bruerne
**Northumberland** Funnywayt'mekalivin, Berwick-upon-Tweed

**North Yorkshire** Dusty Miller, Low Laithe
**Nottinghamshire** Langar Hall, Langar
**Oxfordshire** Le Manoir aux Quat'Saisons, Great Milton
**Somerset** Ston Easton Park, Ston Easton
**South Yorkshire** Greenhead House, Sheffield
**Suffolk** Mr Underhill's, Stonham
**Surrey** Gemini, Tadworth
**Tyne & Wear** 21 Queen Street, Newcastle upon Tyne
**Warwickshire** Restaurant Bosquet, Kenilworth
**West Sussex** Stane Street Hollow, Pulborough
**West Yorkshire** Haley's, Leeds
**Wiltshire** Toxique, Melksham

## Scotland
**Grampian** Green Inn, Ballater
**Highland** Kinacarra, Kinlochmoidart
**Lothian** La Potinière, Gullane
**Strathclyde** Cameron House Hotel, Georgian Room, Alexandria

## Wales
**Clwyd** Swiss Restaurant Imfeld, Hawarden
**Dyfed** Tŷ Mawr, Brechfa
**Gwynedd** Plas Bodegroes, Pwllheli

# The *Guide*'s longest-serving restaurants

The *Guide* has seen many restaurants come and go. Some, however, have stayed the course with tenacity. (Qualification for this list is that the restaurant must be in each edition of the *Guide* subsequent to its first entry.)

| | |
|---|---|
| Connaught, W1 | 41 years |
| Gay Hussar, W1 | 37 years |
| Porth Tocyn Hotel, Abersoch, Gwynedd | 37 years |
| Gravetye Manor, East Grinstead, West Sussex | 33 years |
| Sharrow Bay, Ullswater, Cumbria | 33 years |
| Dundas Arms, Kintbury, Berkshire | 31 years |
| French Partridge, Horton, Northamptonshire | 29 years |
| Walnut Tree Inn, Llandewi Skirrid, Gwent | 29 years |
| Black Bull Inn, Moulton, North Yorkshire | 27 years |
| Pool Court, Pool in Wharfedale, West Yorkshire | 25 years |
| Rothay Manor, Ambleside, Cumbria | 25 years |
| Sundial, Herstmonceux, East Sussex | 25 years |
| Chez Moi, W11 | 23 years |
| Le Gavroche, W1 | 23 years |
| Summer Isles Hotel, Achiltibuie, Highland | 23 years |
| Timothy's, Perth, Tayside | 23 years |
| The Capital, SW3 | 22 years |
| Miller Howe, Windermere, Cumbria | 22 years |
| Cringletie House, Peebles, Borders | 21 years |
| Old Fire Engine House, Ely, Cambridgeshire | 21 years |
| Ubiquitous Chip, Glasgow, Strathclyde | 21 years |
| White Moss House, Grasmere, Cumbria | 21 years |

# Introduction

The world of food is much written about: Saturday/Sunday supplements, daily and weekend newspaper columns, specialised magazines, magazine features, at every turn, cookbooks and guidebooks. *The Good Food Guide* sails on, 42 years since its birth, bringing not so much the opinions and hand-me-down verdicts of experts, but the accounts of ordinary people who have told us of their experiences at the public dining tables of Britain. *The Good Food Guide* is a publication informed by consumers and produced for consumers.

Some guidebooks have a small, necessarily dedicated, band of paid inspectors who do the groundwork, make reports and deliver assessments. Many rely on support from within the industry they are assessing, or take advertisements, or charge for entries in the publication itself. *The Good Food Guide* does not work like that. There are no advertisements; it is self-supporting. Its reporters are no small band, but the whole army of its readers who inundate the office with letters, postcards and comments. It is our function to stem the tide momentarily, con the portents and report the conclusions in this year's edition.

The *Guide*'s essence lies in those reports from the front-line of meals taken in celebration, on holiday, or in the normal course of business. Of course, we check them out, to ensure that they are not the outpourings of some fond relation for a favourite nephew's restaurant; and to make some judgement on the prejudices or enthusiasms of the reporter. We do this by asking a smaller band of men and women – still consumers, still part of the real world and not two-dinners-a-day people – to make inspections on our behalf and at our expense. This gives us a two-level insight into the success or otherwise of a restaurant or catering business. No new entry in this book gains its place without a commissioned inspection. A restaurant may retain its entry in a subsequent year by virtue of consumer reports alone, though important changes, such as that of chef or owner, mean a re-inspection before acceptance.

Our success, therefore, depends on readers continuing to support us in this practical way. Not only should they buy the book (last year's edition will have been superseded in countless ways), but they should make use of the report forms at the end. The postage is free: all we need is a moment of their time. 'Forgive the writing, but I did this in the car on the way home' prefaces many of our letters. As we may save them the cost of a very bad meal, their gesture in reporting to us may help us to repeat the trick, with even greater accuracy, in years to come.

## The new realism

Nineteen ninety-three was the year when a certain realism crept into the arithmetical calculations of restaurateurs rich and poor. The hard knocks of recession had found them with fewer customers, higher bills and closer financial monitoring, especially from the banks. Rather than simply charging more and hoping to ride it out, a number of enlightened people began to think in terms of offering more of what people wanted, at a price they could afford, to attract them back into restaurants. At the end of the '80s there was a real chance that good cooking was going to price itself out of the market – rather as bespoke tailoring and hand-built cars had largely done in earlier decades. Chefs of note were cooking for an ever-richer clientele, in premises that became more luxurious by the minute. There is certainly an argument for defending centres of excellence, in cooking as much as in scholarship; but there is a counter-argument that would decry the dreadful spurious imitations that spring up in their wake.

The new realism has had some effect on this tendency. It has come as a surprise to many chefs that good food need not be made from luxury ingredients; that foie gras may be a good thing, but too much is extravagance. At the beginning of the year, a £5 lunch scheme was initiated by Nick Lander at the *Financial Times*, himself a former restaurateur. It was taken up by many in London and a few in the shires. A similar scheme for £10-a-head dinners was introduced by the London *Evening Standard* in the spring and was joined by restaurants throughout the capital. Not all restaurants were equally competent, but the interesting lesson was that a sound meal could be produced at a fair profit margin, for this sum. Even if the overheads of any city-centre business were too high to make it feasible as a permanent feature, it did give cause to reassess the arithmetic in the light of flagging occupancy levels.

This experiment in philanthropy emphasised the existence of two sorts of eating house. On one hand there were the places fully kitted for the grand life, on the other were havens of good food, but operating on altogether more basic lines. More and more, the public is being shown that clever cooks do not always need tablecloths on which to present their art and that it is the overheads – the bevies of attendants, the marbled halls, the silver, the linen and the deep-pile carpets – that swallow money like a hungry dragon.

Economic practicality used once to be the preserve of Chinese and Indian restaurants, or was the fabled quality of eating out in France and other countries bordering the Mediterranean. It stemmed from intelligently and deeply dug foundations: find a good location *but* do

17

not spend too much on the premises (property in France, and many other European countries, is cheaper than it is in Britain); invest only from profits (do not put yourself too much in hock to the bank before you have seen a customer); keep the business under control (employ family members, who will work for minimal wages while the business is finding its feet); offer good value and watch the customers come through the door. The same rules can, of course, be applied to extremely horrid restaurants, which is why we write this guide – to laud the saints, not the sinners.

## Milking the customers: a practice still with us

As we pass into the middle-'90s, there seems to be a common presumption that the restaurant scene is now a paradise of consumer-friendly and public relations-conscious establishments, and that the old suspicion that waiters, chefs and owners were anxious to relieve us of as much money as they could without our noticing has been laid to rest for good and all. This atmosphere of distrust was one reason for *The Good Food Guide* in the first place.

But sadly, no: some of the very newest and most popular operations are guilty of some shameful tricks, all designed to push up profits without the customer being too aware of it. The price of a main dish may be considered a fair indicator of the level of expenditure likely to be incurred when eating out. But if you're charged, in a far from luxurious establishment, £3 for a bottle of Hildon mineral water, plus a cover charge when even the *plates* for bread and butter have not been provided, you are likely to feel put out. And if there's a 15 per cent service charge on top, you could well decide that enough is enough.

While the recession may have forced proprietors to reduce their headline prices to persuade customers through their doors, some of them load the other costs to the point of virtual deceit. No wonder the public sometimes feels restaurants are combat zones.

## Taste, flavour and fun

A meal outside the home is more complicated than just food on a plate, whatever its quality. It is a social event with all the intricacies of an eighteenth-century court ballet. Meals are often memorable for the occasion, the conversation, the open hospitality of the restaurant staff, the buzz and fizz of the atmosphere in the restaurant itself, the quality of the wine cellar, or the mere coincidence of fine weather, a beautiful situation and your own good fortune. The cooking may come quite far down the list of why you had such a good time. However, it is not wise to forget it altogether – which is what some restaurant designers and publicists think can be done.

Chefs, too, are guilty of the same misapprehension: if it sounds exciting on the menu and looks wonderful on the plate, how it tastes does not really matter. This is a recipe for disaster, and one we have too often sampled. It may be self-evident that an editor of an eating guide should insist on the importance of taste and flavour, but it is these two elements that are sometimes first thrust out of the window in the genuine and necessary effort of running a restaurant. Yet the kitchens that give most consistent pleasure are those which get their tastes right, season judiciously and quite obviously sample the food before dishing it up to the customer. For them, the question of trendiness and fashion does not exist – except insofar as it sets up certain expectations in the minds of the diner; good food, clever flavours that build into a harmony, intelligent technique that neither masks nor leaves too naked, are all that is needed.

There is of course fashion in taste, trend in flavours, just as much as in ingredients or recipes. We do not like too much stodge and flour with our meat any more, we actually like the aromas of the charcoal grill, and we find too many mousses flabby and distracting. These are not questions of moral worth, they are shifts of fashion. Chefs need to respond. But they are not excuses for forgetting the basic techniques, for producing food without seasoning, or for piling anything fashionable into one hotch-potch construction.

It may also seem strange for an editor of a food guide to urge that restaurants should be there for enjoyment. They are centres of happiness. That they also act as fuelling stops on the route through life is incidental (though not unimportant). Going out to dinner should be an act of celebration, however small, not an opportunity to pick holes. Too much preciosity surrounds writing and thinking about restaurants. Chefs are not philosophers usually: they are doers and enablers. We attend their table as a pleasure, not as some arcane theoretical exercise. It is often said that *The Good Food Guide* receives only letters of complaint and niggling criticism. But this is not so: the majority of our post is affirmative, containing endorsements of good places to eat. If we voice criticism, it is only to make them better. Restaurants are a joy founded on the hard work of others. This book celebrates that.

Tom Jaine

# 'Non-fumeurs? Il y a la terrace!'

## The French anti-smoking laws – is there a lesson for Britain?

**Elizabeth Carter** – freelance food writer and journalist

It's the first day of your holiday in France, and it's pouring with rain. You need money, so you dash into the nearest bank. Inside, the clerk takes a deep, contemplative drag on his cigarette as he regards your traveller's cheque. Your eyes begin to water; beneath a prominently displayed no-smoking sign the other clerk and his customer settle down to a convivial smoke and chat.

Back outside, you decide to have a drink while you wait for the rain to stop. You plunge into the nearest café but are instantly driven out by the thick fug of tobacco smoke. You take an outside table, only slightly damp; most of the rain is kept off by the awning. And you thought France would be an even more pleasant place now that it had passed anti-smoking laws!

A law certainly went into effect in France on 1 November 1992. In broad terms it requires designated smoking areas in bars, cafés, hotels, restaurants and discothèques, as well as in the workplace. It completely bans smoking, in principle, in certain public buildings like post offices and banks.

But the law was doomed from the start – no one took it seriously. Television news set the tone, in the last week of October, by featuring jokey interviews with bar- and café-owners, who brushed the law aside. The shrugs, the streams of cigarette smoke blown contemptuously into the camera, endorsed the same view: if non-smokers did not like the owners' premises, they could go elsewhere. A stream of TV chat shows were enlivened by one of, or all, the guests lighting up in the studio (now a no-smoking area in compliance with the law) and blowing smoke at the presenter. Such behaviour became de rigueur, even if the guest didn't habitually smoke. Defence of personal liberty became a hot topic throughout the media. Tremendous coverage was given, by both TV and newspapers, to the outbreak of defiant, handwritten signs pinned by owners to bar and café doors. Most proclaimed '*Bar des Fumeurs*', others banned non-smokers outright, or condescendingly promised to serve them as long as they didn't make a fuss.

The press's attention tended to be concentrated on Paris, but my experiences in the South mirrored its view. The only time smoking bothers me is when I'm in a restaurant, halfway through a meal, and people at the next table, having finished theirs, light up. It's not an uncommon occurrence in England, but in France the odds of it happening are higher; more French people smoke. I also usually avoid cafés, unless I can sit on the terrace. I remember 1 November because I was looking forward to the law's introduction. It was a wet Sunday. The seven bar/cafés in my Provençal hill village were as unapproachable as ever in such weather; one had even stuck up a 'Bar des Fumeurs' sign. There had been no attempt to comply with the smoking law.

When I tried to obtain a copy of the booklet explaining the law, issued by the Fédération Nationale de l'Industrie Hôtelière, only one proprietor could lay his hands on a copy. Others had trouble recalling its existence. Had they considered complying with the law? Shrugs all round. Non-smokers have always sat out on the terrace; no one had ever complained.

I was in Aix-en Provence the following Tuesday. The large café opposite the main post office sported two handwritten signs, offering smoking and no-smoking rooms. I pushed my way in, past the crowded bar, through the thick cigarette smoke, into a back room used for the storage of spare gas cylinders; there I sat and drank my coffee in splendid isolation. But I felt like a social outcast; it was what I wanted, but I was away from the front-of-house action, the life and colour of the bar. For lunch I chose a simple café which served an excellent set menu; I had previously enjoyed the food, but been put off by the smoking. I decided to give it another try. I sat at one of the two no-smoking tables, which were in the centre of the room, surrounded by smokers' tables. Few people were smoking; it was bearable. Halfway through the meal a couple took the remaining no-smoking table, and immediately lit up. I think it was the fact that ashtrays were on both no-smoking tables that stopped me from protesting. And the fact that both the proprietor and the waiter smoked.

The thrust of the law is to provide protection for the non-smoker through minimum ventilation requirements – i.e. certain spaces between tables, and limits on the number of tables in an establishment, depending upon the system of ventilation: windows and doors, fans, air-conditioning, some combination of these. Unless they have a complete air-conditioning system, the easiest way for proprietors to comply with the ventilation requirements is to put smokers at tables near windows, open fireplaces, by the terrace, and as far from the kitchen and lavatories as possible – in short, at the best tables.

In practice, this doesn't happen. Non-smokers have been turned into second-class citizens. They get the table by the lavatory door, or slap-bang in the middle of the room, where they can be knocked into, and get the full blast from any smokers around them. A strange quirk of the law permits the proprietor to determine just how many tables should be set aside for smokers and non-smokers, justified by an observation that the proprietor will best know his customers' needs.

Whereas the intent might have been to carve out smoking areas in an essentially non-smoking environment, the opposite effect has been achieved.The law actually codifies smoking in public eating areas in France; it provides very little comfort – often none – for the non-smoker.

I telephoned a number of Michelin/Gault Millau-recommended restaurants. Few, generally the very best, had made any provision for non-smokers indoors. It's difficult to express in words how one receives a Gallic shrug down the telephone. But try responding to the phrase 'Une table non-fumeur? Il y a la terrace' with 'et s'il pleut?' ('What if it's raining?') and you'll understand what I mean.

The lively Quai du Port in Marseilles, a 300-yard stretch of bars, cafés, bistros and restaurants, ranging from cheap drinking dives and frites-with-everything cafés to smart guide-recommended establishments, gives an encapsulated view of the law in action. At lunch-time the place is packed with *le tout Marseilles*; this is a working city with little tourism. On fine days eating is no problem – every establishment has its patch of pavement, elegantly or tattily covered, depending on the price range. Everyone sits outside. But when the Mistral strikes, or when it's raining...? The staff in Chez Caruso were very pleasant. If they book in advance, non-smokers can have a private room, otherwise they get a shrug. The bar nearby directed me up a wobbly spiral staircase to the upper floor. The lavatories were there too. The grandest restaurant of all, the Miramar, had seven indoor tables for non-smokers, complete with ashtrays. The huge bistro on the corner had eight, also with ashtrays. And that seemed to be it. Of some 30 or so eating and drinking establishments, only a handful were bothering to acknowledge the law.

What were what the motives of the French lawmakers? They have passed into law something that achieves the opposite of what was intended. Non-smokers have always had a raw deal in France. It's still chic to smoke, and cigarettes are cheap – a pack of 20 Marlboro costs 13.80F (about £1.65) – and there's currently little social pressure to give up. Phillipe Boucher,of the Comité Nationale Contre le Tabagisme (National Committee Against Smoking), states that no publicly funded information is available about passive smoking, and that anti-smoking subjects are rarely raised in French newspapers.

Boucher claims that the press is 'definitely not on the side of the non-smoker', adding that most of the prominent French restaurant critics smoke and are indifferent to non-smoking areas in restaurants. The general public therefore remains fairly ignorant as to the effects of passive smoking.

The law is the direct result of a report, commissioned by the Minister of Health, on public health in France, with an emphasis on preventable disease. The report came out strongly against smoking. Among its recommendations were raising the price of cigarettes, a total ban on all tobacco advertising, and protection of non-smokers in public places. But in the face of the strong opposition marshalled by the tobacco lobby, the French press and bar- and restaurant-owners, the French government compromised, framing the law in such a way that smokers retain the upper hand. Although proprietors can, in theory, be fined 3,000F–6,000F (£360–£720) for not implementing the law, a nice piece of fine tuning states that they cannot be held responsible if a customer smokes in a non-smoking section. This explains the frequent presence of ashtrays on non-smoking tables. If a non-smoking table is the only one available to a smoker, the received message is to go ahead and smoke. Who's complaining? Certainly not the cowed non-smokers. There's a joke in Paris: a man walked into a pizzeria on the Champs-Elysées, and asked the waiter, 'Where is the non-smoking section?' The waiter removed an ashtray from a nearby table, and said, 'Here!'

The French also have a strong sense of personal liberty. It stems from an education system which is gruelling, allowing little time for rebellion, combined with the pressure in provincial France to conform – this is a country where everything closes at 12.30 for lunch. All that is left to the French is to ignore laws of which they disapprove. It's no surprise therefore that the anti-smoking laws were unanimously laughed off, and six months later were all but forgotten. When all the fuss and publicity fizzled out, France just carried on smoking, where and when it liked.

The French press views the successful British anti-smoking campaign with some horror, and like to report with glee what it regards as vicious discrimination against smokers. It's all a question of attitude and application. In Britain the social pressure not to smoke is strong. It's not unusual for smoking in the workplace to be banned, for restaurants to offer non-smoking areas, for hotels, with the luxury of space, to discourage smoking in their dining-rooms. Even pubs have changed. More and more are offering non-smoking areas, or rooms. And it's all voluntary.

In December 1991 the British government issued a code of practice, called 'Smoking in Public Places'. It is, in effect, a gentleman's agreement, aiming to make 80 per cent of public places smoke-free by the end of 1994. In 'Health of a Nation', a White Paper of July 1992, the government spelled out its position: if the code of practice doesn't achieve sufficient progress by the end of 1994, it will consider legislation to move things forward more rapidly. By adopting a softly, softly approach, it has created the climate in which the idea could catch hold with the public. According to ASH (Action on Smoking and Health), public opinion in Britain is very much in favour of smoke-free areas. But this has been built up over the last two or three decades: initially, through the prodding of public interest groups and the medical profession; then, by the increasing attention paid to the dangers of smoking by newspapers and TV.

But how does all this affect the holidaymaker in France who wants a meal, or a drink, away from the intrusive smell of tobacco? Not a lot. Phillipe Boucher regards the law as a step forward, but feels that tourists can make an important contribution. 'I hope foreign visitors will put the pressure on, by asking, "Where is the non-smoking section?"' He's also keen on complaining. But do the French complain? He admits not. 'The French public says it is for the anti-smoking lobby, but rarely raises its voice. If you have the guts to complain, you will find that the people around you will support you.'

I don't have the guts. Do you? I'll stick to the terrace, and look out for the guide to restaurants with genuine non-smoking areas that the Comité Nationale Contre le Tabagisme is hurriedly putting together. It will be thin, but useful.

# Anatomy of a restaurant bill

What's in a restaurant bill? As you stare at a meagre breast of chicken, or at two scallops sliced in half to make them seem like four, the answer is likely to be: 'A lot of profit, and not much fun for me.'

There can be very little connection between the shelf-value of goods and their final price in a restaurant. This sometimes gives rise to misunderstandings and resentment. At other times, the customer reckons there is perceived fair dealing, or is willing to pay the price irrespective of its real value in goods consumed.

A price on a menu conveys two messages. The first is about the object being sold. The second is more general: it is the cost of a ticket of entry to this particular establishment. The more energy (and money) invested in making the restaurant and the social event of dining desirable, the more the relationship between actual commodity and raw cost is weakened. This is partly a matter of overheads consuming a larger and larger share of the restaurant's turnover as each succeeding layer of elaboration is planned and staffed, from the greeting at the door to the final goodbye at the cloakroom counter. But it is also a matter of theatre, of creating substance out of thin air. You, the customer, may pay for fame or notoriety.

This 'ticket' aspect of dining out is nowhere more obvious than in a restaurant that charges a single inclusive price for a meal. The same £20, £25 or even £42 buys soup and chicken or prawns and lobster. The price of materials is hardly an issue. The restaurant costs the menu as a whole, working on the 'swings and roundabouts' system. Customers do not necessarily shop around the menu for the 'best' value; as many will opt for chicken as will order lobster, so whatever profit is made on the first can offset the cost of the second. The end is the same amount of money. The price is what people are prepared to pay for the total experience.

All this is laid out in varying degrees of detail in the final reckoning, which may have you lying sleepless in bed as it slowly dawns on you that an evening that was intended to cost £50 in fact cost £100; or it may give rise to a pat on the back for your astuteness. Whichever, the bill should be an accurate record of what was consumed that night.

The rules and regulations surrounding bills are few, though they are of course supported by extensive legislation relating to the sale of goods and services, and common law. The customer needs to be told the amount of the debt, but the law does not insist on it being done in a specific way. A VAT receipt, on the other hand, must show the VAT registration number, though the amount of VAT need not be separately expressed. Some places, especially large hotels with machine accounting, issue bills that do not qualify as VAT receipts. The reasoning behind this is arcane, but if you need to claim a bill as a refundable expense on your own account, or from a VAT-registered employer or client, you have to ask for a separate receipt.

There are also places that do not give you the bill they have presented for payment, but tear off a little strip at the bottom which forms a receipt. The reason usually given is that they need the bill itself for accounting purposes.

As they are unfettered by regulation, bill-writers can be more or less economical with the facts (the truth *must*, of course, be there to see). It does not matter whether the account is made up by hand or by machine, each can be as opaque as the other. Some bills say no more than 'Food £X; Drink £Y; Total £Z'. This is not very helpful, indeed a *bête-noire* with many of our readers, but it is all that is required. Verbal justification can be sought for the total and is bound to be forthcoming.

Machine accounts can be programmed for more or less information. It is probably in the owner's interests to provide more – for example, a pre-programmed till that gives the price for each item, thus reducing loss through mistakes. Even the most Luddite amongst us should therefore welcome the machine's arrival on the scene. It would help if the software designers worked on making the text more comprehensible to the naked eye, but in almost every case the facts are there: they just need ferreting out of the bewildering succession of digits.

Manual bills are something else. They are often illegible. Waiters and clerks develop speed-writing techniques to hasten their production. Addition, if done by brain and eye, is often out of kilter – hence the date getting into the act in the mythological expensive restaurant. These drawbacks, at least, are not repeated by machines, which will invariably be accurate once the information has been fed in.

It is sometimes forgotten by the customer that bill-writing is a terrible consumer of time in a busy restaurant. It may even be the sole occupation of a member of staff. The person in charge of bills has to collate information from myriad pieces of paper – for individual orders to the bar, cellar or kitchen – to produce a tidy, accurate finished account. At the end of the day, all the scraps of information have to tally for the establishment's own accountant.

As customers in restaurants tend to move in waves, it follows that bills are often needed in groups of 10, 20 or more. In his youth, the Editor of this guide worked in a restaurant that was the far side of a ferry trip from the nearest large town. The last ferry departed at

11 o'clock in the evening. Half an hour before then the restaurant would be happy and relaxed (assuming the kitchen had produced all the courses by then). Come 10 minutes to the hour, faces would have reddened, breathing shortened. 'Where's the bill?' would come from every table. Woe betide you if the bills were not ready.

In order to deal with such exigencies, acceleration and abbreviation are necessary. It may even underlie many restaurants' espousal of the fixed-price menu, which makes the production of bills much simpler. Similarly, if ever you come across a wine list which deals in bands of prices rather than a different price per bin, this too may be due to ease of administration rather than consideration of your pocket.

None of these practices has much to do with the awful truth: the total you have to meet before leaving the table. But so as to make you more sympathetic, to soften the blow or, it may be, quite the contrary, consider the following.

A restaurant charges £10 for a steak, from which £1.49 will be paid in VAT. You pay by credit card, so a further 25p (2.5 per cent of £10) goes on the credit card handling charge. The restaurant now has £8 to play with. Ignore the vexed problem of tipping or inclusive service, but bear in mind that in many city restaurants staff costs will be 25–30 per cent of turnover (£8.51), running costs at least 15 per cent and fixed costs at least 15 per cent. This leaves about £3.15 for the purchase of the food – and, if the restauratuer is lucky, some contribution to profit. The gap, therefore, between the cost of materials and their price on the menu is bound to be very large.

The inexorable pressure of costs is one reason why restaurateurs adopt that irritating practice of loading up the margins on little things. It used to be the cover charge and the array of extra vegetables. Today, the cover charge has returned in many (ostensibly cheap) London places, where bread and olives are an extra menu item; and everyone plays the same trick with mineral water. The obvious area for creative charging is the bar, from where the multiple Camparis, the brandies and the little nibbles are merged into a single horrifying figure on the reckoning. Because there is far less room for manoeuvre, many places that make a single inclusive menu charge seem much more expensive than their rivals. You can only wait for the final bill to compare the bottom lines.

Not every restaurant works or subscribes to the same arithmetic. The recession has put great pressure on expensive places and has certainly kept price rises to a minimum. Restaurateurs have also worked on the principle that if prices are low, the flow of customers will be greater. Full houses give them a chance to break the gridlock of the old arithmetic.

It is also true that a restaurant staffed by family, in premises funded out of inherited or earned capital, will work to very different arithmetic from one supporting a large salaried staff and heavy repayments to the bank. The collapse in property values and drop in interest rates have encouraged restaurateurs to accept smaller margins and kept bills lower than they might be, but there are limits to financial flexibility if these two criteria apply.

There is a sense in which it is 'unfair' that a hotel with low margins due to the property being inherited and the staff being father, mother, brother, two sons and a daughter should be able to charge the same as one subject to crippling overheads. Perhaps the latter should have never gone into business at all, but in the palmy '80s, when the game seemed to be to charge as much as possible, not as little, such faulty economics seemed feasible. Now reality, if not business failure, has set in.

Should we expect, therefore, any sort of relationship between the cost of the meat or fish on our plate and the end price? Should a breast of chicken cost radically less than a fillet steak? The answer is probably never. By making more on the chicken, restaurants are able to keep the price of luxuries within bounds. They can accept a lower percentage profit on lobster which is subsidised by soup and the near-ubiquitous fish-cakes. If we start scouring the menu for best value, we may fly in the face of our own natural preferences (some of us *like* soup and chicken).

You go to an expensive restaurant. You are shocked by the bill. Was it worth it? Were you had for a sucker? Before you return a loud affirmative, ask yourself this. Was at least some of the price paid for superior artistry? A chef is worth the price of his or her skill. Were the materials, even common workaday ones, of manifestly superior quality? Good butter costs more than twice the price of ordinary butter. A free-range, hand-reared chicken is three times dearer than a battery-farmed one. Wild salmon may cost much more than farmed. Fresh lobster is very expensive; frozen comparatively cheap. Leave aside the question of trimmings and minor ingredients – the wild mushrooms, the truffle juice, the extra-virgin olive oil, the perfectly formed vegetables from the garden – even the essentials will cost the good restaurant three or four times the amount spent by the bad. Sometimes the differences are not obvious, but their justification has to be in the taste, the flavour, the experience. *That* is why some people will happily pay £50 for a dinner, while others cringe at £10. Expensive may be good value, cheap can be bad.

# Trends abroad: here tomorrow?

As we read more, view more, fly and drive more, the cooking of the Western world assumes a worrying homogeneity. Or does it? The reports that follow, from France, Italy and the USA, show how other countries have responded to the market's apparently insatiable appetite for change and development, and raise interesting possibilities concerning the way in which our own restaurant culture may evolve in Britain.

## France

**Paul Wermus – Paris-based food journalist**

Nouvelle cuisine has died. Long live natural values and the produce of the land. Green leaders such as Antoine Waechter and Brice Lalonde seem to have inspired France's leading chefs, who, for the most part, have adopted their colour.

Top names such as Michel Rostang, Guy Savoy and Joël Robuchon have undergone a sea-change in their approach and opened bistros and rôtisseries in addition to their temples of haute cuisine. And if you cast an eye over the menus of the great restaurants you will re-discover the dishes of two generations ago. This revolution at the stove is a cause for rejoicing, not only among dieticians but also for doctors, who are noting an improvement in the livers of their patients. People will drink less and eat better – such will be the new slogan of the masters, who, almost by chance, in recent years have lost their legendary portliness. Today's customers no longer have the same confidence in chefs who carry prominent paunches. The new kitchen boys all look like mannequins. Vegetables old and new are in vogue again. Even in the most highly rated establishments the customer can enjoy a single snack dish accompanied by a bottle of mineral water. If you are visiting France, here is what you can eat in the new bistrots of the great chefs.

In Paris, Michel Rostang (two stars in Michelin) supervises La Butte Chaillot, 112 avenue Kléber in the 16me. Here you can eat spit-roasted farm chicken accompanied by mashed potatoes, or a tasty stuffed breast of veal with rosemary. The cost will be about 220Fr.

At Guy Savoy's Bistrot de l'Etoile, 19 rue Lauriston in the 16me, the menu is neo-bourgeois: sauté of veal, French toast (pain perdu) with apples, accompanied by a vin de pays de l'Aude or a house Bordeaux. The meal will cost about 240Fr.

At his other Bistrot de l'Etoile, 75 avenue Niel, in the 17me, you can sample 'vulgar' cuisine, with an embarrassment of choice including calf's head, boiled beef and cod in a garlic cream sauce – all for about 200Fr.

Staying in the 17me arrondissement we stop at 10 rue Gustave Flaubert, at Au Bistro d'à Côté Flaubert (proprietor Michel Rostang), with a menu recalling the Lyonnaise cooking which Rostang used to serve in the old days. Dishes of yesteryear include a salad of lentils and saveloys, and andouillettes à la ficelle. The suggested wines are in pitchers and the cost of the meal is about 250Fr.

Francis Vandenhende, proprietor of Le Manoir de Paris (three toques and 17/20 in Gault Millau) has diversified by opening La Niçoise at 4 rue Pierre Demours. This is recommended to lovers of the flavours of the South of France, particularly the hallmark garlic and olive oil. Typical dishes are grilled tuna steak with fresh tomatoes, and lamb with macaroni. The cellar is essentially Provençal. The lunch menu at 140Fr is without equal.

At La Marlotte, 55 rue Cherche Midi, in the 6me, everything is rustic, even the décor: the terrine of tongue, the fricassee of veal with chervil and the pavé of cod are some of the specialities of the house. Prices here average 250Fr.

Also in the 6me arrondissement is L'Arbuci at 25 rue Buci. Here the rôtisserie rules. Spit-roasted meats and poultry are the focus of meals costing about 220Fr. This tendency to simplicity has also spread to the three-star restaurants. Paul Bocuse has not hesitated to serve a modest Bresse chicken, a loin of veal or even the famous ancestral dessert, crème brûlée.

Lasserre at 17 avenue F-D. Roosevelt (two Michelin stars), in the 8me, has created a small haven for traditional cooking. On his menu are fillets of mullet, and a caviare of aubergines. The same approach is found at Taillevent at 15 rue Lamennais (three Michelin stars): fillet of lamb, pigeon tart, a salad of mixed leaves, to say nothing of an infinite variety of crisply served vegetables.

Alan Senderens, the chef at Lucas Carton, 9 place de la Madeleine, has returned to the tastes of old-time cooking: shank of veal en cocotte, roast cod accompanied by potatoes with olives and sliced calf's kidneys.

Even Le Tour d'Argent at 15 quai Tournelle, in the 5me, knows how to cook simply. It offers baby mullet, a salad of black olives and herbs, and roast duck.

A stopover at Joël Robuchon at 32 rue de Longchamp (three Michelin stars), in the 16me, is de rigueur. Joël, considered by his peers to be number one, has no problems about serving his well-heeled clientele with a skirt of lamb, or a modest dish of grilled mushrooms. He has also inaugurated a cheaper branch, quieter though always full, called Le Parc Victor-Hugo at 55 avenue Raymond Poincarré, which has no compunction about serving herrings, terrines and unpretentious vins de pays.

The trend to simplicity is not confined to Paris. For just one example, try Le Côte d'Or at Saulieu in Burgundy, where Bernard Loiseau, who gained his third Michelin star last year, is honouring his predecessor, Alexandre Dumaine, by daring to serve a banal but succulent potato purée, veal offal and his famous fatted chicken.

Is it the effect of the continuing recession or is it that French cuisine is reflecting the leanings of the country toward economy? Away with sophisticated dishes, the cuisine of artifice and conspicuous effort. Goodbye, too, to astronomic bills. French cuisine is at last honouring the money-saving inclination and family values which never go out of fashion.

## Italy

**Leslie Forbes – freelance food journalist**
Italians are a deeply conformist race who rarely value the eccentric, whether in clothes or in cooking, a trait which for years saved their regional food from bastardisation. It took them so long to get around to nouvelle cuisine that while we were rediscovering northern Italy's culinary peasant roots, they were busy pulling them up, with help from such internationally influenced chefs as Milan's Gualtiero Marchesi.

Judging an olive oil competition in Umbria this year, I was served tortured smoked salmon by a local chef who told me proudly that after training with Marchesi he has rejected all those 'housewife's dishes that they are still cooking in less cosmopolitan regions in the south'. His cooking was about as regional as powered cappuccino. Ironically, Marchesi, having inspired a host of less talented provincial imitators, closed his *nuova cucina* restaurant last year. Informed sources allege that prices were so shatteringly expensive that anyone seen there was immediately suspected of corruption, not something to be ignored in Italy's new squeaky-clean regime.

Last spotted eating at the London Italian restaurant Riva, Marchesi is now doing *vecchia cucina* near Bergamo: Italian gastronomic history as theme park. But then he has often taken cues from that home of the theme park and westernmost outpost of the Med, California – as have many of the so-called new-wave northern Italian restaurants in Britain.

Fashionable Italian food here has been pushed through a fine sieve of British and American squeamishness. If we were really influenced by Italians, we would now be tucking into dishes such as the tripe in herbal vinegar and the eel skewered on branches of bay that I had at the Locanda dell'Amorosa in Tuscany. We would be slurping up the *stracotto* of horse that Gidleigh Park's owner, Paul Henderson, had at Dal Peccatore near Mantua, and the tripe lasagna enjoyed by Gidleigh's chef, Shaun Hill.

Unlike truffles, ingredients such as eel, horse and tripe are widely available in Britain, and good Italian cooks have always respected two things: regional and seasonal ingredients. Until recently, no Italian would have dreamt of putting chargrilled French goats' cheese and products from opposite ends of Italy (Naples' sun-dried tomatoes and Modena's balsamic vinegar, say) on a pizza. That took a French-trained Austrian – Wolfgang Puck in Los Angeles. As Priscilla Carluccio found while searching for products for her London delicatessen (Carluccio's in Neal Street, Covent Garden), 'People in Emilia Romagna had still never heard of Puglia's pasta and Neapolitans didn't know what *bresaola* was, while in Britain and America we can pluck dishes from all regions'.

If any current northern Italian trend is likely to succeed in Britian, it is the *enoteca*. Once merely a regional supermarket, with the arrival of designer-labelled products and a young generation of Italian diners raised on fad food as well as fast food, the *enoteca* has become a sort of wine bar meets deli (but about as far removed from our 1970s wine bars as the Uffizi is from a postcard shop), serving glasses of wine and rustic-chic dishes based on its own packaged local products. The Milanese food empire, Peck, with one shop entirely devoted to products of the pig and another to every known variety of roasting poultry, was one of the first to see the idea's potential. Now, in a Modena *enoteca*, you might have a slice of Taleggio cheese with a spoonful of fruit *mostarda*, in Rome, a glass of Frascati and a slice of *focaccia* covered in artichokes *sott'olio*, in Spoleto, *crostini neri* – toast spread with a paste of black truffles.

As the Italian food importer Pietro Pesci said, 'The thing Italians do best is simplicity – like a new sauce I had in southern Italy called *strozzapreti* ("priest-choker": so good it choked the priest), made of chickpeas, wild sage and a twist of lemon. Southern Italians are good at simplicity – and it is so difficult to do.' And to sell.

Pesci believes southern Italian cooking has been underrated because of its very simplicity – and because the north has always been better at marketing. He would like to see an *enoteca*-style café open here with products, recipes and cooks entirely from Puglia and Campania. He may be on to something. In fact, it was not a Tuscan or Ligurian olive oil that won the competition I judged in Umbria, but an unknown Pugliese one from the south (which put a lot of aristocratic Tuscan noses out of joint) – an indication, perhaps, that our gastronomic compass may be changing direction.

# New York

**Paul Dymond** – freelance journalist

In Manhattan the cupboard is bare. Household kitchen cupboards in brownstones, co-ops, duplexes and lofts contain barely one tin of soup. Andy Warhol's cupboard was the exception, but the can of Campbell's was for his art, not his lunch.

Upper East Side apartments may be cluttered with bags from Bloomingdale's, tickets for the Lincoln Center and back issues of *The New York Review of Books*, but the corner known as the kitchen will have an unlived-in look. Not a few New Yorkers consider ignorance of how to operate their own oven a source of pride.

Domestic science was relegated long ago to allow pursuit of the art of eating out. Why cook after a long day in the hothouse of business when the island is jammed with restaurants? Why cook at home when there are restaurants devoted to home cooking? The key to New York City is its love, not of food, but of eating. The plentiful hot-dog stands of Midtown satisfy the impulse-in-transit while immigrants continue to rebuild, annually, the foundations of one of the most sophisticated restaurant cultures on earth.

Refugee restaurateurs from Hong Kong and Cuba are among the latest to have impressed the spoilt-for-choice citizens and visitors who regularly chew the big apple. Bayamo, 704 Broadway, bordering the East Village, and serving Cuban-Chinese stir-fried duck with chilli and beans, neatly demonstrates the tendency to hybrid dining.

Considerable competition (sometimes, literally, cut-throat) combined with low-priced raw materials defeats high rents to yield excellent-value menus. Ultimately, everyone eats out in New York every day because it is relatively cheap in terms of both home-earned and foreign-exchanged dollars.

A chance encounter with a friend on a busy street corner, at a fund-raising evening at the Whitney Museum or, more likely, in a restaurant, involves the exchange of recently acquired enthusiasm for another restaurant as integral and natural to the conversational gambit. As in a Woody Allen movie such as *Broadway Danny Rose*, which begins and ends in the Carnegie Deli, Seventh Avenue and West 54th Street, famous for indifferent service and *New York Times* Sunday edition-size pastrami-on-rye, your life's story may start, finish and be defined in restaurant analogy.

An anecdote about eating well uptown and downtown might revolve around comparing the Four Seasons, decorated by Picasso and housed in Mies van der Rohe's landmark Seagram Building, Park Avenue at East 52nd Street, with *Godfather*-inspired Ballato, on the outer limit of Little Italy in East Houston Street.

Dinner at the Four Seasons, renowned as the site of banquette-reserved, power-brokered deals, is fixed now to a $37.50 *carte*. A supper of seafood and linguine with sardines, plum tomatoes, pine-nuts, raisins and fennel at Ballato is $7.50. Each is exceptional, and unparalleled – at the price – in London.

Midnight feasting at Banana Café, East 22nd Street, north of Union Square, may provoke jokes about the endemic disposition of Manhattan chefs towards novelty for its own sake but the squab-and-shiitake lasagne in East 22nd Street is, against the odds, a succulent riposte.

That a destination such as Banana Café might be a trend-setter is an unlikely proposition: London chefs have already proved they can turn out dishes of equal invention. But their counterparts in New York have the advantage of working under lower overheads for a broader-based clientele with higher expectations.

London has begun, unwittingly, to take its cue from New York by developing multifarious preferences which are increasingly distant from standard European tradition. The redoubtable dynamism across the Atlantic is a harbinger of what may happen when enough people abandon hope of ever again re-stocking their cupboards.

# The grape goes global

Andrew Jefford – wine correspondent of the London *Evening Standard*

I got off the train at Melbourne, after a three-hour journey through
Victoria's reassuring landscape of grasslands and gums. It was a
deliciously warm, open-necked sort of an evening. A taxi-driver in
shorts and tee-shirt asked me if I wanted a cab. As I got into the car, I
saw a local restaurant guide open on the dashboard.

We talked – about restaurants, about food, about wine. He was a
good-looking 40-year-old divorcee with a 50-bottle wine collection,
plenty of vineyard visits under his belt, and a close knowledge of
what was worth eating and what wasn't in Melbourne. He told me
exactly where to go that evening; I failed to find it, but I ate well
anyway. Melbourne's Moomba festival was on, 'reflecting the
fundamental values of Victorians and Australians – mateship,
tolerance, community support and participation'. The city was
cruising and grazing.

He drove me to the airport the next day, and I interviewed him for a
radio feature, impressed by his knowledge and lack of self-
consciousness about wine. All taxi-drivers have forthright opinions,
but it was refreshing to find them targeted elsewhere than at society's
scapegoats. I told him about the glories of British ale, and promised to
help him discover them if ever he came over. His name was Andy
Osborne. We shook hands, and parted.

What was special about the encounter? Only this: it happened. As a
wine journalist, my visit to Australia was long overdue. Australian
wine production has developed spectacularly in response to the
uncomplicated interest and enthusiasm of people like Andy Osborne
– people who, 30 years ago, wouldn't even have drunk wine, let
alone owned up to an interest in it. Something similar has happened
right around the world: the last two decades have seen a startling
democratisation and internationalisation of the wine scene. Our
encounter was a drop or two of water in that wave.

The son of a former *régisseur* of Château Lafite makes wine in the
Pyrenees – the Victorian Pyrenees, an old goldmining district north of
Ballarat. When I met him, Dominique Portet of Taltarni, he'd just got
back from a sales trip to Finland; he told me about the visit he'd made
to the Himalayas in the previous year, to plant Chardonnay and
Altesse for the King of Bhutan. His brother Bernard makes wine at
Clos du Val in California. John Worontschak, the son of a Ukrainian
émigré to Australia, is one of England's best winemakers – for
Thames Valley vineyards, and as a consultant to the Harvest Wine

Group. When we last spoke, he'd just travelled out to do more consulting in the Czech Republic. Hugh Ryman, the son of a well-known former stationer, couldn't make a meeting we were to have had some months ago since he had suddenly to fly to Hong Kong – to tie up a deal by which he will make wine with the Australian Penfolds group in Moldova. An Israeli viticulturalist from the Golan Heights Winery gave me a first-hand account of food shortages in the former Soviet Union following his consultation to the aspiring wine producers of Kazakhstan (a wiry fellow to start with, he lost a kilo in two weeks). Two of the best white wines from Spain and Argentina which I've tasted in the last four months were made by a jet-hopping Bordelais, Jacques Lurton. Twenty years ago, no one in Bordeaux travelled much further than their neighbouring appellation – and then it was only to shake their heads sadly and say how much better things were at home.

'This global wine-sharing frenzy is reflected on our wine merchants' and supermarkets' shelves. Britain's biggest-selling two wines are still German Liebfraumilch and Italian white Lambrusco (the latter, by the way, a creation for the British market – it is almost unknown in Bologna, its home town); but Australian, Chilean and Bulgarian wines have stormed to prominence in the last few years, and exotica such as New Zealand Riesling, Canadian Icewine, Israeli Dry Muscat and Mexican Petite Syrah are the kind of thing with which the buyers are outdoing each other at present.

It's not, as the French like to hope, simply fashion which is bringing about these changes; it's taste, and tastes. Forget the names, soak all the labels off the bottles, and you would still have a 'New World' and an 'Old World'.

I'll explain. We could call Old World wines those of 'late complexity'. Their tastes work like this: in youth, the wines are bright, but tight and terse, and the tongue tends to perceive splinters of flavour rather than a harmonious whole. There may be little aroma. The wines then go through a dull period; and finally they pull round (the timescale varies according to the wine's relative grandeur) and grow into a gentle eloquence and expressivity. All wines begin by suggesting 'primary' fruit flavours (cherry, blackcurrant and so on) and end with a wider, more allusive range of 'secondary' flavours (earth, meat, tobacco leaf and many more). The point about the Old World way was that it ensured that a wine achieved its majority to coincide with the acquisition of these secondary flavours.

New World tastes work differently: they are founded on 'early fruit'. Viticulture and winemaking are tailored to emphasise primary rather than secondary flavours. In youth, therefore, the wines are enormously, overwhelmingly appealing, full of scent, supple in structure, and packed withfruit; some of the best may then draw in their horns before slowly fattening and simmering down to an unpredictable old age, while others may turn gradually to cardboard and dust. But most will have been drunk by then anyway.

Consumers have always wanted to drink wines of early fruit as well as wines of late complexity; indeed one reason why Beaujolais and Muscadet had the success they did in the 1960s and 1970s was that they offered early fruit when most of what was available required a wait for late complexity. The 'New World' countries – Australia and New Zealand in particular – have come near to perfecting the wine of early fruit; that was what turned people like Andy Osborne on to wine. The 'Old World' has long since perfected the wine of late complexity. Now both are trying to learn each other's tricks. But if the wine market is going to grow in the years ahead, and if more and more people are going to go out to eat, and if they are going to feel happy drinking wine when they do so, then the evangelists will be wines of early fruit. The older, richer and wiser may fall back and comfort their old age with wines of late complexity, but the new market wants something riper, softer and simpler. Indeed it is possible that many wine drinkers will never acquire a taste for the wines of late complexity, just as many of those who listen to music will settle for communicative rock, and never go near Mahler or Shostakovitch.

Many restaurateurs have glimpsed this imperfectly as yet; there is a 10-year time lag between restaurant wine lists and the wine ranges of Oddbins or Safeway. To some extent this is understandable: a list should reflect the tastes of the clientele, and those who eat out in restaurants, broadly speaking, are wealthier, older and wiser wine drinkers than those who shop in supermarkets; they are more attuned, therefore, to the pleasures and delinquencies of wines of late complexity. It's changing, though. We're all looking for fruit in young wines, even the most expensive; fewer of us want to age wine – or pay to have someone else age it for us. Even the producers realise this: taste a range of top Bordeaux châteaux from 1989 and 1990, and you'll find them a world away from what the same properties might have produced in 1975 and 1976. Indeed the 1975 clarets are museum pieces; that much tannin will never be allowed to climb into a bottle of Bordeaux red wine again.

So what are the directions in which wine lists should be moving? How should they evangelise as well as comfort and reward?

## France: a widening circle

France first. No, not Bordeaux and Burgundy, but vins de pays. Vins de pays are where much of the creativity in French winemaking lies at present; the producers of vins de pays are the only ones in France allowed to do what they like, where they like – and to tell us on the label which grape variety they've used. That makes them the

Australians of France (indeed quite a few of them *are* Australians). There could be few better ways of beginning a list than with a range of eight to ten crackingly good vins de pays. These could come from anywhere in France: it's the producers that count. Hardy (Dom. de la Baume/Chais Daumière) and Skalli are two big names, but there are even better little ones. The best of the wines should be bursting with early fruit – but fruit held and shaped by the freshness which Europe can always provide, and which Australia and California find more difficult.

What of France's classic wines? Restaurateurs want them; customers want them; I want them, too. But I want the best of them only; Bordeaux from those châteaux struggling to produce intelligible, accessible fine wines for a fair price (Léoville-Barton, Lynch-Bages, Haut-Bages-Libéral, Hanteillan, Sociando-Mallet would be typical names); Burgundy from those growers, like Seysses at Domaine Dujac, Barthod, Leclerc or Lafarge, who have the vision and tenacity to refuse the compromises which so often make the burgundy experience an unhappy one.

France's classicism, of course, is a great deal more than just Burgundy and Bordeaux. The Loire's best Chenin Blanc wines are among the most underrated whites in the world: Savennières, for example, from the now-biodynamic Joly estate or the less expensive two Clos du Papillon estates; Vouvray from Huët, Foreau or Brédif. Red Chinon and Bourgueil, from growers like Druet or Joguet, can let rip with some of the most exciting early fruit you'll find anywhere. The Syrah/Shiraz star is one of the fastest-rising in the wine firmament, unrivalled for perfume and sheer coruscating power in the northern Rhône; and in Crozes-Hermitage (Jaboulet's Thalabert, Graillot, Belle and others) you'll find what is possibly France's best-value appellation at present. Broad-hewn, hawthorn-scented northern Rhône whites offer a fascinating alternative to often platitudinous Chardonnay. South-western France has been a while leaving rustic excess behind it, but Cahors and Madiran and even Gaillac all now have their virtuosi (Clos Triguedina, Alain Brumont at Château Montus and Jean Cros respectively). France is still very much with us, even though there is now a world beyond it.

## Europe: unearthing treasures

Italy's wine renaissance is now well under way, and no nation on earth can provide wines with the attack and vibrancy of an Italian red. Piedmont's classics (from Aldo Conterno, Aldo Vajra, Elio Altare and others) have never been better. The country is also beginning to turn its treasury of grape varieties to good account, as wines like the rose-scented Vernaculum from Villa Ligi in the Marches, the eerie musk-laden reds based on the Negroamaro grape (Copertino, Salice

Salentino), or the muscular Aglianico (Aglianico del Vulture, Taurasi) show. Whites still pad along some way behind, but no list should be without one or two of the Alto Adige's perfumed varietals – and the fruits of Italian individuality, such as Sicily's own answer to the Côtes de Gascogne, Terre di Ginestra.

Portugal is, potentially, another Italy; the reverence for the aged bottle there means that early fruit is often still buried by tannin, but both grape varieties (Fernão Pires, Loureiro, Sousão, Touriga Nacional) and regions (Alentejo and Douro) have a huge amount to give. As in France and in Eastern Europe, the success of an Australian (Peter Bright at JP Vinhos) is catalysing native talent. In Spain, Ribera del Duero, Navarra, Toro and Valencia are four DO regions where fruit is hanging on through the sometimes exhaustive ageing process Spaniards give their wines, while Rueda and Galicia are both producing increasingly impressive nettle-fresh whites.

Germany's fine wines, neglected for so long, deserve a renaissance: the best wines of the Mosel and Rheingau (and they don't come better than Fritz Haag or Franz Künstler) have spellbinding delicacy: a good Kabinett or Spätlese from these areas is never too sweet to accompany food (particularly fish) well, while its naturally low alcohol content makes it restaurant-perfect for the car age. (It is not uncommon for a full bottle of Mosel or Saar Kabinett to contain no more alcohol than than half a bottle of Châteauneuf or Australian Chardonnay.) The best dry (trocken) and, particularly, half-dry (halbtrocken) wines of Germany's south, meanwhile (like those produced by Müller-Catoir or Lingenfelder in the Rheinpfalz), have all the ripe, balanced fruit which the early fusillades in the trocken revolution lacked. Simply avoid any German wine which happens to be cheaper than everything else.

Eastern Europe is a vast wine playground at present; Australians are flying in by the planeload, though it's largely to make varietals to a £2.99 formula for supermarkets. Better wines may follow. For most restaurant wine lists, a watching brief is what's required, especially since recent tastings suggest a period of anarchy may be approaching, as cash-hungry wineries dump large stocks of mediocre wine at any price they can get. The best Bulgarian reds, however, from top wineries like Russe, seem likely to consolidate their lead. This year has brought much-needed improvements in packaging, and those who sense opprobrium in the public drinking of Bulgarian red will not do so for much longer.

## The New World: a tightening focus

There is now so much on offer from Australia, New Zealand, America, South Africa and Chile that only a clear sense of what each does most successfully will reveal which is the best choice. From Australia, drinkers want fat, ripe, sun-drenched Chardonnays, often oaked to hell, because there's nothing else in the world like them, and they are, quite simply, a lot of fun to drink. Penfolds and Rosemount are leading players, but there are plenty of small challengers. For white wines which work with more considered, European inflections, look to Leeuwin in Western Australia, Mountadam in the Adelaide Hills, or Coldstream Hills in Victoria's Yarra Valley. Australian Rieslings (from the likes of Petaluma or Hill Smith) are so good they cannot stay off keen-edged wine lists for much longer; and a Marsanne or two (from, say, Château Tahbilk and Mitchelton) provide the Rhône comparisons intelligent diners will want.

'It is Australian red wines, though, which offer the world's best value at present. Barossa Valley Shiraz (St Hallets, Rockford, Basedow) is as great a regional style as Bordeaux Cabernet, and Penfolds' blenders can stretch it beyond Barossa confines with remarkable success; Coonawarra Cabernet (there's one in most ranges, but Wynns and Lindeman's Limestone Ridge and St George shape its definition) is the chief rival. Once again, regions like Western Australia (Cape Mentelle, Moss Wood, Cullens) and the Yarra Valley (Yarra Yering) produce tighter-grained fruit, more likely to run to later glory.

New Zealand is already providing some of the world's best Sauvignon Blancs (Montana, Cloudy Bay, Hunter's, Villa Maria) and Chardonnays (Martinborough, Cloudy Bay, Morton Estate, Te Mata, Villa Maria); it could easily add Riesling, were demand to require it, and its Loire-style and Bordeaux-style red wines improve almost daily.

America is less easy to categorise, since aspiration and profit fight, sometimes furiously, for the steering wheel. Cabernet and Cabernet blends can be great if occasionally forbidding (Caymus, Diamond Creek, Niebaum-Coppola's Rubicon, Newton, Ridge); and Pinot Noir is surprisingly accessible (Calera, Mondavi, Saintsbury, Sanford). The best Chardonnays are silkily delicious (Chalone, Cuvaison, Kistler). But Randall Grahm of Bonny Doon makes a plausible case for wholescale uprooting and replanting with the varieties of Southern France (Mourvèdre and Grenache) and Northern Italy (Barbera, with Dolcetto and Nebbiolo to follow). California's phylloxera and virus problems will certainly mean uprooting and replanting; though with what remains to be seen. Zinfandel (from Ridge, Grgich Hills, or more inexpensively, Stratford) and Petite Syrah (Ridge, Inglenook) provide a native idiom, with their Grand Canyon-like mouth-scenery.

South Africa's success in Britain so far has been based largely on inexpensive supermarket whites, and those following the estate trail have found quality patchy: whites can be slight and trivial; reds over-pressed and over-aggressive; and packaging, too, about as up to date as a 1950s fridge. But the Cape will make superb wine country once vine material is improved and a sense of style forged: those estates and producers already halfway there include Backsberg, Boschendal, Neil Ellis, Glen Carlou, Hamilton Russell, Klein Constantia, Villiera, Vriensenhof and Warwick.

Chile, finally, is another wineland of great promise, already partially realised in Cabernet Sauvignons and Merlots of insistent, driving purity and depth (Errazuriz, Montes, Santa Rita, Los Vascos). White wines have been less impressive, but there are signs of improvement from the likes of Errazuriz and Santa Carolina.

It may be food which draws a customer to a restaurant, but wine plays an important part in keeping him or her coming back. Wine culture is in a phase of rapid expansion at present: like the English language in Shakespeare's day, the creative possibilities seem endless, the substance itself enticingly pliable. Andy Osborne is excited by it; I am too; and we're not alone. Harvest this richness.

# Vintage Chart

SYMBOLS:

△ = immature
● = mature
▽ = drink up
□ = wines unlikely to be found in Britain, or undeclared vintages for port and champagne, which come from regions where only certain years are 'declared' or marketed as vintage wines.
★ = vintages not yet 'declared' or marketed (port, champagne)

All figures and symbols apply to the best wines of each vintage in each region.

Vintages have been rated on a 1 to 20 point scale (20 being the best).

| | 1 | 2 | 3 | 4 | 5 | 6 | 7 | 8 | 9 | 10 | 11 |
|---|---|---|---|---|---|---|---|---|---|---|---|
| 1992 | 12△ | 12△ | 13△ | 8△ | 15△ | 15△ | 14△ | 14● | 18△ | 16△ | 15△ |
| 1991 | 14△ | 12△ | 13△ | 12△ | 14△ | 14△ | 13△ | 12● | 14● | 16△ | 13● |
| 1990 | 17△ | 18△ | 14● | 19△ | 19△ | 19△ | 19△ | 19● | 19△ | 18△ | 18△ |
| 1989 | 19△ | 19△ | 17● | 19△ | 17● | 19△ | 20△ | 18● | 18△ | 16△ | 18△ |
| 1988 | 18△ | 19△ | 16● | 18△ | 18△ | 15● | 16△ | 17● | 19△ | 18△ | 17● |
| 1987 | 14● | 13● | 15● | 10● | 13● | 15● | 8● | 12● | 12● | 14● | 11● |
| 1986 | 19△ | 18△ | 14● | 17△ | 14● | 18● | 16△ | 18● | 16● | 15● | 16● |
| 1985 | 18● | 18● | 18△ | 15△ | 19● | 16● | 18△ | 16● | 17● | 18● | 19● |
| 1984 | 13● | 10● | 12● | 13● | 11▽ | 12▽ | 8● | 10▽ | 12▽ | 14● | 13● |
| 1983 | 18△ | 17● | 18● | 18△ | 14▽ | 17● | 16△ | 14▽ | 18● | 19△ | 17● |
| 1982 | 19● | 19● | 16● | 14● | 13▽ | 15▽ | 13● | 13▽ | 13▽ | 16● | 15● |
| 1981 | 16● | 15● | 15● | 13● | 11▽ | 8▽ | 16△ | 17● | 16● | 13● | 12● |
| 1980 | 11▽ | 10▽ | 11▽ | 12● | 13▽ | 11▽ | 13● | 12▽ | 8▽ | 14● | 14● |
| 1979 | 16▽ | 18▽ | 17▽ | 14● | 14▽ | 16▽ | 14● | 14▽ | 10▽ | 15● | 14● |
| 1978 | 17● | 17● | 17● | 12● | 18● | 17● | 15● | 18● | 12▽ | 19● | 18● |
| 1977 | 9▽ | 9▽ | 7▽ | 6▽ | 7▽ | 10▽ | 5▽ | 8▽ | 7▽ | 8▽ | 7▽ |
| 1976 | 16▽ | 14▽ | 16▽ | 17● | 14▽ | 14▽ | 18● | 16▽ | 18● | 18● | 14▽ |
| 1975 | 16● | 17● | 17● | 18● | 4▽ | 6▽ | 16● | 15▽ | 14▽ | 10▽ | 9▽ |
| 1974 | 12▽ | 10▽ | 9▽ | 8▽ | 11▽ | 10▽ | 8▽ | 11▽ | 10▽ | 9▽ | 11▽ |
| 1973 | 13▽ | 12▽ | 11▽ | 12▽ | 10▽ | 14▽ | 13▽ | 16▽ | 14▽ | 12▽ | 13▽ |
| 1972 | 8▽ | 8▽ | 6▽ | 9▽ | 12▽ | 10▽ | 8▽ | 6▽ | 5▽ | 14▽ | 15▽ |
| 1971 | 15● | 16● | 18● | 16● | 18● | 17▽ | 16● | 18● | 19● | 17● | 17● |
| 1970 | 18● | 17● | 16● | 14● | 13▽ | 13▽ | 16● | 16▽ | 11▽ | 16● | 18● |
| 1969 | 11▽ | 9▽ | 8▽ | 13▽ | 16▽ | 17▽ | 18● | 16▽ | 13▽ | 18● | 17▽ |
| 1968 | 7▽ | 5▽ | 5▽ | 3▽ | 4▽ | 4▽ | 9▽ | 11▽ | 5▽ | 6▽ | 5▽ |
| 1967 | 12▽ | 12▽ | 11▽ | 17● | 13▽ | 14▽ | 13▽ | 12▽ | 17▽ | 16● | 18▽ |
| 1966 | 17● | 18● | 16▽ | 14▽ | 16▽ | 17▽ | 15● | 18● | 16▽ | 17● | 18▽ |
| 1965 | 3▽ | 3▽ | 3▽ | 6▽ | 2▽ | 3▽ | 6▽ | 7▽ | 4▽ | 8▽ | 6▽ |
| 1964 | 14▽ | 16▽ | 11▽ | 6▽ | 14▽ | 14▽ | 18● | 14▽ | 15▽ | 17▽ | 16▽ |
| 1963 | 5▽ | 5▽ | 3▽ | □ | 11▽ | 14▽ | □ | □ | 8▽ | 7▽ | 8▽ |
| 1962 | 14▽ | 15▽ | 16▽ | 17● | 16▽ | 18▽ | 15● | 14▽ | 14▽ | 17▽ | 16▽ |
| 1961 | 20● | 20● | 18▽ | 16▽ | 14▽ | 16▽ | 14● | 16▽ | 18▽ | 20● | 19● |

1 = Red Bordeaux: Médoc & Graves
2 = Red Bordeaux: St-Emilion & Pomerol
3 = Dry white Bordeaux
4 = Sweet white Bordeaux: Sauternes & Barsac
5 = Red burgundy
6 = White burgundy
7 = Loire (sweet)
8 = Loire (dry)
9 = Alsace
10 = Northern Rhône
11 = Southern Rhône
12 = Midi
13 = Champagne
14 = Rioja
15 = Vintage port
16 = Red Portuguese
17 = Barolo & Barbaresco
18 = Tuscany
19 = Mosel–Saar–Ruwer
20 = Rhinelands
21 = Australia
22 = New Zealand
23 = California

| 12 | 13 | 14 | 15 | 16 | 17 | 18 | 19 | 20 | 21 | 22 | 23 | |
|----|----|----|----|----|----|----|----|----|----|----|----|----|
| 15△ | ★ | 16● | ★ | 16△ | 14△ | 13△ | 18△ | 17△ | 16△ | 15● | 19△ | 1992 |
| 16△ | ★ | 16● | 18△ | 16● | 13△ | 14△ | 13● | 14● | 18△ | 18● | 19△ | 1991 |
| 19● | ★ | 18△ | □ | 17● | 18△ | 20△ | 20△ | 20△ | 17● | 15● | 18△ | 1990 |
| 18● | ★ | 18△ | □ | 17● | 18△ | 13● | 19△ | 18△ | 10● | 19● | 14● | 1989 |
| 19● | ★ | 17● | □ | 11● | 17△ | 19△ | 17● | 17● | 16● | 14● | 15● | 1988 |
| 14● | □ | 16● | 17△ | 15● | 14● | 14● | 6▽ | 7▽ | 18● | 16● | 12● | 1987 |
| 16● | 15● | 17● | □ | 9▽ | 15● | 17● | 11▽ | 13● | 19● | 18● | 14● | 1986 |
| 18● | 19● | 19● | 19△ | 19● | 20△ | 19● | 15▽ | 15● | 17● | 17● | 19● | 1985 |
| 13● | □ | 13● | □ | 14▽ | 8▽ | 9▽ | 3▽ | 5▽ | 18● | 15▽ | 13● | 1984 |
| 18● | 16● | 15● | 18△ | 18● | 13▽ | 15▽ | 16▽ | 14▽ | 14● | □ | 12▽ | 1983 |
| 17▽ | 17● | 16● | 13● | 15▽ | 19● | 17● | 7▽ | 8▽ | 19△ | □ | 15● | 1982 |
| 17▽ | 16● | 17● | □ | 10▽ | 13▽ | 14▽ | 8▽ | 10▽ | 13▽ | □ | 14▽ | 1981 |
| 15▽ | 10▽ | 16▽ | 16△ | 17● | 11▽ | 13▽ | 3▽ | 4▽ | 18● | □ | 17● | 1980 |
| 15▽ | 17● | 14▽ | □ | 14▽ | 14▽ | 17● | 11▽ | 12▽ | 16● | □ | 14▽ | 1979 |
| 18▽ | 12▽ | 19● | □ | 15● | 18● | 16● | 9▽ | 9▽ | 18● | □ | 16● | 1978 |
| 10▽ | □ | 6▽ | 20△ | 16● | 11▽ | 16▽ | 5▽ | 8▽ | 14▽ | □ | 12▽ | 1977 |
| 12▽ | 18● | 13▽ | □ | 12▽ | 14▽ | 13▽ | 19● | 17● | 17● | □ | 14▽ | 1976 |
| 12▽ | 14▽ | 15▽ | 13▽ | 13▽ | 12▽ | 17▽ | 17● | 18● | 18● | □ | 14▽ | 1975 |
| □ | 9▽ | 14▽ | □ | 10▽ | 16▽ | 14▽ | 3▽ | 4▽ | 11▽ | □ | 18● | 1974 |
| □ | 14▽ | 17▽ | □ | 6▽ | 13▽ | 16▽ | 11▽ | 10▽ | 14▽ | □ | 17● | 1973 |
| □ | □ | 7▽ | □ | 12▽ | 10▽ | 9▽ | 6▽ | 7▽ | 13▽ | □ | 15▽ | 1972 |
| □ | 17▽ | 9▽ | □ | 9▽ | 18▽ | 18▽ | 20● | 19● | 20● | □ | 14▽ | 1971 |
| □ | 16▽ | 19● | 18● | 17▽ | 17▽ | 16▽ | 12▽ | 11▽ | 14▽ | □ | 17● | 1970 |
| □ | 14▽ | 12▽ | □ | 9▽ | 14▽ | 14▽ | 16▽ | 13▽ | □ | □ | 16▽ | 1969 |
| □ | □ | 10▽ | □ | 9▽ | 13▽ | 17▽ | □ | □ | 14▽ | □ | 19● | 1968 |
| □ | 13▽ | 12▽ | 16● | 14▽ | 16▽ | 18▽ | 17● | 17● | 15▽ | □ | 14▽ | 1967 |
| □ | 16▽ | 15▽ | 18● | 19● | 15▽ | 16▽ | 16▽ | 16▽ | 19● | □ | 16▽ | 1966 |
| □ | □ | 8▽ | □ | □ | □ | □ | □ | □ | 15▽ | □ | 18▽ | 1965 |
| □ | 17▽ | 20● | □ | □ | 19▽ | 18▽ | 17● | 15▽ | □ | □ | 16▽ | 1964 |
| □ | □ | 12▽ | 20● | 16▽ | □ | □ | 12▽ | 12▽ | 17▽ | □ | 16▽ | 1963 |
| □ | 15▽ | 13▽ | □ | □ | 13▽ | 16▽ | 14▽ | 16▽ | 18● | □ | 13▽ | 1962 |
| □ | 16▽ | 10▽ | □ | □ | 18▽ | 15▽ | 10▽ | 12▽ | □ | □ | 15▽ | 1961 |

# London

---

## Adams Café £

map 10

77 Askew Road, W12 9AH
081-743 0572

COOKING 1*
COST £15–£23

The Café must have been the hit of the year for East Acton. The hordes in search of couscous enabled the Boukraas to transform their greasy-spoon into a tiled labyrinth of Tunisian delight. They have added a new room, a new kitchen, a better bar and generally spruced everything up. The surreal transformation which used to be engineered at teatime by putting candles on the tables and covering the glass display cabinet with a north African shawl now works the other way. Bleary workers of a morning are served coffee and sliced white toast in a room out of *Beau Geste*. Refurbishment has seen an expansion to the menu, but what everyone remarks upon are the little appetisers (meatballs, olives and a pot of harissa), the briks or, as an alternative, 'Fatima's fingers' (filo rolls filled with minced beef) and the couscous (all four versions). The couscous itself is dry and fluffy (though some claim it is not as fragrant as the best that memory can supply), the sauce copious. Service, even with the larger, busier set-up, remains endlessly willing. North African wines – and the place must have the biggest slate of Tunisian vintages in London – all cost £7.95. House French is £5.95. A small corkage charge (55p) still applies if you want to bring your own.

CHEF: Abdel Boukraa  PROPRIETORS: Abdel and Frances Boukraa  OPEN: Mon to Sat, D only; 7.30 to 10.30  CLOSED: bank hols, 2 weeks Aug  MEALS: alc (main courses £5.50 to £7.50). Cover 95p  SERVICE: not inc  DETAILS: 60 seats. Private parties: 36 main room, 24 private room. Vegetarian meals. Children welcome. Wheelchair access. Music

---

## Ajimura £

NEW ENTRY  map 15

51–53 Shelton Street, WC2H 9HE
071-240 0178

COOKING 2*
COST £13–£52

This claims to be the longest-serving Japanese restaurant in London. 'Of all of them, it has been my favourite because it is so relaxed and helpful to vegetarians' is the firm comment of one reader and might serve as general pointer to the fact that this place is pitched to London's demands, not those of ethnic Japanese or people seeking the Japan experience. Hence service is friendly and cheerful, materials are more English than is sometimes the case, and it has a self-confessed 'bohemian' character – not the first word you would think of in connection with Japanese restaurants. Recent meals have confirmed the quality of the sushi, of non-standard variants like spinach wrapped in seaweed, of sometimes good bean curd and excellent stocks. The menus offer lots of variation, including a pre-theatre meal – another first for Japanese restaurants, we think. Drink the chilled saké. House wines are £7.

CHEFS: Susumu Okada and Tatsuo Tanizawa   PROPRIETORS: Susumu Okada and Harumi Okada   OPEN: Mon to Sat, exc Sat L; 12 to 3, 6 to 11   CLOSED: bank hols   MEALS: alc (main courses £6.50 to £15). Set L £7.50 to £8.50, Set pre-theatre D £12.50, Set D £19 to £35   SERVICE: 10%   CARDS: Access, Amex, Diners, Visa   DETAILS: 60 seats. Private parties: 30 main room, 20 private room. Vegetarian meals. Children welcome. No smoking in sushi bar. Music. Air-conditioned. Fax: 071-497 2240

## Alastair Little
map 15

49 Frith Street, W1V 5TE
071-734 5183

COOKING 4*
COST £25–£69

'Of course there are shortcomings. These are centred mainly on the premises, now seven years old and in need of rejuvenation.' This is the comment of a dyed-in-the-wool supporter. The restaurant is conceived on minimalist lines, can be noisy and will not gratify the linen-and-frills brigade. The cooking retains an edge, continues to surprise, has real flavour and is quite simply better than that of most places that produce food in this style. Service surprises some by its lack of formality, but should in reality please everyone for its naturalness and essential sense of hospitality. On the down side, the price is high (and most London restaurants complain that prices are high because of the overheads, which evidently are diminishing here) and output can sometimes be uneven. This can cause venomous reaction on the part of the customer. 'It is difficult to catch up with the latest variations on a theme. For instance, bread-and-butter puddings sampled in one month ranged from a classic firm-set version to one using pannetone and another that oozed creamy custard topped by a beautifully crisp crust.' Is this Alastair Little not making up his mind, or never ceasing to be satisfied? Responses may depend on whether the experiment was successful the last time. The menu changes at every meal. The best dish of the year for one reader was sea bass just seasoned and grilled to surface crispness, to accompany it a salad of sun-dried tomatoes, olives and flat-leaved parsley. The simplest techniques are studied: pasta tastes of something, with no additions needed, but becomes sublime with morels and asparagus, or delightful with pesto. No expense is spared by the kitchen in getting proper ingredients – one good cause of the prices – thus morels again (fresh, of course) in a risotto, and foie gras infusing a duck terrine. Standards do reappear: lamb with flageolets and chicken wrapped in cabbage are two that get regular mention. If only we were rich enough to follow the kitchen at every turn: a chef looking for a way to do spicy Thai sausages (here served with oysters) found the best in town were from this restaurant. Amateurs eagerly await Mr Little's forthcoming recipe book. The wine list rises from £12 and displays a similar knowledge of the subject allied to restless exploration. There is a chance of a discovery, therefore, though a Guigal Côtes du Rhône at more than three times the cost price may leave us wondering at the margins.

CHEF: Alastair Little   PROPRIETORS: Mercedes Andre-Vega, Kirsten Pedersen and Alastair Little   OPEN: Mon to Sat, exc Sat L; 12 to 3, 6 to 11.30   MEALS: alc (main courses £16 to £24). Set L £10 (2 courses, bar only) to £20   SERVICE: not inc   CARDS: Access, Amex, Visa   DETAILS: 36 seats. Private parties: 14 private room. Vegetarian meals. Children's helpings. No music. Air-conditioned

## Alba

map 11

107 Whitecross Street, EC1Y 8JH
071-588 1798

COOKING 1*
COST £24–£40

Convenient for the Barbican complex, for audience and participants alike, Alba offers north Italian cooking (the likes of truffles, artichokes and asparagus). The Georgian terraced house has been stripped and cleaned for restaurant use and staffed by willing people. On the 'approved' list are bresaola (whether of beef, horse or venison), panzerotti alle noci (pasta filled with spinach and ricotta, with a cream and walnut sauce), and a carpaccio of veal with Parmesan, rocket and truffle oil. There is much evidence of the grill in the main courses, especially fish, though breast of chicken pointed with rosemary and balsamic vinegar, and venison cutlets marinated in red wine and served with polenta are two fried dishes that have been mentioned. Sweets trundle round on a trolley; otherwise there are the Italian cheeses. 'The proprietor advised us on the wine, a Pio Cesare Gavi, which was excellent' was a comment from a wise drinker wanting guidance from a list of three dozen Italians, none expensive, some worth investigating. House wine is £7.50.

CHEF: Armando Liboi   PROPRIETOR: Rudi Venerandi   OPEN: Mon to Fri; 12 to 3, 6 to 11   MEALS: alc (main courses £7 to £12)   SERVICE: 12.5%, card slips closed   CARDS: Access, Amex, Diners, Visa   DETAILS: 45 seats. Private parties: 60 main room. Vegetarian meals. Children's helpings. Wheelchair access (1 step). Music

## Albero & Grana

NEW ENTRY   map 13

Chelsea Cloisters,
89 Sloane Avenue, SW3 3DX
071-225 1048 and 1049

COOKING 2
COST £26–£44

The name is not that of a comedy duo from the world of Spanish vaudeville, but reference to the sand of the bullring and the red of the lining of the matador's cape (bunfight rather than bullfight come the evening when the bar 'was six deep in trendies dressed in black, drinking designer beer – Spaniards know how to party'). *La movida* has arrived. The bar in this brightly coloured, ('vibrantly designed' is one term) restaurant is to the front. Tapas are of a higher standard than in most places that hide behind the word in London. The bar, but not the restaurant, is open at lunch-times. Angel Garcia is a new-wave chef born not of the pretty-pretty tendencies of nouvelle cuisine (it happened in Spain too) but of the more expressive and robust reappraisal that has happened in recent years. This may mean that not every dish is what it seems ('The escabèche was not technically escabèche,' maintained one), but may result in noticeable flavour: calves' kidneys with sherry sauce had the real taste of sherry, not merely a waft of the bottle's neck. Good produce may be left unsullied:

baby lamb Segovian-style was indeed plainly roasted with salted skin and milky flesh, served with roast new potatoes; butifarra (sausages) with ceps, garlic and parsley were also robust enough for any hard-working body, even if the sauce were scant. Lasagne with black pudding (morcilla) and a green pimento sauce has satisfied some, but left others wondering at the sticky pasta and the mildness of the morcilla. Desserts include a sweet lemon and tomato tart with meringue topping. Service can be so laid back that it collapses. The wine list is surprisingly unadventurous, given the possibilities. It does have a sound range of familiar Riojas. House wines are £8.50.

CHEF: Angel Garcia  PROPRIETORS: County Supplies Ltd  OPEN: all week, exc Sun D; 7.30 to 11 (bar 6 to 12)  MEALS: alc (main courses £9.50 to £16). Tapas menu (£2 to £6) SERVICE: not inc (10% for 7 or more)  CARDS: Access, Amex, Diners, Visa  DETAILS: 120 seats. Private parties: 300 main room. Vegetarian meals with prior notice. Children's helpings on request. Smart dress preferred. Music. Air-conditioned. Fax: 071-581 3259

## Al Bustan

map 13

27 Motcomb Street, SW1X 8JU
071-235 8277

COOKING 1*
COST £31–£48

In a snazzy Belgravia terrace dotted with antique shops, this stands out as a reliable source of Lebanese food. A few tables are set up outside, and the interior is predictably plush with lots of trellis work, greenery and smartly laid tables packed closely together. Service is helpful. The menu offers an assortment of Lebanese and Middle Eastern specialities, with the meze a major attraction. Cold items range from tabbouleh and labneh ('rich and cheesy' strained yogurt drizzled with olive oil) to goats' cheese salad. Well-reported hot items have included grilled chicken wings with garlic sauce, Lebanese lamb sausages, and chickpeas stewed with garlic, olive oil and tomato. Dishes score highly on freshness and authenticity. High-protein main courses rely heavily on the chargrill, but a few raw meat dishes are also available and fish is at market price – suggesting regular fresh supplies. Sweets feature 'perfectly executed' Lebanese pastries. The cover charge includes a harvest festival of raw vegetables, plus warm flat bread dotted with sesame seeds. The short wine list has some Lebanese bottles which are worth exploring – although there is not much under £20. House French is £15.

CHEF: Mrs R. Atalla  PROPRIETORS: Mr and Mrs R. Atalla  OPEN: all week; noon to 11 (10 Sun)  CLOSED: 25 and 26 Dec  MEALS: alc (main courses £8.50 to £10). Cover £2. Minimum £10  SERVICE: 10%  CARDS: Access, Amex, Diners, Visa  DETAILS: 65 seats. 6 tables outside. Private parties: 25 main room, 7, 10 and 15 private rooms. Vegetarian meals. Children's helpings. Smart dress preferred. Wheelchair access (2 steps). Music. Air-conditioned

'We called for a snack lunch on Saturday. We can confirm the quality of the smoked salmon, the smoked salmon pâté and the house wine. The barman was no asset, however – sullen and reluctant to serve us at 1.55. He whipped my empty wine glass away before our food arrived and announced to the staff, ''Now we can all go home.'' I ignored him and ordered a refill. The rest of the staff were wonderful, however, and obviously loathed him – hope he wasn't mine host.'  On eating in Yorkshire

## Alexandra

map 10

507 Kingston Road, SW20 8SF
081-542 4838

COOKING 1*
COST £20–£33

Formerly Café Normand, this converted terraced house near Raynes Park
station was renamed in celebration of Eric Lecras' young daughter. The
intimacy of the place appeals and service is discreet. Eric works to a daily-
changing blackboard that retains some of its rich creamy Normandy dishes –
generously filled crêpes dieppoises, pork in calvados – but also looks south for
salad of crottin chavignol and grilled red mullet niçoise. Many dishes have
been favourably reported: gently steamed asparagus tips on a bed of salad
leaves with a classy walnut oil dressing; pigeon breasts with armagnac, cream
and redcurrant sauce; calf's liver with basil; 'intense' strawberry sorbet; and
puits d'amour (home-made meringues filled with light chocolate mousse
served with custard cream). Tarte Alexandra is a fine, light pastry with
caramelised sliced apples flamed with calvados, while cafetière coffee is an
increasingly strong brew. Fixed-price lunches are reckoned to be excellent
value. Around 20 French wines are keenly chosen and fairly priced examples
from the major growing regions. House wine is £7.85.

CHEF/PROPRIETOR: Eric Lecras  OPEN: Tue to Sun, exc Sat L and Sun D; 12 to 2, 7 to 10
CLOSED: 26 to 28 Dec  MEALS: alc (main courses £9 to £11). Set L £10.55 (2 courses), Set
Sun L £12.75  SERVICE: 12.5%  CARDS: Access, Visa  DETAILS: 55 seats. 6 tables outside.
Private parties: 30 main room, 30 private room. Vegetarian meals with prior notice.
Children's helpings Sun L. Smart dress preferred. Music

## Al Hamra

map 14

31–33 Shepherd Market, W1Y 7RJ
071-493 1954 and 6934

COOKING 2
COST £29–£42

A reporter waxes lyrical about this: 'It has that special air of confidence,
bonhomie and charm of Lebanon in the old days (in my imaginings). Also a
slight air of danger, almost wickedness. Piquant!' Most people are attracted to
the array of hot and cold meze, which runs to more than 40 items, including
praiseworthy tabbouleh, 'terrific' moutabal, warak inab (stuffed vine leaves),
hummus kawarmah (topped with diced lamb and pine-nuts), muhamara
(crushed nuts with hot sauce), falafel and kibbeh. Main courses are mainly
lamb and chicken subjected to the chargrill: sharwarma is shredded lamb
marinated in vinegar, spices and onions 'grilled on kiosk' (a revolving spit).
Finish with sticky pastries or elegantly sliced fresh fruit. The cover charge of
£2.50 pays for olives, bread and raw vegetables. To drink, you can choose
between mint tea, Turkish coffee, Iyran yogurt or arak. Otherwise there is a
modest but pricey wine list. House wines start at £11.

CHEF: Mahir Abboud  PROPRIETORS: Riad Nabulsi and Hassan Fansa  OPEN: all week;
noon to midnight  CLOSED: 25 Dec and 1 Jan  MEALS: alc (main courses £8 to £9). Cover
£2.50. Minimum £10  SERVICE: not inc  CARDS: Access, Amex, Diners, Visa  DETAILS: 75
seats. 4 tables outside. Private parties: 80 main room. Vegetarian meals. Children's
helpings. Wheelchair access. Music. Air-conditioned

## All Saints £

| NEW ENTRY | map 12 |

12 All Saints Road, W11 1HH
071-243 2808

COOKING 1
COST £15–£39

The clientele here is precisely what you would expect in deepest Portobello. 'I was wearing platform clogs, leggings and a white T-shirt that could have done with a wash; I fitted in just fine' was how one reader put it, adding that it took her two tries to find a chair that did not collapse. The cooking might be said to fit, too. Generously portioned, not too expensive and generally eclectic, it has improved by leaps and bounds. There is a good turn-out for the breakfast menu (10 to 12 Monday to Saturday), better for lunch, with blackboard specials supplementing the constant repertoire, then a daily-changing menu for dinner. Eclectic is again about the only adjective for a list that runs from sweet potato and spinach curry with banana chutney, cod with salsa verde and mustard fruits, to lamb and olive burger with tsatsiki, aubergine, feta and hummus. Flavours are broad, and the place tries to make the food taste of whatever was signalled by the menu, so that penne with tomatoes, basil and Parmesan was not just an apology for tomato sauce. Bulk is given its true value here, as in a goats' cheese salad filled out with decent sourdough bread. And humour is not far away, at least not for the one who ordered chocolate nut brownie with ice-cream, to be faced with 'a slab of brownie topped with two balls of ice-cream, skewered with a banana with a head of half an apricot'. The wine list is short but cheap. House wines are £7.50.

CHEF/PROPRIETOR: Rupert Smith  OPEN: all week, exc Mon L and Sun D; 12.30 to 3.30 (11 to 4 Sun brunch), 7.30 to 11.15  CLOSED: bank hol Mon  MEALS: alc (main courses L £3.50 to £4.50, D £7 to £10.50)  SERVICE: not inc, card slips closed  CARDS: Access, Diners, Visa  DETAILS: 50 seats. Private parties: 20 main room, 20 private room. Vegetarian meals. Children welcome. Music

## Al San Vincenzo

map 11

30 Connaught Street, W2 2AE
071-262 9623

COOKING 3
COST £24–£42

Our criticisms of this small family-run restaurant in last year's edition were not well received, yet they reflected an admitted (by some) reality that there was a dip in palatability as Mr Borgonzolo undertook the long exodus from Cheam (where he started) to the West End. No criticisms this year, however, proclaim his many supporters, themselves exiles from the sun and song of Italy. 'Southern Italian cooking is robust, substantial and simple. I don't know of a restaurant in Italy that presents such invention while maintaining tradition,' asserts a knowledgeable regular. There is no trendiness on the menu (unless zampone with lentils is trendy), but rather bold cooking of pasta – orecchiette with black olives, capers, chilli and Parmesan – or pork products – salsiccia con foglie de broccoli. Tongue with pickles and venison with juniper and an agrodolce sauce are examples of more robustness in the meat department, and many comment on the ability to produce recipes that stray not at all on to hackneyed Italian paths. As Italian products get better exposure here, so the cheeseboard improves. Panettone bread-and-butter pudding or baked apples with grappa are desserts with a Mediterranean tilt that satisfy British appetites.

The wine list is short but good. It is wise to listen to advice. House wines are £9.50.

CHEF: Vincenzo Borgonzolo  PROPRIETORS: Vincenzo and Elaine Borgonzolo  OPEN: Mon to Sat, exc Sat L; 12.30 to 2.15, 7 to 10.30  MEALS: alc (main courses £9.50 to £14.50)  SERVICE: not inc  CARDS: Access, Visa  DETAILS: 22 seats. Private parties: 8 main room. Vegetarian meals with prior notice. Children welcome. Smart dress preferred. No cigars/pipes in dining-room. Music

## Anna's Place

map 11

90 Mildmay Park, N1 4PR
071-249 9379

COOKING 2
COST £21–£35

For all its affiliation to Swedish cooking, the long-running Anna's Place belongs to leafy Newington Green. In the front section the tables are so serried they could make up a chequerboard, but beyond them is a spacious middle ground with the bar which gives on to a garden for picnics on those northern nights when the sun never sets. The menu, which may be explained to you in great detail by Anna or her daughter ('the long descriptions were confusing, especially since nearly everything was noted as "very nice" or "my favourite"'), does not change its essential framework of gravlax (one of London's first), Swedish marinated herrings, biff Strindberg, and Swedish waffles with blueberries and cream. But other dishes – for instance, a game tart, courgette ravioli, sea bream with herb sauce, calf's liver with cider glaze, and a gratin of fresh fruit – come and go with tastes and seasons. The welcome, service and cooking still manage enthusiasm and freshness. There may be details that get rubbed at the corners, but the gloss still shines encouragingly. The place remains popular because the prices are never silly. The same could be said of the wine list. House wine is £7.

CHEFS: René Christiensen and Mark Stocks  PROPRIETOR: Anna Hegarty  OPEN: Tue to Sat; 12.15 to 2.15, 7.15 to 10.45  CLOSED: 2 weeks Christmas and Easter, Aug  MEALS: alc (main courses £7 to £12.50)  SERVICE: 10%  DETAILS: 45 seats. 5 tables outside. Private parties: 12 main room. Vegetarian meals. Children's helpings. Wheelchair access. Music

## Argyll

map 13

316 King's Road, SW3 5UH
071-723 8986

COOKING 3
COST £19–£49

Oh! to boulevard down the King's Road and dive into the cool and airy premises of this restaurant. The bleached floor, spacious tables, mixed bag of second-hand dining chairs, and generally civilised air impart a relaxed elegance to a visit here. 'Elegant' may well be an epithet for Anand Sastry's cooking; it certainly lacks no effort of arrangement. But Sastry's signature of little central piles of comestibles apart, the food has much to recommend it: palpable freshness, variety of recipe and immediacy of flavour; wild mushrooms, offal and pulses seem to bulk large; and it does not outface. The only criticism is that sauces can be at the sweet end of the spectrum. Dishes such as artichoke and salsify soup, scrambled egg on a brioche with wild mushrooms, ragoût of chicken with mustard seeds, braised oxtail (these from a bargain £10 lunch), ravioli of foie gras with lentils and Sauternes, peppered tuna niçoise, and navarin of lamb with aubergines and thyme sauce have met with strong approval. Banana parfait with caramelised bananas, or roast pear with an orange and ginger caramel keep up the momentum. The Argyll is one of the less expensive – and successful – new-wave London restaurants born out of the recession. Trend-spotters will identify many of the growers and properties on the wine list, which is up to date, but not at giveaway prices. House wines are £10.50 to £12.

CHEF: Anand Sastry  PROPRIETORS: Christian Arden and Anand Sastry  OPEN: Mon to Sat, exc Mon L; 12 to 2.30, 7 to 11  MEALS: alc (main courses £9 to £14). Set L £8.50 (2 courses) to £10  SERVICE: not inc  CARDS: Access, Amex, Diners, Visa  DETAILS: 60 seats. 3 tables outside. Private parties: 60 main room. Vegetarian meals. Children's helpings on request. No cigars/pipes in dining-room. Wheelchair access. Music. Air-conditioned. Fax: 071-352 1652

## Arisugawa ✷✖

| | |
|---|---|
| 27 Percy Street, W1P 9FF | **NEW ENTRY** map 14 |
| 071-636 8913 | COOKING 2* |
| | COST £12–£60 |

This large basement restaurant with seating round a sushi bar, a private tatami room and tables set up Japanese-style (take your shoes off) is popular with the Japanese business community. It gets rather jolly in the evenings, with raffles for a free dish on the next visit, and everyone is very friendly and welcoming. The food is grand as well. Sometimes the details are not as finely tuned as in the classier, and quieter, places, but perhaps the evening will turn out more enjoyable. Sushi and sashimi are so quickly turned over that freshness is guaranteed, stocks for soups are excellent and so are the noodles. Some dishes will surprise the unwary, as will always be the case if the nooks and crannies of a Japanese menu are fully explored; here the strong fermented soy with squid was the brave man's forfeit.

CHEF: Akira Takeuchi  PROPRIETOR: Mrs Masako Yamamoto  OPEN: Mon to Sat, exc Sat L; 12.30 to 2.30, 6 to 10  MEALS: alc (main courses £6 to £20). Set L £5 to £14, Set D £20 to £38. Cover £1 D  SERVICE: not inc L, 15% D, card slips closed  CARDS: Access, Amex, Diners, Visa  DETAILS: 100 seats. Private parties: 20 main room, 50 private room. Vegetarian meals. Children's helpings. Smart dress preferred. No smoking in dining-room. Music. Air-conditioned. Fax: 071-323 4237

## Les Associés

| | |
|---|---|
| 172 Park Road, N8 8JY | map 10 |
| 081-348 8944 | COOKING 1* |
| | COST £25–£55 |

'Trying to book on Sunday/Monday [when the associates dissociate] for the following Tuesday proved the most difficult part of our evening,' reports a local; once you are inside, friendly French intimacy dissipates metropolitan organisational angst. Gilles Charvet's half-dozen starters and main courses change regularly and are carefully crafted. The miniature feuilletés of snails left one enthusiast doubting if he had had better in France; loin of rabbit was braised so as to leave juices loitering deliciously in the meat tissues; and the vegetable side dishes, included in the main-course price, have shone on their own. 'The service leaves you to judge for yourself' as the menu winningly puts it. Most verdicts are favourable: 'The smaller associate was as friendly as ever,' writes one, while others have forgiven slightly expensive pricing when generosity of spirit is shown – in this case, by the provision of a small plate of (uncharged) cheeses to see down the remains of a bottle of Rasteau. The wine list is terse, exclusively French and requires £15 to give you any element of choice. House wines are £9.80.

CHEF: Gilles Charvet   PROPRIETORS: Gilles Charvet, Dominique Chéhere and Didier Bertran   OPEN: Tue to Sat, exc L Tue and Sat; 12.30 to 2, 7.30 to 10   CLOSED: 1 week Easter, Aug   MEALS: alc (main courses £13 to £15). Set L £15.95, Set D £27 to £35 SERVICE: not inc, card slips closed   CARDS: Access, Visa   DETAILS: 36 seats. Private parties: 20 main room, 20 private room. Vegetarian meals. Children's helpings. Wheelchair access. Music

## Au Jardin des Gourmets 🍾

map 15

5 Greek Street, W1V 6NA
071-437 1816

COOKING 2
COST £27–£52

'All French restaurants should look like this,' commented a reader satisfied by the Jardin's cool spaciousness, the plethora of atmospheric paintings, and the refreshing draught through open windows on a hot summer's day. On the first floor is the restaurant, with a pair of very fine rooms for private parties; the ground floor houses the brasserie. The Jardin is one of Soho's longest-running French-style places. People come here for the wine as much as for the food – the list is a treasure-trove. 'The entire staff seemed concerned our Pape-Clément was on form,' commented one happy drinker. The cooking this year has not had such good reports but may change now that new chef Simon Wills has been appointed. The menu has not surprised for novelty but has reassured for conservatism. The amiability of the staff and the happy ambience have pleased. The wine list maintains its affinity for burgundy, but many customers will be happy to settle for the menu's suggested wines by the glass. Great depth is shown: for example, 1961 is represented by eight clarets, but these are nicely spread between Fourcas-Hosten and Beychevelle. Similar balance is shown in more recent vintages: there is a fondness for excellent value from the likes of Fronsac and Bourg, and reliable Beaujolais counterpoints a very fine Côtes de Nuits. This is a peach of a list that shows consideration and permits extravagance. House wines are from £8. CELLARMAN'S CHOICE: Montagny, premier cru, Les Vignes sur le Clou 1990, A. Roy, £19.50; St-Emilion, Ch. Rolland-Maillet 1986, £21.

CHEF: Simon Wills   PROPRIETORS: Au Jardin des Gourmets Ltd   OPEN: Mon to Sat, exc Sat L; 12.15 to 2.30, 6 to 11.15   MEALS: alc (main courses £11 to £16). Set L and D £10.75 (2 courses) to £19.50. Cover £1   SERVICE: 15%, card slips closed   CARDS: Access, Amex, Diners, Visa   DETAILS: 150 seats. Private parties: 55 main room, 12, 18 and 55 private rooms. Vegetarian meals. Children's helpings. Smart dress preferred. No-smoking area. Wheelchair access. Music. Air-conditioned. Fax: 071-437 0043

Card slips closed *in the details at the end of an entry indicates that the total on the slips of credit cards is closed when handed over for signature.*

## L'Aventure

map 11

3 Blenheim Terrace, NW8 0EH
071-624 6232

COOKING 1
COST £28–£42

'We felt young (a nice feeling!),' reminisced two ladies of mature years who ventured into this neighbourhood restaurant tucked away in a quiet leafy cul-de-sac off Abbey Road. Sadly they found the service painfully slow, although the food made some recompense. At the beginning of the '80s the cooking here was fashionable; it has hardly changed over the years, although a few in-vogue ideas and ingredients have been grafted on. The setting is countrified, the food is comforting though details may be skimped. The short, daily-changing fixed-price menu (handwritten in untranslated French) might include sauté duck livers with warm vinaigrette, veal chop with herbs and shallots, roast quails with morels, and tarte au citron. Reporters have spoken well of scallops on a bed of spinach, mussels in flaky pastry, rack of lamb with whole cloves of garlic, acceptable îles flottantes and 'nicely matured' soft cheeses. The wine list is French, regional and apposite. House wine is £10.50.

CHEF: Christian Bretèché   PROPRIETORS: Catherine Parisot and Chris Mitas   OPEN: all week, exc Sat L; 12.30 to 2.30, 7.30 to 11   MEALS: Set L £18.50, Set D £25   SERVICE: not inc   CARDS: Access, Amex, Diners, Visa   DETAILS: 38 seats. 6 tables outside. Private parties: 42 main room. Vegetarian meals with prior notice. Children's helpings. Smart dress preferred. No cigars in dining-room before 11pm. Music

## Bahn Thai

map 15

21A Frith Street, W1V 5TS
071-437 8504

COOKING 1*
COST £21–£60

Much cleaning, building and painting has taken place in this two-storeyed restaurant, often said to be home to more authentic Thai cooking than anywhere else in the capital. The ground floor has been brightened, made open to the street and given a more street-food menu to cope with casual grazing. Upstairs is cleaner than it was and the menu is as it used to be. There is a good range of dishes, both in terms of recipe and in use of materials such as venison and wild boar, and a very bold use of chilli (compromising on heat for the British palate is not one this restaurant's characteristics). Other materials, particularly fresh vegetables and herbs and some shellfish, are often interesting, not least because direct supply lines are maintained with Thailand. Prawn dishes are notably succulent and enjoyable, from tom yum goong to butterfly prawns and plum sauce. Service is often, though not always, obliging, but the hectoring tone of the menu about the customer's obligations over payment and tipping may get on people's nerves. The wine list is very much better considered than at most restaurants of this kind, perhaps because the owner is an Englishman. The notes are cogent, the wines are very decent, and the prices are not impossible. House wines are £7.95.

Not inc *in the details at the end of an entry indicates that no service charge is made and any tipping is at the discretion of the customer.*

CHEF: Penn Squires  PROPRIETORS: Bahn Thai plc/Philip Harris  OPEN: all week; 12 to 2.45, 6 to 11.15 (12.30 to 2.30, 6.30 to 10.30 Sun)  MEALS: alc (main courses £6 to £20). 'Small Eats' menu downstairs (£4 to £8.50). Cover 75p upstairs D. Minimum £4.50 downstairs  SERVICE: 12.5%, card slips closed  CARDS: Access, Amex, Diners, Visa  DETAILS: 100 seats. 2 tables outside. Private parties: 50 main room, 20, 25 and 30 private rooms. Vegetarian meals. Children's helpings on request. Wheelchair access (1 step ground floor; also men's WC). Music. Air-conditioned. Fax: 071-439 0340

## Bedlington Café £          map 10

24 Fauconberg Road, W4 3JY        COOKING 1
081-994 1965          COST £9–£23

This really is a café. In the day it helps the local children to fizzy drinks and does the greasy-spoon act; by night it converts to an open secret of fantastic value for vigorous Thai cooking in spartan and cramped surroundings. There is no alcohol licence, not much comfort and lots of customers – giving rise to phased bookings. Laotian bamboo salad, one person reported, was typical of the place in that it made little concession to Western tastes – lashings of chilli and lime juice, and an unfamiliar aroma 'made it a dish for the adventurous'. Quasi-Cantonese dishes like sweet-and-sour pork or beef with oyster sauce are also praised. Service can be charming, or quirky.

CHEF: Mrs S. Srisawad  PROPRIETORS: Mr and Mrs Priyanu  OPEN: all week; 8am to 2pm, 6.30 to 10  MEALS: alc (main courses £2.50 to £5). Unlicensed, but bring your own: corkage 50p  SERVICE: not inc  DETAILS: 35 seats. 6 tables outside. Vegetarian meals. Children's helpings. No-smoking area. Wheelchair access (1 step). No music

## Belgo £          map 11

72 Chalk Farm Road, NW1 8AN        COOKING 1
071-267 0718          COST £19–£46

'I can quite understand that familiarity with mussels can breed contempt,' says a regular of this mussels-and-beer house on the Chalk Farm Road. 'It looks like a building site from the outside,' but then so does the neighbourhood. Belgo has worked: 'unswervingly good value' may be one reason; sticking to a formula may be another. 'The menu barely changes,' said one report, which failed to note that moules bières et lardons had been upgraded to moules congos, with lemon grass and coconut. Once safe haven from the street is achieved, mount steps to a bridge across the kitchen zone, then descend to close-set tables – non-smokers beware, 'Japanese high tar don't mix with mussels' – gnomic inscriptions on the walls, and some whacky furnishing detail by fashionable young architect Anand Zenz. It's all good fun, though service is fast and furious: 'There are plenty of staff, but often they're inexperienced and have difficulty with English.' Mussels are the stars, so are chips, so is the beer – try one of the barman's selections. Quantity and value are never in question, and the success of other dishes such as the salad of pigeon, asparagus hollandaise and fish stew Flemish-style is happily affirmed. Even the vegetables get honourable mention. The tables are turned round every two hours, so do not expect a leisurely night. House wine is £8.50.

CHEF: Philippe Blaise   PROPRIETORS: André Plisnier and Denis Blais   OPEN: all week;
12 to 3, 6 to 11.30 (noon to 11.30 Sat and Sun)   CLOSED: Christmas and New Year
MEALS: alc (main dishes £5 to £13.50). Set L and D £9.75 (2 courses)   SERVICE: 15%, card
slips closed   CARDS: Access, Amex, Diners, Visa   DETAILS: 80 seats. Vegetarian
meals. Children's helpings on request. No cigars/pipes in dining-room. No music.
Fax: 071-267 7508

## Bentley's   **NEW ENTRY**   map 14

| 11–15 Swallow Street, W1 7HD | COOKING 3 |
| 071-734 4756 and 287 5025 | COST £29–£75 |

Bentley's was a name to conjure with in the old days of London fish
restaurants. This year it has undergone a renaissance and a resurgence of good
cooking in the hands of Richard Corrigan. Fingers are crossed that this may be
allowed to continue. Downstairs is the oyster bar – pure English, the fittings
glowing as they used to be, and a place to eat simply. Upstairs, the dining-room
is a reconstruction of an old English chop house, but the menu is utterly at odds
with this image. Fish remains the principal ingredient, even though Richard
Corrigan's main claim to fame has hitherto been black pudding, and the
handful of meat dishes are good enough to hold their heads up high in any
situation. Corrigan is crazy about the raw material: the oysters are wonderful,
the fish is spanking fresh, and so large a menu is only maintained by military
self-discipline and rigour. He is properly creative, able to turn to a classic like
poached turbot with a nage of vegetables and parsley and a sauce mousseline,
or give added depth and flavour to the prime ingredient in something like
steamed sea bass with squid, limes, black beans and ink pasta. Warm terrine of
eel, truffle and bacon vinaigrette, or scallops with couscous, tomato and
coriander are but two things that will not be found in many other places in
London. The danger is that too many flavours and too much exuberance may
overbalance the dish. Some of the trimmings, like the half-lemons in gauze,
remind you of the good elements of old English restaurants. Other things, like
the tables in military rows, or the service that some people have encountered,
are best forgotten. The wine list, like the menu, has nothing old hat about it. It
is a tremendous range, carefully priced to avoid West End shock, with
impressive makers like Roty from Burgundy and Saintsbury from California.
House wines start at £9.75.

CHEF: Richard Corrigan   PROPRIETORS: Boddingtons plc   OPEN: Mon to Sat; 12 to 2.30,
6 to 10.30   CLOSED: Christmas, Easter, bank hols   MEALS: alc (main courses £11 to £28)
SERVICE: not inc   CARDS: Access, Amex, Diners, Visa   DETAILS: 70 seats. Private parties:
16 private room. Vegetarian meals with prior notice. Children's helpings. Smart dress
preferred in restaurant. No music. Air-conditioned. Fax: 071-287 2972

*'The proprietor said my tie didn't go with my jacket – so I took it off. Perhaps the increased
aesthetic sense has overflowed from the new chef?'* On eating in Lancashire

*'The pigeon had been around a long time. Its pâté was a dry tasteless heap of a meatlike
substance served on what I understand is called "a bed of lettuce". The bed had been slept
in for some time.'* On eating in Scotland

## Bertorelli's £

map 15

44A Floral Street, WC2E 9DA
071-836 3969

COOKING 1
COST £18–£40

In the basement is the café (pizzas), at street-level the restaurant (nouveau Italian). Art deco is the intended mood, which means quite bright and cheerful and designerish enough for the Covent Garden crowd, plus the theatre-goers who find it conveniently placed with generous hours. 'I would go again' is a frequent remark that follows a lambasting of the performance of the immediate past, so something must be right. After listening to a waiter assert that salmon should be red rare in the centre – 'It's the chef's speciality, sir' – one reader was not so sure. However, Maddalena Bonino can mastermind a fair dish of pasta, and a meal of warm mushroom, pine-nut and rocket tart followed by grilled marinated poussin on roasted peppers with a salsa verde convinced one reporter, even if the next meal (under pressure after the opera) was not so good. The owners have discovered the delights of old-fashioned Italian restaurants, so have a cover charge (which they justify by compulsory supply of bread, olives and gherkins) and a service charge which they describe as 'recommended, though discretionary'. The wine list works from an Italian base and includes some good makers (Collavini, Antinori, Borgogno, Isole e Olena). House wines are £7.95.

CHEF: Maddalena Bonino   PROPRIETORS: Groupe Chez Gérard Ltd   OPEN: restaurant and café Mon to Sat (café menu Sat L restaurant); 12 to 3, 5.45 to 11.30   CLOSED: 25 Dec   MEALS: alc (main courses café £5 to £7, restaurant £6.50 to £13). Cover £1.50   SERVICE: 12.5%, card slips closed   CARDS: Access, Amex, Diners, Visa   DETAILS: 80 seats. Private parties: 30 main room. Vegetarian meals. Children's helpings on request. No-smoking area. No cigars/pipes in dining-room. Wheelchair access (1 step; also WC). Music. Air-conditioned. Fax: 071-836 1868

## Beth's

NEW ENTRY   map 11

3A Downshire Hill, Hampstead, NW3 1NR
071-435 3544

COOKING 1
COST £14–£40

From Keats to Hungry Hussar, back to Keats, this restaurant is now called Beth's, after the chef, Beth Coventry, who has moved here from a long stint at Green's. What Hampstead has long lacked is a useful, attractive and relaxed place to eat at, though it has pubs and theme parks aplenty. This place is designed to be relatively affordable, its conditions induce relaxation, and the food will pass muster. There is a pair of rooms, pine-panelled then painted, with a particularly effective colour scheme. In the day a large window allows floods of light, at night sconced candles enchance romance. Beth Coventry's most famous dish is fish-cakes. Though she is the mother of their re-invention, the versions sampled here have not been classics, though palatable. Steak, kidney and mushroom pudding will put hairs on anyone's chest. The menu is in the modern mould. The wine list is very interesting, with every sign of doing more than just going to the latest fashionable merchant. There are unfamiliar yet inexpensive bottles (from £7.95) that repay the effort. Tunnel Hill Pinot Noir from Australia, Jermann's Vinnae or Dom. Hautes Noelles Gamay are all excellent, as is much of the rest.

CHEF: Beth Coventry   PROPRIETOR: Angela Collins   OPEN: all week; 12.30 to 3, 7 to 11.30 (12.30 to 11 Sun)   CLOSED: 2 days Christmas, 2 days Easter   MEALS: alc (main courses £7.50 to £12). Set L £7.50 (2 courses), Set Sun L £8.50   SERVICE: not inc   CARDS: Access, Amex, Visa   DETAILS: 50 seats. 3 tables outside. Private parties: 30 main room. Vegetarian meals. Children's helpings L. Wheelchair access (1 step; also WC). Music. Fax: 071-431 3544

## Bibendum 🍾

map 13

Michelin House,
81 Fulham Road, SW3 6RD
071-581 5817

COOKING 4*
COST £24–£81

'The cooking here builds on simplicity and is very strong as a result.' 'This is the best restaurant I have been to in this country in 10 years,' write two independent witnesses converted to this restaurant of immense style with cooking of deceptive simplicity. Others are not so convinced by the cramped tables of two lined against one wall, or the apparently incessant smoking going on around them; they find the food over-simple, or lacking impact; they are certain that it is expensive. The setting is the first floor of the old Michelin building. Its great quality is the light – day or night. This maximises space, allows the personality to expand, and is gently managed by intelligent furnishings. The service is generally good, pursuing the same line of simplicity espoused by the cooking. Resentment is sometimes occasioned by the difficulty of getting a booking, and by the 15 per cent service charge, but neither of these factors is in the waiters' control. The quality of the food depends first on the balance between straightforwardness and clever ideas, and secondly on the exact yet rounded flavours that are brought out. A meal in the spring – the seat-covers green in homage to the new season, daffodils brightening the palest sunshine – consisted of a red wine risotto with confit of duck and an intense brandade of salt cod as first courses, grilled calf's kidney with mushrooms and cream and fillet of cod with spicy lentils as main dishes, followed by apple crumble. Coffee with bitter truffles rounded everything off. This meal was typical of the place and worked magnificently because every element was on song. Olives have been delicious this year – the youngest and fruitiest of crops. Bread is bought in. Failures certainly occur and are the more glaring because there is no mask of complexity, nor the kindly dimming of perceptions afforded by blandness. The wine list is worth taking time over. Even if money is short, ask the sommelier for advice and hope to be startled. The choice from the lesser appellations is of great interest and £20 will get you a worthwhile novelty. The Italians and New World wines are also worth investigating; only Spain and Germany get short shrift. The classic regions, of course, are very serious indeed. House wines start at £9.50. The Oyster Bar (Tel: 071-589 1480) is the small room downstairs to the left of the covered court that forms the narthex to the Conran Shop. Presumably, in the early days of Michelin tyres, it was the foreman's office and the covered court was the fitting bay. Now, on a busy day, tables spill out from the centre (almost) to cover the public space. The menu is more than just shellfish, but the oysters, the crab, the langoustines and the thick, fragrant mayonnaises served with them are excellent. Piedmontese peppers are up to scratch; so are focaccia, Caesar salad and a plate of squid with black-bean sauce. The place is busy and cheerful, with shoppers popping in, or people just wondering what the good life's like. That's Brompton Cross.

CHEFS: Simon Hopkinson and Matthew Harris   PROPRIETORS: Paul Hamlyn, Sir Terence Conran and Simon Hopkinson   OPEN: all week; restaurant 12.30 to 2.30 (3 Sat and Sun), 7 to 11.30 (10 Sun); Oyster Bar noon to 10.30 (noon to 3.30, 7 to 10 Sun)   CLOSED: Christmas, Easter Mon   MEALS: alc (main courses restaurant £12 to £20, Oyster Bar £7.50 to £11.50). Set L £25   SERVICE: 15%, card slips closed   CARDS: Access, Amex, Visa
DETAILS: restaurant 72 seats, Oyster Bar 40 seats. Private parties restaurant: 80 main room. Vegetarian meals. Children's helpings. No children inside Oyster Bar. Wheelchair access. No music restaurant. Music Oyster Bar. Air-conditioned restaurant. Fax: 071-823 7925

## Billboard Café  £                                               map 11

222 Kilburn High Road, NW6 4JP                        COOKING 1
071-328 1374                                          COST £15–£36

'Unique in the area' may pardon some faults in this warehouse conversion while recognising the virtues of relaxed yet lively atmosphere, cheerful service and sometimes vivid cooking, with pasta getting the votes for the best feature. Italy is the main inspiration, the chargrill the main instrument, but vegetables get almost as much emphasis as meat and fish. Lots of regulars, perception of fair value and occasional live music show that Kilburn needs it, warts and all. Brunch is available on Saturdays and Sundays for £6.25. The short wine list is more Italian than anything – sort of like the food. House wines are £6.95.

CHEF: Nasser Nateghi   PROPRIETORS: Nasser Nateghi and Lindsay Smith   OPEN: Mon to Sat D, Sat and Sun L; 12 to 2.45, 6.30 to 12.45   CLOSED: bank hols   MEALS: alc (main courses £4.50 to £12). Set D £10 to £15.   SERVICE: 10%, card slips closed   CARDS: Access, Visa   DETAILS: 65 seats. Private parties: 65 main room. Vegetarian meals. Children's helpings. Smart dress preferred. Wheelchair access. Music. Air-conditioned

## Bistrot Bruno                      │ NEW ENTRY │    map 15

63 Frith Street, W1V 5TA                              COOKING 2*
071-734 4545                                          COST £26–£41

Out of the sea shall rise a creature...no monster this, but out of the fish and seafood restaurant L'Hippocampe rises a bistro under the same ownership, though in partnership with Bruno Loubet, one of England's brighter stars in the cooking firmament. 'If I were trying to send up pretentious modern décor I could have hardly done better than here, with its uneven streaks of painted concrete for walls, all in khaki-related colours, and, at the far end, a solitary charcoal drawing of, possibly, four witches. Uncomfortable chairs around small tables jammed close together' is how one reader ends his report. The message is clear, taste apart, that here we have a bistro in modern form that will provide little by way of comfort no matter what the food. Bruno Loubet does not actually cook here; he does that at the Four Seasons Hotel (see entry, London). His role is more consultative, with a bash at the stoves when he has time to spare. The hallmark of his downmarket cooking is high flavour – 'squid stood out with its nippy seasoning' – applied to good materials that arouse interest in today's climate. Things such as ox cheek, tripe, confit of duck, marinated herrings, sauerkraut and split-peas compete with inexpensive Breton or

Galway oysters, scallops (on puff pastry with a home-made piccalilli), snails with tomato, polenta, parsley and garlic, and white pudding with barley and pumpkin. Slow cooking is a technique as much enjoyed here as fast, and grilling is in minor key. High hopes at the beginning have not always been met as the operation settled in. It is not so much the conception as the details of the execution. Texture and weight get attention from critics: an excess of oil or fat, and the use of the wrong sort of oil, send the dishes out of balance. Desserts show an enquiring mind and some new variations that should be welcome. Stewed apple with rosemary nearly worked; baked apple with a prune and armagnac ice-cream definitely did. Filter coffee is no great shakes but the chocolate-enrobed sorbet petits fours, one direct transplant from Loubet's practice at the Four Seasons, are received with rapture. The bill manages to say 'service not included' three times on a small docket. Is this a record? The wine list may be short, but it manages to include sound new-wave names from around the world at no more than normal profit margins. House wine starts at £8.50.

CHEFS: Bruno Loubet and Desmond Yare   PROPRIETORS: Pierre and Kathleen Condou
OPEN: Mon to Sat, exc Sat L; 12.15 to 2.30, 6.15 to 11.30   CLOSED: 25 Dec to 1 Jan   MEALS:
alc (main courses £10 to £12)   SERVICE: not inc   CARDS: Access, Amex, Diners, Visa
DETAILS: 50 seats. Vegetarian meals with prior notice. Children welcome. Wheelchair
access. Music. Air-conditioned. Fax: 071-287 1027

## Bistrot 190  £
map 13

190 Queen's Gate, SW7 5EU
071-581 5666

COOKING 1
COST £18–£42

It is still as full as ever, a harbinger – when it opened – of many current London tendencies. The restaurant is part of the Gore Hotel, with a bar on the other side of the front hall, and Downstairs at One Ninety (see entry, London) doing for fish what Antony Worrall-Thompson has done for the rest of our dining habits. You cannot book at the Bistrot unless you are a member of the Restaurateurs' Association of Great Britain. Queues build up, therefore, usually in the bar, involving somewhat byzantine negotiations about credit cards and bills. The room is resplendent still with swags of dried flowers and wall-covering rafts of prints and old photos, the bistro effect confirmed by bare tables and floors. The bill starts totting up with the breads and nibbles, though no waiter says so as the basket is offered. Things done Downstairs appear on the menu here, hence Cajun-spiced and blackened John Dory with a chilli salsa and another that was close to a cucumber raita, and chargrilled squid with ditto. There is also the meat: lamb shank and beans, rump steak and chips, duck confit with mash, leeks and onions. Dell'Ugo (see entry, London) dishes also get an outing: the AWT pizza, for example, though one who had tried both said the Soho version was vastly superior. The New York and Italian influences are still apparent, mediated by Englishness when it gets to sticky toffee pudding or fried skate and lemon butter. The chaos induced by crowds means that performance is not as even as it might be, but on a good night the value is impressive, the cooking accurate, everybody's cheerful and the world seems to flock here. 'I was even asked if I was Harold Pinter,' said one bemused but satisfied client. The wine list is never long, and varies every month according to which wine merchant has been asked to do the choosing – a good wheeze for all concerned. Prices are not high. House wines are £9.50.

CHEFS: Antony Worrall-Thompson and Chris Millar   PROPRIETORS: 190 Queensgate plc   OPEN: all week; noon to 12.30am (11.30pm Sun)   CLOSED: 25 and 26 Dec   MEALS: alc (main courses £5 to £13.50). Set L £7.50 (2 courses) to £10   SERVICE: not inc (10%, card slips closed, for 6 or more)   CARDS: Access, Amex, Diners, Visa   DETAILS: 55 seats. Private parties: 70 main room, 24 and 24 private rooms. Vegetarian meals. Children's helpings on request. Music. Fax: 071-581 8172

## Blue Elephant                                                     map 10

4–6 Fulham Broadway, SW6 1AA                                   COOKING 1*
071-385 6595                                                   COST £28–£56

In Bangkok there are some restaurants so large the waiters have roller-skates. In the Blue Elephant, in deepest Fulham, they would have trouble negotiating the bridges over pools and water features – not to mention the steps – but the scale seems almost as big. Through thick fronds of a man-made jungle, customers can be seen to the horizon's rim and they all seem remarkably jolly. Some readers report that a Thai banquet is a better choice than free association from the menu, while others have approved the clear flavours of the fish stew (homok talay) redolent of aniseed, the exceptionally spicy laab phed (marinated duck breast served warm, with onion) and the paper-wrapped prawns. Not everything is as sharp as in some of London's other Thai restaurants: for example, the tom yang koom (spiced prawn soup) may yield barely a murmur of aroma and the noodles seem just workaday. The real reason to go there is for the event, plus the orchid handed to departing women guests; be prepared to pay over the odds for the setting and the size. The wine list may be short but includes good, and high-priced, names. House wines are £8.95.

CHEF: Rungsan Mulijan   PROPRIETORS: Blue Elephant International Ltd   OPEN: all week, exc Sat L; 12 to 2.30, 7 to 12.30 (10.30 Sun)   CLOSED: 24 to 26 Dec   MEALS: alc (main courses £6.50 to £14.50). Set L £19.50, Set D £25 to £28. Cover £1.50 (alc only)   SERVICE: 15%   CARDS: Access, Amex, Diners, Visa   DETAILS: 250 seats. Private parties: 100 main room, 20 to 100 private rooms. Vegetarian meals. Children welcome. Smart dress preferred. Wheelchair access (2 steps; also WC). Music. Air-conditioned. Fax: 071-386 7665

## Blueprint Café                                                    map 11

Design Museum, Butlers Wharf, SE1 2YD                          COOKING 1*
071-378 7031                                                   COST £24–£42

The Unique Selling Point of a room with a view has been rather topped by Sir Terence Conran's other Butlers Wharf extravaganzas, but the point still needs to be made. 'We went on Guy Fawkes weekend and were treated to a free show like no other' was a happy piece of timing. If the breeze becomes nippy a seat on the balcony may be like the quarter-deck on the Titanic, but the riverside site is remarkable. The staff are cheerful and committed, and the cooking steers the course it set at the beginning: bright, modern, nothing too weird, but hardly a mousse or old-fashioned sauce in sight. 'They make as good a Caesar salad as most London places,' commented someone used to current convention, and langoustines mayonnaise, kedgeree, tuna with guacamole and tomato salsa, and rabbit leg in pancetta with parsley mash and tapénade are other items given a 'yes'. It is all done freshly, sometimes with a bit too much crudeness, sometimes also at an aggregate price that is felt to be just 'a tad over the odds', but in surroundings as bright and modern as the recipe book. The wine list sticks sensibly below £20 (except for a handful of specials) and has pleased for its ready appreciation of changing tastes and fashionable makers. Try the Umani Ronchi Cumaro 1989 at £17.50 or Schlumberger's Gewurztraminer at £14.50. House wines start at £8.50.

CHEF: Lucy Crabb   PROPRIETOR: Sir Terence Conran   OPEN: all week, exc Sun D; 12 to 3 (3.30 Sun), 7 to 11   CLOSED: 25 Dec   MEALS: alc (main courses £7 to £12)   SERVICE: 15%, card slips closed   CARDS: Access, Amex, Diners, Visa   DETAILS: 85 seats. 22 tables outside. Private parties: 90 main room. Vegetarian meals. Children's helpings. Smart dress preferred. No pipes in dining-room. Wheelchair access (also WC). Music. Fax: 071-378 6540

## Bombay Brasserie                                          map 13

Courtfield Close,
Courtfield Road, SW7 4UH                              COOKING 1
071-370 4040 and 373 0971                            COST £21–£53

The allure of the Brasserie is the giant scale and faded magnificence of the surroundings, coupled with an interesting menu of unfamiliar dishes. Some would have it that refurbishment would burnish the image, while others still succumb to the charms of the conservatory, even if the main restaurant feels regimented, the long march to the lavatories depressing, and the lighting penumbrous at best. Meat, for instance in a lamb koorma or a chicken xakuti (a Goan speciality), is well trimmed, though meagre in quantity; spicing may be interesting – the chicken xakuti fragrant with cardamom – with a strong hot finish; the breads, for instance yellow and buttery saffron nan, can be delicious. With the main course arrive vegetables (three for the day), which may be arresting, or may be past it. Portion size is generally small; temperatures are often worryingly haphazard. Lunch-time buffets are praised for their better value. The wine list is mainly French, short and on the dear side. More New World wines might accompany the food more sympathetically. House wine is £9.75.

CHEF: Udit Sarkhel   PROPRIETORS: Taj International Hotels   OPEN: all week; 12.30 to 3, 7.30 to 12   CLOSED: 25 and 26 Dec   MEALS: alc (main courses £10 to £19.50). Set L £13.95. Minimum £20 D   SERVICE: not inc   CARDS: Access, Diners, Visa   DETAILS: 175 seats. 25 tables outside. Private parties: 100 main room, 100 private room. Vegetarian meals. Children's helpings L. Smart dress preferred. Wheelchair access (3 steps; also WC). Music. Air-conditioned. Fax: 071-835 1669

## Boyd's ▮                                                  map 12

135 Kensington Church Street, W8 7LP                 COOKING 2
071-727 5452                                          COST £23–£54

The lightness of the interior relaxes: through the ante-chamber which was once a shop (slightly domesticated with some stripped-pine furniture) you hop up three steps to the top-lit back room with its many plants. 'The complete lack of fussiness is the best sign of their self-confidence. Simplicity can be very exposing. No faults here.' This was the verdict of a couple who came to town and ate a tagliatelle and smoked salmon salad with Parmesan, wild mushrooms with red wine sauce on brioche, chargrilled turbot, a three-star ginger crème brûlée, and a trio of home-made ices with some tropical fruit. For sure, there is a certain pattern to Boyd Gilmour's cooking: he favours pasta salads; he often serves scallops with rocket and a Chinese vinaigrette, beef with shallots and garlic, or honey-roasted duck with lime. Simplicity is indeed a virtue, but here it has not always succeeded in imparting intense flavours or sound balance to a dish. The restaurant remains, however, a haven of peace, with the added bonus of an excellent wine list. It might be said that a gap has opened between the interest and excitement offered by the wines and that maintained by the food. Half-bottles are provided intelligently and the hundred-odd bottles encompass a wonderful range from the honest simplicity of a half-dozen Bordeaux petits châteaux to heights scaled with a Kistler Chardonnay from Sonoma or Guigal Côte Rôtie. The several interesting house wines are offered by the glass. Prices are fair. House wines are from £9.30. CELLARMAN'S CHOICE: Cloudy Bay, Chardonnay 1991, £23.10; Médoc, Ch. Patache D'Aux 1982, £18.75.

CHEFS: Boyd Gilmour and Jane Watkins   PROPRIETOR: Boyd Gilmour   OPEN: Mon to Sat; 12.30 to 2.30, 7 to 11   CLOSED: 2 weeks Christmas, bank hols   MEALS: alc (main courses £10 to £14). Set L £14   SERVICE: not inc   CARDS: Access, Amex, Diners, Visa   DETAILS: 40 seats. Private parties: 40 main room. Vegetarian meals. Music. Air-conditioned. Fax: 071-221 0615

## Brackenbury £

map 10

129–131 Brackenbury Road, W6 0BQ
081-748 0107

COOKING 3
COST £16–£30

In Paris, a 'bistro' offered minimal comfort but, if you were lucky, very good food. The cooking was never intended to be complicated; the importance lay in making it taste nice, and it never cost too much. In Britain, 'bistros' produced simple food in vaguely French discomfort at a relatively low price. Their attraction was the Gallic package, very rarely food quality. The Brackenbury in Hammersmith changes that. Of comfort there is none, and walls are bare. If the staff are rushed off their feet, the service may not even be the frank and natural thing it usually is. The food is rarely the product of extended or complicated techniques, but it is so consistently pleasant to eat, and so cheap, that it stands head and shoulders above its competitors. The concept falls down when the consumer puts on the hat of the high falutin gastro-critic, or when people expect too much of an event. The Brackenbury does not set out to be a destination theme park; it tries to feed people. An early luncher passed by the bar and found the waitress grating a giant hunk of Parmesan to go with that day's tagliatelle carbonara. Not many restaurants this cheap have that sort of respect for raw materials and people's palates. The noodles were home-made, the sauce rich and unctuous, and the counterpoint added by the pork scratching style of crisp bacon was exact: a perfect lunch dish at a perfect price. Economy is achieved here by scaling down the quantities when dealing with luxury items. Misunderstanding may arise if the customer thinks the bargain should be even more of a give-away. The menu is kept short, with certain semi-constants or regulars like the plate of savouries to begin, or the potato pancake with sour cream and salmon caviare. The tone is one of sensible eclecticism – not all is French, but not all Cal-Ital either; there are some oriental things, and some Middle Eastern, but not often simple British. A few dishes rely too heavily on oil, rather than sauce, for happy digestion, but mostly the balance is very fine. What appeals most is the willingness to use lots of different ingredients (try the crostini of lambs' brains), the genuineness of everything (no short cuts), and the assurance of the seasoning. Desserts are often good: the crème caramel and tarts are steady attractions. Coffee is strong. The wine list also has friendly prices, starting at £7.50; the choices are interesting, and the list is not too long. One regular visitor has noted that the staff change much less frequently than in most London restaurants. This says quite a lot about the Brackenbury's approach to the whole business.

CHEF: Adam Robinson   PROPRIETORS: Adam and Katie Robinson   OPEN: all week, exc L Mon and Sat and Sun D; 12.30 to 2.45, 7 to 10.45   CLOSED: Christmas, Easter, bank hols   MEALS: alc (main courses £4.50 to £10)   SERVICE: not inc   CARDS: Access, Amex, Visa   DETAILS: 55 seats. 5 tables outside. Private parties: 12 main room. Vegetarian meals. Children's helpings. No cigars/pipes in dining-room. Wheelchair access. No music

## Brady's £

map 10

513 Old York Road, SW18 1TF
081-877 9599

COOKING 1
COST £13–£20

Luke and Amelia Brady have found their experiment with an upper-crust fish restaurant has worked. Fish and chips are the staple, tables there are but no cloths, and fish sparkles straight out the sea. Not everything is battered; grills as well as poached fish are always available and salmon fish-cakes are made from the whole fish, not just scraps and offcuts. With most of the better chippies being on the north side of the river, Wandsworth needs this. The wine list is notional but there are good beers as well as house wines from the Ardèche at £6.50.

CHEF: Luke Brady   PROPRIETORS: Luke and Amelia Brady   OPEN: Mon to Sat, D only, and Sat L; 12.30 to 2.30, 7 to 10.45   CLOSED: Christmas, 1 week Aug, bank hols   MEALS: alc (main courses £4 to £5)   SERVICE: 10%   DETAILS: 38 seats. Children's helpings. Wheelchair access (1 step; also WC). Music

## Brasserie du Marché aux Puces

map 11

349 Portobello Road, W10 5SA
081-968 5828

COOKING 1
COST £17–£35

A sandspit away from the beach of Portobello fashionables keeps this brasserie the right side of pretension and 'nothing like a club' to which membership is an intangible secret – thus spake one who counts himself no Notting Hillbilly. It might also be said that a pleasing drabness is a sort of virtue. There is nothing drab about the food, though, even if the finishes are scrubbed and muted. The cooking produces modern variations that may shock, like haggis in filo with quince purée and apple jelly, when earlier it had been doing a down-the-line haggis and neeps. The food is dependable and exactly pitched for a neighbourhood place – not too dear, not too complex. Borrowings from vegetarian and Indian styles give rise to versions of veggieburgers or dhal with courgette and tomatoes, or 'Indonesian rice' sitting next to fairly straight kidneys Turbigo or grilled rib-eye steak and onion rings. Risottos are enjoyed, so are desserts like raspberry mousse with honey and brandy-snaps. The place is up-front and relaxed, and great for morning coffee and croissants (from 10am daily, and 11am on Sunday). The wine list is short and sharp, with house wines at £7.50 and £7.95.

CHEF: Robert Price   PROPRIETOR: Philip McMullen   OPEN: all week, exc Sun D; noon to 11 (4 Sun)   CLOSED: bank hols   MEALS: alc (main courses £6.50 to £9.50). Set L £9.95   SERVICE: not inc   DETAILS: 35 seats. 7 tables outside. Private parties: 40 main room, 30 private room. Vegetarian meals. Children's helpings. Wheelchair access (1 step). Music. Air-conditioned

## Brasserie Faubourg                                        map 10

28 Queenstown Road, SW8 3RX                     COOKING 1
071-622 6245                                          COST £20–£36

Londoners who are unable to emulate Peter Mayle's Provençal escapades may find solace in this clean, attractive brasserie. It is a family business: François Closset (formerly of Mon Plaisir; see entry, London) cooks, while his wife Nicole is a courteous, attentive hostess who runs the front-of-house. The short menu offers generous helpings of classic dishes with noticeable provincial overtones: fish soup with rouille and croûtons, boned guinea-fowl with cider vinegar, monkfish with leeks and shallots, pavé of beef with red wine and shallots. Salads are in keeping: the Lyonnaise version includes smoked belly pork, croûtons, poached egg and tarragon vinegar. Desserts range from chocolate marquise to raspberry mousse with coulis. 'The food is always full of taste, fresh and fulfilling, yet never cloying or heavy,' note loyal supporters, who list lamb, stuffed mussels, and pear tart among their favourites. Six wines from Provence feature on the modest French list. House wine is £8.95.

CHEF: François Closset   PROPRIETORS: François and Nicole Closset   OPEN: Mon to Sat, exc L Mon and Sat; 12 to 2.30, 7 to 11   CLOSED: bank hols, 10 Aug to 2 Sept   MEALS: alc (main courses £11 to £12). Set L £9.50 (2 courses). Cover 95p   SERVICE: not inc   CARDS: Access, Amex, Diners, Visa   DETAILS: 34 seats. Private parties: 35 main room. Vegetarian meals with prior notice. Children welcome. Wheelchair access (1 step). Music. Air-conditioned

## Buchan's £                              NEW ENTRY   map 10

62–64 Battersea Bridge Road, SW11 3AG           COOKING 1
071-228 0888                                          COST £17–£34

There are no kilts to be seen, but the theme of this wine bar/restaurant is Scotland. The name is in deference to author John Buchan, and the list of 39 wines is bolstered by 39 malt whiskies. Sit and drink at the bar or graduate to the beautifully light eating area at the back with its pitched glassed roof, plants and pictures. A few Scottish ideas colour the menu – haggis with mashed tatties, salmon steak with tiny oatmeal dumplings and fried aubergines, oatmeal mackerel fillets with red fruit dressing – although ideas are pulled in from around the globe. This is a kitchen that can deliver richly flavoured chilled pigeon and hazelnut consommé, a maverick Stroganov of calf's liver and pigeon with Grand Marnier, confit of duck with bubble and squeak, and koulibiac of vegetables. Mishaps and disappointments in the vegetables and sweets are more than redeemed by the 'wonderful' Scottish and Welsh cheeses and by the brilliant wines. 'This place is worth coming to for the booze alone,' exclaimed one couple: not only properly made Pimms and Broughton Greenmantle Ale, but sensational Wolf Blass Cabernet Sauvignon and Tim Adams Semillon from South Australia. House wines are £8.75.

CHEF: Alain Jeannon  PROPRIETORS: Jeremy and Denise Bolam  OPEN: all week; 12 to 2.45, 6 to 10.45 (7 to 10 Sun)  CLOSED: 25 and 26 Dec  MEALS: alc (main courses £6.50 to £14). Set Sun L £9 (2 courses) to £11  SERVICE: net prices, card slips closed  CARDS: Access, Amex, Diners, Visa  DETAILS: 70 seats. 4 tables outside. Private parties: 50 main room. Vegetarian meals. Children's helpings on request. Wheelchair access (1 step; also WC). Music. Air-conditioned. Fax: 071-924 1718

## Bu San £ map 11

43 Holloway Road, N7 8JP  COOKING 1*
071-607 8264  COST £14–£56

The world map that adorns the menu shows that the Korean port of Bu San is the nearest point to Japan on the Asiatic mainland. Appropriately, Young Hyung Lee's comfortable restaurant near Highbury and Islington station offers a mix of Korean specialities plus a few from across the water. Classic dishes such as yuk hoe (Korean steak tartare), kim-chee, bulgogi and gu sho ga ya ki (sliced beef grilled in ginger sauce) line up alongside sashimi, sukiyaki and 'healthy' shabu-shabu. Fish and vegetarian dishes show up strongly and the kitchen prides itself on flamboyant sculptural presentation. Visitors have appreciated the helpful attentions of the head waiter, who is happy to assist with dishes that are cooked at the table: 'He was much more adept than we were with the rounded chopsticks and the button mushrooms,' admitted one couple. Tea and saké are the preferred drinks; otherwise you might order Japanese beer or ginseng brandy. The modest list of around 20 wines does not venture farther than France and Italy. House wine is £6.85.

CHEF: Young Hyung Lee  PROPRIETORS: Young Hyung and Tea Sun Lee  OPEN: all week, exc L Sat and Sun; 12 to 2.30, 6 to 11 (11.30 Fri and Sat)  CLOSED: 25 Dec, 1 Jan  MEALS: alc (main courses £4.50 to £18.50). Set L £4.20 to £6.50 (1 course and coffee/tea), Set D (2 people) £27.90 to £45.50  SERVICE: 10%  CARD: Visa  DETAILS: 46 seats. Private parties: 50 main room. Vegetarian meals. Children's helpings. Smart dress preferred. Wheelchair access (also WC). Music. Air-conditioned

*An asterisk (\*) after the 1 to 5 cooking mark at the top of an entry signifies that the* Guide *and its readers think that the restaurant is a particularly fine example within its rating.*

*London round-ups listing additional restaurants that may be worth a visit can be found after the main London section.*

## Buzkash ✹ £

map 10

4 Chelverton Road, Putney, SW15 1RH  COOKING 1
081-788 3182 and 0599  COST £17–£40

Two restaurants, this one and its sister, the Caravan Serai (50 Paddington Street, W1M 3RQ, Tel: 071-935 1208), serve Afghan food to London. Their menus, and seemingly their personnel, are interchangeable. Each has a seriously Afghani interior, which is 'kitsch' or charming depending on how you enjoyed the meal, mostly indicating the warrior heritage of your waiter even if swords are now beaten into frying-pans. The melding of Persian and Indian flavours gives rise to a sometimes intriguing set of dishes more aromatic or gentle than in a curry house, more tinged with sweetness. Lack of throughput or carelessness may sometimes mean lack of lustre or freshness, but reports have favoured the breads, the pilau with almonds and orange, chicken with chilli, and aubergine cooked with pepper and tomatoes and finished with the ever-present yogurt. Service may be stately or chatty. House wine is £9.95.

CHEF: Mr Padsha  PROPRIETOR: Hassan Khan  OPEN: Mon to Sat; 12 to 3, 6 to 11
CLOSED: 24 to 26 Dec  MEALS: alc (main courses £5 to £11.50). Set L £7.95. Cover 75p
SERVICE: 10%  CARDS: Access, Visa  DETAILS: 52 seats. 6 tables outside. Private parties:
40 main room, 20 private room. Vegetarian meals. Children welcome. Smart dress
preferred. No smoking in 1 dining-room. Music

## Le Cadre

map 10

10 Priory Road, Priory Park, N8 7RD  COOKING 1*
081-348 0606  COST £20–£40

Resolutely French, this place hankers after the bistro school of happiness, though the cooking is not slap-dash, nor the welcome ever surly. The blackboard, one adventurer was pleased to report, is cheaper and more generously portioned than the short *carte*, but none could cavil at the prices. A fixed-price spring menu that offered moules marinière, asparagus hollandaise, daube of beef provençal, or civet of rabbit with red wine among a concise choice of six dishes per course sets out clearly the prospectus. Other meals have included sardines with tomato and capers, feuilleté of sweetbreads with wild mushrooms and praline mousse with coffee custard, or spinach pancakes topped with Gruyère, and that rabbit again, with a mustard sauce. It comforts and it pleases: an enviable achievement. The small wine list is the tip of the iceberg. Look out for additional bottles on display. House wines are £8.50.

CHEF: Yannick Chuat  PROPRIETORS: David Misselbrook and Marie Fedyk  OPEN: Mon to
Sat, exc Sat L; 12 to 2.30, 7 to 11  CLOSED: 25 to 30 Dec, bank hols  MEALS: alc (main
courses £10.50 to £11.50). Set Mon to Fri L £10.50 (2 courses) to £12.50, Set Mon to Thur D
£12.50, Set Fri and Sat D £15.50  SERVICE: not inc  CARDS: Access, Amex, Diners, Visa
DETAILS: 50 seats. 6 tables outside. Private parties: 60 main room. Vegetarian meals.
Children welcome. Smart dress preferred. Music

---

*All letters to the* Guide *are acknowledged with an update on latest sales, closures, chef changes and so on.*

---

## *Café des Arts*

[NEW ENTRY]   map 11

82 Hampstead High Street, NW3 1RE         COOKING 1
071-435 3608         COST £24–£40

Fagin's Kitchen (theme: Dickensiana; period: late '60s) has gone off to the great restaurant quarter in the sky; its successor in this seventeenth-century building in Hampstead village is more Pacific-rim than Pentonville. The décor is all terracotta tiles, pine panelling and sea-drift collages in bleached marine colours; only the coal fire (fake) and Victorian knick-knacks hark back to the days of the Dodger. Everyone remarks that chef, managers and most of the waiting staff are women (noticeable enough 'in black tights with minimal skirts') which, reports one, 'makes for friendly treatment of guests who happen to be women'. Lunch and dinner menus are supplemented by daily specials (seared marlin with papaya and sweet chilli salsa is typical). You sign up for a dish in either the small or large version. Successes have included chargrilled radicchio 'as it should be', with sweet marinated vegetables and coriander vinaigrette; squid and pancetta on a bed of mixed leaves ('all the flavours complementing each other pleasingly'); and an 'exquisitely pink' roast duck breast on a bed of wilted spinach. Among the desserts, warm chocolate espresso cake is much approved. Certain liaisons, however, have been felt overly dangerous: seared duck livers were infelicitous with baked crottin; tuna tataki (seared again, but only just) was questionable with lentils. A clagginess ('claggy bread, claggy livers, claggy walnut pie') dogged one diner, and the 12.5 per cent service charge is widely resented. 'We will happily deduct the fixed service charge immediately for any customer not satisfied with this arrangement,' manager Jacky Kitching says; note it well. The wine list is modest in range and price. House wines are £7.95.

CHEF: Sally Holme   PROPRIETOR: Brian Stein   OPEN: all week; 12 to 4, 6 to 11.30 (11 Sun) CLOSED: 25 and 26 Dec, 1 Jan L   MEALS: alc (main courses £6.50 to £9.50)   SERVICE: 12.5%, card slips closed   CARDS: Access, Amex, Diners, Visa   DETAILS: 65 seats. 4 tables outside. Private parties: 25 main room. Vegetarian meals. Children welcome. No cigars/ pipes in dining-room. Music

## *Café Fish*

map 14

39 Panton Street, SW1 4EA         COOKING 1*
071-930 3999         COST £22–£45

'Very French in character,' note reporters about this bustling, high-ceilinged dining-room, which opens out on to the pavement, just off the Haymarket, in good weather. Every inch of the white and sea-green walls is cluttered with pictures and prints emphasising the piscatorial theme. The place buzzes with noise and atmosphere, especially when the pianist is playing in the evening. 'One would not come here for peace or privacy,' observed a couple. Fish and vegetarian dishes dominate the menu, which takes in roast monkfish with celeriac and rösti potatoes, provençal fish casserole and Stilton gnocchi with spinach, as well as kedgeree and huge plates of fish and chips. Most people reckon that the bouillabaisse (a d-i-y version with 'tons of fish and sauce served separately') is a better bet than the fish soup. Also look for the *plats du jour*, which usually include more exotic species such as chargrilled marlin steak and Jamaican perch with lentils. Crème brûlée is a competent version and apple tart has been 'brilliant'. The cover charge includes an appetiser of salmon mousse plus French bread, and there is good cappuccino to finish. Service is generally sharp and holds up well even under enormous pressure. The downstairs wine bar is a useful meeting place and serves light meals. The wine list is dominated by reasonably priced whites, especially Chardonnays. House Blanc de Blancs is £7.95.

CHEF: Andrew Magson   PROPRIETORS: Groupe Chez Gérard Ltd   OPEN: Mon to Sat, exc Sat L restaurant; 12 to 3, 5.45 to 11.30; wine bar 11.30 am to 11 pm   MEALS: alc (main courses £7 to £14). Cover £1.25   SERVICE: 12.5%, card slips closed   CARDS: Access, Amex, Diners, Visa   DETAILS: 90 seats. 3 tables outside. Private parties: 50 main room. Vegetarian meals. Children welcome. No-smoking area. No cigars/pipes in dining-room. Wheelchair access (restaurant only). Music. Fax 071-436 5227

## Café Royal ▼

map 14

68 Regent Street, W1R 6EL
071-437 9090

COOKING 2
COST £24–£87

London has very few restaurants like the Café Royal which are major-league historical monuments in their own right, with a social history to match. This year has seen the re-creation of a few (Quaglino's, and the Criterion), but the Café Royal is still unique in its assets: a marvellous *fin de siècle* interior – all gilded caryatids, mirrors, painted ceilings and red plush, and a bevy of cultural bigwigs to cite as past clients. Herbert Berger continues to superintend the dragging of this institution into the late twentieth century. Forte needs to finish the job by getting rid of the fusty smell to the Grill Room, which must be potentially the most magical place in town for a dinner, and generally smartening up the level of detail and decoration. The ambience is not helped by the transit-camp feel to the bar, vestibule and, sometimes, the Brasserie, where bewildered tourists and daily shoppers outnumber people who realise the value of the institution; fortunately the staff, whether old-school or fresh-faced, seem properly motivated. Berger's reforms have had a year in the Brasserie, much less than that in the Grill Room, but whether he runs an old or new menu, the standard of craft and quality control is evident. Recommended Brasserie dishes include a pressed terrine of provençale vegetables, spicy paprika sausage with an onion and potato salad, a confit of duck with lentils and red wine sauce, and haddock with English mustard sauce. Lemon tart or hot apple and almond tart show appreciation of pastry work. In the Grill Room prices are very much higher, and classic skills are trotted out with facility in dishes such as a 'mosaïque' of leek and lobster with truffle oil dressing, foie gras terrine with a magret of smoked duck in a little salad, rib steak with bone marrow, and crown of lamb with Mediterranean vegetables and pesto. The Grill Room does not pretend to stray beyond the universally acceptable and slightly luxurious, but if management could get all the trappings right and perhaps shift the prices down, it could be a fine example of the genre. More reports, please. There is canny differentiation between the wine lists in the Brasserie and the Grill Room; the Brasserie culls a neat selection from its neighbour and, at the same time, offers a saving to the customer of a few pounds on a bottle. The grander Grill provides wide range and fine quality, at a premium. But even here prices are not outrageous and the less profligate can content themselves with the decent 'Regional Selection' and more than adequate Italian wines. All-in-all, clever buying and intelligent selling are in evidence here. House wine is £10.50 (Brasserie) or £14.75 (Grill).

CHEF: Herbert Berger  PROPRIETORS: Forte Restaurants  OPEN: Grill Mon to Sat, exc Sat L; 12.30 to 3, 6 to 11. Brasserie Mon to Sat; 12 to 3, 6 to 11  CLOSED: some bank hols (telephone to check)  MEALS: Grill alc (main courses £14.50 to £22); Set L £22.50, Set D £32. Brasserie alc (main courses £7.50 to £13); Set L and D £14.75 (2 courses) to £17.75 SERVICE: not inc  CARDS: Access, Amex, Diners, Visa  DETAILS: Grill 80 seats, Brasserie 100 seats. Private parties: Grill 80 main room, Brasserie 150 main room; 21 banqueting suites. Vegetarian meals. Children's helpings Brasserie. Jacket and tie Grill. Smart dress preferred Brasserie. No-smoking area Brasserie. Wheelchair access (also WC). Music. Air-conditioned. Fax: 071-439 7672

## Canteen

NEW ENTRY    map 10

Unit G4, Harbour Yard,
Chelsea Harbour, SW10 0XD
071-351 7330

COOKING 3
COST £24–£50

The best tables are in the conservatory, looking directly on to the marina of Chelsea Harbour, the new development beyond Lots Road. While some restaurants have struggled on the site, the magic of the names of Michael Caine, the backer, and Marco Pierre White, the supervising chef, was enough to give this one a terrific send-off. The harlequinade and suits of cards form the design motif of a split-level room that is more plush and stylish than any canteen, even if the floor is parquet not carpet and the waiters wear black 501s. Diamonds are forever? Time and fickle fashion will tell. The menu does not change a great deal, so that consistency should be assured. If you cannot cook rump of lamb with tian of aubergines right after doing it for eight months, who can? Well, they still got it wrong here (tough, overcooked) in July, having begun the training in the previous December. On the other hand, dishes like scallops with lemon and cinnamon have been well received for as many months, as has calf's liver, bacon and sage – 'with a stock sauce that is as good as any in London'. Risotto – saffron or black squid ink – with shredded calamari on the top, is often enjoyed, though again consistency – the hallmark of quality for any brasserie – is sufficiently lacking for one version to be grand, and the other to be improperly cooked at the same table. The aim of the repertoire is simplicity, but not without art. Hence there are sauces, and there is balance, not the simplicity of British cooking with a lump of protein unadorned. Desserts will meet approval for their direct flavours in a lemon tart, a flat and broad crème brûlée, a feuillantine of summer fruits, tarte Tatin of pears or tiramisù with gold leaf. Coffee and breads are excellent. Service has been generally welcomed as responding well to popularity, though the practice of telephoning for confirmation of a booking is annoying for some. The wine list is applauded for fashionability and sense, though not for its lack of half-bottles.

CHEF: Steve Terry  OPEN: all week; 12 to 3, 6.30 to 12 (12.30 to 3.30, 7 to 10.30 Sun) MEALS: alc (main courses around £7 to £14.95). Cover charge £1  SERVICE: not inc CARDS: Access, Visa  DETAILS: 200 seats. Private parties: 70 private room

## Cantina del Ponte ▢ NEW ENTRY ▢ map 11

Butlers Wharf Building,
36C Shad Thames, SE1 2YE
071-403 5403

COOKING 2
COST £23–£48

This Italian restaurant is the latest stage in the construction of Sir Terence
Conran's gastrodome on the South Bank. Like its Francophile neighbour, Le
Pont de la Tour (see entry), it benefits from a wonderful site and view, as well
as al fresco eating in good weather. It suffers, however, from an impossible
maze of streets to negotiate once you are over Tower Bridge. The giant mural
embracing foodie Italy gives every clue to the theme, if the pizza dough
manipulation was not enough. The considered design – everything from
waiters' stations to chairs and tables – is probably sufficient to betray the
Conran stamp, and the 15 per cent service charge will only confirm it. Whether
the prices will make people think of this as a true canteen is open to question.
There will be no doubting the Italian influence, though once it has been
learned that the chef (born in England) worked for seven years in Australia,
people may think his style more Pacific-rim than ethnic Italian. Pizzas and
focaccia vie with calamari and linguine, but is there much Italian about
chargrilled squid with spinach, tomatoes, leeks and chilli, or salmon with
samphire and marinated cucumber? What matters is that in general the cooking
works: simple food, boldly handled, with Mediterranean flavours (but not
recipes) dominating. A first course of scallops on top of slices of grilled
aubergine with blobs of pesto showed how simplicity can work to everybody's
advantage, but a main dish of overcooked swordfish demonstrated the reverse
of the coin. Others, however, have reported good minestrones, decent calamari
stuffed with risotto and peas, well-kept cheese with moscatel-studded focaccia,
and enjoyable if rich sweets on a panna cotta theme. The wine list is as
interesting as any from this stable, and is kept sensibly short. There are some
grappas and a pair of eaux-de-vie from Bonny Doon in California. If you need
to build up your store cupboard, Italian items are for sale. House wines
are £9.50.

CHEF: Louis Loizia  PROPRIETORS: Sir Terence Conran, Joel Kissin and David Burke
OPEN: all week, exc Sun D; 12 to 3, 6 to 11  MEALS: alc (main courses £7 to £12.50)
SERVICE: 15%, card slips closed  CARDS: Access, Amex, Diners, Visa  DETAILS: 139 seats.
13 tables outside. Private parties: 20 main room. Vegetarian meals. Children welcome.
Wheelchair access. Music. Fax: 071-403 0267

## ▲ The Capital ♥ map 13

22–24 Basil Street, SW3 1AT
071-589 5171

COOKING 4
COST £25–£71

After celebrating its twenty-first birthday, this hotel looks set to run and run.
So used are we to giant corporations that it is hard to recall that The Capital is
very much the creation of a single man – with help. Though it boasts the
attributes of many larger places, its small scale and relative intimacy attracts
people. The dining-room is a plain shape but 'the boudoir decoration with
heavily ruched drapes and two beautiful chandeliers is very pretty,
complemented by handsome china and table settings,' remarked someone who

found the price structure muddling. At dinner there is a short set-price menu and a *carte*. For the latter, you pay a base price of £25 then add supplements for every dish listed. The only certainty is that the end total will be high. At lunch there are two set-price menus. People appreciate the value of these, and of the set dinner menu, if they find the balance acceptable. Some have maintained that mousses appear with everything; others find too great an emphasis on fish and shellfish (and wild mushrooms they could add). Philip Britten is best at understated finesse: a sole and tomato mousse with a soubise sauce is cited, so too is a tart of oysters and leeks with morels and vin jaune. He can refine a robust dish, not out of existence, but into something very sophisticated: his duck confit is a favourite. And he is a dab hand with fish: steamed brill on roasted red peppers with a sauce of scallops and tarragon, for instance. The successes continue into dessert: hot soufflés are a must, ice-creams very fine, pastry is delicate, substance is solved by apricot crumble with a sauce mousseline. Lack of flamboyance can sometimes mean lack of impact, just as the normally exemplary service can go awry. Further evidence of The Capital's desire to set itself apart from its big brothers lies in the wine list, which tries to satisfy modest needs, with such things as Crozes-Hermitage and simple Touraine bottles. This is though, essentially, a list in the grand style, including a page of magnums and offering several opportunities for comparison with runs of vintages of single properties, for instance Ch. Cos d'Estournel. House wine starts at £10.50. CELLARMAN'S CHOICE: Touraine, 'Le Vin de Levin', £12.50; Beaune, Cuvée Nicolas Rolin, 1988, Jadot, £29.50.

CHEF: Philip Britten   PROPRIETOR: David Levin   OPEN: all week; 12 to 2.30, 7 to 11.15
MEALS: alc (£25 plus supplements). Set L £20 to £25, Set D £25. Minimum £25 D   SERVICE: net prices, card slips closed   CARDS: Access, Amex, Diners, Visa   DETAILS: 35 seats. Private parties: 12 and 24 private rooms. Car park. Vegetarian meals. Children's helpings on request. Smart dress preferred. No music. Air-conditioned   ACCOMMODATION: 48 rooms, all with bath/shower. Lift. Room only £175 to £294. Children welcome. Pets by arrangement. Afternoon teas. Air-conditioned. TV. Phone. Confirm 1 day ahead. Fax: 071-225 0011 (*The Which? Hotel Guide*)

---

## Le Caprice                                                          map 14

Arlington House,
Arlington Street, SW1A 1RT                                         COOKING 3
071-629 2239                                                     COST £29–£52

Le Caprice is reputed to be full of celebrities, a rich man's playground. It fills the role with nonchalant ease: witness the visitor soon surrounded by three stage heroes on an early evening visit. But ordinary people who come here are welcomed. Some find it a peculiarly satisfactory restaurant: 'I came here feeling headachy and migrainous. I emerged feeling invigorated,' reported one happy diner. 'It was the first time I learned that the lady who looks after the cloaks is married to the pianist. We just love this place. Hats off to the owners and chefs,' added a second. The setting is simple and cool, even if the tables are turned over with aplomb to cope with the reservations. Part of the secret lies in owner-occupation and strong motivation of the staff. Another lies in the cooking, which may not always be of the very best, but generally achieves a satisfying consistency and essential standard. One person's squash risotto was as mushy as it sounds; another's Caesar salad was almost wilting. But a third's Middle Eastern hors d'oeuvre were attractive and full of contrasting tastes, and grilled marinated vegetables were 'a splendid cornucopia, a careful assortment of the pedestrian and the exotic'. The list could go on and on for food that succeeds in being safe yet trendy. Prices are held in user-friendly check (except for the cover charge) for the area. The same applies to the wine list, which manages a wide geographical range, a big price spread and a pair of very decent house selections at £8.50.

CHEFS: Mark Hix and Tony Carey   PROPRIETORS: Christopher Corbin and Jeremy King   OPEN: all week; 12 to 3 (3.30 Sun), 6 to 12   CLOSED: D 24 Dec to L 2 Jan   MEALS: alc (main courses £7.50 to £15). Cover £1.50   SERVICE: not inc   CARDS: Access, Amex, Diners, Visa   DETAILS: 70 seats. Vegetarian meals. Children welcome. No cigars in dining-room. Wheelchair access. Music. Air-conditioned. Fax: 071-493 9040

## Casale Franco
map 11

134–137 Upper Street, N1 1TQ   COOKING 1
071-226 8994   COST £22–£51

In a mews off Upper Street the queues snake towards this cavernous warren on two floors decorated with strings of garlic. Its popularity stems from apparent economy (though it may add up to more than you first thought), good pizzas and pasta, cheerful service, and the comfort that comes from numbers of like-minded people. There is no booking except at lunch (but you cannot get a pizza then or as a single-plate meal after 8pm), and meals may be accelerated to cope with the people next in line. As well as the pizzas, which are large and excellent, a full slate of mainstream Italian fare is offered, plus the modern standards such as grilled vegetables, bresaola or squid with polenta. The execution is mixed. People appreciate the generosity of portions, yet sometimes regret the approximate seasoning and indistinct flavours. The Italian wine list is not too dear and has plenty of worthwhile bottles. The house white, Locorotondo from Puglia at £8.50, is much enjoyed.

CHEF: Mario Pensa   PROPRIETORS: Gisella and Franco Pensa   OPEN: Fri to Sun L, Tue to Sun D; 12.30 to 2.30, 6.30 to 11.30 (11 Sun)   MEALS: alc (main dishes £6.50 to £18.50). Cover £1. Minimum £6.50   SERVICE: not inc (10% for 5 or more)   CARDS: Access, Visa   DETAILS: 140 seats. 10 tables outside. Private parties: 40 main room. Vegetarian meals. Children welcome. Smart dress preferred. No-smoking area. Wheelchair access. Music. Air-conditioned. Fax: 071-359 5569

## Chanterelle
map 13

119 Old Brompton Road, SW7 3RN   COOKING 1
071-373 5522 and 7390   COST £17–£32

'An old favourite,' exclaim a couple who, like most customers, appreciate the polite atmosphere and good value of this long-established South Kensington bolt-hole. Some have hinted that the fixed prices are creeping up and the kitchen is prone to lapses, but mostly the place is sound. The menus move with the times, taking on board rabbit sausage with chestnut purée, ceviche of halibut with celeriac and avocado, grilled fillet of salmon with saffron butter, and roast saddle of boar with prune and armagnac stuffing, as well as the more traditional game pie and rack of lamb. Desserts are the likes of treacle tart and poached pear with butterscotch sauce. Lunch is a bargain. Wine prices are kept within limits and the list offers plenty of decent drinking from France and the New World. House wine is £7.60.

CHEF: James McKenzie  PROPRIETOR: Fergus Provan  OPEN: all week; 12 to 2.30, 7 to 11.30  CLOSED: 5 days Christmas  MEALS: Set L £11.50 to £13.50, Set Sun L £13, Set D £14.50 to £20.50. Minimum £11.50  SERVICE: not inc (12.5% for 6 or more)  CARDS: Access, Amex, Diners, Visa  DETAILS: 50 seats. 2 tables outside. Private parties: 20 main room. Vegetarian meals. Children welcome. Smart dress preferred. Wheelchair access. No music

## Cheng-du £

map 11

9 Parkway, Camden Town, NW1 7PG
071-485 8058

COOKING 1
COST £18–£47

Chinese feasts or banquets here are described as 'superiore' or 'classico' but they contain no saltimbocca or spaghetti, more likely a very acceptable and accessible version of Szechuan cooking served in modish and still smart surroundings. The spiced dishes like Hunanese hot-and-sour pork, Kung-po hot chilli prawns, spring onions with black bean and green chilli, and sautéed squid with a hot bean sauce have been approved. The wine list is better than many, though almost all the whites have alternative vintages, but prices are kept in check. House Italian costs £7.80.

CHEF: Mr Lam  PROPRIETORS: Redfern Enterprises Ltd  OPEN: all week; 12 to 2.30, 6.30 to 11.30  MEALS: alc (main courses £4 to £15). Set L and D £17.80 (minimum 2)  SERVICE: 12.5%  CARDS: Access, Amex, Visa  DETAILS: 85 seats. Private parties: 20 main room. Vegetarian meals. Children welcome. Smart dress preferred. Wheelchair access. Music

## Chez Liline

map 10

101 Stroud Green Road, N4 3PX
071-263 6550 and 272 9719

COOKING 1
COST £19–£43

Liline is no longer the proprietress and chef Mario Ho Wing Cheong has taken over the reins of this, the original Mauritian fish restaurant whose sibling is La Gaulette in Cleveland Street (see entry, London). The style has not changed a jot. It is still that melting pot of Chinese (soy sauce, ginger, lemon grass), Indian (chilli and saffron) and French (cream sauces) that is Mauritian cooking. The materials are either from Billingsgate or warm-water species flown in from the Indian and Pacific oceans. The methods are more intrusive than plain old English ways of dealing with fish, but people seem to enjoy shellfish done with onions, tomatoes and chilli, or red snapper with ginger and spring onions as much as grilled sea bass with fennel. No one writes home about elegance or comfort here, though value is still acceptable. More reports of the progress of the new regime would be welcome. The wine list is principally of whites, arranged by grape type. Value is very fair, and the range acceptable. House wines are £8.50.

CHEFS: Mario Ho Wing Cheong and Pascal Doudrich   PROPRIETOR: Mario Ho Wing
Cheong   OPEN: all week, exc Sun D; 12.30 to 2.30, 6.30 to 10.30 (11 Fri and Sat)   CLOSED:
bank hols   MEALS: alc (main courses £10 to £17). Set L and D £12.75 (not Sat D) to £22 (4
or more people). Minimum £9.75   SERVICE: not inc   CARDS: Access, Amex, Diners, Visa
DETAILS: 50 seats. Private parties: 22 main room. Vegetarian meals with prior notice.
Children's helpings. Music

## Chez Moi
map 12

| 1 Addison Avenue, W11 4QS | COOKING 3 |
| 071-603 8267 | COST £22–£44 |

Within striking distance of the BBC in its Shepherd's Bush laager; supported
with affection by families that have lived round the corner for years; a place to
take visiting business: Chez Moi continues to serve many constituencies.
Although long established, it manages to achieve a freshness of welcome and
attention that wins new friends, and to produce food that is at once familiar
(rack of lamb has been cooked on every menu since inception) and sufficiently
aware of changes in taste to have current appeal. This is a neighbourhood
restaurant par excellence that has never rested on its laurels. The menu
acknowledges these different streams with 'Chez Moi traditionnel' on one side
and 'Quelque chose de différent' on the other. Thus can be ordered rack of lamb
with a mustard and herb coating or rolled fillets of sole with a celeriac purée
and caviare sauce (traditionnel), or fast-marinated tuna followed by chicken
cooked in the Thai style (différent). Lunch is much cheaper than the evening
menu and should be better supported than it is, both for the value and
consistent standard. The classic regions get fair representation in the wine list,
though prices can never be give-away. House wines begin at £8.

CHEF: Richard Walton   PROPRIETORS: Richard Walton and Colin Smith   OPEN: Mon to
Sat, exc Sat L; 12.30 to 2, 7 to 11   CLOSED: bank hols   MEALS: alc (main courses £11 to
£14). Set L £14   SERVICE: not inc   CARDS: Access, Amex, Diners, Visa   DETAILS: 45 seats.
Vegetarian meals with prior notice. Children's helpings. No pipes in dining-room.
Wheelchair access (1 step). No music. Air-conditioned

## Chez Nico
## at Ninety Park Lane
NEW ENTRY   map 14

| 90 Park Lane, W1A 3AA | COOKING 5 |
| 071-409 1290 | COST £35–£95 |

Nico Ladenis' principal restaurant did not receive an entry in last year's edition
of the Guide because he was between stoves, so to speak, as we went to press.
He has now settled in his new surroundings, formerly the 'gourmet' restaurant
of the Grosvenor House Hotel next door on Park Lane. He has refurbished
completely, retaining only the means of access, along a canopied path from
Park Lane to the front door. The room is a large one, reached by a pair of
anonymous ante-chambers, but itself full of light and flashing reflections from
a plethora of mirrors. Without fireworks of design or ornament, it seems what it
is: a generous space devoted to the service of food in much comfort. Some
would condemn it for being stolidly bourgeois, but for the first time in Nico's

career there seems to be no shoe-horning, no contradiction between place and pursuit. There is continuity between his earlier restaurants and this one in both personnel (family and staff) and food, though the conversion of the menu from French- to English-language will surprise and please many. Pleasure has also been registered at the inclusive price of the lunch menu, which offers genuine choice for a cost that many consider a palapable bargain. 'One remembers the powerful flavour of the ceps risotto, the rich gamey sauce with the boudin blanc with caramelised apples, and the melting lemon filling to the tart. Miniature work is a delight – tiny tartlets and biscuits served as canapés and petits fours' was the satisfied comment of one who had seized the opportunity. Lunch dishes are understandably simpler than those on the *carte*, less likely to contain luxuries, but still packing a punch of flavour as in a remarkable potato and garlic cream soup, salmon with sorrel, a sole with lobster sauce, lamb cutlets with haricots blancs, a dark chocolate tart, apple tart (still one of the best), or a nougat glace with peach liqueur sauce. The dinner menu is long, the price fixed for two courses, with puddings and coffee extra. Supplements are carried by lobster, caviare and the classic tournedos Rossini. Some of the intensity for which this kitchen was famed has vanished in an effort to lighten sauces and compositions, thus there have been readers who were underwhelmed by a particular dish – not a common complaint *chez* Nico. What has not changed is the careful arrangement, almost harking back to the days of nouvelle cuisine, of food on a plate. It is usually self-contained in the centre, and needs to be unravelled vertically to get the desired effect of texture and flavour contrasts. Things which have satisfied are numberless, but comment might be restricted to extolling the brioche with foie gras topped by a slice of orange given a caramel glaze. That vertical slice gives all the texture changes, the richness, sweetness and sharpness all in one forkful. It throws into relief the relative mildness of a salad of red mullet arranged around a salad of tomato and cucumber with dill or tarragon – pleasing but not so memorable. Among main dishes, that similar contrast between the bold and the tremulous was met at a table which sampled the calf's sweetbreads wrapped in Parma ham with a scattering of sweet candied lemon zest and a limpid stock sauce. The underlying layer was braised cos or Webb lettuce with a smearing of hollandaise, and some golden saffron potatoes gave a slight balance of neutrality – a brilliant dish. Its neighbour was a fillet of brill given a hedgehog skin with a slice of bread criss-crossed then fiercely browned. Fine texture changes and extremely good fish were vitiated by characterless oregano potatoes and a warm vinaigrette that had insufficient punch to point up the main ingredient. The rest of the meal – bread, cheeses, sensationally simple desserts, matchless petits fours, good deep coffee – marched in unison with the foregoing. It is when the wine list (from £18) is reached that most people wince. There are half-bottles and an attempt to get a range that is affordable, but people find the prices difficult to cope with.

CHEFS: Nico Ladenis and Paul Flynn   PROPRIETORS: Nico and Dinah-Jane Ladenis   OPEN: Mon to Sat; 12 to 2, 7 to 11   MEALS: Set L £25 to £35 (inc wine), Set D £42 (2 courses). Minimum £42 D   SERVICE: net prices, card slips closed   CARDS: Access, Amex, Diners, Visa   DETAILS: 70 seats. Private parties: 80 main room, 20 private room. Vegetarian meals. No children under 6. Smart dress preferred. No pipes in dining-room. Wheelchair access (1 step; also WC). No music. Air-conditioned

## Chinon £

map 12

23 Richmond Way, W14 0AS                    COOKING 3*
071-602 4082 and 5968                       COST £18–£52

All change near Shepherd's Bush as Barbara Deane and Jonathan Hayes move
one door up this terraced shopping street caught in a maze of one-way traffic
south of the green. One door equals two floors, for now the set-up is a bar and
café, with good food too, at street level, then down some stairs to the restaurant
(dinner only), which is open to the terrace and garden behind. Jonathan Hayes
works virtually single-handed and his cooking is ambitious, therefore the
menu stays short so that he can do the numbers. Occasionally, this may mean a
lack of balance, but rarely is there anything that does not attract. A meal in the
summer confirmed the quality. A melting goats' cheese, exactly the right
strength, was given a crust of herbes de Provence and sun-dried tomatoes, a
bed of red peppers and a perfumed vinaigrette. It also had fresh peas, some
lentils, broad beans, asparagus and spring onions for trimmings that stopped
short of fussy only because of their quality. Then there was a squid stuffed with
tomato and aubergine one end, pesto the other. There were main courses of
scallops with a garlic butter sauce and a parcel of Chinese leaf over mashed
potato, their giant roes sitting pumply atop a dish of sugar snaps, or a slice of
calf's liver, a chunk of sweetbread, and a diminutive kidney with a carrot and
Sauternes sauce given a kick of paprika. Desserts are distinguished – the prune
and almond tart with orange-flower water is an example; cheeses are carefully
bought. Everything is first-rate, with less of the doctrinaire take-it-or-leave-it
that used to characterise the place in some people's reports. The wine list is
none too long, from superior sources, with range enough to cope with two
styles of service, and seems about to undergo further development. House wine
is £8.50.

CHEF: Jonathan Hayes   PROPRIETORS: Barbara Deane and Jonathan Hayes   OPEN:
restaurant Tue to Sat, D only; 6.30 (7 Sat) to 10.30. Bar/brasserie Mon to Sat; 12 to 2.30, 5 to
11   CLOSED: bank hols   MEALS: alc. Minimum £10   SERVICE: 12.5%, card slips closed
CARDS: Access, Amex, Visa   DETAILS: restaurant 30 seats, bar/brasserie 30 seats. Private
parties: 34 main room. Vegetarian meals with prior notice. No children under 10.
Wheelchair access. Music. Air-conditioned

## Christopher's

map 15

18 Wellington Street, WC2E 7DD              COOKING 1
071-240 4222                                COST £24–£63

Since those glory days when the opening of this still fashionable restaurant
occupied inches of space in the dailies, the exceptionally well-sited room at the
top of a neo-mannerist staircase a hop and jump away from the opera has
chugged along doing good business for a well-heeled bunch of lunchers in the
opinion and service industries and a more miscellaneous group at night. There
is a stylish bar at ground-floor level, with lots of buzz. The cooking is, of course,
with an American tilt, for this is a take-off of a big-city restaurant over there.
The big differences lie in the accents of the clientele, the steep prices for the
food and the standards of consistency. The obvious things to eat are the grills
and the salads. Thus New York-style strip steak with tobacco onions

(deep-fried rings) and a green salad with plenty of dressing and good trimmings of chervil to vary the flavour was unexceptionable. So was plain calf's liver with candied onions and pancetta, and no complaints either about smoked tomato soup, Caesar salad or carpaccio. It is when matters get a little more complex that some errors of seasoning may creep in. The upper-class American or French choices on the wine list give away the nature of the place. House wines are from £10.

CHEF: Adrian Searing PROPRIETOR: Christopher Gilmour OPEN: all week, exc Sat L and Sun D; 12 to 2.30 (11.30 to 2.30 Sun brunch), 6 to 11.30 MEALS: alc (main courses £8 to £17.50). Set pre-theatre D £15 to £19 SERVICE: not inc (12.5%, card slips closed, for 7 or more) CARDS: Access, Amex, Diners, Visa DETAILS: 120 seats. Private parties: 100 main room, 32 private room. Vegetarian meals. Children's helpings on request. Smart dress preferred. No music (exc private parties). Fax: 071-240 3357

## ▲ *Claridge's* 🍷 NEW ENTRY map 14

Brook Street, W1A 2JQ COOKING 3
071-629 8860 COST £33–£86

Enter Claridges without a tie at your peril. This is the resort of crowned, and formerly crowned, heads, where proper respect for the niceties of life is expected. If everyone swallows their prejudices, this is the fun of the place. The courtly dining-room is as good a spot as any to study the tarantelles of classical service, and to taste cooking in the grand tradition. This has been updated by chef Marjan Lesnik to take it beyond archaeological curiosity, but it is still of that particular breed: the grand hotel. None the less, it produced a lunch that started with a salad of pleurottes dressed with pumpkin oil and nut oil that managed to get texture (by frying some of the mushrooms crisp, leaving others to yield up their soft fleshiness) as well as taste, then went on to a best end of lamb (dressed exactly *comme il faut*, of course) with an almond crust and a light gravy, reinforced by a properly cream-laden gratin dauphinois and not such good broccoli, and finished in slightly less flourishing style with a passable brûlée and an acceptable savarin off the trolley. As with all such big kitchens, the framework and the principal items may be just so, but details can nag. In a small corner of the building is the Causerie – designed before the Second World War as a haven for ladies who lunch. It is still an intimate restaurant, serving smorgasbord as ever, where the cast list can surprise. Do not expect anything cheap here. With the marvellous Manzanilla of Barbadillo appearing alongside Harveys Bristol Cream we can be assured that the management knows its clientele and is happy to oblige. Elsewhere on the wine front, the obligation extends to the provision of the finest – four first growths from 1970 are characteristic of the style – with a suitable mark-up regime which catches in its tail relatively modest Loires and Rhônes. None of this surprises; less expected though are a few simple decent wines offered below £16 and half-bottles, notably some well chosen bourgeois clarets, at approachable prices. House wine is £14.50. CELLARMAN'S CHOICE: Chablis 1991, Durup, £24.75; Médoc, Ch. la Tour-de-By 1986, £27.90.

*🍾 denotes an outstanding wine cellar; 🍷 denotes a good wine list, worth travelling for.*

CHEFS: Marjan Lesnik and John Williams   PROPRIETORS: The Savoy Group plc   OPEN: all
week, exc Sat L (Causerie open); 12.30 to 3, 7 to 11.15   MEALS: alc (main courses £16 to
£28). Set L £21 (2 courses) to £32, Set D £27 to £35. Cover £1   SERVICE: net prices, card
slips closed   CARDS: Access, Amex, Diners, Visa   DETAILS: 120 seats. Private parties: 36
main room, 15 to 210 private rooms. Vegetarian meals. Children's helpings on request.
Jacket and tie. Wheelchair access (also WC). Music. Air-conditioned   ACCOMMODATION:
192 rooms, all with bath/shower. Rooms for disabled. Lift. B&B £156 to £361. Children
welcome. Baby facilities. Afternoon teas. Sauna. Air-conditioned. TV. Phone. Confirm 1
day ahead. Fax: 071-499 2210

## Clarke's 🍾

map 12

124 Kensington Church Street, W8 4BH                                   COOKING 4
071-221 9225                                                       COST £30–£50

'If I owned a restaurant, it would be like this' was the thought of a reader
struck by the civility of the place, split between ground floor and airy basement
towards Notting Hill Gate, but definitely part of the Kensington set. Sally
Clarke has a shop as well, for breads, sweets, coffee, wine, cheese and the like.
The basement, shared by a kitchen on view to many of the tables, avoids the
usual claustrophobia of such rooms: what any restaurant designer must think
'the curse of the lower ground floor'. The distinctive character of dinner here is
that the menu is given; there is no choice. At lunch, there are three alternatives
at each course for a set price, and many prefer the meal for that very reason. For
all the possible drawbacks of dinner – and they are well rehearsed in the
course of a year – people vote emphatically with their feet: the place is packed.
The dangers most often encountered, apart from simply not liking what is on
offer, are that there is not enough food – this is not a glutton's paradise – and
that the cumulative effect lacks either balance or weight. The style is not
complicated, methods are direct, and there is no masking by palate-bashing
sauces. Most dishes depend on counterpoint of the elements, often themselves
relatively unsullied. If this does not work (in the eyes of the eater at least), the
dish falls down. The point, of course, is that many find they do work, that
eating here leaves you fresh and ready for the fray, and that the social touch is
light and welcoming as well. A meal that consisted of leek and wild mushroom
broth with scallops, fresh pasta, thyme and truffle shavings, then slow-cooked
duck leg with roasted red endive and fennel and a pine-nut glaze, plus some
soft polenta well seasoned with sage, before cheeses (always good), then
Bramley apple fritters with red fruit cream, was beyond fault on any of the
grounds mentioned above. Clarke's has a remarkably high strike-rate. The
wine list, too, will be remembered for its Californian choices, none of them
overpriced, its good selection of wines by the glass, and its upper-crust yet
concise set of French and Italian bottles. It is a model of composition. Wines
start at £8. CELLARMAN'S CHOICE: California, Qupé, Marsanne 1991, £19;
Morey St-Denis, Clos Des Ormes 1987, Lignier, £35.

---

*The 1995 Guide will be published before Christmas 1994. Reports on meals are most
welcome at any time of the year, but are extremely valuable in the spring. Send them to
The Good Food Guide, FREEPOST, 2 Marylebone Road, London NW1 1YN. No stamp
is needed if posted in the UK.*

---

CHEFS: Sally Clarke and Elizabeth Payne  PROPRIETOR: Sally Clarke  OPEN: Mon to Fri; 12.30 to 2, 7 to 10  CLOSED: 2 weeks Christmas, 1 week Easter, 2 weeks summer, bank hols  MEALS: Set L £22 (2 courses) to £26, Set D £37  SERVICE: net prices, card slips closed  CARDS: Access, Visa  DETAILS: 90 seats. Private parties: 12 main room. Vegetarian meals. Children welcome. No-smoking area. Wheelchair access. Air-conditioned. Fax: 071-229 4564

---

## ▲ Connaught ♥  map 14

Carlos Place, W1Y 6AL  
071-499 7070

COOKING 4  
COST £38–£122

'A restaurant is either good or bad; fashion is irrelevant.' This is the axiom of a well-fed man who knows what he likes. He saw in the New Year at the Connaught with foie gras ('here the kitchen makes decent Melba toast'), a whole wild duck carved at the table, some mange-tout, a half of Ch. Montrose 1982, a layered confection of meringue and mousse of (imported) strawberries, a glass of Muscat de Beaumes de Venise and an espresso coffee. 'There were worse ways of starting the year,' he concluded. His bill was well into three figures and he called the whole experience impressive. It certainly was that. The panelled dining-room glows, the silver gleams, the glasses glint, the cutlery is sharp, and so are the creases to napkins, cloths and waiters' trousers. Change is inconceivable here. Generations of staff have been trained at the Connaught, then have passed on their accumulated knowledge; so have the customers. Even if you are not someone whose grandfather made a habit of coming here every month, you will want to give the impression that he did. The ritual, which starts with the ceremonial passage through the slight corridor entrance – food to the left and right and commis waiters everywhere – is imposing and may be daunting to those unfamiliar with it. The menu needs decoding, but interpretation is readily offered. There are two strong suits: classic British cooking of game, grills and roasts, and French haute cuisine of a sort rarely found in Britain today. Although the odd disappointment in quality of food is registered – 'Is there one rule for the set menu and another for the carte?' asked a couple who wished they had stayed with the dearer option – the level of achievement is outstanding and the service, set in pre-war aspic, is a manoeuvre of mystifying complexity. The wine list disregards non-Europeans, which does not mean that the wines are therefore simply old-fashioned, classic and mature. Big names such as Latour, Jaboulet and Ladoucette may predominate, but that is not altogether a bad thing. Italy shows remarkable strength; well-aged Volpaia and Vicchiomaggio Chiantis stand out. Good halves from elsewhere and reliable bourgeois clarets afford reasonable, but still interesting, drinking. House wine is £11.50 for a carafe.

---

*See the inside of the front cover for an explanation of the 1 to 5 rating system for cooking standards.*

*The text of entries is based on unsolicited reports sent in by readers, backed up by inspections conducted anonymously. The factual details under the text are from questionnaires the* Guide *sends to all restaurants that feature in the book.*

---

CHEF: Michel Bourdin   PROPRIETORS: The Savoy Group plc   OPEN: restaurant all week,
Grill Room Mon to Fri; 12.30 to 2, 6.30 (6 Grill Room) to 10.30   CLOSED: Grill Room bank
hols   MEALS: alc (main courses £11 to £40). Set L £25, Set Sun L Grill Room £30, Set D
Grill Room £35. Minimum £25   SERVICE: 15%, card slips closed   CARDS: Access, Amex,
Visa   DETAILS: restaurant 75 seats, Grill Room 35 seats. Private parties: 10 and 22 private
rooms. Car park. Vegetarian meals with prior notice. No children under 6. Jacket and tie.
Wheelchair access (also men's WC). No music. Air-conditioned   ACCOMMODATION: 90
rooms, all with bath/shower. Rooms for disabled. Lift. Room prices on application.
Children welcome. Afternoon teas. TV. Phone. Fax: 071-495 3262 (*The Which? Hotel Guide*)

## Connolly's

| | NEW ENTRY | map 10 |

162 Lower Richmond Road, SW15 1LY                      COOKING 2
081-788 3844                                           COST £21–£29

After a sabbatical last year, Eamonn Connolly is back in the kitchen of this
restaurant in a small parade of shops. At the front is a sheltered courtyard filled
with greenery; inside are two dining-rooms lit by spots in the ceiling and
candles on the tables. Blue and yellow is the colour scheme. Tables of various
shapes and sizes are neatly laid out, although one visitor remarked at the
'motley' collection of chairs. Kate Connolly is a welcoming, 'hearty' hostess
backed up by neatly turned-out waitresses. Menus are fixed-price for two or
three courses and the cooking has a modern cosmopolitan touch, travelling far
and wide for beef carpaccio, Mediterranean prawns with Thai dressing, and
sweet-and-sour pork fillet. The traditional British tendency appears in the
shape of Cullen skink, boiled bacon with pease pudding, and sticky toffee
pudding. Approved dishes from recent reports have included duck mousse
with a fruity sauce, wild boar and apple sausages, rack of lamb, and poussin
with spring onions and soy sauce. Braised ox tongue with spinach and red
wine sauce was 'absolute bliss' for one reporter. Connolly's crème brûlée is an
unusual version served in a wine glass: a thinnish brûlée flecked with
chocolate in a strong caramel sauce topped with a blob of ice-cream. The wine
list is short and sensibly priced, although it is 'nothing to shout about'; beer is
also available. House wine is £8.50.

CHEF: Eamonn Connolly   PROPRIETOR: Kate Connolly   OPEN: all week, exc Sat L and Sun
D (Sat L by arrangement for parties); 12 to 2.30, 7 to 10.30 (12.30 to 4 Sun)   CLOSED: bank
hols   MEALS: Set L £9.95 (2 courses) to £15.95, Set D £12.95 to £15.95   SERVICE: not inc
CARDS: Access, Amex, Visa   DETAILS: 40 seats. 10 tables outside. Private parties: 46 main
room. Vegetarian meals. Children's helpings. Smart dress preferred. No pipes in dining-
room. Wheelchair access (1 step). Music

## Cork & Bottle ♥ £

map 15

44–46 Cranbourn Street, WC2H 7AN                      COOKING 1
071-734 7807 and 6592                                 COST £18–£35

'My father enjoyed sampling four different wines by the glass – you don't often
get the opportunity in Cheshire,' commented a reporter who used this classic
wine bar for refreshment and sustenance before *and* after the theatre. The all-
day opening (including Sundays) is a real bonus for wine buffs, who
appreciate time to browse through the ever-changing list. The food also

continues to evolve. Fish shows up strongly in specials such as tartare de loup (sea bass mousse with sauce tartare wrapped in smoked salmon), grilled cod steak with Creole sauce, roulade of salmon and carp, and monkfish with pineapple coulis and jalapeño and coriander pesto. Salads, such as Greek and Malaysian versions, are regularly mentioned in reports, as are the breads and filter coffee. Strawberry mille-feuille has been 'pretty and pretty good'. This place remains a rarity, a wine bar worth visiting for the wines. Prices are fair. Last year a special season reintroduced grateful customers to the pleasures of 'proper Beaujolais'. Half-bottles are forsaken on grounds of cost, but the gap is filled with good wines by the glass. House wines are £8.95. CELLARMAN'S CHOICE: Hawkes Bay, Church Road Chardonnay, 1992, McDonald, £13.95; Margaux, Ch. Labégorce-Zédé 1986, £18.95.

CHEF: Louis Egham   PROPRIETORS: Cork & Bottle 1991 Ltd   OPEN: all week; 11am to 11.30pm (noon to 10 Sun)   CLOSED: 25 and 26 Dec, 1 Jan   MEALS: alc (main courses £4 to £10)   SERVICE: not inc   CARDS: Access, Amex, Diners, Visa   DETAILS: 80 seats. Private parties: 20 main room, 20 private room. Vegetarian meals. No pipes in dining-room. Music. Air-conditioned. Fax: 071-483 2230

## Criterion

NEW ENTRY   map 14

224 Piccadilly, W1V 9LB
071-925 0909

COOKING 1
COST £21–£41

This giant basilica of a restaurant – the tiling and character of the light also remind some people of a turn-of-the-century swimming-pool – has been restored and embellished by the restlessly energetic Bob Payton, of pizza pies and Stapleford Park (see entry, Stapleford). His intention, other than rendering us the service of seeing this neo-Byzantine structure of the 1870s, was to establish a North American Italian-style restaurant. Yet, what tendency there is has been towards modern Britain and away from Italy, but between the ribeye steaks and fries, Caesar salads, sausages and herbed mashed potatoes, there still lurk thin-crust pizza, salmon carpaccio, mushroom risotto fritters and other Italian-inspired dishes. Reaction to the food has been that it promises more than it delivers. Polenta with mushrooms and herb cream was mushy and unseasoned; 'coil' of sausage with mashed potato needed more life than it gained from a mustard aïoli that came with it. Enthusiasm for tomato needs to be muted. The location – by the statue of Eros at Piccadilly Circus – is great, so is the place. Staff and service excite differing responses. The short wine list has modish names and decent prices from £8.90.

CHEF: Brian Baker   PROPRIETORS: Bob Payton and Rocco Forte   OPEN: Mon to Sat; noon to 11.30   CLOSED: 25, 26 and 31 Dec, bank hols   MEALS: alc (main courses £7.50 to £12). Set L and D £10 (2 courses). Minimum £4   SERVICE: not inc, card slips closed   CARDS: Access, Amex, Diners, Visa   DETAILS: 140 seats. Vegetarian meals. Children welcome. No cigars/ pipes in dining-room. Wheelchair access (also WC). No music. Fax: 071-839 1494

---

*'We also liked the residents' bar, which was well stocked and provided with a book in which one recorded one's drinks (this system seemed to engender scrupulous honesty in the guests – one even recorded the number of ice cubes he'd taken).'* On eating in Scotland

## Crowthers

map 10

481 Upper Richmond Road West, SW14 7PU
081-876 6372

COOKING 2
COST £24–£34

A couple who have been supporting this smart little East Sheen restaurant since it opened in 1982 continue to sing its praises and enjoy its pleasant surroundings, blessed absence of music and 'wonderful' cooking. The repertoire evolves slowly – a few Mediterranean touches have been taken on board – but, as Philip Crowther points out, 'We would be lynched if we took some dishes off the menu.' Meals are fixed-price for two or three courses and the style is represented by feuilleté of scallops, leeks and oyster mushrooms with light curry sauce, grilled aubergine with tomato, feta cheese and pesto, sauté calf's liver with onion, sage and madeira, and roast guinea-fowl with toasted pine-nuts, wild mushroom and marjoram sauce. Parfait of three chocolates comes with coffee-bean sauce; crêpes are served with praline and caramel ice-cream. Service is reported to be 'excellent'. The list of around 50 wines is keenly priced and there is a better-than-average choice of halves. House wines are £8.50.

CHEF: Philip Crowther   PROPRIETORS: Philip and Shirley Crowther   OPEN: Tue to Sat, exc Sat L; 12 to 2, 7 to 10.30   CLOSED: 1 week Christmas, 2 weeks summer   MEALS: Set L £12.50 (2 courses) to £15.50, Set D £14.50 (2 courses) to £19   SERVICE: not inc CARDS: Access, Visa   DETAILS: 32 seats. Private parties: 32 main room. Vegetarian meals. Children's helpings. Smart dress preferred. Wheelchair access (1 step). No music. Air-conditioned

## Dan's

**NEW ENTRY**   map 13

119 Sydney Street, SW3 6NR
071-352 2718

COOKING 1*
COST £21–£38

Dan Whitehead describes his attractive neighbourhood venture as a 'restaurant and garden', and the prospect of outdoor eating is one of the obvious attractions. The frontage looks more 'country' than 'King's Road', but inside is a cool, quite spacious dining-room with well-spaced tables and mustard-coloured walls. The music can be thumpingly loud. Chef Thierry Rousseau offers a long, affordable *carte* as well as fixed-price menus for lunch and dinner. The tone is French, with inflexions of modern British. Starters such as timbale of Stilton mousse with pears and deep-fried king prawns with Pernod mayonnaise are creditable, but invention and 'sharp flavourings' really get going in the main courses. Standards here are 'on something of a roller-coaster', but there is enough ability at the heart of it to recommend. Favourably reported dishes have included deeply flavoured crab bisque, fine duck magret with 'a gingered-up sauce', braised liver in red wine sauce, nougat glace with raspberry coulis and chocolate cake with cherry sauce. The handwritten, fairly priced wine list is mostly French with a few New World items tucked away for good measure. House wine is £9.50.

---

*A report form is at the back of the book; write a letter if you prefer.*

---

CHEF: Thierry Rousseau PROPRIETOR: Dan Whitehead OPEN: Mon to Sat, exc Sat L;
12.30 to 2.30, 7.30 to 10.45 CLOSED: 25 Dec to 2 Jan MEALS: alc (main courses £6.50 to
£10.50). Set L £10 (2 courses) to £12.50, Set D £14 (2 courses) to £16.50 SERVICE: not inc
CARDS: Access, Amex, Diners, Visa DETAILS: 50 seats. 9 tables outside. Private parties:
34 main room, 12 and 34 private rooms. Vegetarian meals. Children's helpings on request.
Smart dress preferred. Wheelchair access (2 steps). Music. Fax: 071-352 3265

## Daphne £
map 11

83 Bayham Street, NW1 0AG
071-267 7322

COOKING 1
COST £16–£31

The general bonhomie between staff and regular customers quickly builds up
the image of a user-friendly, cheerful restaurant where families are welcome,
vegetarians are looked after and everyone enjoys the atmosphere. The setting is
a terraced house on a busy Camden Town street, but suspension of disbelief is
quickly enforced and the blue horizons and shaded squares of Cyprus are
summoned by the imagination, by a roof garden for summer eating, and by the
food. The fish meze is especially popular, encompassing chargrilled fish and
shellfish as well as taramasalata and other dips. Blackboard specials bring in
more unfamiliar items – for instance, cuttlefish casserole, or deep-fried balls of
aubergine and feta cheese. Finish with Greek sweetmeats; drink island or
Greek wines. The house wines are from Beaujolais and cost £8.50.

CHEFS: L. Georgiou and K. Zacharias PROPRIETORS: Panikos and Anna Lymbouri OPEN:
Mon to Sat; 12 to 2.30, 6 to 11.30 MEALS: alc (main courses £5.50 to £9.50) SERVICE: not
inc CARDS: Access, Visa DETAILS: 85 seats. 10 tables outside. Private parties: 30 main
room. Vegetarian meals. Children's helpings. Wheelchair access (1 step; also WC). Music

## Daphne's
| NEW ENTRY | map 13

112 Draycott Avenue, SW3 3AE
071-589 4257

COOKING 1*
COST £25–£46

Daphne's was something special way back when bright young things (like the
eponymous founder) were called Daphne. Early 1993 saw the faded rose, in a
coma since the '80s, given a kiss of life so passionate as to render it
unrecognisable to former habitués; the name received a last-minute reprieve.
There are several rooms; the favourite is the long one at the back, where plants
climb up the walls to the glass-paned ceiling. The menu gets more complicated
as the day draws on (brunch, lunch and dinner) without ever swimming too
deeply out into its chosen spawning-ground. All the dishes come in single
price-portions, which means some find 'starters' too big or 'main courses' too
small; most, though, like the flexibility of constructing a meal at will. Edward
Baines, from the same owner's Soho restaurant Est (see London round-up),
took the precaution of brushing up his linguine and risotti in Milan before
Daphne's swanned back into circulation, and dishes like agnolotti verdi with
ricotta and walnut salsa, risotto milanese or wild mushroom with grilled
polenta show that the spirit of Italy has been thoroughly ingested. Desserts are
less inventive, but properly made. The tedious aspects of the place are the
smokers, the celebrities and the people who take themselves for celebrities.

'Service was attentive though a touch amateurish, despite the panache of various superior beings dancing attendance.' The presentable wine list begins at £8.50, and is equally divided among Italians, French and New Worlders.

CHEF: Edward Baines   PROPRIETOR: Mogens Tholstrup   OPEN: all week; 12 to 3 (11 to 4 Sun brunch), 7 to 11.30   CLOSED: 25 Dec   MEALS: alc (main courses £7.50 to £14) SERVICE: 15%, card slips closed   CARDS: Access, Amex, Diners, Visa   DETAILS: 120 seats. 10 tables outside. Private parties: 50 main room, 50 private room. Vegetarian meals. Children welcome. Smart dress preferred. No cigars in dining-room. Wheelchair access (2 steps). No music. Air-conditioned. Fax: 071-581 2232

## dell'Ugo £

map 15

56 Frith Street, W1V 5TA
071-734 8300

COOKING 1
COST £20–£40

This club-sandwich of a restaurant is deservedly popular. It offers a menu of 'free-form combinations of everyone's favourite ingredients' at accessible prices, in unstuffy surroundings which can be more (upstairs) or less (downstairs) elaborate. It responds to a need. Sometimes it also serves good food, usually very passable, and if it attracts a higher rate of complaint than many of its colleagues it is because numbers give it a statistical disadvantage. The menu shows Antony Worrall-Thompson's love of breads, peasant earth and wayward combinations that often work surprisingly well. Mussels in a broth of lentils, wilted greens and coriander, a tart of Swiss chard and potato, plain oysters, an AWT pizza (topped with aubergine and Mediterranean vegetables – a sort of bruschetta to order), duck confit with olive oil mash, chargrilled quail (only one of them) with pumpkin ravioli and sage butter were the components of a meal that finished with tarte Tatin flavoured with rosemary, pear poached in red wine served with Gorgonzola, and caramelised rice pudding with a dried fruit compote. When things like this are successful, and not extortionate, then small wonder at the popularity. The staff are hang-loose and amiable, and the place is not meant to be comfortable in the plush sense. The wine list changes every month or so depending on which merchant is being spotlit. House wine is £8.25.

CHEF: Mark Emberton   PROPRIETORS: Simpsons of Cornhill plc   OPEN: Mon to Sat, exc Sat L restaurant; 11am to 12.30am (ground floor), 12.15 to 3, 6.30 to 12.30 (restaurant) MEALS: alc (main courses £6 to £11)   SERVICE: not inc   CARDS: Access, Amex, Diners, Visa   DETAILS: 200 seats. 6 tables outside. Private parties: 60 main room, 16 private room. Vegetarian meals. Children's helpings on request. No pipes in dining-room. Wheelchair access ground floor (also WC). Music. Air-conditioned

## ▲ Dorchester ♥

map 14

Park Lane, W1A 2HJ
071-629 8888

COOKING 3
COST £28–£90

This giant of a hotel can never be said to lumber. In its re-awakened form, after a refurbishment to bring it into a decade whose jet-set includes nationalities and cultures more diverse than ever, it is proud of its Chinese restaurant, the traditionally ornate Grill and gourmet Terrace, and the Club for pursuit of pleasure at the end of the day. The Dorchester is so international that it has almost lost its focus. The cooking at the Terrace, displayed in a giant menu of dishes calculated to titivate but never challenge, remains stuck in the groove of artful decoration and surprisingly muted flavours. This may cause irritation if a vivid tricolour terrine of peppers tastes only of cream, or if breads, apparently varied, seem to be essentially of the same characterless dough, but it can also work supremely well if the food is light, meant to be light, and needs to be light. Delicacy is a grand thing in a dish such as veal chop stuffed with sweetbreads, with a chive cream, or chicken stuffed with shiitake mushrooms served with polenta and livers. This latter creation benefited from the livers (atop red cabbage), which gave a bit of punch. The menu majors on shellfish for first course and seems to place unexpected elements in counterpoint. The object of mixing carpaccio with a vegetable terrine was lost one one pair of diners. The Terrace does offer a paradigm of a certain sort of hotel food, at a considerable price. It also has music and dancing and lots of waiters. The setting, *Magic Flute* Egyptian overlaid with chinoiserie, is grandiose. The Oriental's best line are the dim-sum at lunch-time: beautifully served, no trundling trolleys, and full of flavour. The main drift of the menu is Cantonese and reports this year have not been so enthusiastic about any difference between it and more expressive and bolder cooking in Chinatown. It may be said to suffer from grand-hotel timorousness but, of course, the service and the comfort are top-notch. The same can be said of the wines, but the list takes us well beyond the normal classics showing a strong New World hand and impeccable choices from Spain and Italy. Prices are high but there are many decent halves and effort is made to include petits châteaux and provincial wines. Nothing, apparently, is available by the glass which is a shame for a place of this scale and reputation. House wines are from £15. CELLARMAN'S CHOICE: Cloudy Bay, Sauvignon 1992, £27; Rully 1988, Chauvenet, £23.50.

CHEFS: Willi Elsner (Grill and Terrace) and Simon Yung (Oriental)   PROPRIETORS: Dorchester Hotel Ltd   OPEN: Grill all week; Terrace Tue to Sat, D only; Oriental Mon to Sat, exc Sat L; 12 (12.30 Grill) to 2.30, 7 (6 Grill) to 11 (11.30 Terrace)   CLOSED: Aug Terrace   MEALS: alc (main courses Grill £11 to £24, Terrace £17 to £19.50, Oriental £9 to £25). Grill Set L £20, Set D £20 to £28; Terrace Set D £25 to £30; Oriental Set L £20, Set D £28   SERVICE: net prices   CARDS: Access, Amex, Diners, Visa   DETAILS: Grill 81 seats, Terrace 81 seats, Oriental 77 seats. Private parties: 18 main room, 6 to 14 in private rooms. Car park. Vegetarian meals. Children welcome Grill and Oriental. Jacket and tie Terrace. Smart dress preferred Grill and Oriental. Wheelchair access (3 steps Terrace; also WC all). Music (Terrace). Air-conditioned   ACCOMMODATION: 252 rooms, all with bath/shower. Rooms for disabled. Lift. B&B £225 to £279. Deposit: £180. Children welcome. Baby facilities. Afternoon teas. Sauna. Air-conditioned. TV. Phone. Confirm 1 day ahead. Fax: 071-495 7351

## La Dordogne

NEW ENTRY   map 10

5 Devonshire Road, W4 2EU
081-747 1836 and 994 7327

COOKING 1*
COST £25–£47

Three rooms in dark green, the walls covered in pictures, red café curtains and Victorian light fittings may be some hint of the image of this French neighbourhood restaurant with a line in oysters and lobsters as well as a classic Anglo-French menu. Tables are spaced and sized for midgets, and silent ones at that. Relatively formal French service may bring you a meal of scallops in an orange sauce, salade gourmande (often enjoyed), monkfish with bacon and port, sole fillets with saffron sauce, or fillet of beef with a Cahors or Quercy wine sauce, potato pancake and wild mushrooms. Desserts – for instance, the crème brûlée served with a caramel ice-cream, or even the big plate of everything – get good mentions too. There is a cover charge, but also a complimentary kir to begin. Some have thought the vegetables not worth the extra charge. The wine list is French, with some Cahors and Jurançon exclusivities. Prices are very fair indeed. House wine is £8.60.

CHEF: Gilles Companie  PROPRIETORS: La Dordogne Ltd  OPEN: all week, exc L Sat and Sun; 12 to 2.30, 7 to 11  CLOSED: bank hols  MEALS: alc (main courses £8 to £12). Cover £1  SERVICE: 10%  CARDS: Access, Amex, Diners, Visa  DETAILS: 80 seats. 6 tables outside. Private parties: 30 main room, 20 and 30 private rooms. Vegetarian meals with prior notice. Children welcome. Smart dress preferred. No pipes in dining-room. Wheelchair access (1 step; also WC). Music. Fax: 081-994 9144

## Downstairs at One Ninety     NEW ENTRY     map 13

190 Queen's Gate, SW7 5EU                                           COOKING 1*
071-581 5666                                                        COST £21–£44

Underneath the Gore Hotel, and Bistrot 190 (see entry) and the bar – which seems to be a meeting-place for a certain section of Kensington as well as the ante-room for the restaurants – is this basement restaurant specialising in fish. It was once all haute cuisine and heavyweights, but Antony Worrall-Thompson, who oversees cooking here and elsewhere, has been bitten by the fast-and-furious bug. Prices went down, the room was whitened and lightened, carpets left out, simple chairs added and bright, bright paintings –'"I think it's a squid," said my mother,' shuddered one reader. There is no denying the inventiveness of the menu, or the range of options that can keep the prices down, or the weight of business that marks its popularity. Creole-blackened John Dory with salsa, rocket and frites, scallops with Moroccan spices and minted couscous, or grilled turbot steak with asparagus and pesto potatoes should be sign enough that little is left plain in the manner of old-fashioned British fish restaurants. A diner who kicked off with crostini was undeniably happy with lobster mixed with mange-tout and other vegetables, scallop nori tempura and a saffron risotto (how's that for a mix of inspirations?) before plunging into a blackberry-and-apple cobbler with cinnamon ice-cream. The success of the place can be greater one day than the next. On bad days, all the advertised spices seem to leech away and cooking techniques – important in this simplicity – go awry. The same might be said of the service – excellent one night, then chaotic another. The wine list is more than a match for this, with relatively unknown growers jostling for attention with the well-established. Prices are fair for SW7 and half-bottles show a steady eye for quality. House wines are £9.50.

CHEFS: Antony Worrall-Thompson and Chris Millar  PROPRIETORS: 190 Queensgate plc OPEN: Mon to Sat, D only; 7 to 12  CLOSED: bank hols  MEALS: alc (main courses £6.50 to £14.50)  SERVICE: not inc (10%, card slips closed, for 6 or more)  CARDS: Access, Amex, Diners, Visa  DETAILS: 110 seats. Private parties: 70 main room, 10 and 30 private rooms. Vegetarian meals. Children's helpings. Music. Air-conditioned. Fax: 071-581 8172

## Eagle £

map 11

159 Farringdon Road, EC1R 3AL
071-837 1353

COOKING 1*
COST £18–£29

'Up and down the City Road...' The rhyme might have been turned for this place (a haven for *Guardian* journalists), so often do local workers use it. The Eagle started a movement: conversion of pubs to restaurants or eating-houses without sacrificing the unforced informality of the original. The London variant often serves Italo-Mediterranean, always substantial and rarely delicate food, and adjusts daily to markets, gluts, bargains and temptations. It is the antithesis of the heat-it-up school of pub cooking: immensely enjoyable, not always consistent, sometimes getting the seasoning or balance wrong, but invariably busy. Eat soup, Bife Aria (a steak done in red wine in a ciabatta bun), pastas, bruschetta, something from the grill, the sausages, or oxtail with real heart to the sauce. The furniture is miscellaneous, the staff keep their temper and people-watching is great. The wines are, like the options for food, chalked above the bar. Most are available by the glass, with little over £10. Beers are good too.

CHEF: David Eyre  PROPRIETORS: Michael Belben and David Eyre  OPEN: Mon to Fri; 12.30 to 2.30, 6.30 to 10.30  MEALS: alc (main courses £6.50 to £9)  SERVICE: not inc DETAILS: 50 seats. 4 tables outside. Vegetarian meals. Children's helpings. Wheelchair access (1 step). Music

## Efes Kebab House £

map 14

80 Great Titchfield Street, W1P 7AF
071-636 1953

COOKING 1
COST £14–£26

The pace is invariably fast at this classic Turkish venue: it is no place to linger – 'one waiter after another arrives to take your order, leaving no time to read the menu'. Little changes and most readers have little to complain about: 'first-rate and excellent' is a typical summing up. Hot and cold starters such as carrots with yogurt, chicken with walnut sauce, stuffed vine leaves and deep-fried diced lamb's liver precede formidable, high-protein offerings from the chargrill. Meat is of excellent quality, the bread is good and Turkish coffee is fine. Efespilsen (Turkish beer) and unusual imported liqueurs back up the short Continental wine list. House French is £7.50. Efes II (complete with live music and belly dancing) is at 175–177 Great Portland Street, W1N 5FD, Tel: 071-436 0600.

CHEFS/PROPRIETORS: Kazim Akkus and Ibrahim Akbas  OPEN: Mon to Sat; noon to 11.30  MEALS: alc (main courses £5 to £9). Set L and D £14 to £15. Cover charge 60p. Minimum £5  SERVICE: not inc (10% for 8 or more)  CARDS: Access, Amex, Visa DETAILS: 150 seats. 15 tables outside. Private parties: 70 main room. Vegetarian meals. Children welcome. Smart dress preferred. Music. Air-conditioned. Fax: 071-323 5082

£ *indicates that it is possible to have a three-course meal, including coffee, a half-bottle of house wine and service, at any time the restaurant is open (i.e. at dinner as well as at lunch, unless a place is open only for dinner), for £20 or less per person.*

## English Garden

map 13

10 Lincoln Street, SW3 2TS
071-584 7272

COOKING 1
COST £21–£30

'This is a spectacularly convenient place if you are shopping at the Peter Jones end of the King's Road, or if you have tickets for the Royal Court Theatre,' says one who finds the atmosphere here cool and bright, uncrowded and more peaceful than most Chelsea spots. The chintz that once determined the character has been eased out by rich creams, but the plants survive in the conservatory to keep up the gardening concept, and the menu still reflects a certain level of Englishness to the cooking (even if the staff may be French). A 'springtime' menu served a trio of mulligatawny, venison and hare that was more reminiscent of winter, but dishes such as sole, scallop and saffron mousse ('a riot of yellow'), grilled liver with glazed onions, and apple syllabub with cinnamon shortbread can be competently produced, though trimmings such as vegetables, coffee and fudge are sometimes less satisfactory. The prices on the *carte* may imply a greater level of achievement, but the wine list is a fair deal. House wines are £9. There is a sister restaurant, English House, at 3 Milner Street, SW3 2QA, Tel: 071-584 3002.

CHEF: Brian Turner   PROPRIETOR: Roger Wren   OPEN: all week; 12.30 to 2.30 (2 Sun), 7.30 to 11.30 (10 Sun)   CLOSED: 25 and 26 Dec   MEALS: alc (main courses £8.50 to £16.50). Set L £15   SERVICE: not inc   CARDS: Access, Amex, Diners, Visa   DETAILS: 70 seats. Private parties: 20 main room, 10 and 20 private rooms. Vegetarian meals. Children's helpings. Smart dress preferred. Music. Air-conditioned. Fax: 071-581 2848

## L'Escargot

NEW ENTRY   map 15

48 Greek Street, W1V 5LQ
071-437 6828

COOKING 3
COST £24–£47

The snail has revived. For long a landmark among Soho restaurants, L'Escargot has been through bankruptcy and emerged in the hands of Jimmy Lahoud, who has installed a super-group among young chefs: David Cavalier and Garry Hollihead. Their careers can be traced in earlier editions of the *Guide*. The intention has been to re-create the old set-up – brasserie on the ground floor, rising to the restaurant on the two upper floors (the third being top-lit, under a hangar-like roof) – but with spanking new decoration and equipment. The refurbishment downstairs has been very successful. A long, deep room with a waist formed by bar and service station makes clever use of the existing layout with its panelling and attractive staircase, coupled with bright and glowing colour from paintings and the upholstery of capacious banquettes. Add to that the touches like butcher's-block trolleys for the flambé work and the individual pottery dishes used for everything (bought from the Craftsmen Potters' Association) and you have a potential winner. The brasserie menu has pursued the route of French cookery rather than the trendier Cal-Ital style espoused by so many Soho places. Criticisms might centre on its lack of seasonality, or its failure to adjust to daily markets. Oeufs en meurette, pig's trotter with sauce gribiche, a giant dish of fruits de mer, and some excellent meat cookery such as venison on a parsnip purée or pot au feu, are markers of high intent. Desserts are as good: for example, crêpes suzette for the traditionalists, chocolate tart for the modernists. It is hoped the two partners on the stove can last the course of enforced fraternity. The restaurant upstairs runs a set-price menu, with food more in the mould of Sutherlands or Cavaliers of yesteryear. We have as yet had few reports on this. The brasserie wine list is not cheap. It has the mix of Old and New World that Londoners have come to expect and a reliable set of house wines (that is, under £20) for those who wish to read no further. The cheapest of these is £8.95.

CHEFS: Garry Hollihead and David Cavalier  PROPRIETOR: Jimmy Lahoud  OPEN: restaurant Mon to Sat, exc Sat L; 12.15 to 2.30, 7 to 11.30. Brasserie all week; 12.15 to 2.30, 6 to 11 (7 to 10.30 Sun)  MEALS: alc (main courses restaurant £12.50 to £14.50, brasserie £7.50 to £13). Set L and D £20, Set pre-theatre D £14 (2 courses)  SERVICE: not inc CARDS: Access, Amex, Diners, Visa  DETAILS: restaurant 84 seats, brasserie 80 seats. Private parties: 42 main room, 36 private room. Vegetarian meals. Children's helpings. Smart dress preferred. No pipes in dining-room. Music. Air-conditioned. Fax: 071-437 0790

## L'Estaminet

map 15

14 Garrick Street, WC2E 9BJ
071-379 1432

COOKING 1*
COST £27–£43

This unpretentious French restaurant continues to please – for warmth, informality and spontaneity. The surroundings are pleasant and unobtrusive; the food is straightforward. Snails 'were deliciously garlicky and oily'; cod roasted with a veal jus was perceived as successful adventure. 'Nos pièces de boeuf' are probably why you should make for Garrick Street: chateaubriand for three (with béarnaise, shallot and pepper sauces) was 'excellent quality, well cooked'; rib, fillet and entrecôte jostle for attention. Pheasant, though, 'looked as if it had been dragged through a can of oil' on one occasion, and proved over-tough on another. Complaint saw it swiftly replaced by 'utterly splendid' bream. Chips and cheeseboard have both won praise. Portions, though, overawe some – which may account for few reports of the half-dozen desserts. The wine list provides producers' names and vintages only intermittently; wine service, too, suggests a dutiful rather than enthusiastic approach to the cellar. House wine ('very satisfactory' for one) is £8.50.

CHEF: Philippe Tamet  PROPRIETORS: Georges Dugarin and Christian Bellone  OPEN: Mon to Sat; 12 to 2.30, 6.30 to 11.30  CLOSED: bank hols  MEALS: alc (main courses £11 to £16). Cover £1.50  SERVICE: net prices, card slips closed  CARDS: Access, Amex, Visa DETAILS: 60 seats. Private parties: 50 main room, 25 private room. Vegetarian meals. Children welcome. Smart dress preferred. No-smoking area. Music

## Faulkner's £

map 11

424–426 Kingsland Road, E8 4AA
071-254 6152

COOKING 1
COST £10–£27

A dose of Ella Fitzgerald on the sound system, a strong cup of tea and fish and chips are a recipe for bliss in many people's eyes, and Faulkner's keeps up the standard a long way from civilisation as we know it. It is a good place for families, with children being offered their own scampi and chips menu, while for adults the fish and chips, battered and done in groundnut oil, are the best thing to concentrate on. No bookings. House white is £5.60 and champagne is cheap.

CHEFS: Michael Webber and Patrick Gibson   PROPRIETOR: Mark Farrell   OPEN: all week; 12 to 2, 5 to 10 (11.30am to 10.30pm Sat, noon to 10pm Sun)   CLOSED: 24 Dec to 2/3 Jan, bank hol Mons   MEALS: alc (main courses £3.50 to £9.50). Minimum £2.50   SERVICE: not inc   DETAILS: 60 seats. Children's helpings. Smart dress preferred. No-smoking area in extension. Music. Air-conditioned. Fax: 071-249 5661

## Fifth Floor                              [ NEW ENTRY ]   map 13

Harvey Nichols,
109–125 Knightsbridge, SW1X 7RJ                              COOKING 3
071-235 5250                                                 COST £23–£50

It cannot have escaped many readers of the daily press that the department store Harvey Nichols has opened a food hall on its top floor, with snazzy own-label packagings of everything from tea to olive oil. Architect Julyan Wickham (he who designed Kensington Place – see entry, London) has created a market square out of the floor: fresh produce in the middle, racks and cold counters down one side, a café at one end and a restaurant and bar down the last long side – with views down on to Sloane Street, or into the servants' quarters of the Hyde Park Hotel. When the sun shines through roof and windows on the morning scene, it is invigorating and fun; as darkness falls, and the shopping crowds dwindle to nothing, the restaurant seems a mite disconnected with life, though the giant porthole into the kitchen makes up for any loss of exterior vision. It makes an excellent lunch-time spot, the more so as quicker meals can be had in the bar. Chef Henry Harris comes from years working at Bibendum (see entry, London) and the style has recognisably stuck. There have been ups and downs both in service and cooking in the first months of operation, but routine has its benefits as well as drawbacks. Lunch is a short menu in the restaurant, dinner both a fuller *carte* and *prix fixe*. The directness of much of the cooking is welcome. Crab Louis is a pile of very fresh and simply dressed crab, an answering pile of leaves, and a pool of fine chillified mayonnaise. White pudding with mustard sauce is a chicken sausage sort of white pudding, but the sauce is raunchy enough to carry the mildness of it all. Rabbit with prunes is served with a gloss finish to the meat from the grill, plump prunes and an oversweet sauce that cloyed in the finish but was none the less a fine production. Cod with sauce romescu was more hazelnut than pimenton – a small portion this, but fresh. Greens and mashed potatoes were simplicity itself and the more welcome. Lime cheesecake was over-gelatined, but the coffee and chocolate-covered coffee beans for nibbling with the espresso were first-rate. This lunch showed the risks of simplicity as well as the bonus. Wherever tastes or techniques showed small flaws, the effect was the greater. Reports of satisfactory items might stretch far, but would not change the style. The wine list is a good-value single sheet which runs through a useful half-century of fashionable names, and offers plenty by the glass. Harvey Nichols' own house wines are £9.50. A much larger listing is available at dinner time; this is serious drinking.

CHEF: Henry Harris  PROPRIETORS: Harvey Nichols  OPEN: all week, exc Sun D; 12 to 3 (3.30 Sat and Sun), 6.30 to 11.30  CLOSED: 25 and 26 Dec  MEALS: alc D (main courses £7.50 to £20). Set L £16.50 (2 courses) to £19.50, Set D £15.50 to £18.50  SERVICE: 12.5%, card slips closed  CARDS: Access, Amex, Diners, Visa  DETAILS: 110 seats. Private parties: 150 main room. Car park. Vegetarian meals. Children's helpings. No pipes in dining-room. Wheelchair access (also WC). Music. Air-conditioned. Fax: 071-235 5020

## First Floor

map 12

186 Portobello Road, W11 1LA
071-243 0072

COOKING 1*
COST £28–£55

This room above a pub on the Portobello Road may well have been furnished from the market itself. Its style fits the multifarious nature of the clientele. It is surprising, however, that such street-wise people have not twigged that the apparently reasonable prices are inflated by an extra charge for vegetables and potatoes, a cover charge in the evening and a 15 per cent 'optional' service charge. This is not a people's diner. The food, though, is as resolutely hip as can be and the style is set by the management no matter who may be chef. So Thai fish-cakes, grilled chorizo and lentils, salmon with a lime and coriander hollandaise, and tuna with guacamole are the dishes you may find on the daily menu, with sticky toffee pudding a predictable finish. Wine prices are not bad at all, and the catholic range, though small, is very acceptable. House wines are £8.75; cocktails are still in demand.

CHEF: Michael Knolson  PROPRIETOR: Raymond Blundell  OPEN: all week, exc Sun D; 10 to 3, 7.30 to 12 (11am to 6pm Sun)  CLOSED: 25 Dec, 1 Jan, Good Fri  MEALS: alc (main courses £9 to £14). Set D £27.50. Cover £1 D  SERVICE: 15%, card slips closed  CARDS: Access, Amex, Visa  DETAILS: 50 seats. Private parties: 38 main room, 12 private room. Vegetarian meals. Children welcome. Smart dress preferred D. No cigars/pipes in dining-room. Music. Air-conditioned. Fax: 071-221 8387

## Florians ♥ £

map 10

4 Topsfield Parade, Middle Lane, N8 8RP
081-348 8348

COOKING 1
COST £15–£36

'North London needs more places like this!' exclaimed a reporter who thoroughly enjoyed the fun and happy mood of Arnie Onisto's well-established restaurant. Good-value, rustic Italian food is prepared with gusto, although pressure of numbers can cause serious culinary hiccup. Service is casual, energetic and patient. The lively wine bar has a simple menu, while the two dining-rooms at the back offer something more serious. The décor, with its magnolia-coloured walls, black wooden chairs and off-white floor tiles, could be thought either back-garage, or as Mediterranean as the food. One meal on a special Tuscan evening yielded good crostini, 'highly flavourful' pappardelle with rabbit, chargrilled stuffed squid, and an unusual vegetarian fritto misto containing artichokes, courgette flowers and aubergines. Further endorsements flow for lobster with tagliarini, calf's liver with wilted spinach and pine-nuts, and cold chargrilled vegetables. To finish, anise and raisin cake comes topped with a dollop of 'drunken' ricotta seriously laced with alcohol. The Italian wines are decent to excellent, with the Chianti of Isole e Olena and an

Amarone from Allegrini standing out. Prices are fair and the intelligent range allows real choice. House wine is £8. CELLARMAN'S CHOICE: Sauvignon Grave del Friuli 1991, Borgo Magredo, £10.75; Rocca Rubia 1988, Santadi, £16.50.

CHEF: Eugene Fadil   PROPRIETORS: Arnie Onisto and Franco Papa   OPEN: all week; noon to 11pm (10.30 Sun)   CLOSED: bank hols, 25 and 26 Dec, 1 Jan   MEALS: alc (main courses £7.50 to £12.50). Bar special £5.95 (2 courses). Minimum £12   SERVICE: not inc   CARDS: Access, Visa   DETAILS: 78 seats. 8 tables outside. Private parties: 50 main room, 22 and 50 private rooms. Vegetarian meals. Children's helpings. No cigars/pipes in dining-room. Wheelchair access. No music

## Four Seasons  £

map 12

84 Queensway, W2 3RL

071-229 4320

COOKING 2

COST £15–£35

The window display of glazed, barbecued ducks and other roast meats attracts customers to this pleasantly spacious Chinese venue in the midst of buzzy Queensway. Most reporters rate the cooking highly: crispy duck ('never better'), ma po bean curd and king prawns with vegetables have been favourably received, although satay 'drenched with peanut sauce' caused some consternation. Other items on the 100-dish menu are Cantonese offerings which generally involve braising a multitude of seafood, eels, long-cooked cheap cuts of pork and oysters. It is also worth delving into the separate menu (written in Chinese), which offers the prospect of more challenging gastronomy. One-plate dishes are excellent value for a quick meal, and toffee bananas make a good finale. Service draws a mixed response: some say it is cheerful and charming, others have been greeted with black looks and a lack of jollity. House wine is £7.50.

CHEF: K.M. Lo   PROPRIETOR: H.L. Yau   OPEN: all week; noon to 11.30   CLOSED: 24 to 26 Dec   MEALS: alc (main courses £3.50 to £8). Set L and D £10.50 to £16   SERVICE: 12.5% CARDS: Access, Amex, Visa   DETAILS: 80 seats. Private parties: 40 main room. Vegetarian meals. Children welcome. Wheelchair access (2 steps). Music. Air-conditioned

## ▲ Four Seasons Hotel

map 14

Hamilton Place, Park Lane, W1A 1AZ

071-499 0888

COOKING 4*

COST £32–£70

Not many would hold a brief for the beauty of this generation of hotels in the West End, and the Inn on the Park, rechristened Four Seasons after its parent company, is no exception. An attempt has been made to take the restaurant beyond the corporate plush-in-a-matchbox, and it gains something from the view of the trees and traffic outside, but the environment still feels very much like a hotel. Bruno Loubet has had an eventful year with his own bistro opening in Soho (see entry under Bistrot Bruno) and rumours of a larger brasserie about to be launched. Whether he will still be in place at the stoves in Park Lane remains a question loudly discussed. In the meantime, however, the food here shows all that expressive panache that he has made his own. It is bolder than that of many of his confrères though based on absolutely sound kitchen techniques. The curse of hotel food – that it must be acceptable to a wide and timorous public – strikes here in the lack of offal and the dependence on prime cuts. This makes the fish dishes and first courses seem more attractive than the main dishes, particularly as Bruno Loubet does not rely as absolutely as some hotel chefs on the charms of shellfish as an appetiser. He does manage to get pronounced flavours into most of what he cooks. A lunch – one of those Mayfair deals at special prices – that started with a brandade pastry, went on to langoustine soup full of saffron, then guinea-fowl with a dark stock sauce sharpened with limes, finished with a compote of cranberries and a liquorice ice-cream. The directness is sometimes vitiated by an accumulation of bits and pieces of trimming around a plate, but if you want earthy and splashy tastes to upper-crust cooking, this is perhaps the best place to try for them. The pastry-work is fine throughout the meal, petits fours are always enjoyed (not forgetting the chocolate bombs of sorbet), and the service is grand hotel but assiduous. The wine waiter's advice should be heeded when threading through the list; if it is not, then the cost may be higher than ever. Louis Jadot makes a guest appearance among the burgundies, there are plenty of halves for once, and the New World is not ignored. House wines start at £12.90.

CHEF: Bruno Loubet   PROPRIETORS: Four Seasons Hotels and Resorts   OPEN: all week; 12 to 3, 7 to 10.30   MEALS: alc (main courses £16 to £24.50). Set L Mon to Sat £25, Set Sun L £28, Set D £40   SERVICE: net prices, card slips closed   CARDS: Access, Amex, Diners, Visa   DETAILS: 45 seats. Private parties: 90 main room. Car park. Vegetarian meals. Children's helpings. Smart dress preferred. No pipes in dining-room. Wheelchair access (also WC). No music. Air-conditioned   ACCOMMODATION: 227 rooms, all with bath/shower. Rooms for disabled. Lift. B&B £235 to £288. Children welcome. Baby facilities. Small dogs welcome. Afternoon teas. Air-conditioned. TV. Phone. Fax: 071-493 1895 and 6629

## French House
NEW ENTRY   map 15

49 Dean Street, W1V 5HL
071-437 2477

COOKING 2
COST £23–£38

'It's as if you were at home, and the cook were a real enthusiast, talented too, but cannot be bothered with the tricky bits.' This was the opinion of one reader who braved the hordes crammed into the pub downstairs (once a Free French HQ, hence the name) to reach the darkly marbled dining-room on the first floor. The menu is changed twice a day, exploring how best to offer emphatically fresh ingredients with high flavour without breaking through cost barriers set up by too many staff or too much luxury. Crude food can result, with too many corners cut like the dish of baked fennel, tomato and aïoli with sourdough that rejoiced in wonderful tomatoes, a charred bulb of fennel, olives and cloves of garlic in a giant pile spiked with an infinity of rosemary twigs and leaves – have you ever tried to eat crisp rosemary? Similarly, salt cod, potato and garlic bake with French beans was 'generous, fishy, greasy, sustaining and genuine' but not sophisticated. Main dishes are often sent out with one sensible vegetable – duck and cabbage, liver and onions, lamb and flageolet beans – reminding the eaters of home yet again. The honesty shines through, the quality of materials is always evident (try the cheese, it will always be of the best), and the cheapness is enviable. Service, in white chefs' tunics, is always informed and intelligent. The wine list sticks to France – a bare two dozen –

but has good makers and very fair prices, though there are no halves. House wine is £8.95.

CHEFS: Margot Clayton and Fergus Henderson   PROPRIETORS: Jon Spiteri, Margot Clayton and Fergus Henderson   OPEN: Mon to Sat; 12.30 to 3, 6.30 to 11.30   MEALS: alc (main courses £6.50 to £10)   SERVICE: not inc   CARDS: Access, Amex, Diners, Visa   DETAILS: 30 seats. Private parties: 30 main room. Vegetarian meals. Children welcome. No music. Fax: 071-287 9109

## Fung Shing  £

map 15

15 Lisle Street, WC2H 7BE
071-437 1539

COOKING 3
COST £18–£52

'It gets better all the time' is a knowledgeable verdict on this premier-league restaurant in the heart of Soho's Chinatown. More auspicious than most of its neighbours, the place emphasises comfort, and its trappings are fairly elegant. Early in the evening it is 'very peaceful'; later it gets extremely crowded, yet service remains acceptable. The mostly Cantonese menu of around 150 dishes has a few Szechuan overtones and features several items seldom found in other London restaurants, including 'double-boiled fluffy supreme shark's fin and braised whole abalone with oyster sauce' (the rarity of these specialities is reflected in the £30 to £35 prices). Otherwise the repertoire covers everything from soft-shell crab with chilli and salt and eel with coriander, to barbecued beef and venison with yellow-bean sauce. Spiced jellyfish with chicken and pickles is an intriguing cold appetiser. The kitchen has delivered some especially good dishes, including steamed prawns with garlic, stewed duck with yams, baked crab with ginger and spring onions, and stuffed aubergine in black-bean sauce which was 'simply magic', according to one enthusiastic reporter. The pedigree of the restaurant is reflected in the wine list, which has some classy clarets and burgundies for around £20. Saké, beer and tea offer alternative drinking. House French is £8.50.

CHEF: Kwan Fu   PROPRIETORS: Forum Restaurant Ltd   OPEN: all week; noon to 11.15   CLOSED: 24 to 26 Dec   MEALS: alc (main courses £6 to £15). Set L and D £11 to £12 (minimum 2). Minimum £8.50 after 6.30   SERVICE: not inc   CARDS: Access, Amex, Diners, Visa   DETAILS: 80 seats. Private parties: 50 main room, 28 private room. Vegetarian meals. Children welcome. Music. Air-conditioned

## La Gaulette

map 14

53 Cleveland Street, W1P 5PQ
071-580 7608 and 323 4210

COOKING 2
COST £22–£58

This small restaurant round the corner from the Middlesex Hospital would put hairs on the chest of any sick person with its pungent aromatic sauces of ginger and spring onion or garlic and herbs. These sauces, or their derivatives, are served with a lot of the fish and shellfish that is the kitchen's staple diet – meat is not on offer. Sylvain Ho Wing Cheong comes from Mauritius and sells both that style of cooking and the warm-water fish that he knew in his childhood. 'The vacqua with ginger and spring onion was simply sensational,' reported one happy client of the bistro at the bottom of the stairs, whose guest had taken the Mediterranean route of grilled prawns with herbs and garlic and a large bouillabaisse for main course. The restaurant food is similar in vein, though dearer, and many people come here to try the lobster or the fresh crab (with those sauces). Be warned, it is a messy dinner, but toothsome. The *carte* steers a steady course from month to month, but the 'arrivage du jour' gives extra variety. It could not be less like a British fish restaurant. Gastronomic menus are available from £24 to £40. House wines are £10.95.

CHEF: Sylvain Ho Wing Cheong  PROPRIETORS: Sylvain and Shirley Ho Wing Cheong
OPEN: Mon to Sat, exc Sat L; 12 to 3, 6.30 to 11  CLOSED: 25 and 26 Dec, bank hol Mons
MEALS: alc (main courses £12 to £19). Bistro Set L and D £10.95 (2 courses); restaurant Set L and D £13.95 (2 courses). Minimum £11.75  SERVICE: not inc  CARDS: Access, Amex, Diners, Visa  DETAILS: restaurant 32 seats, bistro 30 seats. Private parties: 40 main room, 40 private room. Vegetarian meals. Children's helpings with prior notice. Smart dress preferred. No pipes in dining-room. Music. Fax: 081-645 7255

## Le Gavroche ▼

map 14

43 Upper Brook Street, W1Y 1PF
071-408 0881 and 499 1826

COOKING 5
COST £38–£120

Someone who had not been here for two years remarked on how much better it was than the last time – no longer cholesterol-bound, everything cleaner and more digestible. So giants can change, they do not only lumber. The restaurant has been described, by critics and the owner alike, as 'club-like'. The green leather look is restful, plutocratic, untroubled by life's problems and faultlessly maintained. Somehow, it avoids the depression usually associated with basements, though it may pick up some from infinite layers of waiting staff and silver domes, plus prehistoric habits such as priced menus given only to the host. 'As my wife was paying, she was somewhat annoyed not to have first-hand sight of what she was letting herself in for,' remarked one irate guest. There have been changes in the repertoire, though oysters Francine and soufflé suissesse survive from what once seemed like an unchanging list, but the dual strands of haute cuisine and adaptations of cuisine bourgeoise still hold firm here. Thus chicken gets barley and beef may be daubed even while knuckle of lamb gets truffles. The ability to pack a punch of flavour is seen in those oysters Francine, perched on lobster quenelles ('absolutely five different tastes, humbling'), or in a staple of any restaurant, the sorbets. The punishing price of the *carte* should be balanced by a memory that the set lunch, which does not stint on luxury ingredients, and which has a more lively repertoire than it once did, is a relative bargain. Price does enter the consideration when it comes to the wines. There has been praise for the sommelier, whose knowledge of his cellar is impressive, 'and whose advice we should have followed' ruefully admitted one dedicated explorer of the bins. Quality apart, the range is of course impressive, but so are the profit margins. These are usually justified by the capital costs involved. Many would wish a different policy were adopted, though the drinker of a 1928 Cantemerle, which had been perfectly cellared, presented and decanted, would disagree.

CHEF: Michel Roux Junior  PROPRIETORS: Le Gavroche Ltd  OPEN: Mon to Fri; 12 to 2, 7 to 11  CLOSED: Christmas to New Year, bank hols  MEALS: alc (main courses £22.50 to £35). Set L £36, Set D £42 to £59. Minimum £50 D  SERVICE: net prices  CARDS: Access, Amex, Diners, Visa  DETAILS: 60 seats. Private parties: 80 main room, 12 private room. Vegetarian meals. Children welcome. Jacket and tie. No cigars/pipes in dining-room. No music. Air-conditioned. Fax: 071-409 0939 and 491 4387

## Gavvers
map 13

61–63 Lower Sloane Street, SW1W 8DH  COOKING 2
071-730 5983  COST £22–£40

This, the first home of Le Gavroche (see previous entry), is intended to be the bustling bargain basement of the Roux empire – with optional bustle ('When I booked I was told to come before 7.45 or after 8.30. At 8 the place was virtually empty'). Bruno Valette returned to the fold in June 1992, and since then the food has been more consistent, though service – by turns over-tense and lackadaisical – has often irritated. The lure is set-price lunches and dinners (the latter with wine, if you wish), which even the finnicky agree offer good value. There are only two choices at each of three courses, but execution and variety – smoked salmon mousse wrapped in smoked salmon, skewered mussels with noodles, roast venison with a 'rich and deeply flavoured' sauce, sea bream with creamed vegetables, calf's liver with gratin dauphinois – are good. On the *carte*, with which few seem to dally, Bruno Valette's Californian experience peeps through, via pea pancakes with broad beans and tomato, or John Dory in a Thai sauce with stir-fried saffron pasta. Desserts are 'first-rate'. Most like the Duboeuf house wine (£11.60 per bottle), perhaps because straying off into the short, predominantly French list puts remarkable upward mobility into the bill.

CHEF: Bruno Valette  PROPRIETORS: Roux Restaurants Ltd  OPEN: Mon to Sat, exc Sat L; 12 to 2.30, 6.30 to 11  CLOSED: bank hols, Easter Sat, Christmas week  MEALS: alc (main courses £10.50 to £15). Set L £12.50 (2 courses) to £14.75, Set D £19.75 to £25.55 (inc wine). Minimum £19.75 D  SERVICE: net prices, card slips closed  CARDS: Access, Diners, Visa DETAILS: 57 seats. Private parties: 35 main room. Vegetarian meals. Children's helpings. Smart dress preferred. Wheelchair access. Music. Air-conditioned

## Gay Hussar
map 15

2 Greek Street, W1V 6NB  COOKING 2
071-437 0973  COST £24–£48

The Gay Hussar is 'for those of good appetite, who like real food, and who know that fat is where the flavour resides'. This, the stoutest, warmest spot in Old Soho, is listed in the same way as a building: because no one will ever create anything like it again, and because what it offers seems worth preserving. The place itself looks like the inside of an artery: red, well-used, occasionally throbbing, always intimate. The food is about as fashionable as thermal underwear, and has the same end result: enormous plates of chicken and barley, duck and potatoes and red cabbage, smoked goose, sausages, stuffed eggs, all slopping with sauce and cream and fat; the soup is a joy – 'green bean soup that is beanier than anyone else achieves'. Vegetables are either raw, pickled or cooked until they have long ceased twitching. Presentation is a question of getting all the food on the plate. To enjoy a meal here to the full you have to be in sympathy with values now largely eroded; one diner, returning after a 25-year break, found himself doubt-ridden. 'Where was the old flair, the spice, the zing in the food? It all edged on the bland. Or have I grown up in the intervening years? Was it always like a German railway-station restaurant or did Victor Sassie instil something in it which is now missing?' Being verbally invited to pay an 'optional' service charge strikes a discordant note when the appeal throughout is to rough-and-ready generosity. The Hungarian wines on the list (for £9 and up) are by no means the best that the country is now producing: the three Bulgarians are better. House wines are £9.

CHEF: Laszlo Holecz   PROPRIETORS: Restaurant Partnership plc   OPEN: Mon to Sat; 12.30 to 2.30, 5.30 to 11   CLOSED: bank hols and public hols   MEALS: alc (main courses £10 to £15). Set L £15.50   SERVICE: 12.5%, card slips closed   CARDS: Access, Amex, Diners, Visa   DETAILS: 70 seats. Private parties: 20 main room, 12 private room. Vegetarian meals. Children's helpings. Smart dress preferred. Wheelchair access (1 step). No music. Air-conditioned

## Gilbert's ▮

map 13

2 Exhibition Road, SW7 2HF
071-589 8947

COOKING 1
COST £22–£42

The restaurant is found right at the bottom of Exhibition Road, handy for South Kensington's museums and the Albert Hall. Furnishings are unassuming: 'It was draughty and our table wobbled,' reflected one wry customer, but it is a very personal operation; 'civilised', the partners call it. 'Whichever lady waited on us was so delightful that it hurts me to make a criticism' was a comment preliminary to regretting delays. The traditional French and English cooking does not aim to be elaborate, more a quasi-domestic interpretation of restaurant fare. 'Our ham tasted like ham used to taste' is the sort of reaction the place seeks for dishes like spiced parsnip soup, gratin of chicory and smoked ham, brioche with mushrooms and madeira, civet of venison and entrecôte maître d'hôtel. The wine list shows enthusiasm and fairness; many bottles are under £15, the range of halves is intelligent and house wines have interest. It displays a nice quirkiness, of a type normally expected from urban exiles in the Welsh mountains or the Yorkshire Dales. House wine is £8.90.

CHEF: Julia Chalkley   PROPRIETORS: Julia Chalkley and Ann Wregg   OPEN: Mon to Sat, exc Sat L; 12.30 to 2, 7 to 10.15   MEALS: Set L £11.50 (2 courses), Set D £13.50 (2 courses)   SERVICE: not inc   CARDS: Access, Amex, Diners, Visa   DETAILS: 32 seats. 2 tables outside. Private parties: 40 main room. Vegetarian meals. Children's helpings. No cigars/pipes in dining-room. Wheelchair access (2 steps). No music. Air-conditioned

'For the main course we ordered squid with green peppers in a black-bean sauce and got beef with green peppers and black-bean sauce. When we asked what had happened we were told that there had been no squid at the market that morning.'
On eating in Edinburgh

## Gopal's of Soho £

map 15

12 Bateman Street, W1V 5TD
071-434 1621 and 0840

COOKING 1
COST £19–£42

'Greenery and mirrors give a deceptive idea of space,' wrote one who felt the tables for two at Gopal's were tight enough, but who accepted that at least the place felt like a real restaurant. There are several curries and dishes from the Carnatic region in south India which repay investigation, such as Mangalore crab, Mangalore mutton and meenu curry (Carnatic fish curry); also worth considering are the Goan mutton xakuti, the aloo chana chat and the Goan murg, which joins the sweetness of coconut to very hot spices. Rice and breads are very passable, and thalis provide for those who like a general selection of dishes. The wine list is short but considered (by consultant David Wolfe). This may explain items such as Ch. la Lagune 1983 and Parent's red burgundy, not often found in an Indian restaurant. House Merlot and dry Loire are £7.90.

CHEF/PROPRIETOR: N.P. Pittal   OPEN: all week; 12 to 3, 6 to 11.30   CLOSED: 25 and 26 Dec
MEALS: alc (main courses £6 to £10.50). Cover £1   SERVICE: not inc   CARDS: Access,
Amex, Diners, Visa   DETAILS: 48 seats. Private parties: 50 main room. Vegetarian meals.
Children welcome. Wheelchair access (1 step). Music. Air-conditioned

## Grahame's Seafare £

map 14

38 Poland Street, W1V 3DA
071-437 3788 and 0975

COOKING 1
COST £17–£44

A favourite old stager, this kosher fish restaurant goes on and on. The interior might be described as old-world New York style, with bench seats and beams. The manageress is the life and soul of the place, much beloved of regular customers: 'very house-proud and well respected by the more light-hearted waitresses.' Excellent fish is grilled, steamed, fried in matzo meal or cooked in milk and butter. Fillet of plaice with latkes and peas, lemon sole with mange-tout, and haddock and chips have been recommended. To start there are gefilte fish, bortsch or chopped herring with rye bread, although sweets such as crème caramel or banana split have not been to everyone's taste. A special fish and chips and coffee deal will set you back only £5. A handful of decent, affordable wines are available. House wine is £8.25.

CHEF/PROPRIETOR: Chetin Ismet   OPEN: Mon to Sat; 12 to 2.45, 5.30 to 9 (8 Fri and Sat)
MEALS: alc (main courses £8 to £19)   SERVICE: not inc, card slips closed   CARDS: Access,
Amex, Visa   DETAILS: 90 seats. Private parties: 40 main room. Children's helpings.
Wheelchair access. No music. Air-conditioned

## Granita £

**NEW ENTRY** map 11

127 Upper Street, N1 1QP
071-226 3222

COOKING 2*
COST £20–£40

The raw concrete frontage on to Upper Street, echoed by the bare-bones decoration inside, has a message that the cooking underlines: the importance is not in the dressing but in the materials themselves. Granita is perhaps a Bauhaus restaurant: form follows function. It also operates satisfactorily as a neighbourhood place. The prices are not forbidding, the service and welcome accommodating, and the food is without a doubt palatable. The short menu changes all the time, says what is cooked and delivers it. A meal in the early summer started with leek and potato soup enriched by crème fraîche before calf's liver with mushroom mash (a good variation, this) and monkfish served plain with new potatoes. The chargrill is often in evidence – a plump, moist piece of salmon given a little edge by the flame, sitting on a bed of lentils, beefed up with a red wine sauce is a good instance – but the cooking is not so unadorned as that might imply. Ahmed Kharshoum is good with pastry, intelligent too with plainness – a chicken breast otherwise just grilled, is marinated first to give it added flavour. Bread is home-made and fair – that too has enough variation (rosemary, for example) to give spice to life. Do not give up on the puddings either. The wine list is in keeping with the style, the most interesting area being sweet wines. If you want a slug of Bukkuram, from an island offshore of Sicily, here is the place to try it. House wines are £7.95 from Dom. de Capion.

CHEF: Ahmed Kharshoum  PROPRIETORS: Ahmed Kharshoum and Vicky Leffman  OPEN: Tue to Sun, exc Tue L; 12.30 to 2.30, 6.30 to 10.30  CLOSED: 10 days Christmas, 5 days Easter, 2 weeks Aug  MEALS: alc (main courses £6.50 to £10.50). Set L £11.50 (2 courses) to £13.50, Set D £18 to £25  SERVICE: not inc  CARDS: Access, Visa  DETAILS: 62 seats. Private parties: 50 main room. Vegetarian meals. Children's helpings. Wheelchair access (1 step). No music. Air-conditioned

## Great Nepalese  £

map 11

48 Eversholt Street, NW1 1DA
071-388 6737

COOKING 1*
COST £10–£31

After a lacklustre patch, this warhorse across the road from Euston Station is back on form. The street and the exterior have seen better days, but crowds come for the food rather than the setting. 'Terence Conran did not do the design here,' observed one visitor, but the place has a genuine warmth that other restaurants merely put on. Service is friendly, good-natured and unerringly helpful. The kitchen is no follower of fashion, but it delivers sound, dependable Indian dishes backed up by a fine showing of authentic Nepalese specialities. Onion bhajia is an 'excellent example of the breed', likewise distinctively spiced vegetable curry. Other highlights have included masco bara (deep-fried lentil cakes), bhutuwa chicken, fish masala, hash ko bhutuwa (barbecued duck curry) and gundroko tarkari (Tibetan processed vegetables). Breads are superb: one reporter reckoned the stuffed paratha was the best she had ever eaten. Basmati rice is spot-on, although the technicolor flecks annoy some devotees of the genre. Nepalese rice pudding is an intriguing spiced sweet; otherwise there is mango kulfi. Drink lager or tea, or try a shot of fiery Nepalese rum. House wine is £6.25 a litre.

CHEF: Mr Masuk  PROPRIETOR: Gopal Manandhar  OPEN: all week; 12 to 2.45, 6 to 11.45  MEALS: alc (main courses £3 to £8.50). Set L £5.50 to £10.50, Set D £10.50. Minimum £5  SERVICE: 10%  CARDS: Access, Amex, Diners, Visa  DETAILS: 48 seats. Private parties: 30 main room. Vegetarian meals. Children's helpings. Music

## Greek Valley £    NEW ENTRY    map 11

130 Boundary Road, NW8 0RH                      COOKING 1*
071-624 3217                                     COST £15–£27

In a pretty residential area just off Abbey Road, this Greek-Cyriot restaurant
has a 'crisp', welcoming atmosphere. Everything is spotless, from the polished
terracotta tiled floor to the immaculately laid tables. A feeling of well-being
pervades the place. Effie Bosnic is a friendly hostess who runs the front-of-
house while her Yugoslav husband cooks. The commitment to real food shows
in the meze – home-made dips, crisp, fresh filo pastries stuffed with spinach
and cheese, home-made loukanika sausages smoked on the premises and
good-looking stuffed vine leaves. Main courses feature classics such as
kleftiko, assorted kebabs, souvlaki and moussaka. Whole roast piglet is an
occasional treat. To finish, it is worth trying the glyko (preserves served resting
on a spoon) as an alternative to sticky pastries. The wine list is a standard
Greek selection with a few interesting additions such as Lac des Roches. House
wine is £6.50.

CHEF: Peter Bosnic  PROPRIETORS: Peter and Effie Bosnic  OPEN: Mon to Sat, exc Sat L; 12
to 2.30, 6 to 12  CLOSED: 25 Dec  MEALS: alc (main courses £5.50 to £8.50)  SERVICE: not
inc  CARDS: Access, Visa  DETAILS: 75 seats. Private parties: 45 main room, 30 private
room. Vegetarian meals. Children's helpings. Smart dress preferred. Wheelchair access
(1 step). Music. Air-conditioned (partly)

## Green Cottage £    map 11

9 New College Parade,
Finchley Road, NW3 5EP                          COOKING 1*
071-722 5305 and 7892                            COST £14–£40

Handily placed between Swiss Cottage and Finchley Road tube stations, this
Chinese restaurant continues to deliver the goods. Cantonese barbecued dishes
such as duck, crispy belly pork and a mixed bag of 'soyed' liver, gizzard, squid
and duck wings show up strongly on the menu. There is also a noticeable
vegetarian presence in the form of fish-flavoured aubergine, oyster mushrooms
with asparagus and 'Buddha's cushion' (stewed black moss with mushrooms
and vegetables). The quality of the the fish shows in steamed sea bass with
ginger and spring onion, which has been 'cooked to bone-leaving perfection';
otherwise there are deep-fried prawn toasts, mixed seafood in a potato basket,
steamed duck with plum sauce and shredded pork with bean paste. Service is
described as 'brief, rapid, minimalist'. Chinese tea arrives automatically and
Tsing Tao and Tiger beers are also available. Saké figures among the basic list
of around 20 wines. House wine is £6.80.

CHEF: T.S. Lok  PROPRIETOR: S.M. Li  OPEN: all week; noon to 11.30  MEALS: alc (main
courses £4.50 to £7.50). Set L and D £11.50 (minimum 2) to £15  SERVICE: not inc  CARDS:
Access, Amex, Visa  DETAILS: 70 seats. Private parties: 40 main room, 14 private room.
Vegetarian meals. Children welcome. Wheelchair access. No music. Air-conditioned

*The* Guide *always appreciates hearing about changes of chef or owner.*

## Greenhouse
map 14

27A Hay's Mews, W1X 7RJ
071-499 3331

COOKING 3
COST £25–£58

The Greenhouse is not a greenhouse, but the ground floor of a mansion block approached from Hay's Mews by a forecourt, which is ornamented at strategic points by those pieces of permanent topiary that solve the problem of daily flowers. An eloquent habitué was moved to remark, 'It provides a welcome and warm home in the cold landscape of mediocre London restaurants where meat is killed a second time, vegetables perish at the hands of ignorant amateurs and customers are served with indifference.' Given the difficulty of achieving a booking, many others must agree. The menu might serve as exemplar of once-current trends (now two years old). There is a vein of English cookery in, for instance, the famed oxtails, faggots in rich gravy, grilled calf's liver with onion gravy and mashed potatoes, and the set of English puddings. Running parallel to this is an expressive and inventive Mediterranean seam, most creative when it comes to fish cookery: this yields dishes such as sea bass with provençal vegetables, sardines on tomato crostini, and a salade niçoise with grilled tuna. Some items defy simple pigeonholes and are all the better for it: mackerel croquettes with lemon butter sauce or cod with cabbage and wild mushrooms, for example. When everything works the approach here can be remarkably expressive, but there are moments when the apparently never-ending stream of customers takes its functional toll so that some things seem done by rote. The very short wine list covers an immense price range within a largely French construction. House wines are from £9.50.

CHEF: Gary Rhodes   PROPRIETOR: David Levin   OPEN: all week, exc Sat L; 12 to 2.30 (3 Sun), 7 to 11 (6 to 10 Sun)   CLOSED: Christmas and New Year   MEALS: alc (main courses £6.50 to £17). Set Sun L £17.50. Cover £1   SERVICE: not inc   CARDS: Access, Amex, Diners, Visa   DETAILS: 90 seats. Private parties: 100 main room. Vegetarian meals. Children's helpings. No children under 6. Smart dress preferred. No pipes in dining-room. Wheelchair access (3 steps). No music. Air-conditioned. Fax: 071-225 0011

## Grill St Quentin
NEW ENTRY   map 13

3 Yeoman's Row, SW3 2AL
071-581 8377

COOKING 1
COST £21–£59

Although the restaurant is in a basement, the high ceiling and large room are successful in disguising this fact. The pictures are more fun than a window view, and fellow-diners offer more variety. The Grill is a public utility for the area. It does the simplest things best: oysters and grilled meats, ice-cream with hot chocolate sauce. Crab can sometimes be dry, steak plates overloaded and inn-style with chips and veg, but a basic reliability renders the place serviceable. Sunday lunch is appreciated in the neighbourhood too. The staff are keen as mustard and nice with it. The wine list is a sound French range with a surprising affection for economy. House wine is £8.20.

*See the back of the* Guide *for an index of restaurants listed.*

CHEF: Jonathan Stanbury  PROPRIETORS: The Savoy Group plc  OPEN: all week; 12 to 3 (3.30 Sun), 7 to 11.30 (6.30 to 10.30 Sun)  MEALS: alc (main courses £8 to £18). Set L £13.50  SERVICE: 12.5%, card slips closed  CARDS: Access, Amex, Diners, Visa  DETAILS: 140 seats. Private parties: 40 main room, 40 private room. Vegetarian meals. Children's helpings weekends. Smart dress preferred. No music. Air-conditioned. Fax: 071-584 6064

## ▲ The Halkin ♥                                                      map 13

5–6 Halkin Street, SW1X 7DJ                                    COOKING 3
071-333 1234                                                  COST £29–£64

The Americans might call The Halkin a 'boutique hotel'. It is not large, it does not have the constant bustle of a grand hotel, but it is in a swish part of town, everyone – including the staff – is dressed by the smartest designers, and it considers most creature comforts. The decorative and culinary themes are Italian, but the stark attack of the original design scheme has been sweetened and softened over the last year: there are potted trees in the front hall, pink (not white) flowers in the dining-room and cream tablecloths. There is still some presence, but not quite the same impact. The management, after a false start, went to Italian chef Gualtiero Marchesi (he of three Michelin stars in Milan) for assistance in running the restaurant. A London branch was set up over here. However, the agreement was set to lapse in summer 1993, though Stefano Cavallini, who has interpreted Marchesi's brief since the restaurant opened, is to stay as chef. The vein of ultra-sophisticated Italian cooking, therefore, is to run. This style may sometimes be so sophisticated that it has no cohesion or point to it: flavours may be light to non-existent, ingredients may not marry. But when it is on form the cooking is unlike any other in London – variety is good for its own sake, some say. Thus, the thinnest slices of turbot are marinated to a startling yellow in saffron and served scattered with sun-dried tomato and preserved bulb fennel. A risotto is blacker than black from squid ink, and as expressively of the sea as could be desired, with wonderfully exact rice. Macaroni is cooked with a sweet, yet not cloying foie gras sauce and helped with positive quantities of black truffle. Sole is given real seasoning with some dried mullet roe; scampi sharpened up with Parma ham. It is a sweet song when in tune. Prices have moderated, so some of the tremendous trimmings that were noted last year have gone. It is still dear, but the dining-room's inhabitants would lead you to expect that, and the set meals are fair value. Idiosyncratic wine prices that tend to the expensive continue to astonish. There is a curious inconsistency that puts Pol Roger at £29.50 (almost cheap) and Hermitage La Chapelle 1984 at £50 (absurdly expensive). There are wonderful names, with the emphasis on Italy. House wine is from £14.

CHEF: Stefano Cavallini  PROPRIETORS: Mr and Mrs Ong Ben Seng  OPEN: Mon to Sat, exc Sat L; 12.30 to 2.30, 7.30 to 10.30  MEALS: alc (main courses £8 to £18). Set L £18 (2 courses) to £24.50, Set D £24.50 to £28.50  SERVICE: net prices, card slips closed  CARDS: Access, Amex, Diners, Visa  DETAILS: 40 seats. Private parties: 70 main room, 26 private room. Vegetarian meals. Children welcome. Smart dress preferred. No cigars/pipes in dining-room. Wheelchair access (also WC). Music. Air-conditioned  ACCOMMODATION: 41 rooms, all with bath/shower. Lift. B&B £225 to £239. Children welcome. Baby facilities. Afternoon teas. Air-conditioned. TV. Phone. Fax: 071-333 1100 (*The Which? Hotel Guide*)

## Harveys

map 10

2 Bellevue Road, SW17 7EG
081-672 0114 and 0115                                    COST £46–£102

This entry is a holding operation (hence no cooking mark), a service to those
who follow the career of the chef-proprietor. As far as the *Guide* can understand,
the restaurant is closed during the autumn of 1993 for refurbishment and
repackaging, to open as a brasserie or neighbourhood gaff. Marco Pierre White
has been widely bruited to be on the verge of agreeing with the owners of the
Hyde Park Hotel to open a luxury restaurant within its premises. No
confirmation is forthcoming. In case nothing happens at all, we shall comment
here on the performance of Harveys restaurant itself during the past year. The
constant refrain of readers has been that the service is poor. It is either because
the waiters themselves are without enthusiasm or civility, or because the
production from the kitchen occasions infinite delay. At the prices charged, this
is considered inadequate. A lady who took a friend to lunch and asked for a
corner table was told 'it was not free', though the restaurant was otherwise
devoid of paying customers. She paid £113 (before tip) for her meal. There have
been fewer tales of Marco Pierre White's presence in the flesh, while he is
constantly seen at the Canteen, his joint enterprise with Michael Caine in
Chelsea Harbour (see entry). In consequence, people have felt that Harveys
lacks both drive and the constant spark of creativity, even if its food is polished.
The lack of proper supervision of the waiting staff merely compounds the
problem. There·have been many plaudits for the cooking, be it for an appetiser
of warmed vichyssoise with oysters, caviare and chives, or an inkfish risotto
that was evilly black and shiny with a gloss of oil, or roast sea bass with a
tapénade that had texture and freshness, a nice counterpoint of sauce vierge,
and (a commonplace here) no green vegetables to give any balance – nor any
available on demand either. Desserts change little, and the coffee at £4 might be
more acceptable if refills were offered. The feeling is definitely of a restaurant
marking time. Even a lunch menu cannot be written out each day, so weary are
the support staff. And to expect anything so lively as a response to the changing
seasons is probably too much; the menu has an air of being carved in stone.
Wines start at just under £20.

CHEF/PROPRIETOR: Marco Pierre White   OPEN: Tue to Sun, exc Sun D; 12.30 to 2, 7.30 to
11.15   MEALS: Set L £24 (2 courses), Set D £55   SERVICE: not inc   CARDS: Access, Visa
DETAILS: 45 seats. No children under 16. No pipes in dining-room. Air-conditioned

## Hilaire ▮

map 13

68 Old Brompton Road, SW7 3LQ                          COOKING 3*
071-584 8993 and 7601                                    COST £26–£66

This little restaurant on the Old Brompton Road, convenient for Christie's if
you have just hocked the silver, survives by gritting its teeth and lowering its
prices. It is a model of the reaction many have welcomed in London this year.
Bryan Webb's cooking has not declined in quality, nor has the service, nor the
attractive setting on the ground floor with its deep bowed windows whence
street life can be put under the microscope. Downstairs is best for a single large

party. The cooking has the hallmarks of proper technique and a pleasing directness that finds expression even in the cheapest menu option. A winter lunch that began with a small appetiser of Glamorgan sausage and deep-fried seaweed with a hint of chilli got into its stride with a tarragon-flavoured celeriac rémoulade served with Serrano ham. The main course of hare with lentils on a sticky, yet well-judged, stock sauce was proof against the bitterest chill; it was happily reinforced by a rich and well-podded crème brûlée. If that sounds a mite pedestrian, then try pigeon and truffle crostini, lamb with tapénade and ratatouille, good English cheeses, then rice pudding and prunes with a sauce that tasted like crème caramel – 'a wonderful range of textures and tastes'. People like the family feel to the restaurant: Webb père does the honours front-of-house while son slaves below. A half-dozen house selection of wines by the glass and a sensible, affordable range of halves reinforce the argument for lunching here. Listed by style, decent clarets fight for attention among more strident Californians, but selection throughout is spot-on. Slightly nervous developments last year have led to consolidation and a reassuring blend of safety and excitement. Prices are not at all bad, but the economically minded need stray no further than the decent house selections. House wines are from £12.75. CELLARMAN'S CHOICE: Coonawarra, Penley Estate, Chardonnay 1990, £19.85; Châteauneuf-du-Pape, Dom. St Benoit 1989, £24.

CHEFS: Bryan Webb and Denise Dunn  PROPRIETOR: Bryan Webb  OPEN: Mon to Sat, exc Sat L; 12.15 to 2.30, 7 to 11.30  CLOSED: 4 days Easter, 4 days Christmas, bank hols  MEALS: alc (main courses £12 to £18.50). Set L £10.95 (2 courses), Set D £16 (2-course supper) to £25  SERVICE: not inc, card slips closed  CARDS: Access, Amex, Diners, Visa  DETAILS: 40 seats. Private parties: 35 main room, 25 private room. Vegetarian meals. Children's helpings. No music. Air-conditioned. Fax: 071-581 2949

## *Ikkyu* £ map 14

67 Tottenham Court Road, W1P 9PA COOKING 1
071-436 6169 and 636 9280 COST £12–£45

An uninspiring door on Tottenham Court Road leads you down to the basement where the setting has been described as 'lived-in Japanese', and the heterogeneous staff have been praised for 'indulging happily our European eccentricities'. It is a busy, economical and enjoyable place, where a single luncher can grab a sushi lunch at the bar or take advantage of something more elaborate like tofu with oyster mushrooms, cuttlefish, skewers of grilled chicken, or offal as in grilled heart, tongue or liver. The cooking is robust but generally very fresh in condition and flavour. Drink saké or beer; green tea is free. House wine is £8.50

CHEF: Y. Sato  PROPRIETOR: M. Kawaguchi  OPEN: Mon to Fri, and Sun D; 12.30 to 2.30, 6 to 10.30  MEALS: alc (main courses £4 to £12.50). Set L £4.80 to £9.30 (2 courses)  SERVICE: 10%  CARDS: Access, Amex, Diners, Visa  DETAILS: 57 seats. Private parties: 12 main room. Vegetarian meals with prior notice. Children welcome. Smart dress preferred. Music. Air-conditioned

*See inside the front cover for an explanation of the symbols used at the tops of entries.*

## Imperial City

[NEW ENTRY]  map 11

Royal Exchange, Cornhill, EC3V 3LL
071-626 3437

COOKING 1*
COST £21–£43

This Chinese restaurant opened in the bowels of the Royal Exchange with
fanfares. The Californian guru of East-meets-West cooking, Ken Hom, was to
be consultant, and the City would have an exciting place for lunch at last. It is a
pity, our inspector remarked, that the entrance could not be cleaned up to make
a better impact on the surface world. Inside, a dragon painted on the side of an
air-conditioning duct sets the tone, but the catacomb is a large one and needs
peopling to gain character. This place is best at lunch; evenings see fewer
clients, and the cooking lacks the tang of immediacy. A worthy attempt is made
to bring regional cooking to foreign palates and there is an estimable avoidance
of MSG. Regionalism, however, may be overshadowed by its Cantonese
intepretation. The menu is also shorter than commonly found, which bodes
well for freshness. A meal that kicked off with the Imperial cold platter –
sesame jellyfish, caramel walnuts, marbled eggs and Szechuan cold peppers
being good items on this – took in northern-style chicken with garlic ('very
crispy, succulent and tasty'), braised red pork casserole ('not fatty, but tender
and flavourful'), fragrant braised aubergine ('rustic and flavourful, stir-fried
after being braised and chilli oil used to add punch'), hearty northern-style
bean-sauce noodles ('a subtle yellow-bean sauce') and spicy Szechuan dan dan
noodles ('stir-fried noodles with pork, spring onion, soy and spicy sauce:
excellent'). Desserts were not so successful. The very sound wine list, mainly
from Bibendum, is arranged by weight and full of fashionable names at
reasonable mark-ups. House wines are £8.50.

CHEF: K.L. Tan  PROPRIETORS: Thai Restaurants plc  OPEN: Mon to Fri; 11.30am to
8.30pm  CLOSED: 24 to 26 Dec, 1 Jan, bank hols  MEALS: alc (main courses £6 to £9.50).
Set L and D £13.50 to £24.50 (minimum 2)  SERVICE: 12.5%, card slips closed  CARDS:
Access, Amex, Diners, Visa  DETAILS: 180 seats. Private parties: 100 main room, 12 private
room. Vegetarian meals. Children welcome. Smart dress preferred. Wheelchair access (also
WC). Music. Air-conditioned. Fax: 071-338 0125

## Inaho £

map 12

4 Hereford Road, Bayswater, W2 4AA
071-221 8495

COOKING 2
COST £14–£33

It's so small, it's almost a booth – and as easily missed. The tiny room holds a
dozen diminutive tables and Japanese 'home style' cooking may be captured as
well here as anywhere in the capital. Chef appears regularly from the kitchen to
help the single server and to advise on the specials or something from the short
menu. There are dishes with real flavour, like the spiced aubergines, decent
sashimi, and a sushi menu which is available in the evening from Wednesday
to Saturday. The restaurant has been adopted by many of the locals, which
contributes to its special charm. Saké is £3 for a small bottle and house wine
is £7.

CHEF: S. Otsuka  PROPRIETOR: H. Nakamura  OPEN: Mon to Sat, exc Sat L; 12.30 to 2.30,
7 to 11  CLOSED: 10 days Christmas and New Year, 4 days Easter  MEALS: alc (main
courses £6 to £11). Set L £8 to £9, Set D £18 to £20  SERVICE: 12%  CARDS: Access, Visa
DETAILS: 20 seats. Private parties: 22 main room. Vegetarian meals. Children welcome. No
cigars/pipes in dining-room. Music

## L'Incontro
map 13

87 Pimlico Road, SW1W 8PH

071-730 6327 and 3663

COOKING 2

COST £27–£66

Venetian cooking, Venetian blinds, even a Venetian antique shop next door –
this corner of a British thoroughfare is determined to remain forever Venice.
The place is smart (prime-minister grey, splashed with the colour of the flowers
on tables) and it is full. The overhead spotlights on the designer chiaroscuro,
which, dim over the course of an evening, may 'give the impression that one is
gradually losing one's sight'; the senses of smell and taste, however, are
gratified by often excellent pasta and risotto. Fish, declared a speciality, is
better in the shell than on the fin, where overcooking may occur; roast quail, its
juices soaked into polenta, was excellent, whereas beef escalopes with a hint of
truffle were very ordinary for £19, and a veal chop came bone-flecked. Desserts
may lack variety. The service is 'upper-crust Italian'. The mainly Italian wine
list contains some fine bottles, but is expensive and unhelpfully arranged.
House red and white wines are £12.50.

CHEF: E. Calboli  PROPRIETOR: I. Santin  OPEN: all week, exc L Sat and Sun; 12.30 to 2.30,
7 to 11.30 (10.30 Sun)  CLOSED: bank hols  MEALS: alc (main courses £12.50 to £21.50).
Set L £13.50 (2 courses) to £16.80. Cover £1.50  SERVICE: 12%  CARDS: Access, Amex,
Diners, Visa  DETAILS: 75 seats. Private parties: 50 main room, 30 private room. Vegetarian
meals. Children's helpings. Smart dress preferred. Wheelchair access. Music. Air-
conditioned. Fax: 071-730 5062

## ▲ Inter-Continental Hotel, Le Soufflé ▼
map 13

1 Hamilton Place, W1V 0QY

071-409 3131

COOKING 4*

COST £36–£85

There is something of a crisis in hotel dining-rooms. Costs have soared, people
have fled, reputations have suffered. No longer are they the be-all-and-end-all
of London catering – a position they nearly achieved in the '70s. This is unfair
to some very fine practitioners whose work does not get as much credit as it
perhaps deserves. Peter Kromberg is one. He has been in this transatlantic liner
of a restaurant for several years. 'My first thought was that the décor of the hotel
was awful; my second, that the restaurant was a little better,' remarked a first-
timer here. An old hand went on to remark at the very high standard of cutlery,
china and glassware – evidently well thought-out and appropriate to the
standard of cooking. Service, too, is constantly praised. The staff seem to know
what's what, the wine waiter is singled out for intelligent helpfulness (at that
price you need guidance), and everybody is much less 'grand hotel' than is
often the case. But it is the food that matters. 'We came to the conclusion that

the meal as a whole was better than its constituent parts' may sound like faint praise, but it included real amazement at the quality of a salmon mousse which surrounded crab-meat before being topped with caviare. This came on a butter sauce with colour from salmon roe. Its contrasts of taste and texture, bland and sharp, were remarkable. So, too, was a ravioli of foie gras served at the same meal, even though the evening dipped at the finish with a bland and boring plate of tropical fruits with apricot mousse. 'We are convinced', states a visitor from Lancashire, 'that this is the best restaurant in London. It has finesse, a light touch and finely judged spicing as well as fragrant dressings. The staff are knowledgeable about the wine and the cheeses, which come round on a giant trolley.' Presentation is often a nice touch from this kitchen: amusing without being precious. The list of dishes that have pleased is very long. Perhaps fish cookery is a strong point; so is the light yet true use of flavours; so are the soufflés. Recent visitors here mused that soufflés at the end are not as brilliant as they could be and that the choice of cheese is restricted for a place of this standard. While nothing comes cheap on the wine list, it does have a distinct feeling of better value. Wines and the service thereof are reported enthusiastically, and while Italy and the antipodes are treated scantily the range for a place of this type is good. There are decent offerings by the glass and an intelligent selection of halves. House wine is £14.50. CELLARMAN'S CHOICE: Sauvignon de Touraine 1992, Marcadet, £11.50; St-Estèphe, Ch. de Pez 1985, £30.

CHEF: Peter Kromberg   PROPRIETORS: Inter-Continental Hotels Group   OPEN: Tue to Sun, exc Sat L and Sun D; 12.30 to 3.30 (12 to 4 Sun), 7 to 10.30 (11.15 Sat)   CLOSED: Aug   MEALS: alc (main courses £14.50 to £23). Set L £25.50, Set Sun L £26 (children under 12 £17.50), Set D £43   SERVICE: not inc   CARDS: Access, Amex, Diners, Visa   DETAILS: 80 seats. Private parties: on application. Car park. Vegetarian meals. Healthy eating options. Children welcome. Smart dress preferred. No-smoking area. Music. Air-conditioned   ACCOMMODATION: 465 rooms, all with bath/shower. Rooms for disabled. Lift. Room only £247. Children welcome. Baby facilities. Afternoon teas. Swimming-pool. Sauna. Air-conditioned. TV. Phone. Fax: 071-409 7460

## Ivy
map 15

1 West Street, WC2H 9NE                                        COOKING 2*
071-836 4751                                                   COST £22–£62

'Big, confident eateries of brasserie inspiration and culinary internationalism are one of the more distinguished features of the restaurant landscape in London,' observes a cosmopolitan expert. The Ivy fits in perfectly. News of its repute has spread far and wide and it gets packed to capacity, with diners crammed elbow to elbow in a room that seems to have the acoustics of 'an indoor swimming-pool'. It hums with noise and activity. The menu is coolly eclectic – English with a Californian suntan, French and Italian inflexions and a sprinkle of Far Eastern spicing. As a reporter remarked, 'Will it be bisque, bruschetta or bang-bang?' Potted shrimps, grilled halloumi, corned beef hash, risotto and cassoulet sit happily together and diners have found much to enjoy. One meal spanned the repertoire: Cornish seafood bisque with a rouille that added 'a tormenting garlic burn', steamed scallops with ginger and spring onions, calf's liver with bacon and sage, salmon fish-cakes on wilted spinach with a sauce flecked with 'rags of sorrel', tarte aux pommes, tiramisù. Most dishes work well, although the sheer pace and turnover of the place may occasionally cause mishaps; prices are on the high side for what is offered, and service can be 'brusque'. The wine list makes amends with a thoroughly modern selection from around the world. House wine is from £8.50.

CHEFS: Mark Hix and Des McDonald  PROPRIETORS: Jeremy King and Christopher Corbin  OPEN: all week; 12 to 3, 5.30 to 12  CLOSED: 25 and 26 Dec, 1 Jan  MEALS: alc (main courses £7 to £18.50). Set Sat and Sun L £12.75. Cover £1.50  SERVICE: not inc CARDS: Access, Amex, Diners, Visa  DETAILS: 110 seats. Private parties: 8 main room, 60 private room. Valet parking Sun. Vegetarian meals. Children welcome. No cigars in dining-room. Wheelchair access. Music. Air-conditioned. Fax: 071-497 3644

## Iznik £

| | NEW ENTRY | map 11 |

19 Highbury Park, N5 1QJ                              COOKING 1
071-354 5697                                         COST £16–£24

This part of north London has a significant Turkish community with several cafés and restaurants dotted around. Iznik stands out because of its comfort, clearly annotated menu, unusual dishes and 'English-friendly service'. By day it is a café, in the evening it delivers 'authentic Ottoman cuisine'. The floor is tiled, artefacts and carpets abound, the lighting is subdued, the music low key, and the atmosphere is conducive to having a good time. Meze are well-reported starters, although portions are diminutive: imam bayaldi, mucver (featherlight courgette and cheese fritters), fava (puréed broad beans with yogurt and mint) and kisir (cracked wheat) have been mentioned. Among the main courses, yogurtlu kebab (minced lamb in a tomato and chilli sauce) and hunkar begendi (diced lamb in aubergine sauce) have pleased. The list of desserts includes crème caramel and bramble mousse as alternatives to Turkish pastries such as sekerpare and revani. The minimal wine list has a couple of inexpensive, gutsy Turkish offerings. House wine is £6.95.

CHEF: B. Pehlivan  PROPRIETORS: Mr A. and Mrs P. Oner  OPEN: all week; 12 to 3, 6.30 to 11  MEALS: alc (main courses £6 to £8.50)  SERVICE: 10%  DETAILS: 54 seats. Private parties: 60 main room. Vegetarian meals. Children welcome. Smart dress preferred. Music

## Jade Garden £                                        map 15

15 Wardour Street, W1V 3HA                           COOKING 1*
071-437 5065 and 439 7851                            COST £14–£49

This is a long-standing, safe haven in Soho for the local Chinese community as well as a multicultural mix of Asians, Italians, English and Americans. Green and brown are the dominant colours, and a curving wooden staircase leading to the gallery eating area is the most eye-catching feature of the place. The menu is Cantonese and the cooking generally hits the target, but occasional mishaps, such as a disastrous wun-tun soup that was like 'dishwater', can mar the picture. 'Our opinions of this restaurant seem to vary with each visit or order' is a fair comment about the performance. However, many dishes have been enjoyed: lobster with ginger and spring onion, fish in sweet-and-sour sauce, sizzling chicken with black-bean sauce, Lohan mixed vegetables, 'vividly flavoured' seafood with fried noodles, and asparagus with crabmeat. The menu also features more esoteric specialities such as ducks' feet with bêche-de-mer (sea cucumber) and fried shark's fin with scrambled eggs. The restaurant is a reputable venue for lunch-time dim-sum (served until 5pm), but we have received no reports on these this year. Service is attentive, although one reporter thought the staff were 'efficient automatans'. Drink tea or Tsingtao beer. House wine is £7.50.

CHEF: Raymond Bignold  PROPRIETORS: L.S. Man, P.W. Man and F.T. Man  OPEN: all week; noon to 11.30  CLOSED: Christmas  MEALS: alc (main courses £4.50 to £15). Set L and D £9.50 to £17 (minimum 2)  SERVICE: not inc  CARDS: Access, Amex, Visa DETAILS: 200 seats. Private parties: 100 main room. Vegetarian meals. Children welcome. No music. Air-conditioned. Fax: 071-494 1336

## Jin £

map 15

16 Bateman Street, W1V 5TB
071-734 0908 and 0856

COOKING 1
COST £13–£38

Tucked away in a quiet backwater between the buzz of Dean Street and Frith Street, this place produces authentic Korean cooking. Tony Wee and his staff are pleasant, constructive and helpful. There is a healthy constituent to the cooking: sesame oil, garlic, seaweed and low fat are its primary flavours and characteristics. The technique of marinating meat and fish and barbecueing at the table is the touchstone of Korean cooking, and the full range – from classic bulgogi to 'great' dahk gui (chicken in chilli and hot saké sauce) – is on offer. Soups are 'fiery and challenging', and the menu also takes in hong cho (sweet-and-sour fish), yuk whe (a version of steak tartare with sugar, pear juice and spices) and chaeyuk pyun (boiled pork with spring onions and garlic). Appetisers and side dishes are always intriguing: kim-chee (pickled cabbage) is essential; also look for seasoned spinach, parjon (a kind of pizza), steamed soya bean cake and bracken stalks when they are available. Some reports suggest that the value for money is questionable, given the size of portions. Ginseng and barley tea reinforce the healthy image; otherwise there is a short, standard wine list. House French is £7.50.

CHEF: Mr Ro  PROPRIETOR: Tony Wee  OPEN: all week, exc Sun L; 12 to 3, 6 to 11 CLOSED: 25 and 26 Dec, 1 Jan  MEALS: alc (main courses £4.50 to £8). Set L £7.90, Set L and D £15.50 to £19.50 (minimum 2)  SERVICE: 12.5%, card slips closed  CARDS: Access, Amex, Diners, Visa  DETAILS: 80 seats. Private parties: 50 main room. Vegetarian meals. Children welcome. Wheelchair access (1 step). Music. Air-conditioned

## Joe's Cafe

map 13

126 Draycott Avenue, SW3 3AH
071-225 2217 and 2218

COOKING 1
COST £25–£44

Chic Eva Jiricna design is the most startling feature and the atmosphere is helped along by 'slick, good-looking waiting staff eager to make sure you don't quibble about the suggested 15 per cent service charge'. The menu is jazzy, fashionable brasserie, and the kitchen team are equally at home with club sandwiches, bangers and mash, sashimi and grilled tuna with peppers in tomato and coriander sauce. Reports have extolled the virtues of tagliatelle with vegetables, steak with frites, and salmon fish-cakes with creamy home-made tartare sauce. Salads are 'beautifully dressed' and incidentals are carefully executed. The list of sweets is in keeping – tarte Tatin, tiramisù, exotic fruit with white rum. Weekend breakfasts (10.30 to 12) and Sunday brunch (11 to 3.30) are popular events. Herb teas, cappuccino and fresh fruit punch bolster the short but quite pricey wine list. House French is £10.80.

CHEF: Jerome Laugénie   PROPRIETOR: Joseph Ettedgui   OPEN: all week, exc Sun D; 12 to 4, 7 to 11.30   MEALS: alc (main courses £7.50 to £15). Sun brunch £5.25. Cover £1. Minimum £7.50   SERVICE: 15%   CARDS: Access, Amex, Diners, Visa   DETAILS: 100 seats. 2 tables outside. Private parties: 12 main room. Vegetarian meals. Children's helpings L and early D. No pipes in dining-room. Wheelchair access. Music. Air-conditioned

## Kalamaras £

map 12

76–78 Inverness Mews, W2 3JQ

071-727 9122

COOKING 2

COST £17–£32

Stelios Platonos set up shop in this 'tatty back alley' in 1966 and continues to deliver some of the most authentic Greek food in London, based on 'recipes of our grandmother's cooking'. Starters are highly praised – melizanes me scordalia (fried aubergine and garlic dip) and crisp flaky tyropites (filo pastry triangles filled with feta cheese and oregano) are regularly mentioned. Appropriately, kalamarakia (deep-fried baby squid) are 'about as good as they can get'. Young lamb is the star among the main courses: some like it casseroled with spinach and lemon juice, others prefer it cooked in the oven with garlic. Fish also shows up well: red mullet, grey mullet and sea bass often appear alongside baked crab, steamed salmon and grilled langoustines. Moussaka draws mixed reports, but baked aubergine topped with mincemeat and béchamel sauce has been 'very cinnamony and good'. To finish, there are pastries or fresh fruit. Twenty Greek wines are in tune with the fair value of the place. House wines are from £7.80. Kalamaras (Micro) at 66 Inverness Mews is equally evocative ('with the door open on to the mews and the breeze wafting in, it was like being back in Greece'); bring your own wine, but the food is of similar quality.

CHEF/PROPRIETOR: Stelios Platonos   OPEN: Mon to Sat, D only; 6.30 to 12   CLOSED: bank hols   MEALS: alc (main courses £5.50 to £10). Set D £15.50. Cover £1   SERVICE: 10%, card slips closed   CARDS: Access, Amex, Diners, Visa   DETAILS: 86 seats. 5 tables outside. Private parties: 12 main room, 28 private room. Vegetarian meals. Children's helpings. Smart dress preferred. Wheelchair access. No music

## Kastoori £

map 10

188 Upper Tooting Road, SW17 7ER

081-767 7027

COOKING 1*

COST £13–£22

'So brilliantly authentic, I thought I was back in Colaba,' noted a seasoned reporter. This vegetarian restaurant continues to draw effusive praise. The décor does not change: the carpets are still pinky/brown and the voluptuous plaster-cast dancing figures remain on the walls. The kitchen can deliver fine south Indian dishes, although Gujarati specialities are the real highlights. The kitchen scores heavily by offering genuine home-made chutneys – in this case three subtly different variations on the theme of green mangoes. The excellent-value Gujarati thali ('quite a feast') shows the capabilities of the kitchen: perfectly risen puris, aubergine curry, potato curry, dhal and good-quality rice. Fresh tomato curry thickened with gram flour has also been first-rate. Elsewhere there have been votes for sev puris, pani-puri, palak paneer and vegetables with bhatura bread. Sunday brings special dishes such as rotlo (millet bread), roast aubergines and khichadi (rice and mung beans). New to the menu are the Thanki family specials from Africa and India. To finish, shrikhand (flavoured curd cheese) is reckoned to be better than kulfi. Salt and sweet lassi and masala tea are recommended, or there is Kingfisher lager plus a minimal wine list. House wine is £6.75.

CHEFS: Dinesh Thanki, Kunchan Thanki and Manoj Thanki   PROPRIETORS: the Thanki family   OPEN: all week, exc L Mon and Tue; 12.30 to 2.30, 6 to 10.30   CLOSED: 2 Jan for 2 weeks   MEALS: alc (main courses £3.50 to £4.50). Set L and D £7.25 (2 courses) to £11.25. Minimum £4   SERVICE: not inc, card slips closed   CARDS: Access, Visa   DETAILS: 84 seats. Private parties: 30 main room. Vegetarian meals. Children's helpings on request. Wheelchair access. Music. Air-conditioned

## Kensington Place ▼                                                      map 12

201 Kensington Church Street, W8 7LX                          COOKING 3*
071-727 3184                                                  COST £21–£50

The casual observer would hardly notice a change to Kensington Place, but this glass-fronted giant, such fun to look into when hurrying up Kensington Church Street, has grown by a third. The absorption of next door has been nearly seamless; the most obvious change is to the working conditions in the kitchens behind, but it is possible that some critical point has been passed as it becomes more like eating in a rowdy university refectory at each visit. Size, popularity, a happy acceptance of large bouts of noise, chatter, greeting, jollity and buzz, and a matter-of-fact approach to the niceties of comfort and overstuffed decorum make this place what it is. The exuberance can be distressing to those who think a restaurant should be a haven of peace and cosseting. Staff strike many customers as efficient and remarkably cheerful, given the circumstances (of course there are lapses). Booking is necessary, but the inveterate dropper-in may find a space at the bar. The size of the place has not changed the nature of the cooking, which remains a remarkable meld of modern brasserie food and classic dishes cooked in the grand manner. Rowley Leigh has, however, been quoted as wishing to devote more time and elaboration to main courses. That he can send out a perfect omelette is as great an achievement (in England) as producing partridge wrapped in cabbage. 'I have been there three times in the last month and the place has grown, not diminished, in my estimation. The cooking manages to offer interesting spices and flavouring – for instance, rabbit with cumin and apricots – and the experience is so refreshingly informal' was an enthusiastic endorsement from one customer. This sentiment has been echoed many times for things like the now famous chicken and goats' cheese mousse with olives, foie gras with sweetcorn pancake, scallops with a pea purée, venison with a beurre rouge and polenta chips, duck with cherries, tiramisù, lemon tart and the big plate of puddings. Coffee is good, bought-in bread is good, and daily specials are always interesting. Prices continue to be very fair value. The majority view is in favour of Kensington Place. Wine-wise, it is a pity that more half-bottles are not on offer, although compensation can be found in the dozen wines available by the glass. The list has expanded steadily but continues to be arranged strictly in price order; strong affinity is shown for Italy and the New World and prices closely reflect quality. There is as much good drinking below £14 as there is above £30. Specific recommendations should be treated circumspectly as things change quickly here. House wines are from £8.75. CELLARMAN'S CHOICE: Côtes du Rhône 1991, Laudun, £15.75; Sonoma County, Ravenswood, Zinfandel 1991, £15.50.

CHEF: Rowley Leigh   PROPRIETORS: Nick Smallwood and Simon Slater   OPEN: all week; 12 to 3 (3.30 Sun), 6.30 to 11.45 (10.15 Sun)   CLOSED: 25 and 26 Dec, 1 Jan   MEALS: alc (main courses £8 to £12.50). Set L £13.50   SERVICE: not inc   CARDS: Access, Visa DETAILS: 130 seats. Private parties: 160 main room. Vegetarian meals. Children's helpings. Wheelchair access (1 step; also WC). Music. Air-conditioned. Fax: 071-229 2025

## ▲ Lanesborough

NEW ENTRY   map 13

1 Lanesborough Place, SW1X 7TA
071-259 5599

COOKING 4
COST £28–£70

The early days at this giant film-set occupying the site of St George's Hospital on Hyde Park Corner were not altogether auspicious. Understandably, it took some time to settle in. However, now it is starting to win friends, if only for the cooking. The building is remarkable. While the columned Dining Room is so lush as to convince, the Conservatory, where cheaper food, and song and dancing, are to be had, seems brasher and more obviously Hollywood. A dinner in the Dining Room is an experience worth having, for all its slight solemnity. 'The china is exquisite, the silver gleams as only very new silver does,' reported a man quite bowled over by the unerring combination of glitz and rich taste. Paul Gayler's menu, as with that in so many of the big hotels, is pitched to his clientele. It reads badly or baldly in many parts: the appetisers seem a simple bunch, the grills depress, much of the list does not inspire appetite. 'Yet quality arrives on the plate. There is no striving for innovation or fashion, though the food is modern and well presented and avoids heavy sauces,' concluded one happy diner who was almost persuaded to give up meat for the attractions of the vegetarian menu. Meals have a spare luxury about them. An appetiser of mushrooms in a tartlet with a hollandaise was followed by a mousse of Arbroath smokies and crayfish wrapped in smoked salmon, before crisp medallions of venison on a potato cake with scatterings of vegetable slivers. 'As someone in search of lost slenderness, this was perfect' was a contented report. Another meal began with a piece of bass on ribbons of leek and carrot with a light cream sauce flecked with caviare, before the pressed vegetable terrine – no binding material – which was invigorated by olives, chives, coriander, chervil, tomato and a well-judged vinaigrette. A tart of sweetbreads had fine puff pastry, a bed of endive, and three nutty, tender sweetbreads caramelised in counterbalance. Main dishes, not to mention the daily trolley of roast beef and Yorkshire, sometimes have an air of Mrs Beeton

113

or the glories of Old England. Thus duck is served with peas (given a gloss by morel mushrooms), and lamb is cooked in hay. The quality of these two dishes was impeccable. Desserts, too, can be throwbacks – at least, a cheese and lemon curd mousse had that effect. Coffee is good, petits fours magnificent but, after all that goes before, in this day and age who wants them? Down at the Conservatory, Paul Gayler is still the man in charge, but the menu is as dashingly modern as the Dining Room's is rooted in the past. It is not so very much cheaper. That here we are in for today's eating in today's style comes across from the very first slice of focaccia glistening with salt that is served while you choose. The cooking can be very successful, as in an oriental black mushroom risotto with coriander, but on other occasions has been reported as missing the mark, for instance, in a stracci of spring vegetables with lentil bolognese (vegetarian creativity here) which suffered from salt, or a handsome plate of mussels with minted peanut sauce that was high on mint and coriander but low on peanut. It almost seems a best bet for lunch, when prices, or appetites, are more manageable. There is music, come evening, in both places, even dancing in the Conservatory on occasion. The wine list will impress for its prices. It has hardly more than a dozen whole bottles at under £20, and rather more that rise to three figures. The range is acceptable, but not unique. House wines, mere packages from the big houses of Cordier and Faiveley, are £14.50 and £17.50 respectively.

CHEF: Paul Gayler  PROPRIETORS: Goodwill Nominees  OPEN: Dining Room Mon to Fri; 12.30 to 2.30, 5 to 12.30. Conservatory all week; 12 to 2.30, 6.30 to 12 (all-day snacks bank hols)  CLOSED: Dining Room bank hols, 3 weeks Aug  MEALS: alc (main courses Dining Room £15.50 to £23.50, Conservatory £11.50 to £20.50). Dining Room Set L £19.50 (2 courses) to £24, Set D £29.50. Conservatory Set L £20.50, Set D £26.50  SERVICE: net prices, card slips closed  CARDS: Access, Amex, Diners, Visa  DETAILS: Dining Room 54 seats, Conservatory 100 seats. Private parties: 75 and 120 main rooms, 12 to 60 in private rooms. Car park. Vegetarian meals. Children's helpings. No children under 6 Dining Room. Jacket and tie (exc L Conservatory). No cigars/pipes in Dining Room. Wheelchair access (also WC). Music. Air-conditioned  ACCOMMODATION: 95 rooms, all with bath/shower. Rooms for disabled. Lift. Room only £194 to £2,938. Children welcome. Baby facilities. Small dogs welcome. Afternoon teas. Air-conditioned. TV. Phone. Fax: 071-259 5606

## Langan's Brasserie
map 14

Stratton Street, W1X 5FD
071-493 6437

COOKING 1
COST £25–£50

This giant strides on, still an essential instrument of the businessperson's lunch, still resort for a medley of people from all walks of life. That is its virtue, and it pioneered the style of a large restaurant capable of cooking passable food at sometimes moderate cost that has now become the *sine qua non* of London eating. Langan's has its infelicities of service which may be acceptable to regulars but much more daunting to first-timers – and a place of this scale should really be accessible to all. The repertoire is conservative – artichoke hollandaise, duck terrine, mixed hors d'oeuvre, roast lamb, black pudding, kidneys and bacon, roast chicken with sage stuffing, rack of lamb, liver and bacon, treacle tart, sorbets and so on – so that the unfamiliar might be surprised at the éclat which this place caused in the first instance when it replaced the Coq d'Or. In two decades, it has aged 50 years. That is a great achievement. We have been unable to confirm the details below as a reply to our questionnaire was unforthcoming.

CHEFS: Richard Shepherd, Dennis Mynott and Roy Smith   PROPRIETORS: Michael Caine and Richard Shepherd   OPEN: Mon to Sat, exc Sat L; 12.30 to 3, 7 to 11.45 (8 to 12.45 Sat) CLOSED: 25 Dec, 1 Jan, Easter, bank hols   MEALS: alc. Cover £1   SERVICE: 12.5%   CARDS: Access, Amex, Diners, Visa   DETAILS: 200 seats. Private parties: 12 main room. Vegetarian meals. Children's helpings. Wheelchair access (1 step). Music. Air-conditioned

## Lansdowne £

**NEW ENTRY**   map 11

90 Gloucester Avenue, NW1 8HX
071-483 0409

COOKING 1*
COST £16–£32

This pub has taken the formula developed at the Eagle (see entry, London) and exported it to the lower skirts of Primrose Hill. Once again, the inside of the place has been ripped out, leaving a barn-like space that is airy rather than claustrophobic. A miscellany of furniture, mostly stripped wood, has been assembled from junk palaces and car boot sales, the wine list and menu are chalked on boards, you order and pay for the food and drink separately at the bar (which can sometimes irk), find a table and wait for your meal to arrive. The menu moves fast. It has less of an emphasis on the grill, less of the Mediterranean about it than the Eagle, but it persists in the concept of good value, giant quantities, bold flavours (sometimes very bold), and natural arrangement. Some things can be a mite dry, or rely on olive oil as the only lubricant; sometimes seasoning is seriously awry. Soups are body-building; risottos and pasta are substantial; chillis are enjoyed, but not to the exclusion of gentler spices; and meat is from the chewier cuts. Try mackerel fillet and couscous, roast leg of lamb with mash and spinach, vine tomato, mozzarella and basil salad, or 'spaghettini' with pesto. If only all pubs tried this route to success. Coffee is good; credit cards are not accepted. The wine list is short, but never overpriced, with some decent bottles from Bibendum and other suppliers. House wines are £7.90.

CHEF: Amanda Pritchett   PROPRIETORS: A.J. Pritchett, K.F. McGrath and A.K. Inglis OPEN: Tue to Sun L, Mon to Sat D; 12.30 to 2.30 (1 to 2.30 Sun), 7 to 10   MEALS: alc (main courses £5 to £10). Set Sun L £12 to £15   SERVICE: not inc   DETAILS: 50 seats. 6 tables outside. Vegetarian meals. Children's helpings L. Wheelchair access (1 step). Music

## Launceston Place ▼

map 13

1A Launceston Place, W8 5RL
071-937 6912

COOKING 2*
COST £23–£50

'This is the civilised crusty compared to Kensington Place's exuberant teenager,' reports one diner, struck by the 'reserved atmosphere, just this side of austere' which makes such a contrast with the sister restaurant (see entry). Elegant table-settings and 'terribly comfortable' chairs entice, while lighting is 'dimmed to decidedly romantic levels'. Another trencherwoman had the opportunity to compare the siblings' ways with foie gras on two successive evenings: it was the Launceston Place version ('with grapes on a bread soaked with juices – sublime') which prevailed. Noisettes of 'the best venison yet', a 'stunningly good' pea and broad-bean soup, and a large bagel-shaped puff-pastry case stuffed full of plump morels and creamy fresh spinach ('good pastry, great mushrooms') have all proved 'worth waiting for'. But wait you may: 'The attitude of the staff was one of total disdain – since we were not regular customers, we obviously weren't worth bothering about' was the experience of one; another found the service slick. Desserts lack the flair of the best of the savoury work, though citrus fruit salad with champagne sorbet proved 'a splendid idea at the end of a rich meal', and a crispy banana fritter was blessedly free from frying-oil. The wine list begins with a dull white at £8.50; it swiftly gets more interesting and more expensive (price governs the order). Among bottles worth a punt are the Langlois-Château 1989 Vieilles Vignes Saumur at £14.75, Reynaud's 1989 Pignan at £24.50 and Mountadam's 1990 Chardonnay at £26.50. House wine is £8.50. CELLARMAN'S CHOICE: Gavi di Gavi, La Raia 1991, £15.75; Weinert, Cabernet Sauvignon 1983, £16.50.

CHEF: Charles Mumford   PROPRIETORS: Nick Smallwood and Simon Slater   OPEN: all week, exc Sat L and Sun D; 12.30 to 2.30 (3 Sun), 7 to 11.30   CLOSED: bank and public hols   MEALS: alc (main courses £9 to £15.50). Set L and D (before 8pm) £12.50 (2 courses) to £15.50   SERVICE: not inc   CARDS: Access, Amex, Visa   DETAILS: 75 seats. Private parties: 120 main room, 14 and 30 private rooms. Vegetarian meals. Children's helpings. No cigars/pipes in dining-room. Wheelchair access. No music. Air-conditioned. Fax: 071-938 2412

## Laurent  £

map 11

428 Finchley Road, NW2 2HY
071-794 3603

COOKING  1*
COST £17–£27

Couscous it promises and couscous is exactly what you get. Laurent Farrugia is nothing if not a specialist, and he is eager to come out front, talk, offer extra helpings and smile a great deal. His 'zero-choice' restaurant (apart from brique à l'oeuf to start and a few sweets) is low on décor, high on atmosphere and colour: plain white walls with prints of Tunisia, gingham check tablecloths, an 'odd selection of glassware', loud conversation. The couscous comes three ways, although the tender, long-cooked lamb version gets most praise – especially when it is topped up with extra merguez sausages. The cooking is invariably on target; massive portions and bargain prices are a bonus. Algerian or Moroccan wine washes it all down well. House wine is £8.60.

CHEF/PROPRIETOR: Laurent Farrugia   OPEN: Mon to Sat; 12 to 2, 6 to 11   CLOSED: last 3 weeks Aug   MEALS: alc (main courses £6.50 to £10). Minimum £6.50   SERVICE: not inc CARDS: Access, Amex, Visa   DETAILS: 36 seats. Private parties: 45 main room. Vegetarian meals. Children's helpings. Smart dress preferred. Wheelchair access (1 step). No music

## Leith's  🍾

map 12

92 Kensington Park Road, W11 2PN
071-229 4481

COOKING  3
COST £40–£64

This large house has always had a certain image of *gravitas*; the rude call it boring, which does not make it a natural choice for a big night out. The prices – never low – apparently militate against this too, but in fact the level of service, the enthusiasm and the warmth of welcome are very consoling, and the cooking has a consistent approach that deserves respect. Leith's does move with the times. It has retreated from its admirable fully inclusive prices and has abandoned the sweets trolley, finally moving into line with the rest of London in this sphere. But it still cooks food with a definite British slant (though not on its vegetarian menu), evinced by dishes like timbale of scallops, clams and oysters with a pea purée or rabbit feuilleté with watercress and horseradish. The duckling, roast and split between two, is the long-runner on the menu, and if the list of first courses seems short, it is because there is still the hors d'oeuvre trolley offering hits one day, near misses the next. Leith's is a genuine enterprise, with produce from the farm and an attempt to do grand cooking without descending into the clichéd luxury of endless shellfish, foie gras and truffles. Sometimes people report that it lacks attack but there are many who appreciate its steady, copper-bottomed existence. The wines are extraordinary both in range and in quality; good sense is manifest throughout. The list is neither over-long nor overpriced and supplementaries to the main listing such as the bin-ends, the 'house selection' and 'recommendations of the month' add to the friendliness and accessibility. Our sole criticism is the relative paucity of halves, with little available by the glass as compensation. House wine is £12.75. CELLARMAN'S CHOICE: Sonoma, Chalk Hill, Sauvignon Blanc 1990, £18.75; Pauillac, Ch. Clerc-Milon 1987, £21.50.

CHEF: Alex Floyd   PROPRIETOR: Prue Leith   OPEN: all week, D only; 7.30 to 11.30
CLOSED: 4 days Christmas, 2 days Aug bank hol   MEALS: Set D £23.50 (2 courses) to £40
SERVICE: 15%, card slips closed   CARDS: Access, Amex, Diners, Visa   DETAILS: 85 seats.
Private parties: 24 main room, 10, 24 and 36 private rooms. Vegetarian meals. Children welcome. Wheelchair access (3 steps). No music. Air-conditioned

## Lobster Pot
map 11

3 Kennington Lane, SE11 4RG                                    COOKING 1*
071-582 5556                                                    COST £18–£50

The streets that surround this restaurant, which occupies the bottom two floors of a very narrow Georgian building, still seem to be suffering from the bomb damage of the last war. Once through the door, however, you are transported to a maritime, not land-based, world. 'It is frankly bizarre' was one observation. 'A series of portholes down one wall reveals a tank of largish tropical fish; upstairs, where coffee and bought-in chocolates can be had, you have to avoid bashing your shins on ships' anchors, propellers, etc. Sea shanties are played in the dining-room.' The business is fish and this is well bought: Hervé Régent can construct grandes assiettes approaching those across the Channel, and people have remarked upon the quality of the sole, prawns and lobster, as well as some less familiar warm-water species. Sauce-making, vegetables and ancillaries may be less accomplished, but desserts have been pronounced excellent. The service by Mme Régent is fine. The menu does not change much. The wine list is very short indeed, and is not too expensive or exciting. House wines are £8.50.

*A report form is at the back of the book; write a letter if you prefer.*

CHEF: Hervé Régent  PROPRIETORS: Hervé and Nathalie Régent  OPEN: Tue to Sun; 12 to 2.30, 7 to 10.45  MEALS: alc (main courses £12.50 to £16.50). Set L £12.50 to £18.50, Set D £18.50. Minimum £12.50  SERVICE: net prices, card slips closed  CARDS: Access, Amex, Diners, Visa  DETAILS: 30 seats. Private parties: 30 main room. Vegetarian meals with prior notice. Children's helpings. Smart dress preferred. No cigars/pipes in dining-room. Wheelchair access (1 step). Music. Air-conditioned. Fax: 071-582 9751

## Lou Pescadou
map 11

241 Old Brompton Road, SW5 9HP
071-370 1057

COOKING 1
COST £25–£43

This large and largely jolly fishery has three sections – a casual bistro, a pink-clothed restaurant area and a conservatory – as well as a 'Rugby Bar' downstairs, decorated with photos of the (French) greats. 'Too bloody cramped' is one view of the restaurant, 'but it keeps the prices down'. The late opening hours are appreciated: 'It's so nice to be able to walk in at 11pm, well after the theatre, and be served food of this quality by friendly but highly professional waiters without any fuss at all.' The menu is built around 'sensitively cooked' fish and seafood; the alternatives are pizza, pasta and salad, with a little (expensive) beef. Shellfish are 'as ever, excellent', and the fish (for which a daily trawl is made) 'impeccable' – monkfish and John Dory both winning praise. Good French bread provides more pleasure than the patchy vegetables; desserts are rough-and-tumble standards. The wine list is barely a list at all, just a few bottles from unspecified sources, but reported quality is good, especially of fish-loving Loire valley Sauvignon (Sancerre, Pouilly-Fumé). House wine is £9.50.

CHEF: Laurent David  PROPRIETORS: Daniel Chobert and Laurent David  OPEN: all week; 12 to 3, 7 to 12  MEALS: alc (main courses £8 to £12.50). Cover £1  SERVICE: 15%, card slips closed  CARDS: Access, Amex, Diners, Visa  DETAILS: 60 seats. 8 tables outside. Private parties: 80 main room, 40 private room. Vegetarian meals. Children's helpings. Smart dress preferred. Wheelchair access (1 step). No music

## Magno's Brasserie
NEW ENTRY  map 15

65A Long Acre, WC2E 9JH
071-836 6077

COOKING 1
COST £20–£46

There has been support for a re-entry of this long-running soi-disant brasserie. It is really a restaurant. Whatever the name, a comfortable French decorative theme gives no offence at all, and the Gallic service succeeds in that certain style of brisk charm. It has long been a resort of theatre-goers who find the cheap deals available at the beginning of the evening a fair bargain. More serious diners will find a menu that mixes the standard entrecôtes and moules marinière with something slightly more enterprising, be it pasta with vodka and bacon, breast of duck with a kick from cloves, or salmon served with salsify. Performance is steady, though a profusion of salt seemed the fate one night for one reporter who also wished that the vegetables had been more careful. Sometimes a lack of detail spoils a perfectly good conception: hence a tabbouleh of seafood was full of good flavours, but the seafood (mussels and squid) should have been bolder. The place may be French, but the summer pudding has been passed as excellent. The wine list makes an effort to find something interesting for wines of the month, and has a fair handful of clarets (note especially the Pomerols) to beef up the range. The range of French brandies is excellent. House wines are £8.50.

CHEF: Gilbert Rousset  PROPRIETORS: Magno Coliadis and Arthur Wastell  OPEN: Mon to Sat, exc Sat L; 12 to 2.30, 5.30 to 11.30  CLOSED: Christmas and bank hols  MEALS: alc (main courses £7 to £14). Set L £12.50 (2 courses) to £15.50, Set pre-theatre D £9.95 (2 courses), Set D £15.50  SERVICE: 12.5%, card slips closed  CARDS: Access, Amex, Diners, Visa  DETAILS: 60 seats. Private parties: 60 main room. Vegetarian meals. Children welcome. Smart dress preferred. Wheelchair access. Music D. Air-conditioned. Fax: 071-379 6184

## Malabar £                                                map 12

27 Uxbridge Street, W8 7TQ                                  COOKING 1
071-727 8800                                                COST £19–£46

The previous histories of restaurant buildings are always a bit of fun to while away a minute's waiting and, just as there are some French places in the West End still sporting Indian motifs from an earlier function as purveyor of curries, the Malabar Indian restaurant is grafted on to the physique of an Italian trattoria. This may make poetic sense in that the service here is brighter, more articulate and less ethnic than many; and the food on the short menu is quite intelligent too. There is a batch of tandoori items, and some enjoyable spicing in things like nimbu gosht (lamb zested with lemon) or long chicken (with cloves and ginger). Some say portions are none too big; breads and vegetables are decent. The short wine list is serviceable and house wines are £8.50.

CHEF: Anil Bist  PROPRIETORS: Jo Chalmers and Anil Bist  OPEN: all week; 12 (12.30 Sun) to 2.45, 6 to 11.15  CLOSED: 4 days Christmas, 1 week end Aug  MEALS: alc (main courses £4.50 to £9.50). Set L and D £11.75 to £29.75 (2 persons). Cover 80p  SERVICE: 12.5% CARDS: Access, Visa  DETAILS: 56 seats. Private parties: 15 main room, 20 private room. Vegetarian meals. Children welcome. No music. Air-conditioned (partly)

## Mandarin Kitchen £                                       map 12

14–16 Queensway, W2 3RX                                     COOKING 2
071-727 9012 and 9468                                       COST £15–£54

Queensway, 'where the Far East meets the Middle East', is well served by this colourful, bustling Chinese restaurant. The room has a retro feel which late '70s nightclubbers will admire, but the real reason for coming here is to plunge into 80-plus different seafood dishes. Lobster is available in six variants; whichever you choose, order the bed of soft noodles to catch the juices. The adventurous may chance crystal king prawn 'with unexpected taste', as the menu puts it, or fish maw with mixed seafood soup, an experience more of texture ('between silky and slippery', in case you were wondering) than of taste. The restaurant's problem is a lack of finesse: coarse ginger and spring onions walloped otherwise choice steamed scallops; eel had sizzled its way towards toughness, though very good gravy made amends. The waitresses, in uniform green blouses and uniform cropped hair, fly around the tables of cosmopolites. The

Arabs drink whisky, the English beer, the Chinese tea – but there is a short, standard wine list. House wine is £6.80.

CHEF: Kwong Wing Man  PROPRIETORS: Helen and Stephen Cheung  OPEN: all week; noon to 11.30  CLOSED: 24 and 25 Dec  MEALS: alc (main courses £5 to £12). Set D £8.90 (minimum 2)  SERVICE: not inc  CARDS: Access, Amex, Diners, Visa  DETAILS: 110 seats. Private parties: 30 main room. Vegetarian meals. Children welcome. Smart dress preferred. Wheelchair access. Music. Air-conditioned

## ▲ Manzi's
map 15

1–2 Leicester Street, WC2H 7BE
071-734 0224

COOKING 1
COST £22–£67

As seafood restaurants go, Manzi's is an institution. Change is not in its nature; it ignores the fact that tastes in food and cooking have moved on. And yet the kitchen is still able to deliver the goods: witness juicy scallops with bacon, crab with avocado, 'rich, well-judged' Breton fish soup and monster grilled Dover sole. A special of grilled tuna has also been favourably reported. Vegetables are a mixed bag – good chips and fresh spinach, but cauliflower 'so undercooked it could not be cut with a fish knife'. Similarly the sweets trolley is an uneven assortment – soft, ripe strawberries, but 'ungainly' fresh fruit salad in 'a viciously tart syrup'. Service can sometimes irritate. The short wine list is notable for its familiar names and lack of information. Carafes start at £8.75. A Docklands branch is at Glengall Bridge, Turnberry Quay, Cross Harbour, E14, Tel: 071-538 9615 – reports, please.

CHEF: Ysid Ali  PROPRIETORS: the Manzi family  OPEN: all week, exc Sun L; 12 to 2.20, 5.30 to 11.40 (10.40 Sun)  MEALS: alc (main courses £7 to £25). Cover £1.60  SERVICE: not inc  CARDS: Access, Amex, Diners, Visa  DETAILS: 120 seats. Private parties: 40 main room. Vegetarian meals. No children under 5. Wheelchair access (3 steps). Music ACCOMMODATION: 15 rooms, all with bath/shower. Lift. B&B £40 to £63. Deposit: 100%. Children welcome. Air-conditioned. TV. Phone. Confirm 1 day ahead. Fax: 071-437 4864

## Maroush/Maroush III
map 11

21 Edgware road, W2 2JH
071-723 0773
62 Seymour Street, W1H 5AF
071-724 5024

COOKING 2
COST £26–£45

'Smart, clean and soothing' sums up the décor and mood of these highly rated Lebanese restaurants. Maroush is in a basement, with live music; Maroush III is a conversion of a plush Western restaurant. Good humour and helpfulness abound. Most visitors opt for the meze ('all competent, some inspired'), which draw effusive comments: falafel ('crispy outside, deliciously moist and subtle within'), cold aubergine and garlic salad with a good dose of chilli to startle the unwary, tongue in yogurt-based sauce ('a revelation to a palate made cynical by fatty pressed tongue from supermarkets'), gently braised, tiny Lebanese sausages, ful medames which provided a 'soothing and balanced background to the more powerful dishes'. Main courses centre on the chargrill, while sweets are a mix of sticky pastries and fresh fruits. House Lebanese wine is

£13.50. Aficionados and the sleepless will embrace the take-away a few yards north on the Edgware Road for doner kebab, filled pitta breads and fruit juices, open until the small hours.

CHEF: Fouad Ladkani   PROPRIETOR: Maarouf Abouzaki   OPEN: all week; noon to 1am
MEALS: alc (main courses £8.50 to £12.50). Cover L £1.50, D £3. Minimun £38 Maroush after 10pm   SERVICE: 10%, card slips closed   CARDS: Access, Amex, Diners, Visa
DETAILS: Maroush 110 seats, Maroush III 40 seats. Vegetarian meals. Children's helpings. Smart dress preferred. Music. Air-conditioned

## Mayflower £

map 15

68–70 Shaftesbury Avenue, W1V 7DF
071-734 9207

COOKING 2
COST £17–£60

The cavernous brown and beige basement may seem 'potentially gloomy', but this restaurant attracts a regular crowd of mainly Chinese customers. 'The whole place was reminiscent of a good family restaurant in a provincial Chinese city,' commented a reporter from the East. The massive menu of around 170 dishes challenges Western palates and intrigues those with knowledge of the cuisine. A wise verdict is to concentrate on one-pot casseroles, seafood specialities, peasant-style items and anything preserved or pickled. There is less support for curries, sizzlers and the more accessible, Westernised dishes. One brilliant meal included white-cut crystal chicken, minced pork and salt fish-cakes, and steamed sea bass with mushrooms, spring onions, coriander and soy (perfectly timed, superbly fresh fish). Soups such as dried scallop and mushroom or preserved egg and pork are out of the top draw, and the selection of bean curd dishes is also good (one version with earthy preserved mushrooms, peppers, aubergines and cabbage dazzled an expert). Service is noticeably courteous and charming by Chinatown standards. House wine is £9.50. The owners recently opened a seafood restaurant, King's Court, at 23 Romilly Street, W1, Tel: 071-287 1637 – reports, please.

CHEF: Fook On Chung   PROPRIETOR: Patrick Tsang   OPEN: all week, D only; 5pm to 4am   CLOSED: 23 to 25 Dec   MEALS: alc (main courses £5.50 to £16.50). Set D £11.50 to £13   SERVICE: not inc   CARDS: Access, Amex, Diners, Visa   DETAILS: 130 seats. Private parties: 40 main room, 40 private room. Vegetarian meals. Children welcome. Smart dress preferred. Music. Air-conditioned

## Melati £

map 15

21 Great Windmill Street, W1V 7PH
071-437 2745 and 734 6964

COOKING 1
COST £15–£34

Deep in X-certificate Soho, this Indonesian hot-spot continues to make new friends and keep its regulars happy. Service is all warm smiles and hearty greetings. The kitchen still delivers some of the most gutsy South-East Asian food in London: hot-and-sour soup, satays, cumi-cumi istimewa (stuffed squid) and kari ayam (Malaysian chicken curry) have all been praised. Vegetarian specialities also stand out: tahu goreng (fried tofu with sweet peanut sauce) and sambal tauco (green beans with chunks of bean curd in a fermented soy bean sauce) have been highly applauded. Bowls of laksa, rice, noodles and composite one-plate dishes such as mee goreng istimewa offer excellent value. Extraordinary desserts, including brilliantly coloured Sam's Triple (layers of puréed avocado, mango and pineapple) and an 'absolutely delicious' concoction of syrup with rambutans topped with coconut milk and grass jelly are great talking points. Drink Indonesian Bintang, Singapore Tiger beer or jasmine tea. House wine is £7.85. Melati's sibling, Minang, at 11 Greek Street, W1V 5LE, Tel: 071-434 1149, serves similar dishes in slightly snazzier surroundings.

CHEF: Hasyim Damuri   PROPRIETORS: S. Alamsjah and Margaret Ong   OPEN: all week; noon to 11.30 (12.30 Fri and Sat)   CLOSED: 25 Dec   MEALS: alc (main courses £4 to £7). Set L and D £15.50 (2 courses) to £19.75 (inc wine)   SERVICE: 10%, card slips closed CARDS: Access, Amex, Diners, Visa   DETAILS: 120 seats. Private parties: 45 main room. Vegetarian meals. Children's helpings on request. Wheelchair access. Music. Air-conditioned

## ▲ Le Meridien Hotel, Oak Room

map 13

21 Piccadilly, W1V 0BH
071-734 8000

COOKING 4
COST £36–£78

'The limed oak panelling, the gilding, the superb Venetian chandeliers and the wide spacing of the tables, coupled with the attentive thoughtfulness of the staff' combine, in the eyes of one seasoned reader, to make the Oak Room one of the most successful grand-hotel restaurants in the capital. This is Le Meridien's 'gourmet' division; the rest of the world goes to the Terrace aloft, which is never as satisfactory. Chef David Chambers, the resident, continues his relationship with Michel Lorain, the foreigner, in producing a menu of considerable interest that might be thought a paradigm of modern French practice. A printed menu is supplemented by a short list of extras, and at lunch-time there is an edited version of the evening offering, plus a cheaper set-price affair. Imagination there is in plenty, with the fish often taking the star turn. Turbot with pink and white peppercorns, cooked with some lemon grass is one example, lobster and spinach in a thin crust with a lobster sauce is a second, and gazpacho of langoustines still gets warm approval. Simple food, such as asparagus with a saffron mousseline or salmon marinated with spices (an haute cuisine version of gravlax), gets more of an outing than might be expected in a place where offal and shellfish seem very much the order of the day. Spicing is a preoccupation, as in the coffee-bean sauce that accompanies the duck, which is given edge by endives rather than the expected citrus or berry flavours. The ancillaries are up to the mark, and people still enjoy the waiters drawing pretty patterns in the coulis and custard from the sweets trolley. The wine list comes dear and is largely French. The New World choices, however, give a little – but not much – financial realism to the pages of classed growths. Given the remarkable quality of some of the new-wave producers in France, it seems a pity that the choices cannot be more adventurous. House wines are £15.50.

*If a restaurant is new to the* Guide *this year (did not appear as a main entry in the last edition)* NEW ENTRY *appears opposite its name.*

CHEFS: David Chambers and Michel Lorain  PROPRIETORS: Meridien Hotels Ltd  OPEN: Mon to Sat, exc Sat L; 12 to 2, 7 to 10.30  CLOSED: bank hols  MEALS: alc (main courses £14.50 to £25). Set L £24.50, Set D £46  SERVICE: not inc  CARDS: Access, Amex, Diners, Visa  DETAILS: 45 seats. Vegetarian meals with prior notice. No children under 3. Jacket and tie. No cigars/pipes in dining-room. Wheelchair access (also WC). Music. Air-conditioned  ACCOMMODATION: 263 rooms, all with bath/shower. Lift. B&B £233 to £260. Children welcome. Baby facilities. Afternoon teas. Swimming-pool. Sauna. Tennis. Snooker. Air-conditioned. TV. Phone. Fax: 071-437 3574

---

## Le Mesurier

**NEW ENTRY**  map 11

113 Old Street, EC1V 9JR
071-251 8117

COOKING 1*
COST £27–£42

The restaurant occupies the ground floor of one of a few old terraced houses, close by St Luke's churchyard. Ring the door for entry, and if you want an architect, go on upstairs to the other half of the Enthoven enterprise. Gillian cooks lunches for a tiny dining-room of half a dozen tables; the menu is from Lilliput too – three choices (some of which may expire before the end of the session). She has remained faithful to her repertoire, which combines dinner-party with sound restaurant practice. An arrangement of mange-tout that have been filled with salmon mayonnaise sits on a flavoursome tomato vinaigrette; medallions of veal moistened with a classic black peppercorn cream sauce, with vegetables that could be more stylish; serious pancakes with soufflé fillings, or hot soufflés on their own should finish the meal. Pastry is good too. In the context of the City, it is a refreshingly personal enterprise. There may be delays but you never feel you do not belong. The wine list is short and sound (Corney & Barrow). House wines are £9.

---

CHEFS: Gillian Enthoven and Loic le Pape  PROPRIETOR: Gillian Enthoven  OPEN: Mon to Fri, L only (D party bookings only 6 to 8.30); 12 to 3  CLOSED: 1 week Christmas, 3 weeks Aug  MEALS: alc (main courses £8 to £12)  SERVICE: 12.5%, card slips closed  CARDS: Access, Amex, Diners, Visa  DETAILS: 26 seats. Private parties: 26 main room. Vegetarian meals with prior notice. No children under 8. Smart dress preferred. Wheelchair access. Music. Fax: 071-608 3504

---

## Mezzaluna New York

**NEW ENTRY**  map 15

Thomas Neal's Centre,
22 Shorts Gardens WC2H 9RU
071-379 3336

COOKING 1
COST £21–£36

Although the entrance to the restaurant is via stairs downwards, once in the apparent basement there opens a court – atrium is the trendy or technical word, depending how you see it – that admits daylight and air. This place is part of a chain, but the other branches are in New York and Aspen. It is also part of a family, but whereas one Grossman, Loyd, appears on television, his brother, Neal, runs the restaurants. Mezzaluna is a pizzeria with a difference. Nearly everything costs about the same; there is thus no obvious difference between the primi piatti and a big pizza. There are a few grilled items – chicken, steak or seafood – that may be recognisable as main dishes and are decently done, but the menu is a sort of monument to unstructured grazing. There are first courses, pasta, pizza, grills and variations (hot or cold) on the theme of carpaccio. All are more or less imaginative, for which read fashionable – *viz* orecchiette with turnip tops and Provolone (which comes over as 'broccoli rabe'). The pizzas are the best thing: done in a handsome wood-fired oven, their dough is good – neither too thin nor too thick – with toppings that have some freshness to them. The design of the place – a sky-like ceiling, lots of mezzalunas (moons and cutters) and handsome table-tops – is busy and successful, the service is cheerful enough, and it makes a good place for lunch. The wine list is short but, particularly for a pizzeria, good. House wines are £8.50.

CHEF: Maurice Maffeo   PROPRIETORS: Mezza London Partners   OPEN: all week; 12 to 3.30, 6 to 1am (10.30 Sun)   CLOSED: 25 to 30 Dec   MEALS: alc (main courses £6 to £11.50). Cover £1 after 7 on live music nights   SERVICE: not inc   CARDS: Access, Amex, Diners, Visa   DETAILS: 92 seats. Private parties: 120 main room. Vegetarian meals. Children's helpings on request. No-smoking area. Wheelchair access (also WC). Music. Air-conditioned

## Mijanou 🍾 🍴

143 Ebury Street, SW1W 9QN
071-730 4099

map 13

COOKING 2*
COST £26–£60

When you have finished going through Mijanou's wine list and the annotated menu (this is for the Winematch system that Neville Blech has introduced), you may be forgiven for thinking *multum in parvo*: Mijanou, near Eaton Square, is not a large restaurant – its two rooms occupy the ground floor and basement – but its heart is big. Sonia Blech has a firmly French background, in contrast to her husband's suave Britishness, and is a self-taught cook. Neither fact can be ignored when savouring her cooking. This is idiosyncratic: it reveals the effects of changes in taste in the last couple of decades, it throws in contributions that are emphatically home-grown, and it is like few other styles in London. Certain tastes feature often: sweet-and-sour, nuts, foie gras and fungi, and strong fruity and floral flavours for dessert. There is an exuberance in composition and display that some find tortured, others entertaining, and that can occasionally misfire completely. The Mijanou is not usually home to *simple* cooking, nor is it especially cheap – though lunch is fair value. People have spoken well of the long-running duck foie gras with a Muscat wine and grape jelly, ravioli of scallops perfumed with lemon grass and crab, and strongly flavoured fillet of beef with a tapénade (and lots of puff pastry) and a mustard and horseradish sauce. If you find soufflé pancakes of banana and pineapple with a Malibu sauce too much to contemplate, there are nutty alternatives in a gâteau Argentin of hazelnuts and almonds, or a gâteau Montelimar made with honey, pistachios and cashews. A mean spirit might condemn the sheer length of the wine list but would be pushed to criticise either the quality or the prices. Fifteen or so excellent choices are offered by the glass from £3. While the Winematch concept is commendable in theory, in practice it becomes less convincing and hardly helpful in the face of a possible nine recommended sections of the list for a single dish. The wines are, however, wonderful. CELLARMAN'S CHOICE: Olivet Lane, Russian River, Chardonnay 1989, Pellegrini, £17.50; Coonawarra, Cabernet/Shiraz 1989, Penley Estate, £20.

CHEF: Sonia Blech PROPRIETORS: Neville and Sonia Blech OPEN: Mon to Fri; 12.15 to 2, 7.15 to 11 CLOSED: 1 week Easter, 2 weeks Christmas, 3 weeks Aug MEALS: alc (main courses £12 to £16.50). Set L and D £12 (2 courses) to £15, Set D 'Menu Dégustation' £36. Minimum £12 L, £18 D SERVICE: not inc CARDS: Access, Amex, Visa DETAILS: 32 seats. 6 tables outside. Private parties: 24 main room. Vegetarian meals. Children welcome. Smart dress preferred. No smoking upstairs. Wheelchair access (3 steps). No music. Air-conditioned. Fax: 071-823 6402

## Mr Kong £

map 15

21 Lisle Street, WC2H 7BA
071-437 7341 and 9679

COOKING 2
COST £12–£32

'I don't think that I have ever had a better Chinese meal or, in this present day and age, had better value for money,' enthused a reporter who entertained friends in this highly popular Soho restaurant. Mr Kong tells us that he was the first to introduce scallops into Chinatown as well as taking on the challenge of cooking venison (sauté in ginger wine). The list of specials is challenging stuff: satay eels, deep-fried crispy duck with yam paste, stuffed fish maw with abalone and prawn paste, boiled 'geoduck' with jellyfish. The full Cantonese menu is dominated by seafood, such as steamed crab, stewed oysters with ginger and spring onion, and fried king prawn with chicken liver, but it also takes in other favourites, including Emperor's chicken, braised belly-pork with preserved vegetables and paper-wrapped chilli spare ribs. There are no desserts, just a refreshing orange. Twenty workaday wines plus saké are on offer, although Chinese tea is probably the preferred accompaniment. House French is £6.80.

CHEF: K. Kong PROPRIETORS: K. Kong, Y.W. Lo, M.T. Lee, K.C. Tang and C.Y. Chau OPEN: all week; noon to 1.45am CLOSED: 4 days Christmas MEALS: alc (main courses £5 to £10). Set L and D £8.60 to £18. Minimum £7 after 5pm SERVICE: net prices CARDS: Access, Amex, Diners, Visa DETAILS: 115 seats. Private parties: 50 main room, 50 private room. Vegetarian meals. Children welcome. Smart dress preferred. Wheelchair access (1 step). Music. Air-conditioned

## Mitsukoshi ⁵✳

map 14

Dorland House,
14–20 Regent Street, SW1Y 4PH
071-930 0317

COOKING 2*
COST £35–£150

This is a Japanese department store and the restaurant occupies the basement. The location determines its convenience for the many Japanese offices nearby, but the cooking merits attention too. The menus revolve round the set meals, the à la carte selection being short. Banquets, at a certain price, are popular and a speciality. The set meals, from special lunches to the sushi course, come well recommended. As the clarets on the wine list currently stand at a choice between Mouton Cadet, or châteaux Cantemerle, Latour, Haut-Brion, Mouton-Rothschild, Lafite or Margaux, it is likely that saké will be the preferred drink.

*See inside the front cover for an explanation of the symbols used at the tops of entries.*

CHEF: Mr Shimada  PROPRIETORS: Mitsukoshi (UK) Ltd  OPEN: Mon to Sat; 12 to 2, 6 to 10  MEALS: alc (courses £4.50 to £27). Set L and D £20 to £120. Cover £1.50  SERVICE: 15%, card slips closed  CARDS: Access, Amex, Diners, Visa  DETAILS: 100 seats. Private parties: 80 main room, 12 and 24 private rooms. Vegetarian meals with prior notice. No children under 2. No smoking in dining-room. Music. Air-conditioned. Fax: 071-839 1167

## Miyama
map 14

38 Clarges Street, W1Y 7PJ
071-499 2443

COOKING 3
COST £22–£61

The diminutive bar on Mayfair's Clarges Street gives way to a subtly arranged restaurant beyond. The staff, in full regalia, are charming and helpful, and language is no problem here. Although the principal menu lists all the variations on the standards that you would expect from a Japanese restaurant, the single sheet of paper with seasonal specialities is one to search for extra side dishes; an alternative sheet lists sashimi for the day. Here and in the City branch (17 Godliman Street, EC4, Tel: 071-489 1937), which is less attractive to the eye, the sushi and sashimi are excellent, and people speak well of the teppanyaki too. Stocks are stronger than those in many other Japanese restaurants. Crab meat and cucumber in rice vinegar proved this year to be less sparkling than hitherto, but a side dish of stuffed aubergine was sensational. House wine is £10.

CHEFS/PROPRIETORS: F. Miyama and T. Miura  OPEN: all week, exc L Sat and Sun; 12.30 to 2.30, 6.30 to 10.30  CLOSED: bank hols  MEALS: alc (main courses £7 to £15). Set L £11.50 to £18, Set D £30 to £36  SERVICE: 15%, card slips closed  CARDS: Access, Amex, Diners, Visa  DETAILS: 65 seats. Private parties: 30 main room, 6 and 12 private rooms. Vegetarian meals. Children's helpings. Smart dress preferred. Wheelchair access (1 step). Music. Air-conditioned. Fax: 071-493 1573

## Monkeys
map 13

1 Cale Street, Chelsea Green, SW3 3QT
071-352 4711

COOKING 3
COST £20–£56

This is one of the most pleasant of Chelsea's restaurants, an ornament to a quiet neighbourhood, which deals with the business of dining as if it were essential to a civilised life, yet not an end in itself. Surroundings are pine-panelled and restful, with pictures, plus monkeys. Prices may reflect the comfortable circumstances of the likely clientele, just as foie gras and caviare on the menu are the kitchen vernacular for residential Chelsea rather than the Mile End Road, but the cooking is no less toothsome for all that. Game is a particular strength, and the style here has not gone overboard for the Mediterranean. Rack of lamb with mint, breast of chicken braised with wild mushrooms, and calves' kidneys and grain mustard show the essential simplicity, informed by French bourgeois cooking. House wine from Bouchard Aîné is £11.

Healthy eating options *in the details at the end of an entry signifies that a restaurant marks on its menu, in words and/or using symbols, low-fat dishes or other healthy eating choices.*

CHEF: Tom Benham   PROPRIETORS: Tom and Brigitte Benham   OPEN: Mon to Fri; 12.30 to 2.30, 7.30 to 11   CLOSED: 25 Dec, 1 Jan, 2 weeks Easter, 3 weeks Aug   MEALS: alc (main courses £13.50 to £18). Set L £12.50 to £17.50, Set D £22.50 to £35. Minimum £17.50 D SERVICE: not inc   CARDS: Access, Visa   DETAILS: 45 seats. Private parties: 50 main room, 12 private room. Vegetarian meals with prior notice. Children's helpings. Smart dress preferred. Wheelchair access (3 steps). Music. Air-conditioned

## Mon Plaisir

map 15

21 Monmouth Street, WC2H 9DD
071-836 7243 and 240 3757

COOKING 1
COST £21–£45

One of the problems of running a French bistro in London these days is that the English do it with rather more style than the ex-patriots. Mon Plaisir, cramming a hundred souls into two floors (not forgetting the table in the corridor), succeeds in being popular, though there are signs that it does not quite succeed in its aims, run by French people or no. It is no-nonsense, relatively quick and convenient for lots of things, such as theatres, galleries and book stores. The cooking is from a menu of the basic elements of French restaurant culture, plus some daily extras. It suits some palates, while others find it boring (the vegetarian dishes), or not thought out enough (the scallops with saffron sauce being five shells on a plate with dollops of sauce and scallops). The place has a considerable trade in lunch-time and pre-theatre meals, which appear better value. The wine list is standard, and house wines are £8.50. The bill at the end of the meal will seem fair if what you need is feeding at the right place at the right time, but expensive if you hoped for a little bit more. Mon Petit Plaisir, a second branch designed for the denizens of Kensington (33 Holland Street, W8, Tel: 071-937 3224), manages to seat people despite cramped conditions and serve up moderate food for a slightly more than moderate bill. Formula French is not enough these days.

CHEF: Daniel Gobet   PROPRIETORS: Alain Lhermitte and J. Baker   OPEN: Mon to Sat, exc Sat L; 12 to 2.15, 6 to 11.15   MEALS: alc (main courses £7.50 to £15). Set L £13.95, Set pre-theatre D £13.95   SERVICE: 12.5%, card slips closed   CARDS: Access, Amex, Diners, Visa DETAILS: 100 seats. Private parties: 32 main room. Vegetarian meals. Children's helpings. Smart dress preferred. No pipes in dining-room. Wheelchair access (1 step). Music. Air-conditioned (partly). Fax: 071-739 0121

## Museum Street Café 🍴✳

map 13

47 Museum Street, WC1A 1LY
071-405 3211

COOKING 2*
COST £19–£30

'No credit cards'; 'Bring your own wine'; 'Last orders 9.15'; 'No smoking'. Thus run the headings to the menu, which sounds a mite forbidding and is certainly single-minded. This tiny café is hard by the British Museum. At the back of a small room is a pastry oven behind a counter and a chargrill and small kitchen beyond. The two chefs are there all the time and employ no other cooks. Bread is baked every day – it forms the emotional base of the whole operation – and much of the menu divides between baking and grilling. A short choice suffices at each meal: both lunch and dinner are at a fixed price. Food, Mark Nathan proudly says, 'tastes as it is described', as, for instance, in a 'chickpea and rosemary soup with red pepper purée and basil oil'. People like the sense that food has been carefully bought, and the conviction that it is freshly cooked. The style can be austere: sauces may be relishes (pesto with chicken, for example), or they may be light accompaniments, as in a balsamic vinegar and shallot dressing with grilled salmon. There is no wish to mask; the Californian lesson has been absorbed. Salads are properly thought out, as in one with goats' cheese with olives and cherry tomatoes, and in a frisée and corn salad with walnuts; they frequently accompany main dishes, particularly at lunch. Many are the mentions of the chocolate tart, or of a dark and rich chocolate cake, but fruit tarts and ice-creams such as gingerbread with cranberry sauce get honours too. Many people remark that this is as close to home cooking as they find in the West End.

CHEFS: Gail Koerber and Mark Nathan   PROPRIETOR: Mark Nathan   OPEN: Mon to Fri; 12.30 to 2.15, 7.15 to 9.15   CLOSED: 1 week Feb, 1 week Easter, 2 weeks Aug, 1 week Christmas   MEALS: Set L £11 (2 courses) to £14, Set D £19.50. Minimum £11. Unlicensed, but bring your own: no corkage   SERVICE: not inc   DETAILS: 24 seats. Private parties: 24 main room. Vegetarian meals. Children welcome. No smoking in dining-room. Wheelchair access (2 steps). No music

## Neal Street Restaurant

map 15

26 Neal Street, WC2H 9PS
071-836 8368

COOKING 2
COST £39–£68

'We agreed that the whole experience was more pleasurable than the sum of its parts,' wrote one who found this restaurant a wonderful place in which to pass a mealtime: comfortable, really good modern art, lots of people to observe – all in all, an event. Yet the prices will deter most and the standard of cooking is sometimes variable. Take a single meal: it started with really good focaccia, took in a plate of wild mushrooms (fresh morels) that had some excitement but did not always come up trumps to the degree the price would seem to demand, then went on to nettle gnocchi with morel sauce. This consisted of indeterminate 'green corks' bobbing in a sauce that owed more to tomatoes than morels. Venison with fungi sauce and mostardadi frutti was all that the Neal Street Restaurant should stand for: it was classic Italian, with beefy flavours and interesting counterpoint. On the other hand, fresh eel, Roman style, left the diner at odds with a lot of skin and bone and a vague lemony, oily, garlic sauce. Vegetables include roasted peppers in their skins (an interesting labour-saving variation); tart of the day may be indeterminate and should be resisted in favour of a rip-roaring panna cotta. Coffee is grand. Antonio Carluccio's food shop next door is as smart and exciting as the restaurant ought to be. The wine list has some good Italians at centre-stage with class acts such as Antinori, Jermann, Mastroberardino and Lungarotti. The house wines are also excellent, as they should be at £12.50.

CHEF: Santiago Gonzales   PROPRIETOR: Antonio Carluccio   OPEN: Mon to Sat; 12.30 to 2.30, 7.30 to 11   MEALS: alc (main courses £12 to £18)   SERVICE: 15%, card slips closed CARDS: Access, Amex, Diners, Visa   DETAILS: 65 seats. Private parties: 12 main room, 24 private room. Vegetarian meals. Children welcome. Smart dress preferred. Wheelchair access (1 step). Air-conditioned. Fax: 071-497 1361

## Neshiko

map 11

265 Upper Street, N1 2UQ
071-359 9977

COOKING 2
COST £21–£70

Japanese music plays in this tasteful, uncluttered dining-room, and the kitchen seems to be making a real effort to produce genuine, well-prepared food. The menu is laid out in true Japanese fashion, with sections devoted to zensai (appetisers), steamed dishes, sunomono (vinegared dishes), grills and so on. Dashimaki is a a rectangular slice of layered omelette with a strong dip, kamo bainiku is pinkish grilled duck on a piquant, chutney-like plum sauce, strongly flavoured teriyaki chicken is served with the Japanese equivalent of 'French fries'. Presentation and artistry are of a high order: vegetable tempura is ingeniously decorated with uncooked noodles and pieces of batter arranged to look like a spray of flowers, while the selection of 'very cool' fresh fruits at the end of the meal is pure visual drama. Set dinners centred around sushi, sashimi and sankaiyaki are worth exploring. Service is accommodating and helpful. Drink green tea, plum wine or saké. House wine is £8.95.

CHEF: Shinji Akamatsu   PROPRIETOR: Margaret Carragher   OPEN: Mon to Sat, exc Sat L; 12 to 2.30, 6 to 11   CLOSED: Christmas, 1 Jan, bank hols   MEALS: alc (main courses £6 to £23). Set L £12 to £40, Set D £15 to £40   SERVICE: 10%   CARDS: Access, Amex, Diners, Visa   DETAILS: 55 seats. Private parties: 30 main room. Vegetarian meals. Children's helpings on request. Music. Air-conditioned

## New Loon Fung  £

**NEW ENTRY**   map 15

42–44 Gerrard Street, W1V 7LP
071-437 3540 and 6232

COOKING 1
COST £16–£42

Situated next door to the prestigious Loon Fung Supermarket, this has been a restaurant of shifting fortunes over the years. The place consists of two large rooms done out in shades of pink, with proper china tableware and considerate staff. The menu is massive, running to almost 300 dishes: sections are devoted to Peking and Szechuan dishes, but the kitchen's roots are in the classic Cantonese tradition. Seafood is a major suit, backed up by ever-improving dim-sum (served from 11.30am to 5pm) and a prodigious assortment of casseroles, hotpots, roast meats and one-plate rice and noodle dishes. Ingredients are good, although seasoned reporters have felt that flavours lack a certain pungency and the presence of Chinese mushrooms *complete with stalks* in a pot of braised eel with belly pork was reckoned to be 'unforgivable'. But there is much to praise: fresh-tasting steamed scallops, sesame prawn toasts, chunky fried aubergine with garlic and chilli, stuffed bean curd with prawn paste and 'superb' Japanese squid with asparagus (minus tips) have all been mentioned. Special functions and banquets are a feature. The wine list offers fair value but few precise details. House wine is £7.

CHEFS: Mr Man and Mr Suen   PROPRIETORS: Loon Fung (UK) Ltd   OPEN: all week; 11.30am to 11.30pm (12 Sat)   CLOSED: 2 to 3 days Christmas   MEALS: alc (main courses £5 to £13). Set L and D £9 (2 courses) to £24   SERVICE: not inc   CARDS: Access, Amex, Diners, Visa   DETAILS: 400 seats. Private parties: 250 main room, 30 private room. Vegetarian meals. Children's helpings. Smart dress preferred. Music. Air-conditioned. Fax: 071-437 3540

## New World £

map 15

1 Gerrard Place, W1V 7LL
071-434 2508

COOKING 1
COST £13–£35

Go at lunch-time. This massive brightly coloured arena still delivers some of the most intriguing dim-sum in the capital and fills to the brim with an eager crowd wanting to experiment with the vast range of morsels on offer. A hierarchy is at work here: long-serving trolley girls trundle round and round ('How many miles do they trudge in a day?' muses a regular), above them are young waiters in red waistcoats and at the top the managers in sharp dark suits and tunics. Among favourite items mentioned this year have been flavoursome cold roast duck, steamed beef dumplings with ginger, stuffed green peppers and 'first-rate' steamed prawn and bamboo dumplings 'bursting with flavour'. Monster helpings of noodle soups are assembled as you watch and it is worth trying the curious delights of congee – authentic rice 'porridge' mixed up with all manner of titbits. The full evening menu tends to disappoint and dinners receive few endorsements. Tea arrives automatically; house wine is £6.05.

CHEFS: Lap Diep and Wai Lam Wong   PROPRIETORS: New World Restaurant Ltd   OPEN: all week; 11am to 11.30pm   CLOSED: 25 and 26 Dec   MEALS: alc (main courses £3 to £9.50). Set L and D £6.60 (2 courses) to £10.50   SERVICE: not inc   CARDS: Access, Amex, Diners, Visa   DETAILS: 600 seats. Private parties: 250 main room, 250 private room. Vegetarian meals. Children welcome. Smart dress preferred. Wheelchair access (lift; also WC). Music. Air-conditioned. Fax: 071-287 3994

## Nico Central

map 14

35 Great Portland Street, W1N 5DD
071-436 8846

COOKING 3
COST £28–£57

This was, as history has told often enough, once the premises of Chez Nico, home of Nico Ladenis, a much-moved chef. He now lives in Park Lane in even grander surroundings, but this place once bid fair for all the laurels of the trade, and now the skeleton of a super-expensive restaurant, overlaid with plainer chairs, more demotic ornament and closer-packed tables, survives as do 'the best loos in London' (talk to the chefs en route). The pitch of the place answers that of Simply Nico in Victoria (see entry, London): none-too-elaborate French cooking, unplagued by 'modern' flavours, on a large and reasonably stable menu at fair prices (for the West End). The cost cannot, however, allow it much comparison to a brasserie. It has its supporters for the cheerful and intelligent reception and for food that often contains lots of flavour even if there have been more notes of unevenness than should be the case with so settled a repertoire. Other niggles revolve around prices for vegetables and the cost of desserts, which are good but simple. Recommendations have come for fish soup, cep risotto, mushroom tart with poached egg and hollandaise, confit of duck, guinea-fowl with beans, and chicken stuffed with mushrooms which 'tasted like a forest'. The place is lively for lunch, while at night it seems less well suited to a cosy neighbourhood night out. The wine list is short, charitable in range – even if the prices are as high as those of the rest of London – and with some good punchy things like Les Collines de Laure from Jean Luc Colombo. House wines are served by the glass (£4).

CHEF: Andrew Jeffs  PROPRIETORS: Nico and Dinah-Jane Ladenis  OPEN: Mon to Sat, exc
Sat L; 12 to 2, 7 to 11  CLOSED: 10 days Christmas, 4 days Easter, bank hol L  MEALS: alc
(main courses £8 to £18)  SERVICE: net prices, card slips closed  CARDS: Access, Amex,
Diners, Visa  DETAILS: 65 seats. Private parties: 18 main room, 10 private room. Vegetarian
meals. No children under 5. Smart dress preferred. No pipes in dining-room. Wheelchair
access (1 step). No music. Air-conditioned. Fax: 071-355 4877

## Noughts 'n' Crosses

**NEW ENTRY**  map 10

77 The Grove, W5 5LL
081-840 7568

COOKING 2
COST £21-£32

This restaurant occupies a corner site on a road parallel to the Broadway. Like
Gaul, it divides into three: two front rooms and a conservatory at the back.
Beyond is a small town garden, 'not a tendril out of place, or a weed in sight'.
Trompe-l'oeil murals make the rooms seem bigger than they are, which thanks
to a certain 'blonde and bleached' decorative treatment are never
claustrophobic. Some have said that the staff are less cheerful than the
furniture, but it does not seem to impair the enjoyment of a largely local
clientele. There is something of a country feel to the cooking here, which may
mean a muddled or uncertain touch in some of the sauces, but which draws
much from different cultures in dishes such as rolled beef fillet with sun-dried
tomatoes and bacon, topped with walnut paste and served with a red wine
sauce, or fillet of pork marinated in a Korean bulgogi sauce served with spiced
yellow beans, honey and ginger sauce. Bread, too, includes some interesting
variations: Parmesan rolls, herb rolls and sun-dried tomato loaves. More signs
of multi-culturalism and creativity come from a meal that included prawn and
bamboo-shoot rolls with a mango, tomato and cucumber salad dressed with
lime; spinach roulade filled with smoked mackerel, grilled monkfish and
aubergine with a lemon-flavoured soured cream sauce; and pigeon with black
pudding and morel mushrooms. Vegetables are elaborate and may misfire.
Everyone seems to enjoy the puddings, swirling decorations and all, whether
the chocolate and chestnut terrine or tiramisù. The good suburban restaurant is
an endangered species and this is one to value. The wine list is short and about
adequate. House wines are from £8.70.

CHEF: Anthony Ma  PROPRIETORS: Jörgen Kunath and Anthony Ma  OPEN: Tue to Sat, D
only, and Sun L; 12 to 2, 7 to 10  CLOSED: 26 Dec to 4 Jan, Aug  MEALS: Set Sun L £10.70
(2 courses) to £14.80, Set D £18.90  SERVICE: not inc (10% for 7 or more)  CARDS: Access,
Amex, Visa  DETAILS: 55 seats. 4 tables outside. Private parties: 55 main room, 28 private
room. Vegetarian meals. Children's helpings Sun L. Smart dress preferred. No-smoking
area. Wheelchair access (1 step). Music

## Now & Zen

map 15

4A Upper St Martin's Lane, WC2H 9EA
071-497 0376

COOKING 1
COST £21-£50

When this stylish Covent Garden-meets-Chinatown jewel in the Zen crown
opened, people flocked to see the décor: the three eating levels linked by open-
plan atrium with fountain, glass and mirrors. But the spectacular design has
not worn as well as it might, perhaps because of the Muzak, perhaps because

the customers do not have the moneyed glitz that would show it off to best advantage. People are attracted by the set-price deal, which gives a pan-Asian (courtesy of the Zen Group) slant to Chinese cooking. However, if the Thai kitchen produces at a slower rate than the Cantonese kitchen, the meal may get muddled. Recommendations come for the dim-sum, with a range that is more catholic than many and not just deep-fried or dumpling items. House wine is £12.

CHEF: Michael Leung   PROPRIETORS: Blaidwood Co Ltd   OPEN: all week; 12.30 to 3, 6.30 to 11   CLOSED: 25 Dec   MEALS: alc (main courses £4.50 to £11). Set L £10.50 (2 courses), Set D £16.80   SERVICE: 12.5%   CARDS: Access, Amex, Diners, Visa   DETAILS: 140 seats. Private parties: 40 main room, 40 private room. Vegetarian meals. Children welcome. Smart dress preferred. Music. Air-conditioned. Fax: 071-437 0641

## Odette's ▮

map 11

130 Regent's Park Road, NW1 8XL                                        COOKING 3
071-586 5486 and 8766                                              COST £19–£46

Summertime in Regent's Park Road can excite even the placid London soul to rhapsody. Plant a few trees and get rid of the cars and you could be anywhere south of the Channel. There is an urban village atmosphere to the smattering of neighbourhood shops – specialist stores sell you anything from old burgundy to cooked meats, antique corkscrews or a handknitted woolly – a good bookshop and restaurants of several hues. Odette's, which is at the Primrose Hill Road end, slots into this scene as the place to eat outdoors, with further choice indoors of a cellar wine bar, a garden room for wet days, and a closely mirrored restaurant in the front. The pattern set by Paul Holmes last year has continued: his modern cooking style, just here and there frenzied, usually demonstrates proper thought for techniques which often successfully coax upstanding flavours from good materials and recipes. A plate of virtual sashimi of brill with coriander and dill and its partner, some smoked scallops with spinach and asparagus, show the kitchen's enjoyment of fish cookery, just as some more scallops, this time with plump capers, olives and ribbon pasta, give an idea of the robustness often met here. Technique and intelligence come through in a shimmering terrine of oysters and scallops wrapped in Parma ham. The angles to modern cooking are evident in a dish of calf's liver with turnip mash, sage and polenta; there is also a willingness to invest in the best, as evinced by leg of Pyrenean lamb with a south-western French garlic potato pie. Desserts are mentioned in dispatches as often as anything else: pear and cranberry tart with cinnamon ice-cream, espresso chocolate tart, and blue plum tart with rhubarb compote – this pâtissier likes pastry, and bakes good bread. Prices have been contained this year, yet service and setting remain the same. The wine bar has its supporters, as it deserves. The wine list is a model of clarity. Bibendum's offerings are well to the fore, which ensures a certain up-to-dateness as well as very few slouches among the choices. Plenty can be had by the glass and the half-bottles have been smartened up. House wines start at £10.25 for Vieille Ferme. CELLARMAN'S CHOICE: Chile, Santa Rita, Sauvignon Blanc 1992, £10.15; St Aubin, premier cru 1989, Prudhon, £19.95.

CHEF: Paul Holmes   PROPRIETOR: Simone Green   OPEN: all week, exc Sat L and Sun D (wine bar Sat L); 12.30 to 2.30, 7 to 11   MEALS: alc (main courses £7 to £12.50). Set L £10   SERVICE: not inc, card slips closed   CARDS: Access, Amex, Diners, Visa   DETAILS: 55 seats. 4 tables outside. Private parties: 30 main room, 8 and 30 private rooms. Vegetarian meals. Children's helpings. No music. Air-conditioned

## O'Keefe's £

**NEW ENTRY**    map 14

19 Dering Street, W1R 9AA           COOKING 1
071-495 0878                   COST £17–£29

'You can book – and those who did got tables round the edge rather than in the crowded middle,' observes a reporter about this up-to-the-minute, all-day café/deli. The shop sells specialities, from organic smoked bacon and salad leaves to tantalising regional cheeses, and the philosophy spills over into the kitchen. What is not shrewdly sourced is made on the premises. The cool, fresh interior might put you in mind of New York, but the cooking has its heart in Italy (although England is not forgotten). Lunch is a simple affair, comprising soups, salads, three main courses, sweets and cheese; dinner (on Thursdays only) is a fixed-price menu. Reports suggest that the kitchen blows hot and cold: spot-on red pepper and tomato soup, beautifully done girolle and porcini risotto, 'boozy' almond and cognac tart, but 'thin' green garlic soup, 'disastrous' focaccia and white peach sorbet that did not really work. Otherwise you might find a cheese and onion tart with chilli jelly, and grilled tuna with tomato, coriander and green olive salsa. Service is sharp and civilised. Breakfasts are available from 8am and food is served throughout the day from Monday to Saturday. A couple of posh beers and freshly squeezed orange juice are alternatives to the short, interesting wine list. House wine is £7.50.

CHEF: Caroline Brett   PROPRIETORS: Romano Crolla and Thomas Dane   OPEN: Mon to Sat L, and Thur D; 12 to 3, 7.30 to 10   CLOSED: 25 and 26 Dec, 1 Jan, Easter Mon, Good Fri, last 3 weeks Aug, bank hols   MEALS: alc (main courses £5 to £8). Set D £13.50. Minimum £6 Mon to Fri L   SERVICE: not inc   DETAILS: 38 seats. 4 tables outside. Vegetarian meals. Children welcome. No cigars/pipes in dining-room. Wheelchair access. No music. Fax: 071-629 7082

## Olivo

**NEW ENTRY**    map 11

21 Eccleston Street, SW1W 9LX          COOKING 1
071-730 2505                   COST £24–£40

This restaurant was once the Ciboure: as fashion-consciously French as this is Italian, and still under the same ownership. The dark blue and ochre colour scheme is certainly striking enough to need no additions of ornament or fussy interference, apart from the almost nautical, almost primitive stencilling at dado height. Customers are happy enough with the speed of service, cheerful food and apparent economy to be content with simple comforts. 'At last, a non-anglicised Italian restaurant where the food is clean-tasting, fresh and not cheese-clogged, soggy or greasy. It is Italian food like you get in Italy,' said one reporter, who may have not been eating at too many of the new-wave Italians of the last year or two. However, the message holds good that the food is straightforward and simple: decent pasta with some variations – lasagne with artichokes, for example; unpretentious but accurate meat cookery – try the kidneys with white wine sauce; good incidentals – the polenta mash was light and well seasoned; but unimpressive pastry – stick to simple desserts. Service is cheerful, so are the customers. The wine list stays Italian and does not often stray over £16. House wines are £8.50.

CHEF: Giorgio Locatelli   PROPRIETORS: J.L. Journade and Mauro Sanna   OPEN: Mon to Sat, exc Sat L; 12 to 2.30, 7 to 11   CLOSED: bank hols, 3 weeks Aug   MEALS: alc (main courses £7.50 to £11). Set L £13 (2 courses) to £15. Cover £1.30   SERVICE: not inc CARDS: Access, Amex, Visa   DETAILS: 45 seats. Private parties: 6 main room. Vegetarian meals with prior notice. Children welcome. No cigars/pipes in dining-room. Wheelchair access. Music. Air-conditioned

## 192 ▮

map 12

192 Kensington Park Road, W11 2ES
071-229 0482

COOKING 2*
COST £19–£43

At the north end of leafy Kensington Park Road is 192, which has taken over the next-door property to grow a little (but '192–194' would not be so snappy a name). It has celebrated 10 years of being hip with a face-lift, and still packs in a 'cosmopolitan, loud, modish clientele'. The downstairs restaurant remains, but the ground-floor wine bar has grown beyond its corridor-like beginnings. Large doses of colour – 'it's like being in the '70s again' – within a strongly architectural frame give life to the far corners of the room. Josh Hampton, an Australian who made a rapid mark at the Canal Brasserie, has taken over the kitchen stoves as the remodelling settles down. The menu is very much in the tradition set by 192's very first cooks, from Alastair Little onwards. It changes often (not quite as often as it did) and pursues inspirational eclecticism. That is the only way to describe items such as fresh herb and Parmesan tabbouleh, Vietnamese squid cakes and sweet chilli dressing, and pork with pear and chilli relish. There is also a classic line that runs through fish and chips (good) to celeriac rémoulade (quite good, but it needed more body from the mayonnaise) and to fillet of beef with red wine sauce (very good indeed). Touches like a purée of spinach and cumin with salmon, or a grand sweet-and-sour sauce with Thai fish-cakes, often enhance a dish. Puddings have not always been a success: 'Chocolate Orgy in fact practised safe sex.' The service is as streetwise as are the customers, but when there are too many of the latter, the former can lose its cool. But hang loose, because the food is worth it. So is the wine. The stock, presented as one of those snappy, no-messing urban lists, has more content than style. It includes Leflaive burgundies, decent simple clarets and top antipodeans. The star turn is the number of offerings by the glass, both standard and large. The quality, value and range of this list are nicely balanced. House wines are from £8.25.

CHEF: Josh Hampton   PROPRIETORS: Anthony Mackintosh, John Armit and Tchaik Chassey   OPEN: all week; 12.30 to 3 (3.30 Sat), 6.30 to 11.30   CLOSED: Christmas, Aug bank hol   MEALS: alc (main courses £6.50 to £13). Set L £8.50 (2 courses)   SERVICE: not inc   CARDS: Access, Amex, Visa   DETAILS: 108 seats. Private parties: 12 main room, 26 private room. Vegetarian meals. Children welcome. No cigars in dining-room. Wheelchair access. Music

## Orso ♟ map 15

27 Wellington Street, WC2E 7DA COOKING 1
071-240 5269 COST £25–£46

This large basement convenient for the opera or theatres, does not change much, save its pretty polychrome china gets a little more chipped. It still attracts a crowd, often smart-set media types anxious for attractive Italian cooking high on flavour and low on fat and bulk that does not take an age to get to table and a place where they feel at home with their fellows and colleagues. The waiting staff can be pretty smart-set too; dismissive, others call them – it all depends if you feel you belong. The menu changes often enough to keep regulars amused, though many will return to a small pizza with anchovies and olives, grilled liver and sweet-and-sour onions, spinach or broccoli with lemon and olive oil (served warmish), and tiramisù, rather than try grilled scallops with roasted peppers, pork chops with mozzarella, sun-dried tomatoes, basil and pine-kernels, and then a slice of Pecorino with a pear. The wine list has a faultless set of Italian bottles, not impossibly priced, though not cheap either, from popular growers. House wines are £9 a litre.

CHEF: Martin Wilson PROPRIETORS: Orso Restaurants Ltd OPEN: all week; noon to 11.45 MEALS: alc (main courses £9.50 to £12.50) SERVICE: not inc DETAILS: 100 seats. Vegetarian meals. Children welcome. No-smoking area. No music. Air-conditioned. Fax: 071-497 2148

## Osteria Antica Bologna £ map 10

23 Northcote Road, SW11 1NG COOKING 1*
071-978 4771 COST £15–£33

'Rustic, crowded, uncomfortable, fun,' notes a reporter of this Clapham restaurant, all decked out in wood. He adds, 'There were lots of extremely pretty waitresses who were excellent with children.' Others have been less well treated, and the sometimes smoky atmosphere and hard seats have caused a little irritation. Aurelio Spagnuolo hails from Sicily and draws inspiration from north and south; his regional loyalties are there for all to see on the menu. The star attraction is the range of assaggi, little morsels that can be shared or turned into a light meal: balls of spicy Sicilian rice stuffed with mozzarella, pugliese potato, mushroom and Pecorino cheesecake, grilled radicchio with rosemary pesto and prosciutto, and garlicky fried spleen on focaccia bread, to name but a few. Added to this is a full repertoire of pasta, salads, polenta and substantial offerings such as kid cooked with almond and tomato sauce. Most items find favour, although one reporter was far from convinced by a dish of cuttlefish pasta. A pastry chef has recently been engaged to give the desserts a lift. The re-creation of local peasant specialities is matched by a commitment to regional Italian wines; the list is a cracker and – like the food – is exceedingly reasonable in price. House wine is £7; a jugful of Sicilian wine is £6.90. A second restaurant, Del Buongustaio, has opened in Putney Bridge Road (see London round-ups).

● *denotes an outstanding wine cellar;* ♟ *denotes a good wine list, worth travelling for.*

CHEFS: Aurelio Spagnuolo and Raffaele Petralia  PROPRIETORS: Rochelle Porteous and Aurelio Spagnuolo  OPEN: all week, exc Mon L; noon to 11, Mon 6 to 11, Sun 12.30 to 10.30  CLOSED: 2 weeks Christmas, bank hols, Easter  MEALS: alc (main courses £5.50 to £9.50). Set L £6.50 (2 courses)  SERVICE: not inc (10% for 5 or more)  CARDS: Access, Amex, Visa  DETAILS: 75 seats. 5 tables outside. Private parties: 25 main room. Vegetarian meals. Children's helpings. Wheelchair access. Music. Air-conditioned

## *Osteria Basilico* £ — **NEW ENTRY** — map 12

29 Kensington Park Road, W11 2EU                             COOKING 1
071-727 9957                                        COST £17–£27

Those who manage to secure a booking at this, Notting Hill's newest Italian, should expect to be part of the frenetic, fun atmosphere. As one diner happily put it, 'I knew one table, my friend knew another. We shouted across for a bit and no one seemed to mind.' Two small rooms, one up and one down, in suitable shades of terracotta and earth, are embellished with dried grass, heavy marble and clay pots, rickety wooden tables and chairs. It is all very Tuscan, very '90s and so packed-out you can hardly wave a napkin. The antipasto buffet looks pretty and is one way to start a meal. Otherwise the menu yields seafood, bruschetta and penne. Minestrone is delicate yet homely: a light stock chockful of root vegetables and summery légumes, not bludgeoned by tomato or pasta. Pan-fried sausage and spinach is well seasoned with nutmeg and some garlic. Mainstays are pizzas, and things that have undergone pan-frying and chargrilling. Rolled fillet of beef filled with Parmesan, ham and garlic came with a tomato sauce, meatballs and grilled polenta. Potato cake with spinach, tomatoes and asparagus was not as good. Arrive hungry for you will certainly not leave that way. Desserts have been disappointing and the tiramisù has been described as 'not the expected pick-me-up but a let-down-flat'. House wine is £6.50.

CHEFS: A. Palano and D. Campioto  PROPRIETORS: Ms T. Levantesi and D. Campioto  OPEN: all week; 12.30 to 3, 6.30 to 11.30 (10.30 Sun)  MEALS: alc (main courses £4.50 to £7.50)  SERVICE: 10%  DETAILS: 90 seats. Private parties: 60 main room. Vegetarian meals. Children's helpings. Music

## *Panda Si Chuen* £                       map 15

56 Old Compton Street, W1V 5PA                       COOKING 1
071-437 2069                                      COST £15–£39

'We are charmed from the moment of entry,' comment regular supporters of this 'immaculate' Soho establishment. The menu of around 100 dishes is a mixed bag: as one reporter noted, it has 'enough Szechuan for me, Cantonese for my wife and guests'. Some of the original Szechuan fire has been tempered, but there are still some authentic specialities to be had. Pelmeni with red chilli oil and garlic is 'a must'. Other recommended dishes have included 'fish-flavoured' shredded pork with aubergine, and anything with cashews and chilli is good. The menu also takes in spiced fish, herb-marinated beef, home-style double-cooked pork and tea-smoked duck as well as hot-and-sour soup, steamed sea bass and lemon chicken. Portions are generous and the value for

money is reckoned to be 'unbeatable'. Drink saké or tea. House French
wine is £7.

CHEF: B. Tsao   PROPRIETOR: K.C. Chew   OPEN: Mon to Sat; noon to 11.30   CLOSED: 25
and 26 Dec   MEALS: alc (main courses £4.50 to £7.50). Set L and D £9.50 to £16.50
SERVICE: not inc   CARDS: Access, Amex, Diners, Visa   DETAILS: 60 seats. 12 tables
outside. Private parties: 48 main room, 15 private room. Vegetarian meals. Children
welcome. Music. Air-conditioned

## Il Passetto  £                                                                 map 14

| 230 Shaftesbury Avenue, WC2H 8EG | COOKING 1 |
| 071-836 9391 | COST £16–£41 |

Tradition dies hard at restaurants like these, so expect a cover charge, and
expect a pepper-toting workforce. The menu remains steady too: a repertoire of
'Britalian' cooking. But the ritual aspects never offend, and the cooking is very
acceptable, either of the fresh pasta and plenty more on the printed *carte*, or of
daily specials – for instance, sea bream or skate – that give a bit of zip to
everyone's choice. It is also very conveniently placed for Theatreland. The wine
list stays with Italy: Lungarotti's Rubesco Torgiano, or a fistful of Barolos will
keep the cold out. House wines are £7.95.

CHEF: Jesus Sanchez   PROPRIETORS: Domenico Forcina and Jesus Sanchez   OPEN: Mon to
Sat, exc Sat L; 12 to 3, 6 to 11.30   CLOSED: bank hols, Christmas   MEALS: alc (main
courses £5.50 to £16). Cover £1   SERVICE: not inc   CARDS: Access, Amex, Diners, Visa
DETAILS: 40 seats. Private parties: 40 main room. Vegetarian meals. Children welcome.
Smart dress preferred. Wheelchair access. Music. Air-conditioned

## Pearl                                                                          map 13

| 22 Brompton Road, SW1X 7QN | COOKING 3 |
| 071-225 3888 | COST £16–£85 |

It must be the Knightsbridge location that gives rise to the Pearl's steep
evening cover charge of £2, which brings you some nibbles. The window
tables assure a view of shoppers' paradise; otherwise the room is simple black
and white modern understatement. Pearl has not completed its year without
blemish, but there is a school that maintains it is among the most consistent
classic Cantonese restaurants in this bracket. 'It compares favourably with
many I have been to in Hong Kong,' says one China hand. He went on to point
out that common-or-garden items like crab 'chips' or sesame prawn toasts have
the advantage of tasting of their original ingredient, soft-shell crabs are not
overladen with batter, and even seaweed is better than the norm. Pastry and
wun-tuns are tender and delicate. In true Cantonese style, fish can be the best
thing to have: 'The bass retained all its glorious flavour; the ginger and spring
onion sauce was subtle enough not to detract, yet enhanced.' Singapore
noodles had heat, yet were fresh-flavoured and perfectly textured. The menu
offers a good range, and the service is admirably pleasant. The wine list tends
to pricey uppercrust bottles, but there is something here for the world as well.
Tea, if taken, is changed regularly through the meal, not merely left to stew.
House wines are £11 or there is saké.

CHEF: Cheung Hong   PROPRIETORS: the Lam family   OPEN: all week; 12 to 3, 6 to 11.30
(11 Sun)   CLOSED: 25 and 26 Dec   MEALS: alc (main courses £5.50 to £13). Set L £12.50
(inc wine), Set D £25 (minimum 2) to £55 (minimum 4). Cover £2 after 6pm   SERVICE: not
inc   CARDS: Access, Amex, Diners, Visa   DETAILS: 90 seats. 18 tables outside. Private
parties: 90 main room, 18 private room. Vegetarian meals. Children's helpings on request.
Smart dress preferred. Music. Air-conditioned. Fax: 071-225 0252

## Le P'tit Normand                                                          map 10

185 Merton Road, Southfields, SW18 5EF                           COOKING 1
081-871 0233                                                     COST £16−£32

Philippe Herrard's comfortable bistro reminds visitors of the kind of café you
might find in Montmartre, and it serves up generous food to match. The kitchen
has its heart in Normandy, although the repertoire is fleshed out with ideas
from other parts of France. The short, printed menu is a classic run through fish
soup, black pudding with apples, duck breast Vallée d'Auge and veal
Normande. A blackboard offers extra specialities, including favourably
reported salad of chicken livers, mille-feuille of smoked salmon and veal
kidneys dijonnaise. Glazed apples on pastry 'beautifully cooked with cream' is
a fine sweet, and the splendid selection of Normandy cheeses is worth
exploring. French waitresses are charming and attentive. There are some
authentic and intriguing aperitifs and an equally impressive selection of
vintage calvados. The wine list is restricted to a handful of choices from
reputable French growing regions. House wine is £7.85.

CHEF/PROPRIETOR: Philippe Herrard   OPEN: all week, exc Sat L; 12 to 2, 7 to 10.30 (11 Fri
and Sat)   MEALS: alc (main courses £8.50 to £9.50). Set L £9.75, Set Sun L £11.95
SERVICE: not inc, card slips closed   CARDS: Access, Amex, Diners, Visa   DETAILS: 35 seats.
Private parties: 25 main room. Vegetarian meals with prior notice. Children's helpings.
Smart dress preferred. No pipes in dining-room. Wheelchair access. Music

## Phuket £                                          NEW ENTRY   map 10

246 Battersea Park Road, SW11 3BP                               COOKING 1*
071-223 5924                                                    COST £16−£34

This bravely named restaurant lies on the busy Battersea Park Road opposite
the Latchmere pub. Tall house plants and ceiling fans strike a tropical note;
mirrors succeed in expanding what is a narrow room; candles provide
illumination for an evening's tender gazing. Tom yung, the famous Thai hot-
and-sour soup, is a barometer dish: a goong version, served in a steamboat, was
'way above average, with small, tender prawns, baby button mushrooms, and
real lemon grass, and the chillies and lemon juice balanced very well'.
Generous starter portions of tord mun (fish-cakes) and goong hom par ('prawns
in the blanket', a kind of prawn/crab spring roll) both showed precision
spicing; a main course of gang gai (red chicken curry) was delicately cooked,
with coconut milk and red curry paste in easy harmony; som tam (papaya
salad) brought one of the prettiest-fleshed of all fruits into an exciting and
successful combination with green beans, carrots, peanuts and chilli.
Rambutan for dessert were 'the real McCoy', served in a dish of iced water;

bananas in coconut milk were soothing if squishy. Service is 'genuinely friendly'. House wine costs £6.50; there is also saké.

CHEF: Miss O. Mungnatee  PROPRIETOR: P. Vatanawan  OPEN: all week, D only; 6 to 11.30  MEALS: alc (main courses £4.50 to £6). Set D £12.50 to £15 (minimum 2)  SERVICE: 10%, card slips closed  CARDS: Access, Amex, Visa  DETAILS: 60 seats. Private parties: 45 main room, 14 private room. Vegetarian meals. Children welcome. Smart dress preferred. No-smoking area. Music. Air-conditioned

## Pied-à-Terre                                                              map 14

34 Charlotte Street, W1P 1HJ                                        COOKING 3*
071-636 1178                                                       COST £28–£56

Any suggestion of starkness here is perhaps dispelled by the playfulness of the modern art (thanks to Richard Hamilton) or the enjoyably decorated plates that give a bit of variety to the place-settings. Simplicity may also give a chance for the food to occupy centre-stage, though some wish the chairs were more yielding. The young proprietors have survived an opening year with great panache and there has been no deviation in style. Richard Neat intends cooking of complexity, costed accordingly, though lunch remains a satisfactory bargain. Many of the effects come from the combination of a single vegetable (roots are favoured) with meat or fish in bold contrast. Complexity or over-ornamentation is not the favoured route to creating an impact. A winter meal began with an appetiser of poached oyster with fennel sauce before the real action began with a 'tagliatelle' of asparagus in a foaming bouillon with some tender, plump langoustines. There was also a roast teal on a bed of turnips. Many have commented on this dish, though some find the bitterness of the turnips overwhelming. The aforementioned winter's day also saw swede croquettes served with pheasant, though venison fillet wrapped with Swiss chard leaves, on a bed of dauphinois potatoes, 'was the best dish, showing real class'. Other meals have taken in scallops on dauphinois potatoes, with girolle mushrooms, then a fillet of turbot on a purée of leek, with lots of deep-fried leek angel-hair and a globe artichoke with some oyster mushrooms and steamed leeks. This second dish was thought by one reporter to have been brilliant as far as the fish and the leeks went, but diluted by the addition of artichoke and mushroom. A case, perhaps, of the doctrine of simplicity being forgotten for once. Desserts often get less praise than the beginnings of the meal, perhaps because there is a little freebie high-class brûlée given out as a chef's gesture before the final course is embarked upon. The pineapple soufflé, served on a slice of the fruit with some sauce of the fruit, was thought to stress the pineapple's flavour without clever counterpoint, and someone made the same observation about putting together a chocolate mousse and a chocolate sorbet. But a mille-feuille of chocolate and another of caramelised banana have both been extolled to the heavens. Service is terribly proper, although it can also be slow. Occasionally it has caused grief. The wine waiter is tremendously knowledgeable and the list does not ignore people who want to drink inexpensively. The choice of growers and properties is sound and length adequate for a fledgling cellar. France hogs the limelight, though Cloudy Bay and a few classy New World wines get walk-on parts. House wines are from £12.

CHEF: Richard Neat   PROPRIETORS: David Moore and Richard Neat   OPEN: Mon to Sat, exc
Sat L; 12.15 to 2.15, 7.15 to 10   CLOSED: last week Dec, first week Jan, last 2 weeks Aug
MEALS: Set L £19.50 and £38, Set D £38   CARDS: Access, Amex, Diners, Visa   SERVICE: net
prices, card slips closed   DETAILS: 40 seats. Private parties: 42 main room, 12 private room.
Vegetarian meals with prior notice. No children under 7. Smart dress preferred. No cigars/
pipes in dining-room. Wheelchair access (3 steps). No music. Air-conditioned

## Pierre Victoire  £

**NEW ENTRY**   map 10

136 Upper Richmond Road, SW15 2SP
081-789 7043

COOKING 1
COST £9–£24

Having wooed the crowds in Scotland, Pierre Levicky has turned his attention
to franchised branches in London. This, the first, is just east of Putney High
Street crossroads. 'Well done!' exclaimed an inspector. 'This is just what
Putney needs.' Mirrors of different shapes dominate the high-ceilinged
ground-floor room, lending a bistro feel to the place – without the posters that
are standard issue in most similar spots. The floors are bare boards, the chairs
are black and candles appear in wine bottles on the tables. Levicky's
burgeoning chain of eating-houses is based on the simple principle that good
food does not need to be expensive. The set lunch at £4.90 is already legendary;
fish soup with Pernod at 90p sounds unbelievable, but there it is on the
straightforward one-page menu. Dishes vary from day to day and the style is a
mix of classic and modern French: steamed mussels with white wine, garlic
and herbs, roast guinea-fowl with raspberry vinegar and orange, and ribeye
steak with shallots and red wine. Reporters have particularly liked melon with
crabmeat and orange and mint dressing, and a dish of monkfish roasted on the
bone with red peppercorns, clams in their shells and an interesting basil and
saffron sauce. The short wine list is cheap and cheerful. House wine is £5.90.
Another branch has opened at 6 Panton Street, SW1, Tel: 071-930 6463 –
reports, please.

CHEF: Nicolas Fontrier   PROPRIETOR: Nick Cowdery   OPEN: all week, exc Sun D; 12 to 3
(4 Sun), 6 to 11   CLOSED: 25 Dec   MEALS: alc (main courses £6 to £9). Set L £4.90, Set Sun
L £5.90   SERVICE: not inc   CARDS: Access, Visa   DETAILS: 120 seats. Private parties: 20
main room, 30 private room. Vegetarian meals. Children's helpings. Wheelchair access (2
steps). Music. Air-conditioned. Fax: 081-785 7902

## Pizzeria Castello  £

map 11

20 Walworth Road, SE1 6SP
071-703 2556

COOKING 1
COST £11–£20

'I have found the Castello to be an old friend, worthy of the trip to SE1,' notes a
woman from SE22. Others sum up this lively pizzeria opposite the shopping
centre as a 'no-nonsense place'. Décor is rough and ready, service is agreeable –
even if the waiters speak little English – and the atmosphere hums. A regular
advises that is worth booking to be sure of getting in: although the place is
open right through the day, evening revolves around two sittings at 7pm and
9pm. At other times you may have to wait 'or get pushed downstairs'. Freshly
baked pizzas from the ovens near the door are the reason for visiting, but pasta

is made on the premises, and the garlic bread is very garlicky (hot and soggy, or crisp, depending on what you like). Accept the 'inevitable', but better-than-average, cappuccino and espresso, drink Peroni beer or quaff the house wine at £5.80 a bottle.

CHEF: E. Adrasti   PROPRIETORS: Renzo Meda and Antonio Proietti   OPEN: Mon to Sat, exc Sat L; noon to 11pm   MEALS: alc (main courses £3 to £5)   SERVICE: not inc (10% for 7 or more)   CARDS: Access, Amex, Visa   DETAILS: 150 seats. Private parties: 30 main room. Vegetarian meals. Children's helpings. Wheelchair access (also WC). Music. Air-conditioned

## Pizzeria Condotti £ map 14

| 4 Mill Street, W1R 9TE | COOKING 1 |
|---|---|
| 071-499 1308 | COST £15–£34 |

'What a good choice for a tête-à-tête,' remarked a couple who visited this place near New Bond Street at lunch-time. They liked the art gallery of prints and paintings on the walls, marvelled at the cleanliness of the place and raved about the pizzas, which are to the Pizza Express specification, of which chain this place is a first cousin. Garlic bread, decent salads (including tuna with beans), cassata and cheesecake are good reinforcements. Service is 'a delight'. Peroni beer and freshly squeezed orange juice are alternatives to the handful of Italian wines. House wines are £7.75.

CHEFS: Mahmoud Eskendry and Nacevr Hammami   PROPRIETORS: Enzo Apicella and Peter Boizot   OPEN: Mon to Sat; 11.30am to midnight   CLOSED: bank hols   MEALS: alc (main courses £5 to £6.50)   SERVICE: not inc (12.5% for 6 or more)   CARDS: Access, Amex, Diners, Visa   DETAILS: 100 seats. Private parties: 50 main room, 50 private room. Vegetarian meals. Children welcome. Wheelchair access (2 steps). No music. Air-conditioned

## Le Pont de la Tour ▮ map 11

| 36D Shad Thames, Butlers Wharf, SE1 2YE | COOKING 3 |
|---|---|
| 071-403 8403 | COST £24–£68 |

A summer meal looking at the river traffic, watching the action on Tower Bridge, and seeing the lights come on as darkness falls is a magical experience. Sir Terence Conran has most things right at this restaurant by the Thames, part of his gastrodome complex, embracing most classes of people and a great range of incomes. Customers at Le Pont de la Tour have to be rich or comfortable, the impecunious can try one of the other locations. They may also have to be quick eaters, as there is great pressure on the tables: 'I was telephoned three times to make sure I was intending to take up my reservation,' remarked one person who was then well pleased by the food and enchanted by the view, although his party was cramped by a table only big enough for one. If bad weather means no outside tables, the restaurant itself, reminiscent of a passenger liner, gives ample cover to try things like a range of fruits de mer, polenta with tomato and basil, wild mushrooms on toast, squid ink risotto with scallops and gremolata, plain Dover sole, rabbit with prunes and pancetta, or venison with green peppercorns, shallots and parsley. This nearly plain cooking frequently nods to inspiration from Bibendum (see entry, London), though the style may have less brio. A tomato and mozzarella salad, followed by corn-fed chicken pan-fried with wild mushrooms and a veal stock and wine sauce, before a simple apricot tart, proved irresistible, a fine example of less equalling more. Service generally gets good notice as does the wine list, which has lots for the serious spender-cum-drinker, but seems to pay attention to the value-for-money lobby as well. The choices are catholic and have some bearing on retail value. Most people have also benefited from the sommelier's advice. The crustacea bar and grill is a lively annexe to the restaurant – music and no bookings, as well as Saturday brunch. House wine is £9.50. CELLARMAN'S CHOICE: Petit Chablis 1991, Gallois, £15.75; Côtes du Rhône Valreas 1990, Sinard £16.50.

CHEF: David Burke   PROPRIETORS: Sir Terence Conran, Joel Kissin and David Burke
OPEN: all week, exc Sat L (Grill open); 12 to 3, 6 to 12 (11 Sun)   CLOSED: 4 days
Christmas   MEALS: alc (main courses £12.50 to £18.50). Set L £25, Set pre- and post-
theatre D £19.50. Sat brunch £14.50 (2 courses) to £17.50. Grill menu (main courses £7.50
to £13.50)   SERVICE: 15%, card slips closed   CARDS: Access, Amex, Diners, Visa
DETAILS: 105 seats. 22 tables outside. Private parties: 9 main room, 22 private room.
Vegetarian meals. Children welcome. Wheelchair access. No music. Fax: 071-403 0267

## Poons £

map 15

4 Leicester Street, WC2H 7BL
071-437 1528

COOKING 1
COST £9–£30

Poons is at the side of the Swiss Centre and looks somewhat like a café, with its pale green walls, rows of Formica-topped tables and bare tiled floor. However, the owners say that major renovation is under way and parts of the restaurant may be closed from time to time. Recent reports have been mixed, but the consensus is still firmly in favour of the cooking. At its best the kitchen delivers authentic Cantonese food based on fresh ingredients and it is 'exceedingly good value'. Stuffed braised bean curd in gravy has been 'bursting with taste and flavour', and spiced stewed brisket with fried noodles is 'no-nonsense café stuff'. Poons is renowned for its wind-dried foods, although not all reporters have been impressed by these. Beyond the hotpots, rice and noodle dishes there are interesting specialities such as chicken casserole with dried fungus and tiger lilies, or 'particularly marvellous' bean curd and aubergine with minced prawn in black-bean sauce. Service can be 'glum'. Drink jasmine tea or a bottle of Tsingtao beer. House wine is £6.50.

CHEF: K.W. Lam   PROPRIETOR: W.N. Poon   OPEN: all week; noon to 11.30   CLOSED:
Christmas   MEALS: alc. Set L and D £6.50 (minimum 2) to £16   SERVICE: not inc
DETAILS: 100 seats. Private parties: 50 main room, 35 private room. Vegetarian meals.
Children welcome. Smart dress preferred. Wheelchair access (also women's WC). Music.
Air-conditioned

'We once arrived to find an establishment apologetically understaffed because a new waitress had knocked herself unconscious opening a bottle of champagne.'
On eating in Gloucestershire

## Quaglino's

NEW ENTRY map 14

16 Bury Street, SW1Y 6AL
071-930 6767

COOKING 3
COST £22–£60

A legend in its own lifetime, forged by intense PR activity as it opened, this restaurant seems set for a fair future. Sir Terence Conran has effected a remarkable transformation of the site, which was once the ballroom of the old '30s Quaglino's. The place seems more an art gallery than a restaurant, with fixtures and fittings by named artists and craftsmen, each giant column a signed work, the uniforms *haute couture*, and an exhibition in the private room. Even the chairs, moulded it is said on the contours of Betty Grable's bottom, get a dressing of a mullet-coloured tassle – all dressed up and looking for a butt. Arching over the lot is the kaleidoscope of a ceiling replicating with colour and light the moods of the weather and natural heavens. The giant room, overlooked by a mezzanine bar and dance-floor, is given structure by a central spine of banquettes and tables (plus altar of crustacea), texture from all the art, metalwork and the varying of table finish (twos are unclothed red tops), and movement by the grand staircase approach for exhibitionists and onlookers alike. The stories about the service and the difficulties of getting a table are largely products of the early months. Though the unfamiliar may find the progress through various stages before the greeter is reached exhausting – and anyone who has been subjected to 'phone call after 'phone call for confirmation of a reservation will be tired of the process – the staff are getting better and less astonishingly arrogant than they at first appeared. The food, and the whole business, are part of that international love-affair with the Paris brasserie. Animated atmosphere, simple food of consistent quality, good value and great surroundings are qualities everyone has tried to repeat. The menu, which is largely made up of good ingredients simply treated, is a paradigm of this type. Oysters, caviare, grilled chicken or steak, shellfish platter, crème brûlée, lemon tart: the list is predictable. Weaving between these items is a vein of New World invention that produces such things as spiced lamb with roast onions, rabbit with prosciutto and herbs, or a layered terrine of chicken, foie gras and leek with a little puddle of lentils and some salad. Most recent reports have applauded both strands for taste, condition and quantity. To produce this level of food for such numbers is achievement indeed. The wine list is fairly priced and runs around the world picking fashionable names, without sacrificing quality. If you insist on spending thousands, there is a longer fine wine list, but who would protest at Bonny Doon Big House Red, Cauhape Jurançon Sec or Olivier Merlin's Mâcon 'La Roche Vineuse'? House wines are £9.50. There is the usual Conran 15 per cent service charge, which never endears a customer to his waiter, especially if there is any dereliction. Some have also questioned the frequent practice of only allowing one-and-three-quarter hours' occupation of any table on busy nights.

---

*The text of entries is based on unsolicited reports sent in by readers, backed up by inspections conducted anonymously. The factual details under the text are from questionnaires the* Guide *sends to all restaurants that feature in the book.*

---

CHEF: Martin Webb  PROPRIETORS: Sir Terence Conran, Joel Kissin, Tom Conran and Keith Hobbs  OPEN: all week; 12 to 3, 5.30 to 12 (2am Fri and Sat, 11 Sun). Antipasti Bar all week; 11.30am to midnight (11 Sun)  CLOSED: 2 days Christmas  MEALS: alc (main courses £8.50 to £17.50). Antipasti Bar (£3.50 to £7)  SERVICE: 15%, card slips closed  CARDS: Access, Amex, Diners, Visa  DETAILS: restaurant 300 seats, bar 100 seats. Private parties: 12 main room, 40 private room. Vegetarian meals. Children welcome. Wheelchair access (also WC). Music. Air-conditioned. Fax: 071-839 2866

## Quality Chop House £ map 11

94 Farringdon Road, EC1R 3EA  
071-837 5093

COOKING 2*  
COST £18–£40

The setting has not changed since Charles Fontaine brought good cooking to the Farringdon Road in 1990. Outside, the look is of a hang-dog café; inside is a re-creation of how it might have been 50 years ago, down to the original Anaglypta and bottles of HP sauce. 'The pews which break the room into compartments were designed by Torquemada, with a ridge at the back that gets the base of the spine, and a seat too narrow for comfort. No one is liable to fall asleep over their meal here.' The reporter who thought this also thought the discomfort worth enduring for the fish soup, the salmon fish-cake on a bed of spinach, and the treacle pudding with custard. The fish-cakes are 'the star of the show' in the view of another, who feels that some things, the confit of duck, for instance, are better than others (he named the game pie). Not every meal gets unqualified approval, but such things as a roast lamb, rocket, Parmesan and goats' cheese salad, toulouse sausage and mash with onion gravy, corn beef hash, and grilled swordfish with a lime hollandaise are praised for their generosity, accuracy of cooking and simplicity. Sunday brunch is a feature. The wine list is short, but the staff, who are very tolerant, know what's what, and the choices are sound. Prices start at £8.

CHEF/PROPRIETOR: Charles Fontaine  OPEN: all week, exc Sat L; 12 to 3 (4 Sun), 6.30 to 12 (7 to 11.30 Sun)  CLOSED: Christmas, L bank hols  MEALS: alc (main courses £5.50 to £10)  SERVICE: not inc  DETAILS: 40 seats. Vegetarian meals. Children's helpings. Smart dress preferred. No cigars/pipes in dining-room. Wheelchair access (1 step). No music. Air-conditioned

## Ragam £ map 14

57 Cleveland Street, W1P 5PQ  
071-636 9098

COOKING 1*  
COST £10–£27

This little restaurant, close to Telecom Tower, is popular at lunch-time with workers from the nearby hospitals and offices. Tables are close enough to make eavesdropping a worthwhile activity, and the old-world politeness of owners and staff adds a further dimension of pleasure to eating here. Do not expect luxury: 'We had not been for several years and decorations have been improved, but no money was wasted in the process' was one observation. This diner went on to confirm the *very* good value for money for predominantly south Indian cooking: 'The best south Indian fish curry I have had for years – a whole mackerel in very hot sauce with excellent coconut rice with seeds and mint leaves in it.' Specialities revolve around dosai (pancakes of rice and lentil flour with various fillings) and vadai, which are cakes made with gram flour. Coconut, given the regional emphasis, gets a strong showing in flavourings and chutneys. The excellent onion bhajias lack any greasy overtones and the cooking generally avoids over-oiling and blandness of flavour. To drink, there are lots of lassis, lager and wine from £6.90.

CHEFS: C.S. Nair and Mojid Ullah   PROPRIETORS: J. Dharmaseelan, T. Haridas and S. Pillai   OPEN: all week; 12 to 2.45, 6 to 11.30   CLOSED: 25 and 26 Dec   MEALS: alc (main courses £2 to £6). Minimum £5.50   SERVICE: 10%, card slips closed   CARDS: Access, Amex, Diners, Visa   DETAILS: 36 seats. Private parties: 40 main room, 24 private room. Vegetarian meals. Children's helpings D. Wheelchair access (1 step; also WC). Music. Air-conditioned

## Rani £

map 10

7 Long Lane, N3 2PR
081-349 4386 and 2636

COOKING 2
COST £14–£29

The Pattni family's converted shop, not far from Finchley Central tube station, continues to set the standard for Indian vegetarian cooking in London. The premises have expanded over the years, but the place has lost none of its friendly intimacy. Few signs of curry-house décor show in the well-spaced glass-covered tables, red and white walls and Venetian window blinds. Mother and daughter-in-law run the kitchen. Their cooking is uncompromisingly authentic, defined by vivid flavours and complex spicing which are sometimes searingly hot, sometimes cunningly subtle. Brilliant home-made chutneys – the hallmark of any genuine Indian enterprise – are always mentioned in reports. Vegetable bhajias with fresh coriander chutney, lentil bhajias with soothing coconut chutney and samosas with date chutney are typical offerings. The choice of curries takes in banana methi, cauliflower and pea, and stuffed aubergine and potato. Also look for the more esoteric and daring daily specials such as stuffed green chillies, tindora (baby cucumbers with potato topped with yogurt sauce) and undhia (fried gram flour and fenugreek balls with exotic vegetables). Codes on the menu indicate whether dishes contain ingredients such as dairy products, sugar or wheat. Ice-creams and Rani Nutty Delight (pistachios, almonds and cashews cooked in milk and sugar) have been enjoyable desserts. The range of drinks includes not only a few wines, lagers and lassi, but several therapeutic herbal teas. Australian house wine is £7.50.

CHEFS: Kundanben Pattni and Sheila Pattni   PROPRIETOR: Jyotindra Pattni   OPEN: all week, exc L Mon and Sat; 12.15 to 2, 6 to 10.30   CLOSED: 25 Dec   MEALS: alc (main courses £4 to £5). Set L £12, Set D £17 to £19. Minimum £8   SERVICE: net prices, card slips closed   CARDS: Access, Visa   DETAILS: 90 seats. Private parties: 60 main room, 23 and 60 private rooms. Vegetarian meals. Healthy eating options. Children's helpings. No children under 6. Smart dress preferred. No-smoking area. Wheelchair access (1 step). Music. Fax: 081-349 4386

£ *indicates that it is possible to have a three-course meal, including coffee, a half-bottle of house wine and service, at any time the restaurant is open (i.e. at dinner as well as at lunch, unless a place is open only for dinner), for £20 or less per person.*

## Ransome's Dock ▼

NEW ENTRY    map 10

35–37 Parkgate Road, SW11 4NP                    COOKING 2*
071-223 1611                                     COST £21–£36

Martin Lam's opening on the former site of Le Chausson – in a handsomely
converted former ice-cream factory on the bank by Battersea Bridge – is good
news for residents south of the river. His aim has been to create a fair-value
place, with conspicuously enjoyable service, in surroundings that are
comfortable without being lavish: very much the current recipe for a good
restaurant. He has succeeded. The repertoire is modern, but with enough
down-home touches to avoid the pitfalls of wildness. Potted shrimps from
Morecambe are almost a standard; otherwise the range takes in cassoulet, liver
with spinach and polenta, lamb with beans and new potatoes, grilled
vegetables with balsamic dressing, and grilled kippers with toast. Sweets are
kept simple: Greek yogurt and honey, divine baked bananas with cardamom
and lemon tart are mentioned. It is a sound production, and the welcome is
very warm. There is a stated intention here to make 'wines accessible to most
people' and this is realised with a generous pricing policy for the broad range
of carefully chosen bottles. Half a dozen are offered by the glass and the house
selection makes for flexibility and much pleasure. House wine is from £9.25.
CELLARMAN'S CHOICE: Favorita del Piemonte 1991, Deltetto, £15.25; Rasteau,
Côtes-du-Rhône-Villages, Dom. La Soumade 1989, £15.

CHEF: Martin Lam    PROPRIETORS: Martin and Vanessa Lam    OPEN: all week, exc Sun D;
11 to 3.30, 5.30 to 11 (12 Sat)    CLOSED: Christmas    MEALS: alc (main courses £8 to £11).
Set L £10.50 (2 courses)    SERVICE: not inc    CARDS: Access, Amex, Diners, Visa    DETAILS:
60 seats. 7 tables outside. Private parties: 50 main room, 40 private room. Car park D.
Vegetarian meals. Children's helpings. No pipes in dining-room. Wheelchair access (1 step;
also WC). Music. Air-conditioned. Fax: 071-924 2614

## ▲ Regent Hotel

NEW ENTRY    map 14

222 Marylebone Road, NW1 6JQ                     COOKING 3
071-631 8000                                     COST £27–£62

This hotel aims to bring the West End to the railway strip of the Marylebone/
Euston roads. It was, of course, once a railway hotel itself but has been
reconstructed and refurbished with Far Eastern money. The busy Jacobethan
frontage on the Marylebone Road has some presence, but it is as nothing to the
gasps of admiration elicited by the atrium in the very centre of the building.
Walls rise sheer around you for five storeys; galleries at first floor give a view of
the marbled, carpeted floors occupied by tea-takers, idle guests and scurrying
staff; palm trees sprout gigantic in their tubs. The dining-room is grand-hotel
classical: airy, spacious and moribund. 'If the food here were served in a
Chelsea restaurant, the crowds would flock to it' was the sage remark of one
satisfied visitor. 'All it needs is a knowledgeable, plentiful clientele' was
another. This is the bane of many hotels. Here, Italian cooking has been chosen.
What is surprising is that it is very passable and has some character. A menu is
divided classically into first courses, pasta and risotto, fish and meat. The
breads include focaccia, grissini and olive bread. The staff are more French than
Italian, so may not understand you if you practise your Tuscan gleanings, but

they serve with a will and a smile. The range of choice is better, or wider, than that in many classically oriented hotels and there is even a children's menu. Lunch, which includes pizza (unless you eat from the fixed-price menu), is lighter in tone and slightly lower in price. Meals have elicited some satisfaction for dishes such as a salad of shrimps, scallops and crayfish with truffle-oil dressing and authentic shavings of the tuber itself. Plump, fresh-tasting and generous was the verdict. Black ravioli filled with lobster were good pasta, with a mild filling and bold sauce. Meat dishes are less evidently Italian. Lamb noisettes with sweetbreads were given a standard, and over-strong, stock sauce and the compulsory trimming of dauphinois. Rabbit may have had a basil sauce, but it was more stock and salt, and the aubergine caviare that lent a Mediterranean tinge was again over-bitter. Anything Italian disappears as the sweets trolley is trundled on stage. This is disappointing hotel fare and could be greatly improved. The wine list is impressively Italian, with all the famous names and many of their new-wave table wines, rather than a series of old Barolos and Valpolicellas. The prices are high and the list has fewer than 10 bottles below £20. There are French and New World selections, but these too are just as pricey. The few half-bottles are mostly over £20. House wines are from £22.

CHEF: Paolo Simioni  PROPRIETORS: Regent International  OPEN: all week; 12 (12.30 Sun) to 3, 7 to 11  MEALS: alc (main courses £9 to £19). Set L £19.50 to £27 (inc wine)  SERVICE: net prices, card slips closed  CARDS: Access, Amex, Diners, Visa  DETAILS: 100 seats. Private parties: 12 main room, 12 to 500 in private rooms. Car park. Vegetarian meals. Children's helpings. Smart dress preferred. No-smoking area. Wheelchair access (also WC). Music. Air-conditioned  ACCOMMODATION: 309 rooms, all with bath/shower. Rooms for disabled. Lift. B&B £211.50 to £329. Children welcome. Baby facilities. Small dogs welcome. Afternoon teas. Swimming-pool. Sauna. Air-conditioned. TV. Phone. Fax: 071-631 8080

## Riva
map 10

169 Church Road, SW13 9HR
081-748 0434

COOKING 3
COST £23–£42

Lots of opera (not too loud), architectural prints and a subdued but space-enhancing paint job make this shop conversion, at the Barnes village end of Castelnau, a pleasing yet unpretentious frame for north Italian cooking that is sometimes among the most exciting that London can offer. Yet be warned that not everyone has the same experience. A scan of the menu shows enticing objects: bocconcini alla contadina (a plate of preserved meats and cheeses); polenta e pesce (polenta with toppings of salt cod and raisins, eel and olives, and pickled herring); and verzada (a plate of cabbage and onions with black pudding). Then the fish, which comes either with pasta or grilled aromatically with herbs: 'My sea bream in a paper parcel was outstandingly fresh and the flavour fully brought out – not smothered with a sauce – by a mixture of shrimps, lobster and seafood.' Meats – for instance, calf's liver with polenta, or grilled chicken with balsamic vinegar – almost pale by comparison. This is northern food, so is quite substantial. In the hands of chef Francesco Zanchetta it is often quite oil-heavy (with good oil), and the polenta can be mushier than people sometimes like. When the place is on song, the successes are palpable; if it misses, people are often unhappy, particularly at some indifferent service. Lombardy is cold, the Veneto has fogs, why then should their natives be rendered so gloomy by the English winter? The intelligently bought wines are Italian. The list is short and to the point and offers sensible range at decent value. House wine is £9.

CHEF: Francesco Zanchetta  PROPRIETOR: Andrea Riva  OPEN: all week, exc Sat L; 12 to 2.30, 7 to 11 (11.30 Fri and Sat, 9.30 Sun)  CLOSED: Christmas, Easter, bank hols  MEALS: alc (main courses £6 to £11.50)  SERVICE: 10%, card slips closed  CARDS: Access, Visa  DETAILS: 50 seats. 2 tables outside. Private parties: 40 main room. Vegetarian meals. Children's helpings. No cigars/pipes in dining-room. Wheelchair access. Music. Air-conditioned

## River Café ♥                                                              map 10

Thames Wharf Studios,
Rainville Road, W6 9HA                                               COOKING 3*
071-381 8824                                                         COST £25–£49

The riverside setting is a draw in the summer, with lots of outside tables and seclusion from the hurly-burly of the street – it is notoriously difficult to get to, so complex are the one-way systems. Sharing the location of Sir Richard Rogers' architectural practice, the restaurant has always worn its function on its sleeve, though surroundings have been upgraded and acoustically improved this year. It long ago moved away from the 'café' of its name, without sacrificing a direct and natural approach to the whole business of feeding people, and with none of the artificial flounce of a top-drawer restaurant. The same might be said of the cooking, which waves the Italian flag and is not afraid to do things straightforwardly. Nor does it flinch at good ingredients. This immediacy and quality is the main appeal. Leg of lamb that has been marinated before grilling is served with mashed potatoes souped up with Parmesan, cream and olive oil and a salsa verde. Sea bass is stuffed to the gills with fresh herbs, grilled and presented with a simple salad of courgettes and mint. Scallops are grilled and put on a plate with borlotti beans flavoured with summer savoury and some grilled radicchio. Without the grill and a tanker of extra-virgin olive oil, the place would sink. Enough herbs, spinach, rocket and saladings are used to keep a smallholder rich. As time goes by, things that were once startling here become more commonplace – chargrilled squid with chilli and rocket, for example – but they are still done memorably. Because of the enthusiasm for materials and the simple cooking, this has become a very good place to try game and venison in season. Simplicity has its drawbacks, mostly that it underwhelms, hence brickbats from readers are not infrequent. They are hurled with greater velocity because prices are never low. It is perhaps the River Café's very freshness of approach that gives rise to the inconsistency. Apart from the food, the kindness to children on Sunday lunch-times, the view and the bills, the other point that excites the first-time visitor is the valet parking. The wine list should please too. All Italian, with a grand list of sweets and stickies, from the best suppliers, with helpful information, it is a pity that it does not have much with age, although it offers an opportunity to try the new names on everyone's lips. House wines are £9.50.

CHEFS: Rose Gray, Ruth Rogers and Theo Randall   PROPRIETORS: Richard and Ruth Rogers, and Rose Gray   OPEN: all week, exc Sun D; 12.30 (1 Sun) to 2.30, 7.30 to 9.30 CLOSED: 1 week Christmas and New Year, bank hols   MEALS: alc (main courses £9 to £17)   SERVICE: 12.5%, card slips closed   CARDS: Access, Visa   DETAILS: 70 seats (110 summer). 10 tables outside. Private parties: 70 main room. Car park D. Vegetarian meals. Children's helpings. No cigars/pipes in dining-room. Wheelchair access (also WC). No music. Fax: 071-381 6217

## Rotisserie
map 12

56 Uxbridge Road, W12 0LP
081-743 3028

COOKING 1
COST £22–£32

The Rotisserie stands out from the tatty businesses on its perimeter (opposite is a subterranean snooker club, once a public lavatory). Half-way down the long room that stretches from the street front and is done out in pine, rattan and natural finishes, it becomes clear from the heat bursting out of the open kitchen that the restaurant is about grilling, both rotary and charcoal. The generous portions of beef are Scotch, hung to develop some flavour and given a slightly sweet wash before grilling. This makes it distinctive. In addition, there are chicken, salmon, liver, duck and, most popularly, rack of lamb. Supporting dishes tend to the modish: tataki of tuna, bruschetta with grilled vegetables, and merguez sausages. The success of the execution is not unqualified, but standards are fair. Chips are straw-like and could taste better. The staff are a pleasure. It is remarkable that such a place can survive in such a location with so few compromises. The fair-priced wine list is short, but goes for a sensible range from all round the world. House wines are £8.25 a carafe.

CHEF: Emmanuel Schandorf   PROPRIETOR: Ian Davies   OPEN: all week, exc L Sat and Sun; 12 to 3, 7 to 11   MEALS: alc (main courses £6.50 to £10)   SERVICE: not inc   CARDS: Access, Amex, Visa   DETAILS: 70 seats. Private parties: 40 main room. Vegetarian meals. Children's helpings. Wheelchair access. Music. Fax: 081-743 3028

## Royal China
map 12

13 Queensway, W2 4QJ
071-221 2535

COOKING 2
COST £21–£67

The Putney branch is undergoing refurbishment, but people in need of glitz Chinese-style can still get their fix here, along with some classy cooking, smooth and gentle service, and dim-sum all through the day. Sunday is seriously popular. The seafood and fish hold most attractions, and dishes that have passed muster include prawns braised with garlic, deep-fried squid balls, shredded chicken with jellyfish in a mustard sauce, fragrant yam duck and baked pork chop with spicy salt. The wine list is reliable if not adventurous. House wines are £8.50.

CHEFS: Simon Man and Wai Hung Law   PROPRIETORS: Playwell Ltd   OPEN: all week; noon to 11.15   CLOSED: 24 and 25 Dec   MEALS: alc (main courses £5 to £15). Set D (minimum 2) £20 to £26   SERVICE: 12.5%   CARDS: Access, Amex, Diners, Visa DETAILS: 110 seats. Private parties: 85 main room, 15 private room. Vegetarian meals. Children welcome. Smart dress preferred. Music. Air-conditioned

## *RSJ* 🍷 £

map 11

13A Coin Street, SE1 8YQ
071-928 4554 and 9768

COOKING 2
COST £20–£39

This restaurant and brasserie, magnificently obsessed by the wines of the Loire valley, would elsewhere be a drinker's Lourdes. Its position, though – perfectly if uncosmetically sited to assuage the hunger pangs of South Bankers, as well as for anyone stranded at Waterloo – means that many visit for sustenance alone. A fundamental pokiness is cleverly disguised; the fact that the brasserie downstairs postdates the restaurant upstairs means that it has the edge in colour and brightness. The menus are not hugely different, though the brasserie emphasises simplicity. Plausible ideas – brill served with a salmon and lobster soufflé and avocado and basil sauce; tagliatelle of shellfish; rabbit saddle stuffed with liver and sun-dried tomatoes then wrapped in Parma ham and roasted, served with a braised rabbit leg – are largely successful; portions, though, 'may look a little as if nouvelle were living at this hour'. Regulars salute regular changes in the menus, and value for money means that the babble of conversation usually drowns out the Ella Fitzgerald tapes. Service – 'accomplished though not particularly cheerful' on one occasion – is mostly 'friendly, welcoming and efficient'. The complexities of the wine list can leave both waiting staff and customers floundering, but put yourself in Nigel Wilkinson's hands and you could enjoy some of the finest white wines available in any British restaurant for £40 or under, with reds (from Bourgueil and Chinon) scarcely less impressive. House wines begin at £9.75.
CELLARMAN'S CHOICE: Saumur Blanc, Ch. de Hureau 1990, Vatan, £16.95; Chinon, Vieilles Vignes, Dom de la Perrier, 1990, J.& C. Boudry, £13.95.

CHEF: Ian Stabler   PROPRIETOR: Nigel Wilkinson   OPEN: Mon to Sat, exc Sat L; 12 to 2, 6 (5.45 Sat) to 11   CLOSED: 4 days Christmas, bank hols   MEALS: alc (main courses restaurant £11 to £13, brasserie £6 to £8.50). Set L and D £13.95 (2 courses) to £15.75
SERVICE: 10%, card slips closed   CARDS: Access, Amex, Visa   DETAILS: restaurant 60 seats, brasserie 40 seats. Private parties: 20 main room, 20 private room. Vegetarian meals. Children welcome. Music. Air-conditioned

## *Rules*

**NEW ENTRY**   map 15

35 Maiden Lane, WC2E 7LB
071-836 5314

COOKING 2
COST £21–£45

'I was taken here for the first time in years and found it considerably improved,' reported a reader desperate to find variety in the Covent Garden area. Rules was established in 1798 and was frequented by many famous writers, artists and actors: 'I remember lunching there with George Orwell and Graham Greene in 1944,' continued our reader, who detailed his recent meal as 'artichoke and ginger soup, salmon fish-cake and sticky toffee pudding'. His guests were well pleased with steak, grouse and kidney pie – good tender meat and light pastry. It would be wrong to say that everything here is fantastic, but the setting is magical – if old-fashioned restaurants interest you – and the service exceptionally amiable. As we went to press, a new 'state-of-the-art' kitchen had just been installed. Game and beef are the sensible things to order and are done well; salmon is moist, wild and reliable as a summer alternative. Puddings mean puddings. There is a special deal for people off to the theatre. The wine list keeps below two dozen bins, but most of them are available in halves and prices are very fair. House wines are £8.50.

CHEFS: Neil Pass and Shaun Falvey   PROPRIETOR: John Mayhew   OPEN: all week; noon to 11.45pm (10.30 Sun)   CLOSED: 24 to 26 Dec   MEALS: alc (main courses £12 to £15.50). Set weekend L £15, Set supper (4 to 6pm) £12.75 (2 courses)   SERVICE: not inc (12.5% for 7 or more, card slips closed)   CARDS: Access, Amex, Visa   DETAILS: 140 seats. Private parties: 9 main room, 18, 30 and 60 private rooms. Vegetarian meals. Children's helpings on request. Wheelchair access. No music. Air-conditioned. Fax: 071-497 1081

## Sabras £

map 10

263 High Road,
Willesden Green, NW10 2RX
081-459 0340

COOKING 2
COST £9–£31

Hemant and Nalinee Desai celebrated 20 years in business in 1993 and still proudly fly the Indian national flags in their modest little café/restaurant near the Willesden Bus Garage. Shades of orange, green and white dominate the décor. The kitchen challenges the vegetarian palate, pulling in ideas from many parts of the sub-continent: 'Brilliant, every dish different' is one verdict. To begin, there is powerful strength in the range of farsan snacks, specialities from Bombay's Chowpatty Beach, and south Indian dosai: bhajias tinged with fenugreek, patras (steamed yam leaves), sev puris and bataka vadas are pointed up with delectable home-made chutneys. Reporters have also enthused about ravaiya (stuffed baby aubergines, bananas and potatoes) and simla mirch bharela (peppers stuffed with spices), while dhals, breads, assorted thalis and exotic vegetables loom large. To finish, you will find sheera, a 'sublime' dessert of semolina, ghee, saffron and spices, as well as home-made kulfi. Bargain-price lunch menus boast that you can 'eat for £1'. Rose lassi is a favourite beverage; otherwise there is a choice of juices, milkshakes and masala tea. The wine list is short and good with house wine at £5.50.

CHEFS/PROPRIETORS: Hemant and Nalinee Desai   OPEN: Tue to Sun, exc L Sat and Sun; 12.45 to 2.45, 6.15 to 10   MEALS: alc (main courses £3.50 to £6). Set L £1 (1 course) to £2.95 (2 courses), Set D £8.50 to £11   SERVICE: 12.5%, card slips closed   CARDS: Access, Visa   DETAILS: 32 seats. Private parties: 32 main room. Vegetarian meals only. Children welcome. Smart dress preferred. No-smoking area. Wheelchair access. Music

## ▲ St James's Court Hotel, Auberge de Provence

map 11

41 Buckingham Gate, SW1E 6AF
071-821 1899

COOKING 3
COST £31–£81

This 'auberge' – though nothing could be less like one – is two minutes' walk from Buckingham Palace. It continues as an outpost of L'Ousteau de Baumanière, the parent restaurant in the French village of Les Baux, with consultant chef Jean-André Charial and the staff 'looking as if they've just got off the boat', according to one reporter who finds visits there a consistent pleasure. The cooking is not as pattern-book as the auberge-style décor. It shows some perception of changes in taste and adds its own novelties in dishes such as king prawns with broad beans served with salmon in a tabbouleh salad, or sea bream served with an orange and star-anise sauce. Classics there are, for the nature of the place demands it: hence foie gras terrine, mullet with basil, olive oil and tomato, or duck with blackcurrant sauce and polenta. A winter dinner of scallops with a honey and raspberry vinegar dressing, quenelles of langoustines with (unseasonal) asparagus en feuilleté, breast of chicken with sage sauce and (unseasonal) baby vegetables, and fillets of sole with white wine sauce and fennel and spinach reminded everyone that this is a summertime restaurant, but also brought a ray of (unseasonal) sunshine into the hearts of the participants. The wine list is restricted to serious prices in the classic areas and the wise drinkers may care to restrict themselves to the southern French bottles carrying the Baumanière label. House wines are £11.50.

CHEF: Bernard Briqué  PROPRIETORS: St James's Court Hotel  OPEN: Mon to Sat, exc Sat L; 12.30 to 2.30, 7.30 to 11  CLOSED: 2 weeks Aug, first week Jan  MEALS: alc (main courses £16 to £22). Set L £22.50, Set D £30 to £40  SERVICE: not inc  CARDS: Access, Amex, Diners, Visa  DETAILS: 60 seats. Private parties: 60 main room. Vegetarian meals. Children's helpings. Smart dress preferred. No music. Air-conditioned
ACCOMMODATION: 391 rooms, all with bath/shower. Rooms for disabled. Lift. B&B £164 to £206. Children welcome. Afternoon teas. Garden. Sauna. TV. Phone. Confirm by 6. Fax: 071-630 7587

## Salloos                                                    map 13

62–64 Kinnerton Street, SW1X 8ER                         COOKING 2
071-235 4444                                             COST £26–£65

The restaurant began as Mr Salahuddin's part-time hobby at his home in Lahore before he set up business in this fashionable mews house on the fringes of Belgravia. His intention was to re-create the highest level of sophisticated cooking from households in Pakistan 'where the cuisine of the Mughal empire is preserved to this day'. Few reporters doubt the finesse and refinement of the cooking, but prices are 'over the top' (particularly as a £1.50 cover charge and 15 per cent service are levied). Tandoori lamb chops really are 'out of this world,' exclaims an expert, although chicken jalfrezi has been 'dry'. Otherwise the repertoire takes in many classic and unusual specialities, such as chicken taimuri (marinated and deep-fried in a spicy batter) and haleem akbari (shredded lamb cooked with wheatgerm, lentils and spices). Pilau rice is 'natural-looking' and excellent, as is nan bread. Conditions in the upstairs dining-room can be 'cramped'; consequently the noise level is fierce. Service is friendly, but can seem pushy as far as ordering is concerned. The creditable – but pricey – wine list has some good selections from Corney & Barrow. House French is £12.50.

CHEF: Abdul Aziz  PROPRIETOR: Muhammad Salahuddin  OPEN: Mon to Sat; 12 to 2.30, 7 to 11.15  CLOSED: bank hols  MEALS: alc (main courses £9.50 to £15). Set L £16, Set D £25. Cover £1.50  SERVICE: 15%, card slips closed  CARDS: Access, Amex, Diners, Visa  DETAILS: 70 seats. Private parties: 70 main room. Vegetarian meals. No children under 6 after 8.30. Smart dress preferred. No music. Air-conditioned

## Les Saveurs  ▼

map 14

37A Curzon Street, W1Y 8EY
071-491 8919

COOKING 3*
COST £28–£60

This restaurant occupies a luxurious basement in the heart of Mayfair. Blond wood and delicate colours lighten the atmosphere to near-vanishing point, but some interest is re-injected by the various pieces of stylish china and glass that come to the table during a meal. The owners are Japanese and the chef is a Frenchman who has learnt his craft at the stoves of the good and the great of the modern French kitchen; he has also done time in the Far East. His familiarity with tip-top international practice is evident throughout his work, and it makes the cooking here the most authentically Parisian and haut-goût Français in England. The waiting staff are also very French, but charming with it. Their ability and tact have been invariably praised. This slightly unlikely combination, in a very unlikely and not immediately attractive location, has meant that the restaurant has altered its tack during the year. The cooking has stayed the same, as has the many-layered service, but prices have gone down. During the rush of blood to the financial head of the capital's restaurants during the winter of 1993, when so many were offering a £5 lunch, Les Saveurs was often thought the winner in bargain terms. The current pricing, though no bargain (set-price lunch, however, must come close to that), is very competitive and you do see labour and effort, as well as taste and flavour, for your money. The cooking is not the new-wave simplicity of English chefs; things get well and truly altered by Joël Antunés. People have spoken well of lightly smoked scallops on a salad with horseradish, rolls of smoked salmon filled with a tartare of lobster, a lasagne of langoustines with mousserons, and even cheek of beef with a Madiran sauce. Desserts may be a grand production: for example, the hot soufflés or the bitter chocolate fondant with a pistachio sauce. A vein of sweetness appears in some of the savoury dishes. Ancillaries – two stages of appetisers, petits fours, bread and so on – are determinedly clever or good. The same could be said of the wine list; the house selection champagne comes from Bruno Paillard and it is difficult to better that. Age is respected, and even relatively modest Médocs such as Ch. La Tour Saint-Bonnet and Ch. Potensac are from 1978 and 1979. All this comes at a very high price. Quality of such consistency, however, should not be ignored. House wine is £15.
CELLARMAN'S CHOICE: St-Joseph Blanc 1990, Cuilleron, £25; Médoc, Ch. Potensac 1979, £29.

CHEF: Joël Antunés   PROPRIETORS: Fujikoshi UK Ltd   OPEN: Mon to Fri; 12 to 2.30, 7 to 10.30   CLOSED: 2 weeks Christmas, New Year, bank hols, 2 weeks Aug   MEALS: Set L £18, Set D £26 (2 courses) to £36   SERVICE: not inc   CARDS: Access, Amex, Diners, Visa
DETAILS: 55 seats. Private parties: 50 main room, 10 private room. Vegetarian meals. Children welcome. Jacket and tie. No pipes in dining-room. No-smoking area. No music. Air-conditioned. Fax: 071-491 3658

---

*'Our meal came to a sudden halt when my partner discovered on his plate a half-live cockroach, approximately half an inch long – a mere youngster. When we eventually caught someone's eye the plate was removed with an apology and a ''You won't be charged for that dish, Sir'', and the meal continued.'*  On eating in Oxfordshire

---

## ▲ Savoy Grill and River Restaurant

map 15

Strand, WC2R 0EU
071-836 4343

COOKING 3
COST £32–£90

This is one London's institutions and therefore in an enviable position. Everyone wants to come here at some stage. The world beats an automatic path to the door, so the place benefits from interest, variety of incident and a sense of event for the casual onlooker. That said, it is very large and reports are as mixed as giant organisations can expect. The Savoy has less of the exact market targeting of smaller places like the Connaught or The Capital; it has to be mother to a surprisingly disparate brood. Small wonder that rapturous praise will follow on the heels of someone's vilification. The River Restaurant is the hotel dining-room; the Grill is the general-purpose restaurant. While the River Restaurant has windows giving on to the trees of the Embankment and the river traffic beyond – tables in the hinterland never have the same allure – the Grill is inward-looking, the view relieved only by ornate fittings and waiters. Many feel the best time for the Grill is lunch, particularly for people-watching. In the River Restaurant, the happiest time is Sunday lunch, when families have jolly get-togethers. The menus are never going to amaze for interest, even if they have length in spades, and the execution has generally been thought either satisfactory or lacklustre, rarely brilliant. As the cost in either place is punishing, this is regrettable. Service, which should have the character of everybody's favourite uncle, has been seen by some as tired and unenthusiastic. The wine list is both manageable and good, even if it is as dear as much of the rest. House wines are £10.75.

CHEFS: David Sharland (Grill) and Anton Edelmann (River Restaurant)   PROPRIETORS: The Savoy Group plc   OPEN: Grill Mon to Sat, exc Sat L; 12.30 to 2.15, 6 to 11.30. River Restaurant all week; 12.30 to 2.30, 7.30 to 11.20 (7 to 10.30 Sun)   CLOSED: Grill Aug, bank hols   MEALS: Grill alc (main courses £12.50 to £21). Set pre-theatre D £26.75 (2 courses) to £29.75. River Restaurant alc (main courses £18 to £30), Set L £25.20, Set D £30.50 (£36.50 Fri and Sat) to £45 (inc wine)   SERVICE: Grill not inc. River Restaurant net prices, card slips closed   CARDS: Access, Amex, Diners, Visa   DETAILS: Grill 100 seats, River Restaurant 160 seats. Private parties: River Restaurant 50 main room, 6 to 60 in private rooms. Vegetarian meals. Children welcome. Jacket and tie. No pipes in dining-rooms. Wheelchair access Grill. Music (Christmas and New Year Grill). Air-conditioned   ACCOMMODATION: 202 rooms, all with bath/shower. Rooms for disabled. Lift. B&B £200 to £306. Children welcome. Baby facilities. Afternoon teas. Swimming-pool. Sauna. Air-conditioned. TV. Phone. Confirm by 6. Fax: 071-240 6040 (The Which? Hotel Guide)

## La Sémillante

map 14

5 Mill Street, W1R 9TF
071-499 2121

COOKING 2
COST £30–£53

Although London saw unexpected vigour in the restaurant sector during a general recession, the tendency was for variations on the cheap and cheerful theme: brasseries, converted pubs, cafés with ambitions, for example. The West End practitioners of full-blown haute cuisine seemed thinner on the ground.

Patrick Woodside, who has worked as pastry chef with many of the big names, is one of those trying this route. As we reported last year, La Sémillante, a former Indian basement restaurant *en plein* Mayfair, has had most (but not all) of its orientalisms removed or overlaid by bright colours in paint, fabric and pottery. The more expensive fixed-price menu displays the young-Turk tendencies of the chef to a T: 'steamed sea scallops en croûte in a skin of sea bream and red mullet nestled on a compote of red peppers spiked with cumin', or 'quail à la crapaudine, with layers of spinach and langoustine resting on a bed of buckwheat pasta and redcurrant jelly'. Sauces tend to be smidgeons, not pools or lakes. Tastes, which lean towards sweetness, are often extremely disturbing: barely seasoned scallops with a smear of red pepper and cumin sauce, liberally sprinkled with candied violets, is a mixture of messages that most palates find difficult. While meat cookery is often soundly based, there can be a lack of balance – especially acidity – to dishes that may reduce their impact. Presentation is remorselessly old new-wave. Desserts are pretty impressive. Readers remember fondly a coffee tart and a lavender bavarois with more crystallised violets. There is almost more art than the spirit can bear, and it slows the service right down. The wine list is short and adequate. House wines are £12.

CHEF/PROPRIETOR: Patrick Woodside   OPEN: Mon to Sat, exc Sat L; 12.15 to 2.15, 7.15 to 11.15   CLOSED: last 2 weeks Aug, last 2 weeks Dec   MEALS: Set L £16 (2 courses), Set D £28   SERVICE: not inc (12.5% for 8 or more), card slips closed   CARDS: Access, Amex, Diners, Visa   DETAILS: 36 seats. Private parties: 50 main room, 15 private room. Vegetarian meals. Children's helpings. Smart dress preferred. No-smoking area. No music. Air-conditioned. Fax: 071-499 4042

## Shogun

NEW ENTRY   map 14

Brittania Hotel, Adams Row, W1   COOKING 2*
071-493 1255 and 1877   COST £25–£56

'As a dining-out experience this rates highly,' commented one seasoned sampler of the capital's Japanese restaurants impressed by the faultless hospitality of Hiromi Mitsuka and amused by the decoration which milks the name of the place of all its symbolism. 'Who would guess that it was the basement of a faceless modern hotel?' he added, struck by the sushi and sashimi, and the dexterity of the chef, though he found the food bland to some extent, though never incompetent. 'It is the first time I have needed to add soy to a chawan-mushi, a light savoury custard with lots of garnish,' he remarked. When this place began, its price was stunning. As more Japanese restaurants have opened, it surprises less. Saké is £3.75 for a small flask.

CHEF: S. Daito   PROPRIETOR: Miss H. Mitsuka   OPEN: Tue to Sun, D only; 6 to 11   MEALS: alc (main courses £8.50 to £17). Set D £30 to £32   SERVICE: 12.5%, card slips closed   CARDS: Access, Amex, Diners, Visa   DETAILS: 65 seats. Private parties: 100 main room. Children welcome. Smart dress preferred. No pipes in dining-room. Music. Air-conditioned

Net prices *in the details at the end of an entry indicates that the prices given on a menu and on a bill are inclusive of VAT and service charge, and that this practice is clearly stated on menu and bill.*

## Simply Nico

map 11

48A Rochester Row, SW1P 1JU
071-630 8061

COOKING 3
COST £30–£39

When Simply Nico was relaunched as Nico Ladenis' brasserie operation, it had a menu apparently carved in stone and an unintentional – it was the publicity that did it – emphasis on steak and chips. The intervening years have seen the menu loosen up, though the fixed-price formula remains, and the restaurant consolidate its position as a place for the neighbourhood (it has a division bell for hungry Members). The modern setting remains a constant, the tables are still a little too close, 'but as most of the customers don't smoke, this doesn't matter,' one reader reported with relief. Another person condemned the French bistro cooking as standards that have been 'messed about'. That seems harsh. The repertoire is refreshingly simple, yet flavours are strong and technique is generally accurate. Recommendations have been enthusiastic for the fish soup, the côte de boeuf with béarnaise, the walnut-dressed potato salad with flakes of cod and a mustard mayonnaise, the escalope of salmon with a herb mayonnaise, confit of duck with onions, simple grilled fish and the pithiviers of quail. Desserts take a steady line as well: crème caramel, apple crumble, armagnac parfait ('it looked a jumble but tasted fine') and home-made ice-creams have been mentioned. Chips and mashed potato are still just the ticket. The service is young and usually enjoyed. The wine list has a more charitable range of prices than it did, starting at £11.

CHEF: Andrew Barber   PROPRIETORS: Nico and Dinah-Jane Ladenis   OPEN: Mon to Sat, exc Sat L; 12 to 2, 7 to 11   CLOSED: 10 days Christmas, 4 days Easter, bank hol L   MEALS: Set L £23, Set D £25   SERVICE: net prices, card slips closed   CARDS: Access, Amex, Diners, Visa   DETAILS: 60 seats. Private parties: 60 main room. Vegetarian meals. No children under 5. Smart dress preferred. No pipes in dining-room. Wheelchair access (2 steps). No music. Air-conditioned. Fax: 071-355 4877

## Singapore Garden Restaurant £

map 11

83–83A Fairfax Road, NW6 4DY
071-328 5314

COOKING 2
COST £18–£40

Singapore Garden fulfils the dual requirement of neighbourhood utility and sound and interesting cooking. Consequently, it is often full. The Lim family recognise their regulars and welcome strangers, service is amiable and the place is comfortable. All of South-East Asia is peeped at through the menu's eyes: Indonesian, Cantonese, Thai and Malay dishes have their place on a stable repertoire supplemented by a specials list that changes periodically. Recommended dishes include soft-shell crab with chilli and garlic, Singapore noodles, laksa, spicy aubergines, squid blachan, chilli crab and lobster when available, and beef rendang. There is now another branch – Singapore Garden II – in an airy basement in the Regent's Park Hotel at 154 Gloucester Place, Tel: 071-723 8233, which is one of the few restaurants where you can get an Asian breakfast. House wines are £7.65, but some support the delicate grass jelly as a non-alcoholic alternative.

CHEF: Mrs S. Lim   PROPRIETORS: the Lim family   OPEN: all week; 12 to 2.45, 6 to 10.45
(11.15 Fri and Sat)   CLOSED: 1 week after Christmas   MEALS: alc (main courses £4 to
£8.50). Set D £14.85. Minimum £9   SERVICE: 12.5%, card slips closed   CARDS: Access,
Amex, Diners, Visa   DETAILS: 100 seats. 3 tables outside. Private parties: 60 main room,
60 private room. Vegetarian meals. Children welcome. No cigars in dining-room. Music.
Air-conditioned

## Snows on the Green                                          map 10

166 Shepherd's Bush Road, W6 7PB                         COOKING 2
071-603 2142                                             COST £20–£42

The tables are part-tiled; lavender hangs on the terracotta-red and corn-yellow
walls; while jars of oil, like the diners in this Shepherd's Bush parade shop and
basement (just by Brook Green), are slowly infused with garlic and rosemary.
Sebastian Snow's cooking, despite the 'new age' tag of one customer, is a
sincere exploration of Provence and beyond into pan-Mediterranean comfort-
food zones. Brandade crostini, chargrilled asparagus, warm salads of Toulouse
sausages and wild rabbit, more chargrilling of polenta with snails, mushrooms
and Gruyère, lemon tart and rich chocolate cake have all won approval. Other
dishes have had a more mixed reception: tongue fat floating in the sauce for a
confit of lambs' tongues proved offputting 'even for a fat lover'; chartreuse of
Bresse pigeon, black pudding and Savoy cabbage was judged 'bland and
boring'; an 'ordinary' shortbread was served with over-cinnamoned pears. In
general, though, the boldness and authenticity are appreciated, even when
execution falters. Service is no less sincere – even ingenuous: 'The waiter
seemed amazed when we said how good the food was.' The wine list is not
ambitious or innovative, but is full of solid bottles from Rosemount, Cuvaison,
Labouré-Roi and their like; look to the Rhône and Italy for best value and best
food matches. House wines are £8.50.

CHEF: Sebastian Snow   PROPRIETORS: Sebastian and Melissa Snow   OPEN: all week, exc
Sat L and Sun D; 12 to 3, 7 to 11   CLOSED: bank hols   MEALS: alc (main courses £7 to £11).
Set L £10.50 (2 courses) to £12.50   SERVICE: not inc   CARDS: Access, Visa   DETAILS: 65
seats. Private parties: 12 main room, 22 private room. Vegetarian meals. Children's
helpings Sun L. No pipes in dining-room. Wheelchair access. Music. Air-conditioned

## Soho Soho  £                                              map 15

11–13 Frith Street, W1V 8TS                              COOKING 1
071-494 3491                                             COST £18–£46

The ground-floor café-bar/rotisserie never seems empty, often has queues and
is a definite utility for the area. Here late lunches and early suppers are popular,
breakfast is served, cider bouché is listed, and the place does not close until
after midnight. On the first floor is a more serious and, in some ways, less
satisfactory restaurant. The dried flowers on the stairs, echoed by perpetual
topiary here and there, underline the culinary theme of Provence and the
Mediterranean, only amplified by the Cocteau-style mural. The view on to a
busy Frith Street, the harlequin patterning of furniture and menus, and the
generally assiduous (sometimes too assiduous for anyone's temper) waiting

team make for a fair ambience. The menu itself, which is composed to a certain formulaic Frenchness but with enough variation to tempt, reinforces this. Tuna is seared and placed on pickled cabbage, there is an estocaficada (a stew of fish and salt cod, garlic and potatoes), and chicken is wrapped in caul with tarragon and tomatoes and dressed with capers. Bread and olives, though left on the table, are charged at £1.50. The wine list has a slight tilt towards the Midi, though only a handful of unfamiliar names and sources catch the eye. Sound it is, as is the mainstream general list that bolsters the provençal specialisation. House wines are £8.95 in the restaurant.

CHEF: Tony Howorth  PROPRIETORS: Neville Abraham and Laurence Isaacson  OPEN: Mon to Sat, exc Sat L restaurant; restaurant 12 to 3, 7 to 12; café-bar/rotisserie 8am to 1am  MEALS: restaurant alc (main courses £9.50 to £13.50); café-bar/rotisserie alc (main courses £5 to £8.50). Cover £1.50 restaurant  SERVICE: 12.5%, card slips closed  CARDS: Access, Amex, Diners, Visa  DETAILS: restaurant 70 seats, café-bar/rotisserie 70 seats. 8 tables outside. Private parties: 60 private room. Vegetarian meals. Children's helpings café-bar/rotisserie. No-smoking area restaurant. Wheelchair access café-bar/rotisserie (1 step). Music. Air-conditioned. Fax: 071-436 5227

## Sonny's
map 10

94 Church Road, SW13 0DQ
081-748 0393

COOKING 1
COST £22–£40

Restaurant, then deli, then café as well, Sonny's has not stopped developing since opening in 1986. It won the hearts of Barnes at first shot: a useful neighbourhood place with lots of style, an informal way of doing things, not too dear and quite with-it in the kitchen department. It has not changed the formula. The volume still can approach that of a rugby team having a jolly, the floor still clatters with rushing feet and it is still busy. The chef who joined in summer 1993 is hot from a big hotel, but the style remains London café-cum-brasserie with bruschetta, salmon rillettes, twice-baked goats' cheese soufflé, liver and mash, or cod with boulangère potatoes, though there may be a little less of the Mediterranean or Cal-Ital about it than there used to be. Matters have always gone up and down a bit here, depending on the press of business. This is still the case, as, for example, in a meal which had goats' cheese soufflé and roast chicken with thick bacon and peas as ups, and a salad of smoked haddock and poached egg and crème brûlée as downs, while scallops were drowned out by aubergine purée and balsamic vinegar. At dinner, the daytime café tables are utilised; a table at the back will prove more comfortable and more fun. There are some nice things on the wine list: Big House Red, St Hallett Merlot, Vinattieri's Chardonnay among others. House wines are £7.95.

CHEF: Alec Howard  PROPRIETOR: Rebecca Mascarenhas  OPEN: restaurant all week, exc Sun D; 12.30 to 2.30, 7.30 to 11. Café all week; 11am to 7pm  MEALS: alc (main courses £7 to £13). Set L and D £12.50 (2 courses). Daytime café menu  SERVICE: not inc  CARDS: Access, Amex, Visa  DETAILS: 70 seats. Private parties: 20 main room. Vegetarian meals. Children's helpings. Smart dress preferred. Wheelchair access. No music. Air-conditioned. Fax: 081-748 2698

**The Good Food Guide** *is a registered trade mark of Consumers' Association Ltd.*

# The Square ♟

map 14

32 King Street, SW1Y 6RJ
071-839 8787

COOKING 3
COST £32–£56

The new giant of St James's – Quaglino's – has not apparently affected the success or popularity of this restaurant of last year's vintage. The Square has indeed got lots of shapes to reinforce the image in the name: 'There are blocks and cubes of strong pastel shades and large paintings of one colour. Chairs are either pink or blue, mixed at random,' reports one reader. 'Slightly Californian,' said another. The place is also blessed with a clean and fresh face that speaks of bright modern comfort. Some have wondered about the real function of the downstairs bar, yet marvelled at the design of the lavatories (blue for a boy and pink for a girl). Philip Howard offers a menu that is curt almost to a fault. 'Roast scallops, wilted endive, Sauternes' may tell you the ingredients, but little about how they are put together. The waiters may not help much either. In the event, the dish proved to be scallops on a bed of endive with a sweet wine vinaigrette; the dressing was too sweet to achieve the intended balance. But wordlessness adds to the adventure, and many people's investigations have borne ripe fruit of satisfaction in dishes such as mullet on green Chinese noodles, calf's liver with a red wine sauce and caramelised carrots, and fillets of sole served in a bowl to hold asparagus, a rich butter sauce and fast-melting tomato Chantilly. Rare-roasted tuna with sesame, coriander and soy, or crab mayonnaise with avocado and pain de campagne have provided punchy, exciting starts. Desserts offer less choice, but lemon tart and crème brûlée have been approved. Sometimes ambition seems to exceed execution, and standards vary. Service is much enjoyed, until a bad day causes all praise to be cancelled. The Square's prices are now in line with the very West End clientele, even though when the place opened it seemed to embrace a new realism in straitened times. Half of the wine list under the heading 'fine wines' appears to attract a premium on price as well as quality; a relatively modest Fronsac, albeit a 1982, costs £30. Conversely, a possibly finer Jean Léon 1983 Cabernet which escapes the 'fine' label is a mere £23.50. Notwithstanding the vagaries of wine economics, this is a very good list headed by 'The Square selection', several of which are offered by the glass. House wines are from £10.50. CELLARMAN'S CHOICE: St-Véran 1991, Dom. des Deux Roches, £18.50; Rioja Reserva, Viña Ardanza 1985, La Rioja Alta, £22.50.

CHEF: Philip Howard   PROPRIETORS: Dailyrare Ltd   OPEN: all week, exc L Sat and Sun; 12 to 3, 6 to 11.45 (7 to 10.30 Sun)   CLOSED: Christmas, Easter   MEALS: alc (main courses £11.50 to £17.50)   SERVICE: not inc   CARDS: Access, Amex, Diners, Visa   DETAILS: 70 seats. Private parties: 14 main room, 25 private room. Vegetarian meals. Children welcome. Smart dress preferred. Wheelchair access (1 step). No music. Air-conditioned. Fax: 071-321 2124

## Sree Krishna £

map 10

192–194 Tooting High Street, SW17 0SF
081-672 4250 and 6903

COOKING 1
COST £11–£29

The Haridas family have been here since 1988 and also run Ragam (see entry, London): both restaurants specialise in south Indian cooking with specialities gleaned from the Keralan coast. A new feature is the short list of 'exotic starters', such as chicken chilli, meat fry and fish fry; otherwise you will find dosai, burnished ghee roast masala, vadai (fried gram-flour doughnut), uthappam (a fiery, pizza-style pancake topped with green chillies, onions and tomatoes) and avial (mixed vegetables with coconut, yogurt and curry leaves). Traditionalists looking for curry-house stalwarts should be satisfied by the full range of dhansaks, bhunas, birianis and the like. The kitchen generally delivers good food, although service does not always meet with approval. Drink lassi or Kingfisher lager. House Italian wine is £6.

CHEF: Mullath Vijayan   PROPRIETORS: T. Haridas and family   OPEN: all week; 12 to 3, 6 to 11 (12 Fri and Sat)   CLOSED: 25 and 26 Dec   MEALS: alc (main courses £2 to £6) SERVICE: 10%, card slips closed   CARDS: Access, Amex, Diners, Visa   DETAILS: 120 seats. Private parties: 60 main room, 60 private room. Vegetarian meals. Children welcome. Smart dress preferred. Wheelchair access (also WC). Music. Air-conditioned

## Sri Siam £

map 15

14 Old Compton Street, W1V 5PE
071-434 3544

COOKING 2
COST £16–£43

Few reporters dispute that Sri Siam holds its place among the premier league of Thai restaurants in the capital: 'outstanding', 'maintains its excellent standard', 'probably the best in Soho' are typical accolades. The cool, long, narrow dining-room is seriously perfumed, while the walls are embellished with abstract prints, gold 'transfers' of butterflies and Thai dolls. Service is generally helpful and brisk. Visitors have plundered the 70-dish menu for well-balanced tom yum soup, mixed hors d'oeuvre (including satays, fish-cakes and stuffed chicken wings with invigorating dips), 'wonderful' roast duck curry with pineapple, tomato and Kaffir lime leaves, steamed flatfish with preserved plum and ginger, rice served in a hollowed-out pineapple and anything with noodles. The repertoire also encompasses regional specialities such as larb (a northern Thai dish of finely chopped meat with ground roast rice on a salad with a hot-and-sour dressing) as well as a full selection of vegetarian dishes. Desserts include some excellent ice-creams as well as exotic fruit. There is a short wine list; otherwise drink jasmine tea or Singha Thai beer. House French is £7.95.

CHEF: Orawan Seniwong   PROPRIETORS: Thai Restaurants plc   OPEN: all week, exc Sun L; 12 to 3, 6 to 11.15 (10.30 Sun)   CLOSED: 25 and 26 Dec, 1 Jan   MEALS: alc (main courses £4.50 to £7.50). Set L £9, Set D £14.95   SERVICE: 12.5%   CARDS: Access, Amex, Diners, Visa   DETAILS: 80 seats. Private parties: 100 main room. Vegetarian meals. Children welcome. Wheelchair access. Music. Air-conditioned

## Sri Siam City

<NEW ENTRY> map 11

85 London Wall, EC2M 7AD
COOKING 2
071-628 5772
COST £21–£50

The City sibling of Sri Siam (see previous entry) has drawn an enthusiastic response from readers seeking authentic Thai food within striking distance of the Barbican. A much-travelled reporter reckons that the décor is some of the most attractive among London's ethnic restaurants: mottled orange-ochre walls, a dribbling stainless steel fountain, good lighting and a mood of intimacy created by the separation of the bar and eating areas. It feels pleasant, smart and sober. The menu is identical to that of the Old Compton Street original (but with higher prices), and many items have pleased: tom yum koong (prawn and coconut soup), sia rong hai (a beef salad), pomfret with spicy chilli sauce, 'red' curry. Bean curd curried with coconut milk and spices is a rare speciality; kong wan (a coconut custard) is the pick of the sweets. The cooking is sharp, although a reporter detected a lack of authentic fire and felt that the kitchen was 'treading the path of minimal heat to avoid upsetting Western business stomachs'. Service veers from 'exquisite' to 'confused'. Like the menu, the wine list echoes the Soho formula and offers a carefully chosen, intriguing selection. House French is £8.50.

CHEF: P. Lerdjirakul  PROPRIETORS: Thai Restaurants plc  OPEN: Mon to Fri; 11.30am to 8pm  CLOSED: 25 and 26 Dec, 1 Jan  MEALS: alc (main courses £6 to £10.50). Set L and D £13.50 to £24.50 (minimum 2)  SERVICE: 12.5%, card slips closed  CARDS: Access, Amex, Diners, Visa  DETAILS: 130 seats. Private parties: 180 main room. Vegetarian meals. Children welcome. No-smoking area. Wheelchair access (lift; also WC). Music. Air-conditioned. Fax: 071-628 3395

## Stephen Bull ♥

map 14

5–7 Blandford Street, W1H 3AA
COOKING 3*
071-486 9696
COST £24–£48

'This place went through an uncertain period, but is now consistently excellent. I dine here twice a month and haven't had even a moderate dish for ages, except once, a smoked rump steak – meat dishes were always more liable to error than fish – but I have had fine smoked loin of pork, very good guinea-fowl, peppered pork, sea bream, mackerel and grey mullet. Steamed puddings are a delight, as are the meringues of brown sugar. Portions are far from "delicate", and I speak as a trencherman.' Thus a report from a seasoned supporter of Stephen Bull's Marylebone restaurant, as distinct from his bistro in the City (see next entry). The interior setting has always been devoid of ornament, relying on clean lines and geometry, though as we prepare for press art is being hung on hitherto bare walls. Lack of flouncing curtains does not mean slovenliness nor unseemliness, simply a direct approach to public eating. The food achieves a distinctive blend of creativity, fashion and proper training in classical cooking. It also steers a clever course between lightness, strength of flavour and sufficient body. The list of recommended dishes is long. Something of the flavour may be caught by mentioning a salad of vegetable tempura; mackerel mousse and a lemon-lime vinaigrette; twice-cooked goats' cheese soufflé (a constant); lamb with Serrano ham, dry sherry and marjoram; black bream with polenta and a provençale red wine sauce; excellent desserts and bread; strong coffee that varies in quality; and fine little cheese biscuits. Service can be hectic, particularly at lunch, but the staff keep smiling. The set-price lunch menu, a novelty for this year, has been appreciated for economy and performance. Good and reliable merchants supply the wine list, which maintains its straightforward, umpompous approach. The range of excellent house wines provides no incentive to stray further, but adventure is rewarded with such delights as Jean-Luc Colombo's Syrah from Cornas, some tremendous burgundies and finely selected Australians. It is a shame that only dessert wines are offered by the glass; meanwhile, decent half-bottles offer some consolation, and prices throughout are fair. House wines are from £10.25. CELLARMAN'S CHOICE: Sauvignon de Touraine 1992, Marcadet, £12; Rhône Cabernet Sauvignon, Dom. la Soumade 1990, Romero, £17.50.

CHEF: Jon Bentham   PROPRIETOR: Stephen Bull   OPEN: Mon to Sat, exc Sat L; 12.15 to 2, 6.30 to 10.30   MEALS: alc (main courses £10 to £15). Set L £14 (2 courses) to £17   SERVICE: not inc, card slips closed   CARDS: Access, Visa   DETAILS: 60 seats. 2 tables outside. Private parties: 55 main room. Vegetarian meals. Children's helpings. No cigars/pipes in dining-room. Wheelchair access (1 step). No music. Air-conditioned. Fax: 071-490 3128

## Stephen Bull's Bistro and Bar ♥

map 11

71 St John Street, EC1M 4AN                        COOKING 2*
071-490 1750                                       COST £22–£34

Enter the bistro through a door off St John Street. As you proceed down the corridor, mark how it opens out into a tall room bare of much ornament, with focal points of Mondrian-style colouring on expanses of wall and the odd papier-mâché sculpture. There is height enough to accommodate a mezzanine for more tables, and a high-level bridge offers opportunity for suicidal customers and staff, or for bun-throwing. As the name implies, this is cheap Stephen Bull. The bargain has been embraced with enthusiasm by local workers and people off to theatre or concert hall at the Barbican, as well as by the world at large. The style, the materials and the skill are not adrift from those on show at Blandford Street (see previous entry), though presentation may be simpler, the amalgam less rich. The menu stays short (it is longest on first courses, some of which may be promoted to main dishes), with some constants like a plate of Spanish ham, chorizo, Manchego cheese and quince paste, or lemon and lime curd pots with lemon crumble biscuits. Nage of fish with red wine, cumin, chickpeas and aïoli, loin of pork stuffed with Gorgonzola and sun-dried tomatoes, and confit of chicken with grilled black peppercorn polenta and a cardamom and orange sauce are recipes which show the original Stephen Bull style. The characteristics of this are an unwillingness to conform to fashion's latest dictates, yet an ability to stay in touch. This is not a place for an amorous evening in candlelight, just a very fine spot for a meal. A good few wines are offered by the glass; range is eclectic, but brief and very much to the point – 40 bottles in all. Good growers such as Forest in Pouilly-Fuissé and Chopin-Groffier further north indicate a steady eye for quality. Prices are very reasonable and there is much below £12. House wines are from £8.95.

CELLARMAN'S CHOICE: Tocai Friulano 1991, Puiatti, £15; Santa Cruz, Grenache, 'Bighouse' 1991, Bonny Doon, £14.50.

CHEF: Stephen Carter  PROPRIETOR: Stephen Bull  OPEN: Mon to Sat, exc Sat L; 12 to 2, 6 to 10.45  MEALS: alc (main courses £8 to £10)  SERVICE: not inc  CARDS: Access, Visa  DETAILS: 90 seats. Private parties: 90 main room. Vegetarian meals. Children's helpings. No cigars/pipes in dining-room. Wheelchair access (1 step). No music. Air-conditioned. Fax: 071-490 3128

## Suntory
map 14

72–73 St James's Street, SW1A 1PH                    COOKING 3*
071-409 0201                                         COST £25–£96

Japanese restaurants in London are more varied than they may at first appear. Not only are there large differencs in the standards of cooking, but they set out to appeal to very different markets. This is definitely one for visiting managing directors, though there is rather more soul to it than some of the highly priced simulacra of airport lounges that also seem to chase the same sector. The menus do not seem so very different, though Suntory has foie gras and lobster nestling among its broiled dishes, but the prices will alert you to some slight variation on the theme. If adventurous, and rich, take advice about the chef's suggestions beyond the shortish menu. These will show some match to the seasons and may include a river of soy milk and jelly, cold shabu-shabu, egg custard with shards of lobster set in agar-agar, or fresh sardine and burdock tempura. There is real cooking here, and the highest standards regarding the raw materials obtain. The ground-floor restaurant is less cheerful than the teppanyaki bar below. The wine list is aristocratic, with house wines starting the bidding at £14.

CHEF: K. Kato  PROPRIETORS: Suntory Ltd  OPEN: Mon to Sat; 12 to 2, 7 to 10  MEALS: alc (main courses £6 to £39.50). Set L £15 to £33.50, Set D £50 to £67  SERVICE: net prices, card slips closed  CARDS: Access, Amex, Diners, Visa  DETAILS: 120 seats. 19 tables outside. Private parties: 100 main room. Vegetarian meals. Children welcome. Smart dress preferred. Wheelchair access. No music. Air-conditioned. Fax: 071-499 7993

## Le Suquet
map 13

104 Draycott Avenue, SW3 3AE                        COOKING 1*
071-581 1785                                        COST £29–£51

An old hand reports that 'it looks just as it always did: giddy Med fishscapes, lots of deep blue, huge flower and bush arrangements, cramped but cheerful and effective.' The waiters, the menu and the wine list all seem to stay the same, and the particular recipe of fresh fish and a cheery casual French atmosphere is enticing. The cooking will please from the point of view of the raw material, but will be less brilliant if you take it dressed up with too many sauces or concoctions. These can be satisfactory, but sometimes the cooking goes overboard on seasoning or flavouring and destroys the very point of being there – the fish. There are lots of simple seafood options, the grills are tip-top, and vegetable cookery has improved. Desserts are still not exciting. The wine list is devoid of vintages and pretty bare of interest. House wines are £9.50.

CHEF: Jean Yves Darcel   PROPRIETOR: Pierre Martin   OPEN: all week; 12.30 to 3, 7 to 11.30
MEALS: alc (main courses £9 to £15). Cover £1   SERVICE: 15%, card slips closed
CARDS: Access, Amex, Diners, Visa   DETAILS: 50 seats. 4 tables outside. Private parties: 14
private room. Vegetarian meals. Children's helpings. Smart dress preferred. Wheelchair
access (also WC). Music

## Surinder's

map 12

109 Westbourne Park Road, W2 5QL                      COOKING 1
071-229 8968                                          COST £21–£28

Of late, little has been heard of this small neighbourhood restaurant where
Surinder Chandwan has held aloft the flag of reasonably priced French food for
several years. When Surinder's opened in 1985, there were few places around
that could supply bistro-style dishes as well or as cheaply in distinctly un-
bistro-like surroundings: no dusty candle-wax drippings or red check
tablecloths here. After a couple of spells of illness, Surinder is back in business.
The formula of a set price for a short daily menu has not altered. Spinach
pancakes or *bloc* of foie gras, then grilled Dover sole, saddle of lamb, or calf's
liver, with vegetables ('could have been more ample'), and a simple dessert
like little pots of chocolate are some of the things on offer. A dinner of game
sausage with red cabbage, followed by venison in a prune sauce and a small
selection of cheese, kept winter chills away and proved fair value. The cooking
can be very workmanlike, the ambience agreeably familiar. The wine list is in
keeping. House wines are £7.95.

CHEF/PROPRIETOR: Surinder Chandwan   OPEN: Tue to Sat, D only; 7 to 11   MEALS: Set L
and D £14.95   SERVICE: 10%, card slips closed   CARDS: Access, Amex, Visa   DETAILS: 45
seats. Private parties: 45 main room. Vegetarian meals. Children welcome. Wheelchair
access (2 steps). No music

## Surya £

map 11

59–61 Fortune Green Road, NW6 1DR                     COOKING 1
071-435 7486                                          COST £12–£21

Regulars confirm that standards are being maintained in this family-run Indian
vegetarian restaurant. Décor is still the same smart green and white, with glass-
topped tables and an atmosphere of 'scrupulous cleanliness'. Mr Tiwari
oversees the dining-room and service is reckoned to be very polite but 'never
smarmy'. Mrs Tiwari's cooking is exact and authentic, and many dishes have
been recommended. Crunchy bhel poori, deep-fried aloo bhonda (potato balls
with some crushed peanuts and onion mashed in), mater paneer, chickpea
curry, very spicy sambar dhal, fluffy fried bhatura bread and 'delightful' pilau
rice were the components of one fine meal. Daily specials are also worth
investigating: for instance, Tuesday brings bread rolls with spicy potato
stuffing and kaddu (pumpkin curry).

▲ *This symbol means accommodation is available.*

CHEF: Mrs H. Tiwari   PROPRIETOR: Mr R.C. Tiwari   OPEN: all week, D only, and Sun L; 12 to 2.30, 6 to 10.30 (11 Fri and Sat)   CLOSED: 24 to 31 Dec, 1 Jan   MEALS: alc (main courses £2 to £3). Set Sun L £4.95, Set D £6 to £11   SERVICE: 10%   CARDS: Access, Amex, Diners, Visa   DETAILS: 32 seats. Private parties: 32 main room. Vegetarian meals. No children under 6 after 7pm. No-smoking area. Wheelchair access (also WC). Music. Air-conditioned

## Tageen

map 15

12 Upper St Martin's Lane, WC2H 9DL

071-836 7272

COOKING 1

COST £21–£34

Tageen is Moroccan, named after those conical terracotta pots brought home by holidaymakers to recreate remembered masterpieces. Tageen is also upper-crust, interpreting for us the cookery of ancient Moroccan courts. Hence bastela, the country's most famed main course: a construction of pastry, chicken (or pigeon) and almond, pointed with saffron, rosewater and spices, then dusted with sugar. Staff decked out in ethnic gear will explain some of these delights, though occasionally their smiles outweigh the clarity of their expositions. Couscous, brik, meshwiya (grilled peppers) and tageens of various complexions (lamb or chicken cooked with saffron, pickled lemon and olives, or artichokes or peas and potatoes, to name but a few) are the staples of the menu, but there are 'one-plate meal' soups such as harira (lentils and chickpeas), as well as grilled fish. Some of the flavours are less aromatic than might be hoped: 'We found a few bites enough and shared everything between ourselves to give variety.' But the bastela makes a visit worthwhile. Certain price reductions are available at lunch-time and at dinner before 7pm. Moroccan wines are among the short selection available. House wines start at £8.50.

CHEF: Maitre Idrissi   PROPRIETORS: ANFA Catering Ltd   OPEN: Mon to Sat, exc Sat L; 12.30 to 2.30, 6 to 11 (11.30 Sat)   MEALS: alc (main courses £8 to £11.50). Cover 90p   SERVICE: not inc   CARDS: Access, Amex, Diners, Visa   DETAILS: 90 seats. 2 tables outside. Private parties: 50 main room. Vegetarian meals. Children's helpings. Wheelchair access (1 step). Music. Air-conditioned. Fax: 071-379 0759

## La Tante Claire ▼

map 13

68 Royal Hospital Road, SW3 4HP

071-352 6045 and 351 0227

COOKING 5

COST £31–£94

'All we can say about this lunch is that it was daylight robbery – so inspired and such good value that the customer felt he was robbing the restaurant.' 'I take world-weary advertising managers here and their jaws drop in astonishment at the first mouthful.' 'To say "I've had the best meal in my life" is not as high praise as I would like it to be.' The clutch of letters about this restaurant in deepest Chelsea is as impressive a group as one could hope for. Praise piles on praise to near surfeit; even those who reflect that 'it could have been more memorable' soon suggest they may have ordered badly. Legions protest at the service charge *and* open credit card slips but then admit the service to be unstuffy, 'so kind' and so perfect that the staff almost deserve a double tip. Some of this effusion of support comes from gratitude: that cooking this good and service this svelte can be available for so little – at lunch on the set-price menu, of course. The room is stylish yet understated, airy yet never glaring, public but with space enough for privacy. 'Mr Koffmann eschews the baroque,' said one who liked the directness of the cooking, no matter how sophisticated it may be. This can extend to many elements, as in the assiette canardière aux deux sauces, or as perhaps in a lunch dish of lentil soup with ravioli of duck confit. Pierre Koffmann likes to give things added depth as in a ragoût of langoustines with strong shellfish stock garnished with a piece of crisp belly pork, or in his chocolate sauce with venison. Some may wish to eat specialities like his stuffed pig's trotter, but he also does more recognisable items from a bourgeois repertoire: a brandade de morue, though of course with some caviare, or a plainish spatchcocked pigeon, though here with some foie gras. His ability lies in eliciting very intense flavours through care, proper recipes and recognition that taste matters. The *carte* is quite long, offering a strangely haute cuisine-dominated set of first courses (foie gras and shellfish or other luxuries) but broadening out with the main dishes. The lunch menu, a short set of daily alternatives, sometimes seems both more accessible and more interesting. Anyone who had an oyster and langoustine ragoût with ginger followed by côte de boeuf with shallots then soup of peaches, nectarines and rhubarb for under £25 in these surroundings would seem lucky indeed. The saintliness of M. Koffmann continues with his socially aware list of relatively inexpensive French regional wines (from £11.90) that help his giant wine list to be affordable. The rest will not, but it does offer hours of reading and good conversation with the sommelier who, needless to say, knows his onions. CELLARMAN'S CHOICE: Côtes de Duras, Sauvignon Blanc 1992, £13.90; Chinon Rouge, Les Allets 1988, £22.80.

CHEF: Pierre Koffmann   PROPRIETORS: Mr and Mrs Pierre Koffmann   OPEN: Mon to Fri; 12.30 to 2, 7 to 11   CLOSED: Christmas and New Year   MEALS: alc (main courses £23 to £28). Set L £24.50. Minimum £45 D   SERVICE: net prices   CARDS: Access, Amex, Diners, Visa   DETAILS: 45 seats. Vegetarian meals with prior notice. Children's helpings. No children under 8. Jacket and tie D. Wheelchair access (1 step; also WC). No music. Air-conditioned. Fax: 071-352 3257

## Thai Garden ⁵⁕ £                                                    map 10

249 Globe Road, Bethnal Green, E2 0JD                              COOKING 2
081-981 5748                                                      COST £10–£30

'Vegetarian food does not have to be bland,' says Jack Hufton, especially if it is Thai. Try the mus mun, a curry of yellow bean curd, onion, potato and peanut sweetened with coconut cream for proof. The Huftons have also allowed themselves the freedom of fish and shellfish, so the appeal of their monochrome-decorated restaurant can be as wide as Bethnal Green permits. Pensri Vichit has a sure palate – Thai cooking, almost more than any other, is a matter of balancing very strong flavours – and the result is excellent. Tom yum soup in clay pots, satay of oyster mushrooms, stir-fried prawns with garlic and pepper, and a benchmark example of pomfret with sweet-and-sour sauce are things that have pleased. Everyone is very friendly; it is wise to book. House wine is £5.95.

CHEF: Mrs Pensri Vichit   PROPRIETORS: Suthinee and Jack Hufton   OPEN: Mon to Sat, exc
Sat L; 12 to 2.45, 6 to 10.45   CLOSED: bank hols   MEALS: alc (main courses £4 to £6.50).
Set L £6.50, Set D £14.50 to £19   SERVICE: 10% (net prices Set L), card slips closed
CARDS: Access, Visa   DETAILS: 32 seats. Private parties: 20 main room, 14 private room.
Vegetarian meals. Children's helpings with prior notice. No smoking in upstairs dining-
room. Wheelchair access (1 step). Music

## Thailand £       map 10

| 15 Lewisham Way, SE14 6PP | COOKING 2* |
| 081-691 4040 | COST £19–£41 |

'Some of the best Thai food I've had, and it does a small set of Laotian dishes as
well,' said a wanderer from north London who urged us to stress that it is
plumb opposite Goldsmiths' College and that 'the unappealing, exhaust-
smutted exterior on a road with heavy traffic is no guide at all to the
immaculate interior, white damask cloths and spotless kitchen'. The cooking is
in the manner of north-eastern Thailand, where many of the people are in fact
of Laotian origin. It is, therefore, the nearest thing to a Lao restaurant in
London. Two sittings in an evening may cause problems at overlap time, but
the food is worth it – very fine cooking of a menu mercifully free of Thai names
so that everyone knows what is what. Chillis are hot here, and there is no
trimming. The wine list is short but sound. Sicilian Cellaro is £8.50.

CHEF/PROPRIETOR: Kamkhong Cambungeot   OPEN: Tue to Sat, D only; 6 to 11 (2 sittings at
weekends)   MEALS: alc (main courses £5.50 to £10.50). Parties £20 per head   SERVICE: not
inc   CARDS: Access, Amex, Visa   DETAILS: 25 seats. Private parties: 25 main room.
Vegetarian meals. Music. Air-conditioned

## Thistells £       map 10

| 65 Lordship Lane, SE22 8EP | COOKING 1 |
| 081-299 1921 | COST £13–£32 |

If the falafel with tahini makes you think you are in an Egyptian restaurant you
would be half-right, for Sami Youssef draws on his native culture for some
favourites, while using his classical European training to produce 'the best
best-end of lamb ever tasted' or breast of duck with cassis. Thistells is a wine
bar-cum-restaurant of a decidedly neighbourhood tilt that can summon up
some really good cooking. Try the horura (three-bean soup with coriander), or
ful medames. Desserts are not so fine. House wine is £7.

CHEF/PROPRIETOR: Sami Youssef   OPEN: all week, exc L Mon and Sat and Sun D; 12 to 3,
7 to 10.30   MEALS: alc (main courses £5.50 to £10.50). Set Sun L £8   SERVICE: 10%, card
slips closed   CARDS: Access, Visa   DETAILS: 40 seats. 4 tables outside. Private parties: 45
main room. Vegetarian meals. Children's helpings. Smart dress preferred. Wheelchair
access. Music

*Several sharp operators have tried to extort money from restaurateurs on the promise of an
entry in a guidebook that has never appeared.* The Good Food Guide *makes no charge
for inclusion and does not offer certificates of any kind.*

## La Truffe Noire ✷

map 11

29 Tooley Street, SE1 2QF
071-378 0621

COOKING 2
COST £24–£55

If ever you find yourself near the London Dungeon, you are not far from La
Truffe Noire. The owners recognise that the area is 'economically
disadvantaged; most people are council-home dwellers with serious
unemployment problems and most of our clients come over from the City'. The
general opinion is that this is a lunch-time place, with a duo of sensibly priced
menus running concurrently with a short *carte* in the formal restaurant, the grill
below and the terrace patio on sunny days. Cooking is often found to be
satisfactory if a touch pedestrian, yet details may be less than perfect.
Approvals have been noted for smoked salmon with dill and cucumber relish,
crab mayonnaise, Canadian lobster with cream and chive sauce, pheasant with
apple and cinnamon purée and sea bass with sweet potato purée. With the odd
exception, desserts have been judged very good indeed – for instance, a
chocolate and orange mousse of fine texture, with a pistachio and mint sauce
that set it off magnificently. Though La Truffe is voted a curate's egg in most
reports, the district needs every break it can get. The wine list is a fairly normal
classic French collection, of no great length. A clutch of fine clarets furnishes
the big city dealers; otherwise Louis Latour seems the favourite maker. House
wines are from £8.

CHEFS: Pascal Lucas and Patrick Lalor   PROPRIETORS: Mr and Mrs M. Alam-Ahmed
OPEN: Mon to Fri (also Sat D May to Sept); 12 to 2.30, 7 to 10.30   CLOSED: bank hols
MEALS: alc (main courses £10 to £20). Set L and D £10 (2 courses) to £19   SERVICE: 12.5%,
card slips closed   CARDS: Access, Amex, Diners, Visa   DETAILS: restaurant 50 seats, grill
40 seats. 10 tables outside. Private parties: 60 main room, 16, 32 and 40 private rooms.
Vegetarian meals. Children's helpings on request. Smart dress preferred. No smoking in 1
dining-room. No cigars/pipes in dining-rooms. Wheelchair access (1 step). Music. Air-
conditioned. Fax: 071-403 0689

## Turner's

map 13

87–89 Walton Street, SW3 2HP
071-584 6711

COOKING 3*
COST £22–£57

'Refurbished since our last visit,' writes one reporter of Turner's, 'it remains a
calm, beautiful room in blue, cream and gold. Only the tarts' knickers at the
windows introduce an inconsistent note.' Brian Turner stills keeps his
customers contented. His social skills are as evident as his successful control of
the kitchen, displaying the same degree of tact and judgement enlivened by
just the right amount of flair and jollity. This may provoke backlash if he
spends more time with one table than another, but it does keep the place
personal. 'The style is deceptively simple with no attempt to extend frontiers,
but the lightness of touch and the instinctive resort to flavour combinations that
work ensure satisfaction' was the conclusion of inspectors who make a point of
coming here when on a visit to London. They have found some economies in
force (why no canapés?), and some cheaper menus, especially at lunch-time,
but no deviation from the correct priorities. Hence a dinner that included crab
salad with ginger to point it up, and a warm salad of sweetbreads with rocket

dressed with walnut oil and mixed with lardons. It went on to a rolled breast of guinea-fowl with an acidulated sauce that gave it the character of poulet au vinaigre, and a fillet of sea bass with a Fleurie sauce and morels, all served with a bouquet of vegetables – 'nothing wrong with these if done well,' our reporters commented defensively, as if to protect Brian Turner from accusations of being out of the culinary swim. A long list of desserts keeps up the standard, but often people elect to skip it and drive through to coffee and excellent petits fours. The price structure almost encourages this. The wine list has an impressive set of Chablis from William Fèvre. It does not really bother with anything beyond France and is definitely not cheap. House wines are £11.50.

CHEF: Peter Brennan   PROPRIETOR: Brian Turner   OPEN: all week, exc Sat L; 12.30 to 2.30, 7.30 to 11.15 (10 Sun)   CLOSED: 1 week Christmas, bank hols   MEALS: alc (2 courses £32). Set L £9.95 (2 courses) to £13.50, Set D £23.50 (2 courses) to £26.50   SERVICE: net prices, card slips closed   CARDS: Access, Amex, Diners, Visa   DETAILS: 52 seats. Private parties: 54 main room. Vegetarian meals. Children welcome. Smart dress preferred. Wheelchair access (1 step). Music. Air-conditioned. Fax: 071-584 4441

## Two Brothers £                          NEW ENTRY   map 10

297–303 Regent's Park Road, N3 1DP                    COOKING 2
081-346 0469                                          COST £13–£32

'In the reaches of Temple Fortune' might be the description of a fledgling geographer, 'across the North Circular' the warning of a tired driver; but wherever, this bustling fish restaurant is worth a trip for very sound cooking across the spectrum of fry it and serve it, to more complex affairs with honestly crafted sauces. The restaurant side takes no bookings and has a queue. It is not a place for a languorous visit, but no one could fault the quality of the welcome, or its enthusiasm. The batter is first-class, the oil as fresh as it could be, and so too is the fish. Hollandaises, mayonnaises and dressings do *not* come out a bottle. The daily specials board may have shellfish and crustacea on offer, but keen supporters urge trial of Tony's Arbroath smokies, or the plump marinated herrings, as well as the plainer fish. Ice-creams will see off any lingering hunger, and coffee is decent. The wine list is headed by the Manzis own Côtes de Duras and is thoroughly sound. House wines are £6.95 for Duboeuf.

CHEFS/PROPRIETORS: Leon and Tony Manzi   OPEN: Tue to Sat; 12 to 2.30, 5.30 to 10.15 MEALS: alc (main courses £5 to £10)   SERVICE: not inc, card slips closed   CARDS: Access, Amex, Visa   DETAILS: 90 seats. Vegetarian meals. Children's helpings. No babies after 6.30pm. No-smoking area. Wheelchair access (2 steps). Music. Air-conditioned

## Upper Street Fish Shop £                          map 11

324 Upper Street, N1 2XQ                              COOKING 1
071-359 1401                                          COST £10–£24

Check tablecloths, heavy silverware, tartare sauce and Heinz tomato sauce on the tables, a loyal following, tea, fried fish and chips: perhaps this is a successful recipe – it is also this cheerful fish restaurant. Not everything is fried for a main course, and for starters the fish soup is enjoyed; and if not that then Irish rock oysters or mussels are done in batter. Puddings, from crumble to summer and back to treacle tart or steamed ginger sponge, are home-made. It puts a gloss on the word 'chippie'.

CHEFS: Alan Conway and Stuart Gamble   PROPRIETORS: Alan and Olga Conway
OPEN: Mon to Sat, exc Mon L; 12 to 2, 5.30 to 10   MEALS: alc (main courses £3.50 to £8.50).
Minimum £6.30. Unlicensed, but bring your own: no corkage   SERVICE: not inc
DETAILS: 50 seats. Children welcome. Wheelchair access. No music. Air-conditioned

## Vegetarian Cottage £    NEW ENTRY   map 11

91 Haverstock Hill, NW3 4RL                                          COOKING 1
071-586 1257                                                        COST £13–£30

You will not find many Chinese vegetarian restaurants in London, yet China has a long and distinguished Buddhist vegetarian tradition. This restaurant, which is up the hill from Chalk Farm tube and is plainly yet pleasingly appointed, brings that tradition to us. Taking advantage of the chameleon-like quality of bean curd, the Chinese vegetarian style imitates meats and fishes. This is similar to our own vegetarian cookery, which offered nut cutlets and vegan hamburgers rather than accept the vegetable world on its own terms. The menu of the Vegetarian Cottage thus lists duck and fish simulated by vegetable protein (though bona fide seafood such as prawns and scallops are also served). Better, perhaps, or more interesting in flavour, are the more direct vegetable dishes: braised mushroom and black moss, Szechuan aubergine and vegetables with turmeric. Mixed gluten balls are also worth a try. Service is amiable and ready to inform; the cooking is acceptable. The wine list is better than many and not expensive. House wines are £6.50.

CHEF: C. Wong   PROPRIETORS: Y.K. Tsui and S.W. Chu   OPEN: all week, D only, and Sun
L; 6 (noon Sun) to 11   CLOSED: Christmas   MEALS: alc (main courses £4 to £5.50). Set Sun
L £7.50, Set D £10.80 to £12.50   SERVICE: not inc   CARDS: Access, Visa   DETAILS: 60
seats. Private parties: 20 main room, 20 private room. Vegetarian meals. Children welcome.
Smart dress preferred. Wheelchair access (1 step). No music. Air-conditioned

## Villandry Dining Room ⅝✳    map 14

89 Marylebone High Street, W1M 3DE                                  COOKING 1
071-224 3799 and 487 3816                                           COST £22–£38

The restaurant grows, its tentacles reaching into parts of the shop that are not needed for sales or display. Its roots lie at the back, in a room some have said reminded them of school, the seats of detention. It has also expanded its hours: no longer just lunch, but breakfast (9.30 to 11.30), tea (3.30 to 5.30) and the occasional dinner. The rush and crush have not altered, though, and it is best to arrive early if you want the whole menu to choose from. The bases of the operation – regular items such as smoked salmon, soups, charcuterie, cheeses – are in symbiosis with the shop, where you can also buy sandwiches. The shop may seem profoundly French, though less so than when it started, but the dining-rooms are more mixed in inspiration: nothing French about Cumberland sausages with cranberry sauce and mash, but nothing very English in the salads either. Some days the cooking works better than on others. The tarts, the rice pudding and particularly the coffee get good notices.

The final total has been known to surprise, for such a bare-bones approach. The wines are supplied by Legrand of Paris, which means that many of the makers are unfamiliar to customers versed in the lists of English shippers. They start at £9.90 – not cheap for a lunch-time café either.

CHEFS: Caroline Symonds and Rosalind Carrarini  PROPRIETORS: Jean-Charles and Rosalind Carrarini  OPEN: Mon to Sat, L only (D third Thur of month, and private parties by arrangement); 12 to 2.30, 7.30 to 9.30  CLOSED: bank hols  MEALS: alc (main courses £7 to £13). Minimum £6.50 L  SERVICE: net prices, card slips closed  CARDS: Access, Visa  DETAILS: 48 seats. Private parties: 45 main room. Vegetarian meals. Children's helpings. No smoking in dining-room. Wheelchair access. Music. Air-conditioned. Fax: 071-486 1370

## Wagamama ⁵✳ £　　　　　　　　　　　　　　map 14

4 Streatham Street, WC1A 1JB　　　　　　　　　　　　　　COOKING 1
071-323 9223　　　　　　　　　　　　　　　　　　　COST £10−£16

'"The way of the noodle" is to make slurping noises while eating – the extra oxygen adds to the taste,' says a note on the menu of this giant Japanese canteen with the motto 'positive eating'. In a minimalist setting of white, pale wood and steel, the kitchen serves up a range of good-value one-pot dishes based around ramen (Chinese-style noodles in broth), soba (buckwheat) and udon (thick, worm-like white noodles) in various combinations with meat, fish and vegetables. 'The food is hot, imaginative and wonderfully flavoured,' commented one contented customer who noted the queues out on the street at 7 in the evening. This is no-frills, satisfying cooking delivered in an enthusiastic but 'devoted' atmosphere, where high fashion and in-vogue philosophy go hand in hand. The 'great staff' take orders on computer terminals and help to make this 'the ultimate fast food'. Japanese tea is free; otherwise drink saké, plum wine or Kirin beer. Three organic wines are also available from £6.80.

CHEF: Ayumi Meada  PROPRIETORS: Wagamama Ltd  OPEN: Mon to Sat; 12 to 2.30 (1 to 3 Sat), 6 to 11  MEALS: alc (main courses £3.50 to £6.50)  SERVICE: not inc  DETAILS: 104 seats. Vegetarian meals. Children welcome. No smoking. No music. Air-conditioned. Fax: 071-323 9224

## Wakaba　　　　　　　　　　　　　　　　　　　map 11

122A Finchley Road, NW3 5HT　　　　　　　　　　　　　COOKING 3
071-722 3854 and 586 7960　　　　　　　　　　　　　　COST £21−£60

The hard-edged design of this place (opposite Finchley Road tube station) does not lose its appeal. Many appalled by the plain surfaces are converted by the quality of the geometry and the materials. It helps, too, that the staff are so engaging, and that the customers are so potentially smart and certainly interesting. The sheer façade broken by a curved frosted-glass window draws the visitor in. He or she may pause to eat at the sushi bar at the back of the room or take a wider choice at table. Whichever, the freshness is exemplary in the sashimi (truly tested by the mackerel), and the ohitashi is as good as any in London, the stock with the noodles quite sweet and strong. The range does not stray far outside the classics of Japanese cuisine, but performance is satisfyingly consistent. House white wine is £8.50, saké is £3.30, or drink green tea or Japanese beer.

CHEF/PROPRIETOR: Minoru Yoshihara  OPEN: Mon to Sat, D only; 6.30 to 11  CLOSED: 4 days Christmas, 4 days Easter  MEALS: alc (main courses £7 to £18). Set D £24 to £33. Minimum £15  SERVICE: 10%  CARDS: Access, Amex, Diners, Visa  DETAILS: 55 seats. Private parties: 55 main room. Vegetarian meals. Children welcome. Smart dress preferred. Wheelchair access (also WC). No music. Air-conditioned

## *Waltons*

map 13

121 Walton Street, SW3 2HP  COOKING 2*
071-584 0204  COST £21–£70

Visitors to London have often heard of Waltons and enjoy its hyper-suave 'domestic' decoration that looks more like a glossy magazine illustration than most such interiors – no hard edges here, all very deeply cosseted. It makes a virtue of Englishness, without indulging in the quaint, and makes common-or-garden restaurant standards sound as if they were part of our heritage. Calf's liver and bacon with an onion marmalade and grain mustard sauce, or breast of Norfolk duck with a passion-fruit sauce, are examples of this. Desserts may sound like something out of the Lake District, headed as they are by sticky toffee pudding. Prices, apart from the neighbourhood-friendly lunch-time deals, are high for the food offered, if not for the location, but the service is well balanced and the atmosphere of an evening can be pleasantly intimate. The place improves with the wine list, which offers a fine fist of clarets and other French wines – more summary for the rest of the world – at not indecent prices. There are worthwhile bourgeois as well as classed growths, plus some Rousseau burgundies which well repay investigation. House wines are £9.

CHEF: Paul Hodgson  PROPRIETOR: Roger Wren  OPEN: all week; 12.30 to 2.30, 7.30 to 11.30 (12.30 to 2, 7 to 10 Sun and bank hols)  CLOSED: 25 and 26 Dec  MEALS: alc (main courses £12.50 to £17). Set L £10 (2 courses) to £14.75, Set Sun L £16.50, Set post-theatre D £21 (2 courses)  SERVICE: not inc  CARDS: Access, Amex, Diners, Visa  DETAILS: 90 seats. Private parties: 40 main room, 6, 12 and 20 private rooms. Vegetarian meals. Children's helpings on request. Smart dress preferred. Wheelchair access (1 step). Music. Air-conditioned. Fax: 071-581 2848

## *Wiltons*

map 14

55 Jermyn Street, SW1Y 6LX  COOKING 3
071-629 9955  COST £33–£80

If you have a fair bit of money, a taste for fresh fish or game cooked English style, like to see the British establishment on its home ground, then take a Pullman booth here (if you can) and eat a meal. Service is motherly and redolent of the club or common-room, but then it is as much a neighbourhood restaurant as any in north London or Richmond – just choose your neighbourhood. The quality of the produce is not in question, though there are many who will not find the ambience relaxing, the cost realistic, or the style to their current taste. House wines are around £13.

CHEF: Ross Hayden  PROPRIETORS: Wiltons (St James's) Ltd  OPEN: Mon to Sat, exc Sat L; 12.15 to 2.15, 6.30 to 10.15  CLOSED: 10 days Christmas, bank/public hols  MEALS: alc (main courses £12 to £26). Cover £1. Minimum £11  SERVICE: not inc  CARDS: Access, Amex, Diners, Visa  DETAILS: 90 seats. Private parties: 30 main room, 18 private room. Vegetarian meals. Children's helpings. No children under 8. Jacket and tie. Wheelchair access (1 step). No music. Air-conditioned

## Zen Central
map 14

20 Queen Street, W1X 7PJ
071-629 8103 and 8089

COOKING 1*
COST £26–£83

The refurbished Rick Mather design, all black and white and as smart, or international, as the clientele that fill it to the very windows – it is a good restaurant to pass by at night – seems to have given the place a new lease of life. The menu adopts a Western approach rather than the long catalogues of Cantonese restaurants, and the repertoire is less traditional than is common in Chinese cooking. This makes dishes such as smoked chicken imbued with spices, lobster with tangerine peel and crushed garlic, or whole sea bass deep-fried and braised with coriander and chilli well worth trying. The kitchen is MSG-free; the dim-sum and dumplings are good; the level of finesse, and the service, can be impressive. The wine list is impressively priced and packs an upper-class punch. House wines are £12.

CHEF: Michael Leung  PROPRIETORS: Blaidwood Co Ltd  OPEN: all week; 12.15 to 2.30, 6.30 to 11.15 (11 Sun)  CLOSED: 3 days Christmas  MEALS: alc (main courses £7.50 to £30). Set D £30 to £45. Cover £1. Minimum £20  SERVICE: not inc  CARDS: Access, Amex, Diners, Visa  DETAILS: 90 seats. Private parties: 80 main room, 18 private room. Vegetarian meals. Children welcome. Smart dress preferred. Wheelchair access. Music. Air-conditioned. Fax: 071-437 0641

## Zoe £
**NEW ENTRY**  map 14

St Christopher's Place,
3–5 Barrett Street, W1M 5HH
071-224 1122

COOKING 2
COST £17–£42

The last restaurant on this site was short-lived. The owners called in London's favourite magician Antony Worrall-Thompson to work his spell and transform its popularity. To begin, he spilt his paint pots in an alarming, or arresting, galaxy of colours – warm umbers, blues and greens – to make what was mainly a basement more lively, more *happening*. He did the same with the menu, which some have likened to a caricature of his current style; it is certainly long and may muddle the reader. Split between 'City' and 'Country', it has many dishes on offer as first or main courses, and has no discernible unity save fashion. 'Country' yields ham hock, parsley pease-pudding and hot potato salad, or braised lamb shank, flageolet beans with garlic and rosemary, and lambs' kidneys with champ, bacon and mushrooms. 'City' tries grilled marinated salmon, bacon and pickled aubergine, grilled squid, rocket and chips, and grilled saddle of rabbit, ancho-chilli sauce and roast pumpkin. Breads are various and are charged extra; free pickles are a giant home-made choice. Service and cooking can be fun. Upstairs there is a slightly cheaper café menu, and a jumping bar is next door. The place works; the difficulty is in retaining even quality. The wine list is short and prices are mainly under £20. The bottles are perfectly decent, the prices only just over the odds. House wine from Duboeuf is £8.25.

CHEFS: Antony Worrall-Thompson and Conrad Melling    PROPRIETORS: Zen Group
OPEN: all week, exc Sun D and bank hols; 11.30am to 11.30pm    CLOSED: 24 to 26 Dec
MEALS: alc (main courses £5.50 to £12). Set L and D £7.50 (2 courses) to £10    SERVICE: not
inc    CARDS: Access, Amex, Diners, Visa    DETAILS: 160 seats. 20 tables outside. Private
parties: 90 main room. Vegetarian meals. Children's helpings. Smart dress preferred. No
cigars/pipes in dining-room. Wheelchair access (2 steps). Music. Air-conditioned. Fax:
071-935 5444

# London round-ups

'Where should we go then?' is sometimes as impossible a question as 'Who is your favourite composer?' and the *Guide*'s full entries may not always supply the answer. You live in the wrong part, your pocket cannot stretch so far, you can't stand curries, fish, liver or vegetables. This supplementary listing is 100-odd places that may help your decision. They have gained approval of other readers, but they may not fit the *Guide*'s specifications, or approval is too guarded for complete description or recommendation. Read on.

## Price guide

For a three-course meal, including half a bottle of house wine, coffee and service, per person.

£ = £20 or under
££ = £20–£30
£££ = £30 or over

**L'Altro**                       W11
210 Kensington Park Road        map 12
071-792 1066 and 1077
Baroque theatre décor (that can sometimes feel rather spartan); fish in modern Italian style. Everything from baby octopus and cuttlefish to monkfish and sea bream.    **££–£££**

**Andrew Edmunds**                 W1
46 Lexington Street             map 14
071-437 5708
Relaxed, some have said arrogant, haunt that's a magnet for Soho trend. Modern British cuisine from a short, interesting menu. Duck breast with mango relish and lamb chops with tapénade have pleased, as have 'grown-up' puddings and decent coffee. Gets busy, so book ahead.    **£**

**Aroma**                          W1
1B Dean Street                  map 15
071-287 1633
Quirky café providing a safe haven from the crush that is Oxford Street. South American music, funky décor, colourful crockery, modern classic sandwiches and a take-away option make this a popular pit-stop. Great coffee is the star attraction: cappuccino, espresso, iced-coffee and ristretto amongst others.    **£**

Branches also at: 36A St Martin's Lane, WC2, 071-836 5110
273 Regent Street, W1, 071-495 4911.

**Arts Theatre Café**             WC2
6 Great Newport Street          map 15
071-497 8014
Basement Italian beneath the Unicorn Theatre. Very informal, with few frills in the way of furnishings and absent-minded service, but home to honest Italian fare. Breads and rustic dishes such as braised chicory in Gorgonzola on focaccia, and grilled sausages with lentils and pancetta, have been better than pastas. Fruit-based desserts are refreshing.    **£**

**Aziz**                           W6
116 King Street                 map 10
081-748 1826
Reliable tandoori restaurant in the heart of Hammersmith. Reported favourite dishes have been king prawn vindaloo served with freshly chopped chillies, chicken Madras and fresh nan bread. Courteous and willing service.    **£**

**Balzac Bistro**                 W12
4 Wood Lane                     map 10
081-743 6787
Well-run bistro for straightforward French food. Fresh fish particularly has

been found reliable, and the chef is said to be happy to adapt anything on the menu, if required. Pleasant service.   £

### Beauchamp Place                               SW3
15 Beauchamp Place                          map 13
071-589 4252
Contemporary menus from the Antony Worrall-Thompson stable. Chef David Wilby's food is colourful, earthy and expressive; choose lighter dishes to avoid too much oil. Alcoves, ochre walls and whimsical outbreaks of mosaic make the most of the basement location. Intelligent wine list.   £–££

### Belvedere                                        W8
Holland Park,                                   map 12
off Abbotsbury Road
071-602 1238
Wonderful park location, perfect for a summer lunch. Food is not as successful as the foliage outside. Modern eclectic menus take in all things fashionable: tagliatelle, tartlets, tortillas and lots of chargrilling. Sweets can be stunning. Light and airy, split-level dining-room and an enjoyable atmosphere.   ££

### Beotys                                           WC2
79 St Martin's Lane                          map 15
071-836 8768/8548
Long-running, family-owned Greek restaurant that's happily old-fashioned. Steady cooking of decent materials; skip the mélange of universal dishes in favour of the authentic Greek – classic calamari, soufflé-like moussaka, souvlakia and 'wonderful' Greek honey pudding. Welcoming and professional service.   ££

### Bodali                                            N5
78 Highbury Park                            map 11
071-359 3444
Unprepossessing Indian run by a husband-and-wife team. Refreshing home cooking more reminiscent of the cafés of Southall than the usual high street establishments. Tender chicken tikka and rogan josh, interesting prawn

curry with apricots, terrific breads. Unlicensed.   £

### Books for Cooks                              W11
4 Blenheim Crescent                         map 12
071-221 1992
Go to the back of the shop, behind the shelves groaning with every conceivable cookery book, to find this tiny lunch-time café. Presumably, customers have had their appetites whetted from so much food reading and are more than ready for imaginative dishes prepared from fresh market ingredients.   £

### La Bouchée                                       SW7
56 Old Brompton Road                      map 13
071-589 1929
Crowded South Kensington place for all French staples. Snails are good, as are profiteroles and tarte Tatin, but fish dishes have been disappointing. Overstretched staff sometimes struggle to cope with the tables – but young visitors may still find it fun.   £

### Le Braconnier                                 SW14
467 Upper Richmond Road West   map 10
081-878 2853
Provincial French cuisine, set-price menus at both lunch and dinner and an agreeable ambience. Execution is passable to good, with pâtés and terrines receiving praise and desserts always popular. The wine list is expensive but the house red is very drinkable.   ££

### Del Buongustaio                             SW15
283 Putney Bridge Road                    map 10
081-780 9361
This ambitiously decorated neighbourhood bistro has a menu that promises to be different. However, the Italian cooking is not always exciting and sometimes underseasoned. Redeeming features are the olives and breads at the start and the genuine tiramisù with an intense chocolate sauce at the finish.   ££

**Café de Colombia** W1
Musuem of Mankind, map 14
6 Burlington Gardens
071-287 8148
Not just for those interested in
ethnography but easily accessible for
anyone needing a break from Cork Street
galleries or Jermyn Street shops. Reviving
cappuccino, cakes, biscuits and salads
from Justin de Blank. Open morning
through till late afternoon.

**Café du Marché** EC1
22 Charterhouse Square map 11
071-608 1609
City warehouse conversion that
understandably buzzes more at noon
than in the evening. The atmosphere and
well-paced service have pleased, and
most find the French cooking consistent
in its reliance on good raw materials and
accompanying herbs. Attractive wines,
less wonderful coffee. **£££**

**Café Flo** NW3
205 Haverstock Hill map 11
071-435 6744
The Belsize Park branch of the brasserie
group, geared to providing Continental
breakfasts and casual meals. French
favourites include mussels, fish soup,
chicken stuffed with crab in a basquaise
sauce and confit of duck. A rapid
turnover of clients may mean tables are
wanted back before long. **£**
Branches also at: 51 St Martin's Lane,
WC2, 071-836 8289
334 Upper Street, N1, 071-226 7916
127–129 Kensington Church Street, W8,
071-727 8142
149 Kew Road, Richmond, Surrey,
081-940 8298.

**Café Rouge** W8
2 Lancer Square, map 12
off Kensington Church Street
071-938 4200
Stylish surrounds for quite a simple
formula: tried-and-tested French dishes,
decent wines and a few snack items, fairly
priced. Call in for coffee and a croissant or
the full (three courses) works. **£**

Branches also at: 140 Fetter Lane, EC4,
071-242 3469
6–7 South Grove, N6, 081-342 9797
19 Hampstead High Street, NW3,
071-433 3404
Hay's Galleria, Tooley Street, SE1,
071-378 0097
390 King's Road, SW3, 071-352 2226
855 Fulham Road, SW6, 071-371 7600
200 Putney Bridge Road, SW15,
081-788 4257
46 James Street, W1, 071-487 4847
Unit 209, Whiteley's, Queensway, W2,
071-221 1509
31 Kensington Park Road, W11,
071-221 449
7A Petersham Road, Richmond, Surrey,
081-332 2423.

**Canal Brasserie** W10
Canalot Studios, map 11
222 Kensal Road
081-960 2732
Perfectly acceptable brasserie meals
within a lofty, modern, music and film
studios space (once Fry's chocolate
factory). Parking is a lot easier, and
outside tables in summer are better
spaced, than in nearby Notting Hill.
Only open for lunch; dinner by
arrangement. **££**

**Le Champenois** EC2
10 Devonshire Square, map 11
Cutlers Gardens
071-283 7888
Subterranean City restaurant with a
menu that's firmly French but with
occasional inconsistent delivery. The
restaurant is open only for lunch but the
champagne and oyster bar stays open
until eight in the evening. **£**

**Chez Gérard** W1
8 Charlotte Street map 14
071-636 4975
Recently revamped premises for this well-
known French bistro have brought the
visuals up to date. Debate still rages over
the reputation for steak-frites but there
are other things on the *carte* to try too.

Service in the other branches seems to experience the occasional hiccup. ££
Branches also at: 31 Dover Street, W1, 071-499 8171
119 Chancery Lane, WC2, 071-405 0290.

### China China                                    W1
3 Gerrard Street                                   map 15
071-439 7511
Fast-paced café for Chinese one-plate dishes. Service is swift and polite. Serves a purpose in the area and it's inexpensive. £

### Christian's                                    W4
1 Station Parade,                                  map 10
Burlington Lane
081-995 0382/0208
Attractive French restaurant that's recommended for Sunday lunch. On the menu might be chargrilled red pepper and mozzarella salad, 'perfectly cooked' trout fillets with parsley sauce and an 'utterly delicious' chocolate and armagnac terrine. A few good wines and lots of liqueurs. ££–£££

### Chutney Mary                                   SW10
535 King's Road                                    map 10
071-351 3113
Anglo-Indian cuisine in colonial-style surroundings, complete with conservatory, ceiling fans and potted palms. Obviously upmarket – prices do not compare with those of a standard curry house – and an interesting menu: lamb narangi and almond chicken korma line up alongside salmon kedgeree and hill station bread-and-butter pudding. ££–£££

### Cibo                                           W14
3 Russell Gardens                                  map 12
071-371 6271 and 2085
Smart clients, bright young staff, modish Italian cooking that is more approximate than brilliant. Fish is the best thing to eat; lots of good Italian wines to drink. ££–£££

### Cottons                                        NW1
55 Chalk Farm Road                                 map 11
071-482 1096
The menu proclaims 'Yard food: Jamaican style', which is a pretty accurate description of this reggae-playing restaurant. The sound-system is turned up loud, the staff are hip and the décor is colourful. The Camden-Caribbean cooking is fair (and fun) and the portions are generous. Fill up on fried fish, rice and peas, breadfruit and 'incredibly rich' chocolate fudge slice with rum. Potent drinks. £

### La Croisette                                   SW10
168 Ifield Road                                    map 11
071-373 3694
French fish cooking from the Pierre Martin empire that's ever-so-slightly formulaic. The old-fashioned pseudo-maritime furnishings are showing some dust. That aside, the plateau de fruits de mer lined with seaweed and laden with crustaceans and shellfish is splendid. Finish with chocolate mousse. £££

### Deals Diner                                    SW10
Chelsea Harbour                                    map 10
071-376 3232
Large, lighthearted American-style diner. Late opening hours and a Chelsea Harbour location. Spicy Thai soup, stir-fries and curries raise interest levels on an otherwise burger-oriented menu. £

### Diwana Bhel-Poori                              NW1
121 Drummond Street                                map 11
071-387 5556
A bhel poori house that's the best of its type. All vegetarian pooris, dosas and kulfis; unlicensed but bring your own. Don't mind the hard seats and no booking policy. £
Another branch at: 50 Westbourne Grove, W2, 071-221 0721.

### Eatons                                         SW1
49 Elizabeth Street                                map 13
071-730 0074
Modest Belgravia bolt-hole with very long-standing reputation. Simple,

familiar cooking that has not been deflected by current fashions; smoked salmon blinis, poached halibut, traditional desserts and coffee ad lib. Good value in an expensive area.  ££

## Emile's                           SW6
144 Wandsworth Bridge Road    map 10
071-736 2418
Popular bistro that's usually packed-out (the Putney branch is roomier with its conservatory extension). Tables are, inevitably, close together. Mix-and-match menus incorporate familiar French dishes alongside more inventive combinations. Minus points for the sauces and wine list; generous portions, good fish cooking and desserts score higher.  ££
Another branch at: 96–98 Felsham Road, SW15, 081-789 3323.

## Enoteca                         SW15
28 Putney High Street          map 10
081-785 4449
Not at all stereotypical Italian, neighbourhood restaurant. Family-run with good front-of-house and a happy atmosphere. Regional cooking that manages not to pander to current fashions – it blazes no new trails but does keep the locals well fed.  ££

## Est                               W1
54 Frith Street                map 15
071-437 0666
Trendy bar/restaurant for Soho media types, best for pasta. Extra-virgin olive oil over mostly everything; chargrilling much in evidence.  ££–£££

## Formula Veneta                   SW10
14 Hollywood Road              map 13
071-352 7612
In a smart West Brompton street that's awash with wine bars and restaurants, Formula Veneta manages to stand out from the crowd. Beautifully delicate pastas, some featuring seafood, of rather delicate portion-size. Summer sees the

garden open, and there are several outside tables at the front.  ££

## Frederick's                        N1
Camden Passage                 map 11
071-359 2888
Well-established restaurant behind Islington's Upper Street, convenient for all the area's antique shops. Food is dyed-in-the-wool French and heavily laced with cream; opt for the lighter choices if tackling three courses.  ££

## Galicia                          W10
323 Portobello Road            map 12
081-969 3539
Tapas bar and restaurant that's home from home for Portobello's Iberian populace. Fundamental furnishings and a heavy fug of black tobacco. Good octopus, caramel cream custard, excellent coffee.  £

## Geales                            W8
2 Farmer Street                map 12
071-727 7969
Notting Hill fish and chip place that's been going for years, and attracts a varied crowd of regulars. Good for a casual meal in low-key surrounds. Finish with apple crumble.  £

## Green's                          SW1
36 Duke Street                 map 14
071-930 4566
Comfortable, club-like wood and leather and banquetted booths in this restaurant and oyster bar. English establishment cooking evoking memories of the nursery; popular with politicians and turf types. Go for good oysters, smoked salmon and a glass or three of champagne.  £££

## Haandi                           NW1
161 Drummond Street            map 11
071-383 45557
The lunch-time buffet is the thing at this Indian amongst Indians in Drummond Street. Great-value lunch buffet at under £6 for as much as you can eat; choose

from a couple of meat curries, vegetarian dishes and a good selection of chutneys. Evenings have been less successful. **£**

### Halcyon Hotel                         W11
129 Holland Park Avenue        map 12
071-221 5411

Leafy, upmarket location for a highly designed dining-room, home to entirely fashionable cooking. Very expensive, very casual, very much the place for vodka (beware of the chilli). Now, a separate vegetarian menu too. Still *the* place for illicit liaisons. **£££**

### Harveys Café                         SW10
358 Fulham Road                 map 11
071-352 0625

Trendy upstairs tenant of pub – food has less impact than the decoration. Mediterranean and Californian-inspired dishes of varied success. Attracts a young crowd. **£–££**

### Hing Lee                              SE1
32 Curlew Street                 map 11
071-403 7919

Civilised Chinese that's handy for visitors to the Design Museum. Extensive menu-choice includes reasonable set dinners; enjoyable spare ribs, Peking duck, fried seaweed and giant prawns. **£**

### Hodgson's                             WC2
115 Chancery Lane               map 11
071-242 2836

An attractive, colonnaded, lofty room functioning as a venue for traditional English eating. Steak and kidney pudding, grilled sea bream and calf's liver are typical of what's on offer. Popular with the business and City crowd. **££**

### Hyde Park Hotel                      SW1
Park Room, Knightsbridge        map 13
071-235 2000

Elegant, marbled hotel with Hyde Park views. Rumour is that Marco Pierre White may be arriving here to take over the kitchen, but no confirmation as the *Guide* went to press. **£££**

### Isohama                              SW1
312 Vauxhall Bridge Road        map 11
071-834 2145

Small and useful Japanese restaurant close to Victoria. Short menu at lunch, extended in the evenings. **££–£££**

### Julie's                              W11
135 Portland Road               map 12
071-229 8331

With its '70s rich-hippy-meets-country-house décor, Julie's is nothing if not offbeat. The upstairs wine bar is funky and accessibly priced, the basement restaurant reserved, romantic and rather expensive. Straightforward English cooking with a few lighter touches. If you're going to drink pink champagne anywhere, drink it here. **££–£££**

### Kagura                               WC2
13–15 West Street               map 15
071-240 0634

Japanese restaurant off Cambridge Circus with an interesting menu. A series of set meals; sashimi, sushi and teppanyaki. **££–£££**

### Kanishka                             W1
161 Whitfield Street            map 14
071-388 0860

Half-meat, half-vegetarian, with two distinct kitchens and chefs. An interesting menu with regional overtones: north Indian, Goan, Mughlai, Kashmiri. Reports have shown first-class tandooris, unusual curries (especially vegetarian), fine spicing, helpful service and an agreeable atmosphere. The lunch buffet may be more prosaic but will certainly offer good value. **£**

### Kaspia                               W1
18–18A Bruton Place             map 14
071-493 2612

Mayfair meeting place for the seriously solvent. Surroundings are wood-panelled and low-key although the customers and prices are anything but. All forms of caviare, likewise vodkas to accompany. Set meals will be less severe on the wallet (the attached shop may put paid to that, however).  **£££**

### Kenny's                                NW3
70 Heath Street                          map 11
071-435 6972
Laid-back Louisiana-style bar and restaurant that's often busy. Admittedly, some of the food's mainstream American – all prime quality and large portions – but there's enough Cajun/Creole influences to keep up the interest. Taped music is to match.  **£**
Another branch at: 2A Pond Place, SW3, 071-225 2916.

### Kettners                              W1
29 Romilly Street                        map 15
071-437 6437
A Soho institution, liked for its stylish, historic building and its pizzas. Non-pizza lovers can choose from the more pedestrian list of burgers, steak and BLT. No bookings taken but groups tend to meet first in the Champagne Bar.  **£**

### Lahore Kebab House                    E1
2 Umberston Street                       map 11
071-488 2551
Basic Formica and furnishings that can only be described as fundamental characterise this East End Indian. Don't come looking for comfort and trappings but for the authentic taste of the sub-continent. Unlicensed; also does take-away.  **£**

### Leith's at the Institute              EC2
Chartered Accountants' House,            map 11
11 Copthall Avenue
071-920 8100
Large basement restaurant with a long bar inside the Institute of Chartered Accountants. Another place for business lunches at fair prices. Food is highly eclectic but flavours are sometimes so mild as to be almost absent. Plus points are affordable, interesting wines and lots of elbow room.  **££**

### Lemonia                               NW1
89 Regent's Park Road                    map 11
071-586 7454
Some love the enormous brasserie-like space occupied by this Primrose Hill Greek-Cypriot restaurant, while others find it noisy and daunting. Either way, folk seem to agree on the food. Freshly prepared meze, kleftiko, afelia, figs and delightfully nutty Turkish delight with coffee.  **£–££**

### Matsuri                               SW1
15 Bury Street                           map 14
071-839 1101
Probably enjoying a higher profile by virtue of its close proximity to Quaglino's, this Japanese newcomer is just as expensive. Basement sushi and teppanyaki bar for very fresh fish and quite stylish sushi. Surroundings are clean as a new pin and utterly soulless.  **££–£££**

### Meson Don Felipe                      SE1
53 The Cut                               map 11
071-928 3237
Well-known, popular tapas bar that's useful for the Young Vic. Undistinguished ingredients but certainly authentically Spanish. Cheerful atmosphere, decent Riojas and dry sherries.  **£–££**

### Le Muscadet                           W1
25 Paddington Street                     map 14
071-935 2883
Long-standing (recently refurbished) French bistro with a pleasant atmosphere and charming waiters. A few ups and downs but the fish is fine, as is the wide selection of ripe French cheeses.  **£££**

### Namaste                               E1
30 Alie Street                           map 11
071-488 9242
Indian that's not run-of-the-mill. An interesting chef cooking from a constantly evolving menu. Exquisite spicing in dishes such as lamb pasanda, venison kebab with a tomato sauce, chicken jalfrezi and prawn dhansak.  **£**

181

**Nautilus** NW6

27 Fortune Green Road map 11

071-435 2532

Prime fish and chips (fried in matzo meal) at this restaurant and take-away. Lots of types of fish, all served in large portions. **£**

**Newton's** SW4

33–35 Abbeville Road map 10

081-673 0977

Clapham brasserie with a light and airy, exposed-brick interior and attractive prints. Contemporary British cooking that's certainly fair but flavours are over-delicate. Service can be frustrating and sometimes slow. **££**

**Nontas** NW1

14–16 Camden High Street map 11

071-387 4579

Friendly and welcoming taverna with rather more to offer than the others that surround it in Camden Town. The small back garden is worth knowing about in summer months. **£**

**Odin's** W1

27 Devonshire Street map 14

071-935 7296

One of the most pleasant restaurant environments in London, with plain, sometimes good English-style food. Excellent service. **£££**

**Ovations** SE1

National Theatre, map 11

South Bank

071-928 3531

Sympathetic pre- and post-theatre dining. The waiters understand the importance of timing and will fit in around any schedule. Mainstream menus of light, health-conscious dishes. Can get block-booked in advance. **££**

**Le Palais du Jardin** WC2

136 Long Acre map 15

071-379 5353

A smart, large, well-lit brasserie that tries to capture the Parisian style and gets away with it. The atmosphere is

enjoyable and the food wide-ranging, from traditional onion soup and beef bourguignonne to more adventurous dishes. **££**

**Patisserie Valerie** SW3

215 Brompton Road map 13

071-823 9971

Grand café with lots of marble and row upon row of classic cakes: fresh fruit-crammed tartlets, florentines, palmiers, lavish cream confections – all washed down with large cups of cappuccino. Savoury items also appear on the daytime menu. **£**

Another branch at: 44 Old Compton Street, W1, 071-437 3466.

**Piccolo Mondo** WC2

31 Catherine Street map 15

071-836 3609

Elegant theatre-land Italian that's used to fitting in the theatre-going crowd. Competent enough production of the usual staples. Happy and obliging staff. **£££**

**La Pomme d'Amour** W11

128 Holland Park Avenue map 12

071-229 8532

Pretty French restaurant that's within walking distance of the park. Classic menus take in artichoke mousse with crab sauce, fennel cake with scallops and confit of duck with Toulouse sausage and lentils. Caramelised apple tart with calvados provided the 'perfect finish' according to one reader. Aim to sit in the conservatory. **££**

**Poons in the City** EC3

2 Minster Court, map 11

Mincing Lane

071-626 0126

Vast City Chinese that's the latest spin-off of the well-known Covent Garden Cantonese. The menu has some interesting points – wind-dried items, for example. Cooking of fair but not outstanding quality, but the location is useful, the seats are comfortable and service cheerful.

## Porters
WC2

17 Henrietta Street     map 15
071-836 6466

Sensible English food at sensible prices; this long-established, large venue is the place to go for bangers and mash. Traditional pies, roasts and hot puddings also feature.    £

## Le Poulbot
EC2

45 Cheapside     map 11
071-236 4379

A distinct need in not-so Cheapside, this Roux Brothers' enterprise is still popular after all these years. Upstairs brasserie and downstairs restaurant (velveteen benches, in cubicles, convey confidentiality and quietness) offering acceptable French food. A lack of affordable wines (no house) can send the bill soaring. Only open for lunch.    ££–£££

## La Poule au Pot
SW1

231 Ebury Street     map 13
071-730 7763

Long-standing, still romantic Gallic restaurant cooking all the traditional staples. Not adventurous but pleasantly reassuring.    ££–£££

## Primates
NW1

257 Royal College Street     map 11
071-284 1059

Apes abound – don't worry they're only stuffed – in this Camden Town eaterie with conservatory extension. Monthly-changing menus advertise a mixture of styles; snail ravioli, loin of pork on saffron risotto, creamy desserts. Makes a change from the faster-food outlets so abundant in the area.    ££

## Quincy's
NW2

675 Finchley Road     map 11
071-794 8499

Small, often crowded, neighbourhood place for fair English cooking with a smattering of French. Wooden tables, candles, excellent service. Choose from the likes of 'truly fishy' bouillabaisse, new season's lamb, 'light and feathery'

bread-and-butter pudding. Pleasing wine list.    ££

## Raoul's Café
W9

13 Clifton Road     map 11
071-289 7313

New-wave Italian in (appropriately) Little Venice. A laid-back attitude, several outside tables, fashionable décor and light, modern cooking make this a good local find.

## Ritz Hotel
W1

Piccadilly     map 14
071-493 8181

Although famous for afternoon tea dances, this (still) fabulous hotel has probably the prettiest dining-room in London. Chef, David Nicholls, employs luxury materials to reasonable effect. Go for the whole experience rather than just for food and revel in soaking up some of the glamour.    £££

## Rossmore
SW10

11 Park Walk     map 13
071-352 3449

Aidan McCormack's new venture has had a total refurbishment since its previous existence. Regularly changing menus should have things to interest. Reports, please.    £–£££

## San Lorenzo
SW3

22 Beauchamp Place     map 13
071-584 1074

Famous as the Italian that Princess Diana (among other faces) frequents when in town. Lesser mortals might find the Knightsbridge prices offputting or the service cool, but the pastas are respectable, and the star-spotting is fun.    £££

## San Remo
SW13

195 Castelnau     map 10
081-741 5909

Unassuming, usefully priced Italian that continues to turn out good meals. Fresh seafood starters, baby chicken in rosemary and garlic, and genuine tiramisù are representative.    ££

## Seoul EC3

89A Aldgate High Street  map 11
071-480 5770

Korean restaurant that's very much a
lunch-time venue, popular with Japanese
businessmen. Stark, workmanlike dining-
room that can feel desolate, but service is
warmer. Food is basic but competent; stay
with the simple dishes sauch as bulgogi
(sautéed beef), steamed fish, kimchi
(pickle) and noodles.  £

## Simon's Bistro NW4

41 Church Road  map 10
081-203 7887

Neighbourhood restaurant clocking up a
Hendon clientele. Varied menus that
change regularly list gnocchi with
salmon, tagliatelle, duck in filo pastry,
straightforward desserts. Affably run.  £

## Soulard N1

113 Mortimer Road  map 11
071-254 1314

Reliable French that continues to be busy.
Portions are generous, the fish specials
are particularly recommended and the
short wine list is much liked.  £–££

## Spice Merchant W2

Coburg Hotel,  map 12
130 Bayswater Road
071-221 2442

International Indian restaurant with
interesting, if somewhat pricey, menu.
Large dining-room that's corporate
enough for suits.  ££

## Spread Eagle SE10

2 Stockwell Street  map 10
081-853 2333

Old Greenwich coaching-inn with a
French chef. Traditional menus, decent
cooking including well-reduced sauces.
Everyone seems to like the décor with its
collected ephemera and the comfortable
atmosphere.  £–££

## Sweetings EC4

39 Queen Victoria Street  map 11
071-248 3062

With a history of over 150 years behind it,
Sweetings can claim to be one of our
oldest fish restaurants, and is certainly a
City establishment. Puddings are equally
traditional. Open only for lunch in the
week – arrive early to secure a seat.  ££

## Tandoori Lane SW6

131A Munster Road  map 10
071-371 0440/0844

Fulham Indian that continues to please
the locals (although cigarette smoke and
poor ventilation have upset more than
one customer). Chicken tikka masala and
mater paneer are recommended; drink
Kingfisher lager.  £

## Tiny Tim NW1

7 Plender Street  map 11
071-388 0402

Inexpensive but not particularly Gallic
neighbourhood French restaurant. Offers
somewhere in Camden Town to eat in
relative quiet, and service is charming
too. Some decent French wines including
house by George Duboeuf, also an
interesting selection of digestifs.  £–££

## Twenty Trinity Gardens SW9

20 Trinity Gardens  map 10
071-733 8838

Well-established, fashionably relaxed
Brixton eaterie. Eclectic cooking that's
basically modern British; traditional
Sunday lunch is popular. Interesting
wines from the affiliated wine company
are offered at very fair prices.  ££

## Vasco & Piero's Pavilion W1

15 Poland Street  map 14
071-437 8774

Modest Italian with a lovely atmosphere.
A mixture of old – prosciutto and melon –
and new – balsamic vinegar, rocket,
shaved Parmesan. Pasta and gnocchi are
made on the premises. Irrestible service
that remains charming rather than
flirtatious.  £–££

**Versilia**                               NW3
250 Finchley Road                     map 11
071-794 7640
Italian specialising in fish: mussels,
seafood crêpes, sea bream, sea bass and
sole were among one evening's selection.
Unusually, the menu also has a
vegetarian page: artichoke flan,
aubergine with cheese, ricotta and
spinach crêpes. Comfortable place;
parking may be difficult.     £–££

**White Horse on Parsons Green**    SW6
1–3 Parsons Green                     map 10
071-736 2115
Hugely popular pub overlooking the
green. Deeply comfortable button-leather
sofas, a lively, good-natured atmosphere,
and Traquair House Ale (brewed in a
Scottish stately home by a laird) explain
the crowds. The other draw is the food –
simple but wholesome hot and cold
meals; decent chips.     £

**White Tower**                            W1
1 Percy Street                        map 14
071-636 8141
Reliable, long-running Greek restaurant
that's hardly changed at all over the
years. This is no plate-smashing place, but
has a genteel atmosphere and pleasant,
old-fashioned service.     £££

**Willoughby's Café-Bar**                  N1
26 Penton Street                      map 11
071-833 1380
Tucked away, between Islington and
King's Cross, this unassuming spot is
home to modern British cooking. The all-
day menu is supplemented with daily
specials. Salmon fish-cakes are a
perennial favourite; award-winning
house wine.     £

**Wilsons**                               W14
236 Blythe Road                       map 12
071-603 7267
Owner Bob Wilson has a penchant for
tartan, which is all over this Shepherd's
Bush restaurant. The menu too has more
than a few Scottish influences – Atholl
brose, Aberdeen beef, salmon – but the
rest is modern British.     £–££

**Wódka**                                  W8
12 St Albans Grove                    map 13
071-937 6513
Polish restaurant with a modern, eclectic
menu that owes almost as much to
Western Europe. One 'admirable dinner'
on a cold evening comprised sorrel soup,
braised hare in chestnut sauce with red
cabbage and a lemony crème brûlée.
Wash everything down with flavoured
vodkas – chilli, bison grass and honey to
name but three.     ££–£££

**Ziani**                                  SW3
45–47 Radnor Walk                     map 13
071-351 5297 and 352 2698
Pretty Italian in a pretty Chelsea street.
Fair cooking of fresh ingredients: wafer-
thin carpaccio of sea bass, roasted
vegetables, cuttlefish with polenta.
Casual but charming service; short wine
list, excellent coffee.     £££

# England

---

**ABBERLEY** Hereford & Worcester                                  map 5

## ▲ *The Elms*

Abberley WR6 6AT
GREAT WITLEY (0299) 896666
On A443, between Worcester and                       COOKING 2
Tenbury Wells, 2m W of Great Witley                   COST £23–£51

There have been easier times than 1993 for Queens Moat Houses, the owners of
this splendid country house (built in the eighteenth century) with fittings and
fixtures to match. While no one has suggested that any problems have taken a
toll in the kitchens – though there are periodic complaints about the boring
breakfasts – the cooking here has shown some signs of lacking both conviction
in taste and a good pastry chef. A succession of evenings seemed to confirm that
salt (or any high-flavour substitute) was missing in nearly everything. This
country-house gentility might be best exemplified in a 'bouillabaisse' of
salmon and monkfish which was nothing of the sort, even though the fish was
admirably fresh and poached in a plainish stock. Prices at least are not too
pressing, 'especially considering the grand surroundings', for dishes such as
terrine of chicken and spinach with a Cumberland sauce, pork stuffed with a
liver parfait and wrapped in bacon, and duck with honey and pink peppercorn
sauce. The wine list is not over-long and the choices are sound, if predictable.
The 'Elms Selection' at the front of the list has some excellent choices at
reasonable prices. House wines are £11.50.

---

CHEF: Michael Gaunt   PROPRIETORS: Queens Moat Houses plc   OPEN: Library Bar Mon to
Sat, L only; 12.30 to 2. Brooke Room all week, D only, and Sun L (L by arrangement for 6 or
more); 12.30 to 2, 7.30 to 9.30   MEALS: alc (main courses £7.50 to £19.95). Set Sun L
£14.95, Set D £16 to £22   SERVICE: not inc, card slips closed   CARDS: Access, Amex,
Diners, Visa   DETAILS: 75 seats. 4 tables outside. Private parties: 75 main room, 18, 32, 46
and 75 private rooms. Car park. Vegetarian meals. Children's helpings on request. Jacket
and tie in Brooke Room. No cigars/pipes in Brooke Room. Wheelchair access (1 step; also
WC). No music   ACCOMMODATION: 25 rooms, all with bath/shower. B&B £82 to £128.
Children welcome. Baby facilities. Afternoon teas. Garden. Tennis. TV. Phone. Fax: (0299)
896804 (*The Which? Hotel Guide*)

---

*The text of entries is based on unsolicited reports sent in by readers, backed up by
inspections conducted anonymously. The factual details under the text are from
questionnaires the Guide sends to all restaurants that feature in the book.*

---

## ABINGDON Oxfordshire        map 2

# ▲ *Thame Lane House* 🍴✳

1 Thame Lane, Culham,
Abingdon OX14 3DS
ABINGDON (0235) 524177
on corner of Thame Lane, off A415        COOKING 2
Abingdon to Dorchester road        COST £24–£38

'A charming little cottage with four tables and a pretty garden,' reported a very satisfied visitor taken by Marie-Claude Beech's *bourgeois* cooking where the 'meat or fish has its flavour brought out, not smothered, by the sauces'. A recited menu gives three or four choices of steady French cooking brightened by modern touches. 'Our faultless lunch included terrine of pork with cornichons, duck breast with braised lettuce and new potatoes, and a pair of sorbets: a very pleasant experience.' Other dishes approved of were a plateau de fruits de mer, salmon with rhubarb, and a gratin of fruits. The experience strikes people in different ways. Sometimes there seem to be errors, and sometimes the evening runs less merrily than it might. A short French wine list offers Ch. Méaume and Ch. Fieuzal among its sound selection. House wines start at £10.

CHEF: Marie-Claude Beech   PROPRIETORS: Michael and Marie-Claude Beech   OPEN: all week, exc Mon L and Sun D; 12.30 to 1.30, 7.15 to 8.45   CLOSED: 1 week Jan, 2 weeks Aug   MEALS: Set L and D £18.50 to £26.50   SERVICE: net prices, card slips closed   CARDS: Access, Visa (3.5% surcharge)   DETAILS: 16 seats. Private parties: 18 main room. Car park. Vegetarian meals with prior notice. Children's helpings with prior notice. No children under 3. Smart dress preferred. No smoking. Wheelchair access (1 step). No music
ACCOMMODATION: 5 rooms, 1 with bath/shower. B&B £28 to £52. Deposit: £15. No children under 3. Garden. TV. Doors close at 11.30. Confirm by 6

## ALDEBURGH Suffolk        map 3

# ▲ *Austins*

243 The High Street, Aldeburgh IP15 5DN        COOKING 1
ALDEBURGH (0728) 453932        COST £19–£31

Legions of artists and musicians are fed and watered at this popular venue during the Aldeburgh Festival, but it maintains its reputation throughout the year. The exterior is pink, while inside is a bar with theatrical overtones and an elegant dining-room tastefully fitted out with paintings and fine furniture. Julian Alexander-Worster makes good use of fish and local produce: 'Having seen several hundred rabbits on the field in which two of our party camped the night before, we were relieved to see it on the menu,' observed travellers from Wales. The menu offers steak, roast beef and lobster, but the kitchen also gets to grips with more complex creations such as filo 'pan' of spiced chicken with almonds or marinated duck breast with braised celeriac. Duo of smoked grouse and venison, cold cucumber and sorrel soup, and poached salmon in herb sauce have been mentioned in reports. Lemon sole with cream and ginger has been outstanding. Desserts such as crème brûlée and orange steamed pudding have also been given the seal of approval. Robert Selbie is a 'worthy host' and service is courteous. The wine list is short, sharp and affordable; otherwise you may find lager and beer 'of types known usually only to experimenting city dwellers'. House wine is £7.15.

CHEF: Julian Alexander-Worster  PROPRIETORS: Robert Selbie and Julian Alexander-Worster  OPEN: Tue to Sat D, and Sun L; 12.30 to 1.45, 7.30 to 9.30  MEALS: Set Sun L £13.75, Set D £19.75  SERVICE: not inc, card slips closed  CARDS: Access, Visa  DETAILS: 30 seats. Private parties: 25 main room. Vegetarian meals with prior notice. No children under 12. No cigars/pipes in dining-room. Music  ACCOMMODATION: 7 rooms, all with bath/shower. B&B £47.75 to £70. No children under 12 (exc babies). Baby facilities. Pets welcome (£5 surcharge for dogs). TV. Phone. Fax: (0728) 453668 (*The Which? Hotel Guide*)

## New Regatta  £

**NEW ENTRY**

171–173 High Street, Aldeburgh IP15 5AN                    COOKING 1*
ALDEBURGH (0728) 452011                                    COST £17–£30

The Mabeys are out to spread 'chunky chips' the length and breadth of East Anglia. From their power-base in Sudbury (Mabey's Brasserie – see entry), they have spread as far as Norwich, and now meet the sea at Aldeburgh where they have taken over this well-loved restaurant and wine bar – more a bistro with marine style. Life has been fast and furious in the first months of occupation, partnerships are settling down, Johanna Mabey has had a baby, and staff take time to work everything out. The place runs more or less to a well-tried formula of a blackboard menu (not visible from every table), food that has moved one step ahead of the old bistro style of the '70s, and fair value. There have been plenty of successes in dishes like cool lovage, celery and bacon soup, chicken liver terrine, medallions of beef with caramelised onions and red wine and herb sauce, and roast loin of lamb with onion gravy. First courses are not complicated – salads, pâtés, local products from Butley-Orford – but main dishes often show intelligence, as in the parcels of wild mushrooms on a pea purée with new potatoes that was a vegetarian choice one night. Economy – lobster for under £12 – is appreciated hereabouts. Close inspection applauds the bare bones but questions some of the finer details of sauce-making and finish. The wine list provides best for lovers of burgundy. There is a steady list printed on one side and a varying selection typewritten on the other. Value is very fair. House wines are £7.25.

CHEF: Robert Mabey  PROPRIETORS: Robert and Johanna Mabey  OPEN: all week (Wed to Sun Oct to Mar); 12 to 2, 7 to 10  MEALS: alc (main courses L £5 to £12, D £7 to £12)  SERVICE: not inc, card slips closed  CARDS: Access, Amex, Visa  DETAILS: 100 seats. Private parties: 80 main room. Vegetarian meals. Children's helpings. No cigars/pipes in dining-room. Wheelchair access (1 step). Music. Fax: (0728) 452011

🚭 *indicates that smoking is either banned altogether or that a dining-room is maintained for non-smokers. The symbol does not apply to restaurants that simply have no-smoking areas.*

£ *indicates that it is possible to have a three-course meal, including coffee, a half-bottle of house wine and service, at any time the restaurant is open (i.e. at dinner as well as at lunch, unless a place is open only for dinner), for £20 or less per person.*

---

**ALDERHOLT Dorset** map 2

## *Moonacre*

| NEW ENTRY |

Fordingbridge Road, Alderholt SP6 3BB
FORDINGBRIDGE (0425) 653142 COOKING 2*
off B3078, between Cranborne and Fordingbridge COST £15–£33

There are summer and winter sides to this cottage restaurant. In summer the extension looking into the garden is best; in winter the dining-room in the cottage itself, with wood fires, beams and low ceilings, comes into its own. In point of fact, it may be worth taking a table in either place, come rain or shine. Barbara Garnsworthy's cooking has the great recommendation of being cheap as well as good. The menu changes near enough daily, and Barbara has little truck with fancy cooking, preferring instead to get good supplies (fish from Poole, meat and game locally, flour from Alderholt Mill, pick-your-own fruit and veg) and impart a bit of boldness with modern recipes. This bears witness in grilled aubergine, red pepper and mushroom salad with basil and garlic; sardines with ginger, garlic, chilli and lime; lambs' kidneys and liver with mustard and bacon on potato pancakes; or John Dory fillets with red pepper, crab and saffron sauce. A dinner that ran through smoked salmon parcels of avocado and cream cheese mousse, a hot soufflé of crab and Jarlsberg cheese, scallops with mushroom, bacon and pesto, chicken with smoked ham and cider sauce, pistachio ice-cream with hot chocolate sauce and a good lemon tart delivered very precisely what it said it would: exact cooking and accurate seasoning. Service is pleasant, without fuss and bother, and the wine list, with quite a lot from Yapp Brothers, is an excellent example of fair range in a small compass at a very reasonable price. House wines are £7.50.

CHEF: Barbara Garnsworthy PROPRIETORS: Barbara Garnsworthy and Edward Bourke OPEN: Tue to Sat D, and Sun L; 12 to 2, 7 to 10 CLOSED: first 2 weeks Feb MEALS: alc (main courses £7.50 to £11.50). Set Sun L £10 (£6 children), Set D Tue to Thur £9 (2 courses) to £11 SERVICE: not inc, card slips closed CARDS: Access, Visa DETAILS: 36 seats. Private parties: 36 main room. Car park. Vegetarian meals. Children's helpings. Wheelchair access (1 step). No music

---

**ALNWICK Northumberland** map 7

## *John Blackmore's* ✕

1 Dorothy Foster Court, Narrowgate,
Alnwick NE66 1NL COOKING 3
ALNWICK (0665) 604465 COST £19–£36

In a town where history is much in evidence, 'Alnwick's second-oldest house' is a claim that carries clout. John Blackmore's is set in a narrow alley close to the castle, and now that all is amity between England and Scotland the beef comes by way of trade, not raid. Age determines the warm stone flags, overlaid with a drop of modern comfort; location explains the warmth and friendliness of welcome – here and there unskilled – derived from bluff North Country manners. John Blackmore's cooking is, however, well mannered. A summer meal took in marinated wild salmon and an avocado and dill sauce, with capers to add point; lambs' sweetbreads with a tomato-basil sauce together with a broccoli mousse; lightly peppered fillet of beef with a liver pâté and port sauce; fresh strawberries, meringue and home-made ice-cream; and a roulade filled with orange cream, with a hot white chocolate sauce. The wine list keeps to three dozen bins, and is careful to avoid breaching £20 too often. The range is wide enough for most palates to be satisfied, if not startled. House wines are £7.80.

CHEF: John Blackmore   PROPRIETORS: John and Penny Blackmore   OPEN: Tue to Sat, D only; 7 to 9   CLOSED: Jan   MEALS: alc (main courses £12 to £13.50). Set D Tue to Wed £15 (inc wine)   SERVICE: not inc, card slips closed   CARDS: Access, Amex, Diners, Visa   DETAILS: 28 seats. Private parties: 30 main room. Vegetarian meals. Children's helpings. Smart dress preferred. No smoking in dining-room. Wheelchair access (2 steps). Music

---

**AMBERLEY West Sussex**                                                          map 3

## ▲ Amberley Castle, Queen's Room ⁵⁄⁶✳

Amberley BN18 9ND
BURY (0798) 831992                                                          COOKING 2
on B2139, between Storrington and Bury Hill                    COST £25–£73

The castle sits in a flat meadow, once defending the coastal hinterland from incursion. Within its square courtyard there now stands a house, part medieval, part modern (the wall paintings in the great hall are worth a look), where hotel and restaurant do business. The service may not always be the most accurate, but often the setting of warm panelled lounges and impressive vaulted hall seduces. The cooking by Nigel Boschetti has not changed its stance from last year. Prices on the *carte* are still very high indeed, some luxuries (particularly lobster) are deployed, but it is the delicate (if not fussy) presentation with intense sauces that catches people's attention. This is not *hearty* cooking. Petits fours (sweet), canapés (pleasant), a red pepper bavarois as appetiser and home-made breads are often commented upon. A meal that was composed of hot-smoked lobster with chervil butter sauce, quenelles of haddock in sesame-seed crust, chicken with glazed chicory and loin of lamb with creamed potato and herbs and baby vegetables pleased one couple, even if another were moved to protest at the exiguous quantities of potato and vegetables in the same dishes. The high-priced wine list includes many good names. There are some good halves and an 'Amberley Castle Value Selection' which provides slight relief. House wine is £11.95.

CHEF: Nigel Boschetti   PROPRIETORS: Joy and Martin Cummings   OPEN: all week; 12 to 2, 7 to 9.30   MEALS: alc (main courses £19 to £23). Set L £13.50 (2 courses) to £16.50, Set Sun L £21.50, Set D £25.50, Set 'gourmet' D £40   SERVICE: not inc, card slips closed   CARDS: Access, Amex, Diners, Visa   DETAILS: 70 seats. Private parties: 48 main room, 12 and 48 private rooms. Car park. Vegetarian meals with prior notice. Children's helpings. Jacket and tie. No smoking in dining-room. No music   ACCOMMODATION: 14 rooms, all with bath/shower. B&B £80 to £225. Deposit: 50%. Children welcome. Baby facilities. Afternoon teas. Garden. TV. Phone. Doors close at 1am. Fax: (0798) 831998

---

**AMBLESIDE Cumbria**                                                      map 7

---

## ▲ *Rothay Manor* ♟ ✳

Rothay Bridge, Ambleside LA22 0EH
AMBLESIDE (053 94) 33605                                   COOKING 2
off A593 to Coniston, ½m W of Ambleside               COST £17–£41

---

'What more could one wish for at these prices?' enthuse a couple who make a
regular pilgrimage to this eminently comfortable, elegant Lakeland retreat.
They are not the only ones who appreciate the space and comfort, the personal
attention of the Nixon families, the cheerful, discreetly supervised female staff
dressed in white blouses and black skirts, the absence of music and the no-
smoking policy. The food has been described as 'good home-made rather than
exciting/original', but it generally pleases. The short dinner menu has only a
few choices at each stage and is priced according to the number of courses
taken. Soups, such as cream of pepper and orange or carrot and marjoram, are
regularly applauded. Other recommended dishes have included Basque
chicken (a thick entire breast was brought to the table before having a sharp,
slightly sweet tomato sauce poured over it), woodpigeon braised in red wine
with herbs, and roast duck with orange and madeira. Of the sweets, strawberry
pavlova, lemon tart, and orange and praline roulade have been conspicuously
good. Details such as the well-stocked cocktail bar, unlimited coffee and petits
fours add to the pleasure. The cheap lunch-time buffet available Monday to
Saturday (main courses around £5) and afternoon tea have become Lakeland
institutions. The sensible will take the wines recommended with each of the
main dishes, leaving the adventurous to track a path through the long, but
carefully compiled list. Prices are fair, and the range is evenhanded in its
enthusiasms. A reasonable number of half-bottles is supplemented by the
offer to charge three-fifths of the whole bottle price if only a half is wanted.
CELLARMAN'S CHOICE: Barossa Valley, Shiraz 1989, Basedows, £11.10; Givry,
'En Choué' 1990, Lespinasse, £17.20.

CHEFS: Jane Binns and Colette Nixon   PROPRIETORS: the Nixon families   OPEN: all week;
12.30 to 2 (12.45 to 1.30 Sun), 8 to 9   CLOSED: Jan, beginning of Feb   MEALS: Set Sun L
£14, Set D £20 (2 courses) to £26   SERVICE: not inc   CARDS: Access, Amex, Diners, Visa
DETAILS: 70 seats. Private parties: 16 main room, 30 private room. Car park. Vegetarian
meals. Children's helpings. Smart dress preferred. No smoking in dining-room. Wheelchair
access (1 step; also WC). No music. Air-conditioned   ACCOMMODATION: 18 rooms, all with
bath/shower. Rooms for disabled. B&B £66 to £116. Deposit: £60. Children welcome. Baby
facilities. Afternoon teas. Garden. TV. Phone. Doors close at 11. Confirm by noon. Fax:
(053 94) 33607 (*The Which? Hotel Guide*)

---

**AMERSHAM Buckinghamshire**                                          map 3

## *King's Arms*

---

High Street, Old Amersham HP7 0DJ                         COOKING 1
AMERSHAM (0494) 726333                                    COST £19–£42

---

John Jennison recently purchased the freehold of this showpiece Tudor inn,
having been a tenant for more than 16 years. Otherwise there have been few
changes. Chef Gary Munday delivers modern cooking, along the lines of

guinea-fowl with wild mushroom and ginger sauce, grilled breast of duck with carrot and juniper sauce, and bean sprouts with mushrooms in filo pastry. Fish and desserts have been praised. Some reporters feel that the place does not justify its prices, although the set lunch offers excellent value. The well-spread list of around 70 wines ranges from house Chilean at £7.75 to some classy clarets and burgundies. Only a few halves are available. Decent bar snacks and well-kept real ales, including Greene King IPA, are served in the dark, heavily beamed bar.

CHEF: Gary Munday  PROPRIETOR: John Jennison  OPEN: Tue to Sun, exc Sun D; 12 to 2, 7 to 9.30  MEALS: alc (main courses £13 to £16). Set L £8.50 (2 courses) to £11.50. Set Sun L £14 to £15, Set Sat D £23. Minimum £8.50  SERVICE: not inc  CARDS: Access, Amex, Diners, Visa  DETAILS: 30 seats. Private parties: 30 main room, 12 and 48 private rooms. Car park. Vegetarian meals. Children welcome. Smart dress preferred. No cigars/pipes in dining-room. No music. Fax: (0494) 433480

---

APPLETHWAITE Cumbria                                                    map 7

## ▲ Underscar Manor 🌟✳

Applethwaite, nr Keswick CA12 4PH
KESWICK (076 87) 75000                                       COOKING 3
off A66, 1½m N of Keswick                                    COST £26–£45

'More interesting than...; more successful than...; as comfortable as...; lovely view over Derwentwater' was the comparative report of someone who was served a 'light soufflé of fish, tasty mushroom soup, slightly overcooked duck, a well-reduced sauce, conventional "modern" vegetables, and a selection of sweets that pleased our rather greedy guest'. Underscar has survived its first year with honours all round: for the deep-pile comfort, yards of chintz and cretonne, 'wonderful, discreet, charming, knowledgeable and not overly zealous' service, sensational position and satisfactory food. The prices are keen for this sort of establishment, which has doubtless helped the tone of comments received. One winter meal began with an appetiser of various meats and couscous, then took in black pudding with kidneys, sweetbreads and liver on a mustard and tarragon sauce, followed by a bowl of pumpkin soup. The main course was venison with juniper and pears on a ceps sauce, served with a macaroni gratin and a plethora of vegetables; then a dessert of chocolate things – ice-cream, ganache and a bi-coloured terrine with raspberries and banana cream 'plus brandied cherries and four sauces'. Diners pay no extra for coffee or for the Pianola music that strums away in the hall. The mainly French wine list is very sound, with enough attention paid to châteaux cheaper than Ducru-Beaucaillou for most to avoid bankruptcy. House wines are from £9.90.

CHEFS: Robert Thornton and Stephen Yare  PROPRIETORS: Pauline and Derek Harrison, and Gordon Evans  OPEN: all week; 12 to 1, 7 to 8.30 (9 Sat)  MEALS: Set L £18.50, Set D £28.50  SERVICE: not inc, card slips closed  CARDS: Access, Amex, Visa  DETAILS: 60 seats. 6 tables outside. Private parties: 40 main room. Car park. Vegetarian meals. No children under 12. Smart dress preferred. No smoking in dining-rooms. No music ACCOMMODATION: 11 rooms, all with bath/shower. D,B&B £75 to £250. No children under 12. Afternoon teas. Garden. TV. Phone. Doors close at midnight. Fax: (076 87) 74904 (The Which? Hotel Guide)

## ASENBY North Yorkshire

map 7

# Crab & Lobster

**NEW ENTRY**

Asenby, nr Thirsk YO7 3QL
THIRSK (0845) 577286
off A168, between A19 and A1

COOKING 2
COST £21–£41

'This place is almost too good to be true,' exclaimed a reporter. From the outside it is an archetypal country pub, with thatched roof, creeper-covered walls and beer garden. But the interior is a very different story. The whole place is filled with an extraordinary clutter of mirrored sideboards, musical instruments and bric-à-brac – even the gents' loo is papered with sheet music. The bar menu is chalked all around the beams, although there are also printed menus. Theakston bitter is on handpump, but the food is firmly in restaurant, not pub, style. Meals in the restaurant begin with good nibbles and a basket of home-baked breads. The repertoire leans heavily towards fish, and dishes such as a gargantuan portion of fish soup and unadorned fresh turbot with dill mayonnaise pleased one diner. Otherwise you might find fish-cakes with tomato and pesto, Scarborough woof with rarebit topping, and salmon and halibut in filo with chive crème fraîche. Reporters have also spoken highly of carrot and coriander soup, rack of pork with toffee apple slices and black pudding, and salmis of pheasant. To finish, chocolate marquise, crème brûlée served in a miniature copper pan, and white chocolate ice in an almond tuile have been outstanding. Service is attentive, even in the crush of customers. The wine list is modern and racy; bottles are decanted into French glass 'pots'. House Duboeuf is £7.95.

CHEFS: David Barnard and Michael Pickard  PROPRIETORS: David and Jackie Barnard
OPEN: all week, exc Sun D; 12 to 2.30, 6.30 to 10 (3 Sun)  MEALS: alc (main courses bar/brasserie £7.50 to £10, restaurant £10.50 to £15.50). Set L and D £12.75  SERVICE: not inc
CARDS: Access, Amex, Visa  DETAILS: 110 seats. 14 tables outside. Private parties: 70 main room. Car park. Vegetarian meals. Children's helpings L. Smart dress preferred. Wheelchair access (1 step). Music

## ASHBOURNE Derbyshire

map 5

# ▲ Callow Hall ⅚✳

Mappleton Road, Ashbourne DE6 2AA
ASHBOURNE (0335) 343403
¼m NW of Ashbourne, off A515

COOKING 1
COST £20–£47

Home-cured bacon and home-made sausages make an encouraging start to the day at this Victorian manor house built by a corset manufacturer, now converted and run with enthusiasm by the Spencers. The decoration does not mask the Victorianism and the cooking makes much of 'the country-house experience': hence the breakfasts, the local Stilton, and the long menu that supports a five- or six-course extravaganza served in a dining-room magnificent in shades of red. Guests will find a surprisingly large range of sea fish – from monkfish to sea bass and beyond – as well as plenty of butcher's meat and poultry. The latterday country-house style of cooking shows through in an affection for fruit such as exotic salads with scallops or with pigeon breast, strawberry with fillet of beef, plums with duck, and apricot with guinea-fowl. Desserts follow suit: one happy reader reflected on the 'explosive' flavour of a mousse made from damsons picked in the orchard (she also recommended the warmth of welcome accorded all guests). The wine list displays solid worth: the price range is bolstered by New World, Italian and Spanish bottles, but the interest concentrates on Bordeaux and Burgundy. House wines are £8.75.

CHEFS: David Spencer and Anthony Spencer PROPRIETORS: David and Dorothy Spencer OPEN: Mon to Sat D, Tue and Sun L (Sun D residents only); 12 to 1.30, 7.30 to 9.30 CLOSED: 25 and 26 Dec MEALS: alc (main courses £12.50 to £17). Set L £13.50, Set D £28 SERVICE: not inc CARDS: Access, Amex, Diners, Visa DETAILS: 60 seats. 3 tables outside. Private parties: 35 main room, 25 and 25 private room. Car park. Vegetarian meals with prior notice. Children's helpings with prior notice. Smart dress preferred. No smoking in dining-room. Wheelchair access (also WC). No music ACCOMMODATION: 13 rooms, all with bath/shower. Room for disabled. B&B £65 to £120. Children welcome. Baby facilities. Pets by arrangement. Garden. Fishing. TV. Phone. Doors close at midnight. Fax: (0335) 343624 (*The Which? Hotel Guide*)

---

**ASTON CLINTON** Buckinghamshire                                    map 3

## ▲ Bell ▮ ⁵⁂

Aston Clinton HP22 5HP
AYLESBURY (0296) 630252                                    COOKING 2
on A41, between Tring and Aylesbury                         COST £29–£68

'For years this has been a Home Counties bastion,' observes a reporter. It has also been the haunt of film stars and politicians and continues to move at a stately pace. The atmosphere is unchanging – 'it seems almost set in stone' – but there have been a few developments of late. David Cavalier's period of residence in the kitchen was a short one: he has moved to L'Escargot (see entry, London) and he has been replaced by Jean-Claude McFarlane. As a result, the thrust of the cooking seems to have reverted to the style of former years – a mix of modern classic French and traditional English of the old school. What shines out is the quality of the raw materials: specially bred Aylesbury ducks, superb lamb, maize-fed chicken, fine salmon. The *carte* is extravagantly expensive and inhabits the world of salmon and ratte potato terrine, duck broth with old port and foie gras ravioli, cod with baby clams and thyme jus, chicken with woodland mushroom sauce, and calvados soufflé. Better value are the daily set menus, and the Bell now has a bistro offering light dishes such as Mediterranean fish soup and goats' cheese salad. Sunday lunch is a relaxed event, although 'unforgivably poor' roast rib of beef, plus a 'prosaic' sweets trolley took the edge off one occasion. Cheeses are British and well chosen, but not always in proper condition ('not ripe enough where ripeness was needed,' commented an aficionado). Service in the green dining-rooms, with their walls featuring wildlife paintings, can vary from immaculate to vague and inattentive. Intelligence about the wine list is muddied by dispatch of the wine shop's stock list, but the restaurant is blessed by a remarkable range, even if prices show a bullishness that is more at home in London. House wines are £9.50.

CHEF: Jean-Claude McFarlane  PROPRIETORS: the Harris family  OPEN: all week; 12.30 to 1.45, 7.30 to 9.45  MEALS: alc (main courses bistro £6.50 to £9.50, restaurant £15.50 to £22). Set L £18.50, Set Sun L £25, Set D £22.50 to £36  SERVICE: not inc, card slips closed  CARDS: Access, Amex, Visa  DETAILS: 120 seats. 17 tables outside. Private parties: 55 main room, 20 and 250 private rooms. Car park. Vegetarian meals. Children's helpings. Smart dress preferred. No smoking in dining-room. Wheelchair access. No music  ACCOMMODATION: 21 double rooms, all with bath/shower. Rooms for disabled. B&B £92 to £187. Children welcome. Baby facilities. Pets welcome. Afternoon teas. Garden. TV. Phone. Doors close at midnight. Confirm 1 day ahead. Fax: (0296) 631250 (*The Which? Hotel Guide*)

---

**AYLESBURY Buckinghamshire**                                                              map 2

## ▲ *Hartwell House* ¦ ⁵⚹

Oxford Road, Aylesbury HP17 8NL                                          COOKING 2
AYLESBURY (0296) 747444                                                  COST £30–£53

Hartwell House's lineage stretches back almost 1,000 years and it has been the natural seat of the high and mighty over the centuries. During the residence of the French Court the roof was converted into a miniature farm where birds and rabbits were reared in cages, and shops were opened in outbuildings by émigrés short of money. Today, the place oozes luxury as a country-house hotel. 'The grounds are a joy. The public rooms are grand. Flowers abound' is a visitor's summary. Chef Aidan McCormack has left for pastures new and the kitchen is now directed by Alan Maw (ex-sous chef at Le Meridien Hotel, London – see entry). First reports suggest that the new regime needs time to settle and attain its own identity; however, the cooking is sound. Dinner revolves around a fixed-price, three-course menu that still has its share of conservative dishes – from smoked salmon to summer pudding – but there is also modern elaboration in the repertoire. Terrine of foie gras with Sauternes jelly, chicken in champagne sauce with truffle-flavoured rice, honey-glazed duck with oriental spices, and Grand Marnier soufflé served with a separate bowl of sauce have been endorsed. But for the prices, the wine list would be beyond criticism. It has range, depth, age and curiosity. Red burgundy from Guyard, Vouvrays from Huet, Alsaces from Schlumberger and a range of Penfolds Grange from South Australia are just some of the names, but those prices... House wine is £11.50. CELLARMAN'S CHOICE: Cloudy Bay, Sauvignon Blanc 1991, Nelson, £24; Ch. de Caraguilles, Corbières 1990, £14.75.

---

CHEF: Alan Maw  PROPRIETORS: Historic House Hotels Ltd  OPEN: all week; 12.30 to 2, 7.30 to 9.45  MEALS: Set L £16.50 (2 courses) to £22.40, Set D £38  SERVICE: net prices, card slips closed  CARDS: Access, Amex, Diners, Visa  DETAILS: 60 seats. Private parties: 18, 30 and 60 private rooms. Car park. Vegetarian meals. No children under 6. Jacket and tie D. No smoking in dining-room. Wheelchair access (also WC). Music. Air-conditioned  ACCOMMODATION: 46 rooms, all with bath/shower. Rooms for disabled. Lift. B&B £98 to £316. No children under 8. Pets welcome (in Hartwell Court). Afternoon teas. Garden. Swimming-pool. Sauna. Tennis. Fishing. TV. Phone. Confirm by 4. Fax: (0296) 747450 (*The Which? Hotel Guide*)

---

Card slips closed *in the details at the end of an entry indicates that the total on the slips of credit cards is closed when handed over for signature.*

---

map 3

# Mims

63 East Barnet Road, Barnet EN4 8RN        COOKING 2
081-449 2974 and 447 1825        COST £20–£35

Visitors have been pleased by the new layout and décor of this suburban restaurant: deep-green walls, parquet floors and light wood chairs have given the dining-room a new lease of life. The atmosphere is friendly and service is calm. Not much changes in the kitchen, which works to a short menu of modern dishes with Mediterranean overtones. A fixed price pays for two courses; desserts are extra. Ali Al-Sersy's cooking roams the world with crab baklava, steamed aubergine with barley, tomato and chilli, roast hake with saffron risotto, and grilled guinea-fowl. From the list of desserts, reporters have raved about the chocolate assortment – 'an unbelievable creation: I have never seen such a rich collection of four or five individual confections on one plate'; otherwise you might find mascarpone charlotte with raspberries or pear and almond tart. Breads are reckoned to be outstanding. The wine list runs to around 50 bins and halves are well in evidence. Around £15 will pay for plenty of acceptable drinking from Europe and the New World. House wine is £8.95.

CHEF: Ali Al-Sersy  PROPRIETORS: Moustafa Abouzahrah and Ali Al-Sersy  OPEN: Tue to Sun, exc Sat L; 12 to 2.30, 6 to 11 (noon to 10.30 Sun)  CLOSED: 1 week Christmas MEALS: Set L £8.50 (2 courses) to £12, Set D £17 (2 courses) to £20.50  SERVICE: not inc CARDS: Access, Visa  DETAILS: 50 seats. Private parties: 50 main room. Car park. Vegetarian meals with prior notice. Children's helpings Sun L. No children under 6. Smart dress preferred. No cigars/pipes in dining-room. Wheelchair access (1 step). No music

map 5

# Armstrongs ▼

6 Shambles Street, Barnsley S70 2SQ        COOKING 2
BARNSLEY (0226) 240113        COST £16–£38

Armstrongs is in a terrace of shops near the town hall. Inside is a long, narrow room dominated by a splendid chandelier and a curving staircase leading to an upstairs eating area. The music moderates from lively jazz to mournful blues as the evening progresses. Service is generally friendly and informal, although it can be short on numbers. Nick Pound offers keenly priced eating, with light lunches and a brasserie-style fixed-price dinner menu as well as the *carte*. He casts his net far and wide to haul in ideas and influences from around the world. China shows up in sea bass with ginger and spring onions or honey-roast duck breast with red wine and soya sauce. Boned poussin stuffed with basil and pine-kernels and marinated salmon with lemon roasted peppers and saffron vinaigrette acknowledge the modern European trend, while there is a British undercurrent in oxtail or silverside braised with 'zero flour' and served, Gary Rhodes-style, with finely diced vegetables. There is always something for vegetarians, such as courgette and blue cheese timbale or avocado and hazelnut salad with baby broad beans. Sweets are equally successful: Atholl brose 'with a whisky tang', 'really zingy' lemon sauce pudding, and peach and hazelnut tart. 'Armstrong's special recommendations' on the wine list will please. An up-to-date, informed character pervades the selection, which includes Mascarello Nebbiolo, decent New World offerings, careful Beaujolais and adequate Rhônes. A tighter rein and a more coherent arrangement of the list might help, perhaps listing by price and ignoring other clever classifications. In all, these are good wines, showing much intelligence. Prices are very fair. House wine is £8.65.

CHEFS: Nick Pound and Lee Hammond  PROPRIETOR: Nick Pound  OPEN: Tue to Sat, exc Sat L; 12 to 2, 7 to 9.30  MEALS: alc (main courses L £3.50 to £9, D £8 to £14). Set D £12.95 (7 to 8, Tue to Fri)  SERVICE: not inc  CARDS: Access, Amex, Visa  DETAILS: 60 seats. Private parties: 30 main room, 20 private room. Vegetarian meals. Children's helpings on request. Wheelchair access. Music

## Restaurant Peano ♟

102 Dodworth Road, Barnsley S70 6HL
BARNSLEY (0226) 244990

COOKING 2*
COST £21–£43

This rather severe, detached Victorian stone house just outside the town centre was previously a dentist's; nowadays, the world at large makes its way more willingly here. Both the bar upstairs and the dining-room on the ground floor mix spare modernism – black, white or wooden – with parlour-palm Victorian comfort. There is plenty of room, perhaps too much – 'It's the sort of place where you tend to talk in hushed voices because sound carries and because you can feel conspicuous sitting in the middle of what could be a largish ballroom' – hence the Muzak. Michael Peano is half-German, half-Italian and Roux-trained, and these different influences result in well-balanced menus with earthy, warm flavours. Risotto with pine-kernels, hazelnuts and cream, for example, was soft and yielding, well-perfumed with basil; red snapper with basil and tomato vinaigrette was both generously portioned and subtle in flavour. Poussin brought more of the Mediterranean to Barnsley with its haricot beans, roast courgette, peppers and fennel; pigeon might arrive on polenta with a thyme jus, and medallions of lamb be partnered by red pepper and olives. Vegetables always seem to include green beans, regulars note; but the carrot purée is delicate and good. Desserts make more concession to local traditions, via sticky toffee pudding or jam sponge with English custard. A fresh cherry and almond tart was substantial, the 'moist but not very almondy' filling and stoned cherries set in fine pastry; poached peach in a biscuit basket with iced vanilla parfait was full of contrast, picture-pretty. Quality of service seems to depend on the number of diners; it can be 'stretched and uneven', though Tracey Peano's charm soon smooths ruffles. The excellent wine list is well annotated and well selected, with France and Italy favoured almost equally. If it seems expensive, that is because producers of the quality of Quintarelli, Puiatti, Rolly-Gassmann, Aldo Conterno, Adhémar Boudin and Ghislaine Barthod do not come cheap; there are very few bottles here which would not be worth a punt. House wines are Italian and cost £9.50. CELLARMAN'S CHOICE: Ch. de Fonsalette 1987, Reynaud, £18.50; Pomerol, Vieux Châteaux Certan 1987, £32.50.

CHEF: Michael Peano   PROPRIETORS: Michael and Tracey Peano   OPEN: Tue to Sat, exc Sat
L; 12 to 1.30, 7 to 9.30   MEALS: alc (main courses £11.50 to £14.50). Set L and D £14.50
SERVICE: not inc, card slips closed   CARDS: Access, Amex, Visa   DETAILS: 45 seats. Private
parties: 45 main room. Car park. Vegetarian meals with prior notice. Children's helpings on
request. Smart dress preferred. No cigars/pipes in dining-room. Wheelchair access (1 step).
Music

---

| BARNSTAPLE Devon | map 1 |
|---|---|

## ▲ *Lynwood House* ✻

Bishops Tawton Road,
Barnstaple EX32 9DZ
BARNSTAPLE (0271) 43695 ............................................... COOKING 1
1m S of town centre, before A377 roundabout ......................... COST £19–£57

This Victorian house on the outskirts of Barnstaple makes a virtue of family
unanimity in its operations. Ruth Roberts and son Matthew look after the
kitchen, John and son Christian run the restaurant. This gives the place a
certain tone, as does the emphasis on home production in the kitchen: visitors
can even buy bottled and preserved items to take home with them, such as
lemon curd, fish soup and jams. While the hotel makes a genuine effort to be all
things to all people, offering bargain lunches, lighter meals for midday,
vegetarian items and so forth, it is for the fish that most people remember it.
Hence the pot of seafood is a constant, but many other dishes will vary
according to the markets and the state of the weather. The wine list is a useful
generalist collection that takes no hostages on price and is sound on selection.
House wines start at £8.25.

CHEFS: Ruth Roberts and Matthew Roberts   PROPRIETORS: John, Ruth, Matthew and
Christian Roberts   OPEN: Mon to Sat (Sun L and D residents only); 12 to 2, 7 to 9.30 (10
summer)   MEALS: alc (main courses £12 to £25). Set L £10.95 (2 courses) to £12.95
SERVICE: not inc, card slips closed   CARDS: Access, Amex, Visa   DETAILS: 50 seats. Private
parties: 80 main room, 20 and 80 private rooms. Car park. Vegetarian meals. Children's
helpings. Smart dress preferred. No smoking in dining-room. Wheelchair access (also WC).
Music   ACCOMMODATION: 5 rooms, all with bath/shower. B&B £47.50 to £67.50. Children
welcome. Dogs in bedrooms only. TV. Phone. Fax: (0271) 79340 (*The Which? Hotel Guide*)

---

| BARTON-UPON-HUMBER Humberside | map 6 |
|---|---|

## *Elio's* £ NEW ENTRY

11 Market Place,
Barton-upon-Humber DN18 5DA ......................................... COOKING 1
BARTON-UPON-HUMBER (0652) 635147 ............................... COST £15–£35

Tucked away in a corner of the market square, this unassuming trattoria feeds
well off the trade and traffic over the Humber Bridge. A reporter felt that
cramped décor was an understatement, although he relished the overheard
conversations and local scandal emanating from nearby tables. The menu is
typical self-respecting trattoria, backed up by a blackboard with fish as the
prime suit. Fine-looking Parma ham, genuine fresh seafood salad, deep-fried

aubergine Parmesan, and pasta soup with beans have caught the attention. Fillet steak with garlic, cream and red wine sauce has been superb, and well-reported fish specials have included grilled bream with a 'perfectly spicy' Mexican-style sauce, turbot in lemon and watercress sauce, and tuna with tomatoes, olives and herbs. Vegetables are well-handled favourites such as ratatouille and cauliflower cheese. Desserts from the trolley are backed up by zabaglione from the kitchen. Service is friendly and professional to a fault, although the pace is likely to be slow. The wine list is standard trattoria, although mark-ups seem rather steep. House wine is £7.50 a litre.

---

CHEF/PROPRIETOR: E.M. Grossi   OPEN: Mon to Sat, D only; 6 to 11   MEALS: alc (main courses £6 to £12). Set D £9.95   SERVICE: not inc   CARDS: Access, Amex, Diners, Visa   DETAILS: 40 seats. Private parties: 40 main room, 16 and 24 private rooms. Vegetarian meals. Children's helpings. Smart dress preferred. Wheelchair access. Music

---

## BARWICK  Somerset                                               map 2

## ▲ Little Barwick House ⅚✳

Barwick, nr Yeovil BA22 9TD
YEOVIL (0935) 23902
off A37, take second left                                        COOKING 2*
opposite Red House pub                                           COST £31–£39

This small Georgian pile stands above the lawns, borders and conifers that mark the limits of the Colleys' kingdom. As the years pass, so do characters – the dogs change, the daughters grow up – but the hospitality is always noticed. The Colleys have an ability to make people feel relaxed quickly. A warm throb of familiarity strikes repeat visitors, for Veronica Colley's strengths – meat cookery, pies, excessively appetising sweet dishes – are invariably on show and remain constant. First courses are mere preludes to venison or feathered game, beef and game pies, rabbit cooked with sage and onion, sensibly straightforward vegetables, and a sweet course such as 'apple and almond tart with the most buttery and crisp pastry base we have ever tasted'. The house and cooking might be your rural idyll. The wine list is a soundly based general survey that picks no pockets by stealth, nor shocks any sensitive palate. Acceptable growers will be persuasively extolled by Christopher Colley. House wines are £8.90.

---

CHEF: Veronica Colley   PROPRIETORS: Christopher and Veronica Colley   OPEN: Mon to Sat, D only (Sun D residents only); 7 to 9 (9.30 Sat)   MEALS: Set D £15.90 (2 courses) to £23.90   SERVICE: not inc, card slips closed   CARDS: Access, Amex, Visa   DETAILS: 40 seats. Private parties: 40 main room, 20 private room. Car park. Vegetarian meals. Children's helpings. No smoking in dining-room. Wheelchair access (1 step). No music. Air-conditioned   ACCOMMODATION: 6 rooms, all with bath/shower. B&B £47 to £74. Deposit: £20. Children welcome. Pets welcome with prior notice. Garden. TV. Phone. Doors close at 11. Fax: (0935) 20908 (*The Which? Hotel Guide*)

---

*'And what was the barman doing (I watched him while I was waiting for someone to come and take my order) pouring red wine from a jug into a bottle, banging in the cork and patting the filled bottled back into the wine-rack behind the bar?'*  On eating in London

## ▲ Fischer's at Baslow Hall ♀ ⁵⅟*

Calver Road, Baslow DE45 1RR                              COOKING 3
CHESTERFIELD (0246) 583259                               COST £21–£52

This imposing Edwardian house sits framed by its tree-lined drive, the mullioned stone windows shedding light on a fair riot of vivid carpet, fervid curtaining, handsome wood panelling and blazing fires. It may not be centuries old, but it has something of the grand manner, as does the cooking. Last year's reports implied some form of glitch: not so this season. Profiting from a classical background, Max Fischer seems capable of depth of flavour through accurate saucing, and refined composition through tact allied to adventure. His pride in dishes such as monkfish and calf's liver served together with a veal jus sharpened with lemon juice, or a pithiviers of rhubarb with honey ice-cream is paralleled by consumers' admiration for calf's liver with sesame seed and an aubergine mousse, lemon sole with tomato and a balsamic dressing, something simple like fillet steak au poivre, or desserts such as mille-feuille of kiwi and lemon mousse with a honey sauce or a trio of citrus (soufflé, tart and sorbet). The set-price menus, offering a choice of maybe half a dozen dishes, seem understated, but the flavour combinations of something like sea bream in puff pastry with Beluga caviare or veal steak with fresh truffle are arresting in their simplicity. Fischer's is one of the more thoroughgoing kitchens in the region: the ancillaries and supporters are all home produced and proper. The cheaper Café Max offers the likes of salmon roulade and paupiette of veal with tomato and Parma ham. Good names predominate on the wine list, although the occasional lapses into the safe and well known discourage total confidence. Prices are fair, especially at the lower end. House wine is £9. CELLARMAN'S CHOICE: Bourgogne Aligoté 1990, Rollin, £15.50; Châteauneuf-du-Pape, Vieux Télégraphe 1988, £23.

CHEF: Max Fischer   PROPRIETORS: Max and Susan Fischer   OPEN: restaurant all week, exc Sun D (residents only); 12 to 2, 7 to 9.30. Café Max Mon to Sat; 12 to 2, 7 to 9.30   CLOSED: 25 and 26 Dec   MEALS: restaurant L £20 (£25), Set D £34. Café Max alc (main courses £7.50 to £12.50)   CARDS: Access, Amex, Visa   SERVICE: not inc, card slips closed   DETAILS: restaurant 52 seats, Café Max 24 seats. 4 tables outside. Private parties: 40 main room, 12 and 24 private rooms. Car park. Vegetarian meals with prior notice. Children's helpings L. No children under 10 D. Children welcome Café Max. Jacket and tie restaurant D. No smoking in restaurant. Wheelchair access (3 steps; also WC). Music Café Max. No music restaurant   ACCOMMODATION: 6 rooms, all with bath/shower. B&B £65 to £120. Children welcome. Afternoon teas. Garden. TV. Phone. Doors close at midnight (*The Which? Hotel Guide*)

CELLARMAN'S CHOICE: *Wines recommended by the restaurateur, normally more expensive than house wine.*

Not inc *in the details at the end of an entry indicates that no service charge is made and any tipping is at the discretion of the customer.*

map 2

# ▲ Bath Spa Hotel, Vellore Restaurant

**NEW ENTRY**

Sydney Road, Bath BA2 6JF
BATH (0225) 444424

COOKING 3
COST £46–£60

Rastafarians unite! Haile Selassie spent years of his wartime exile in this Italianate house on the slopes of a hill that is crowned by Ralph Allen's Sham Castle. After the Emperor it became a nurses' home, then Forte converted it into a shameless palazzo for travellers. A touch of whimsy – two teddy bears at the entrance studying menus, or mice made from bread and chocolate – may reconcile the fearful to paying a steep price for Jonathan Fraser's cooking in the Vellore Restaurant, which occupies what was once the ballroom. A cheaper but creditable version is available in the light and airy Alfresco 'for not much money at all, plus a chance to rub shoulders with Nigel Havers,' reported one starstruck reader. There is a short *carte* and a daily menu, with less whimsy in the cooking than might be feared. A terrine of goats' cheese and smoked garlic layered with aubergine and pimentos proved full of flavour yet never out of balance, pepper-seared venison with mulled pears was also finely balanced between sweet and sour, with a nice neutrality to the trencher of sweetcorn beneath. It was bettered by duck that coped with excess fattiness, was perfectly tender, yet had taste, and came with caramelised prunes, apricots and plums. Fancy reasserts itself at dessert with the description 'strawberry indulgence behind bars', which seems to be sorbet under a sugar cage, but 'three chocolate puddings' were just that, and appreciated. The wine list tries hard to present a user-friendly face, but the prices rather inhibit the role. It is arranged by weight rather than geography with some impressive choices, including plenty from the New World, adequate numbers of older vintages in clarets but not burgundies, and a collection of bottled waters for the curious. Bath is a spa, after all. House wines are £16 or £18, which gives some idea of the baseline.

CHEF: Jonathan Fraser  PROPRIETORS: Forte Hotels  OPEN: all week, D only, and Sun L; 12.30 to 2, 7 to 10  MEALS: Set D £34  SERVICE: not inc, card slips closed  CARDS: Access, Amex, Diners, Visa  DETAILS: 100 seats. Private parties: 150 main room, 60, 60 and 200 private rooms. Car park. Vegetarian meals. Children's helpings. Smart dress preferred. No-smoking area. Wheelchair access (also WC). Music. Air-conditioned  ACCOMMODATION: 98 rooms, all with bath/shower. Rooms for disabled. Lift. B&B £109 to £198. Deposit: 1 night. Pets welcome on ground floor. Afternoon teas. Garden. Swimming-pool. Sauna. Tennis. TV. Phone. Confirm by 4. Fax: (0225) 444006

# Beaujolais

5A Chapel Row, Queen Square,
Bath BA1 1HN
BATH (0225) 423417

COOKING 1
COST £16–£35

Jean-Pierre Augé has an exact and accurate view of the appeal of his restaurant on the south side of Queen Square. 'The customers come for a night of fun without protocol. We are now serving the children of our first years, who want to know where their parents used to go for a romantic date. It is a restaurant for locals, who know it will never change and is not going to improve!' It was just such an improvement – the decoration of the back part – that led one reader, who had not been there for some years, to regret the passing of an era. The Beaujolais is a bottle without a bottom, the staff are usually cheerful, and it runs with very few pretensions, serving fair-value, resolutely French food, in fairly large portions: chicken liver pâté, a salad with croûtons and poached egg, galantine of chicken, leg of lamb steak with a goulash-style sauce, venison casseroled with shallots and honey, crème brûlée and apple tart. The crowds beg for more, even after 20 years, wanting familiarity, not finesse. The wine list is a short and inexpensive one, with wines from Languedoc and Provence being the main draw. House wines are £8.50.

CHEFS: Jean-Christophe Larras and Jacque Dubini  PROPRIETORS: Jean-Pierre Augé and Phillippe Wall  OPEN: all week, exc Sun L (bank hols, Mothering Sun and other 'special' days only); 12 to 2, 6 (7.30 Fri and Sat) to 11  CLOSED: 1 Jan, early Jan, 25 Dec  MEALS: alc (main courses £10 to £14). Set L £9, Set D £17.50  SERVICE: not inc  CARDS: Access, Amex, Visa  DETAILS: 85 seats. 5 tables outside. Private parties: 50 main room, 25 private room. Vegetarian meals. Children's helpings. No-smoking area. Wheelchair access. Music

## Garlands

7 Edgar Buildings, George Street,
Bath BA1 2EE
BATH (0225) 442283

COOKING 1
COST £24–£34

The broad pavement of George Street protects this small restaurant from the immediate rush of traffic. The last 12 months have seen the Bridgemans converting the back of the shop into a small café-bar for lighter, cheaper and quicker food; a case of responding to the market. Tom Bridgeman moves with the times inasmuch as filo turnovers come garnished with olives and sun-dried tomatoes, or a pigeon salad is served with pickled red cabbage and oyster mushrooms, but his essential style is one of gradual change, not revolution. Hence fillet of pork is served with a grain mustard and thyme sauce, chicken with mushrooms and cream, duck with apple and calvados. No harm in this, though some have commented on rather too much cream and insufficient bite to the sauces, and a touch too much bite to the vegetables. For dessert soft fruits in brandy-snap baskets with a honey ice-cream were 'a particularly felicitous combination'. The café means that there is an espresso machine. The wine list is set out according to grape varieties with some decent producers among them, be they Ch. Siran, Droin's Chablis, Firestone's Cabernet Sauvignon or Quady's Essencia. House wines are Duboeuf at £9.75.

CHEF: Tom Bridgeman  PROPRIETORS: Tom and Joanna Bridgeman  OPEN: all week, exc Mon L; 12 to 2.15, 7 to 10.30  MEALS: Set L £12.75 (2 courses) to £14.95, Set D £18.75. Café-bar menu (£3.50 to £8)  SERVICE: not inc  CARDS: Access, Amex, Diners, Visa  DETAILS: 26 seats. Private parties: 14 main room, 35 private room. Vegetarian meals on request. Children welcome. Smart dress preferred. No-smoking area. Wheelchair access (also WC). Music

The Good Food Guide *is a registered trade mark of Consumers' Association Ltd.*

## ▲ *Priory Hotel* ✸

| Weston Road, Bath BA1 2XT | COOKING 3 |
|---|---|
| BATH (0225) 331922 | COST £28–£57 |

'We came for dinner, having not been for ages and ages. It seemed exactly the same as our last visit: same chef, same maître d'hôtel, same good food, and good vegetables. It was full of what seemed like business people.' And tourists, our reporter might have added, had it been in the summer season. This does not alter the essential accuracy of her comment. The hotel established its style some years ago and has stuck to it. The house is in one of Bath's earliest suburbs, so is not without garden, though space has been occupied by new bedroom wings in the intervening years. This is a country-house hotel in all but name and location, with the generous lounges, oil paintings, high prices and elaborate service that go with the bracket. For all that, it does it very competently and Michael Collom is a chef of settled skills, evinced in dishes such as black pudding on an apple galette, carefully composed terrine of foie gras, leek and guinea-fowl, scallops on a pastry tart case with provençal tomatoes, or desserts of the order of apple and blackberry strudel served with a cinnamon ice-cream. The wine list is as dear as the rest of the place. If an Ochoa Tempranillo can be charged at £21 when it rarely costs more than £6 retail, then someone's margins are high. House wines are £14.50.

CHEF: Michael Collom   PROPRIETORS: Select Country Hotels plc   OPEN: all week; 12.30 to 2, 7 to 9.15   MEALS: alc (main courses £8 to £15). Set L £20.50, Set D £29.50 to £32 SERVICE: not inc, card slips closed   CARDS: Access, Amex, Diners, Visa   DETAILS: 65 seats. Private parties: 45 main room, 10 private room. Car park. Vegetarian meals. Children's helpings. Jacket and tie. No smoking in dining-room. Wheelchair access (also WC). No music   ACCOMMODATION: 21 rooms, all with bath/shower. B&B £85 to £185. Deposit: 1 night. Children welcome. Baby facilities. Afternoon teas. Garden. Swimming-pool. TV. Phone. Fax: (0225) 448276

## ▲ *Queensberry Hotel, Olive Tree*

| Russel Street, Bath BA1 2QF | COOKING 2 |
|---|---|
| BATH (0225) 447928 | COST £18–£42 |

The bland repetitiousness of a Georgian terrace house (albeit one near the Assembly Rooms) lends itself to reinterpretation, once you are through the door. Not everyone goes in for indiscriminate conservatism and the Rosses have chosen to rework their basement bistro (their word for it) with strong, bare colourwashes, tiles and much light. From the ground floor upwards, in the rooms of their town house hotel, subdued elegance reigns in more predictable manner. The restaurant's ambience fits well with the style of cooking: bright and modern, sometimes inventive, coupled with a strong vein of the Anglo-French consensus achieved in the '70s. For starters, a version of carpaccio with a mustard cream sits happily next to salmon fish-cakes with a lemon hollandaise, a provençal fish soup with the trimmings, and a duck terrine with spiced chutney and toasted brioche. Main-course guinea-fowl with pears, tarragon and cream does not seem out of sorts with its neighbouring seafood risotto, braised beef with prunes and armagnac, or a mixed grill of lamb with black pudding, mint sausage and a mustard sauce. Herbs and flavourings are definitely assertive and modern (i.e. from everywhere). People have talked warmly of the fish-cakes, the fish soup, the liver and bacon, some of the fish offered (Thursday is the day for more fish cookery), and long slow dishes like a pot-au-feu that was good in everything but the trimming of the oxtail. Ingredients are fine, but there is an up-and-downness to the cooking, a missing of detail, that sometimes disappoints. Chips are excellent, as are the dauphinois. Pastry can be heavy, but few can resist hot chocolate soufflé, and one customer 'did not lick his plate after pears with a peach sabayon, but came close to it'. The wine list is as sharply aware of current trends as is the menu, and its prices are as carefully pitched to what Bath and district prefer to spend. The house selection may start at about £9.50.

CHEFS: Stephen Ross, Rupert Pitt and Janice Wilmot   PROPRIETORS: Stephen and Penny Ross   OPEN: Mon to Sat, exc Mon L; 12 to 2, 7 to 10.30   CLOSED: 2 weeks Christmas   MEALS: alc (main courses £7.50 to £13). Set L £10.50, Set D £17   SERVICE: not inc, card slips closed   CARDS: Access, Amex, Visa   DETAILS: 50 seats. Private parties: 50 main room, 30 and 20 private rooms. Vegetarian meals. Children's helpings with prior notice. Wheelchair access (2 steps; also WC). Music   ACCOMMODATION: 22 rooms, all with bath/shower. Rooms for disabled. Lift. B&B £89 to £140. Children welcome. Baby facilities. Afternoon teas. TV. Phone. Fax: (0225) 446065 (*The Which? Hotel Guide*)

## ▲ Royal Crescent Hotel, Dower House

16 Royal Crescent, Bath BA1 2LS                           COOKING 3
BATH (0225) 319090                                          COST £27–£66

Dining is done not in the hotel itself, but in the dower house – down a short and serpentine path across pretty gardens, the deliciously petite building flanked by pavilion and mews. Opinions differ as to the success of the setting within: some feel that the orange and apricot dining-room and over-furnished lounge are 'disappointing for one of the best addresses in the world'; others acclaim the dower house as 'a magnificent place to eat dinner in'. The mixed clientele poses problems for the kitchen; an inspector found her eyeline filled with 'gentlemen in dark glasses accompanied by young ladies with purple lipstick and skirts that barely covered their bottoms'. Nevertheless, the food, fairly described as 'post-classical', does its best to keep minds on plates, by dint of taking top-quality ingredients and pitching them into emphatic, imaginative but unfrightening flavour contrasts: sweetbreads with minted vinaigrette, scallops on a gingery jus, monkfish with red wine fish gravy, cannon of lamb spiked with pesto on a black olive gravy. Mousse-filled turbot poached in a morel cream and John Dory braised in butter and served with a *vin jaune* sauce were 'both excellent. We swopped at half-time and could not decide which was better. Full marks to kitchen.' High scores have been awarded to meunière of codling with red wine gravy, beef fillet in juniper sauce ('intense flavour full of the hunt and the forest'), chocolate soufflé with an orange sauce, and a parfait of rhubarb. The menu states that vegetables 'are lightly cooked'; one respondent had scrawled 'there *is* a limit' on her copy, and sent her undercooked potatoes back to the kitchen, from where they returned, improved. 'Lovely chocs' appear

ENGLAND

with coffee. Service, even when few diners are present, is 'not of the highest order', but reporters have sprung to the defence of the wine list, pointing out that in such surroundings it is not expensive and that the selection is an unblinkered one, with a good choice of halves. The house wines start at £11.50.

CHEF: Steven Blake  PROPRIETORS: Queens Moat Houses plc  OPEN: all week; 12.30 to 2, 7 to 9.30 (10 Sat)  MEALS: alc (main courses £17 to £19). Set L £14.50 (2 courses) to £18.50, Set D £28  SERVICE: not inc, card slips closed  CARDS: Access, Amex, Diners, Visa DETAILS: 70 seats. 4 to 10 tables outside. Private parties: 70 main room, 20 to 70 in private rooms. Car park. Vegetarian meals. Children's helpings 5.30 to 9.30pm. No children under 7 D. Smart dress preferred. No cigars/pipes in dining-room. Wheelchair access (1 step). Music  ACCOMMODATION: 42 rooms, all with bath/shower. Rooms for disabled. Lift. B&B £98.50 to £360. Children welcome. Baby facilities. Afternoon teas. Garden. TV. Phone. Doors close at midnight. Confirm by 2. Fax: (0225) 339401 (*The Which? Hotel Guide*)

## Woods £

9–13 Alfred Street, Bath BA1 2QX  
BATH (0225) 314812 and 422493

COOKING 1  
COST £17–£32

Set in fine Georgian premises opposite the Assembly Rooms, Woods continues to offer excellent value in pleasant surroundings. Owner David Price is a devotee of the Sport of Kings and the walls of the restaurant are lined with racing prints and memorabilia. Set lunch and dinner menus plunder the globe for satay squid, roast leg of lamb with olive and smoked garlic butter, and fillet of cod with tomato and basil. Reporters have endorsed carrot and cumin soup, chicken breast in herb boursin sauce, and veal steak with garlic. Vegetables are crunchy, the cheeseboard is excellent and sweets have included a perfect iced nougat in strawberry coulis. The cut-price weekday 'happy supper menu' is worth investigating, and lighter dishes such as fish soup, steak sandwiches and grilled goats' cheese with warm onion marmalade are on offer in the brasserie. Occasionally dishes do not match their menu descriptions and the music can intrude, but this is generally a reliable place. The wine list veers between pricey clarets and affordable bottles from the New World. House wine is £8.10.

CHEFS: Mary Alley and Kirk Vincent  PROPRIETORS: David and Claude Price  OPEN: Mon to Sat; restaurant 12 to 2.30, 6.30 to 10.30; brasserie 11am to 11pm (11 to 3 Sat)  CLOSED: 25 and 26 Dec, 1 Jan  MEALS: alc (main courses brasserie £4.50 to £8, restaurant £12). Set L £8 (2 courses) to £10, Set D £12 (Mon to Fri) to £18.95 (Mon to Sat)  SERVICE: not inc CARDS: Access, Amex, Visa  DETAILS: 140 seats. 6 tables outside. Private parties: 70 main room, 40 private room. Vegetarian meals. Children's helpings. Smart dress preferred. No cigars/pipes in dining-room. Wheelchair access (2 steps; also WC). Music. Fax: (0225) 443146

'The restaurant is split-level, no I can't describe it more than that, its got a tented ceiling and pine tables, etc. A notice taped to the till instructed us to ''chant Hare Krishna and be happy'' – I didn't and I wasn't.'  On eating in Yorkshire

'A huddle of orderlies killed time by the far window. When our food began to arrive, there was a mass move towards us, like forwards advancing for a scrum.'  On eating in Edinburgh

BEAMINSTER Dorset · map 2

## ▲ *Bridge House* ¦✳

Prout Bridge, Beaminster DT8 3AY
BRIDPORT (0308) 862200, code changes
to (01308) April 1994

COOKING 1
COST £17–£39

'On the sunniest day of the year anywhere would seem wonderful, but the Bridge House surpassed itself,' enthused a reporter. The building, just down the hill from the town square, is a thirteenth-century clergy house with beautifully laid out gardens and some modern extensions. Inside, the dining-room is 'comfortable olde England, just right for Hardy country', although another visitor found the atmosphere 'very gloomy and church-like'. Lindsay Wakeman buys wisely and cooks ably within limitations. The regularly changing *carte* might feature John Dory with orange and mushroom stuffing, roast best end of lamb with mint and lemon sauce, and guinea-fowl braised in red wine with wild mushrooms. Similar dishes also appear on the daily table d'hôte. One enjoyable lunch included Poole mussels with fennel and cream, vichyssoise ('charmingly packed in a bowl of ice'), fillets of Dover sole with almonds, crème brûlée with a 'hidden kick of brandied prunes' and passion-fruit mousse with orange sauce. The wine list is well spread, sensibly chosen and fairly priced. House wines start at £7.50.

CHEFS: Lindsay Wakeman and Peter Pinkster PROPRIETOR: Peter Pinkster OPEN: all week; 12.30 to 1.45, 7 to 8.30 (9 Sat and all days summer) MEALS: alc (main courses L £5.50 to £6, D £9.50 to £15). Set L £11.95, Set D £15.45 to £16.45 SERVICE: not inc, card slips closed CARDS: Access, Amex, Diners, Visa DETAILS: 36 seats. 3 tables outside. Private parties: 48 main room, 14 private room. Car park. Vegetarian meals with prior notice. Children's helpings on request. Smart dress preferred. No smoking in dining-room. Wheelchair access. No music ACCOMMODATION: 14 rooms, all with bath/shower. Rooms for disabled. B&B £35 to £92. Deposit: £25. Children welcome. Pets welcome (not in public rooms). Afternoon teas. Garden. TV. Phone. Doors close at 11.30. Confirm by 6. Fax: (0308) 863700 (*The Which? Hotel Guide*)

BECKINGHAM Lincolnshire · map 6

## *Black Swan* ¦✳

Hillside, Beckingham LN5 0RF
NEWARK (0636) 626474
off A17 to Sleaford, 5m E of Newark-on-Trent

COOKING 2*
COST £23–£40

The river runs quietly past the Black Swan's car park; the elevated village bypass rather less so, yet inside this sixteenth-century former pub roadside noise is quickly forgotten. 'I liked it' was one reporter's comment on the décor of the L-shaped restaurant, 'but some of the others said it was a mite too pink.' Beams redeem the pinkness, and a 'summer garden lunch-time menu' replaces pink with green and deep blue. Value continues to be a major draw: 'My initial intention had been to select from the *carte* but I felt that I just had to test the lowest-priced set dinner that I've seen for a long time. It was excellent. It was reminiscent of the meals one can get in the French provinces.' The set-price menu may begin with a complimentary dish, such as rabbit terrine with finely chopped celery in a light curry sauce; starters might be a soup (crab, with salmon quenelles, or quail and oyster mushroom with sherry) or seafood ravioli with a salmon and lumpfish caviare sauce. Escalope of sea bream with spinach was well matched by a buttery saffron sauce; chicken breast stuffed with apricot and cased in pastry, with a port wine sauce, also pleased. 'Slightly odd food combinations' sometimes intrude, like hot ratatouille tartlet topped with Stilton; but never at pudding stage, where strawberry and chocolate soufflé was 'scrumptious', an individual plum and almond tart fresh and good, and an 'extremely light' chocolate mousse served with an unusually refreshing caramel sauce. Service, in white gloves ('a touch of Indian army somewhere?'), is pleasant and unobtrusive, and the 50-bottle wine list fair. The annotations are welcome, but producers' names could be noted more systematically. House wines ('the dry white was respectable, the red lacked tannin') are £7.60.

CHEFS: Anton Indans and Claire Rogers   PROPRIETORS: Anton and Alison Indans   OPEN: Tue to Sun, exc Sun D; 12 to 2, 7 to 10   MEALS: alc (main courses £12 to £14.50). Set L and D £14.75   SERVICE: not inc   CARDS: Access, Visa   DETAILS: 35 seats. Private parties: 28 main room, 12, 14 and 28 private rooms. Car park. Vegetarian meals. Children's helpings. Smart dress preferred. No smoking in dining-room. Wheelchair access (also WC). Music

---

## BERWICK-UPON-TWEED Northumberland                                    map 7

### *Funnywayt'mekalivin*

41 Bridge Street,
Berwick-upon-Tweed TD15 1ES
BERWICK-UPON-TWEED (0289) 308827 and 386437

COUNTY OF THE YEAR RESTAURANT

COOKING 2*
COST £11–£28

'My principles are high, but the price isn't,' says Elizabeth Middlemiss. Bravo! Her converted plumber's shop in the old town continues to delight a stream of visitors. 'Warmth, generosity and sincerity mark it out' is a typical comment. She has now started opening for light lunches on a regular basis – a service greatly appreciated by the people of Berwick: salads, savouries and local cheeses are backed up by house wines and Normandy cider. In the evening a four-course meal at a set time can provide hours of pleasure. Consider a typical dinner from June: a complimentary glass of white port with appetising nibbles, then tomato and mint soup with three kinds of freshly baked bread, then rack of Scottish lamb with mint and gooseberry sauce plus glazed beetroot, cabbage with juniper and garlic and potato puffs. Rounding things off on this occasion were strawberries with cream and shortbread, plus unlimited coffee with petits fours. The diners could also have plumped for cheese – perhaps Bonchester, Lanark Blue, Cotherstone or Teviotdale. The verdict: 'A lovely evening followed by a walk around the town ramparts overlooking the sea.' Like everything else about the place, the eminently affordable short wine list is well thought out and balanced. House wines start at £6.50.

CHEF: Elizabeth Middlemiss   PROPRIETORS: Mr and Mrs Middlemiss   OPEN: Mon to Fri L, Wed to Sat D; 11.30 to 2.30, 7.30 for 8   CLOSED: bank hols   MEALS: alc (main courses £4 to £6.50). Set D £18.50. Minimum £2 L   SERVICE: net prices, card slips closed   CARDS: Access, Visa   DETAILS: 34 seats. Private parties: 26 main room, 8 private room. Vegetarian meals (with prior notice D). Children welcome. No smoking L, no smoking during meal D. Wheelchair access (1 step). Music

**BEXHILL** East Sussex map 3

## Lychgates

Church Street, Old Town,
Bexhill TN40 2HE
BEXHILL (0424) 212193

COOKING 2
COST £18–£32

The white clapboard house near the churchyard, the gate of which has lent its name, is home and hearth to the Tysons and has that character of personal welcome when you visit. Although the South Coast can be more moribund than some parts of the country – it must occasionally seem as if the clientele is slipping away – John Tyson sticks to his last. Classically trained, his techniques are more polished than at other catering outlets in the neighbourhood, yet it is not simply Escoffier regurgitated: a Brazilian fish stew given the zip of spices and the mellow flavour of saffron, or a little crab, dill and Pernod omelette as a first course are evidences of that. Other offerings on a spring menu included a salad of pigeon and beetroot followed by chicken stuffed with pear and ginger, or braised rabbit with whisky, lemon and honey. Menus are set-price with a pair of offerings at dinner and a much cheaper one at lunch. No service charge is made or expected. The wine list is cursory for the classic French regions, because the Tysons realise that their price has soared beyond Bexhill budgets. Instead, French country wines and bottles from the New World make up the bulk of the list, at very fair prices. House wines are £8.75.

CHEF: John Tyson  PROPRIETORS: John and Sue Tyson  OPEN: Tue to Sat, D only (L Easter Sun and Mothering Sun; other days by arrangement); 12.30 to 2, 7.30 (7 Sat) to 10 (10.30 Sat)  CLOSED: 25 Dec to 1 Jan, 2 weeks school summer hols  MEALS: Set L £10 (2 courses) to £12.95, Set D £18.50 to £21.95  SERVICE: card slips closed  CARDS: Access, Visa  DETAILS: 28 seats. Private parties: 18 main room. Vegetarian meals (vegans with prior notice). Children's helpings. No children under 8 D. No cigars/pipes in dining-room. Wheelchair access. No music

**BILBROUGH** North Yorkshire map 5

## ▲ Bilbrough Manor ⅔✴

Bilbrough, York Y02 3PH
TADCASTER (0937) 834002
off A64, 4m NE of Tadcaster

COOKING 1*
COST £23–£57

The house is an intriguing piece of Edwardian architecture, with much potential character: a double hall divided by a columned arcade, a generous drawing-room and an impressive panelled dining-room. It is a pity, for some visitors, that the glasses are unnecessarily fussy, the flowers ditto, doilies are whipped out at every turn and the decoration is slightly out of sync. The cooking can be good: people have enjoyed the definite country-house style of Andrew Pressley's devilled kidneys and mushrooms in a piquant sauce, lobster tarts, guinea-fowl and apple meringue pancake (to cite one set meal taken in the spring), or the relatively plain cooking for Sunday lunch, or a meal such as mussels 'billy bye', chicken served with a warm salad of spring vegetables and artichoke, and a bakewell tart to finish. Others, however, have found the taste notes at fault: much too much sweetness in the sauces, flavourless bread, overheated vegetables and sometimes inaccurately cooked meat. Service is professional. The wine list, too, is a reliable canter through sound suppliers from all over. Price range should console the impecunious and house wine is £11.95.

CHEF: Andrew Pressley   PROPRIETORS: Mr and Mrs Colin C. Bell   OPEN: all week; 12 to 2, 7 to 9.30   CLOSED: 25 to 29 Dec   MEALS: alc (main courses £10.50 to £19). Set L £10.50 (2 courses) to £14.50, Set D £20 to £30   SERVICE: not inc, card slips closed   CARDS: Access, Amex, Diners, Visa   DETAILS: 78 seats. 5 tables outside. Private parties: 46 main room, 12 and 20 private rooms. Car park. Vegetarian meals. Children's helpings L. No children under 10. Jacket and tie. No smoking in dining-room. Wheelchair access (also WC). Music   ACCOMMODATION: 13 rooms, all with bath/shower. B&B £77 to £150. No children under 10. Afternoon teas. Garden. TV. Phone. Fax: (0937) 834724

---

**BILLESLEY Warwickshire**                                                  map 2

## ▲ *Billesley Manor* ♟

Billesley B49 6NF

STRATFORD-UPON-AVON (0789) 400888
off A422, 2m W of Stratford-upon-Avon

COOKING 2*
COST £25–£62

After the hurly-burly of a tourist's timetable, devoted to the hot pursuit of Shakespeare in nearby Stratford-upon-Avon, soothing respite at this Tudor manor house may be in order. The place may be slightly hard to find; one reader reported that after the sign on the A422 there is no further direction when another right-hand turn is required. It may also suffer from some of the drawbacks of a fancy country hotel – 'everybody spoke in whispers'; 'the waiting team spoke French between themselves too audibly'. But the continued presence of Mark Naylor in the kitchen does mean a steady hand in the pot and some satisfactory cooking, even if *carte* and dinner prices are stiffer than the more realistic set-price lunch. The culinary mode is modern classicism: dishes such as duck with honey and black peppercorns, lamb with basil and turnip purée, and monkfish with bacon and mustard give enough variation on tired master-recipes to appeal to jaded palates. Some things, however, never change, like the array of vegetables produced at main-course time, or the quality of the crème brûlées. The wine list is succinct and, apart from some diffidence about claret vintages, shows intelligent if cautious selection. Alsace remains strong. Especially pleasing half-bottles and bin-ends merit consideration. House wine is £10.50. CELLARMAN'S CHOICE: Menetou-Salon 1991, Clément, £18.75; Hautes Côtes de Beaune 1990, Demangeot, £17.75.

CHEF: Mark Naylor   PROPRIETORS: Queens Moat Houses plc   OPEN: all week; 12.30 to 2, 7.30 to 9.30 (10 Fri and Sat)   MEALS: alc (main courses £17 to £23). Set L £17, Set D £26 SERVICE: not inc, card slips closed   CARDS: Access, Amex, Diners, Visa   DETAILS: 75 seats. 6 tables outside. Private parties: 8 main room, 14 to 100 in private rooms. Car park. Vegetarian meals. No children under 12. Jacket and tie. No cigars/pipes in dining-room. Wheelchair access. No music   ACCOMMODATION: 41 rooms, all with bath/shower. B&B £99 to £160. Children welcome. Afternoon teas. Garden. Swimming-pool. Tennis. TV. Phone. Doors close at 1am. Confirm by 6. Fax: (0789) 764145

BIRCH VALE Derbyshire

map 5

## ▲ *Waltzing Weasel* £

COUNTY OF THE YEAR RESTAURANT

**NEW ENTRY**

New Mills Road, Birch Vale,
Hayfield SK12 5BT
NEW MILLS (0663) 743402
on A6015, ½m W of Hayfield

COOKING 1*
COST £17–£37

Every report mentions the views – of the valley and of Kinder Scout – to be seen from the restaurant windows of this former pub: 'four-star comfort in a pub setting'. There is plenty of the local about the pub part, and the restaurant and new rooms give added dimension. George Benham, who cooks here, has been in the *Guide* before, when he was at the Lamb at Shipton-under-Wychwood. His honest cooking, founded on good materials, a direct style and decent technique, has won northern converts for plain lobster, guinea-fowl with apples and calvados, accurately cooked steaks and roast beef, and plenty of vegetables English-style. Puddings have not had the same plaudits, but first courses of smoked venison, gravlax, hot cheese soufflés and warm salad of duck breast have hit the mark. Bar snacks and a carvery are available at lunchtime. The wine list has plenty of range and is sensibly priced with above-average house wines at £7.75.

CHEF: George Benham   PROPRIETORS: Lynda and Michael Atkinson   OPEN: all week; 12 to 2, 7.30 to 9   CLOSED: 25 Dec   MEALS: alc D (main courses £5.50 to £12.50). Set D £18.50 (2 courses) to £22.50. Bar carvery L Minimum £18.50   SERVICE: not inc, card slips closed   CARDS: Access, Visa   DETAILS: 30 seats. Private parties: 36 private room. Car park. Vegetarian meals. Children's helpings. No children under 5. Smart dress preferred. Wheelchair access (1 step). Music. Air-conditioned   ACCOMMODATION: 8 rooms, all with bath/shower. Rooms for disabled. B&B £40 to £90. Deposit: £10. No children under 5. Pets by arrangement. Garden. Fishing. TV. Phone. Doors close at 12.30am (*The Which? Hotel Guide*)

BIRDLIP Gloucestershire

map 2

## ▲ *Kingshead House* ▼

Birdlip GL4 8JH
GLOUCESTER (0452) 862299

COOKING 2
COST £22–£43

There is a nice sense of occupation in this stone house that was once a coaching-inn high on the Cotswold scarp, but is now a country restaurant with few of the irritations of false elaboration, ornament and fuss. The presence of 'Lord John Russell's Iced Pudding', an orange and lemon ice-cream bombe with Cointreau sauce, might indicate leftish leanings, as well as a propensity to cook British revival dishes, but Judy Knock's sources are much wider than that: chicken with an oriental spiced pancake, torte aux fromages with a soubise sauce, koulibiac, and rosettes of beef with gremolada are some instances of wide reading and willing experimentation. Lunch, as imaginative as the choice for dinner, may be eaten in restaurant or bar, or take advantage of the sunshine in the garden beyond. Cheerful girls serve, as well as Warren Knock himself. Seventy-odd wines provide an informed global tour and with a strong bias to well-made middle-range bottles rather than the exalted. Prices are fair. Notes

could be edited to allow for a simpler read. House wine is from £8.95.
CELLARMAN'S CHOICE: Trentino, Pinot Bianco, 'Alle Pergole' 1989, Longariva,
£12.75; Côtes du Luberon, Ch. de Mille 1986, Pinatel, £11.50.

CHEF: Judy Knock  PROPRIETORS: Warren and Judy Knock  OPEN: Tue to Sun, exc Sat L
and Sun D; 12.30 to 1.45, 7.30 to 10  CLOSED: 26 Dec, 1 Jan  MEALS: alc L (main courses
£6.50 to £9.50). Set D £22.50 to £24.50  SERVICE: not inc (10% for 6 or more)  CARDS:
Access, Amex, Diners, Visa  DETAILS: 34 seats. 4 tables outside. Private parties: 34 main
room. Car park. Vegetarian meals. Children's helpings. Smart dress preferred. Wheelchair
access (also WC). Music  ACCOMMODATION: 1 room, with bath/shower. B&B £35 to £50.
Deposit: £10. Children welcome. Pets by arrangement. Garden. Doors close at 11.30.
Confirm by 6

---

## BIRKENHEAD Merseyside

map 5

# Beadles

15 Rosemount, Oxton, Birkenhead L43 5SG
051-653 9010

COOKING 1
COST £22–£30

'It's fine – exactly as it has been for the last 15 years and presumably will be as
long as the Gotts choose to continue' is the verdict of a devotee who has been
supporting this restaurant from the start. The décor is dominated by Roy Gott's
collection of prints, which are regularly swapped with ones in his own home.
Bea Gott's cooking depends on the market and great trouble is taken with
suppliers. She rings the changes, taking inspiration from Asia, California and
Italy, as well as from France. This translates into a short, monthly-changing
menu that might include confit of duck leg with butter beans, suprême of
chicken with wild apricots, calf's liver with onion marmalade and balsamic
vinegar, and tiramisù. The daily fish dish might be hake with aubergines and
red pepper sauce. Ice-creams and sorbets are made on the premises. Roy Gott is
always eager to chat about the wines, which offer catholic drinking at keen
prices. House wine is £6.50.

CHEF: Bea Gott  PROPRIETORS: Roy and Bea Gott  OPEN: Tue to Sat, D only; 7.30 to 9
CLOSED: 2 weeks Aug  MEALS: alc (main courses £9 to £9.50)  SERVICE: not inc
CARDS: Access, Visa  DETAILS: 34 seats. Private parties: 30 main room. Vegetarian meals
with prior notice. No children under 7. Wheelchair access (1 step). Music

---

## BIRMINGHAM West Midlands

map 5

# Chung Ying £

16–18 Wrottesley Street, B5 4RT
021-622 5669

COOKING 2
COST £11–£42

Now that the Arcadian Complex has neared completion, this long-standing
restaurant near the Birmingham Hippodrome has some youngblood rivals on
its doorstep. Competition has kept the kitchen on its toes: 'getting better and
better,' enthused one reporter. This is a Cantonese warhorse of a place, with
a hefty menu running to more than 300 dishes. Lunch-time dim-sum are one
of the high points and the choice of around 40 items provides pleasure,
entertainment and outstanding value: 'It doesn't hurt that after eating our fill,

the bill is unbelievably low,' commented a family who feasted on slithery charsiu cheung-fun, deep-fried squid with sweet-and-sour sauce, paper-wrapped prawns, stuffed green peppers, and beef dumplings with ginger and spring onion. Elsewhere, there have been votes for the accessible delights of hot-and-sour soup, Peking spare ribs, and stuffed duck with crab sauce. Authentic casseroles, hotpot, barbecued meats and one-plate rice and noodles are good for a quick meal. Also consider some of the more challenging stuff: steamed pork pie with salted egg, shredded eel, goose webs with mushrooms, and 'home-made venison'. Service is noticeably helpful and interested. The wine list holds no surprises, but prices are fair. House wine is £8.50.

CHEF/PROPRIETOR: Sui Chung Wong  OPEN: all week; noon to midnight (11 Sun) CLOSED: 25 Dec  MEALS: alc (main courses £6 to £8). Set D £9.50 (minimum 2 people) to £12.20 (minimum 6 people). Minimum £5  SERVICE: not inc  CARDS: Access, Amex, Diners, Visa  DETAILS: 200 seats. Private parties: 120 main room, 120 private room. Vegetarian meals. Children welcome. Smart dress preferred. Music. Air-conditioned. Fax: 021-666 7051

## Chung Ying Garden  £

| NEW ENTRY |

17 Thorp Street, B5 4AT
021-666 6622

COOKING 1
COST £17–£42

After a spell in the doldrums, this Chinese restaurant is regaining much of its old form. It is arguably the glitziest of its kind in Birmingham's Chinese quarter, with thick carpets, massive marbled pillars and vast eye-catching murals covering the walls. The menu – a Cantonese monster, 360 dishes long – is virtually identical to that of its near neighbour the Chung Ying (see previous entry): dim-sum, barbecued meats, sizzlers, casseroles and one-plate rice and noodle dishes backed up by some intriguing chef's specialities such as sliced fillet of beef with ground walnuts, quick-fried shredded duck with jellyfish and celery, and frogs' legs with bitter melon. A reporter who remembers the restaurant's heyday was particularly impressed by steamed spare ribs in plum sauce, spicy squid stuffed with minced prawn and braised bean curd in black-bean sauce. Service can be temperamental, especially at off-peak times. The short wine list has some decent and appropriate drinking, especially among the whites; otherwise drink tea. House wine is £8.50.

CHEF/PROPRIETOR: Siu Chung Wong  OPEN: all week; noon to midnight  MEALS: alc (main courses £5.50 to £10.50). Set D £9.80 to £16  SERVICE: not inc, card slips closed CARDS: Access, Amex, Diners, Visa  DETAILS: 350 seats. Private parties: 200 main room, 40, 60 and 70 private rooms. Vegetarian meals. Children welcome. Smart dress preferred. Wheelchair access (also WC). Music. Air-conditioned. Fax: 021-622 5860

## Henrys  £

27 St Paul's Square, B3 1RB
021-200 1136

COOKING 1
COST £18–£39

St Paul's Square is dominated by a blackened church dedicated to industrial pioneer James Watt and stands in the heart of Birmingham's revamped jewellery quarter. It is a surprising location for an up-market Chinese restaurant, but close enough to the city centre to be popular. The low, white building reminded one reporter of a 'ranch-house bungalow', while the interior is extravagantly stylish. Napkins are sculpted into wine glasses, large vivid prints adorn the walls and it feels soothing. Service is noticeably friendly and welcoming. The menu of around 100 dishes shows some fashionable touches – king prawn satay, sizzling loin of lamb with yellow-bean sauce, fried chicken in crispy bird's nest, grilled salmon in black-bean sauce – but it also has a traditional Cantonese undercurrent. The results may sometimes seem rather bland to those used to the more assertive flavours of Chinatown restaurants, but ingredients are fresh and the cooking is sound. One creditable meal produced paper-wrapped spare ribs, steamed king prawns in garlic sauce, stuffed crispy duck and fried aubergines with black-bean sauce. House wine is £8.

CHEF: W.C.W. Choi   PROPRIETOR: Henry Wong   OPEN: Mon to Sat; 12 to 2, 6 to 11 (11.30 Fri and Sat)   CLOSED: bank hols   MEALS: alc (main courses £6 to £8.50). Set L and D £13 SERVICE: not inc   CARDS: Access, Amex, Diners, Visa   DETAILS: 140 seats. 32 tables outside. Private parties: 140 main room, 40 private room. Vegetarian meals. Children's helpings. Smart dress preferred. Music. Air-conditioned

# Maharaja £

23–25 Hurst Street, B5 4AS
021-622 2641

COOKING 1
COST £13–£30

Nat Batt set up this civilised little restaurant more than 20 years ago and it still finds favour with Indian families, business people and theatregoers from the nearby Hippodrome. The small dining-room is discreetly done out in shades of peach and grey; service is gracious and polite to a fault. The menu is a sensibly chosen repertoire of stoically traditional Punjabi dishes highlighted by good ingredients and distinct, fresh spicing. Reporters have endorsed 'wonderfully moist' chicken tikka, creamy lamb pasanda and intense, vividly flavoured king prawn bhuna masala. Vegetables also receive praise: lotus roots with peas excites those with inquisitive palates, with its 'earthy, almost fungal flavour and firm woody texture,' according to one expert. Ask about the chef's specials and the 'dhal of the day'. Pilau rice is authentically fragrant and breads are up to the mark. The wine list is a short, creditable selection; most bottles will leave change from £10. House wine is £6.70.

CHEF: Bhupinder Waraich   PROPRIETOR: N.S. Batt   OPEN: Mon to Sat; 12 to 2.30, 6 to 11.30 CLOSED: last week July   MEALS: alc (main courses £5 to £7). Set L £7.50 (2 courses), Set D £10.60. Minimum £7   SERVICE: 10%, card slips closed   CARDS: Access, Amex, Diners, Visa   DETAILS: 62 seats. Private parties: 30 main room. Vegetarian meals. Children welcome. Wheelchair access (1 step; also WC). Music. Air-conditioned

Healthy eating options *in the details at the end of an entry signifies that a restaurant marks on its menu, in words and/or using symbols, low-fat dishes or other healthy eating choices.*

The Guide *relies on feedback from its readers. Especially welcome are reports on new restaurants appearing in the book for the first time.*

## Sloans ♟

27–29 Chad Square, Hawthorne Road,
Edgbaston, B15 3TQ
021-455 6697

COOKING 2
COST £18–£46

'Consistently excellent,' pronounced one Sloans regular who took advantage of a 'club discount' so that he could entertain clients with greater facility. This is Birmingham's closest approach to a serious restaurant, though the amount of feedback we get about it may hint that Birmingham is happier at places that make less demands on ambition or finance. The most enterprising dishes are offered at lunch, which is not expensive, leaving the evening *carte* a fairly staid run through prime meats for main courses, and a less-than-exciting slate for beginnings. But the cooking is all done to a standard, whether boudin blanc on a bed of creamed leeks, a warm salad of pigeon, fillet of beef with wild mushrooms, or lamb with soubise sauce. The wine list is very good and not over-priced. One visitor from out of town was less than impressed by the wine service or the knowledge to support the list, but others found the many half-bottles some consolation. House wines are £8.75.

CHEF: Simon Booth   PROPRIETORS: Roger Narbett and John Narbett   OPEN: Mon to Sat, exc Sat L; 12 to 2.30, 7 to 10.30   CLOSED: 1 week after Christmas, bank hols, (exc 25 Dec)   MEALS: alc (main courses £9 to £15). Set L £8.50 (2 courses) to £12   SERVICE: not inc   CARDS: Access, Amex, Diners, Visa   DETAILS: 60 seats. Private parties: 85 main room. Car park. Vegetarian meals. Children's helpings L and before 8 D. Smart dress preferred. No-smoking area. Wheelchair access (1 step; also WC). Music. Air-conditioned. Fax: 021-454 4335

---

**BIRTLE** Greater Manchester

map 5

## ▲ Normandie ▮

COUNTY OF THE YEAR RESTAURANT

Elbut Lane, Birtle BL9 6UT
061-764 3869 and 1170
off B6222

COOKING 4
COST £21–£49

Park the car not many metres away from the settlement tanks in front of the strange accretion of buildings that make up this hotel (the beginnings were a tiny pub on the hillside above Birtle); the view across Greater Manchester is impressive. Behind and beyond are rough pasture and moor. But the cooking at the Normandie is no country bumpkin affair – quite the opposite, and that goes for the service ('No service charge is made or expected,' say the menus and bills) and welcome too. The hotel bustles with a city-centre edge to it: there are business people staying the night and quite a lot of entertaining, as well as the usual leavening of private customers out for the evening. Pascal Pommier cooks with great assurance. He is as able to construct an absolutely classic eggs florentine, as he is to produce a fillet of sea bass with aubergines and tomatoes in a thoroughly modern manner. He can make something simple – for instance, pasta with oyster mushrooms and a madeira sauce – memorable by judicious seasoning and balance, or he can construct a complex pig's trotter stuffed with Jerusalem artichoke, sweetbreads, mushrooms and shallots. Desserts do not desert him: a pear tart with cinnamon ice-cream had more taste than most pear

215

dishes achieve; a pile of shortbreads layering three different mousses was 'too rich, but I noticed it was all disposed of'. There is a cheaper set-price menu which also contains some good cooking, though the choices may be less eye-catching; however, steamed pudding with vanilla sauce and pears caught the swooning raptures of one reporter. A comforting page of modestly priced French country wines appears early in the list. Thereafter, although prices reflect quality, the upper end appears to be subject to a formula that presses hard on the wallet. Quality is assured, with as much care devoted to the New World as to the classic areas; of special note are bourgeois clarets, including two Fronsacs and noteworthy Rhônes and Mosels. There is a careful and adequate range of halves. House wines start at £11.50.

CHEF: Pascal Pommier  PROPRIETORS: Gillian Moussa and Max Moussa  OPEN: Mon to Sat, exc L Mon and Sat; 12 to 2, 7 to 9.30  CLOSED: 2 weeks from 26 Dec (open 25 Dec), 1 week Easter, bank hols  MEALS: alc (main courses £10.50 to £18.50). Set L £12.50 (2 courses) to £15, Set D £18.95  SERVICE: card slips closed  CARDS: Access, Amex, Diners, Visa  DETAILS: 60 seats. Private parties: 60 main room. Car park. Vegetarian meals. Children's helpings on request. Smart dress preferred. No cigars/pipes in dining-room. Wheelchair access (1 step; also WC). Music  ACCOMMODATION: 23 rooms, all with bath/shower. Rooms for disabled. Lift. B&B £49 to £79. Children welcome. Baby facilities. Garden. TV. Phone. Confirm by noon. Fax: 061-764 4866

---

**BISHOP'S TACHBROOK Warwickshire**　　　　　　　　　　　　　　　map 2

# ▲ *Mallory Court* ♥

Harbury Lane,
Bishop's Tachbrook CV33 9QB
LEAMINGTON SPA (0926) 330214　　　　　　　　　　　　　　COOKING 3*
off B4087, 2m S of Leamington Spa　　　　　　　　　　　　COST £29–£82

This Midland magnate's mansion evokes the 1920s both from the outside, with its fine gardens, to deep within, though there are some late twentieth-century, florid touches here and there, even if the vast majority of the décor shows thought and taste. 'It is idyllic on a hot summer's evening: drinks on the terrace, the dining-room shaded, windows screened by shrubbery, the wood panelling offset by lemon-yellow tablecloths and complemented by comfortable chairs, large tables and proper eating equipment.' So ran the eulogy of one who returns most years and finds the standards in the kitchen exacting, the conception attractive, elegant and modern, though sometimes dished out on a scale that has respect for local, rather than national, requirements. There is a fixed-price menu at lunch-time, but in the evening there is only the *carte*, with a rather muddling system of supplements to the basic charge, which may obscure the fact that this is a very expensive restaurant indeed. Cooking therefore has to be good and it usually is. Modern conceptions include dishes such as grilled scallops with squid ink, pepper and garlic sauces, fillet of brill with black taglioni and langoustine sauce and feuilleté of pear with ginger caramel sauce and lime sorbet. However, traditionalists used to grand hotels will not be disappointed by a Dublin Bay prawn mousse wrapped with smoked salmon served with caviare and quail's egg, or crab with avocado and pink grapefruit, or main dishes such as lamb with dauphinois potatoes, calf's liver with limes, and beef and foie gras. Though large portion-size has been mentioned, the overall effect of the cooking has been increasingly light. Once, Mallory was in the vanguard of the 'hollandaise movement' but cholesterol-awareness has struck here too. The wines cater unashamedly for the big spenders and the mark-up regime does nothing to disappoint. However, with halves scattered liberally across the range and genuine care going into selection from Beaujolais, petits châteaux and the Rhône, huge expense is not compulsory – at least on the wines. Excellence extends beyond the classics to Italy and the New World. House wines are from £8.95 white, £13.25 red. CELLARMAN'S CHOICE: Bianco 1991, Avignonesi £18.50; Corbières, Ch. Les Ollieux Romanis 1990, £13.25.

CHEF: Allan Holland  PROPRIETORS: Allan Holland and Jeremy Mort  OPEN: all week; 12.30 to 2, 7.30 to 9.45  MEALS: alc (basic charge £31.50, supplements for main course £8.50 to £10.50). Set L £20.50 (2 courses) to £24.50  SERVICE: net prices, card slips closed  CARD: Access, Visa  DETAILS: 50 seats. Private parties: 50 main room, 50 private room. Car park. Vegetarian meals. No children under 9. Smart dress preferred. No cigars/pipes in dining-room. Wheelchair access. No music  ACCOMMODATION: 10 double rooms, all with bath/shower. B&B £100 to £210. No children under 9. Afternoon teas. Garden. Swimming-pool. Tennis. TV. Phone. Doors close at midnight. Fax: (0926) 451714

---

**BLACKPOOL** Lancashire                                                    map 5

## September Brasserie

15–17 Queen Street, Blackpool FY1 1PU                        COOKING 2*
BLACKPOOL (0253) 23282                                       COST £22–£42

How many restaurants in Blackpool serve samphire with their monkfish plus ginger and coconut at lunch-time? How many also manage it at dinner? This says much about the September Brasserie: there is not a lot of competition from Blackpool's burger and chip shops. The place is on the first floor above a hairdresser's; the kitchen is open to view, as is the outside world through big windows (though the sea is only visible from one carefully chosen spot); the tables are left bare at lunch; and table napkins are paper, not linen. These last points hint at 'brasserie', though local skinflints complain that prices are quite high for the description. Think about the samphire – there for the taking, Michael Golowicz says. You can also eat cream-dripping mussels, salt herrings with potato pancakes and a tad of caviare, Cumbrian air-dried ham with melon and dandelion leaves, grilled halibut, tempura of king prawns, sea bass with pesto and saffron, beef with wild mushrooms, or pork with buckwheat and raisins on a redcurrant and thyme sauce. The cooking here is serious, the waiters are devoted, the welcome is happy, and the place needs all the support possible to keep Blackpool on the map. The wine list is kept sensibly short, but every bottle has something to say (and rather long notes with which to say it). Prices are very fair; house wines are from £8.75.

---

*Restaurateurs justifiably resent no-shows. If you quote a credit card number when booking, you may be liable for the restaurant's lost profit margin if you don't turn up. Always phone to cancel.*

---

CHEF: Michael Golowicz   PROPRIETORS: Michael Golowicz and Pat Wood   OPEN: Tue to Sat; 12 to 2.30, 7 to 9.30   CLOSED: 2 weeks summer, 2 weeks winter   MEALS: alc (main courses L £6 to £7, D £12 to £14)   SERVICE: not inc, card slips closed   CARDS: Access, Amex, Diners, Visa   DETAILS: 40 seats. Private parties: 40 main room. Vegetarian meals. Children's helpings. Smart dress preferred. Music

---

## BLACKWATER Cornwall

map 1

# Pennypots

Blackwater TR4 8EY
ST DAY (0209) 820347
off A30, ¾m W of village centre

COOKING 2*
COST £23–£40

'It's clear that the chef, Kevin Viner, can't stop cooking. Everything – the rolls in a woven basket of bread, wonderful canapés delivered to us direct from the kitchen by Kevin himself, and so on through the meal – is made with love and devotion on site.' This accurate judgement by a visitor is good reason for Pennypots' success; people like such industry, embellishment and effort. It is also a warning that little comes unadorned. All began with the roadside cottage on the old Blackwater to Redruth road: it was plain enough at heart, but now is vehicle for every sort of decoration. The general reaction to the heartwarming ambience and supercharged style – even the crème brûlée has a spun-sugar cage – is very positive. Generosity marks dishes such as scallops with a tagliatelle of cucumber and a basil beurre blanc, beef with heaps of wild mushrooms, lamb on a sweetish port and blackberry sauce, and turbot with vermouth and oysters, basil and saffron. Vegetables come in droves. Leave space for a dessert, such as cinnamon crème brûlée with a prune and armagnac sauce, or nectarines and plums in a brandy butter with a further cream sauce, a piece of brioche and an apricot ice-cream. Coffee is bottomless; pastries are another chance for Kevin to show his skill. The service wins hearts and minds. The wine list is set out by country and includes some high-class bottles (a few as high as Dom. de la Romanée-Conti's Romanée-St-Vivant 1982), and plenty as useful as Chante Cigale's Châteauneuf or Kanonkop's Pinotage. House wines are £6.95.

---

CHEF: Kevin Viner   PROPRIETORS: Kevin and Jane Viner   OPEN: Tue to Sat, D only; 7 to 10   CLOSED: 3 weeks winter   MEALS: alc (main courses £12.50 to £14). Set L £15.95   SERVICE: not inc, card slips closed   CARDS: Access, Visa   DETAILS: 30 seats. Private parties: 20 main room, 10 private room. Car park. Vegetarian meals with prior notice. Children's helpings. No smoking before 10pm. Wheelchair access (1 step). Music

---

*Several sharp operators have tried to extort money from restaurateurs on the promise of an entry in a guidebook that has never appeared.* The Good Food Guide *makes no charge for inclusion and does not offer certificates of any kind.*

*Prices quoted in the* Guide *are based on information supplied by restaurateurs. The prices quoted at the top of each entry represent a range, from the lowest meal price to the highest; the latter is inflated by 20 per cent to take account of likely price rises during the year of the* Guide.

---

# ▲ La Belle Alliance ♥ ¾✗

White Cliff Mill Street,
Blandford Forum DT11 7BP                                    COOKING 1*
BLANDFORD (0258) 452842                                     COST £24–£35

'People dress up and treat a visit to La Belle Alliance as a special event, but
with a cosy lounge area and an intimate dining-room the atmosphere is
conducive to lively chats across the aisles,' reported a satisfied reader who
remembered a meal that included Nile perch, new to her – and most of us – as
a fish for English plates. Her words capture the mood well. This late-Victorian
house is on the way out of town (round the one-way system, towards
Shaftesbury): spring and summer see it buried in flowers, while within doors,
well-padded upholstery banishes thoughts of discomfort. The place is very
much a family affair, and the sense of teamwork is infectious. A pair of fixed-
price menus elicits comments of 'skill and competence'; dishes include scallops
thermidor, braised lentils with smoked salmon and prawns, goats' cheese
soufflé with a calvados sauce, sirloin steak with walnut and Stilton sauce, and
breast of pigeon on a bed of cabbage. Some see the kitchen attempting a
marriage between fashion (lentils) and traditional British expectations of meals
out (smoked salmon and prawns). Vegetables may be contained within a tulip
of puff pastry, and puddings are eagerly anticipated. Try the bread-and-butter
pudding or the iced chocolate terrine. Locals feel the Davisons have got the
balance between expense, event, friendliness and fuss just right. On the wine
side, careful attention to buying has resulted in a compact but eventful wine
list. Good burgundies vie with a fine 1982 Rioja and sound selection from the
antipodes. Prices are generous to the customer. House wines are £8.95.
CELLARMAN'S CHOICE: Napa, Edna Valley, Chardonnay 1989, £21.85;
Montagne-St-Emilion, Ch. Tour Musset 1988, £15.50.

CHEF: Philip Davison   PROPRIETORS: Lauren and Philip Davison   OPEN: Tue to Sat (and
bank hol Sun), D only (Tue to Sat L by arrangement); 7 to 9.30 (6.30 to 10 Sat)   MEALS: Set
D £15.95 to £19.95   SERVICE: not inc, card slips closed   CARDS: Access, Amex, Visa
DETAILS: 32 seats. Private parties: 38 main room. Car park. Vegetarian meals. Children
by arrangement. No smoking in dining-room. Wheelchair access (1 step). Music
ACCOMMODATION: 6 rooms, all with bath/shower. Rooms for disabled. B&B £40 to £66.
Children by arrangement. Baby facilities. Pets welcome (not in public rooms). TV. Phone.
Doors close at midnight. Confirm by 6

## Mauro's £

88 Palmerston Street, Bollington SK10 5PW                   COOKING 1*
BOLLINGTON (0625) 573898                                    COST £15–£37

As we went to press, Vincenzo Mauro and family were planning to buy an
adjacent building to provide a bar and extra space in their long-established
Italian restaurant. Otherwise little changes. The cooking comes from the old
school: complimentary appetisers have been appreciated, pasta is made on the
premises, and the minestrone is 'authentic' stuff. Otherwise, the menu moves

in familiar trattoria territory with prosciutto, gnocchi, chicken cacciatora and saltimbocca alla romana. Fish specials change daily. Vegetables are plentiful, even if the choice is sometimes rather predictable. Home-made sweets are from the trolley. Regulars continue to support the restaurant, but not everyone is happy with the performance of the kitchen or the overall set-up. Service in particular comes in for harsh criticism: reporters feel that the waitresses need to be much sharper and more professional. Set lunch is a bargain and the wine list has fair mark-ups and plenty of decent drinking from the major Italian regions. House wine is £8.10.

CHEF/PROPRIETOR: Vincenzo Mauro   OPEN: Tue to Sat, exc Sat L (Sun L first Sun of month); 12 to 2, 7 to 10 (10.30 Sat)   MEALS: alc (main courses £8.50 to £15). Set L £8.75   SERVICE: not inc (10% for 6 or more)   CARDS: Access, Amex, Visa   DETAILS: 48 seats. Private parties: 58 main room. Vegetarian meals. Children's helpings. Smart dress preferred. Wheelchair access (also WC). Music

---

**BOLTON ABBEY North Yorkshire**                                      map 5

## ▲ Devonshire Arms, Burlington Restaurant ♥ ⁵⁄ₓ      | NEW ENTRY |

Bolton Abbey BD23 6AJ
BOLTON ABBEY (0756) 710441                                   COOKING 2
at junction of A59 and B6160, 5m NW of Ilkley               COST £29–£61

No expense has been spared in restoring this old coaching-inn. Opulence, elegance and comfort ooze. Several luxurious lounges are filled with furnishings, antiques and portraits from Chatsworth. The Burlington Restaurant is an airy room done out in green and white, with a Georgian-style conservatory offering views of the lawned gardens and the hills beyond. Gavin Beedham's menu is at a fixed price for five courses, although supplements abound. The cooking is in the modern mould, with a peppering of influences from the Mediterranean and the Orient enlivening dishes such as tea-smoked brill with lemon and almond dressing, and Gressingham duck with plum sauce and hazelnut dumplings. Brilliant appetisers, including lasagne layered with chicken livers, oyster mushrooms and sun-dried tomatoes followed by richly flavoured mushroom consommé, started one meal on a high note. Main courses are remarkable for the quality of the ingredients: noisettes of lamb were full of 'rich local flavours'; well-hung fillet of beef came with parsley purée on a claret and pink peppercorn sauce. Vegetables can be 'overplayed' but desserts restore the balance: 'I have never had such decorative spotted dick and the crêpes suzette were prepared at the table.' Reservations seem to centre on the cost of the experience. The wine list is refreshing in its relative brevity and willingness to cast its net wide; the fear of an overbearing number of overpriced classics is not sustained. Grandeur there is, but the suppliers make sure that the list is well leavened with interest from Italy, Alsace and the antipodes. There are a few half-bottles. House wines are £10.50.
CELLARMAN'S CHOICE: Chablis 1991, Dampt, £25.50; Haut Médoc, Ch. Villegeorge 1987, £32.50.

CHEF: Gavin Beedham  PROPRIETORS: Duke and Duchess of Devonshire  OPEN: all week;
12 to 2, 7 to 10 (9.30 Sun)  MEALS: Set L £16.95 to £21, Set D £27.50  SERVICE: 10%, card
slips closed  CARDS: Access, Amex, Diners, Visa  DETAILS: 70 seats. Private parties: 24
main room, 10, 20 and 24 private rooms. Car park. Vegetarian meals. Children's helpings.
No children under 12. Jacket and tie. No smoking in dining-room. Wheelchair access (also
WC). No music  ACCOMMODATION: 40 rooms, all with bath/shower. Rooms for disabled.
B&B £85 to £110. Children welcome. Baby facilities. Dogs welcome. Afternoon teas.
Garden. Swimming-pool. Sauna. Tennis. Fishing. TV. Phone. Confirm by 6. Fax: (0756)
710564 (*The Which? Hotel Guide*)

---

## BOTLEY Hampshire
map 2

## Cobbett's

15 The Square, Botley SO3 2EA  
BOTLEY (0489) 782068

COOKING 1  
COST £25–£51

In 1994, Charles and Lucie Skipwith will celebrate 20 years at the helm of this
long-standing restaurant in a half-timbered cottage. Lucie was born and
brought up in Bordelaise country and many of her dishes reflect her culinary
roots. The cooking is dubbed 'cuisine réalistique' which, in her words, is 'a
combination of French country farmhouse cooking with the subtleties of
compatible flavourings and herbing coupled with sensible portions and
attractive presentation'. Fish is from South Coast trawlers; some game is
supplied by a local sportsman, the rest is shot by Charles Skipwith himself;
herbs are grown in the garden, and ice-creams are made on the premises. This
careful integrity translates into a menu that might feature guinea-fowl and
pistachio terrine, smoked fish and seafood in aspic with watercress mousse,
pigeon breasts with gin and juniper sauce, and noisettes of lamb with bigarade
sauce. Desserts range from chocolate marquise to pink grapefruit bavarois. A
crop of fairly priced French regional wines are bolstered by a few from the New
World. House wine is £9.85.

CHEF: Lucie Skipwith  PROPRIETORS: Charles and Lucie Skipwith  OPEN: Mon to Sat,
exc L Mon and Sat; 12 to 2, 7.30 (7 Sat) to 10  CLOSED: 2 weeks winter, 2 weeks summer
MEALS: alc (main courses £10.50 to £13). Set L £15.50  SERVICE: not inc  CARDS: Access,
Visa  DETAILS: 40 seats. Private parties: 50 main room, 8 and 14 private rooms. Car park.
Vegetarian meals. Smart dress preferred. No cigars/pipes in dining-room. No music. Fax:
(0489) 799641

---

## BOTTESFORD Leicestershire
map 5

## La Petite Maison
**NEW ENTRY**

1 Market Street, Bottesford NG13 0BW  
BOTTESFORD (0949) 42375  
just off A52 Nottingham to Grantham road

COOKING 1  
COST £18–£39

Originally the local butcher's, this is now a delightful franglais 'country bistro'.
The old chopping block is still in place, along with oak beams and a genuine
Victorian fireplace; posies from the garden and William Morris-style wallpaper
reinforce the tone of cool, charming intimacy. Andrew and Beverley Goodson

are courteous, relaxed hosts, while the kitchen delivers 'what custom demands, with a nod to the changing seasons'. The repertoire changes monthly, taking in asparagus with hollandaise, leek and crab timbale, roast duckling with honey and lemon sauce and fillet steak, backed up by fish of the day. Baking is done in-house: 'Bread of Heaven!' exclaimed a reporter embarking on a highly pleasurable Sunday lunch. This meal suggested a kitchen that knows its stuff: duck liver pâté was 'evocative of fine foie gras without the tachycardia', poached fillet of salmon bathed in garlicky olive oil was beguilingly simple and sparky, then came 'suave and frosty' chocolate marquise. The unpretentious wine list is well scattered geographically and mark-ups are reasonable. House wine is £8.50.

CHEF: Adrian Hutchinson   PROPRIETORS: Andrew and Beverley Goodson   OPEN: Tue to Sun, exc Sun D; 12 to 2, 7 to 10   CLOSED: 2 weeks Jan   MEALS: alc (main courses £10 to £15). Set Sun L £9.95, Set D £13.95   SERVICE: not inc   CARDS: Access, Amex, Visa
DETAILS: 38 seats. 2 tables outside. Private parties: 38 main room. Car park. Vegetarian meals. Children's helpings. Wheelchair access. Music

---

**BOUGHTON LEES Kent**                                                map 3

▲ *Eastwell Manor* ⁵⅄

Eastwell Park, Boughton Lees TN25 4HR
ASHFORD (0233) 635751
on A251, 3m N of Ashford

COUNTY OF THE YEAR RESTAURANT

COOKING 3*
COST £16–£65

Heading north out of Ashford, the traveller will pass an amazing gatehouse in full-dress 'Tudorbethan' which was once the entrance to Eastwell. Continue on the road to find the real gap in the fence, bump over a whole army of sleeping policemen and drive up to what is now but a rump of a very large Edwardian castellated manor house surrounded by '3,000 acres of Kent countryside'. Impressive, yes, but when you get indoors the decoration and setting are a mite funereal. The cooking, however, is remarkable in parts (though let down by the bread and pastry). A parcel of smoked salmon wrapped round a brandade of sole flavoured with caviare was of ethereal lightness and brilliantly balanced between sharp and quietly sweet, with garlic and oil to give boldness and caviare lending its edge. A main course of lobster with dill mayonnaise was served with slices of lightly marinated salmon and brill on a bed of sprouting grain and spinach, and a gutsy gazpacho sauce. What impressed here was the relationship of all the components, which melded into perfect harmony. Equal satisfaction has come from a dinner that began with oxtail and vegetables in a pastry case and was followed by a piccata of lamb and beef with roasted garlic on a bed of potatoes perfumed with pesto. The garlic remained in the brain for half a day, the memory of the meal for much longer. The top prices here are castle scale, their impact only modified by the cheaper set-price options, the cheapish weekday 'Country-house lunches' or the consolation that the kitchen is free with luxuries once money is up front. Money is also the problem with the wine list. Search hard and long through the lesser regions if economies are in force. The choice is staid, but adequate; the clarets are classic. House wines start at £12.50.

CHEF: Mark Clayton   PROPRIETORS: Queens Moat Houses plc   OPEN: all week; 12.30 to 1.45, 7.30 to 9 (10 Fri and Sat)   MEALS: bar alc L (main courses £4.10 to £5.95). Restaurant Set L £12.75 (2 courses) to £16.50, Set D £24.50 (also 2-course Set L and D £32.50)   SERVICE: not inc, card slips closed   CARDS: Access, Amex, Diners, Visa   DETAILS: 85 seats. Private parties: 56 main room, 30 private room. Car park. Vegetarian meals. Children's helpings on request. Jacket and tie. No smoking in dining-room. Wheelchair access (2 steps; also WC). Music   ACCOMMODATION: 23 rooms, all with bath/shower. Lift. B&B £100 to £260. Children welcome. Dogs welcome (not in public lounges). Afternoon teas. Garden. Tennis. Snooker. TV. Phone. Doors close at midnight. Confirm by 6. Fax: (0223) 635530 (*The Which? Hotel Guide*)

---

**BOURNEMOUTH Dorset**                                                          map 2

## *Sophisticats*

43 Charminster Road,
Bournemouth BH8 8UE                                              COOKING 2
BOURNEMOUTH (0202) 291019                                     COST £26–£39

Someone called Bournemouth 'a gastronomic wilderness of coach-party food'. It may not be quite that, but John Knight and Bernard Calligan have been holding the torch for fair eating for many years against a fairly sombre backdrop. Few people write about the allure of Sophisticats' outer setting ('nondescript' is a term used); once through the door, most will comment on the somewhat kitsch decorative theme that features cats in various shapes and forms. There is, however, consistent praise for the welcome and the steady appeal of the cooking: the almost timeless menu develops slowly from a firm base of tried favourites such as crab gratin, satay, veal with calvados and cream, 'Javanese' fillet steak marinated in soy, wine and spices, seriously gloopy meringues, or finally, if you are lucky, a hot soufflé. The moveable dish is the fish, which depends on the market and is often a good bet. As the partners observe, they get greyer with the years, but not their customers, who might include a restaurant-full of public health inspectors on an annual conference, or holidaymakers pleased at last to find a haven. The wine list is equally traditional but with a page of extras to round it out, none of which is overpriced. House wines are £7.75.

CHEF: Bernard Calligan   PROPRIETORS: John Knight and Bernard Calligan   OPEN: Tue to Sat, D only; 7 to 9.30   CLOSED: 2 weeks Feb, 1 week July, 2 weeks Nov   MEALS: alc (main courses £10.50 to £12)   SERVICE: not inc   DETAILS: 34 seats. Private parties: 16 main room. Vegetarian meals. Children welcome. Smart dress preferred. Wheelchair access (also WC). Music

---

*'The maître'd here is definitely an undertaker with an evening job.'*
On eating in London

*'Just to complete the impression that you have wandered accidentally into a disco instead of a restaurant, a huge light above the kitchen door intermittently bathes the whole room in its glow, like a storm in a silent movie. On particularly busy nights this system must represent quite a considerable risk to epileptics.'* On eating in London

---

## *Porthole Eating House* 🍾

3 Ash Street,
Bowness-on-Windermere LA23 3EB
WINDERMERE (053 94) 42793

COOKING 2*
COST £27–£45

A couple who arrived during the 'inauguration' of cobbled Ash Street by the local MP found Gianni Berton dressed up as a Regency beau, wife Judy looked like a matronly serving wench and the waiter had donned a grey wedding suit. Live music-hall ditties were being played in the restaurant. The Porthole has always been high on eccentricity and this is part of its enduring charm. It is a noisy, jolly place with rough stone walls and bare wooden tables close together: 'spartan without being utilitarian,' as one reporter observed. Gianni is a cycling enthusiast: memorabilia fill the dining-room and he sponsors the annual 25-mile Porthole Time Trial around the Lakes. The menu remains a 'cocktail of Italian, French and English dishes' and most interest centres on the list of weekly specialities. Venetian recipes are from Gianni's mother, while Aunt Ancilla from Lucca has provided a Tuscan trend. The Bertons also take full advantage of Lakeland produce for potted wild trout, traditional onion and sorrel tartlet ('a meal on its own', with light crumbly pastry), grilled Windermere char and thick slices of roast loin of Lakeland lamb on a herb stuffing marinated in garlic and rosemary. Vegetables, such as beetroot tops with bacon, show some imaginative touches. Vegetarian options include mille-feuille of six kinds of wild mushrooms. Very good brown bread is baked on the premises. Sweets tend to be standard offerings, such as sticky toffee pudding and tiramisù. National loyalty brings Italy to the forefront of the wine list, while the French classics have to take their place. The range is excellent, with fine growers throughout and an impressive New World listing. Prices remain fair. House wine is £9.50. CELLARMAN'S CHOICE: Russian River Valley, Dutton Ranch, Chardonnay 1991, £24; Crozes-Hermitage, 'Les Meysonniers' 1989, Chapoutier, £13.

CHEF: Michael Metcalfe   PROPRIETORS: Judy and Gianni Berton   OPEN: Wed to Mon, D only (L by arrangement for parties); 6.30 to 11   CLOSED: mid-Dec to end Feb   MEALS: alc (main courses £8.50 to £12)   SERVICE: not inc, card slips closed   CARDS: Access, Amex, Diners, Visa   DETAILS: 36 seats. Private parties: 26 main room, 26 private room. Vegetarian meals. Children's helpings. Music. Fax: (053 94) 88675

## ▲ *Bradfield House* ⅝✕

Sudbury Road,
Bradfield Combust IP30 0LR
SICKLESMERE (0284) 386301
on A134, 4m S of Bury St Edmunds

COOKING 2
COST £24–£35

Since their arrival in 1988 Roy and Sally Ghijben have turned this fine-looking seventeenth-century house into a country restaurant-with-rooms. The half-timbered building stands in two acres of gardens complete with scented yew hedges, listed trees, a herb garden and a croquet lawn. The interior is a rustic blend of antique furnishings, colourful pictures and vases of fresh flowers. Roy's cooking is in keeping. His style is a mix of traditional English and French rural – taking in mushroom soup, guinea-fowl pie, breast of duck with apple and calvados sauce and pan-fried fillet of beef dijonnaise. Fillet of lamb – perhaps cooked with rosemary and served with tartlets of redcurrant jelly and onion paste – draws regular praise. Vegetables such as nut squash, endive and 'very crisp' baked cabbage are from the garden. Sally's desserts continue the same theme with elderflower sorbet and raspberry coulis or lemon posset in brandy-snap basket. In addition she runs the front-of-house with aplomb. A sound wine list from Lay & Wheeler provides a well-balanced selection with a strong French bias, but also with representatives from other countries. Half-bottles show up well. House wines are £7.40.

CHEF: Roy Ghijben    PROPRIETORS: Roy and Sally Ghijben    OPEN: Tue to Sat, D only; 7 to 9 (9.30 Sat)    MEALS: alc (main courses £11 to £14.50)    SERVICE: net prices, card slips closed    CARDS: Access, Visa    DETAILS: 36 seats. Private parties: 26 main room, 14 private room. Car park. Vegetarian meals with prior notice. Children's helpings before 7pm for hotel residents. No children under 9. Smart dress preferred. No smoking in dining-room. Wheelchair access (1 step; also WC). Music    ACCOMMODATION: 4 rooms, all with bath/ shower. B&B £45 to £80. Deposit: £20. Children welcome. Baby facilities. Garden. TV. Phone. Doors close at midnight. Fax: (0284) 386301 (*The Which? Hotel Guide*)

---

**BRADFORD** West Yorkshire                                              map 5

## ▲ *Restaurant Nineteen* ♟

North Park Road, Bradford BD9 4NT                          COOKING 4
BRADFORD (0274) 492559                                      COST £26–£52

'It carries less ceremonial baggage than many of its local competitors, yet the food is actually more interesting.' This comment about Stephen Smith's cooking omits to mention that its field of action, a fine late-Victorian industrialist's house in a leafy, carriage-trade section of Bradford (the sort of place described in *Room at the Top*) is pretty ceremonious. The wedding-cake decoration of the pair of dining-rooms makes no bones about ornament, and service by Robert Barbour is punctilious, even if his helpers are less suave. The style is thoroughgoing, though sometimes it may seem as if too much is attempted with dishes like rabbit with braised ham hock and a mustard pudding with the rabbit's offal on the side in a pastry case, or braised ox tongue with celeriac and cheese pudding. Yet these often work magnificently. Stephen Smith has also moved with the times: sautéed polenta, lamb's kidney, pancetta and mushrooms lightly spiced with curry, or fillet of hake with spring vegetables and coriander are as 'fashionable' as anything in Yorkshire. The format is a three- or four-course dinner at a very fair (reduced from last year) price, including coffee. The overall quantity may be large, especially when taking the canapés into account. But the message this year is that the food has high flavour here. It has texture and skill as well, evinced by those puddings already mentioned, and an ability to achieve contrasts that have real interest. It is wise to stay alert until the end, for the best for some comes when rhubarb and ginger crème brûlée with a rhubarb sorbet is offered, or apple and raisin pancakes with a rum-and-raisin ice-cream. Again, little is left to stand alone, but ornament does not obscure the intention. The wine list, showing intelligent and considerate range, is characterised by the Rhônes starting with Guigal Côtes du Rhône at £11.50 and capped with Côte Rôtie, Les Jumelles 1978 for £55. Succinct, presented accurately and with no fuss, it is exemplary. The distribution of half-bottles is a little patchy. House wines are from £9.50. CELLARMAN'S CHOICE: Chardonnay, Il Marzocco 1991, Avignonesi, £24.50; Côtes du Rhône 1989, Guigal, £11.50.

CHEF: Stephen Smith   PROPRIETORS: Stephen Smith and Robert Barbour   OPEN: Mon to Sat, D only; 7 to 9.30 (10.30 Fri and Sat)   MEALS: Set D £16.50 to £28   SERVICE: not inc, card slips closed   CARDS: Access, Amex, Diners, Visa   DETAILS: 36 seats. Private parties: 30 main room. Car park. Vegetarian meals with prior notice. No children under 10. No cigars/pipes in dining-room. Music   ACCOMMODATION: 4 rooms, all with bath/shower. B&B £60 to £70. Children welcome. TV. Phone. Doors close at midnight (*The Which? Hotel Guide*)

---

**BRADFORD-ON-AVON** Wiltshire                                                    map 2

## ▲ *Woolley Grange* ❦ ✳

Woolley Green,
Bradford-on-Avon BA15 1TX
BRADFORD-ON-AVON (0225) 864705                                  COOKING 3
on B3105, 1m NE of Bradford-on-Avon                             COST £23–£44

Gardening seems to have stayed centre-stage in the culinary life of Woolley Grange. Nigel Chapman reports a seed company's congress that finished with a tour of the kitchen plot guided by chef Colin White, a wizard with the garden hoe as well as the salt pot. In sunlight, when old stone is set off by green lawns, pools and flowerbeds, the place is enviable; at dusk, it is atmospheric. Within doors the Grange shows its age (seventeenth century overlaid by Victorian) through character, and the ingenuity of the conversion by the loggia's fine roof timbers. Although a place that welcomes children, indeed, makes a point of it, the Grange's prevailing ambience may, after infants' bedtimes, be quite subdued. None of this is the fault of the management, who are invariably cheerful. Colin White has now settled in, produces strongly Mediterranean food – lamb with ratatouille is consistently praised, polenta is often mentioned – and manages to take notionally boring materials and convert them to something tasty: 'My guinea-fowl was the best for years.' The slightly miscellaneous look to his lists of ingredients has been reduced in the past year, and dishes such as calf's liver with sage and avocado, a salad of roast peppers with feta cheese and pine-nuts, cod with potato crust and a tomato and caper sauce, brill with onion and orange, and venison with a chutney of pears and red wine sauce are now more in the original Colin White vein when he was cooking at his restaurant in Cricklade. Grilled tuna with Thai spices and black beans or crab-cakes with spiced tomato salsa are homages to modernity and multiculturalism: both have been praised. Price apart, Woolley Grange is pitched to be more 'fun' than many country sepulchres. Tennis court and swimming-pool resound to summer cries, hamburgers and club sandwiches (from the cheaper 'terrace' *carte*) are downed with gusto come lunch-time, and staff maintain good cheer. The wine list has taken a leap forward. It has a reassuring orderliness, and customer friendliness is displayed in a dozen modestly priced wines from the French regions. Buying is safe rather than exciting, but the range is good and merciful restraint is shown on the number of bins stocked. Bourgeois clarets, Australian wines and the Rhône valley stand out, and halves, although few, demonstrate care. House wines are £9.85. CELLARMAN'S CHOICE: Pinot Grigio 1991, Jermann, £23.70; Beaujolais-Villages, Ch. de la Grande Grange 1990, £14.50.

CHEF: Colin White    PROPRIETORS: Nigel and Heather Chapman    OPEN: all week; 12.30 to 2, 7.30 to 10    MEALS: alc light L (main courses £4.50 to £11.50). Set Sun L £17, Set D £28    SERVICE: not inc, card slips closed    CARDS: Access, Amex, Diners, Visa    DETAILS: 54 seats. 6 tables outside. Private parties: 40 main room, 20 in 2 private rooms. Car park. Vegetarian meals. Children's helpings. No smoking in dining-rooms. Wheelchair access (1 step; also women's WC). No music    ACCOMMODATION: 20 rooms, all with bath/shower. Rooms for disabled. B&B £80 to £165. Children welcome. Baby facilities. Pets welcome. Afternoon teas. Garden. Swimming-pool. Tennis. Snooker. TV. Phone. Doors close at midnight. Fax: (0225) 864059 (*The Which? Hotel Guide*)

---

**BRAITHWAITE Cumbria**                                                                          map 7

## ▲ *Ivy House* ✹✱

Braithwaite CA12 5SY
BRAITHWAITE (076 87) 78338                                                        COOKING 1
just off B5292 Keswick to Braithwaite road                          COST £22–£26

For ivy, read green; there is a lot of it about – inside and out. The bold decoration of this essentially handsome dwelling causes some debate: 'Still, taste is a tricky thing' was the conclusion of one report. The dinner menu, giving a palate cleanser (sorbet) or booster (soup) as an alternate second course, has a steadiness of repertoire that gives rise to cries of approval. First courses are often fruity – a salad with some liqueur, avocado with raspberry vinaigrette, or pear with smoked chicken – and main dishes can sometimes be inspired by the orchard too – pork with apples, venison with three berries, duck with cherries, all figuring on the same menu one May night. Come dessert, sticky toffee pudding is a constant. Service is neither charged nor expected. The wine list shows a lot of good thinking, with notes to guide you. Some excellent makers figure, and the prices are very fair. The emphasis is not on length but on value. House wine is £6.95.

CHEFS: Wendy Shill and Peter Holten    PROPRIETORS: Nick and Wendy Shill    OPEN: all week, D only; 6.30 to 7.30    MEALS: Set D £17.95    SERVICE: not inc, card slips closed    CARDS: Access, Amex, Diners, Visa    DETAILS: 32 seats. Private parties: 12 main room. Car park. Vegetarian meals. Children's helpings. Smart dress preferred. No smoking in dining-room. Music    ACCOMMODATION: 12 rooms, all with bath/shower. B&B £28 to £98. Deposit: £20. Children welcome. Baby facilities. Dogs by arrangement. Afternoon teas. TV. Phone. Doors close at 11 (*The Which? Hotel Guide*)

---

*See the inside of the front cover for an explanation of the 1 to 5 rating system for cooking standards.*

---

## BRAMPTON Cumbria map 7

# ▲ Farlam Hall

Brampton CA8 2NG
HALLBANKGATE (069 77) 46234 COOKING 2*
on A689m, 2½m SE of Brampton (not at Farlam village) COST £35–£44

'Difficult to find when roads are blocked by snow in May,' commented a couple who lighted upon this family-run country-house hotel and thawed out with an excellent afternoon tea with home-made cakes. They clearly enjoyed their stay: 'The unobtrusive friendliness made us relax from the instant of arrival until the sad moment of departure.' This hotel, built in the seventeenth century and enlarged in the nineteenth, stays in character with its small lake (and island), ivy-clad stone walls, antiques, deeply comfortable sofas, and Victorian dark-blue plaster ceiling in the dining-room. Dinner usually runs to five courses (including a sorbet and coffee) and one typical meal shows the style. Spinach with Stilton and nutmeg in a filo 'money bag' set the ball rolling, then came a sorbet of winter fruits before duck breast with calvados sauce and apples ('cooked to pink perfection'), and pieces of superb stir-fried venison in a potent soy sauce with unadorned vegetables. Blue Wensleydale featured on the cheeseboard, while desserts included delicate fruit bavarois and fruit salad with honey ice-cream. Little extras, such as individually cooked canapés, are those of a serious enterprise. Reporters still feel that the wine list could be moved up a notch to match the quality of the food, but it offers a fair selection and prices are not outrageous. House wines start at £8.95.

CHEF: Barry Quinion  PROPRIETORS: the Quinion and Stevenson families  OPEN: all week, D only; 8 for 8.30  CLOSED: 25 to 31 Dec  MEALS: Set D £27.50 to £28.50  SERVICE: not inc, card slips closed  CARDS: Access, Amex, Visa  DETAILS: 45 seats. Private parties: 45 main room. Car park. Vegetarian meals with prior notice. No children under 5. Smart dress preferred. No cigars/pipes in dining-room. Wheelchair access (3 steps). No music  ACCOMMODATION: 13 rooms, all with bath/shower. D,B&B £86 to £196. No children under 5. Pets welcome. Afternoon teas. Garden. TV. Phone. Doors close at 11.30. Confirm by 2. Fax: (069 77) 46683 (*The Which? Hotel Guide*)

## BRAY Berkshire map 2

# ▲ Waterside Inn ♛

Ferry Road, Bray SL6 2AT
MAIDENHEAD (0628) 20691 COOKING 4*
off A308 Maidenhead to Windsor road COST £37–£110

Waterside has had a good press this year, as it flies the flag of modern classical French cooking as a sign of determination to win through the bouts of recession and never to let standards slip. People have also spoken well of the accommodation. Comfort and cleverness appear in a small space that on the face of it was not designed for luxury breakaways. This riverside inn with a large extension to house the dining-room, two small pavilions for coffee and drinking in the diminutive garden, and electric launch for playing at river rats (for £35 an hour) is a mecca for high days and holidays for many. One reader was moved to note 'that customers always look happy here, not always the case in such places'. The existence of the set-price lunch, which keeps costs understandable if not in check, is a boon to many people planning an outing. The restaurant is decorated in a manner far removed from historical English kitsch – it is modern French kitsch instead. There is a riverbank part, where most people want to sit, and a part to the rear with views over the heads of those who bagged the best tables. The food is built round the enduring values of French cookery, with fashion dictating that it lightens sauces, uses more olive oil, explores with greater vigour the flavours of things like basil or saffron, but never deserting the primacy of the truffle, foie gras, snails and eggs. Although pitched to the super-rich market of the sort which gathers in West End hotels, the menu does not sink to their frequent banality, offering variety of cooking techniques and finishes. Though there have previously been many notes of dispute about the cooking of meat, no one has ever questioned the brilliance of the pastry-work (just look at the two-tiered finish with the coffee). While dispatching the complexities of kidneys and sweetbreads with lettuce and a béarnaise, the kitchen can also produce a lobster bisque of amazing power, and a navarin of lamb fragrant with the perfumes of an early summer vegetable basket. Cheeses are from Philippe Olivier and mainly French; coffee is excellent. Though the petits fours will satisfy many, the desserts, like a sablé of pears or pancakes filled with passion-fruit soufflé, will put the finish on any celebration, no matter what anniversary. Wines remain very expensive and even the normal bolt-holes for the economically minded are secured with very firm prices. Range is very fine with grand names falling off every page. House wine is £17.50. CELLARMAN'S CHOICE: Chablis, Sélection des Frères Roux 1990, £27; St-Julien, Ch. Talbot 1987, £29.

CHEFS: Michel Roux and Mark Dodson  PROPRIETOR: Michel Roux  OPEN: Tue to Sun, exc Tue L (Sun D Apr to 6 Oct only); 12 to 1.30 (2.30 Sat and Sun), 7 to 10  CLOSED: 6 weeks from 26 Dec  MEALS: alc (main courses £24 to £32). Set L £28 to £35, Set D £55.50. Minimum £30  SERVICE: net prices  CARDS: Access, Diners, Visa  DETAILS: 75 seats. Private parties: 80 main room, 8 private room. Car park. Vegetarian meals. No children under 12. Smart dress preferred. No cigars/pipes in dining-room. Wheelchair access (1 step). No music. Air-conditioned  ACCOMMODATION: 6 rooms, all with bath/shower. B&B £110 to £150. Deposit: £60. No children under 12. TV. Phone. Fax: (0628) 784710

---

**BRIGHOUSE** West Yorkshire                                    map 5

*Brook's* ✸✶                                              NEW ENTRY

6–8 Bradford Road, Brighouse HD6 1RW                    COOKING 1*
HUDDERSFIELD (0484) 715284                              COST £25–£30

Just as the ambience and décor are 'curiously mixed' – 1930s and 1940s music, overhead fans, dark wooden floor and staircase, and cream-coloured walls covered in Pennine naive paintings – so Brighouse is not exactly an obvious setting for haute cuisine. Yet Savoy-trained Darrell Brook has carved a niche for his particular brand of it. Ingenuity is high in the list of priorities: four years of weekly menus and hardly a dish repeated – 1,200 to date – goes the record. This may give rise to an initially worrying affair like 'charcuterie wrapped in Parma ham' which turned out to be 'a sausage ball, Limpopo-coloured with lurid pink salami distinguishable from the rest of the filling; it was, however, delicious, strong meat indeed. Its richness was increased by a sauce of mozzarella and port wine.' These were the words of an inspector who was surprised at every turn, but went away happy. The cooking is strong, sometimes outlandish, often heavy with oil or rich sauces, but it tastes grand and the cooks get the timings right. To be fair, not everything is quite so novel: for example, chicken marinated in plum sauce with mooli and spring onion, sirloin steak with garlic and saffron dip, or cod with black noodles and spinach in a Noilly Prat sauce. Desserts will continue the culinary fun and games. When coffee is served, the paper tablecloths are ready for your doodles – wax crayons are supplied and the best pictures get displayed. The wine list is very satisfactory; Marqués de Cáceres, Gaston Hochar and Wolf Blass are just some of the good names, and prices are fine. House wines are £6.95.

CHEF: Richard Ullah   PROPRIETOR: Darrell Brook   OPEN: Mon to Sat, D only, and Mothering Sun L (other L by arrangement); 6 to 11 (7 Sat)   CLOSED: Jan (telephone to check)   MEALS: Set D £14.75 (2 courses) to £18.50   SERVICE: not inc   CARDS: Access, Visa   DETAILS: 50 seats. Private parties: 70 main room, 20 private room. Vegetarian meals. Children's helpings on request. Smart dress preferred. No smoking in dining-room. Wheelchair access (2 steps). Music

---

**BRIGHTON** East Sussex                                                    map 3

## Black Chapati

12 Circus Parade, New England Road,
Brighton BN1 4GW                                                   COOKING 2
BRIGHTON (0273) 699011                                           COST £15–£34

After a period when it seemed to be floundering, the Black Chapati has resurfaced and is back on top form. The action takes place in a small dining-room at the foot of a 1960s office block, with black-topped tables and framed 1920s sheet music on the white walls. This is arguably the most distinctive and curiously fascinating Indian restaurant in Britain, because it is run by an Englishman with a maverick view of Asian cuisine. The slogan on the receipts says 'real Indian foods', although 'Indian' is perhaps the wrong word for Stephen Funnell's cooking. Taking risks with authenticity can be a dangerous game, but this restaurant thrives on riskiness. Asian spicing and vivid contrasts of flavours and textures are combined with up-to-the-minute cooking techniques to produce a menu that might take in breast of woodpigeon with Japanese udon noodles and coriander pesto, home-made Goan pork sausages with lentils and red pepper chutney, and roast rack of lamb with aloo bharta and tomato dhal. Reporters have singled out smoked duck salad with sweet mustard sauce, pan-fried scallops with hot coriander and ginger sauce, and roast haddock fillet marinated in lemon with Gujarati salad. Sweets encompass crème brûlée and bread-and-butter pudding as well as mango and pistachio kulfi. The two-course 'recession-beating' menu (available Tuesday to Thursday evenings) is remarkable value and Sunday lunch is a well-reported buffet. As well as a modest selection of wines there are rare ciders and unusual bottled beers such as Jeanne d'Arc lager. House wine is £7.95.

CHEFS/PROPRIETORS: Stephen Funnell and Lauren Alker  OPEN: Tue to Sat D, and Sun L; 1 to 3, 7 to 10.30  CLOSED: 1 week Christmas, 1 week June  MEALS: alc (main courses £9.50 to £11.50). Set Tue to Thur D £8.50 (2 courses). Sun L buffet £7.95 to £8.95  SERVICE: 10%, card slips closed (not inc Sun L)  CARDS: Access, Amex, Visa  DETAILS: 30 seats. 2 tables outside. Private parties: 30 main room. Vegetarian meals. No children after 9pm. Wheelchair access. Music

## Langan's Bistro

| 1 Paston Place, Brighton BN2 1HA | COOKING 1* |
|---|---|
| BRIGHTON (0273) 606933 | COST £22–£42 |

Although Peter Langan is now long dead, his portrait still adorns the menu of this eponymous restaurant that is the furthest from London his spirit ever managed to wander – except Los Angeles, which was not a success. The intended ambience of pictures and settled plush is similar to the parent in Stratton Street (see entry, London) though the service is less formidable and more amiable. The menu, which works the old-fashioned wrinkle of a cover charge (not found much beyond London these days), is short and simple and, for the level of ambition, expensive. However, there are not many places in Brighton where decent food of the likes of fish soup, open ravioli of wild mushrooms with sorrel, monkfish with pine-nuts, and guinea-fowl with shallots can be found in such sympathetic surroundings. The wine list is short, and house wine is £7.70.

CHEF: Mark Emmerson  PROPRIETORS: Michael Caine and Richard Shepherd  OPEN: Tue to Sun, exc Sat L and Sun D; 12.30 to 2.30, 7.30 to 10.30  MEALS: alc (main courses £13.50 to £15). Set L £14.50. Cover 75p  SERVICE: 10%  CARDS: Access, Amex, Diners, Visa  DETAILS: 48 seats. Children's helpings. Music. Air-conditioned

## ▲ Topps Hotel

| | NEW ENTRY |
|---|---|
| 17 Regency Square, Brighton BN1 2FG | COOKING 1 |
| BRIGHTON (0273) 729334 | COST £29–£34 |

A Regency square, a pair of Regency houses and a comfortable and attractive conversion are ingredients for a sure-fire success in Brighton. The Collins run an enviable small hotel, with a restaurant in the basement, just large enough to cope with residents and a few outsiders. The cooking is better than just a pit-stop before a trip down the pier (now, unfortunately, derelict), but Pauline Collins does not intend overdressing the food or tempting her customers away from well-worn paths. A dinner that included queen scallops with garlic butter, salmon pancakes, veal escalopes with sage and lemon, rack of lamb plainly cooked, lots of vegetables and some excellent home-made ice-cream left the participants remarking that they would have been head-over-heels with relief if this had been the dining-room of *their* hotel. The menu is a set price for two courses and coffee; puddings are extra. The wine list is serviceable and house wines from Ropiteau are £7.50.

▲ *This symbol means accommodation is available.*

CHEF: Pauline Collins  PROPRIETORS: Paul and Pauline Collins  OPEN: Mon, Tue and Thur to Sat, D only; 7 to 9.30  CLOSED: Jan  MEALS: Set D £18.95 (2 courses)  SERVICE: net prices, card slips closed  CARDS: Access, Amex, Diners, Visa  DETAILS: 24 seats. Private parties: 16 main room. Vegetarian meals. Children's helpings. Smart dress preferred. No music  ACCOMMODATION: 14 rooms, all with bath/shower. Lift. B&B £45 to £99. Children welcome. TV. Phone. Fax: (0273) 203679 (*The Which? Hotel Guide*)

## *Whytes*

**NEW ENTRY**

33 Western Street, Brighton BN1 2PG  COOKING 1*
BRIGHTON (0273) 776618  COST £25–£34

Whytes lies in an area of 'well cared-for terraced houses cheek-by-jowl with virtual dereliction', where Brighton fades imperceptibly into Hove. The narrowness of the house poses problems well solved by small tables with beech chairs opposite banquette seating. The menus reveal assiduous balance: soups and fish dishes change daily, the rest every six weeks or so; vegetarians, traditionalists and those with more exotic tastes are all catered for. Ian Whyte's cooking is technically assured – Roquefort and leek in a filo parcel was skilfully cooked, and its accompanying cranberry and ginger sauce offered clean, if sweet, contrast. Duck liver pâté, though, gave 'no feeling of a kitchen fretting over complexity or depth of flavour'. Some combinations (calf's liver with mango, for example) work 'magnificently', while others (chestnut and orange with guinea-fowl, for example) are less inspired. Puddings may plod, too: chocolate mousse and praline parfait with chocolate sauce soothed rather than excited. Service, essentially from Jane Whyte, is calm, well paced and assured. The short wine list is somewhat eccentric, with some wines described in full and given welcome tasting descriptions, while others drift on to a page bereft of even vintage and producer information. Prices for the identifiable wines are reasonable: house Côtes du Luberon is £6.95.

CHEF: Ian Whyte  PROPRIETORS: Ian and Jane Whyte  OPEN: Mon to Sat, D only (L, pre-theatre D and some Suns by arrangement); 7 to 9.30  MEALS: Set D £14.50 (2 courses) to £17.95  SERVICE: not inc  CARDS: Access, Amex, Visa  DETAILS: 38 seats. Private parties: 30 main room, 14 private room. Vegetarian meals. Children welcome. Music

---

**BRIMFIELD  Hereford & Worcester**  map 2

## ▲ *Poppies* ♥ ✳

The Roebuck, Brimfield SY8 4WE
BRIMFIELD (0584) 711230  COOKING 3*
on A49, 4m S of Ludlow  COST £21–£55

This popular village pub/restaurant-with-rooms can get very busy. The contrast between dark wooden bar and light, cane-chaired dining-room across the corridor (named 'Poppies', striking the right summer-meadow note) remains as stark as ever, but good food is to be had in both. 'Carole Evans remains enthusiastically committed to keeping this remarkable enterprise at its peak,' reports a regular. The increasing emphasis on organic ingredients can be tasted. 'Simple but exquisitely executed' was one verdict on a meal from the bar menu, where imagination (buckwheat pancakes stuffed with smoked haddock and leek, and roast monkfish with a mustard sauce) pitches in with populist tradition ('tasty lamb hotpot with delicious potato topping' and chicken in Dunkerton's cider pie). Across the way, a warm scallop salad with crispy bacon and garlic croûtons offers 'a salmagundi for the '90s', with nasturtium and borage flowers adding flamboyance to the 'bright assortment of salad leaves'. Fillet of lamb, 'perfectly cooked to exact pinkness', came with a spinach tartlet which resembled a 'light quiche with fresh crumbly pastry', and its mint and redcurrant sauce was 'concentrated, sweet without being syrupy and potently infused with fresh mint'. Beef with a red wine and shallot sauce is perfectly contrasted by the celeriac purée on which it is served, and grilled monkfish also found 'a piquant counterpoint' with a mustard sauce. Truly splendid farmhouse cheeses rival the grand platter of desserts as the most popular way to finish the meal. The wine list, like the cheese list, is informatively annotated and full of variety and originality. Anyone prepared to explore the nooks and crannies of the list will find character and quality at every turn, from Sauzet, Leflaive and Vernay to Conterno and Parker Coonawarra Estate. Halves and bin-ends are good, too. Prices begin at £7.50.

CHEF/PROPRIETOR: Carole Evans   OPEN: Tue to Sat; 12 to 2, 7 to 9.30   CLOSED: 2 weeks Feb, 1 week Oct   MEALS: alc (main courses bar £5.50 to £8, restaurant £14.50 to £19)   SERVICE: not inc, card slips closed   CARDS: Access, Amex, Visa   DETAILS: restaurant 36 seats, bar 36 seats. 4 tables outside. Private parties: 40 main room, 16 private room. Car park. Vegetarian meals. Children's helpings on request. Smart dress preferred. No smoking in 1 dining-room. No music   ACCOMMODATION: 3 rooms, all with bath/shower. B&B £35 to £60. Deposit: £30. No children under 10. Pets by arrangement. Garden. TV. Phone. Confirm by 6. Fax: (0584) 711654 (*The Which? Hotel Guide*)

---

**BRINKWORTH** Wiltshire                                                    map 2

## *Three Crowns* £                                        NEW ENTRY

The Street, Brinkworth SN15 5AF
BRINKWORTH (0666) 510366                                COOKING 1
on B4042 Malmesbury to Wootton Bassett road            COST £14–£28

This stone-built country pub is a local asset. It has a popular family garden, good draught beers, a delightful atmosphere and an enterprising chef/landlord who knows how to cook. Above all, it has retained its identity: no bookings are taken, you order at the bar, and meals are eaten in the lounge or the airy flagstoned conservatory. Service is swift and charming, even under pressure. Standard pub snacks are served at lunch-time, but the real action takes place on the full blackboard menu. No starters are available, but the range of dishes is 'mind-blowing'. Exotic fish is the star of the show and supplies come from as far away as Australia: barramundi with Noilly Prat sauce and 'fragrant' cold poached salmon have been recommended. Other praised dishes include tagliatelle with smoked cheese sauce, sauté medallions of venison with redcurrant jelly and red wine sauce, and spot-on fillet steak with Stilton and prawn sauce. Dishes come with six different vegetables. Chocolate and Grand Marnier mousse served in a chocolate cup is a worthwhile sweet. The wine list is a cracker: prices are kept in check, the New World shows up strongly and the notes make colourful reading (Vacqueyras is a 'solid puncher, chunky and dusty-edged'). House wines are £7.95.

CHEFS: A. Windle and A. Gale   PROPRIETORS: Mr and Mrs A. Windle   OPEN: all week; 12 to 2, 6 to 9.30   MEALS: alc (main courses £4.50 to £12.95)   SERVICE: not inc   CARDS: Access, Amex, Diners, Visa   DETAILS: 85 seats. 18 tables outside. Car park. Vegetarian meals. Children's helpings. Smart dress preferred. Wheelchair access (1 step). Music

---

**BRISTOL Avon**　　　　　　　　　　　　　　　　　　　　　　　　　　　map 2

## Bell's Diner ⅙✳ £　　　　　　　　　　　　　　　 | NEW ENTRY |

1 York Road, Montpelier, Bristol BS6 5QB
BRISTOL (0272) 240357
take Picton Street off Cheltenham　　　　　　　　　　　　COOKING 1
Road (A38) – runs into York Road　　　　　　　　　　　　COST £16–£36

Shirley Anne Bell opened this bistro-style restaurant in 1976 and ran it for five years before being bought out by one of the staff. When interest waned, she returned and reports suggest that the place is back on top form. It is not easy to find, and the setting is a converted corner shop in 'a not particularly inviting area', but the atmosphere is anything but bleak: 'On a freezing night, warm staff and warming open fires drew us into this super oasis,' commented travellers from Cardiff. The restaurant consists of a series of connecting rooms with polished floorboards, original fireplaces and prints of old Bristol on the light-grey walls. The cooking depends on the shrewd buying of quality ingredients. Both the regularly changing *carte* and set menus offer exceptional value. Fish might range from salmon and raisins in filo pastry to blue-fin tuna grilled with olive oil. Reporters have approved of light, up-to-the-minute dishes such as endive and kohlrabi salad with hot bacon and tomato dressing, pigeon breast on crostini with plums, and delicately poached chicken breast with salsa verde. Honey custard and quinces, and pears poached in Beaujolais with cinnamon ice-cream have been admirable finales. The wine list matches the menu for price, with plenty of drinking for around £10. House wine is £7.25.

CHEFS/PROPRIETORS: Shirley Anne Bell and Peter Taylor   OPEN: Tue to Sat, D only, and Sun L; 12 to 3, 7 to 10   CLOSED: 1 week Christmas, 1 week end Aug   MEALS: alc (main courses £8 to £12.50). Set Sun L and Tue to Sat D £10   SERVICE: not inc (10% for 8 or more)   CARDS: Access, Visa   DETAILS: 55 seats. Private parties: 30 main room, 18 private room. Vegetarian meals. Children's helpings. No smoking in dining-room. Music

---

## Harveys ▌　　　　　　 　　　　　 | NEW ENTRY |

12 Denmark Street, Bristol BS1 5DQ　　　　　　　　　　COOKING 3
BRISTOL (0272) 277665　　　　　　　　　　　　　　　　COST £25–£52

There was a time when this restaurant, housed stylishly in giant medieval vaults beneath its wine merchant owners' nondescript neo-Georgian offices, cornered the Bristol market in power dining. The design was early Conran, there was money about – and look at the wine list. The last year or two have seen a new and younger team attempt to recapture the position. A coat of paint has lightened the burden of the vaults; good modern pictures and a boost in wattage finish the job. Now it is only marred by dreadful music – and that from the sponsors of the Leeds Piano Competition. Ramon Farthing has been brought in from the Cotswolds to spruce up a menu that was in international mode, but now sports more lively dishes such as turbot on crab and leeks with a spiced olive dressing, or red mullet cooked with sesame oil with a mushroom, orange and apple salad. The food is never less than full dress, but the litany of accompaniments will interest the reader, not bore him. More importantly, the cooking is accurate, the flavours are revealed and the techniques are honest. That vegetable cooking may be messy is regrettable, but the desserts – even a wholly conservative crêpes suzette – are up to par and cheeses are properly kept. Prices, despite the intended economy lunch menu, seem to creep up on the unwary, so that the restaurant will retain its charms for prosperous customers. A range of sherries by the glass (not all of them from Harveys) is offered, as are several ports. The clarets are pedigree, but are supported by petits châteaux with some age at modest prices. Elsewhere, big names figure like Latour, Jaboulet and Jadot, but these run alongside Roux, Barjac and Juillot. Italy and Spain are unambitious, while the antipodes is only a little less so. House wines are £12. CELLARMAN'S CHOICE: Barossa Valley, St Hallett Cabernet/Merlot 1990, £15; Sancerre 1991, Paul Prieur, £17.50.

CHEF: Ramon Farthing  PROPRIETORS: Harveys of Bristol  OPEN: Mon to Sat, exc Sat L; 12 to 2, 7 to 10.45  CLOSED: bank hols  MEALS: alc (main courses £16.50 to £19). Set L £16.50 (2 courses) to £27, Set D £29  SERVICE: net prices  CARDS: Access, Amex, Diners, Visa  DETAILS: 120 seats. Private parties: 100 main room, 20, 36 and 60 private rooms. Valet parking D. Vegetarian meals. Healthy eating options. No children under 8. Smart dress preferred. Music. Air-conditioned. Fax: (0272) 253380

## *Howards*

1A–2A Avon Crescent, Hotwells,
Bristol BS1 6XQ                                                           COOKING 1
BRISTOL (0272) 262921                                              COST £20–£36

With a view of the Clifton Suspension Bridge, SS *Great Britain* just round the corner, and the Nova Scotia pub ('one of Bristol's few remaining traditional pubs,' a conservationist reader remarks) next door, this bistro on the docks has quite a lot of the city's recent history on its doorstep. Add to that the fact that the premises were the site of Bristol's first transport café and you have the makings of a thesis. There is not a lot of 'caff' about the decoration today, politely called Regency, nor about the cooking, which covers crab pancakes with lemon grass and ginger, Thai chicken wrapped in filo then deep-fried and served with a pimento sauce, and breast of chicken with lobster in a lemon and dill sauce. Standards are usually acceptable and the young staff's efficiency comes over agreeably. The wine list may be short, but is fair value with little priced at more than £20, and including a pinot blanc from Luxembourg. House wines are £7.25, and extra bottles are listed on a blackboard. Howards Bistro at Nailsea – Tel: (0275) 858348 – is run by the same team.

*All entries in the* Guide *are rewritten every year, not least because restaurant standards fluctuate. Don't trust an out-of-date* Guide.

CHEF: David Roast   PROPRIETORS: Christopher and Gillian Howard   OPEN: Mon to Sat,
exc Sat L (Sat L and Sun by arrangement); 12 to 2.30, 7 to 11.30   MEALS: alc (main courses
£10 to £13.50). Set L £13, Set D £15   SERVICE: not inc   CARDS: Access, Amex, Visa
DETAILS: 60 seats. Private parties: 35 main room. Vegetarian meals. Children's helpings.
No-smoking area. Wheelchair access. Music

## Hunt's

| | |
|---|---|
| 26 Broad Street, Bristol BS1 2HG | COOKING 3 |
| BRISTOL (0272) 265580 | COST £25–£41 |

Once there was a restaurant called Markwick and Hunt, now there's
Markwick's and there's Hunt's. The fission has benefited Bristol's financial
downtown. Hunt's occupies a former tea and coffee merchant's premises, with
the old fittings adding interest to the small ante-room bar. Andy Hunt has
continued to mine the vein established at the old joint venture, one which was
first worked when Stephen Markwick had Bistro 21 and Andy helped him out.
It is steady bourgeois French cooking with a few variations, but none so
worrisome as to alarm. Salade niçoise, provençal fish soup and spinach ravioli
with ricotta may be dishes that promise much sunshine, but the strengths lie in
more northerly cooking: things like venison and guinea-fowl terrine with
chicken liver pâté and spiced onions, eggs Benedict, calf's kidney with
mustard, tarragon and brandy, or veal cutlet with mushrooms, bacon and
madeira. Rack of lamb with fresh figs and three spices showed off some of the
potential of the variations; steamed celeriac with parsley, potato galette and
nicely creamy spinach were comforting signs of steady ability extended to the
ancillaries. Fish is on a separate menu and comes direct from Cornwall. For
dessert, think of hot soufflé. Four dozen wines run across a generous range;
prices are none too steep. House wines start at £8.75.

CHEFS: Andrew Hunt and Haydn Neal   PROPRIETORS: Andrew and Anne Hunt   OPEN:
Tue to Sat, exc Sat L (Sun and Mon by arrangement for private parties); 12 to 2, 7 to 10.30
(pre- or post-theatre by arrangement)   CLOSED: 1 week Christmas, 1 week Easter, 2 weeks
summer   MEALS: alc (main courses £11.50 to £16.50). Set L £9.95 (2 courses) to £11.95
SERVICE: net prices, card slips closed   CARDS: Access, Visa   DETAILS: 40 seats. Private
parties: 26 main room, 26 private room. Vegetarian meals with prior notice. Children's
helpings. Smart dress preferred. Wheelchair access (1 step). Music

## Lettonie 🍷

| | |
|---|---|
| 9 Druid Hill, Stoke Bishop BS9 1EW | COOKING 4 |
| BRISTOL (0272) 686456 | COST £25–£51 |

The location is true suburbia, the far side of the Downs. The house is part of a
shopping parade, and the room itself has been variously described as '1930s
semi front room', 'an eastern European living-room, comfortable but verging
on the austere', and 'disconcerting, with a mirror down one side reflecting you
from the opposite wall'. While the food is anything but understated, the service
can be less than garrulous, though always willing. This makes for a slightly
serious atmosphere. Martin Blunos, however, continues to cook very well
indeed. His menus do not change with alarming speed, and he has an apparent

preoccupation with offal, but few dispute the quality. 'The temptation to be original for originality's sake is avoided; everything is there for a purpose,' remarked one reader who had benefited from the cheaper lunch menu and could thus afford a good bottle of wine. Dinner will kick off with a hot appetiser, often a cheese soufflé with onion marmalade. Then choose between an intense chicken consommé, or a tartlet of nettles and spinach with quail's eggs and Ardennes ham, or the signature dish of scrambled duck egg with caviare, blinis and vodka, before main dishes of rump of lamb with garlic fritters and sweetbreads rolled in bacon, the lamb piled over a bed of mashed potatoes, or stuffed pig's trotter full of morels (another constant here). Brill stuffed with salmon and carrot, and sauced with cream and basil, showed that Martin Blunos' hand is as delicate with fish as with meat. 'And vegetables are properly dealt with here,' someone else chimed in. An apple croustade with caramel ice-cream, a tart of sun-dried bananas and almonds, and a mango biscuit ice-cream are some of the desserts which will always please, even if the flavours are not as exciting as those displayed in the first two courses. This is a restaurant that grows on you, perhaps because of the evident commitment of both chef and Siân Blunos, who looks after the customers. The wine list is unpushy and retains its good sense, emphasising the many more-than-decent bottles now available and buying from merchants who combine interest and reliability. Prices are neither high nor particularly low, and half-bottles are well chosen. Real strengths are white burgundy, Rhônes and a flight of modest clarets. House wine is from £9.95. CELLARMAN'S CHOICE: Ch. Thieuley 1991, £19.10; St-Emilion, Ch. Pipeau 1986, £19.15.

CHEF: Martin Blunos   PROPRIETORS: Martin and Siân Blunos   OPEN: Tue to Sat; 12.30 to 1.30, 7.30 to 9.30   CLOSED: 2 weeks Aug, 2 weeks Christmas   MEALS: Set L £15.95 to £29.95, Set D £29.95   SERVICE: not inc   CARDS: Access, Amex, Visa   DETAILS: 24 seats. Private parties: 24 main room. Vegetarian meals with prior notice. Children welcome. Smart dress preferred. Music

## Markwicks ▮

43 Corn Street, Bristol BS1 1HT                                    COOKING 3*
BRISTOL (0272) 262658                                             COST £18–£44

Some years ago, Stephen and Judy Markwick caught Bristol's stomachic imagination by offering food of very high quality at sensible (silly) prices at their Bistro 21. The consequence was capacity business. The Markwicks may now be more mature, their restaurant an elegant and characterful vault (once a safety deposit) in the centre of the city's lawyerland and money market, but they still catch the breath of the careful with their eminently cheap, yet properly cooked, meals. This is the Markwicks' response to recession, and it works. 'Markwicks exudes the air of the best Paris restaurants (e.g. Allard) and this is sedulously but unobtrusively cultivated. Markwick is one of the steadiest of British chefs,' writes one supporter, 'especially now he has finished his love affair with salt,' noted another. The menus strike chords in the memory while keeping up with current tastes – salmon on a bed of cabbage or baked cod with tomato and chilli salsa and mashed potato – balanced by an ever-constant presence of provençal fish soup and dishes such as guinea-fowl with apples, calvados and cream, various ragoûts of fish, orange and Grand Marnier pancakes, and peaches with a lemon and brandy sabayon. This is studied, 'rounded' cooking; someone also said 'strong but shy' cooking. Materials, methods, overall approach and the front-of-house are all well up to scratch. On the wine side, recession has reinforced good habits. At Markwicks the already good house wines have been augmented both in number and in quality and, while the remainder of the list is a delight, it is here that most customers will linger. Stray a little and mature Rhônes, excellent Alsaces and more than decent antipodeans are found; reach the end of the list and the reward is a mouthwatering bin-end page. Prices fairly reflect quality throughout, but bin-ends apart Italian and Australian wines might reward longer study. House wines are from £9.50. CELLARMAN'S CHOICE: Wairau River, Sauvignon Blanc 1992, £15; La Volte 1991, Antinori, £18.

CHEFS: Stephen Markwick and Sara Ody  PROPRIETORS: Stephen and Judy Markwick  OPEN: Mon to Sat, exc Sat L; 12 to 2, 7 to 10.30  CLOSED: Christmas, New Year, Easter, 2 weeks Aug, bank hol Mons  MEALS: alc (main courses £12.50 to £16). Set L £9.50 (2 courses) to £11.50, Set D £19.50  SERVICE: net prices, card slips closed  CARDS: Access, Amex, Visa  DETAILS: 50 seats. Private parties: 30 main room, 6 and 20 private rooms. Vegetarian meals. Children's helpings on request. No music. Fax: (0272) 262658

## Melbourne's £

74 Park Street, Bristol BS1 5JX  
BRISTOL (0272) 226996

COOKING 1  
COST £16–£25

This is a cheerful and inexpensive spot, encouraging bring-your-own on the wine front (no corkage) and now revelling, after a refurbishment, in even more Australianisms and increased seating. Some people find the cooking perfunctory, others enjoy it for fair value – though the set lunch has now disappeared except on Sundays. The cheerful bistro cooking is augmented by daily blackboard specials such as salmon and sole with tomato and lobster sauce, or sea bass with oyster mushrooms. Desserts range from sticky toffee pudding to apple pie and bread-and-butter pudding. Service can be slow, perhaps depending on the number of diversions. The wine list is there to help those who forget to bring their own. House wine, from Australia, is £6.25.

CHEFS: C.J. Cowpe and M.V. Read  PROPRIETORS: A.P. Wilshaw, N.J. Hennessy and C.J. Cowpe  OPEN: Tue to Sun, exc Sat L and Sun D; 12 to 2, 7 to 10.30  MEALS: alc (main courses £6.50 to £8.50). Set Sun L £10 (2 courses) to £11.50, Set D £13.25 to £15  SERVICE: 10%, card slips closed  CARDS: Access, Amex, Visa  DETAILS: 110 seats. Private parties: 20 main room (Tue to Thur only). Vegetarian meals. Children's helpings Sun L. No cigars/pipes in dining-room. Wheelchair access (2 steps). Music. Fax: (0272) 250825

## Michael's

129 Hotwell Road, Clifton, Bristol BS8 4RU  
BRISTOL (0272) 276190

COOKING 1*  
COST £21–£38

A sensitive soul commented that Hotwell Road is on the seedy side of town, though improvements are in train, and that the restaurant is opposite a bikers' boozer, though traffic noise rarely intrudes. Plum-coloured walls and a vaguely Victorian theme soon wrap the customer in another world. 'The value of

Michael's is its consistency and longevity. It carries on, while many in the city shine briefly, then fade' is the judgement of one who does the Bristolian rounds. Twenty years may have seen changes in dishes offered on set-price menus with more than adequate choice; changes that may be more in the trimmings than in the substance – the mango and lime chutney with terrines of venison and duck, olive oil and dill dressing with smoked salmon, ginger sauce and crispy leeks with scallops, olive sauce with monkfish, and of course a de rigueur vegetarian dish. Service is casual but never unfriendly. The serviceable wine list is fairly priced, with house wines at £8.25.

CHEF/PROPRIETOR: Michael McGowan   OPEN: Tue to Sat, exc Sat L; 12 to 2, 7 to 11
CLOSED: 1 Jan, last week Aug   MEALS: Set L £12.50 to £17.50, Set D £22.50   SERVICE: not inc (10% for 5 or more, card slips closed)   CARDS: Access, Visa   DETAILS: 45 seats. Private parties: 50 main room, 20 and 40 private rooms. Vegetarian meals. Children welcome. Smart dress preferred. No smoking in dining-room. Wheelchair access (1 step; also WC). Music in bar/lounge. Air-conditioned

## Muset ▼

12–16 Clifton Road, Clifton,
Bristol BS8 1AF                                                          COOKING 1*
BRISTOL (0272) 732920                                                COST £23–£30

It is quite a giant of a restaurant, slung out among basements and mezzanines along the base of the building. 'The location may be terrible, but there's loads of character,' reflect the owners. The place survives for its value-for-money, up-front ways of doing business and its encouragement, despite a good, cheap, short wine list, of B.Y.O. (bring-your-own) on the Australian principle. Someone with a picky approach might say the output is so great it has to resort to quick-fix procedures, but the chefs make their own sauces and ice-creams. The choice may sometimes be conventional, but never dull, and turnover is very rapid. There has been a noticeable shift towards dishes in the American/Italian style, pasta being a big hit. Soups can be solid but worthy, while other dishes such as salmon-and-sole mousse, avocado pear with a salad of marinated chicken, simple mozzarella, tomato and bacon salad, chicken stuffed with herbs and cheese, duck with spinach and wild mushrooms, or fish of the day from the blackboards listing specials meet general approval. Less enthusiasm is noted for desserts, though ice-creams go down well. A new, cheaper branch, called Bistro Musette, has recently opened at 19–23 Colston Street, Bristol, Tel: (0272) 227757. The 40-bottle wine list offers fine value and canny selection; Stag's Leap from Srafer vies with Léoville-Poyferré at the top end and decent Australians jostle with reliable bourgeois at around the £10 mark. CELLARMAN'S CHOICE: Ch. Léoville-Poyferré 1985, £19.95; Taltarni, Fumé Blanc 1990, £10.25.

CHEFS: D. Wheadon and P. Baker   PROPRIETORS: A.J. Portlock and D. Wheadon   OPEN: Mon to Sat, D only; 7 to 10.30   MEALS: Set D £13.50 (2 courses) to £15.50   SERVICE: 10%, card slips closed   CARDS: Access, Visa   DETAILS: 150 seats. Private parties: 45 main room. Vegetarian meals. Children early evening only. Wheelchair access (1 step). Music. Air-conditioned. Fax: (0272) 732920

## Rocinante's £

| | |
|---|---|
| 85 Whiteladies Road, Bristol BS8 4NT | COOKING 1 |
| BRISTOL (0272) 734482 | COST £15–£29 |

This colourful tapas bar in a converted shop premises on the main Clifton drag is unashamedly young at heart. It buzzes. Live music raises the decibel level at weekends. The kitchen is committed to organic meat and vegetables, and farmed fish is barred. Daily deliveries of seafood mean that dishes change regularly: 'wonderful' sardines, bream and John Dory are grilled; salmon and sea bass are baked or poached; squid is put into casseroles and octopus into salads. The tapas are substantial and the menu ventures further afield for bouillabaisse, keftedes (Greek meat balls) and falafel. Spicy chickpeas, skewers of chargrilled lamb and gooseberry fool have received favourable mention. Weekday breakfast is served from 9am, while Sunday brunch (10am to 2pm) is a lively family occasion. Unusual Spanish and Portuguese bottled beers supplement the short, affordable wine list. House wine is £7.25.

CHEF: Barny Haughton   PROPRIETORS: Barny Haughton and Mathew Pruen   OPEN: all week; 12 to 3, 6 to 11   MEALS: alc (main courses £4.50 to £8.50). Set L £7.75 (2 courses) to £8.95   SERVICE: not inc (10% for 6 or more)   CARDS: Access, Visa   DETAILS: 100 seats. 6 tables outside. Private parties: 100 main room, 30 private room. Vegetarian meals. Children welcome. Wheelchair access (3 steps; also WC). Music

---

**BROADHEMBURY** Devon                                          map 1

## Drewe Arms £

| | |
|---|---|
| Broadhembury EX14 0NF | |
| BROADHEMBURY (040 484) 267, changes to | |
| (0404) 841267 early 1994 | COOKING 2* |
| off A373, between Cullompton and Honiton | COST £16–£40 |

There are so many blackboards here that you may be forgiven for thinking that the Burges were once schoolteachers. In fact, Kerstin Burge is a talented and natural cook, Nigel an 'amazingly calm and kind landlord'. Their site of operations is a thatched pub – perhaps slightly hard to find – in a village that epitomises picturesque, fireside Britain to an extreme. The Burges offer not just the ales that the character of the place seems to demand, but also a fine set of fish dishes, some meat, and the full slate of pub specials like sandwiches, cheese and so on. 'The seafood platter was a half-lobster, thickly sliced gravlax, sweetly marinated pickled herring which reminded me of my Danish childhood, a mass of prawns and some unnecessary mock roe and Danish caviare,' rhapsodised one reporter. Others speak of the dressed crab, simple grilled sardines, scallops with hollandaise sauce, turbot with a herby hollandaise, salmon with sorrel, and John Dory with cream and onion sauce. The menu depends on the catch, and the quality is remarkable. The meal may be eaten in the bustling first bar, atmospheric with all the trappings of old English domesticity. No matter how much food is cooked, there is no drift towards restaurant habits. The wine list is kept alive by local merchant Chris Piper at Ottery. The range is good for a pub and the prices are very fair. House wines are £6.95.

CHEF: Kerstin Burge   PROPRIETORS: Kerstin and Nigel Burge   OPEN: all week, exc Sun D restaurant; 12 to 2, 7 to 10   MEALS: alc (main courses bar £5 to £8.50, restaurant £12). Set L and D £16.95   SERVICE: not inc   DETAILS: 36 seats. 8 tables outside. Private parties: 25 main room. Car park. Vegetarian meals with prior notice restaurant. Children's helpings. Wheelchair access (1 step; also WC). No music

---

**BROADWAY** Hereford & Worcester                                                     map 2

## ▲ *Collin House*

Collin Lane, Broadway WR12 7PB
BROADWAY (0386) 858354                                                     COOKING 2
on A44, 1m NW of Broadway                                                  COST £19–£39

This charming sixteenth-century Cotswold-stone house once belonged to a wool merchant and it has retained an air of domesticity, with lots of antique furniture and china. It reminded one visitor of staying in the residence of 'an upper-class family who have fallen on hard times but are still charming to know'. Reports suggest that the lack of custom is starting to take its toll; however, the kitchen continues to maintain its high standards. Dinner is a wide-ranging *carte*, priced according to the main course taken: local meat and game show up strongly and fish is delivered fresh each day. Residents have spoken highly of twice-baked soufflés (perhaps Parmesan and cheddar with a 'zingy' sweet pepper sauce), fish grill with tarragon hollandaise, pigeon breast cooked pink with tart blackcurrant sauce, oxtail casserole, and fillet of beef with red onion marmalade and burgundy sauce. Sweets are a blend of the light (lemon posset, 'wonderful' ice-creams) and the weighty (bread-and-butter pudding, treacle tart). A set menu operates at lunch-time, along with highly praised bar snacks. Service is consistently polite. The wine list is well spread and puts little strain on the wallet. House wine is £9.60.

CHEFS: Mark Brookes and Anthony Ike   PROPRIETOR: John Mills   OPEN: all week; 12 to 1.30, 7 to 9   MEALS: alc bar L (main courses £6.50). Set L £14.50, Set D £15 to £23. Bar menu L Mon to Sat   SERVICE: not inc, card slips closed   CARDS: Access, Visa   DETAILS: 30 seats. 4 tables outside. Private parties: 30 main room. Car park. Vegetarian meals. Children's helpings Sun L. Smart dress preferred D. No cigars/pipes in dining-room. Wheelchair access (1 step; also WC). No music   ACCOMMODATION: 7 rooms, all with bath/shower. B&B £45 to £99. Deposit: £40. Children welcome. Garden. Swimming-pool. Doors close at midnight (*The Which? Hotel Guide*)

## ▲ *Dormy House* 🍴✳

Willersey Hill, Broadway WR12 7LF
BROADWAY (0386) 852711                                                     COOKING 1*
just off A44, 1m from centre                                               COST £23–£55

Visitors are likely to be enchanted by the setting: this converted seventeenth-century farmhouse stands high on the wooded escarpment above the town with the Vale of Evesham opening out in the distance. 'It's my favourite hotel,' comments a regular visitor from the North, who adds that 'the staff work wonderfully as a team'. Improvement and extension have changed the complexion of the place, although it still proudly exhibits its oak beams, rafters and mellow Cotswold-stone walls. John Sanderson's cooking is complex, and ingredients seem to tumble over each other, as in seasonal specialities from the *carte* such as pot au feu of salmon, turbot and sea bass with baby vegetables and a salmon and crab ravioli, or pan-fried breast of guinea-fowl with its leg filled with chicken and morel mousse on a bed of home-made saffron noodles. Table d'hôte menus offer the prospect of light relief in the shape of tian of white crabmeat with tomato mayonnaise and grilled salmon with stir-fried vegetables and a soy, honey and sherry sauce. Cheeses from Androuet come with French lettuces and toasted walnut bread. Wines are good, but resort is made too often to the big names. The coverage, however, is broad and there are many fine bottles at reasonable prices. House wine is from £8.75.

CHEF: John Sanderson PROPRIETOR: Jorgen Philip-Sorensen OPEN: all week, exc Sat L; 12.30 to 2 (2.30 Sun), 7.30 to 9 (7 to 9.30 Sun) CLOSED: 25 and 26 Dec MEALS: alc (main courses £17 to £20). Set L £16, Set D £25.50 to £33 SERVICE: not inc CARDS: Access, Amex, Diners, Visa DETAILS: 80 seats. Private parties: 40 main room, 8 and 14 private rooms. Car park. Vegetarian meals. Children's helpings 5 to 7.30pm. Smart dress preferred. No smoking in 1 dining-room. Music ACCOMMODATION: 49 rooms, all with bath/shower. Rooms for disabled. B&B £55 to £110. Children welcome. Baby facilities. Pets welcome (not in public rooms). Afternoon teas. Garden. TV. Phone. Doors close at 12.30am. Confirm by 6. Fax: (0386) 858636 (*The Which? Hotel Guide*)

## Hunters Lodge

High Street, Broadway WR12 7DT
BROADWAY (0386) 853247

COOKING **2**
COST £19–£41

'We liked the lounge with nibbles, wobbly tables and lots of fat, good-natured cats,' reflected one family who found this plant-clad house a haven for lunch. The Friedlis have restricted the number of days they are open to give themselves more time for family and friends, but it is worth trying to sample Kurt Friedli's classically based cuisine that disdains much fashion yet manages to extract flavour from properly made sauces and respect for materials. 'I am very English and get withdrawal symptoms in France and its imitators from lack of vegetables,' wrote one who applauded the excellent choice that accompanied her roast lamb which came after a prawn and vegetable strudel with honey and yogurt sauce. Perhaps the same English taste prompted wild praise for a chocolate, rum and raisin cheesecake, and a crème caramel with caramel that was strong but never bitter. Set-price meals are very fair value. The wine list is soundly conventional, with house wines at £7.70.

CHEF: Kurt Friedli PROPRIETORS: Kurt and Dottie Friedli OPEN: Wed to Sat D, Sat and Sun L; 12.30 to 2, 7 to 9.30 CLOSED: first 2 weeks Feb, first 3 weeks Aug MEALS: alc (main courses £9.50 to £13). Set L £13.50, Set D £15 SERVICE: not inc CARDS: Access, Amex, Diners, Visa DETAILS: 35 seats. Private parties: 35 main room. Car park. Vegetarian meals. Children's helpings. No children under 8 D. No cigars/pipes in dining-room. Wheelchair access (2 steps; also WC). No music

---

*Dining-rooms where live and recorded music are never played are signalled by* No music *in the details at the end of an entry.*

## ▲ Lygon Arms

| | |
|---|---|
| Broadway WR12 7DU | COOKING 2* |
| BROADWAY (0386) 852255 | COST £31–£64 |

This must be nearly the most famous 'olde inn' of Britain, and it sits on the Cotswolds' most trampled high street. In the barrel-vaulted great hall with its medieval overtones, Clive Howe has put on show his interpretation of British cooking. This is unique in the region, if not the country, and deserves support. His fertile brain, mulling over old recipe books and modern price-lists, has yielded various compromises of old and new that are worth eating: venison faggots with beetroot and onion, raised pie of guinea-fowl and apricot, home-smoked salmon with anchovy sauce, and venison with apple and mustard sauce. In parallel with these are the more simple grilled food, or 'modern' dishes such as seafood salad with orange and ginger, or a brochette of seafood with a red wine and parsley dressing. Although the intentions are clear, sometimes the tastes verge too much on the over-sweet or over-vinegared to allow complete success. Perhaps the greatest achievements are at the dessert stage: gooseberry crumble tart, an old-fashioned flummery, or a crème brûlée of rhubarb and ginger. The wine list is sound enough, though not arresting. Some effort has been made to offer bottles at below £20, though none at all to supply half-bottles. House wines are £12.

CHEF: Clive Howe  PROPRIETORS: The Savoy Group plc  OPEN: all week; 12.30 to 2, 7.30 to 9.30  MEALS: alc (main courses £17.50 to £22.50). Set L £19.50, Set D £29.75  SERVICE: not inc, card slips closed  CARDS: Access, Amex, Diners, Visa  DETAILS: 90 seats. 8 tables outside. Private parties: 90 main room, 20, 40 and 76 private rooms. Car park. Vegetarian meals. Children's helpings. Jacket and tie. Wheelchair access (also WC). Music ACCOMMODATION: 65 rooms, all with bath/shower. Rooms for disabled. B&B £103 to £153. Children welcome. Pets welcome. Afternoon teas. Garden. Swimming-pool. Sauna. Tennis. Snooker. TV. Phone. Confirm by 6. Fax: (0386) 858611 ( *The Which? Hotel Guide*)

---

**BROCKENHURST** Hampshire                                                    map 2

## Le Poussin 🍴

| | |
|---|---|
| The Courtyard, Brookley Road, | |
| Brockenhurst SO42 7RB | COOKING 4 |
| LYMINGTON (0590) 23063 | COST £22–£50 |

The entrance is between Bestsellers bookshop and Robert Bruce hairdressers. Dive through to a courtyard and diminutive dining-room with statutory pictures of chickens on the walls. This is a family enterprise, purposely kept small. The owners seem to gather or kill, as well as cook, many of the ingredients. The menu offers a choice of two items in each course, and an option on what length of meal you would like. Most reports this year have been very satisfactory. A few have found persistent error, not least one diner whose fish was overcooked, whose rabbit was without texture, and who found the sauces too similar and too reduced and overpowering. By contrast, many have rejoiced in the fair pricing, the nicely personal attention and the accurate cooking and saucing. Though dishes are not fussy, they often involve several elements – as in 'Fruits of the Forest', a plate of pigeon, venison and rabbit in a port sauce, or the other popular trio, this time of seafood, cooked with olive oil and herbs. London visitors have enjoyed the boldness of flavour, even in venison terrine or ballottine of chicken – two things that often underwhelm. The short menu occasionally gives rise to lack of contrast: hence, one unlucky day when it began with two terrine alternatives, and each had pistachio, and venison was listed as a main dish as well as a first course. This may contribute to the fair charging, as there should be little waste. The desserts, among them a passion-fruit tart with its sorbet, a hazelnut and honey terrine with crème anglaise, and a poached pear with a pear sorbet, again get the votes for elegant and sufficient simplicity allied to proper flavour. Good intentions on the wine front are largely met; range is fair, as are most of the prices barring a few curious exceptions. All seven house wines are offered by the glass and, even better, the halves, although not numerous, provide genuine choice and interest, especially among the whites. House wines are from £8.95.

CHEF: Alexander Aitken  PROPRIETORS: Alexander and Caroline Aitken  OPEN: Wed to Sun, exc Sun D; 12 to 2, 7 to 10  MEALS: Set L £10 (2 courses) to £16, Set Sun L £12.50 (2 courses) to £15, Set D £20 (2 courses) to £30  SERVICE: not inc  CARDS: Access, Visa
DETAILS: 25 seats. 3 tables outside. Private parties: 30 main room. Vegetarian meals with prior notice. Children welcome. No smoking in dining-room. Wheelchair access (also WC). No music. Fax: (0590) 22912

---

**BROMSGROVE Hereford & Worcester**　　　　　　　　　　　　　　　　　　map 5

## ▲ Grafton Manor | NEW ENTRY

Grafton Lane, Bromsgrove B61 7HA
BROMSGROVE (0527) 579007　　　　　　　　　　　　　　　　　　COOKING 1*
1½m S of Bromsgrove, off B4091　　　　　　　　　　　　　　　　COST £26–£51

'The crumbling red sandstone façade seemed to have crumbled a little more,' said one who was taken by the manor's peace, its garden, the church joined to it as if by an umbilical chord, and the strong and atmospheric decoration of the public rooms. The herb garden is a winner and snippets of herbs crop up time and time again on everything. Englishness, not just of a country garden, pervades much of the style – for instance, in the soups, sometimes the best part of the meal – or proudly local materials, although this quality has been overlaid by a modern set of recipes like carpaccio, gravlax or skate grilled with olive oil. Such a tendency does not stop the appearance of country originals such as sea trout terrine with spinach and samphire and a nettle sauce, or lamb sliced quite thinly across the leg, pan-fried after marinating in red wine, then served with quince jelly. Not everything works as it should, particularly from the point of view of taste. But this view is contradicted by one fervent adherent of a dessert of bread-and-butter pudding with cardamom, lime and mango custard, and of a main-course confit of duck with a kumquat and apricot sauce. Though the kitchen is by now long practised, technical error is not always absent. The wine list is priced on the high side, though help is at hand from the New World and a decent range of house wines starting at £8.95.

CHEF: Simon Morris   PROPRIETORS: the Morris family   OPEN: all week, exc Sat L; 12 to
1.30, 7.30 to 9   MEALS: Set L £20.50, Set Sun L £16.95, Set D £19.95 to £28.50   SERVICE:
not inc, card slips closed   CARDS: Access, Amex, Diners, Visa   DETAILS: 50 seats. Private
parties: 45 main room, 12 private room. Car park. Vegetarian meals. Children's helpings
with prior notice. Smart dress preferred. No cigars/pipes in dining-room. Wheelchair access
(1 step). No music   ACCOMMODATION: 9 rooms, all with bath/shower. Rooms for disabled.
B&B £85 to £150. Children welcome. Garden. Fishing. TV. Phone. Doors close at midnight.
Confirm 2 days ahead. Fax: (0527) 575221 (*The Which? Hotel Guide*)

---

**BROXTED** Essex                                                                                   map 3

## ▲ *Whitehall*

Broxted CM6 2BZ
BISHOP'S STORTFORD (0279) 850603                                              COOKING 2
off B1051, 3m SW of Thaxted                                                  COST £29–£56

It looks like an ancient monument, so many beams are there. But everything is
done up in the best possible taste, and no one notices the strange contrast of the
artificial azure of the swimming-pool and the soft tones of knapped flints and
lichen-covered tiles on the church next door. Paul Flavell has continued his
stint at the stoves, imparting welcome steadiness. Though the cooking carefully
stops short of bold robustness, there are some first courses like smoked
haddock with champ and a mustard sauce, sweetbreads with butter beans,
garlic and bacon, or fillet of red mullet with green beans, tomato and sweet
potato, that might well double up as main dishes. People speak highly of the
'menu surprise' ('even with fish and chips served in newspaper'), which is the
kitchen's response to the markets, though these have already been combed
quite widely to support a menu that is long by many standards. Finesse is the
quality most often mentioned, with items such as vension with ginger and a
blackberry sauce, or the hot pastry dishes at the end, or even the ice-creams –
vanilla and tarragon – getting worthy mentions. The wine list is best for
Australia and comes mainly from Corney & Barrow. House wines are a steep
£13.50.

CHEF: Paul Flavell   PROPRIETORS: the Keane family   OPEN: all week, exc Sat L (by
arrangement only); 12.30 to 2, 7.30 to 9.30   CLOSED: 26 to 30 Dec   MEALS: Set L £19.50,
Set D £19.50 to £33.50   SERVICE: not inc, card slips closed   CARDS: Access, Amex, Diners,
Visa   DETAILS: 60 seats. Private parties: 120 main room, 12 and 120 private rooms. Car
park. Vegetarian meals. Children's helpings with prior notice. Smart dress preferred.
No cigars/pipes in dining-room. Wheelchair access (2 steps; also WC). No music
ACCOMMODATION: 25 rooms, all with bath/shower. Rooms for disabled. B&B £75 to £155.
Children welcome. Afternoon teas. Garden. Swimming-pool. Tennis. TV. Phone. Doors
close at midnight. Fax: (0279) 850385 (*The Which? Hotel Guide*)

---

*All letters to the* Guide *are acknowledged with an update on latest sales, closures,
chef changes and so on.*

*All details are as accurate as possible at the time of going to press, but chefs and owners
often change, and it is wise to check by telephone before making a special journey. Many
readers have been disappointed when set-price bargain meals are no longer available.
Ask when booking.*

---

BRUTON Somerset                                                            map 2

## ▲ Claire de Lune  £

2–4 High Street, Bruton BA10 0EQ                                    COOKING 1*
BRUTON (0749) 813395                                                 COST £16–£34

Thomas and Kate Stewart's recession-beating strategy seems to have paid off:
'things are looking up,' observed a reporter. The atmosphere remains
congenial: the place has a 'Normandy feel', noted one visitor, 'shabby but
friendly'. Kate Stewart is a perfect host, and her attributes are 'generally, but
not always, shared by her staff'. The bar has a grill menu; this plus a fixed-
priced menu are offered in the restaurant (you can have just one course if you
wish), and lunches are now served during the week. Luxury ingredients are
generally eschewed for reasons of economy, and the cooking has moved into
less ambitious territory. Among dishes mentioned this year are terrine of
salmon with fleurette sauce, melon with Sauternes sorbet, turbot bonne femme
and pan-fried breast of duck. For one diner the high point was a 'really
powerful hazelnut praline ice-cream in a tulip basket sailing in a sea of warm –
not hot or almost cold – chocolate sauce'. He added that the ice-cream 'should
be sent up to London on the first train every morning for consumption at
Paddington for breakfast'. The wine list provides plenty of instruction for
drinkers: the 'around the world' selection is worth exploring. House wines
are from £7.95.

CHEF: Thomas Stewart   PROPRIETORS: Thomas and Kate Stewart   OPEN: Tue to Sun, exc
Sun D; 12 to 2, 7 to 10   CLOSED: First week Jan, 1 week Aug   MEALS: alc (main courses
£5.50 to £12). Set Sun L £5.95 (1 course) to £9.95, Set D £11.95 (1 course) to £16.95
SERVICE: not inc   CARDS: Access, Visa   DETAILS: 50 seats restaurant, 20 seats bar. 7 tables
outside. Private parties: 50 main room, 30 private room. Vegetarian meals. Children's
helpings Sun L and bar. Smart dress preferred. No cigars in dining-room. Music
ACCOMMODATION: 3 rooms, all with bath/shower. B&B £25 to £35. Deposit: 25% (for
bookings over 1 month ahead). Children welcome. Pets welcome (not in bedrooms). TV

## Truffles

95 The High Street, Bruton BA10 0AR                                COOKING 2
BRUTON (0749) 812255                                                 COST £21–£39

Once home to weavers, this terraced cottage in the heart of Bruton now
provides a cosy, pretty-in-pink setting for Martin Bottrill, who combines his
firmly founded technical skills with delicate invention. Gravlax sprinkled with
fresh coriander and smoked trout and oak-leaf salad came accompanied by
cucumber dressed orientally (soy and sesame), while avocado mousse
contrived to be both 'light and dense', served with avocado slices in a 'creamy,
tangy' Roquefort dressing. Pigeon breast touched down on slices of sautéed
black pudding, the apple and shallot sauce setting off in piquant pursuit; pan-
fried sea bass, meanwhile, found gentler contrasts in a celeriac choucroute, and
a filo basket filled with smoked chicken was 'very satisfactory' with wild rice.
Desserts are no less impressive: 'a wonderful banana terrine', for example,
'dense and creamy, with fine layers of rich dark chocolate', or more mousses –
white, brown and bitter dark chocolate – or Greek yogurt and honey. Service

by Denise Bottrill is 'solicitous but unstuffy', and the wine list pitches France and the New World into creative conflict. Mark-ups are reasonable, and there are plenty of halves. House wine from Duboeuf is £7.95; the more interesting (and oakier) Dom. de l'Aigle Chardonnay is £13.95.

CHEF: Martin Bottrill   PROPRIETORS: Martin and Denise Bottrill   OPEN: Tue to Sat (and bank hol Mon) D, and Sun L (weekday L by arrangement); 12 to 2, 7 to 9   MEALS: Set Sun L £12.95, Set D £19.50   SERVICE: not inc   DETAILS: 20 seats. Private parties: 25 main room. Vegetarian meals. No children under 8. Smart dress preferred. Wheelchair access (1 step). No music

---

**BUCKLAND Gloucestershire**                                             map 2

## ▲ *Buckland Manor* 🍷 ⁵⁄✳

Buckland WR12 7LY
BROADWAY (0386) 852626                                          COOKING 2*
on B4632, 2m SW of Broadway                                   COST £29–£66

'We arrived as the bells were being rung – Monday night is practice night,' reported one couple who were not put off one jot and who enjoyed the immaculate service. As the belfry is right next to this exact rendering of what a Cotswold manor should be, it is hard to escape the chimes when the ringers set about it. But it all adds to the atmosphere. When it comes to cooking, the style becomes rather more refined and international than the Cotswolds were ever used to. A little brochette of fish with basil, olive and tomato, or salad of endive, lambs' leaves and foie gras may be followed by a fricassee of chicken with clams, cream and Gewurztraminer, or duck with blackcurrant, the leg confit with prunes. The presentation and slightly small portions – of vegetables, especially – accord with the manner. Desserts continue the vein, but then everything is cooked with precision and with all the proper skills. The wine list covers pages with endless notes and a worrisome layout, but there are some excellent Italians and New World choices, lots of half-bottles and plenty to choose for under £20, even from the classic regions. House wines are from £8.95. CELLARMAN'S CHOICE: Napa Valley, Duckhorn, Sauvignon Blanc 1989, £19.90; South Africa, Thelema, Cabernet Sauvignon 1988, £18.30.

CHEF: Martyn Pearn   PROPRIETORS: Roy and Daphne Vaughan   OPEN: all week; 12.30 to 2, 7.30 to 9   MEALS: alc (main courses £17 to £20.50). Set Sun L £18.50   SERVICE: not inc, card slips closed   CARDS: Access, Amex, Visa   DETAILS: 38 seats. 6 tables outside. Private parties: 10 main room. Car park. Vegetarian meals. No children under 8. Jacket and tie. No smoking in dining-room. No music   ACCOMMODATION: 10 rooms, all with bath/shower. Rooms for disabled. B&B £135 to £270. No children under 12. Afternoon teas. Garden. Swimming-pool. Tennis. TV. Phone. Fax: (0386) 853557 (*The Which? Hotel Guide*)

---

*An asterisk (\*) after the 1 to 5 cooking mark at the top of an entry signifies that the* Guide *and its readers think that the restaurant is a particularly fine example within its rating.*

⁵⁄✳ *indicates that smoking is either banned altogether or that a dining-room is maintained for non-smokers. The symbol does not apply to restaurants that simply have no-smoking areas.*

---

## BURFORD Oxfordshire                                                    map 2

## ▲ Lamb Inn ⅗

Sheep Street, Burford OX18 4LR                          COOKING 1
WITNEY (0993) 823155                                    COST £15–£46

Since the fifteenth century, this picturesque Cotswold inn has retained a
special place in the life of Burford. It conjures up thoughts of 'ye olde England':
flowers adorn the building and garden, there are stone floors and winter log
fires, and brass and porcelain gleam everywhere. At dinner much elaboration
can be seen in filo baskets filled with scallops, cockles and mussels in ginger
butter, roast quail stuffed with chicken and mushroom mousseline, and
tenderloin of pork on a bed of spinach and basil cream. Generally the kitchen
succeeds in its efforts, although occasional protests about 'over-generous
helpings' of 'tasteless' braised pheasant, and 'heavy' profiteroles suggest that
not all is sweetness and light. Sunday lunch is a favourably reported occasion
that kicks off with Buck's Fizz; on Sunday evenings a buffet is available
between 7.30 and 8.30pm. Staff are reckoned to be 'very nice'. Substantial
helpings of bar food plus Wadworth real ales also attract the customers. The
wine list runs to 70 bins, halves show up well and the selection is keenly
chosen to suit most wallets. House wines are £7.50.

CHEFS: Pascal Clavaud and David Partridge   PROPRIETORS: Richard and Caroline de Wolf
OPEN: restaurant Mon to Sun, D only, and Sun L; 12.30 to 1.45, 7.30 to 9. Bar all week,
L only; 12 to 2   CLOSED: 25 and 26 Dec   MEALS: alc (main courses £8.50 to £16.50).
Set Sun L £15, Set D £18.50. Bar meals L   SERVICE: not inc   CARDS: Access, Visa
DETAILS: 56 seats. Private parties: 20 main room. Car park. Vegetarian meals. Children's
helpings on request. Smart dress preferred. No smoking in dining-room. Wheelchair access
(2 steps). No music   ACCOMMODATION: 13 rooms, all with bath/shower. Rooms for
disabled. B&B £42.50 to £80. Children welcome. Baby facilities. Pets with prior notice.
Garden. TV. Doors close at 11. Confirm by 6. Fax: (0993) 822228 (*The Which? Hotel Guide*)

## BURNHAM MARKET Norfolk                                                  map 6

## Fishes' £

Market Place, Burnham Market PE31 8HE                   COOKING 1*
FAKENHAM (0328) 738588                                  COST £16–£36

'It is on form this year,' writes a regular visitor to this part of the coast where
the location ensures really good fish. The double-fronted premises offer
restaurant, sitting-room (though this may be partly invaded by the restaurant at
the busiest times) and a fish counter for do-it-yourself addicts. It is best out of
season. Summer sees too many people in Burnham Market, and the restaurant
itself may lose some efficiency. 'The cooking is sound and reliable; the menu
varies little, with crab and fish-cakes usually present, recently skate with black
butter was particularly good,' runs one description. A set-price meal at lunch is
fair value; the *carte* does indeed run over familiar ground with crab, oysters,
smoked fish and a changing list of fresh catches, served with salads and
potatoes. Gillian Cape stresses her direct and uncluttered approach to the
business: 'It is not a place for the pompous; do not condemn us for what we are
not trying to do.' The wine list keeps short, with house wines at £6.50.

CHEFS: Gillian Cape, Carole Bird and Paula Ayres   PROPRIETOR: Gillian Cape   OPEN: Tue to Sun, exc Sun D; 12 to 2, 6.45 to 9 (9.30 summer)   CLOSED: Christmas and 3 weeks Jan/Feb   MEALS: alc (main courses £5.50 to £12.50). Set L £8.95 (2 courses) to £12.25 SERVICE: not inc, card slips closed   CARDS: Access, Amex, Diners, Visa   DETAILS: 48 seats. Private parties: 14 main room. Vegetarian meals with prior notice. Children's helpings. No children under 5 after 8.30pm. Smart dress preferred D. Wheelchair access (1 step). No music

---

**BURPHAM** West Sussex                                                              map 3

## *George and Dragon*                                    **NEW ENTRY**

Burpham BN18 9RR
ARUNDEL (0903) 883131                                                     COOKING 1
off A27, 1m E of Arundel, signed Warningcamp                    COST £21–£30

The passing trade is not great. This eighteenth-century inn with restaurant is at the end of a three-mile single-track no-through road. This may be why the first sign that greets you is a request to walkers to remove their boots. The dining-room does not conform to that hirsute image, but nor does the cooking pretend to a false aristocracy. People have spoken of the robust enjoyment of dishes like a substantial soup of Stilton and onion, or king prawns wrapped in a plaice fillet as a first course, and even more of the steak with onion and wine sauce, or lamb with a herb hollandaise. Marianne Walker is herself Swiss, so her tuition on rösti has been absorbed by staff and customers alike. The sweets trolley groans with goodies which are fallen upon by the appreciative audience as if the rest of the meal never existed. Bar food is served all week except for Sunday evening. The simple enough mainstream wine list should suit most people. House wines are £8.95.

CHEFS: Kate Holle, David Futcher and Michael Collis   PROPRIETORS: Marianne and George Walker   OPEN: restaurant Mon to Sat, D only, and Sun L; 12 to 1, 7.30 to 9.30. Bar meals all week, exc Sun D; 12 to 1.45 (2.15 Sun), 6.30 to 9.45   CLOSED: 25 Dec   MEALS: Set Sun L £14.50, Set D £14.50 (2 courses) to £17.50   SERVICE: 10%, card slips closed CARDS: Access, Visa   DETAILS: 40 seats. 6 tables outside (bar food). Private parties: 40 main room. Car park. Vegetarian meals. No children under 8. Smart dress preferred. No cigars in dining-room. Wheelchair access (also WC). No music. Air-conditioned (partly)

---

**BURTON UPON TRENT** Staffordshire                                    map 5

## ▲ *Dovecliff Hall*                                    **NEW ENTRY**

Dovecliff Road, Stretton,
Burton upon Trent DE13 0DJ
BURTON UPON TRENT (0283) 31818                                 COOKING 2
½m off A38, between Stretton and Rolleston          COST £19–£49

The Hines have taken immense care over the last six years in restoring the garden setting of this late-Georgian mansion. It has 'among the loveliest dining-rooms I have seen, neither insistently period nor over-restored, with panelling and mouldings in earth tones, terracotta and moss green,' reflected one reader. It is piquant that the china is Villeroy & Boch, even in the stronghold of the Potteries. Service is not entirely English either, nor the cooking, given one person's main dish of honey-roast duck breast served on a plum and ginger sauce with pancakes (in fact pasta) of leg meat, bean sprouts and hoisin sauce. This adaptation from Peking had 'more masculine, less sweet flavours' than in its usual manifestations, but also less textural contrast; and the vegetables were those you would use to accompany the Sunday roast. In general, the menus here 'feature a selection from the categories that clients demand'. This may lead to easy eating with not too much excitement, but it is a fair recipe for success if it is done well. Thus moules marinière with a cream-laden sauce, a good salad of lobster with light vinaigrette, salmon with samphire and neutral sauce, densely chocolate truffle cake with poached cherries, and decent but unremarkable vanilla ice-cream made up a very satisfactory dinner. A pianist doodles in the hall, the service is attentive, and it makes a very useful spot for the district. The wine list canters round the world. The best section is claret; burgundies rely on Chanson and Jadot; other countries have short sets of decent makers. Prices can be quite high. House wines are from £9.95.

CHEFS: J. Mountney, Mrs H. Hine and I. Johnson  PROPRIETORS: Mr N.O.and Mrs H. Hine  OPEN: all week, exc Sat L and Sun D; 12 to 2, 7 to 9.30  CLOSED: 1 week after Christmas, 2 weeks summer  MEALS: Set L £8.50 (2 courses) to £10.50, Set Sun L £13.95, Set D £17.50 to £29  SERVICE: not inc  CARDS: Access, Visa  DETAILS: 85 seats. 4 tables outside. Private parties: 85 main room, 16 and 50 private rooms. Car park. Vegetarian meals. Children's helpings. Smart dress preferred. Wheelchair access (also WC). No music  ACCOMMODATION: 7 rooms, all with bath/shower. B&B £60 to £100. Children welcome. Garden. TV. Phone. Doors close at midnight. Fax: (0283) 516546

---

**BURY ST EDMUNDS Suffolk**                                              map 3

## Mortimer's  £

30 Churchgate Street,
Bury St Edmunds IP33 IRG                                         COOKING 1
BURY ST EDMUNDS (0284) 760623                                   COST £18–£40

'A meal at Mortimer's continues to put one in good humour. The food, the atmosphere and the company combine to give a result at once civilised and natural,' writes a devoted fan of this long-established fish restaurant. The menu changes daily depending on the catch and the kitchen thrives on old-school simplicity: crab pâté, delicately crisped grilled tiger prawns, Loch Fyne oysters, Dover sole, grey mullet with fennel, skate with black butter and capers. The freshness of the ingredients shines through, although sometimes portions can seem 'gargantuan'. To finish, lemon chiffon was described as a 'subtle, refreshing syllabub', although 'insipid' mango ice-cream was less impressive. The reasonably priced wine list features some reliable names, with whites as the main attraction. House wine is £7.65. The sister restaurant, Mortimer's on the Quay in Ipswich (see entry), operates in similar fashion.

---

Not inc *in the details at the end of an entry indicates that no service charge is made and any tipping is at the discretion of the customer.*

---

CHEF: Kenneth Ambler  PROPRIETORS: Kenneth Ambler and Michael Gooding  OPEN: Mon to Sat, exc Sat L; 12 to 2, 7 to 9 (6.30 to 8.15 Mon)  CLOSED: 24 Dec to 6 Jan, last week Aug, first week Sept  MEALS: alc (main courses £7 to £16)  SERVICE: not inc  CARDS: Access, Amex, Diners, Visa  DETAILS: 60 seats. Private parties: 12 main room. Vegetarian meals. Children's helpings on request. Smart dress preferred. No-smoking area. Wheelchair access (1 step; also WC). No music. Fax: (0284) 752561

---

**CALSTOCK Cornwall**  map 1

## ▲ Danescombe Valley Hotel ♥ ⠜

Lower Kelly, Calstock PL18 9RY
TAVISTOCK (0822) 832414  COOKING 2*
½m W of Calstock on riverside road  COST £31–£39

A loyal customer, returning each year, observes how prices have gradually increased. This partly reflects the labours of improvement and the increase in amenities. None the less, essential character is unchanged: a small yet handsome house perched above the Tamar, with views all round; a husband-and-wife team, 'where the wife is as elusive as the husband effusive'; a fine wine cellar; and good cooking for dinner that comes with no choices on the menu. 'The food is worth the asking price. Our meal began with ricotta cheese pie on a bed of salad with a vinaigrette. This simple-sounding dish looked stunning and had none of the drying effect of ricotta. Next came duck with balsamic vinegar sauce which we found too astringent, but the balance was redressed by the almond sponge, pears poached in marsala and some crème fraîche.' This was a meal of accurate composition (the big collection of local cheeses has been omitted from the list) and refined sensibility. Martin Smith castigates us for not giving sufficient details of his wife's cooking, of playing down the work that goes into something apparently simple. It is like that, and it gets much approval. The wine list needs time to be read, with comments much longer than the factual content. But the bottles are a steal and well chosen. Italy seems a strong point, until you get to the mere half-dozen clarets: a tempting handful.

CHEF: Anna Smith  PROPRIETORS: Martin and Anna Smith  OPEN: Fri to Tue, D only; 7.30  CLOSED: Nov to Mar, exc Christmas  MEALS: Set D £27.50  SERVICE: net prices, card slips closed  CARDS: Access, Amex, Diners, Visa  DETAILS: 12 seats. Private parties: 12 main room. Car park. Vegetarian meals with prior notice. No children under 12. No smoking in dining-room. No music  ACCOMMODATION: 5 rooms, all with bath/shower. D,B&B £97.50 to £175. Deposit: £50. No children under 12. Garden. Doors close at 11.30. Confirm 1 day ahead. Fax: (0822) 832414 (*The Which? Hotel Guide*)

---

*The Guide is totally independent, accepts no free hospitality, and survives on the number of copies sold each year.*

*The text of entries is based on unsolicited reports sent in by readers, backed up by inspections conducted anonymously. The factual details under the text are from questionnaires the Guide sends to all restaurants that feature in the book.*

CAMBRIDGE Cambridgeshire                                                    map 3

## Midsummer House

Midsummer Common,
Cambridge CB1 1HA                                                    COOKING 2*
CAMBRIDGE (0223) 69299                                               COST £32–£65

The upright house between the Common and the Cam – a terror to find, so ask
in advance – has a glorious garden and conservatory, which is the real seat of
the action. People applaud it for atmosphere and elegance. Hans Schweitzer is a
chef who has worked in London and places of international resort, and
Midsummer House does not fall into the mould of country restaurants. This can
be seen from its prices, which locals sometimes find daunting. Moreover, the
repertoire of dishes includes metropolitan habits of mind in starters such as
tea-smoked seafood brochette on an avocado and papaya salsa, and foie gras
with apple and a cassis sauce; followed by aiguillette of beef with garlic mash
and red wine sauce, and chicken armoricaine, ending with pistachio parfait
with marinated strawberries, and hot soufflés of passion-fruit paired with
lemon grass and lime. Bold simplicity is not the style – the beef came with a
bundle of haricots verts and a timbale of carrot. The meat was adjudged tender,
the sauce not overpowering; it was altogether better than the brochette before it
that had dried too much in the cooking. Bolder dishes like carbonnade of
venison and hare have worked, even if the pear that served as adjunct was
redundant. And simpler dishes – a champagne and oyster soup, for instance –
can also be effective: 'It was in fact a grand white wine and mushroom velouté
with some poached oysters.' There is a general sense that the touch is not
always sure in finishing these dishes, though the effort is appreciated. The
service is generally keen and young, though one person found the staff
unhelpful about the whole business of finding the place and parking. There are
wines aplenty, many wine notes and high prices on an enlarged list. Halves are
not ignored. France has the biggest concentration and some good people like
Crochet, Guigal, Clerc and Trapet. The Californian choice is small but good.
House wines are £13.50.

CHEF: Hans Schweitzer   PROPRIETORS: Hans Schweitzer and Chris Kelly   OPEN: Tue to
Sun, exc Sat L and Sun D; 12 to 2, 7 to 10   MEALS: Set L £13.95 (2 courses) to £40, Set D £24
(2 courses) to £40   SERVICE: not inc   CARDS: Access, Amex, Diners, Visa   DETAILS: 120
seats. 12 tables outside. Private parties: 60 main room, 16 private rooms. Vegetarian meals.
Children's helpings. Smart dress preferred. Wheelchair access (also WC). Music. Fax:
(0223) 302672

## Twenty Two ♥

22 Chesterton Road, Cambridge CB4 3AX                               COOKING 2
CAMBRIDGE (0223) 351880                                             COST £27–£38

The new owners of this friendly and unpretentious terraced-house restaurant –
bar-less and pretty-pink as before – are lecturers at the local catering college.
They have resisted the temptation to change the formula – value for money and
a surprising degree of variety within the confines of a set dinner menu – which
continues to please. Chris Gorham, behind the stove, tries still harder than his

predecessor, but success is not yet uniform: sliced pigeon breast came overdressed on a purée of root vegetables, 'wreathed in sweet, winy redcurrant sauce and all under a cloud of deep-fried, finely shredded onion. The composition overwhelmed the pigeon itself as I progressed through layers of increasing sweetness.' Yet wild mushroom salad, a pastry parcel with scrambled egg and herbs, and breast of Barbary duck left one party unable 'to pinpoint a favourite dish as all was so much enjoyed'. Desserts are particularly strong: grapefruit and Pernod mousse 'possessed a brave, grown-up bitter-sweetness', while a rhubarb tart 'in a pretty puddle of red-ribboned custard' deftly avoided soggy-bottom syndrome. Service is friendly and well timed. The wine list is excellent: the selections and the descriptive notes are right on the ball. Prices begin at £7.95, and £9.65 will bring you the vivacious Stratford Zinfandel and the gutsy Dom. de Limbardie; £20 puts almost everything, much of it fine, within reach. CELLARMAN'S CHOICE: Ch. Musar 1986, Gaston Hochar, £14.95; Chardonnay, La Serre, Vin de Pays d'Oc 1991, £9.65.

CHEF: Chris Gorham   PROPRIETORS: David Carter and Louise Crompton   OPEN: Tue to Sat, D only (L by arrangement); 7.15 to 9.45   CLOSED: 25 and 26 Dec   MEALS: Set D £19.50 to £23   SERVICE: not inc   CARDS: Access, Visa   DETAILS: 30 seats. Private parties: 34 main room, 12 private room. Vegetarian meals. No children under 12. Smart dress preferred. Music

---

**CAMPSEA ASH Suffolk**                                                        map 3

## ▲ Old Rectory

Campsea Ash IP13 0PU
WICKHAM MARKET (0728) 746524                                        COOKING 2
on B1078, 1m E of A12                                                COST £25–£31

Stewart Bassett runs the Old Rectory his own way. It is his home, but he takes in paying guests, cooks and looks after their needs. The place has a formal old-style dining-room, all silver and polished wood, although most people eat in the conservatory overlooking the mature gardens. The fixed-price menu runs to four courses with well-kept British cheeses before the desserts. Fish, such as hot terrine of salmon and halibut, normally begins the meal, followed by meat or game – either plainly roasted or given some elaborate touches, as in lightly spiced beef with turmeric rice and pickled quince. The individualistic cooking can triumph magnificently or go awry in the course of a single meal. One impressive dinner included a starter of red snapper and spinach mousse layered together on a pool of excellent butter sauce in which 'all the flavours melded perfectly and a masterpiece resulted'. Similarly a dessert of light sponge sandwiched with whipped cream and napped with a 'divine' chocolate sauce was reckoned to be superb. In between, however, was breast of guinea-fowl with red wine and wild mushrooms that was 'comparatively boring', with little flavour. Wines are generous in range and in price. A plunge into antiquity with three 1945 clarets at under £60 can be well balanced with careful, almost cheap New World selections. Excellent Alsaces and Mosels and beefy Languedocs and Spanish wines cater for all tastes. Half-bottles feature too. House wine is £9. CELLARMAN'S CHOICE: Pinot d'Alsace 1991, Faller, £11.75; Ch. Léoville-Poyferré 1987, £14.50.

CHEF/PROPRIETOR: Stewart Bassett  OPEN: all week, D only; 7.30 to 8.30  CLOSED: Christmas  MEALS: Set D £18.50  SERVICE: not inc  CARDS: Access, Amex, Diners, Visa  DETAILS: 40 seats. Private parties: 30 main room, 18 and 40 private rooms. Car park. Vegetarian meals with prior notice. Children welcome. Smart dress preferred. No smoking during meals. Wheelchair access (also WC). No music  ACCOMMODATION: 7 rooms, all with bath/shower. B&B £30 to £46. Deposit: £10. Children welcome. Garden. Doors close at midnight. Confirm by noon (*The Which? Hotel Guide*)

---

**CANTERBURY Kent**                                                    map 3

## ▲ Sully's

County Hotel, High Street,
Canterbury CT1 2RX                                          COOKING 2
CANTERBURY (0227) 766266                                    COST £20–£45

'Odd to see black-suited clergy in this pink setting: more appropriate in the old wood-panelled dining-room I remember here from the 1950s – when some still wore gaiters,' recalls a reporter who chose this old-school town hotel as the place for a family reunion lunch. Chef Eric Marin-Gavignet does not shy away from foie gras and caviare, and is not afraid of elaboration, especially where the *carte* is concerned: roast sea bass with ink sauce and julienne of chicory, mille-feuille of confit of duck with apple and a salad dressed with balsamic vinegar, and savarin of couscous with ratatouille flavoured with coriander are typical dishes. Fixed-price lunch and dinner menus inhabit less high-flown territory, and dishes such as avocado salad with prawn mousse and yogurt dressing, and chicken suprême with creamed horseradish sauce have been endorsed. 'Delicious' apple strudel, lemon tart and summer pudding have been well-liked sweets. Sunday lunch also receives its share of praise, although the practice of wheeling joints around under silver domes is not to everyone's taste. The wine list is dyed-in-the-wool French and does not come cheap, but a few additional Italians are promised. House wine is currently £8, although a change of supplier was mooted as we went to press.

CHEF: Eric Marin-Gavignet  PROPRIETORS: Laughing Water Hotels Ltd  OPEN: all week; 12.30 to 2.30, 7 to 10  MEALS: alc (main courses £12 to £16). Set L £12 (2 courses) to £14.50, Set D £14.50 (2 courses) to £18.50  SERVICE: not inc  CARDS: Access, Amex, Diners, Visa  DETAILS: 50 seats. Private parties: 18 main room, 30, 100 and 130 private rooms. Car park. Vegetarian meals. Children's helpings. Smart dress preferred. No pipes in dining-room. Wheelchair access (also women's WC). No music. Air-conditioned  ACCOMMODATION: 73 rooms, all with bath/shower. Rooms for disabled. Lift. B&B £74.50 to £110. Deposit: 1 night. Children welcome. Baby facilities. Afternoon teas. TV. Phone. Confirm by 6. Fax: (0227) 451512

---

*All letters to the* Guide *are acknowledged with an update on latest sales, closures, chef changes and so on.*

*The 1995 Guide will be published before Christmas 1994. Reports on meals are most welcome at any time of the year, but are extremely valuable in the spring. Send them to* The Good Food Guide, *FREEPOST, 2 Marylebone Road, London NW1 1YN. No stamp is needed if posted in the UK.*

---

## ▲ *Manor House Inn* ⁵⁺✳ £

Carterway Heads,
Shotley Bridge DH8 9LX
EDMUNDBYERS (0207) 55268　　　　　　　　　COOKING 1
on A68, 3m W of Consett　　　　　　　　　COST £13–£25

Four bedrooms are the latest addition to this ever-popular inn set in the remote reaches of the moors, although its location by the main road ensures that the place is invariably full. Meals can be eaten in the bar or in the cosy restaurant. Jane and Elizabeth Pelly change their menus regularly, work with local produce and plunder the globe for ideas ranging from sausage and mash to bream with lime sauce. Soups such as fennel and almond get the thumbs-up, and other dishes might include herrings with dill and crème fraîche, roast guinea-fowl with wild mushrooms and South African bobotie. Tyne salmon is baked and served with sorrel butter, and North Country cheeses come with home-made apple chutney. Sweets, such as chocolate and hazelnut tart, honey ice-cream and apricot and almond Betty, have been 'mouthwatering'. Most of the plentiful vegetables are grown for the restaurant by two keen local gardeners. Portions are hefty and the value for money is excellent. Butterknowle Bitter and Thatcher's cider are alternatives to the modest, keenly priced wine list. House wines are £7.

CHEFS: Jane and Elizabeth Pelly　PROPRIETORS: Anthony, Jane and Elizabeth Pelly
OPEN: all week; 12 to 2.30, 7 to 9.30 (9 Sun)　CLOSED: 25 Dec　MEALS: alc (main courses £3.50 to £8). Set L and D £15　SERVICE: not inc, card slips closed　CARDS: Access, Visa
DETAILS: 100 seats. 6 tables outside. Private parties: 50 main room. Car park. Vegetarian meals. Children's helpings. No children in public bar. No smoking in 1 dining-room. Wheelchair access (2 steps; also WC). Music　ACCOMMODATION: 4 rooms. B&B £18.50 to £37. Children welcome. Baby facilities. TV. Doors close at 11

## ▲ *Aynsome Manor* ⁵⁺✳

Cartmel LA11 6HH
CARTMEL (053 95) 36653　　　　　　　　　COOKING 1
½m N of Cartmel village　　　　　　　　　COST £17–£33

The Varley family run this sixteenth-century manor house in the peaceful Cartmel Valley. Short breaks are the mainstay of their business and travellers continue to be impressed by the food. Game from Holker Hall estate has been greatly enjoyed: breast of pheasant ('undamaged by any shot pellets') wrapped with locally smoked bacon and served with redcurrant and port sauce was the highlight of one reporter's meal. The five-course, fixed-price dinner menu is dyed-in-the-wool traditional hotel cooking along the lines of mushrooms with ham and pasta, tomato and orange soup, medallions of beef fillet served on a croûton with red wine and shallot sauce, and poached salmon with pink peppercorn and vermouth sauce. Vegetables have been 'absolutely first-class' and the sweets trolley is still loaded with creamy, alcoholic desserts. The well-spread wine list has a better-than-average showing of halves and plenty of creditable drinking for under £15. House wines are £9.

CHEFS: Victor Sharratt and Chris Miller   PROPRIETORS: Tony and Margaret Varley   OPEN: Mon to Sat, D only, and Sun L (Sun D residents only); 12.30 for 1, 7 to 8.30   MEALS: Set L £10.50, Set D £18.50   SERVICE: not inc, card slips closed   CARDS: Access, Amex, Visa   DETAILS: 28 seats. Private parties: 28 main room. Car park. Children's helpings. No children under 5. Smart dress preferred. No smoking in dining-room. No music   ACCOMMODATION: 13 rooms, 12 with bath/shower. B&B £49.50 to £102. Children welcome. Baby facilities. Pets welcome (not in public areas). Afternoon teas. Garden. TV. Phone. Doors close at midnight. Fax: (053 95) 36016 (*The Which? Hotel Guide*)

## ▲ Uplands ⁵⚹

Haggs Lane, Cartmel LA11 6HD
CARTMEL (053 95) 36248
2½m SW of A590, 1m up road
opposite Pig and Whistle

COOKING 3*
COST £19–£37

A house in the country rather than a country house, Uplands enjoys wonderful views to Morecambe Bay from its dining-room (there are field glasses in the lounge for the short-sighted). It also has two acres of garden, a series of rooms (in pink, grey and blue, with pictures to match) that soothe, and a pair of owners – Diana at the front, Tom in the kitchen – who provoke loyalty as well as approbation. Uplands is 'in the Miller Howe manner': John Tovey is a founding partner here, and the Peters worked for him for many years. The manner embraces the short menus that offer no more than three choices, a second course of soup (served with a whole loaf of sweetish brown bread per table), and an emphasis on home invention rather than the grand tradition of Anglo-French cookery. The frequent combination of fruit with savoury ingredients, as in a warm salad of pigeon with pineapple or fillets of sole stuffed with smoked salmon and kiwi fruit, is a hallmark. Surprising vegetables are another leitmotif. A list one day included okra stir-fried with sesame oil, beetroot with lime, cabbage with bacon, potatoes with cream, cheese and garlic, and new season's carrots. Some people find all these flavours intrusive and too varied to make for harmony. Few ever criticise the standard of ingredients or the level of skill deployed, and because everything is done with brio, it all works better than can be imagined. Puddings are enjoyed. The emphasis is on good value, to all our benefit, so the faff and fol-de-rol of fancy dining is kept to a minimum. Value is also a mark of the wine list, which is short, does not go in for anything too outlandish (red burgundies consist of three from Louis Latour), and is best for its New World bottles. House wine is £7.

CHEF: Tom Peter   PROPRIETORS: John Tovey, and Tom and Diana Peter   OPEN: Tue to Sun; 12.30 for 1, 7.30 for 8   CLOSED: 1 Jan to 23 Feb   MEALS: Set L £13.50, Set D £24   SERVICE: not inc, card slips closed   CARDS: Access, Amex, Visa   DETAILS: 28 seats. Private parties: 12 main room. Car park. Vegetarian meals with prior notice. Children's helpings on request. No children under 8. Smart dress preferred. No smoking in dining-room. Wheelchair access (also WC). Music   ACCOMMODATION: 5 rooms, all with bath/shower. D,B&B £65 to £130. No children under 8. Pets welcome. Garden. TV. Doors close at midnight. Confirm by 5 (*The Which? Hotel Guide*)

**CASTLE COMBE** Wiltshire                                    map 2

## ▲ *Manor House Hotel* 🍸❋                    NEW ENTRY

Castle Combe SN14 7HR
CASTLE COMBE (0249) 782206
on B4039, 3m NW of junction with A420                   COOKING 2
                                                        COST £27–£69

This is the workplace of Franco Campioni, one of the few on the waiting side
who has won the coveted designation of Meilleur Ouvrier de Grande Bretagne.
This gives assurance, perhaps, of entirely correct service in a manor house that
has long been a preferred destination for tea on the lawn in summertime, when
the village at its gates is looking its most picturesque. Prices on the *carte* are
evidently high enough to pay for new roofing, but set-priced menus are closer
to reality. The description 'smoked fillet of beef draped in a sauce flavoured
with tomato, rosemary and foie gras' sounds more like an instruction from the
interior decorator, and a decorator's hand is at work in the presentation, as
carefully picked out as the frieze in the dining-room. But reports have it that the
cooking is sounder than this suggests: a summer lunch produced a warm
asparagus mousse with saffron sauce; salad of quail with spiced pears and
walnuts; pigeon breast on a pea purée with glazed shallots; a fish casserole
with water-chestnuts and mussels that was less anaemic than it looked;
followed by a hot caramel soufflé with a caramel ice, and warm pear tart with
white chocolate. In the main, the food is as correct as the service, even if lacking
the brio that might come from less formal surroundings. The wine list ranges
wide, drawing safely on the big names in Burgundy but showing more
excitement in Italy. Clarets show good sense with decent Côtes de Bourg as
well as first growths from respected vintages. Prices, even in the house
selection, start rather high and rise relentlessly. House wines are £14.55.

CHEF: Mark Taylor   PROPRIETORS: Manor House Hotel Ltd   OPEN: all week; 12 to 2, 7 to
10   MEALS: alc (main courses £19.50 to £21.50). Set L £16.95, Set D £32   SERVICE: not inc,
card slips closed   CARDS: Access, Amex, Diners, Visa   DETAILS: 70 seats. 12 tables
outside. Private parties: 10 main room, 10, 12 and 20 private rooms. Car park. Vegetarian
meals. Children's helpings. Smart dress preferred. No smoking in dining-room. Wheelchair
access (3 steps; also WC). No music   ACCOMMODATION: 36 rooms, all with bath/shower.
Rooms for disabled. B&B £105 to £315. Children welcome. Baby facilities. Pets welcome
(£10 per night). Afternoon teas. Garden. Swimming-pool. Tennis. Fishing. TV. Phone.
Doors close at 2am. Confirm by noon. Fax: (0249) 782159 (*The Which? Hotel Guide*)

---

**CASTLE HEDINGHAM** Essex                              map 3

## *Rumbles Castle* 🍸❋                         NEW ENTRY

4 St James Street,
Castle Hedingham CO9 3EJ
HEDINGHAM (0787) 61490, changes to
(0787) 46149 November 1993                              COOKING 1
                                                        COST £16–£36

This is the second of Joy Hadley's restaurants, reflecting upward mobility from
her Cottage in Felsted (see entry) to a Castle. The Castle is no castle, but is
surely ancient, with twisted beams everywhere to be seen. The repertoire
offered here is identical to that at Felsted, and execution every bit as good.

While the Cottage is dinky and domestic, the Castle offers more space and greater comfort. See the entry under Felsted for comments about food and wine.

CHEFS: Joy Hadley, Steven Urry and Laura Thompson   PROPRIETORS: Joy Hadley and Martin Donovan   OPEN: Wed to Sat, D only, and Sun L (also L Dec and other days by arrangement); 12 to 2, 7 to 9   MEALS: alc (main courses £10 to £12.50). Set Sun L £12.50, Set Tue to Thur D £12.50   SERVICE: not inc   CARDS: Access, Visa (2% discount for non-card payments)   DETAILS: 30 seats. Private parties: 30 main room. Vegetarian meals. Children's helpings. No smoking in dining-room. Wheelchair access (1 step; also WC). No music

---

**CHADDESLEY CORBETT  Hereford & Worcester**                                    map 5

## ▲ *Brockencote Hall* ⁑

Chaddesley Corbett DY10 4PY
CHADDESLEY CORBETT (0562) 777876
on A448, Kidderminster to Bromsgrove                           COOKING 1*
road, just outside village                                      COST £21–£50

The impressive classical house, built by a brewer in the early part of this century, has been refurbished and decorated to a pleasing pitch. Views from the dining-room are enhanced by the extensive park and lake, just as the approach from the road convinces the humblest visitor that he is to the manor born. Giving an impression of luxury underlies the attentive service, and the manner of presentation and cooking is in the established tradition of country mansions both here and in France. Not much thrills the questing spirit, but at the same time everything is workmanlike and fulfils most expectations. Prices are also well up to expectation. A dinner that may consist of lobster ravioli and lobster sauce, fillet of beef on braised white cabbage (served with minced beef and foie gras), followed by meringue swans flavoured lightly with rosewater and filled with champagne ice-cream, seems to utilise all the high-cost ingredients known to man, but then may also provide lacklustre vegetables and poor coffee. Lunch is inexpensive by contrast. The experience, as a place for a cosseted visit, is often recommended. The wine list tries to balance the range of highly priced burgundies and clarets with some sensible choices from the Loire and Alsace. Financial consideration also dictates a useful short run of New World bottles. House selections start at £9.90.

CHEF: Eric Bouchet   PROPRIETORS: Alison and Joseph Petitjean   OPEN: all week, ext Sat L; 12.30 to 1.45, 7 to 9.30 (10 Sat)   MEALS: Set L £16.50 to £33.50, Set D £21.50 to £33.50   SERVICE: net prices, card slips closed   CARDS: Access, Amex, Diners, Visa   DETAILS: 50 seats. Private parties: 40 main room, 15 and 20 private rooms. Car park. Vegetarian meals. Children's helpings L. Smart dress preferred. No smoking in dining-room. Wheelchair access (also WC). No music   ACCOMMODATION: 17 rooms, all with bath/shower. Rooms for disabled. Lift. B&B £75 to £115. Children welcome. Baby facilities. Afternoon teas. Garden. Fishing. TV. Phone. Doors close at midnight. Confirm by 6. Fax: (0562) 777872

---

Net prices *in the details at the end of an entry indicates that the prices given on a menu and on a bill are inclusive of VAT and service charge, and that this practice is clearly stated on menu and bill.*

---

## CHADLINGTON Oxfordshire

map 2

## ▲ Manor ▮ ⁵⨯

Chadlington OX7 3LX
CHADLINGTON (0608) 76711, changes to
(0608) 676711 April 1994

COOKING 1
COST £32–£38

'Not a restaurant-with-rooms, more a hotel with fabulous bottles,' observes a reporter about this solid-looking Cotswold-stone 'edifice'. The immediate setting is beautiful: from the rooms (named after birds) you can 'look out on idyllic pastoral scenery and the fattest, cleanest, most attractive sheep – on all sides'. Meals are taken in a high-ceilinged dining-room with an ornate fireplace capped by a large marble pediment. Chris Grant cooks a five-course, fixed-price dinner menu which changes from day to day. Many dishes have pleased: broad bean and hazelnut soup, grapefruit soufflé, venison with crabapple and wine sauce, duck breast in orange and wine sauce, and sticky toffee pudding have been 'outstanding'. Vegetables, including parsnip purée, kale and chopped leeks, have also been highly rated. The food is reckoned to be satisfying and substantial without seeming weighty. Wines are treated with respect, and enthusiasm is reserved only for the classic areas; Spain, Italy and the New World are all eschewed. Within this narrower-than-usual confine, the range is intelligent and very fairly and accurately priced, including many less expensive bourgeois clarets, Beaujolais and Loires, balanced with an extraordinary range of the fine and ancient. Halves are very good. House wine is £8.

CHEF: Chris Grant   PROPRIETORS: David and Chris Grant   OPEN: all week, D only; 7 to 9
MEALS: Set D £25.50   SERVICE: net prices, card slips closed   CARDS: Access, Visa
DETAILS: 20 seats. Private parties: 20 main room, 12 private room. Car park. Vegetarian
meals with prior notice. Children's helpings. No smoking in dining-room. Music
ACCOMMODATION: 7 rooms, all with bath/shower. B&B £60 to £120. Children welcome.
Garden. TV. Phone. Doors close at 11

## CHAGFORD Devon

map 1

## ▲ Gidleigh Park ▮ ⁵⨯

Chagford TQ13 8HH
CHAGFORD (0647) 432367 and 432225
from Chagford Square turn right at
Lloyds Bank into Mill Street, take right
fork after 150 yards, follow lane for 1½m

COOKING 4*
COST £45–£80

The long, half-timbered Edwardian shipping magnate's house clings to a ridge lying between the moor and the valley, before a further plunge to a nascent, tumbling river, littered with giant boulders, which then levels off to the broad acres of pavilioned croquet lawn and woodland beyond. It is a pretty magical place, but has become so by dint of hard labour. Standards are impressive, as they might be at the price, but Gidleigh has the presence of a grand establishment, humanised by the strong personalities of owner Paul Henderson and chef-director Shaun Hill. They are, however, not so strong as to

259

be indispensable: 'I had two meals here, the first good, the second very good. I sent my congratulations to Mr Hill after the second, only to be told that he was not cooking that night.' There is an easy assurance to much of the cooking. A summer lunch that included ragoût of vegetables, which was wonderfully rich, yet lacked the worrying heaviness of meat, also took in perfect scallops with lentil coriander sauce, aromatic with ginger as well as all the other spices; foie gras in a terrine with a strongly stocky jelly, and some apple dressed with clear honey which was so intensely sweet that it acted as seasoning; a bourride of chicken that was more elegant than a provençal affair, yet nearly as enjoyable; a whole steamed John Dory with caviare cream that allied simplicity with the voluptuous; cheeses from Britain that the staff always know about; lemon tart with caramelised bananas – a welcome as well as enjoyable variation; and a chocolate parfait with cherries in a port sabayon glazed under the grill. The last dish was the only one that seemed not to work: too sickly, not enough cherries, temperatures at odds. Petits fours and especially the canapés are tip-top; breads are interesting and properly baked. Breakfasts also engender letters of support: how many places offer haddock fish-cakes with parsley sauce? What needs to be stressed here is that the whole experience is enjoyable: just remember to save up for it. Try a family lunch, as raucous as you want, then adjourn for croquet: everything is supplied, and a pavilion verandah shelters you from sun or rain – all's well with the world. For those with a less relaxed schedule, the lengthy wine list can confidently be forsworn in favour of the well-kept wines by the glass; thus ever-changing wines allow experiment and variety, especially for smaller groups. Elsewhere, random drawings from the wine list bring out Zind-Humbrecht Alsaces, well-aged Vouvray from Foreau, Nelson Late Harvest Riesling, and a not overlong range of clarets. We have noted before that while prices are never low here, it is worth spending a little more since the mark-up policy continues to favour the upper reaches. Allow time for this glorious list. Paul Henderson's comments are astute and succinct.

CHEF: Shaun Hill   PROPRIETORS: Kay and Paul Henderson   OPEN: all week; 12 to 2, 7 to 9 MEALS: Set L £36 to £46. Set D £46 to £51.   SERVICE: net prices, card slips closed CARDS: Access, Amex, Diners, Visa   DETAILS: 35 seats. Private parties: 8 main room, 30 private room. Car park. Vegetarian meals with prior notice. Children's helpings. Smart dress preferred. No smoking in dining-room. Wheelchair access. No music ACCOMMODATION: 14 rooms and cottage, all with bath/shower. D,B&B £170 to £350. Children welcome. Baby facilities. Pets welcome in bedrooms. Afternoon teas. Garden. Tennis. Fishing. TV. Phone. Fax: (0647) 432574

---

**CHARINGWORTH Gloucestershire**                                      map 2

## ▲ *Charingworth Manor* ▼ ✳        | NEW ENTRY |

Charingworth GL55 6NS
PAXFORD (038 678) 555                                      COOKING 2*
on B4035, 2½m E of Chipping Camden                          COST £23–£47

The ancient house, in 50 acres, is of a type: stone, gables, mullions, beams indoors – the works. Beds may be four-poster, there is a series of dining-rooms in pink, lavender grows in abundance, and the swimming-pool – all Hollywood classical – in the Leisure Spa adds a surreal touch. New boy

William Marmion has been showing his paces in the kitchen, producing food recognisably in the country-house tradition with enough variation to give a little edge. A meal of salmon with basil on a hollandaise followed by venison with a pear spiced with cinnamon and a blueberry sauce, finishing with chocolate and orange terrine 'had vim and vigour' one person opined, even if she decried the stodgy texture of the dessert, wished the coffee were stronger, but wrote home about the bread. Service – all silver domes and over-flounce – does not always have quite enough assurance to match the surroundings. Only the top names get on to the wine list; from Italy that means Conterno, Gaja and Villa di Vetrice; in Spain, Imperial Reserva and Pesquera. There is a canny eye foı good value among the clarets, including decent vintages from Ch. Liversan, Lascombes and Fombrauge. Prices can soar, but there are half-bottles and some excellent wines by the glass including, at the time of writing, Krug, a Montagny from Leflaive, and Châteauneuf Bosquet des Papes. What is absent is a solid foundation of decent, modestly priced wines. House wines are from £11. CELLARMAN'S CHOICE: Pinot Grigio, 'Collio' 1991 Puiatti, £19.50; Médoc, Ch. La Tour Saint-Bonnet 1986, £21.75.

CHEF: William Marmion PROPRIETORS: Blandy Brothers and Co Ltd OPEN: all week; 12.30 to 2, 7 to 9 (9.30 Fri and Sat) MEALS: Set L £15.50, Set D £29.50 SERVICE: not inc, card slips closed CARDS: Access, Amex, Diners, Visa DETAILS: 48 seats. Private parties: 48 main room, 14 and 36 private rooms. Car park. Vegetarian meals. Children's helpings. Smart dress preferred. No smoking in dining-room. No music ACCOMMODATION: 24 rooms, all with bath/shower. B&B £85 to £180. Deposit: £50. Children welcome. Baby facilities. Pets welcome (not in public rooms). Afternoon teas. Garden. Swimming-pool. Sauna. Tennis. Snooker. TV. Phone. Doors close at 11. Confirm by 11am. Fax: (038 678) 353 (*The Which? Hotel Guide*)

**CHEDINGTON Dorset** map 2

## ▲ *Chedington Court* 🍷

Chedington DT8 3HY
CORSCOMBE (0935) 891265 COOKING 2
off A356, 4½m SE of Crewkerne COST £31–£39

The Court is an early-Victorian edifice built of honey-coloured ham stone with mullion and transom windows, haunch and plain gables with ball-and-spear finials. There are stunning views from every main room in the place. The dining-room is in keeping with the old-fashioned country elegance of the rest of the hotel: gold-coloured, satiny wallpaper, paintings all around and a flower-filled conservatory tacked on. Dinner is a four-course fixed-price menu (plus cheese and coffee); it shows modern touches (warm salad of sauté pigeon breast, grilled venison with pink peppercorn sauce), as well as a fondness for more stoically traditional ideas (duck liver parfait with Cumberland sauce, kidneys in mustard sauce, roast loin of pork with apple and sage sauce). Starters and mains are split by an intermediate course that might range from watercress soup or baked escalope of salmon with saffron sauce to carefully made courgette charlotte with tomato and basil sauce. Conventional sweets such as raspberry fool and profiteroles are from a trolley, ditto the cheeses. The cooking is generally sound although it can lack vigour and is unlikely to challenge the palate. The range of the wine list is remarkable in both its geographical and economic spread. Half-bottles are very fine. A rigorous editorial eye is required to tidy the copy and trim the bin numbers. House wine is from £7.50. CELLARMAN'S CHOICE: Mercurey Blanc, Ch. de Chamirey 1990, £19.50; Brouilly, Ch. des Tours 1991, £14.50.

CHEFS: Hilary Chapman and Christopher Ansell Green   PROPRIETORS: Philip and Hilary Chapman   OPEN: all week, D only; 7 to 9   CLOSED: 3 Jan to 3 Feb   MEALS: Set D £27.50 SERVICE: net prices, card slips closed   CARDS: Access, Amex, Visa   DETAILS: 26 seats. Private parties: 8 main room, 22 private room. Car park. Vegetarian meals. No children under 10. Smart dress preferred. No cigars/pipes in dining-room. Wheelchair access (2 steps; also WC). Music   ACCOMMODATION: 10 rooms, all with bath/ shower. B&B £53.50 to £117. Deposit: £30. Children welcome. Baby facilities. Pets welcome (not in public rooms). Afternoon teas. Garden. Golf. Snooker. TV. Phone. Doors close at midnight. Confirm by 6. Fax: (0935) 891442 (*The Which? Hotel Guide*)

---

**CHELTENHAM Gloucestershire**                                                    map 2

## Bonnets Bistro ⊰✕                                         | NEW ENTRY |

12 Suffolk Road, Cheltenham GL50 2AQ
CHELTENHAM (0242) 260666                                                  COOKING 1*
on A40, S of town centre at junction with Bath Road          COST £23–£37

The place was originally called Bonnets Bistro at Staithes. Staithes is a Yorkshire fishing village where traditional bonnets (hence exhibit A, draped over a wall-lamp) are still worn; posters and photographs underline the theme. But the view (through swathed, pelmeted and sashed windows) of elegant Regency houses and stately town trees, as well as the restaurant's ceiling rosettes and friezes, are all distinctively Cheltenham; smoke-free air from start to finish is gratifyingly futuristic. Part-owner Paul Lucas is responsible for the cooking, but his enthusiasm for customer relations sometimes sees him more out front than out back. The food is 'modern, colourful bistro, a bit on the wild side, and rather heavy on the cholesterol'. The Cornish mussels were good, though the sauce owed more to the onion family than to marine essences; ragoût of lamb was contemporary, pink, vegetable-flecked – the product not of oven hours but of lightning assembly, with a sauce in which tomato purée held sway; vegetables were 'over-soft, going on for wettish'; ravioli parcels of apples and raisins came sugar-dusted and served with a good, thin custard. Clear, intense flavour contrasts are the aim of the seasonally changing menu: for example, summer brings a caramelised bacon salad roused by sherry vinegar, Scottish salmon startled by grapefruit butter sauce, and a 'dessert' of Camembert baked in pastry with port and redcurrant sauce. The 21 wines are not cheap, but include some good bottles (like Villa Maria's Sauvignon Blanc, at £15.95). House wine is £9.95.

CHEF: P.R. Lucas   PROPRIETORS: R.E. Lucas and P.R. Lucas   OPEN: Mon to Sat, exc Sat L; 12 to 1.30, 7.30 to 10   CLOSED: 26 to 31 Dec, 2 weeks June, bank hols   MEALS: alc (main courses £7 to £12)   SERVICE: not inc, card slips closed   CARDS: Access, Amex, Diners, Visa   DETAILS: 30 seats. Private parties: 24 main room, 10 private room. Vegetarian meals with prior notice. Children's helpings with prior notice. No children under 8. Smart dress preferred. No smoking in dining-room. Wheelchair access. Music

## Le Champignon Sauvage  ♥

24–26 Suffolk Road,
Cheltenham GL50 2AQ
CHELTENHAM (0242) 573449

COOKING 3
COST £27–£49

A reader extolled the prints hanging on the walls of this 'decorously set', simply decorated dining-room, which give variety to the theme of fungi in all their glory. The Everitt-Matthiases have stayed loyal to the idea that a restaurant should be French, producing fancy food, even as the rest of us move towards some concession to Englishness (menus, cheeses, etc.) and to a more rumbustious style of cooking. Here, 'colombine de saumon, purée de petits pois, son garniture printannière' manages one grammatical and one spelling mistake, but convinces the customers that the place means business. The rillettes 'might have even been made by the de rigueur two forks,' wrote one impressed by the industry and by the flavour of a lunch that started with those rillettes, accompanied by lightly pickled vegetables, salmon with a vivid beetroot sauce, chicken with roast leeks and a crisp potato crust, a warm and bitter chocolate tart, and a fine tray of French cheeses. Fault was not in the presentation or the trimmings, but in the lack of salt. Service depends on Helen Everitt-Matthias, who knows her onions (and her cheeses), and will advise you happily about the excellent wines. These suffer from an old-fashioned mark-up regime, which happily puts modest wines at approachable prices but thereafter, less happily, puts too many wines into unreasonably high brackets. Nevertheless, the wine list is much enjoyed, the pleasure derived both from the geographic range and the consistent quality. A few more halves, clarets, Alsaces and white burgundies would be welcome. House wine is £8.50.
CELLARMAN'S CHOICE: Hawkes Bay, Aotea, Sauvignon Blanc 1990, £12.50; Chinon, Dom. de Briançon 1986, £10.95.

CHEF: David Everitt-Matthias  PROPRIETORS: David and Helen Everitt-Matthias  OPEN: Mon to Sat, exc Sat L; 12.30 to 1.30, 7.30 to 9.30  MEALS: Set L £17.50, Set D £27 to £30  SERVICE: not inc  CARDS: Access, Amex, Visa  DETAILS: 30 seats. Private parties: 30 main room. Vegetarian meals with prior notice. Children welcome. Smart dress preferred. Wheelchair access (1 step; also WC). Music. Air-conditioned

## Epicurean

On the Park, Evesham Road,
Cheltenham GL52 2AH
CHELTENHAM (0242) 222466

COOKING 3*
COST £22–£66

'Elegant' seems a fair description for this spacious, gracious cool grey and yellow collection of rooms (the sitting areas are perhaps small, proclaimed an inveterate mover-around) that occupies the ground floor of a Regency villa, now a hotel. Patrick McDonald's determination is impressive, and so too, wrote one admirer, is his consistency. Old hands will still be greeted by his tip-top appetiser of black pudding, apple and potato purée, but constant affection does not mean a stick-in-the-mud approach across the whole menu. Some people castigate him for being expensive, but he is generous with fine materials, and lunch can be a positive bargain, reconciling many to higher bills incurred in the evening. A dinner in the spring involved parsley soup filled with scallops and oysters, a carpaccio of beef with shredded white radish dressed with truffle oil, a dish of scallops and squid and asparagus with a risotto and some ratatouille which had the diner wishing for more protein to balance the starch, and a superb lemon tart to finish. Depth of flavours is recognised, for instance, in a plainish confit of duck with potato purée and a red wine sauce. This gets dressed up with foie gras on the dinner menu. Elegance of presentation combines with a light touch where necessary, for example, in a carpaccio of salmon with more truffle oil. The repertoire is quite large, taking in shank of lamb for neo-peasants, pig's trotter, not stuffed with sweetbreads and a mousseline as in so many places, but done over with minced cheek and served after a slow braise with deep-fried sage, truffle jus and confit of onions for the gourmand, and lobster ravioli with Jerusalem artichoke for the delicately constituted. Service is correct but slow, so is the kitchen. The wine list is wide enough, dear enough, but includes 59 bottles under £20, claims Mr McDonald. House wines from Parisot or Doudet-Naudin start at £9.75.

CHEF: Patrick McDonald   PROPRIETORS: Patrick and Claire McDonald   OPEN: Tue to Sun, exc Sun D; 12.30 to 2.30, 7.30 to 10   CLOSED: 2 weeks Jan   MEALS: Set L £12.50 (2 courses) to £35, Set D £22.50 to £45 (gourmet menu – whole table only)   SERVICE: not inc, card slips closed   CARDS: Access, Amex, Diners, Visa   DETAILS: 32 seats. Private parties: 32 main room, 20 private room. Car park. Children's helpings on request. Wheelchair access (1 step; also WC). No music. Fax: (0242) 511526

## Mayflower £

32–34 Clarence Street,
Cheltenham GL50 3NX                                            COOKING 1
CHELTENHAM (0242) 522426 and 511580                            COST £12–£48

Gold lamps hang over the windows of this town-centre Chinese restaurant. The interior is spacious and airy, with bold colour schemes and lotus-flower pictures on the walls. Service is polite and attentive. The menu charts its way through an assortment of familiar Pekinese and Szechuan specialities, with some Cantonese dishes for good measure. Reporters have endorsed many items: crispy spring rolls, garlic and chilli broccoli, fragrant spiced fish slices, sizzling king prawns with garlic and fillet steak mandarin, Szechuan seafood hotpot, and celery with black bean and chilli, while minced beef with bean curd and chilli made one visitor from Hong Kong feel very much at home. Vegetarians have plenty of choice. Prices are 'certainly not cheap', but the quality is high. This is a Chinese restaurant with an interest in wine: the owners hold regular tastings and the list of around 120 bins is impressive of its kind. House wine is £7.95.

CHEFS: Mr C.F. Kong and Mrs M.M. Kong   PROPRIETORS: the Kong family   OPEN: all week, exc Sun L; 12 to 1.45, 5.45 to 10.45 (11.15 Fri and Sat)   CLOSED: 25 and 26 Dec   MEALS: alc (main courses £5 to £9.50). Set L Mon to Sat £6.50, Set D £14.50 to £27.50   SERVICE: not inc   CARDS: Access, Amex, Diners, Visa   DETAILS: 80 seats. Private parties: 80 main room, 50 private room. Vegetarian meals. Children welcome. Wheelchair access (1 step). Music. Air-conditioned. Fax: (0242) 251667

# Abbey Green and
# Garden House ♀ ⅙✳

1 Rufus Court, Northgate Street,
Chester CH1 2JH                                        COOKING 2
CHESTER (0244) 313251 and 320004                       COST £15–£37

Rufus Court is a small shopping development modelled on the Rows of
Chester. Intending visitors to the Abbey Green (vegetarian) or the Garden
House (meat, fish and vegetarian) restaurants may therefore have to negotiate
some stairs to gain entry at first-floor gallery level. Once through those doors,
vegetarians stay downstairs, carnivores go up – two restaurants, two kitchens,
no contamination. Should the dining-rooms combine – as they do on quiet
nights when the world may be concentrated upstairs – the kitchens still stay
apart. Since the move into these handsome Georgian premises (new
development, old buildings), Abbey Green has re-invented itself: its milieu
and cooking 'stop vegetarians feeling like pulse-eating do-gooders who dislike
good food' was one response. This diner went on to eat aubergine and basil
daube on flageolet beans, which showed that pulses can be good for you and
taste decent too. He had begun with lightly spiced parsnip soup, the common
response to which is that it is too lightly spiced, but the poppadum that comes
with it is appreciated. There are plenty of other dishes where the spicing or
seasoning are spot-on: for example, duck with Egyptian sauce of yellow split
peas and shallots. Other meat/fish dishes from the upstairs menu that have
given pleasure include ravioli of crab and prawn with coriander, lime and
ginger butter, and a pancake filled with marinade of beef in a ginger beer sauce
– both dishes signal a love of ginger and originality. The vegetarian food
manages not to be too heavy. One person's view was that puddings let the
place down. Whereas savoury stodge had been cleverly avoided, it was
encountered head-on come sweet. And coffee, too, would have been better if
stronger. All round, however, this is a place to encourage, and Chester needs
that. The wine list, though moving through rapid change, is excellent and not
overpriced. Duncan Lochhead tastes widely and well, giving useful notes and
seeking out good growers from all around. Firestone and Konocti in the USA,
Mountadam from Australia, Marqués de Murrieta from Rioja: all these give
confidence. House wines are £8.50.

CHEFS: Roger Hyde and Simon Shaw   PROPRIETOR: Duncan Lochhead   OPEN: Mon to Sat;
12.30 to 2.30, 6.30 to 10   MEALS: alc L (main courses £4.50 to £7.50). Set D £18.50 to
£19.50   SERVICE: not inc, card slips closed   CARDS: Access, Visa   DETAILS: Abbey Green
55 seats, Garden House 55 seats. 7 tables outside. Private parties: 55 main room, 55 private
room. Vegetarian meals. Healthy eating options L. Children's helpings on request. Smart
dress preferred. No smoking in dining-room. Music. Fax: (0244) 327604

---

*Prices quoted in the* Guide *are based on information supplied by restaurateurs. The prices
quoted at the top of each entry represent a range, from the lowest meal price to the highest;
the latter is inflated by 20 per cent to take account of likely price rises during the year of
the* Guide.

---

# ▲ *Chester Grosvenor Hotel, Arkle* ♟

| | |
|---|---|
| Eastgate Street, Chester CH1 1LT | COOKING **4** |
| CHESTER (0244) 324024 | COST £30–£73 |

This, the high-flying restaurant of the town's swishest hotel, is, as might be expected, decorated by a portrait of the beast – Arkle, that is. It gallops away with the prices, but the weary can rest their feet in the library lounge, which acts as ante-room to the restaurant itself. Although this sort of cooking and this sort of restaurant have lost favour in times of recession, the chefs here have not deviated from the task of modern haute cuisine. Truffles are as common as mushrooms in this kitchen's store-cupboard. The menu has an edge to it that gives life to many dishes: ragoût of lobster with a creamed soup of spinach and nutmeg, scallops with chicory and lemon, oysters served with a 'brandade' of fennel and a little caviare. A plate of offal – sweetbreads, trotter, foie gras and tongue – is still produced, with a sauce that complements yet refreshes, and fish cookery includes sea bass with a rich lobster sauce, studded with lobster meat, broad beans (skinned) and spinach. Vegetables are given their right priority – different and apt for each dish. The success continues through cheese to desserts like a hot apricot soufflé with a ginger ice-cream, or a tarte Tatin with a crème brûlée. Complexity is not a problem here. A combination of scallops and foie gras, with truffle, garlic, onions, Sauternes and a rich meat reduction, sounds impossible, but it can work: 'We asked for spoons to finish the sauce.' Lunch is cheaper and more like the product of a fancy British hotel dining-room. The hotel also has a brasserie which has been through some chequered times, although reports are more satisfactory this year. The wine list is giant and the staff are able to discuss it. Long runs of single châteaux are complemented by intelligent choices from less pricey regions: the Loire, Spain and Italy, for example. Not everything is over £20 and there is a decent set of halves. House wines are £9.95. CELLARMAN'S CHOICE: Te Kauwhata, Rongopai, Sauvignon 1989, £21.50; Savigny-Lès-Beaune 1988, Jacob, £22.50.

CHEFS: Paul Reed and Simon Radley   PROPRIETORS: Grosvenor Estate Holdings   OPEN: Mon to Sat, exc Mon L; 12 to 2.30, 7.30 to 10.30   CLOSED: bank hols   MEALS: alc (main courses £17 to £25). Set L £18 (2 courses) to £22.50, Set D £37.50   SERVICE: not inc CARDS: Access, Amex, Diners, Visa   DETAILS: 45 seats. Vegetarian meals. Children's helpings. Jacket and tie. No cigars/pipes in dining-room. Wheelchair access (also WC). Music. Air-conditioned   ACCOMMODATION: 86 rooms, all with bath/shower. Rooms for disabled. Lift. B&B £124 to £209. Deposit: 1 night. Children welcome. Baby facilities. Afternoon teas. Sauna. Air-conditioned. TV. Phone. Confirm by noon. Fax: (0244) 313246

---

| CHICHESTER  West Sussex | map 3 |
|---|---|

# *Droveway* 🍴

| | |
|---|---|
| 30A Southgate, Chichester PO19 1DR | COOKING **1** |
| CHICHESTER (0243) 528832 | COST £22–£39 |

This place used to be called Thompsons, but owners Elly and Jonas Tester decided to change the name and make several other alterations: regulars reckon that these have been for the better. The original barn-like interior on the first floor now has the added attraction of a comfortable reception lounge which has 'softened' the mood of the place. Menus vary regularly, more specials (particularly fish) are on offer and a weekly vegetarian menu is also available. Sunday lunch shows that Jonas Tester is quite at home with traditional soups, roasts and fresh vegetables, while more ambitious dinner menus provide plenty of scope for flexing culinary muscles. Terrine of lamb with sun-dried tomatoes, leek and asparagus charlotte, calf's liver with shredded celeriac and balsamic vinegar sauce, and herb-crusted noisettes of pork with apricot sauce are typical dishes. Sweets are reckoned to be the stars of the show: chocolate quenelles with Grand Marnier sauce and summer fruit vacherin have been drooled over. Wine evenings are a feature and the wine list is peppered with reliable names at affordable prices. House wine is £8.50.

CHEF: Jonas Tester  PROPRIETORS: Elly and Jonas Tester  OPEN: Tue to Sun, exc Sun D; 12.30 to 2, 7 to 10 (post-theatre by arrangement)  CLOSED: first 2 weeks Jan  MEALS: alc (main courses £9.50 to £14). Set L £10.50 (2 courses) to £14.50, Set Sun L £15  SERVICE: not inc, card slips closed  CARDS: Access, Amex, Visa  DETAILS: 40 seats. Private parties: 30 main room. Vegetarian meals. Children's helpings. Smart dress preferred. No smoking in 1 dining-room. Music

## Little London 🍴 £ | NEW ENTRY

38–39 Little London, Chichester  
CHICHESTER (0243) 537550

COOKING 1  
COST £19–£45

It proclaims itself 'Mediterranean', with a full licence to offer lamb with aubergines and courgettes and a garlic sauce or, more unexpectedly, rabbit Spanish-style with pears and turnips on a large menu that runs in tandem with a short table d'hôte as Mediterranean as moules à la crème. Some reports have not been enthusiastic, but in the main, production of dishes like warm salad of seafood and bacon with a tarragon mayonnaise, seafood pancakes, salmon with lime, and beef with shallots and red wine have been approved, as have cheerful service and the general utility of the place in a town strangely bereft of decent restaurants. The wine list is another little bit of France (mainly) and house wines are £7.95.

CHEF: Ashley Abady  PROPRIETORS: Philip Cotterill and Thierry Boishu  OPEN: Mon to Sat; 12 to 2.30, 6 to 11  MEALS: alc (main courses £8.50 to £19). Set L and D £9.50 (2 courses) to £12.50. Light L and supper menu  SERVICE: not inc  CARDS: Access, Amex, Diners, Visa  DETAILS: 85 seats. 3 tables outside. Private parties: 40 main room, 16 private room. Vegetarian meals. Children's helpings. Smart dress preferred. No smoking in 1 dining-room. Wheelchair access (1 step). Music

£ *indicates that it is possible to have a three-course meal, including coffee, a half-bottle of house wine and service, at any time the restaurant is open (i.e. at dinner as well as at lunch, unless a place is open only for dinner), for £20 or less per person.*

*All details are as accurate as possible at the time of going to press, but chefs and owners often change, and it is wise to check by telephone before making a special journey. Many readers have been disappointed when set-price bargain meals are no longer available. Ask when booking.*

CHILGROVE  West Sussex                                                          map 3

## White Horse Inn 🍾

Chilgrove PO18 9HX
EAST MARDEN (024 359) 219                                            COOKING 1*
on B2141, between Chichester and Petersfield                    COST £26–£40

'The village green in front – unspoilt as yet – makes this a great family
meeting-place at weekends and ideal for helicopters during the week,'
comment the owners of this prestigious eighteenth-century inn. A bonus is the
glorious setting in the lee of the South Downs, although the place is rightly
renowned for its magisterial wine list. Reporters also continue to sing the
kitchen's praises. Neil Rusbridger can cook traditional stalwarts such as oxtail,
braised beef with vegetables, and syllabub, as well as embarking on more
ambitious up-to-the-minute ideas (tartare of salmon with tapénade, breast of
woodpigeon with celeriac purée, champagne risotto with woodland
mushrooms). Daily fish specialities and desserts are recited verbally. Cheaper
light dishes, lunches and fixed-price suppers are served in the bar.
Notwithstanding our normal disparagement of wine lists that need an evening
to be read, Barry Phillips' now commands legendary status; it is very good,
packed with ancient clarets dating back to 1919, and makes a more than
respectable stab well beyond the classics. The less knowledgeable are helped
with decent house wines by the glass. House wines are from £9.50.

CHEF: Neil Rusbridger  PROPRIETORS: Dorothea and Barry Phillips, and Neil Rusbridger
OPEN: Tue to Sun, exc Sun D; 12 to 2, bar 6 to 10, restaurant 7 to 9.30 (10.30 during
Chichester theatre season by reservation)  CLOSED: last week Oct, 3 weeks Feb  MEALS:
alc (main courses £9.50 to £11.50). Set L £17.50, Set D £23  SERVICE: 10%, card slips
closed  CARDS: Access, Diners, Visa  DETAILS: 75 seats. 4 tables outside. Private parties:
35 main room, 10 to 35 in private rooms. Car park. Vegetarian meals. No children under 14.
No cigars/pipes in dining-room. Wheelchair access. No music. Air-conditioned. Fax:
(024 359) 301

CHINNOR  Oxfordshire                                                            map 2

## Sir Charles Napier Inn 🍾

Sprigg's Alley, nr Chinnor OX9 4BX
HIGH WYCOMBE (0494) 483011
off B4009, take Bledlow Ridge                                        COOKING 2
turn from Chinnor, 2m up hill                                        COST £25–£43

The road climbs out of Chinnor past some apparently post-holocaust quarry
workings, wanders through Chiltern beech woods, and arrives at a plateau that
lets the spirit breathe. At the end of the narrow lane is this unassuming-
looking pub that the Griffiths family have converted into their own version of a
pub-restaurant. Enjoy the al fresco dining on a good day, the various bits of art
for sale, the champagne on tap (the only one in Britain) and the relaxed
atmosphere of a long-running business which no one would call regimented.
The style must be idiosyncratic, because half the world finds it irritating while
the other half adores it. The prices tend to be high, the cooking can be
inconsistent and the service casual (some even claim offhand) to a fault. When

it works, the form is simple and true: tartare of salmon with cucumber and a dill cream dressing; scallops with a pile of wilted rocket and a very good oil and vinegar dressing; plain boiled lobster with chive butter; lambs' kidneys and black pudding with a grain mustard sauce; and little chocolate pots that were better than the bread-and-butter pudding. Vegetables may not be a strong point. A set-price two-course lunch menu provides a cheaper alternative. The diner may find his or her meals influenced by the weather and the mood. But the delightful wine list from some of the best merchants should help. Antipodeans feature as strongly as fine French, and a few recently added Italians complement strong Rhônes and Riojas. Half-bottles are magnificent, but bargain hunters should turn straight to the bin-end list. A page of digestifs should not be ignored. Prices remain firm at the upper reaches, but with so much else on offer this is hardly a problem. House wine is £9.75.

CHEF: Batiste Tolu   PROPRIETORS: the Griffiths family   OPEN: Tue to Sun, exc Sun D (also bank hol Mons); 12.30 to 2.30 (3.30 Sun), 7.30 to 10   MEALS: alc (main courses £8.50 to £12.50). Set L and Tue to Fri D £13 (2 courses)   SERVICE: 10% Set L, 12.5% D, card slips closed   CARDS: Access, Amex, Diners, Visa   DETAILS: 80 seats. 10 tables outside. Private parties: 50 main room, 30 and 50 private rooms. Car park. Vegetarian meals. Children's helpings L. No children under 7 D. Smart dress preferred. No cigars/pipes in dining-room. Wheelchair access. Music. Fax: (0494) 484929

---

**CHISELDON** Wiltshire                                                                map 2

# ▲ *Chiseldon House Hotel, Orangery*                    NEW ENTRY

New Road, Chiseldon SN4 0NE
SWINDON (0793) 741010                                                    COOKING 1
on B4005, ½m W of A345, 4m SE of Swindon                       COST £23–£40

You eat in the so-called orangery of this Regency house, identified by large murals of orange trees in a colour scheme of pinks and greens, and probably accompanied by a significant section of Swindon's business community. Christopher Fisher maintains a fair standard at stable prices: 'The evening price has not changed for two years, despite the chef's tendencies towards morels, foie gras and truffles,' writes the manager with feeling. The range is enlivened by the use of spices such as grated ginger with a warm salad of chicken, five-spice powder with sea bass, or spiced chickpeas in a salad of bacon, although this had the diner diving through inches of greenery to locate the meat. This last might have been an inauspicious start, but the rest of the meal that included venison with wild mushrooms, John Dory with tomato, a duo of iced lemon parfait and hot lemon tart, and some well-kept British cheeses was enjoyed. Home cooking gets supported here: bread, pasta and even sun-dried tomatoes are done in-house. The wine list takes a small sip from each producing country, the Italians perhaps coming off best. Half-bottles are scanty. House wines are £10.50.

---

*If a restaurant is new to the* Guide *this year (did not appear as a main entry in the last edition)* NEW ENTRY *appears opposite its name.*

---

CHEF: Christopher Paul Fisher  PROPRIETOR: S. Ehrnlund  OPEN: all week; 12 to 2, 7 to 9.30  MEALS: alc light L (main courses £5 to £10). Set Sun L £9.95, Set L £11.95 (2 courses) to £14.95, Set D £17.95 (2 courses) to £24.95  SERVICE: not inc, card slips closed CARDS: Access, Amex, Diners, Visa  DETAILS: 70 seats. 4 tables outside. Private parties: 70 main room, 18 and 18 private rooms. Car park. Vegetarian meals. Children's helpings. Smart dress preferred. No-smoking area. Wheelchair access (also WC). Music ACCOMMODATION: 21 rooms, all with bath/shower. B&B £55 to £110. Afternoon teas. Garden. Swimming-pool. TV. Phone. Confirm by 8. Fax: (0793) 741059

---

**CHOBHAM Surrey**　　　　　　　　　　　　　　　　　　　　　　　map 3

## Quails

1 Bagshot Road, Chobham GU24 8BP　　　　　　　　　　　COOKING 1*
CHOBHAM (0276) 858491　　　　　　　　　　　　　　　　COST £19–£40

This edge-of-town restaurant is useful for a shopping trip as well as an evening out, so the Wales try to hit the lunch-time market with a weekday, fixed-price French regional brasserie menu that is kinder on the pocket than the full *carte*. On one visit the theme was Provence, with salade niçoise, ratatouille tarts, a provençal braised beef dish, and red mullet with capers and olives. The place is a converted shop and has a central bar that splits the dining areas; some say it has more of an evening than daytime feel, but this does not detract from the thoroughly competent cooking. Saddle of lamb wrapped in filo with a pesto filling and a basil-scented gravy, or guinea-fowl with capers and green lentils wrapped in smoked bacon may indicate that Christopher Wale has taken modern lessons – he even serves salmon with tapénade – so that the menu is not the usual Surrey canter through post-nouvelle cuisine. Occasional slips of details (stale bread, a pigeon salad with no dressing, cold cheese) only point up the satisfactory whole. The wine list could show some neighbours the way, with intriguing choices available from the New World and French classics, particularly the Rhône. New-wave makers are given their due and prices are kept in check. There is an encouraging first page of French country wines from £8.95: Savoie, Buzet and Cahors are three to start with.

CHEF: Christopher Wale  PROPRIETORS: the Wale family  OPEN: Tue to Sun, exc Sat L and Sun D; 12 to 2, 7 to 10  MEALS: alc (main courses £7.50 to £12). Set Sun L £12.95, Set Mon to Fri L and D £15.95 (inc wine)  SERVICE: not inc  CARDS: Access, Amex, Diners, Visa DETAILS: 46 seats. Private parties: 46 main room. Car park. Vegetarian meals. Children welcome. Wheelchair access (also WC). Music. Air-conditioned

---

**CHRISTCHURCH Dorset**　　　　　　　　　　　　　　　　　　map 2

## Splinters
　　　　　　　　　　　　　　　　　　　　　　　　　　| NEW ENTRY |

12 Church Street, Christchurch BH23 1BW　　　　　　　　COOKING 1
CHRISTCHURCH (0202) 483454　　　　　　　　　　　　　COST £28–£43

This place is in the centre of Christchurch, at the entrance to the pedestrian centre that leads to Christchurch priory; parking is said to be a problem. There is so much wood involved in furniture, fittings (some brass as well) and structure that small wonder the restaurant was called Splinters. The new team on the boards comes from the Bath Spa Hotel (see entry, Bath), and thus is more used to soft fabrics than bare table-tops. The cooking shows the influence, but the setting remains fairly strenuously simple. Prices are not so low. There is, however, competence in a *carte* plus daily specials that might include an onion confit tart with herb butter sauce, casserole of kidneys and sweetbreads with a caper and tomato sauce, John Dory fillets with a tomato butter sauce, and duck with a jasmine tea sauce. Vegetables tend to be the same, irrespective of what was ordered (swede with John Dory?). Trimmings show something of the kitchen's background, and the wine list will do for a start. House wines begin at £9.

CHEFS: Robert Rees and Kerry Oliver   PROPRIETORS: Robert Wilson and Timothy Lloyd
OPEN: Mon to Sat, exc Mon L; 12 to 2.30, 7 to 10.30   MEALS: alc (main courses £10 to £15)
SERVICE: not inc   CARDS: Access, Amex, Diners, Visa   DETAILS: 40. Private parties: 12
main room, 22 private room. Vegetarian meals. Children's helpings. Smart dress preferred.
Wheelchair access. Music. Fax: (0202) 483454

---

CLAYGATE Surrey                                                                          map 3

## Le Petit Pierrot

4 The Parade, Claygate KT10 0NU                                               COOKING 2
ESHER (0372) 465105                                                          COST £23–£33

'Hugely enjoyable' is one enthusiastic verdict on the Brichots' restaurant, which some people think resembles a circus tent. Jean-Pierre changes his entire menu every six weeks and rings the changes with a catalogue of new ideas that split their allegiance between classic and modern French cooking. A full menu is available at both sessions and the short set lunch is particularly good value. Crab and saffron soup, quail's eggs in pastry with sauce paloise and salmon tartare are typical starters, while main courses may range from navarin of lamb and sauté calf's liver in red wine sauce to stuffed halibut on beurre blanc with salmon eggs. Exotic sorbets, pear and almond tart and chocolate gâteau are typical desserts. Annie Brichot is a pleasant and able hostess who is well supported by capable staff. The wine list strays no further than France and prices are fair. House wines are £8.25.

CHEF: Jean-Pierre Brichot   PROPRIETORS: Jean-Pierre and Annie Brichot   OPEN: Mon to
Sat, exc Sat L; 12.15 to 2.20, 7.15 to 10.15   MEALS: Set L £9.95 (2 courses) to £16.85, Set D
£18.95   SERVICE: not inc   CARDS: Access, Amex, Diners, Visa   DETAILS: 32 seats. Private
parties: 35 main room. Vegetarian meals with prior notice. No children under 8. Smart
dress preferred. No pipes in dining-room. Wheelchair access (1 step). Music. Air-
conditioned. Fax: (0372) 465105

---

*Restaurateurs justifiably resent no-shows. If you quote a credit card number when booking, you may be liable for the restaurant's lost profit margin if you don't turn up. Always phone to cancel.*

*The 1995 Guide will be published before Christmas 1994. Reports on meals are most welcome at any time of the year, but are extremely valuable in the spring. Send them to The Good Food Guide, FREEPOST, 2 Marylebone Road, London NW1 1YN. No stamp is needed if posted in the UK.*

**CLEEVE HILL  Gloucestershire**                                    map 2

## ▲ *Redmond's* 🍾 ✳

Cleeve Hill, Cheltenham GL52 3PR
CHELTENHAM (0242) 672017                                     COOKING 3*
on B4632, 3m NE of Cheltenham town centre                    COST £22–£45

'You can see the races from here with a telescope,' reports someone dead keen
on horseflesh who likes to be well fuelled into the bargain. For sure the view –
of Cheltenham, the Malverns and the wild west beyond – is spectacular. Bit by
bit, this unassuming house has succumbed to the Haywards' attentions: 'quite
magnificent fabrics,' said one; 'really good prints,' added the next. The
simplicity of the house's origins is never overlaid in a riot of luxury, but lots of
taste makes it a pleasing stopover. The cooking, which always has a slight
angle to it or something interesting, also shows taste. Celeriac soup has a mild
curry glaze; seafood chowder comes with lemon grass and ginger; skate wing
also comes with ginger; pork fillet is cooked in sesame oil; a tart of baked egg
custard with vanilla has crème fraîche seasoned with nutmeg. Spices are high
on Redmond Hayward's shopping list: they are rarely misused, though one
diner remarked that the rosemary utterly overpowered the mushroom in a
mushroom soufflé tartlet. The menu is kept short to ensure seasonality, and it
changes all the time. Prices have remained firm, but are being reduced as we
write. A meal in winter began with an appetiser of mussels with a parsley
sauce before skate with a lime and ginger butter sauce. The tang of the sauce
gave life to the fish. After that, some guinea-fowl with sherry and truffle sauce
was neither mean with the truffle nor overbalanced by the sherry. Wild duck
was also tried; it came with a mild thyme sauce and an apple and onion tart –
'Neither dish was over-decorated; each was cooked to the second.' A sweet dish
of banana soufflé recalls that hot soufflés are a strong point here. It came with a
rum and coconut crème brûlée that was novel but did not quite work – the rum
too strong, the coconut a gritty texture. Cheese is always approved and is
usually British, with an occasional French item to give a zip. Pippa Hayward is
the dominant, often the only, front-of-house presence. Her knowledge of the
wine list is exemplary and 'she is a genuinely unaffected hostess' who, for
instance, 'made light of an awkward two-year-old and helped the parents relax
and enjoy their meal'. The determined effort to bolster the low to mid-price
range of wines, which brings in more of the likes of Guigal's Côtes du Rhône
and a decent Alsace Pinot Blanc to the house list, is nothing but good news.
This is a place for experiment, with immense care going into the selection of
half-bottles. Those in search of the old and venerable – at the time of writing
the most mature claret is 1981 – will be disappointed. Compensation abounds,
however, in this wonderful, succinct list. House wines are from £9.25.
CELLARMAN'S CHOICE: Margaret River, Ashbrook, Sauvignon Blanc 1990, £17;
Médoc, Ch. Sénéjac 1987, £17.25.

---

✳ *indicates that smoking is either banned altogether or that a dining-room is maintained
for non-smokers. The symbol does not apply to restaurants that simply have no-smoking
areas.*

---

CHEF: Redmond Hayward   PROPRIETORS: Redmond and Pippa Hayward   OPEN: Tue to Sun, exc Sat L and Sun D; 12.30 to 2, 7.15 to 10   CLOSED: first week Jan   MEALS: Set L £17.50, Set Sun L £22.50, Set D £32.50   SERVICE: net prices, card slips closed   CARDS: Access, Amex, Visa   DETAILS: 32 seats. Private parties: 28 main room, 12 and 28 private rooms. Car park. Vegetarian meals with prior notice. Children's helpings. No smoking in dining-room. No music   ACCOMMODATION: 5 rooms, all with bath/shower. B&B £49 to £65. Children welcome. Baby facilities. TV. Doors close at midnight. Confirm by 3

---

**CLITHEROE** Lancashire                                                          map 5

## *Auctioneer*

New Market Street, Clitheroe BB7 2JW                            COOKING 2
CLITHEROE (0200) 27153                                          COST £19–£32

Negotiating the intricacies of Clitheroe's one-way system may delay your finding the Auctioneer, but once on New Market Street this cottage-style former pub is obvious enough. Despite irritating music, paper napkins and artificial (silk) flowers, the cosiness is genuine, based as much on the warmth and capability of Frances Van Heumen as externals such as floral wallpaper and Victorian lace curtains. Henk Van Heumen, assisted by Michael Heathcote, continues to shop well and modify the menu inventively, particularly through a series of regional fixed-price menus; dinner and Sunday lunch are also fixed-price (but weekday lunch is à la carte). Fish impresses: marinated, grilled queen scallops are served with 'superb' tuna; evidently fresh hake was not overawed by its accompaniment of grapes, banana and flaked almonds; baked fillet of pike 'had nearly no bone in it'; and tusk, red bream, sea bream and Dover sole are all trawled from the quays from time to time. Game pie, pigeon breast served with a venison medallion, baron of lamb and a pulse-heavy cassoulet have been praised, and vegetables have moved up a notch. Dainty portions, particularly of the starters, 'may outrage local trenchermen', and being offered bread too late is galling for all; the young waiting staff rarely seem to stay long enough to absorb Frances Van Heumen's much-praised skills. The wine list is reasonably priced and gratifyingly annotated; house wines are £9, and for £15 there is wide choice.

CHEFS: Henk Van Heumen and Michael Heathcote   PROPRIETORS: Henk and Frances Van Heumen   OPEN: Tue to Sun; 12 to 1.30, 7 to 9 (9.30 Sat)   MEALS: alc L (main courses £7 to £8.50). Set Sun L £12.50, Set D £14.50 (2 courses – not Sat) and £19.50. Minimum £6.25 L and £14.50 D   SERVICE: not inc   CARDS: Access, Visa   DETAILS: 48 seats. Private parties: 24 main room. Vegetarian meals. Children's helpings L. No babies. Smart dress preferred. Music

---

*'This restaurant should not in our view feature in the* Guide *because it has a curious policy of only providing dinner apparently when the chef is feeling like it.'*
On eating in Kent

*'I think the young waiter had a bet on with his colleagues about how many times he could ask if everything was all right: he asked us both individually after each course and by the end of the meal I was ready to hit him if he asked me again. (He did: I didn't.)'*
On eating in Kent

---

COCKERMOUTH Cumbria                                                                          map 7

## Quince & Medlar ✳ £

13 Castlegate, Cockermouth CA13 9EU                                            COOKING 1
COCKERMOUTH (0900) 823579                                                      COST £17–£26

A double end-of-terrace house is seat for the Le Vois' kitchen restaurant, and
family life. As in so many owner-occupied restaurants, life and work are
intermingled from morn to night. Three-quarters of the customers at this
vegetarian restaurant are not vegetarians at all. This says something for the 100
per cent thoroughness of the approach – everything fresh, everything home-
made – and for its palatability. The main dishes have a substantial ring to them
– crusty nut rings, Jerusalem artichoke and aduki-bean bake, potato and green
lentil galette – but they are enlivened by intelligent use of toppings (cheese,
say, or nuts), sauces and a willingness to deploy herbs, like the tarragon with a
carrot, apricot and chickpea roulade. Desserts will keep the boat floating, and
prices are not high. The wine list avoids the upper reaches, yet is a fistful of
proper wines. House French is £6.80.

CHEF: Colin Le Voi   PROPRIETORS: Louisa and Colin Le Voi   OPEN: Tue to Sun, D only;
7 to 9.30   CLOSED: 3 weeks Jan/Feb, 10 days Nov, Sun and Mon New Year to Easter
MEALS: alc (main courses £6.50 to £7.50)   SERVICE: not inc, card slips closed   CARDS:
Access, Visa   DETAILS: 26 seats. Private parties: 14 main room. Vegetarian meals. No
children under 6. Smart dress preferred. No smoking in dining-room. Music

---

COGGESHALL Essex                                                                            map 3

## Baumann's Brasserie

4–6 Stoneham Street, Coggeshall CO6 1TT                                       COOKING 1
COGGESHALL (0376) 561453                                                       COST £16–£30

This place has a sympathetic atmosphere, enhanced by the pictures that have
been a constant attraction since the brasserie was founded by the late Peter
Langan, and reinforced by the staff, who manage a happy welcome and nice
balance between efficiency and formality. The menu is sensibly priced and
offers firm favourites rather than novel constructions. A pair of pâtés, a pair of
salmon numbers, a soup and a salad might make up the first courses; beef,
chicken, liver and pork the meats for main dishes. Pork comes with red
cabbage, chicken with bubble and squeak, bacon and mushrooms. Lunches are
especially good value and the wine list offers bottles from excellent sources at
prices that are never greedy. House wines are £8.50.

CHEFS: Mark Baumann and Douglas Wright   PROPRIETORS: Baumann's Brasserie Ltd
OPEN: Tue to Sun, exc Sat L and Sun D; 12.30 to 2, 7.30 to 10   CLOSED: 2 weeks early Jan
MEALS: alc (main courses £10 to £14.50). Set L £9.95   SERVICE: not inc   CARDS: Access,
Amex, Diners, Visa   DETAILS: 74 seats. Private parties: 74 main room (Sat L only).
Vegetarian meals. Children's helpings. Smart dress preferred. Wheelchair access. Music

---

*The* Guide *relies on feedback from its readers. Especially welcome are reports on new
restaurants appearing in the book for the first time.*

---

COLCHESTER Essex                                                                    map 3

## *Warehouse Brasserie* £

12 Chapel Street North,
Colchester CO2 7AT                                                      COOKING 2
COLCHESTER (0206) 765656                                      COST £17–£28

Colchester's premier eating house, off St John Street in the town centre, has
become something of a local institution and continues to please a loyal band of
followers from Essex and beyond. 'Unfailingly delicious meals' is a typical
comment. It can get crowded, but the atmosphere is always congenial and
service is friendly. The value for money remains excellent and the quality of the
cooking rarely falters. The fixed menu is backed by an ever-interesting choice
of daily specials. There are influences from France, the Mediterranean and the
Far East as well as a thoroughgoing vegetarian presence. The kitchen delivers
excellent crab bisque, wild rabbit croustade with tarragon, wild salmon with
sorrel sauce and quail salad, as well as curried nut loaf, pan-fried falafel, and
spinach and mushroom filo parcels. Meals are flexible: have three courses or
simply a single light dish such as warm salmon salad or twice-baked cheese
soufflés. The selection of quality ingredients extends to organically reared beef;
bread is baked on the premises. Desserts range from home-made brown bread
ice-cream to Eton mess (a blend of strawberries, meringue and fresh cream).
Reporters have praised the espresso and cafetière coffee, while the choice of
drink includes freshly squeezed juices. The fairly priced wine list has a
noticeable tilt towards the New World. French house wine is £6.95.

CHEFS: Anthony Brooks and Stuart Mott   PROPRIETORS: Anthony Brooks and Mel
Burley   OPEN: Mon to Sat (pre- and post-theatre D by arrangement); 12 to 2, 7 to 10
MEALS: alc (main courses £5.50 to £10)   SERVICE: not inc   CARDS: Access, Visa
DETAILS: 80 seats. Private parties: 100 main room. Vegetarian meals. Children's helpings.
Wheelchair access. No music. Air-conditioned

COLERNE Wiltshire                                                                map 2

## ▲ *Lucknam Park* ▼

Colerne SN14 8AZ
BOX (0225) 742777                                                        COOKING 4
off A420 at Ford, 6m W of Chippenham                      COST £32–£70

'I could only make lunch: *only*! – would that all my lunches were so good,'
wrote one who fell on this 'lap of luxury, absolutely pukka' hotel not far from
the Colerne airfield (used only in time of war, says the management) on the hills
beyond Bath and Bristol. The slightly straggling front elevation (Georgian)
alerts the eye, the main public rooms soothe it. The reconstructed stables
behind, where conferences, beds and other amenities are located, are neat as
neat, and the dining-room has a very sub-Tiepolo painted ceiling, very long
tablecloths, and pictures that need replacing with something good. Michael
Womersley has made his mark here. 'I had salad of confit of rabbit leg, with its
saddle pan-fried, on a bed of pickled cucumber and carrot with a truffle
vinaigrette: meltingly delicious, gently gamey, the touch of the Orient was

sure-footed and gave interest and subtlety. Squid was presented three ways – braised, chargrilled and fried – with a provençal sauce. This was just right for a sultry day, the different methods of cooking kept up the pace of the dish and the sauce had a sunny depth. Beignets of exotic fruits with vanilla ice-cream and mango coulis were neither heavy nor greasy.' Quite a lunch, showing marks of skill and discretion at most turns, and exact technique. Dinner has an elevated set price, but the lunch cost is realistic, with no stinting. First courses are often miniature main dishes – for instance, venison wrapped in cabbage and braised with celery, or mille-feuilles of lambs' tongues, sweetbreads and kidneys with roast shallots. This gives you a chance to have a fish main course, something Michael Womersley does very well. His enthusiasm for grouping elements of a dish, instanced above, manifests itself in other items such as a pair of soufflés with a lemon posset, or exotic fruit cooked three ways. Even smoked salmon goes out with a partner of gravlax. The service demonstrated a 'sixth sense' of what is needed next at a table; it is certainly more old-world professional than is found in many country-house hotels. The wine list is extremely long, very fine and makes no concession to economy. There are some modestly priced enjoyable wines, such as decent bourgeois Médocs, Sauvignon de St-Bris, St-Véran and two pages of French provincials, whose prices start at £15. Thereafter costs rocket upwards and the usual money-saving routes are closed. Italy and the Loire stand out, Alsace is slightly wanting and New Zealand is barely mentioned. Effort has been made to accumulate good halves. House wine is £15. CELLARMAN'S CHOICE: Chinon, Clos du Saut au Loup 1988, £20; Chianti Classico 1988, Isole e Olena, £26.

CHEF: Michael Womersley  PROPRIETORS: Lucknam Park Hotels Ltd  OPEN: all week; 12.30 to 2, 7.30 to 9.30 (9.45 Sat)  MEALS: Set L £19.50 (2 courses) to £22, Set D £39.50  SERVICE: not inc, card slips closed  CARDS: Access, Amex, Diners, Visa  DETAILS: 85 seats. Private parties: 85 main room, 2 to 24 in private rooms. Car park. Vegetarian meals. Children's helpings. No children under 10. Jacket and tie D. Wheelchair access (also WC). Music  ACCOMMODATION: 42 rooms, all with bath/shower. Rooms for disabled. B&B £100 to £340. Children welcome. Baby facilities. Afternoon teas. Garden. Swimming-pool. Sauna. Tennis. Snooker. TV. Phone. Doors close at 1am. Fax: (0225) 743536 (*The Which? Hotel Guide*)

---

CONSETT  Co Durham                                                    map 7

## *Pavilion* £

2 Station Road, Consett DH8 5RL                          COOKING 1*
CONSETT (0207) 503388                                     COST £12–£46

'The whole world seems to come here to celebrate something' was the comment of one who was more than happy to find this big, yet constantly busy Cantonese restaurant where any birthday, anniversary or event is enough to elicit a complimentary cake from the management. In truth, the food does not need extra incentives; it is fresh, wholesome and very good value. 'We had a shellfish blow-out with buckets of wine and could not fault the food or the bill,' wrote another happy eater. Service is friendly and the menu is vast, spanning sizzlers, Canton, Peking and 'health and vegetarian'. House wine is £6.70.

CHEF: Wan Yip   PROPRIETORS: the Yip family   OPEN: all week D, Thur to Sat L; 12 to 2,
6 to 10.30   CLOSED: 24 to 26 Dec, 1 Jan   MEALS: alc (main dishes £6 to £11). Set L £6.95,
Set D £13.50 to £18   SERVICE: not inc, card slips closed   CARDS: Access, Amex, Diners,
Visa   DETAILS: 100 seats. Private parties: 100 main room. Vegetarian meals. Children's
helpings L and early D. No children under 6. Smart dress preferred. Music. Air-conditioned

---

## COOKHAM Berkshire                                                    map 2

# Alfonso's                                            `NEW ENTRY`

19–21 Station Hill Parade,
Cookham SL6 9BR                                            COOKING 1
BOURNE END (062 85) 25775                               COST £19–£31

The Baena family rule the roost in a small parade of shops hard by Cookham
station. They have a strong, even vociferous, local following and the realism
induced by such support keeps prices sensible for cooking that sounds as if it
should cost far more. A pair of quail with bacon and morels is not a normal
offering in a £16.50 set-price deal and the scale of the menu itself, with
classically inspired dishes over a very wide range, is unexpected. Perhaps this
is the reason for the support. Yet service is a second reason, for attention from
Sr Baena is constant and appreciated. An inspection meal yielded lambs'
kidneys with a sherry sauce, halibut with a tarragon cream sauce, and îles
flottantes with an enriched custard glazed (toughened) under the grill. The
wine list is as fairly priced as the food; Torres and Berberana keep the Spanish
flag aloft. House wines are £7.50.

CHEF: Richard Manzano   PROPRIETORS: Mr and Mrs Alfonso Baena   OPEN: Mon to Sat,
exc Sat L; 12.30 to 2, 7 to 10 (10.30 Fri and Sat)   CLOSED: 2 to 3 weeks Aug   MEALS: Set L
£12.50, Set D £16.50   SERVICE: not inc   CARDS: Amex, Diners, Visa   DETAILS: 34 seats.
Private parties: 34 main room. Car park. Vegetarian meals. Children's helpings. Smart dress
preferred. No pipes in dining-room. Wheelchair access (also WC). Music

---

## COPPULL MOOR Lancashire                                             map 5

# Coppull Moor                                         `NEW ENTRY`

311 Preston Road, Coppull Moor PR7 5DU                     COOKING 2
CHORLEY (0257) 792222                                   COST £22–£35

'This unique experience must be observed and tasted and touched,' exclaimed
a reporter in florid mood – all the more remarkable because the setting is
unprepossessing, to say the least. The restaurant is in a redundant pub on the
main road with a large car park. Inside is a series of little rooms that someone
has cared about: visitors have noted the remarkable attention to detail in the
two dining-rooms – lace tablecloths, first-class glassware 'designed for serious
drinkers', Villeroy & Boch plates, and spirit lamps on the tables. The menu is
fixed price for five courses and changes daily with the market. Consider this: to
begin, avocado mousse set on a pool of yogurt scattered with crabmeat and
spring onion, then rich cream of onion soup with a dollop of broccoli purée in
the middle; next, pheasant and venison pie with Cumberland sauce and rolled
loin of lamb with beef tournedos and apple sauce accompanied by

'interestingly handled' vegetables (perhaps buttered kohlrabi, fanned roots of mooli and baby fennel with mixed peppers). To finish, a selection of excellent sweets includes sticky toffee pudding, spotted dick and choux pastry swan, rounded off with mature Stilton and first-class coffee. Sunday offers an intriguing brunch running to several courses. 'No gratuities please; service is with our compliments,' says a note on the menu. Wines are adequate: there are a few gems but generally there is an over-reliance on decent, safe names. Prices are fair (from £8) but half-bottles are notable by their absence.

CHEFS: Barry Rea and Paul Dicken   PROPRIETOR: Barry Rea   OPEN: Tue to Sun; 12.30, 8 for 8.30   CLOSED: first 2 weeks Feb   MEALS: Set L £17.50, Set Sun brunch £16.50, Set D £19.50 (Tue to Thur) to £24.50 (Fri to Sun)   SERVICE: net prices, card slips closed   CARDS: Amex, Diners   DETAILS: 26 seats. Private parties: 12 main room, 12 and 12 private rooms. Car park. Vegetarian meals. Children under 14 by arrangement. Smart dress preferred. No smoking in dining-room. Music

---

**CORBRIDGE Northumberland**                                                            map 7

## Valley £                                          | NEW ENTRY |

Old Station House, Station Road,
Corbridge NE46 2HZ
HEXHAM (0434) 633434 and 633923                              COOKING 1
off B6321 S of Corbridge towards Riding Mill                 COST £16–£36

The restaurant is in the nineteenth-century Old Station House, one of Britain's oldest passenger railway stations. Owner Mr Aziz offers a unique 'train service': a suitably attired waiter meets parties from Newcastle Station, escorts them on the train and takes their orders. The restaurant itself consists of four connecting rooms, with the smallest one right on the platform. It is flamboyantly done out with aquamarine and gold wallpaper, swathed drapes, and marble pillars supporting illuminated coloured globes. Side tables are graced with bronze statuettes topped with tasselled lampshades. Uniformed waiters offer pleasant and prompt service. The menu has its share of familiar bhunas, dhansaks and tandooris, but those in the know go for the more esoteric chef's recommendations such as murgh-e-khazana, a creamy dish of chicken with lentils plus a few blobs of honey stirred in at the last moment, and mangsho pesta ke shadi, which is topside of beef cooked with pistachio nuts. The freshness of the ingredients and the vivid spicing continue to impress regulars who have praised 'exemplary' vegetable pakoras, 'monster' king prawns served on a puri pancake, king prawn chilli masala, mushroom bhaji and pilau rice ('good enough to eat on its own'). Prices are 'sensible' rather than cheap. Kingfisher lager is the preferred drink, though the wine list is perfectly decent. House French is £6.50.

CHEF: Titu Ahad   PROPRIETOR: S.N. Aziz   OPEN: Mon to Sat, D only; 6 to 11 (private parties weekday L and Sun by arrangement)   CLOSED: 25 Dec   MEALS: alc (main courses £4.50 to £9.50). Set D £40 (2 people) to £75 (4 people)   SERVICE: not inc   CARDS: Access, Amex, Diners, Visa   DETAILS: 70 seats. Private parties: 40 main room, 10 and 20 private rooms. Car park. Vegetarian meals. Children's helpings. Smart dress preferred. Wheelchair access. Music

**CORSE LAWN** Gloucestershire                                    map 2

## ▲ *Corse Lawn House Hotel* ❦ £

Corse Lawn GL19 4LZ
GLOUCESTER (0452) 780479 and 780771                    COOKING 3
on B4211, 5m SW of Tewkesbury                          COST £19–£58

There cannot be many places that offer calf's brains with black butter in the normal course of events, but Baba Hine has the temerity of a good cook at ease with her materials. Needless to say, the brains were good, as have been hot crab sausage with tomato sauce and chickpeas, grilled king prawns with garlic and wild rice, breast of guinea-fowl with armagnac, barbecued fillet of pork with apple fritters, the set of upwards of a dozen cheeses, and 'a fascinating selection of petits fours' with coffee. The Hines have improved and cared for this tall early eighteenth-century house with add-ons for some 15 years, yet the pond, the giant green before the doors and the essential style of the place have not altered, the breakfasts have got better and better, 'and the supply of watercolours by Mrs Hine's mother seems inexhaustible'. However, though loose covers may have faded a little, there is change in the air as the bar converts in part to a bistro, offering bilingual menus of British or French dishes, in an attempt to offer a cheaper alternative to the restaurant, or to beef up the already popular bar trade. Though people see only slight development in the repertoire, they enjoy the fairly high flavours that come across with the food, and the use of very good materials. Hop shoots, elvers, local meats, fish and game, and really excellent vegetables (which are not messed about) make for a satisfying style that is never coarse, but often properly robust. The wine list continues to offer a good range and plenty in halves or by the glass. House wines are £9. CELLARMAN'S CHOICE: St-Véran, Les Grandes Bruyères 1991, Luquet, £21.50; Corbières, Ch. Les Ollieux 1990, £15.20.

CHEF: Baba Hine   PROPRIETORS: Baba, Denis and Giles Hine   OPEN: all week; 12 to 2, 7 to 10   MEALS: alc (main courses bistro £6 to £10, restaurant £13 to £20). Set L £15.95, Set bistro Sun L £10.50 (2 courses) to £12.50, Set D £23.50   SERVICE: not inc, card slips closed   CARDS: Access, Amex, Diners, Visa   DETAILS: 50 seats. 10 tables outside. Private parties: 75 main room, 20 and 35 private rooms. Car park. Vegetarian meals. Children's helpings. Wheelchair access (also WC). No music   ACCOMMODATION: 19 rooms, all with bath/shower. Rooms for disabled. B&B £70 to £90. Children welcome. Baby facilities. Pets welcome. Afternoon teas. Garden. Swimming-pool. Tennis. TV. Phone. Doors close at midnight. Confirm by 6. Fax: (0452) 780840 (*The Which? Hotel Guide*)

---

**COSHAM** Hampshire                                             map 2

## *Barnards* £

109 High Street, Cosham PO6 3BB                          COOKING 2
COSHAM (0705) 370226                                     COST £18–£38

'Modest,' said a visitor, who added that the quality of the cooking was 'delightfully, surprisingly excellent'. There are no signs of great expenditure on furnishings and decoration, though habitués have welcomed the addition of some ventilation and a general smartening-up and improvement of the pleasing shop conversion. But the Barnards' intentions are not *grande luxe* – just good food, lots of effort and plenty of smiles at the welcome. This warms people's hearts, and gains David Barnard respect for sound execution of conventional dishes such as asparagus en feuilleté with hollandaise, mussels in aspic with a ratatouille, best end of lamb with a crumb crust, fillet steak with a vol-au-vent of snails and a red wine sauce, and excellent desserts such as a banana parfait on a caramel sauce. What pleases are the care, the thoroughly self-sufficient approach and the modesty. The à la carte choice is supplemented by a shorter fixed-price affair, and there are daily specials, particularly of fish. Gastronomic evenings are held regularly. The wine list is very short, but adequate. House wines are £7.95.

CHEF: David Barnard   PROPRIETORS: David and Sandie Barnard   OPEN: Tue to Sat, exc Sat L; 12 to 2, 7.30 to 10   CLOSED: 1 week Christmas, 2 weeks Aug   MEALS: alc (main courses £12.50 to £16). Set L and D £13.50   SERVICE: net prices, card slips closed   CARDS: Access, Visa   DETAILS: 26 seats. Private parties: 26 main room. Vegetarian meals. Children's helpings. Wheelchair access (1 step). Music

---

**CRANLEIGH Surrey**                                                                          map 3

# La Barbe Encore

High Street, Cranleigh GU6 8AE                                          COOKING 1*
CRANLEIGH (0483) 273889                                              COST £24–£34

This used to be called Restaurant Bonnet, after the owners. They remain, but the name has changed. If you are coming from Guildford, the restaurant is at the far end of the High Street. Follow the signs to the public car park (just before the restaurant and the only place to park) and walk through. The result is much the same as before (physically) with cheaper menus and less of an emphasis on post-nouvelle cuisine. The aim is a neighbourhood bistro-style restaurant serving well-prepared food. 'Our customers said they liked a mixture of traditional and modern dishes,' reported Jean Pierre, which may explain why moules marinière, oxtail and snails share a menu with ratatouille in filo pastry or salmon fish-cakes. There has been a general simplification, but not at the expense of quality. A first-course tart of poached egg on a bed of creamed leeks with a hollandaise sauce showed fine pastry work; the second-course guinea-fowl with olives, and rolled pork escalopes in a port sauce (alouettes sans tête), and the desserts – meringue glacée and apple tart – were all competent. Îles flottantes have been reported as less expert. The place has not a lot of character, but the view through to the kitchen and the amiable service may make up for it. The wine list is very short and not inspired. New house wines are £9.50.

CHEF: Jean Pierre Bonnet   PROPRIETORS: Jean Pierre and Ann Bonnet   OPEN: Tue to Sun, exc Sat L and Sun D; 12 to 2, 7 to 10 (10.30 Sat)   CLOSED: 25 and 26 Dec   MEALS: Set L £13.95 (2 courses) to £15.95, Set D £16.95 (2 courses) to £18.95   SERVICE: not inc   CARDS: Access, Amex, Visa   DETAILS: 60 seats. Private parties: 60 main room. Children's helpings on request. No-smoking area. Wheelchair access (1 step; also men's WC). Music

CROYDE Devon                                                    map 1

## ▲ *Whiteleaf at Croyde* ♀ ⁑✳

Croyde EX33 1PN                                          COOKING 2
CROYDE (0271) 890266                                    COST £21–£31

'The Whiteleaf is definitely a guesthouse,' insists David Wallington, which is a view endorsed by visitors to this clean and neat, small and friendly outfit. Having reduced the number of bedrooms, he has also suggested that eight people are probably the maximum he can handle for dinner – given the fact that this is a one-man culinary show that runs on inspiration and flair. Not for him the sweat-free option of a set menu – just the opposite. On any night you may well find at least half a dozen starters and a similar number of main courses, four different vegetables and a plethora of desserts. Added to this is the sheer industry of the place, with home baking as a major activity. One couple simply listed the delights in note form: 'excellent quenelles of salmon, fish soup, rack of lamb, "untortured" vegetables, sorbet, strawberry crumble.' French, Italian and English provenances embrace the menu, so you may find rillettes with home-made pickles and fegato alla veneziana alongside game pasties with crab apple jelly, 'high-rise' Yorkshire puddings and roast grouse. But the work does not end there: breakfast is an extraordinary choice of first-class ingredients, from local hog's pudding to undyed kippers. The intention to please is extended to the wine list; the range encompassed in a relatively small number of bins is remarkable, but while Italy retains most favoured status, clarets and Rhônes are fine. Half-bottles abound. A weak spot is perhaps Burgundy, where resort to safety is too readily taken. Prices though are very fair throughout. House wine is £7.65.

CHEF: David Wallington   PROPRIETORS: David and Florence Wallington   OPEN: all week, D only; 6.30   CLOSED: Christmas and New Year, 2 weeks Apr, 2 weeks July, 2 weeks Oct   MEALS: Set D £17.25 to £21.75   SERVICE: net prices, card slips closed   CARDS: Access, Visa (2.45% surcharge)   DETAILS: 16 seats. 3 tables outside. Private parties: 16 main room. Car park. Vegetarian meals. Children's helpings. Smart dress preferred. No smoking. No music   ACCOMMODATION: 3 rooms, all with bath/shower. B&B £34.50 to £54. Deposit: £25. Children welcome. Baby facilities. Pets welcome in bedrooms. Garden. TV. Phone. Doors close at midnight. Confirm by 5 (*The Which? Hotel Guide*)

CROYDON Surrey                                                  map 3

## *34 Surrey Street* £

34 Surrey Street, Croydon CR0 1RJ                       COOKING 1
081-686 0586                                            COST £18–£36

Surrey Street is the site of 'the oldest fruit and veg market in downtown Croydon', according to the proprietor of this lively American-style restaurant in a listed building. The interior surprised one visitor: 'To the left is the bar with tables set out for lighter fare; the main attraction was a sea-horse constructed from blue balloons. Well, I guess we were in Croydon!' To the right is the restaurant; otherwise you can relax in the conservatory and listen to some live jazz. Exotic seafood is the star of the show, and the daily board lists up to 18 species from moonfish and marlin to red snapper and rainbow runner. San

Francisco, Florida, the Deep South and Mexico provide the culinary inspiration, which means lots of marinating, chargrilling and 'blackening'. Monkfish has been 'quite heavenly'. The standard menu is a fast run through Cajun 'popcorn' prawns, chimichangas (sauté vegetables in a tortilla), fajitas, salads and pasta. Vegetables such as fried zucchini sticks are charged extra. Cocktails are worth sampling, although it may be best to bypass the Long Island iced tea. Affordable New World wines dominate the short list, with plenty of drinking by the glass. House wines are £7.95.

CHEF: Malcolm John   PROPRIETORS: Harbour Lights Restaurant Group   OPEN: all week, exc Sat L and Sun D; 12 to 3, 7 to 10.45   CLOSED: bank hols   MEALS: alc (main courses £5 to £10). Set L and D Mon to Fri £12.95 to £15.95   SERVICE: not inc   CARDS: Access, Amex, Diners, Visa   DETAILS: 70 seats. Private parties: 90 main room. Vegetarian meals. Children's helpings. Smart dress preferred. Wheelchair access (also WC). Music

---

**CRUDWELL Wiltshire**                                                              map 2

## ▲ *Crudwell Court* ⅚✳

Crudwell, nr Malmesbury SN16 9EP
MALMESBURY (0666) 577194
on A429, 3m N of Malmesbury

COOKING 1
COST £18–£53

'An exceptional family country haven' is a reader's verdict on this 300-year-old converted rectory by the ancient church. It is a place with a pleasant, homely feel. Inside is a panelled dining-room overlooking the rose garden and water-lily pond. Chris Amor cooks to a menu that has around six choices at each stage and flavours can be both subtle and forthright. A starter of collops of Scottish mealy pudding and quail with red wine and shallot sauce is an 'exciting' blend of richness and delicacy; warm terrine of salmon and crab with cream and chive sauce has been equally impressive. Middle of Cotswold lamb with rosemary and grilled breast of duck with blackberry and Cassis have been darkly, pungently sauced and served with 'respectable' vegetables. Sticky toffee pudding with butterscotch sauce is reckoned to be an outstanding sweet; otherwise you might find lemon soufflé with raspberry coulis or white and dark chocolate torte. Service is friendly and amenable. The wine list has a substantial, well-spread selection and prices are kept within reason. House wines are £9.75.

CHEF: Chris Amor   PROPRIETORS: Nick Bristow and Iain MacLaren   OPEN: all week; 12 to 2, 7 to 9.30   MEALS: Set Sun L £11.50, Set Mon to Sat L £14.50, Set D £19.50 to £24.95   SERVICE: not inc, card slips closed   CARDS: Access, Amex, Diners, Visa   DETAILS: 80 seats. Private parties: 50 main room, 30 private room. Car park. Vegetarian meals. Children's helpings on request. Smart dress preferred. No smoking in dining-room. Wheelchair access (also WC). Music   ACCOMMODATION: 15 rooms, all with bath/shower. B&B £47 to £114. Deposit: £20 to £50. Children welcome. Baby facilities. Pets welcome. Afternoon teas. Garden. Swimming-pool. TV. Phone. Doors close at 11. Fax: (0666) 577853 (*The Which? Hotel Guide*)

---

Card slips closed *in the details at the end of an entry indicates that the total on the slips of credit cards is closed when handed over for signature.*

---

CUCKFIELD  West Sussex                                              map 3

## ▲ Ockenden Manor ❧✳

Ockenden Lane, Cuckfield RH17 5LD
HAYWARDS HEATH (0444) 416111                          COOKING 2
off A272, 2m W of Haywards Heath                      COST £24–£54

The Goodmans run a friendly ship in the centre of Cuckfield. 'I could not have met a nicer crowd,' reports one reader, impressed by this slice of living history – the building dates back to the sixteenth century – with views of the church spire and a classic English setting. Indoors, the wood-panelled dining-room and elaborate plasterwork complete the expectations of manorial grandeur set up by the approach. Other visitors have remarked that the staff seem less than knowledgeable about what actually goes into the cooking. None the less they have praised new chef Geoff Welch, who has brought a more modern sensibility to bear on the menu that may offer as a first course pig's trotter stuffed with pork and duck livers and herbs, then braised in honey, sliced and served with a salad, or a main-course breast of chicken stuffed with crab, with a pilaff and a tarragon sauce. This British style of cooking does not stray too far out of bounds, and has pleased as much with simple oysters and fresh cured salmon, crème brûlée and sticky toffee pudding, as with confit of duck with lentils. The wine list is very long and superior. 'Superior' might also describe its prices. Clarets are a particular strength. House wines are £9.75.

CHEF: Geoffrey Welch   PROPRIETORS: Mr and Mrs H.N.A. Goodman   OPEN: all week; 12.30 to 2, 7.30 to 9.30   MEALS: alc (main courses £12.50 to £20). Set L £16.50 to £17.50, Set D £25.50 to £28.50   SERVICE: not inc   CARDS: Access, Amex, Diners, Visa   DETAILS: 70 seats. 10 tables outside. Private parties: 40 main room, 12 and 75 private rooms. Car park. Vegetarian meals. Children welcome. Jacket and tie. No smoking in dining-room. Wheelchair access (also WC). No music   ACCOMMODATION: 22 rooms, all with bath/ shower. B&B £68 to £155. Deposit: £50. Children welcome. Baby facilities. Pets by arrangement. Afternoon teas. Garden. TV. Phone. Doors close at midnight. Confirm by 6. Fax: (0444) 415549 (The Which? Hotel Guide)

---

DARLINGTON  Co Durham                                              map 7

## Cottage Thai                                    | NEW ENTRY |

94–96 Parkgate, Darlington DL1 3PJ                   COOKING 1
DARLINGTON (0325) 361717                              COST £11–£44

Within walking distance of the railway station and opposite the Civic Theatre, this Thai restaurant is a local asset. The frontage may seem plain, but the interior has been exotically done out with plants and all kinds of Thai artefacts, pictures and carvings. One corner is set aside for ceremonial meals eaten sitting on cushions round a low table. Thai waitresses in full costume are overseen by the ever-helpful lady of the house. The 70-dish menu covers all the main strands of the cuisine and there is much to recommend. Kanom cheeb (wrinkly steamed dumplings), cod with green beans and curry paste, tiny fish-cakes and crispy wrapped king prawns have been fine appetisers. Elsewhere, reporters have been won over by 'glorious' tom yum soup, roast duck curry, curiously named 'son-in-law' egg, pla chien (wonderfully complex, but mundanely described as fish in a special sauce with ginger) and blisteringly hot squid salad. The only quibble seems to relate to rather high dinner prices. The wine list does not venture far, but most drink tea and Singha Thai beer. House wine is £7.50.

CHEF/PROPRIETOR: Malinee Burachati   OPEN: Mon to Sat; 12 to 1.45, 6.30 to 10.30   MEALS: alc (main courses £6.50 to £9.50). Set L £4.95 to £5.40, Set D £14 to £24   SERVICE: not inc   CARDS: Access, Visa   DETAILS: 50 seats. 20 tables outside. Private parties: 50 main room. Vegetarian meals. Children welcome. Smart dress preferred. Wheelchair access (1 step; also WC). Music

## Victor's

84 Victoria Road, Darlington DL1 5JW         COOKING 1*
DARLINGTON (0325) 480818         COST £14–£39

'Victor' – alias Peter Robinson – is 'a fine host' according to a long-standing devotee of this well-established restaurant not far from the station. After 10 years in residence, the Robinsons still make their own breads, ice-creams, sorbets and chocolates, and are staunch supporters of local produce. The kitchen makes good use of everything from wild pigeons shot by a customer and an annual supply of kid from a nearby farm to a fine array of up to 12 cheeses all produced within a 35-mile radius of Darlington. The fixed-priced dinner menu always begins with an appetiser 'to get the taste-buds going', before dishes such as stir-fried five-spice beef with watercress, roast duckling with lime and almond stuffing, and braised ox tongue with caper sauce. Fish has been praised, and vegetables are invariably interesting. The short wine list is affordable, particularly as the Robinsons have a policy of marking up all bottles by a standard amount of £3. Californian house wine is £8.

CHEFS: Peter and Jayne Robinson, and Trudie Neave   PROPRIETORS: Peter and Jayne Robinson   OPEN: Tue to Sat; 12 to 2, 7 to 10.30   CLOSED: 25 Dec to 1 Jan   MEALS: Set L £8.50, Set D £25   SERVICE: not inc, card slips closed   CARDS: Access, Amex, Diners, Visa   DETAILS: 32 seats. Private parties: 32 main room. Vegetarian meals. Children's helpings. Wheelchair access (2 steps). Music

---

**DARTMOUTH Devon**         map 1

## ▲ Billy Budd's

7 Foss Street, Dartmouth TQ6 9DW         COOKING 1
DARTMOUTH (0803) 834842         COST £15–£34

Foss Street was reputedly once home to the original of Chaucer's shipman. Today the ships are yachts, the sailors cheerful pleasure-seekers. Cheerful might describe Gilly Webb's handling of the front-of-house and could, with ease, extend to Keith Belt's cooking. Fresh food is treated sensibly as in skate with black butter, guinea-fowl with red wine, mushrooms and fresh pasta, and best end of lamb. Other reports have mentioned the twice-baked cheese soufflé, smoked salmon parcels with avocado salsa, and sweets, such as chocolate and Cointreau pots, bread-and-butter pudding and summer pudding when in season. Proceedings may extend somewhat when the yachts are all in harbour together and neither kitchen nor service can keep up with the flotilla. Lunch-time snacks are available from £1.60 to £5 and can be useful if you want to avoid pubs. The wine list keeps to essentials and house wines are £8.50.

---

CHEFS: Keith Belt and Tony Dingle   PROPRIETORS: Keith Belt and Gilly Webb   OPEN: Tue to Sat; 12 to 2 (1.30 Sat), 7.30 to 9.30   CLOSED: 1 week Nov, 1 month Feb, bank hols (telephone to check)   MEALS: alc D (main courses £11 to £13). Light L menu. Minimum £10.95 D   SERVICE: not inc, card slips closed   CARDS: Access, Visa   DETAILS: 35 seats. Private parties: 30 main room. Vegetarian meals with prior notice. Children's helpings. No children under 7 D. Smart dress preferred. Wheelchair access (1 step). Music ACCOMMODATION: 2 twin rooms. B&B £29. Deposit: 50%. TV

---

## Carved Angel 🍾

2 South Embankment, Dartmouth TQ6 9BH
DARTMOUTH (0803) 832465

COOKING 4*
COST £35–£65

This Dartmouth landmark – Tudor in style from without, 'light and airy' from within – provides a choice of views. The nautically inclined can watch boats bobbing in the harbour; those more interested in the ebb and flow of soup and sauce can gaze into the open-plan, live-action kitchen. The blue Colin Kellam pottery is the other thing everyone notices; some with pleasure, while others have felt that 'basins rather than plates for the main courses lead to food degenerating into a homogeneous mush in which individual components disappear', and are no more pleased by 'modern, square-ended spoons and forks, almost painful to use'. The food offers the same synthesis of local craft and brisk modernity. Even those who query execution admit that ingredients are of the freshest and finest. 'Although dishes sound at first to be highly composed, the many ingredients are used judiciously, every ingredient serving to add to the completeness of the finished dish. I particularly liked the fact that British ingredients are used to great effect, and traditional skills such as preservation techniques are employed adding depth and contrast to the meal,' reported one, thrilled with chargrilled breast of guinea-fowl 'lifted to new heights by a compote of onion and orange and a pool of soured cream topped with freshly roasted and ground coriander seed', and by Ticklemoor cheeses accompanied by home-pickled grapes of such flavour that the recipe was requested (and provided). Other frisson-yielding strokes have included an elderflower sauce with avocado and melon; orange, olive and anchovy butter with turbot ('the olive and anchovy were wonderfully subtle and gave a warm background savoury flavour to offset the orange and fish'); a 'wonderful' ragoût of turbot, sole and scallops ('exemplary – briefly seared and meltingly tender') in a saffron, pimento and fennel fumet; and 'the best steak my husband has ever had. It was worth the 140-mile round trip.' Nibbles, vegetables, salads and desserts (such as 'a fresh ice-cream heart containing divine chunks of ginger and toffee-ish meringue, served in a lake of delicious coffee cream') are lauded too. Things are not always perfect (and complaints have been received): presentation is sometimes simpler than the price would suggest; herbs can be used over-enthusiastically; and service varies from 'very pleasant and helpful' to 'muddled' or worse – 'When there were only two tables left, the kitchen turned inwards on itself and partied with glasses of wine to the extent that we could not get another cup of coffee and the adjacent party could not get their bill.' House wines here are not cheap at £14, but they are well selected and stimulating. The list itself begins at £11 and is classic, well-organised, rather grand and francophile. The aperitif and digestif section, much of it available by the glass, is good, and there are plenty of halves. CELLARMAN'S CHOICE: Wairau River, Sauvignon Blanc 1992, £15; Dom. de Trevallon 1987, Durrbach, £18.

---

CHEFS: Joyce Molyneux and Nick Coiley   PROPRIETORS: Joyce Molyneux and Meriel Matthews   OPEN: Tue to Sun, exc Sun D; 12.30 to 2, 7.30 to 9.30   CLOSED: 6 weeks from early Jan   MEALS: alc (main courses £15 to £24). Set L £23 (2 courses) to £28, Set Sun L £30, Set D £38 (2 courses) to £43   SERVICE: net prices   DETAILS: 48 seats. Private parties: 38 main room, 12 and 20 private rooms. Vegetarian meals. Children's helpings. Smart dress preferred. Wheelchair access. No music

---

## The Exchange

| 5 Higher Street, Dartmouth TQ6 9RB | COOKING 1* |
| DARTMOUTH (0803) 832022 | COST £18–£38 |

If you like conservation, talk to owner Nigel Way when he passes through en route for his other place, the Royal Castle Hotel. The restaurant is housed in a seventeenth-century merchant's house, once the local employment exchange (hence the name), and has been impressively restored to give restaurant space on two floors. Joc Wetherley's cooking is by no means historical; it grasps current fashion for dishes such as turkey escalope with thyme and apricot sauce, duck with spiced honey sauce, and salmon with langoustines and green tagliatelle. For a place that calls itself 'brasserie' in a town such as Dartmouth, the evidence of home enterprise – for instance, the daily bread – is encouraging. The lunch menu concentrates on cheaper and lighter affairs, and fish is given equal weight to meat. 'Brasserie' is a loose description, perhaps to encourage the public to think 'informal', which vitiates none of the enthusiasm among kitchen or front-of-house staff. The wine list has little truck with bottles over £20 – a sensible policy when the choice can be as fair as this. House wines are £9.45.

---

CHEF: Joc Wetherley   PROPRIETORS: Nigel and Anne Way   OPEN: Tue to Sat; 12 to 2, 7 to 9.45   CLOSED: second week Jan to 1 Mar   MEALS: alc (main courses £9.50 to £14)   SERVICE: not inc, card slips closed   CARDS: Access, Visa   DETAILS: 45 seats. Private parties: 60 main room. Vegetarian meals. Children's helpings. No cigars/pipes in dining-room. Music

---

DEDHAM Essex                                                                        map 3

## ▲ Fountain House 🍷 ⁵⚹

| Dedham Hall, Brook Street, | |
| Dedham CO7 6AD | COOKING 1 |
| COLCHESTER (0206) 323027 | COST £21–£28 |

Evidence of James Sarton's interest in art abounds on the walls of this house – carefully called a guesthouse, not a hotel – set in grand gardens within a frame of classic English landscape (this is Constable country). It is a very personal operation, and if the personalities of the owners are not in evidence, the ambience may suffer from lack of character. Wendy Sarton's cooking is plain to a fault. 'Melon and strawberries as a first course were just that; not a hint of dressing,' exclaimed one visitor who found the cooking sound, but playing second fiddle to the wine list. Such good bottles may indeed be best with plain food like stuffed mushrooms or fresh asparagus, followed by kidneys with mustard sauce, sirloin with garlic butter and good, plain vegetables.

Temptations to expand the sampling may arise at pudding time. One of the best features of the list is the special effort to obtain half-bottles. This must be one of the best ranges available, though surprisingly it is more interesting for regions other than Bordeaux. The whole bottle choice is well rounded (strong on Germany too), fairly priced and uses some of the best growers. The Italian, American and Australasian sections are very fine; prices remain fair. House wines are £7.50. CELLARMAN'S CHOICE: Marlborough, Sauvignon 1992, Allan Scott, £14; Victoria, Mount Langi Ghiran, Shiraz 1990, £14.

CHEF: Wendy Sarton  PROPRIETORS: James and Wendy Sarton  OPEN: Tue to Sat, D only, and Sun L; 12.30 to 2.30, 7.30 to 9.30  MEALS: Set L £15.50, Set D £17.50  SERVICE: not inc, card slips closed  CARDS: Access, Visa  DETAILS: 32 seats. 10 tables outside. Private parties: 50 main room, 16 private room. Car park. Vegetarian meals. Children's helpings. Smart dress preferred. No smoking in dining-room. Wheelchair access. Music ACCOMMODATION: 6 rooms, all with bath/shower. Rooms for disabled. B&B £34 to £57. Children welcome. Baby facilities. Garden. TV. Doors close at midnight

## ▲ *Le Talbooth* 🍾

Gun Hill, Dedham CO7 6HP
COLCHESTER (0206) 323150
on B1029, off A12, 6m NE of Colchester

COOKING 2
COST £29–£57

The softly flowing river laps the lawns of this jettied and gabled black and white house. Get through the doors and curtains take over from tie-beams as the dominant motif, but it is all very Olde England and goes down well with the custom. A new chef at Le Talbooth has heralded a new policy. Gone are the big-spending '80s, when haute cuisine ruled and the restaurant 'perhaps lost touch with its local support'. Now you get steak and kidney pie, chateaubriand, half a lobster with cold asparagus soufflé – simple dishes and recognisable materials in familiar forms. The simplicity may extend to getting the recipe for chicken bonne femme muddled with chicken bourguignonne – in the opinion of one avid reader of *Gastronomique* – but the principle seems a good one. Reports, however, are so far mixed, with too many comments about insipidity for comfort. Desserts have had a fair press: pastry has been praised, an almond and amaretto tart had the contrast of buttery pastry, nutty filling and fruity trimmings of raspberries off to a T, and a mille-feuille of pear with bitter chocolate sauce was particularly recommended. Coffee and petits fours help give a strong finish to the meal, though bread has been nothing to write home about and canapés have consisted of mixed nuts. The prices and the service speak of serious intentions – inability to rustle up a fresh orange juice and the mixed character of the cooking make one wonder. Lay & Wheeler oversees the excellent wine list, which is neither overlong nor overpriced and perhaps outshines the quality and reliability of the food. House wine is £10.50.

CELLARMAN'S CHOICE: Savennières, Clos du Papillon 1990, Baumard, £19.25; Old Block, Shiraz 1990, St Hallett, £17.95.

CHEF: Henrik Iversen  PROPRIETOR: Gerald M.W. Milsom  OPEN: all week; 12 to 2, 7 to 9  MEALS: alc (main courses £10.50 to £17.50). Set Sun L £19.95, Set L and D (exc Sat D) £19.50  SERVICE: 10%, card slips closed  CARDS: Access, Amex, Visa  DETAILS: 70 seats. Private parties: 85 main room, 24 private room. Car park. Vegetarian meals. Children's helpings. Smart dress preferred. No cigars/pipes in dining-room. No music  ACCOMMODATION: 10 rooms, all with bath/shower. B&B £82.50 to £137.50. Children welcome. Baby facilities. Garden. TV. Phone. Fax: (0206) 322752

---

**DENT Cumbria**  map 7

## ▲ *Stone Close* ⁵⁄* £

Main Street, Dent LA10 5QL  COOKING 1
DENT (053 96) 25231  COST £10–£18

Walkers and their families used to extol the home-cooking virtues of this café and guesthouse in picture-postcard farming cottages in a picture-postcard village. Stairs creak, beams intrude and the fires in the cast-iron ranges burn brightly. Since our last recommendation, Pat Barber and Graham Hudson have ceased to offer evening meals to all comers, while still cooking their hearts out during the day. Walkers will have to refuel mid-hike henceforth. The style – 'unfussy cooking for hungry people' – remains identical, with vegetable bakes, big salads, thick soups, apple pie and Wensleydale cheese. So does the good value and tolerant service: 'We had a two-year-old crawling about and it didn't disturb them.' Breakfasts are good if you stay the night. There is a tiny wine list and house wines cost £7.60 for a litre bottle.

CHEF: Patricia Barber  PROPRIETORS: Graham Hudson and Patricia Barber  OPEN: all week; 10.30am to 5.30pm  CLOSED: Jan and Feb, mid-week Nov to mid-March  MEALS: alc (main courses £3 to 4.50)  SERVICE: not inc  DETAILS: 45 seats. Private parties: 45 main room. Vegetarian meals. Children's helpings. No smoking. Wheelchair access (also WC). Music  ACCOMMODATION: 3 rooms. B&B £16 to £28. Deposit: £10. Pets welcome. Afternoon teas (*The Which? Hotel Guide*)

---

**DISS Norfolk**  map 6

## ▲ *Salisbury House* ⁵⁄*

84 Victoria Road, Diss IP22 3JG  COOKING 1*
DISS (0379) 644738  COST £29–£44

'A country house, but within a town' is the paradox that the Davies like to use as a shorthand description of their Victorian brick house encrusted with bay windows and creepers, adorned by a conservatory and protected by a ring of garden and double-glazing from the heat and dust of downtown Diss. The feel of the decoration, the 'tons of reading matter, fruit, and games' in the trio of bedrooms, and the personal welcome of the proprietors themselves all contribute to the 'country' epithet, as does the French and 'modern British' style of cooking: that certain refined richness that is met most often among the broad acres of mansions now put out to guests. Parsnip and orange soup finished with cream, monkfish and tomato fondue and rosemary butter sauce, chicken breast stuffed with a duck mousse and served with a port sauce, and beef fillet with Beaujolais sauce were followed by chestnut mousse surrounded by caramel sauce – the richness self-evident, the competence spoken for. The wine cellar is generously provided with half-bottles, even some older vintages in reds, and the general range is worth exploring. Javillier, Leroy, Guigal and Vincent are big names to bandy about, and there are clarets of like status. Some of the years need careful thought, and Barry Davies' advice on a 1969 Latour or 1973 Palmer in halves may be worth hearing. House wine is £7.55.

CHEF: Barry Davies   PROPRIETORS: Barry and Sue Davies   OPEN: Tue to Sat, D only (Tue to Fri L by arrangement 12.15 to 1.45); 7.30 to 9.15   CLOSED: 1 week Christmas, 2 weeks summer   MEALS: Set L and D £18.75 (2 courses) to £27   SERVICE: not inc   CARDS: Access, Visa   DETAILS: 34 seats. 2 tables outside. Private parties: 20 main room, 14 and 20 private rooms. Car park. Vegetarian meals with prior notice. Children's helpings. Smart dress preferred. No smoking in dining-room. Wheelchair access (1 step). Music
ACCOMMODATION: 3 rooms, all with bath/shower. B&B £39 to £67. Deposit: £20. Children welcome. Garden. TV. Doors close at 12.30am. Confirm by 6 (*The Which? Hotel Guide*)

## Weavers

**NEW ENTRY**

Market Hill, Diss IP22 3JZ
DISS (0379) 642411

COOKING 1
COST £14–£30

'A jolly place with good food and value,' reports someone relieved to find this spot in Diss, an attractive town in itself, but not overburdened with places to stop. 'Weavers is run by nice jolly ladies, who welcome everyone whether with push chairs or zimmer frames,' she continues. Under a mural of Diss market, surrounded by the beams and plasterwork of a weaver's house (*circa* 1400), people jostle for a sight of the menu on the blackboard and order some of the fish fresh in from Lowestoft: 'My Dover sole was enormous, moist, tender and wonderful; my husband's skate with black butter was all it should be.' Puddings can be gooey: an ice-cream pavlova with honey and raspberry sauce may not be correct but was great; a sticky toffee and banana pie ensured that no more work was done that day. Coffee is light. The more expensive and full menu at dinner – when upstairs is brought into operation – ranges wider than this description, but the cooking has much the same quality of generosity. The wine list may also be termed generous, for prices are not high, but the choices (especially French country and Australian wines) are very adequate. House wine is £7.95.

CHEF: William Bavin   PROPRIETORS: William and Wilma Bavin   OPEN: Mon to Sat, exc Sat L; 12 to 2, 7 to 9.30   CLOSED: 1 week from 24 Dec, 1 week from Aug bank hol Sun   MEALS: alc (main courses L £4.50 to £6.50, D £8.50 to £11)   SERVICE: not inc, card slips closed   CARDS: Access, Diners, Visa   DETAILS: 80 seats. Private parties: 45 main room, 45 private room. Vegetarian meals. Children's helpings. Smart dress preferred. No smoking before 2 L, 9 D. Wheelchair access. Music

*If a restaurant is new to the Guide this year (did not appear as a main entry in the last edition)* NEW ENTRY *appears opposite its name.*

---

**DORCHESTER Dorset** map 2

## *Mock Turtle*

34 High West Street, Dorchester DT1 1UP COOKING 1
DORCHESTER (0305) 264011 COST £19–£36

Who would have thought that Dorchester might see Cajun-blackened halibut
with a chilli salsa on the menu of one of its most popular eating-houses? The
Mock Turtle is a well-designed modern, open-plan restaurant that seats a fair
crowd – 'perhaps they should not do so many covers' was the reflection of one
person who has found them a little inconsistent from week to week. The menu
is quite adventurous, with cheerful dishes like rabbit, mushroom and bacon
pie, or lamb served on coriander rice with a piquant sauce, or baked crumbed
chicken breast sitting on an artichoke purée with a Dorset Blue Vinny cheese
sauce. Fish comes in fresh from Weymouth, where the Hodders have another
restaurant, Perry's (see entry), and gives variety to the seasonal menu. It helps
having Eldridge Pope as your local wine merchant and the list relects its
proximity. House wines are £7.95.

CHEFS: Raymond Hodder and Caroline Stevenson PROPRIETORS: Raymond, Alan and
Vivien Hodder OPEN: Mon to Sat, exc L Mon and Sat; 12 to 2, 7 to 10 CLOSED: 26 Dec
MEALS: Set L £9.50 (2 courses) to £12, Set D £16 (2 courses) to £22 SERVICE: not inc
CARDS: Access, Visa DETAILS: 60 seats. Private parties: 60 main room. Vegetarian meals.
Children welcome. Wheelchair access (1 step). Music

---

**DORKING Surrey** map 3

## *Partners West Street*

2, 3 and 4 West Street, Dorking RH4 1BL COOKING 3
DORKING (0306) 882826 COST £15–£48

This ancient house, hard on the side of the street with parking a distance away,
has been thoroughly made over – ground floor and the floor above – to give a
late-Elizabethan dining experience. People appreciate the no-smoking zone
downstairs, but regret when it is not offered or explained to them. People also
appreciate the efforts made by a kitchen to be all things to all men; to offer high
and low prices. This means that there are several strains to the output: some
things are boring, others more exciting. Pursuit of economy may not be to
everyone's benefit. When properly taxed, there is good food to be had. 'My
duck was marinated in mango and soy. This just cut the richness,' said one
person who had started with skate served with spinach and mushrooms done
to his special order. Other people have endorsed the twice-cooked goats'
cheese and hazelnut soufflé, the mushroom ravioli with mixed vegetables,
seafood casserole with squat lobster sauce, and rendezvous of fish with
vermouth and cream sauce. Pastry cooking is excellent here, as is the
cheeseboard. Some of the 'plainer' food has impressed less. Service seems too
often left in the hands of the unskilled, especially when the food is at these
prices. The wine list is acceptable but could be more exciting. House wines are
£9.95. For details of Partners Brasserie, see entry under North Cheam, Surrey.

CHEFS: Tim McEntire, Adrian Walton, Paul Ager and Nathan Darling   PROPRIETORS:
Partners Restaurants plc   OPEN: Tue to Sun, exc Sat L and Sun D; 12.30 to 2, 7.30 to 9.30
MEALS: alc (main courses L £8 to £15, D £14 to £16).   Set L £9.95, Set D £19.95   CARDS:
Access, Amex, Diners, Visa   SERVICE: net prices, card slips closed   DETAILS: 43 seats.
Private parties: 36 main room, 18 and 36 private rooms. Vegetarian meals. Children's
helpings Sun L. No children under 5 D. Smart dress preferred. No-smoking area.
Wheelchair access (2 steps). No music

---

**DORRINGTON Shropshire**                                                    map 4

## ▲ *Country Friends*

Dorrington SY5 7JD
DORRINGTON (0743) 718707                                       COOKING 3
on A49, 5m S of Shrewsbury                                     COST £24–£41

'Peaceful it isn't, right on the narrow A49 with its heavy traffic.' Once you are
inside, though, the noise of internal combustion disappears; the logs on the
hearth spit gently; and the pink and chocolate colour scheme, modulated by the
carnations and conifer sprigs on the tables, completes the sense of warm
restfulness. The Whittakers' shopping and bread-making (slices of dark,
almost chocolatey Shropshire Brown, unbleached white rolls, and a rosemary-
flavoured wholemeal roll) are as good as ever, and the cooking is never less
than steady. Result: 'I don't think it would be possible to have a bad meal
here.' Certainly, halibut with wild mushrooms and smoked oysters left one
practised eater wondering whether she had ever had such an exciting fish dish
('The fish was meltingly *à point*, and full of flavour', while heating the
Abergavenny smoked oysters in the fish stock lent it 'an almost decadent,
slightly toffeed flavour'). Other approved dishes include salmon with a lime
crust, duck breast marinated in ginger with a plum sauce, and wild rabbit
saddle cooked pink and juicy, set around a spinach stuffing containing the
chopped rabbit liver. Some feel that a less ambitious approach to vegetables
would reap dividends. Desserts call variously on gin, white chocolate, poppy
seeds and 'surprisingly translucent' caramel sauce. Smoking is banned in
principle, 'but occasionally one [smoker] gets through the net'. The wine list,
printed with the hyperopic in mind, contains jolly bottles such as Penfolds' Bin
389 and Beaucastel Châteauneuf; producers' names, though, are occasionally
omitted (critically for the Chablis), and there are no notes or descriptions.
Prices begin at £9.50.

CHEF: Timothy Greaves   PROPRIETORS: Charles and Pauline Whittaker   OPEN: Tue to Sat;
12 to 2, 7 to 9 (9.30 Sat)   CLOSED: Christmas, last 2 weeks July, Oct half-term mid-week
PRICES: alc (main courses £11 to £14). Set L and D £16.90   SERVICE: not inc   CARDS:
Access, Amex, Visa   DETAILS: 45 seats. Private parties: 45 main room. Car park. Vegetarian
meals with prior notice. Children welcome. No smoking while others eat. Wheelchair
access (1 step). No music   ACCOMMODATION: 3 rooms, 1 with bath/shower. B&B £35 to
£42. Deposit: £20. Children welcome. Garden

---

*'To finish: peach soufflés. I was not intending to have a second soufflé but one of my party
passed out and I ate her pudding.'*   On eating in the Channel Islands

---

**DREWSTEIGNTON Devon**                                      map 1

## ▲ *Hunts Tor House* ✸

Drewsteignton EX6 6QW                                    COOKING 2
DREWSTEIGNTON (0647) 21228                              COST £23–£27

After years of struggling for planning permission, Sue and Chris Harrison now
have a bona fide restaurant as part of their guesthouse. But there are limits. The
dining-room is restricted to a maximum of eight people, non-residents must
book in advance and acceptance is determined by the numbers game – a full
house of guests means that enquiries from outsiders will be declined. This
sensitively restored private residence on the village square has a little garden
that supplies the kitchen with organic produce. Reporters are seduced and
beguiled by its very special style. Sue Harrison cooks a no-choice set dinner
that changes regularly and looks to Devon for supplies and inspiration. 'After
one of Chris Harrison's lethal cocktails,' writes a contented soul, 'dinner started
with a delicious salmon and spinach terrine.' Following on was lamb charlotte
lined with aubergines, then lemon soufflé on a caramel and Grand Marnier
sauce, and finally local cheeses. Other diners have mentioned broccoli mousse
with tomato coulis, chicken with soy sauce and ginger, and almond parfait
with raspberry coulis. Visitors might also be treated to smoked pigeon and
lentil salad, boned baby guinea-fowl stuffed with mushrooms and spinach on
an elderberry sauce, and sticky toffee pudding. The wine list is short, but few
dispute the quality or the price. House Duboeuf is £7.

CHEF: Sue Harrison   PROPRIETORS: Sue and Chris Harrison   OPEN: all week, D only; 7.30
(book 1 day ahead)   CLOSED: end Nov to end Feb (telephone to check)   MEALS: Set D
£17   SERVICE: not inc   DETAILS: 8 seats. Private parties: 12 main room. Vegetarian meals
with prior notice. No children under 14. Smart dress preferred. No smoking in dining-
room. Music   ACCOMMODATION: 4 rooms, all with bath/shower. B&B £25 to £50. Deposit:
£10 per night. No children under 14. Pets welcome in bedrooms. Doors close at midnight.
Confirm by 3 (*The Which? Hotel Guide*)

---

**DRYBROOK Gloucestershire**                                map 2

## *Cider Press* ✸                            | NEW ENTRY |

The Cross, Drybrook GL17 9EB                              COOKING 2
DEAN (0594) 544472                                      COST £21–£41

An old-fashioned cider press stands near the door of this pretty little country
restaurant in the heart of the Forest of Dean. Apple-patterned curtains hang in
the windows and the tables are named after varieties of cider apple, while corn
dollies, dried flowers and pictures of fruit reinforce the rustic mood of the
place. Despite the name, the cooking has a distinct Mediterranean slant,
although it also looks to the English past for inspiration. The menu is
refreshingly short and might feature smoked venison and orange salad dressed
with extra-virgin olive oil, home-made black pasta with oyster mushrooms,
beef en daube and fried goose breast with black cherries and kirsch sauce. Fish
is delivered twice a week: monkfish with lime sauce and lobster with garlic
butter have been heartily endorsed. Reporters have also commented favourably

on smoked mackerel and apple pâté and a sixteenth-century dish of Cotswold lamb stuffed with apples, sage, garlic and cloves and basted with cider. Vegetables are steamed. Cheeses always include a strong Welsh contingent including Pencarreg and Llanboidy, while desserts are often fruity confections such as pear roulade. Bernadette Fitzpatrick is a charming hostess. The short, reasonably priced wine list suggests a noticeable allegiance to organic production. House wines start at £7.50.

CHEF: Christopher Challener   PROPRIETOR: Bernadette Fitzpatrick   OPEN: Wed to Mon, D only (Wed to Sun L by arrangement); 7 to 10 (1 day's notice D Sun and Mon 31 Oct to 30 Apr)   MEALS: alc (main courses £8 to £16.50)   SERVICE: not inc   CARDS: Access, Amex, Visa   DETAILS: 24 seats. Private parties: 30 main room. Vegetarian meals with prior notice. Children welcome. Smart dress preferred. No smoking in dining-room. Wheelchair access (also WC). Music

---

**EAST BOLDON** Tyne & Wear                                                                  map 7

## Forsters

2 St Bedes, Station Road,
East Boldon NE36 0LE
091-519 0929                                                                   COOKING 3*
on main Newcastle to Sunderland road                                    COST £26–£39

'Our only complaint was that our daughter's duck was neither tender nor crisp. Result? No charge for it.' Out of disaster can come shining triumph and the Forsters won this customer over with hospitality, the ability to cook (bar this item), and the charm of the place – though few tourists would send a postcard from East Boldon. Barry Forster's style is understated neo-classicism, avoiding the wild side of modernism, yet having proper regard for prime materials, intense flavours in his sauces, and a lack of mannerisms when building up a dish. Reports speak favourably of crisp (this time) breast of duck with black pudding and olive oil mash, and chicken breast with a mild garlic and sage mousse stuffing. The range of joints and ingredients does not take in a lot of offal or funny bits – it runs counter to the region's taste perhaps. Bitter lemon tart with thick cream is all it says it is, and the crème brûlée has the perfect crisp topping. Sue Forster copes – often single-handedly – with the front-of-house and impresses everybody. The wine list is compact – names like Viénot, Duboeuf, Dry Creek and Chapoutier give reliability, but length is not so great as to permit variety. House wines are Duboeuf at £7.65.

CHEF: Barry Forster   PROPRIETORS: Barry and Sue Forster   OPEN: Tue to Sat, D only; 7 to 10.30   MEALS: alc (main courses £11 to £13)   SERVICE: not inc   CARDS: Access, Amex, Diners, Visa   DETAILS: 28 seats. Private parties: 30 main room. Car park. Children's helpings. No children under 10. Smart dress preferred. No cigars/pipes in dining-room. Wheelchair access (2 steps). Music

---

*Several sharp operators have tried to extort money from restaurateurs on the promise of an entry in a guidebook that has never appeared.* The Good Food Guide *makes no charge for inclusion and does not offer certificates of any kind.*

---

## ▲ Grand Hotel, Mirabelle

Jevington Gardens, Eastbourne BN21 4EQ                    COOKING 2*
EASTBOURNE (0323) 410771                                  COST £26–£59

Cocooned from the mad whirl of Eastbourne and the intemperate bite of sea-front squalls by a womb of pastel drapery, this high-ceilinged, low-windowed restaurant, with its entrance separate from the hotel, continues to please both palates and nerves. Mitchell and Wiggins buy only ingredients: bread, pasta, pastry and chocolates are all made in the kitchen, and most of the dishes on the *carte* bear the hallmarks of enthusiastic industry – monkfish, itself cocooned in Parma ham, Dover sole plumped out with spinach mousseline, asparagus-flecked scrambled egg cased in puff pastry with a wild mushroom sauce, noisette of veal peeping from beneath a leek-and-chive soubise. The set-price lunch and dinner menus are simpler, though varied: conservatives salute the mobile daily roast, yet salmon and mussels paired with carrot and coriander, or chicken breast rusticised with green lentils and a braised ham sauce, please the wilder at heart. Cheeses and desserts are much lauded – 'I have never had a poor course at the Mirabelle,' reports one diner, replete with chocolate crème brûlée. Service is good, though it can slow towards the end of the evening. Non-smokers and smokers may both care to note that lighting-up time is 2 at lunch and 9 in the evening. The wine list stretches from white Lambrusco (distressing at any price, but especially so at £13.50) to Dom. de la Romanée Conti's 1982 La Tâche (£110). It lacks the sparkle to tempt abandonment of the six-wine 'house selection' offered by the glass (£2.50 to £3.10) or bottle (£12.50 to £15.50).

CHEFS: Keith Mitchell and Neil Wiggins  PROPRIETORS: De Vere Hotels  OPEN: Tue to Sat; 12.30 to 2.30, 7 to 10  CLOSED: 1 week Jan, 2 weeks Aug  MEALS: alc (main courses £16 to £22). Set L £14.50 (2 courses) to £17.50, Set D £20.50 to £27.50. Minimum £20.50 SERVICE: not inc, card slips closed  CARDS: Access, Amex, Diners, Visa  DETAILS: 50 seats. Private parties: 50 main room, 70 to 400 private rooms. Car park. Vegetarian meals. Children's helpings. Smart dress preferred. No cigars/pipes in dining-room. Wheelchair access. No music. Air-conditioned  ACCOMMODATION: 161 rooms, all with bath/shower. Rooms for disabled. Lift. B&B £67 to £134. Children welcome. Baby facilities. Pets welcome (not in lounges or gardens). Afternoon teas. Garden. Swimming-pool. Sauna. Snooker. TV. Phone. Confirm by 7. Fax: (0323) 412233

## ▲ Lower Pitt ⅝✕

East Buckland EX32 0TD
FILLEIGH (0598) 760243                                    COOKING 2
2m N of A361, 4m NW of South Molton                       COST £23–£33

For students of vernacular architecture, Lower Pitt is a useful example of an Exmoor longhouse: and of twentieth-century conservatory construction for enthusiasts of recent social history. Lower Pitt's charms may depend on the weather and the time of year: the hardy will feel no lowering of spirits, but many would rather it were sunny. The Lyons have soldiered on through rain and shine, composting their organic vegetables in order to get second prize in the county council's recycling competition with one hand, while energetically tracking down local suppliers and growers with the other. Materials may be changed by the time they reach the table: pork comes pan-fried with cider and mustard, lamb is cooked Kashmiri-style, while chicken is given sesame oil, root ginger and lemon grass. Lower Pitt offers that country-restaurant style of local goods and one-world recipes. There are no complaints as to the food, especially when the meal finishes with something like sticky toffee banana split (another sure marker of the style) or chocolate roulade. And, on sunny days at least, there are no complaints about the cheerfulness of greeting and happiness of ambience. The wine list will please everyone by having Ch. Musar 1986 at an advantageous price, and a perfectly reasonable general selection for the rest of the world. House wines number a baker's dozen and run from £8.50 to £13.90.

CHEF: Suzanne Lyons   PROPRIETORS: Jerome and Suzanne Lyons   OPEN: Tue to Sat, D only; 7 to 9   MEALS: alc (main courses £9 to £10)   SERVICE: not inc, card slips closed   CARDS: Access, Amex, Visa   DETAILS: 32 seats. Private parties: 16 main room, 16 private room. Car park. Vegetarian meals. No children under 5. Smart dress preferred. No smoking in dining-room. No music   ACCOMMODATION: 3 rooms, all with bath/shower. D,B&B £55 to £110. Deposit: 10%. No children under 12. Garden. Doors close at 11. Confirm by 6. Fax: (0598) 760243 (*The Which? Hotel Guide*)

---

**EAST GRINSTEAD  West Sussex**                                           map 3

## ▲ *Gravetye Manor* ▮ ✳

Vowels Lane, East Grinstead RH19 4LJ
SHARPTHORNE (0342) 810567                                    COOKING 2*
off B2028, 2m SW of East Grinstead                           COST £35–£73

No one will question the magnificence. The house, built in 1598, was taken by the scruff of the neck at the turn of the century by pioneering gardener William Robinson, who repanelled the rooms and did up the gardens (they alone make the visit a necessity). Gravetye was then improved and consolidated (and here and there added to) by Peter Herbert, himself a pioneer of the country-house hotel movement. The comfort is as deep as the upholstery, the atmosphere as palpable as the wood-smoke from the fires. The place is best enjoyed as a destination for a day: gardens, woodland, a meal, a cup of tea. Sometimes a hint of regimentation surfaces at night: if there are lots of people, they are processed in waves. Stephen Morey's menu seems attractive, but would be more informative if prices were given to anyone other than the host (what happens if the party is going Dutch?). It may also suffer from variation of ingredients – a rocket and corn salad turned out to be endive and watercress on one occasion – and from meagreness: a smoked haddock and leek mousse was 'tiny'. While standards can be satisfactory in dishes such as saddle of rabbit wrapped in bacon, stuffed with prunes and served on polenta, or venison with red cabbage and glazed onions – perhaps meat cookery comes off the best – there has been comment that tastes do not always get through the dome lifting and plating – truffle ravioli with fugitive flavour, no ginger discernible with a breast of duck. Techniques have sometimes also been awry, for instance a disintegrating haddock mousse, or a solid, unimpressive bread-and-butter pudding. Though the set-price meals offer better value, the cost of it all (and you have to add VAT to the menu prices) is very high. The same might be said of the wines. The range is brilliant, but at a price. The cost, however, supports a remarkable superstructure that is worth every effort to preserve. If you want a bargain, the Australian and New Zealand bins are the best bet. House wines are £15.50 for generic burgundy from Louis Latour (then add the VAT).

CHEF: Stephen Morey   PROPRIETORS: Peter Herbert and Leigh Stone-Herbert   OPEN: all week; 12.30 to 2, 7.30 to 9.30 (9 Sun)   MEALS: alc (main courses £16 to £23 – plus VAT). Set L £22, Set Sun L £26, Set D £26 (all plus VAT)   SERVICE: inc (but VAT added)   CARDS: Access, Visa   DETAILS: 50 seats. Private parties: 8 main room, 20 private room. Car park. Vegetarian meals. Children's helpings. No children under 7. Smart dress preferred. No smoking in dining-room. Wheelchair access. No music   ACCOMMODATION: 18 rooms, all with bath/shower. B&B £108 to £240. Deposit: £108. No children under 7 (exc 'babes in arms'). Baby facilities. Garden. Fishing. TV. Phone. Doors close at midnight. Confirm by 9am. Fax: (0342) 810080 (*The Which? Hotel Guide*)

---

**EASTON ON THE HILL  Northamptonshire**                                           map 6

## *Exeter Arms* £

Stamford Road, Easton on the Hill PE9 3NF
STAMFORD (0780) 57503                                             COOKING 1
off A43, 2m SW of Stamford                                     COST £14–£30

The signs by the side of the road proclaim this pub and restaurant's true pride: meat. David Waycot cooks on a chargrill and the beefsteaks are to be recommended. There are alternatives – even lobster – and they are carefully cooked for the most part. The plates may be piled with extra bits that are deemed essential to enjoyment but are not. The service is cheerful and obliging and there is a pleasant intermingling of pub and restaurant trade so that diners, while getting proper tables, are not banished to some food ghetto while the rest of the world enjoys itself. House wine is £8.50.

CHEF/PROPRIETOR: David Waycot   OPEN: Tue to Sun; 12 to 3, 7 to 10.30   MEALS: alc (main courses £5.50 to £12)   SERVICE: not inc   DETAILS: 60 seats. 10 tables outside. Private parties: 60 main room, 10 private room. Car park. Vegetarian meals. Children's helpings. No-smoking area. Wheelchair access (also WC). Music

---

**EDENBRIDGE  Kent**                                                               map 3

## *Honours Mill*

87 High Street, Edenbridge TN8 5AU                               COOKING 3
EDENBRIDGE (0732) 866757                                         COST £19–£44

The name, which might describe a retirement home for senior civil servants, has grainier origins, as recalled by the props in this bright, upstairs restaurant at the southern end of Edenbridge's long, straggling High Street. Both the cane-furnished downstairs bar and the intimacy of upstairs charm the diner (who must remember to dodge the low rafters), with pond views and fresh flowers, pretty plates and glasses, deft lighting and original pictures; the weatherboarded exterior promises much less. Lunch remains the bargain, where you can eat three courses (and coffee) for less than the price of a bottle of Muscadet on the wine list; one of the dinner options includes a half-bottle of wine. In the kitchen, the aim is high; some feel that execution strains on tiptoes to match it, occasionally tottering – as when an over-smoky, over-wine-charged sauce 'blitzed' an intricate snail vol-au-vent, or when lamb cleverly dressed in green (a herb stuffing, a Savoy overcoat) proved 'tough and unappetising'. But the ideas are always good, fundamentals (terrine of red mullet served with a well-made beurre blanc, or properly dressed salad leaves beneath sliced duck breast) are firmly in place, and some of the fancier flights, like the 'tasty and unusual' sweetbread sausage with green peppercorns on a bed of lentils, work memorably. Desserts (from passion-fruit and orange tart to winter and Sussex pond puddings) please; petits fours are skilled; and gratitude for generous helpings has replaced jibes about not-so-nouvelle cuisine. Service is 'kind and helpful'. The wine list makes a fairly determined attempt to recoup revenue, and £15 does not get you far; the range of halves is good, though.

CHEFS: Neville Goodhew and Martin Radmall  PROPRIETORS: Neville, Duncan and Giles Goodhew  OPEN: Tue to Sun, exc Sat L and Sun D; 12.15 to 2, 7.15 to 10  MEALS: Set L £14.50 to £31.75, Set D £20.50 to £31.75  SERVICE: net prices  CARDS: Access, Amex, Visa  DETAILS: 40 seats. Private parties: 40 main room. Vegetarian meals with prior notice. Children's helpings Sun L. Smart dress preferred. No music

---

ELTON Cambridgeshire                                                    map 6

## Loch Fyne Oyster Bar  £

The Old Dairy, Elton PE8 6SE
OUNDLE (0832) 280298
off A1 at A605 junction (Peterborough                        COOKING 1
to Northampton road), then 3m                                COST £15–£36

The long, low conversion of a former model dairy to the estate is kept as plain and simple as the headquarters of the Loch Fyne operation in Scotland. This makes it eminently suitable for a lunch, less so for a romantic tryst in the evening. The choice of fish depends on the day's delivery from Scotland, but may include hot smoked salmon, perhaps salmon or halibut, a selection of shellfish and, of course, oysters. Applause has come for the Loch Fyne kippers, as well as for the oysters, and for the straightforward approach to fish cookery. Less praise is heard for the ancillaries, and the service sometimes appears untutored. Afternoon teas with home-made cakes are also available. The wine list stays short, with house Gros Plant and the house claret both very drinkable and costing £7.95.

CHEF: Alan Haran  PROPRIETORS: Loch Fyne Oysters Ltd  OPEN: all week; 9am to 9pm (10 Fri and Sat)  MEALS: alc (main courses £5 to £12)  SERVICE: not inc  CARDS: Access, Amex, Visa  DETAILS: 100 seats. 8 tables outside. Private parties: 60 main room, 12 and 60 private rooms. Car park. Vegetarian meals. Children's helpings. Wheelchair access (also WC). Music

---

**ELY Cambridgeshire** map 6

## *Old Fire Engine House* ♥ ✱

25 St Mary's Street, Ely CB7 4ER COOKING 1
ELY (0353) 662582 COST £21–£35

The excitement for many customers is two-fold. What wines will they find on Michael Jarman's list of bin-ends, and will there be any good paintings on show in the gallery room? As the years roll by, the Old Fire Engine House – an exact description – has added more than mere cooking to the ingredients of its strong appeal to locals and visitors alike. There is the varied character of the rooms, from small yet welcoming bar to modern and comfortable lounge upstairs, to the large dining-room with undulating floor that is reached by passing before the kitchen. There is also the fresh and unforced service that makes you feel like a human being. Then there is the food. 'Farmhouse cooking' is a useful description. A certain sense of history exists in some of the recipes, and a sense of continuity in the menu itself. Elaboration is kept to a minimum, especially with the first courses, and slow-cooking is a favoured technique for main dishes. Desserts have a timeless appeal. At times expectation falls short of the image. The wine list is a gem of considered choice and economy. The bin ends give adventure at little cost. House wines are £6.60 but it is worth spending more for the fun of it. CELLARMAN'S CHOICE: Chardonnay 1991 Marqués de Casa Coucha, £9.40; Côtes de Bourg Ch. Pont du Roy 1988, £9.

---

CHEF: Terri Kindred PROPRIETORS: Ann Ford and Michael Jarman OPEN: all week, exc Sun D (by arrangement); 12.30 to 2, 7.30 to 9 CLOSED: 24 Dec to 6 Jan, bank hols MEALS: alc (main courses £9.50 to £13) SERVICE: not inc CARDS: Access, Visa DETAILS: 60 seats. 8 tables outside. Private parties: 36 main room, 12, 24 and 36 private rooms. Car park. Vegetarian meals. Children's helpings. No smoking in 1 dining-room. Music

---

**EMSWORTH Hampshire** map 2

## *Spencers*

36 North Street, Emsworth PO10 7DG COOKING 2
EMSWORTH (0243) 372744 COST £16–£35

There are not many gas-lit restaurants in Britain – this is one of them and it dimly adds to the atmosphere of nook and cranny, small corners and little touches. The apprehensive may be comforted that it was not the cause of the fire which interrupted one reader's meal for 15 minutes while the brigade was called. While the light reflects off polished tables, Denis Spencer enlivens a conventional set of choices with orientalisms in dishes such as grilled chicken Java, or beef tien la, cooked with peppers, red wine and chilli. Smoked foods, as in salmon, scallops and mackerel, give a certain character to the menu. Competence was confirmed in a meal of asparagus tart with cream cheese and an asparagus and chive sauce; pigeon breasts with apricots and a port sauce; and a multi-layered sorbet terrine on a blackcurrant sauce. The wine list is short, with the New World contributing some useful single-figure drinking. House wines are £8.25.

CHEF: Denis Spencer   PROPRIETORS: Denis and Lesley Spencer   OPEN: Tue to Sat, exc Sat L; 12.30 to 2, 7.30 to 10.30   MEALS: alc L (main courses £6 to £7.50). Set Tue to Thur D £16 (2 courses) to £19.50, Tue to Sat £19.50 to £22   SERVICE: not inc, card slips closed   CARDS: Access, Amex, Visa   DETAILS: 45 seats. Private parties: 26 main room, 12 private room. Vegetarian meals. Children welcome. Smart dress preferred. No cigars/pipes before 10pm in dining-room. Music. Air-conditioned

---

## EPWORTH Humberside                                                          map 5

### Epworth Tap ▌ ⁵✳ £

9–11 Market Place, Epworth DN9 1EU
EPWORTH (0427) 873333                                              COOKING 2
3m S of M180, junction 2                                          COST £17–£28

John Wynne has taken a seat slightly nearer the back of this essential wine bar (essential, that is, to anyone with a palate on Humberside). Ill-health has forced him to work less, but the wine list is still a winner, and the food, under the supervision of Helen Wynne, continues to evolve. 'I discovered that my wife was using our best amontillado to make the chicken liver pâté,' he reports, 'so I substituted an old (and cheaper) oloroso.' Would that everyone were so generous. The food here has character and is by no means out of touch with bigger-city thinking. A red pepper sauce made with the best olive oil comes with the spinach and smoked salmon terrine; jambon persillé is transmogrified into ham with a riesling jelly; beef is dropped in favour of farmed venison; duck is served with a honey and five-spice sauce; and the spare ribs continue their steady sale. Good materials, good cheeses and really fresh vegetables are three more components for a meal distinguished by ever-present enthusiasm. The careful and considerate eye of John Wynne assures wines displaying any uncertainty are offered at bargain prices. Italy is as strongly represented as anywhere, with nicely matured Chiantis of top quality – Isole e Olena and Selvapiana – and Piedmont from Mascarello; but with Vouvray from Huet, Rolly-Gassmann Alsaces and a fine range of claret choice is difficult. Excellent halves and fair prices reign throughout. House wine is £7.95. CELLARMAN'S CHOICE: Zeltinger Himmelreich Riesling Kabinett 1988, Mönchhof, £7.95; Keyneston Estate, Shiraz/Cabernet 1989, Henschke, £14.50.

---

CHEFS: Helen Wynne and Noreen Smith   PROPRIETORS: Helen and John Wynne   OPEN: Wed to Sat, D only; 7.30 to 10 (10.30 Sat)   MEALS: alc (main courses £5.50 to £8.50). Set D £15.95   SERVICE: not inc, card slips closed   CARDS: Access, Amex, Visa   DETAILS: 70 seats. Private parties: 30 main room, 24 private room. Vegetarian meals with prior notice. Children welcome. Smart dress preferred. No smoking in 1 dining-room. Wheelchair access (3 steps). Music

---

⁵✳ indicates that smoking is either banned altogether or that a dining-room is maintained for non-smokers. The symbol does not apply to restaurants that simply have no-smoking areas.

£ indicates that it is possible to have a three-course meal, including coffee, a half-bottle of house wine and service, at any time the restaurant is open (i.e. at dinner as well as at lunch, unless a place is open only for dinner), for £20 or less per person.

---

ERPINGHAM Norfolk map 6

## ▲ *Ark*

The Street, Erpingham NR11 7QB
CROMER (0263) 761535 COOKING 2
on A140 Cromer road, 4m N of Aylsham COST £17–£35

'Cosy', 'quiet' and 'rural' are fair descriptions of Mike and Sheila Kidd's well-established cottage restaurant. 'Now that we have rooms, we could be open evenings all week, so worth a phone call.' There seems to be some dispute about the mood of the place, but there is little argument about Sheila's cooking. Her short handwritten menus cover a lot of territory and bristle with vivid ideas without ever becoming modish: aubergine three ways; rocket, mango and Parma ham salad; beef daube with olives and gremolada; spring lamb, herb roasted with flageolet beans; grilled salmon with herb butter and sun-dried tomato sauce. A trio of vegetarian pâtés with home-baked bread has been most enjoyable, while saddle of hare in herb cream has been 'memorable'. Vegetables are crisp and 'wonderfully fresh', and cheeses are from the farmhouse. Sweets have included luxurious, creamy trifle, spot-on brown-bread ice-cream, and tangy lemon tart. One party's Sunday lunch yielded beef cooked to perfection and 'by far the best roast potatoes we had ever eaten'. An abandoned enthusiasm infuses the wine list with scrawled additions here, prices slashed there and an invitation to discuss price and state of maturity of as yet unrevealed magnums. For the timid a careful selection of almost cheap house wines makes life possible; for the knowledgeable some really cracking wines are on offer, but as details are not always clear an enquiry may help. Meanwhile the Chianti from Villa de Vetrice and the Cloudy Bay wines look like bargains. House wines are from £7.50.

CHEFS: Sheila and Bec Kidd PROPRIETORS: Mike and Sheila Kidd OPEN: Tue to Sat, D only, and Sun L; 12.30 to 2, 7 to 9.30 CLOSED: Oct MEALS: Set L £11.75, Set D £15.75 (2 courses) to £20. Minimum D £15.75 SERVICE: not inc DETAILS: 36 seats. Private parties: 36 main room, 30 private room. Car park. Vegetarian meals. Children's helpings. Smart dress preferred. No smoking in dining-room. Wheelchair access (also WC). No music ACCOMMODATION: 3 rooms, 2 with bath/shower. Rooms for disabled. D,B&B £55 to £95. Children welcome. Baby facilities. Garden. TV

EVERSHOT Dorset map 2

## ▲ *Summer Lodge*

Evershot DT2 0JR COOKING 3
EVERSHOT (0935) 83424 COST £25–£65

'It is the general result that is so good,' reports one diner. 'Service, décor, flowers, drinks, food, pre-dinner titbits and coffee all make one purr.' Those who stay, rather than simply dine, at this Georgian country house ('*so* cared for') in Hardy country agree that 'the overall experience of pleasure' is its distinction, generous breakfasts and afternoon teas adding to the contentment of lunch and dinner. Changes during the year include the recruitment of Martin Lee from Le Manoir aux Quat'Saisons. Attention to detail is evident, from nibbles (smoked salmon in filo pastry, grilled John Dory and yellow peppers on cocktail sticks), through 'outstanding' home-baked bread to the 'eight types of mint' served, on one occasion, with coffee. Consistency has improved, and the choice of ingredients and methods, thought one analyst, is 'perfectly suited to a country-house hotel with older and wealthier clients whose tastes are likely to be on the conservative side'. Conservative perhaps, but not timid: lobster ravioli, pan-fried calves' sweetbreads on a spinach and Sauternes sauce, and John Dory in a tomato liquor with basil sauce indicate creative effort; only mussels on cardamom cabbage rang false. Special requests are met sympathetically: a red wine sauce with fish was replaced by white; appetisers of battered fresh herring were so enjoyed they were served on request as a main course. Soups (mushroom and sherry, parsnip and ginger, tomato and mint, leek and potato) are admired, as is the habit of leaving the tureen on the table for second helpings if wished; vegetables, though, are a little too al dente for some. Puddings gratify, from home-made ice-creams to individual pavlovas. Service, slow sometimes, is always friendly. The wine list begins with a flourish of sherries by the glass and ends with fine vintage cognac from Hine; between lies a richly upholstered wine list of classical cast. House wine is from £9.95. CELLARMAN'S CHOICE: Sylvaner 1990, Rolly-Gassmann, £16.50; Fixin, 'Les Chenevrières' 1988, Moncaut, £24.

CHEF: Martin Lee   PROPRIETORS: Nigel and Margaret Corbett   OPEN: all week; 12.30 to 1.45, 7 to 9   MEALS: alc (main courses £15.50 to £22.50). Set Sun L £17.50, Set L £17.50 (2 courses) to £19.50, Set D £25   SERVICE: not inc, card slips closed   CARDS: Access, Amex, Visa   DETAILS: 50 seats. 10 tables outside. Private parties: 70 main room, 8 and 20 private rooms. Car park. Vegetarian meals. Children's helpings. No children under 8 D. Smart dress preferred. No smoking while others eat. Wheelchair access (2 steps; also WC). No music   ACCOMMODATION: 17 rooms, all with bath/shower. Rooms for disabled. B&B £100 to £200. Deposit: £50. Children welcome. Pets welcome. Afternoon teas. Garden. Swimming-pool. Tennis. TV. Phone. Doors close at midnight. Fax: (0935) 83005 *(The Which? Hotel Guide)*

---

**EVESHAM Hereford & Worcester**      map 2

## ▲ *Evesham Hotel,*
## *Cedar Restaurant* ❢

Cooper's Lane, Evesham WR11 6DA       COOKING 2
EVESHAM (0386) 765566       COST £16–£40

The Jenkinsons remain in firm control of this family-run, family-oriented hotel with a giant cedar of Lebanon on the lawn. The tree was planted in 1809, there are mulberry trees elsewhere in the grounds that have a few centuries on that, and the house was first put up in 1540. Endless changes have been seen since then, not least the reconstruction of the original front: 'As no one can detect we've done it,' writes John Jenkinson, 'there's no need to mention it.' The strenuous efforts made by the hotel to please and entertain its customers – hence the constant flow of jest on all the menus, wine lists and other productions from the hotel office – pay off in satisfaction, and the Cedar Restaurant is not exempt. The cooking is substantial, eclectic and fair value. It looks for high flavours and uses devilling, cheese toppings, curry powder and spices to achieve its ends in dishes such as Soyer's chicken, 'Belshaw Puffs' (choux buns with Parmesan, spring onion, coriander and cream cheese), and 'rendezvous of seafood' with curry powder, dill and paprika. You can bet that puddings are in keeping, whether rhubarb fool, sticky toffee, or cherry and nut strudel. The cheerful production of the food is topped by the wine list (and endless lists of hard liquors too). This covers every country except France and has some distinguished items in its pages, whether Vega Sicilia 1960, a good range of South Africans, Trefethen from California, and Heitz. Value is excellent, the choice is beguiling. House wines are from Chile and cost £8.40.

CHEF: Ian Mann   PROPRIETORS: the Jenkinson family   OPEN: all week; 12.30 to 2, 7 to 9.30   CLOSED: 25 and 26 Dec   MEALS: alc (main courses £7 L to £16.50)   SERVICE: net prices, card slips closed   CARDS: Access, Amex, Diners, Visa   DETAILS: 55 seats. Private parties: 12 main room, 15 private room. Car park. Vegetarian meals. Children's helpings. No cigars/pipes in dining-room. No music   ACCOMMODATION: 40 rooms, all with bath/shower. B&B £58 to £92. Children welcome. Baby facilities. Pets welcome (not in public rooms). Afternoon teas. Garden. Swimming-pool. TV. Phone. Confirm by 5. Fax: (0386) 765566 (*The Which? Hotel Guide*)

---

**EXETER Devon**                                                                            map 1

## Lamb's  £                                                          | NEW ENTRY |

15 Lower North Street, Exeter EX4 3ET                                  COOKING 1
EXETER (0392) 54269                                                   COST £16–£30

'Lamb's turned a tiresome journey from London to Penzance into a merry jaunt, and we didn't need any supper at the end of it' was the message from one travel-weary writer. The young team that have opened this place, in the shadow of Exeter's Victorian iron bridge (a sort of south-western Holborn Viaduct), have won hearts and minds with their willingness to please, their intelligent approach to the wine list, their prices, and their determination to make everything (except the cheeses) themselves using organic vegetables and decent materials. One new regular comments that it takes something to surprise a seasoned native but Lamb's has done it with some interesting new flavours. Prawns and duck may be home-smoked, or something unexpected inserted into a dish, like caraway into bubble and squeak. This very creativity may sometimes result in unevenness, but Exeter revels in the effort. Special place should be left for desserts: old-fashioned bread-and-butter pudding, hot cherry tart with kirsch ice-cream, and amaretto parfait with coffee-bean sauce have all been commended. The wine list may be small, but it changes often enough and draws from a wide enough range, and the staff – refreshingly – actually know what they are selling. House wines are £7.50.

CHEF: Paul George Bending   PROPRIETORS: Ian and Alison Aldridge   OPEN: all week, exc Sat L; 12 to 2, 6 to 10.30 (10 Sun)   MEALS: alc (main courses £6 to £11.50). Set L and D (until 7pm) £8 (2 courses)   SERVICE: net prices, card slips closed   CARDS: Access, Visa   DETAILS: 42 seats. 2 tables outside. Private parties: 26 main room, 26 private room. Vegetarian meals. Children's helpings. No-smoking area. Music. Air-conditioned. Fax: (0392) 431145

## ▲ St Olaves Court Hotel

Mary Arches Street, Exeter EX4 3AZ                    COOKING 2
EXETER (0392) 217736                                  COST £23–£37

This Georgian merchant's house with mulberry tree courtyard and fountain has
had a good year – as hotel and as restaurant. People evidently find the Wyatts'
cheerful welcome a tonic and have approved David Mutter's cooking of a
modernish menu that is priced by the course. Without sacrificing good looks, it
is only with desserts that presentation comes centre-stage – that's the influence
of the spun-sugar cage. Otherwise there is a certain attractive spareness to the
cooking of first courses such as a warm salad of halibut with pesto, crab cakes
with basil and spring onions, or tourte of chicken with trompettes-de-mort and
thyme sauce, or main dishes like pork en crépinette with lentils and wild
mushrooms, mullet with Noilly Prat and scallops, or guinea-fowl with potato
galette and madeira sauce. Desserts get continual notice: for instance, a steamed
jam sponge with vanilla custard, meringue swans with strawberries and a
caramel sauce – the stuff to make a grown man drool. Chef's tasty appetisers,
hand-made chocolates, coffee: these get approval too. The wine list has some
useful 1982 clarets, a trio of South Africans including a Boschendal
Gewurztraminer and no excessive prices. House wines are £10.50.

CHEF: David Mutter   PROPRIETORS: Raymond and Ute Wyatt, and Peter Collier   OPEN: all
week; 12 to 1.45, 6.30 to 9.30   CLOSED: 26 Dec to 4 Jan   MEALS: alc (main courses £11.50).
Set L £13.50   SERVICE: not inc, card slips closed   CARDS: Access, Amex, Diners, Visa
DETAILS: 58 seats. 5 tables outside. Private parties: 40 main room, 18 private room. Car
park. Vegetarian meals. Children's helpings on request. Smart dress preferred. No cigars/
pipes in dining-room. Wheelchair access (3 steps). No music   ACCOMMODATION: 15
rooms, all with bath/shower. Rooms for disabled. B&B £45 to £90. Children welcome.
Baby facilities. Pets welcome. Afternoon teas. Garden. TV. Phone. Confirm by 5. Fax:
(0392) 413054

---

**EXMOUTH Devon**                                                    map 1

## Barnaby's Restaurant                          | NEW ENTRY |

9 Tower Street, Exmouth EX8 1NT                       COOKING 1*
EXMOUTH (0395) 269459                                 COST £22–£32

Rumour has it that the building was once used for making coffins. Now it
comes as a happier package, though the wrapping still needs some attention:
'chairs are second-hand rather than antique' was a polite way of putting it. But
the Aylwards are young and putting their all into the food and wine (and
raising a family – hence the name, after their son). The menu, priced by the
choice of main course, may sound on the wild side of British creativity, as in
baked paw-paw with lemon and ginger, lemon grass and sorrel soup, venison
with Gruyère and a red-wine sauce, basil ice-cream and blackberry ice-cream,
but it does seem to work. A relatively staid lamb's sweetbreads with madeira
sauce and baked polenta with mushrooms, ginger and Gruyère were entirely
successful. The cheese with the venison did not do much more than add a not
unwelcome richness. Scallops with laverbread and a cream and citrus sauce
were first-rate. Ginger may get everywhere, even detected in carrots with

mustard seed served as a vegetable, though not surfacing in desserts except as a brandy-snap basket. The enthusiasm seems catching. The lack of greed in wine pricing is also encouraging, making it difficult to choose which bargain. Range is very fair, and James Aylward has obviously drunk the samples, if his notes are anything to go by. Anything priced at less than £12 is available by the glass.

CHEF: James Aylward  PROPRIETORS: James and Sally Aylward  OPEN: Mon to Sat, D only (party bookings any time); 7 to 9.30  CLOSED: Mon mid-Sept to mid-July  MEALS: alc (main courses £9 to £13). Set D £14.95 to £18.95  SERVICE: not inc, card slips closed  CARDS: Access, Visa  DETAILS: 35 seats. Private parties: 24 main room, 20 private room. Vegetarian meals. Children's helpings on request. Wheelchair access (1 step). Music

---

**EYTON** Hereford & Worcester                                    map 2

## ▲ *Marsh* 

Eyton HR6 OAG
LEOMINSTER (0568) 613952                          COOKING 1
off B4361, 2m NW of Leominster                    COST £33–£41

This is a masterpiece of half-timbering, set in landscaped lawns and flowerbeds. The Gillelands are rightly proud of their restoration of this medieval hall-house and of their equal facility with secateurs and dibber. They play the hosts with enthusiasm; Martin's conversation rarely flags while Jacqueline slaves over the hot stove. Prices may lead you to think otherwise but the cooking is quite simple, though the skill with baking is worth stressing. Smoked mackerel puffs with fennel and cucumber, or a prawn moussse wrapped in smoked salmon, come before a middle course of home-grown salad and are followed by a centrepiece of brill and salmon with a saffron sauce, or breast of duck with an apricot stuffing. Desserts such as the Alsace rhubarb tart with orange ice-cream may give pastry-work a chance to shine. Some felt that the wine list has a patchy spread: six red Rhônes and but one claret, no red burgundies and four varietals from South Africa. House wines kick off with a Herefordshire Reichensteiner for £9.75, but the cheapest red is £11 which, like the menu price, seems over the odds.

CHEF: Jacqueline Gilleland  PROPRIETORS: Martin and Jacqueline Gilleland  OPEN: all week, D only (L by arrangement); 7.30 to 9  MEALS: Set D £27.50  SERVICE: net prices, card slips closed  CARDS: Access, Amex, Diners, Visa  DETAILS: 24 seats. Private parties: 24 main room. Car park. Vegetarian meals with prior notice. No children under 10. Smart dress preferred. No smoking in dining-room. No music  ACCOMMODATION: 5 rooms, all with bath/shower. B&B £74 to £100. Deposit: £15. Children welcome. Baby facilities. Garden. TV. Phone. Doors close at midnight. Confirm by 6 (*The Which? Hotel Guide*)

---

*See the inside of the front cover for an explanation of the 1 to 5 rating system for cooking standards.*

*Prices quoted in the* Guide *are based on information supplied by restaurateurs. The prices quoted at the top of each entry represent a range, from the lowest meal price to the highest; the latter is inflated by 20 per cent to take account of likely price rises during the year of the* Guide.

---

## Read's 🍷

Painter's Forstal, Faversham ME13 0EE
FAVERSHAM (0795) 535344                                                    COOKING 3*
on Eastling road, 1m S of Faversham                                    COST £23–£48

One diner felt that the building might be taken for a school or a surgery; inside, though, all is lightness and forgetting, and impeccable table settings focus the mind on the business in hand. A new kitchen and garden extension are scheduled for completion by the time this *Guide* is in print; meanwhile, craft and care continue to hold sway in the old kitchen. The communicative menus (set-price three-course for both lunch and dinner) describe a remarkable range, considering that choices are sensibly limited to between four and seven dishes per course: lunch might begin with 'creamy and correctly seasoned' asparagus soup, three elegant smoked fish mousses ('they're very good at fish and fish pâtés') or, for those eyeing each others' waists, a variety of citrus fruit segments with a fresh pineapple sorbet. Lateral thinking provides good combinations, such as the chicory rémoulade accompanying fillet steak tartare, and technical difficulties (a Montgomery cheddar soufflé posed on a provençale sauce) are not shirked. Everyone, though, wants an old favourite once in a while, as often as not here given a new twist: crisp-skinned, moist-fleshed duck with caramelised oranges and a Grand Marnier sauce suggested 'masterly' skills to one diner; venison loin is sweetly foiled by chestnut purée and kumquat marmalade; fillet of beef is fortified with black pudding, bacon and onions on a Guinness sauce. 'The image', among desserts, brings the undecided a little bit of everything (which might include 'wonderful crème brûlée'). Service is 'unfussy but professional', and the revamped, tidied-up wine list is a success, beginning with a 'best buys' selection of 40 wines between £11 and £16, before spreading its wings and gliding up to annotated heights, most of them French. Prices are very fair and half-bottles well chosen. House wine is £11.
CELLARMAN'S CHOICE: Morey St-Denis 'En la rue de Vergy' 1989, B. Clair, £26.50; Margaret River, Cape Mentelle, Cabernet Sauvignon 1990, £16.

CHEF: David Pitchford   PROPRIETORS: David and Rona Pitchford   OPEN: Tue to Sat; 12 to 2, 7 to 10   CLOSED: late Aug   MEALS: Set L £14.50, Set D £29   SERVICE: not inc, card slips closed   CARDS: Access, Amex, Diners, Visa   DETAILS: 40 seats. 2 tables outside. Private parties: 60 main room, 12 private room. Car park. Vegetarian meals. Children's helpings. Smart dress preferred. Wheelchair access (1 step). Music. Fax: (0795) 591200

## Rumbles Cottage

Braintree Road, Felsted CM6 3DJ
GREAT DUNMOW (0371) 820996                                            COOKING 1
on B1417, between A130 and A120                                        COST £18–£36

By having three in the cooking team, Joy Hadley feels able to offer the same menus at her two restaurants (see Rumbles Castle, Castle Hedingham) without diminution of standards. Stick-in-the-mud she never is and her repertoire often seems to take the most surprising combinations and, in the eyes of regular and local customers, make them work. It is perhaps accents that she seeks the hardest: that given by Stilton in a roulade of pork, or ginger with a peanut sauce for fillet of beef, or the strength of olives in an olive ring with two pepper sauces. Some have found the traditional things work the best, like smoked halibut with horseradish – though even that had quite a lot of extra elements not mentioned here. A main course of haddock accentuated by orange and lemon rind proved to be overpowered by them and a vegetarian pancake of spinach, mushroom and courgettes with tomato sauce and pesto proved to be unexpectedly bland. The experiments sometimes need more work, but people have spoken well of lamb with onion marmalade, smoked trout with horseradish, and chicken with turmeric and cumin, cooked with yogurt. Desserts 'are not for slimmers' if you have chocolate mint slice, though less weight would be gained, and less enjoyment too, with mango and melon fruit salad with honeyed yogurt topping. The Cottage is indeed a cottage, and the style has been described as tea-room. The wine list is sensibly priced and probably has something for everyone, a fair proportion coming from reliable Lay & Wheeler. House wines start at £7.60.

CHEFS: Joy Hadley, Steven Urry and Laura Thompson   PROPRIETORS: Joy Hadley and Martin Donovan   OPEN: Tue to Sat, D only, and Sun L (also L Dec and other days by arrangement); 12 to 2, 7 to 9   MEALS: alc (main courses £10 to £12.50). Set Sun L £12.50, Set Tue to Thur D £12.50   SERVICE: not inc   CARDS: Access, Visa (2% discount for non-card payments)   DETAILS: 50 seats. Private parties: 25 main room, 8, 10 and 10 private rooms. Vegetarian meals. Children's helpings. Wheelchair access (1 step). No music

---

**FLITWICK** Bedfordshire                                                                map 3

## ▲ Flitwick Manor ⁵✳

Church Road, Flitwick MK45 1AE
FLITWICK (0525) 712242                                              COOKING **2**
off A5120, S of Flitwick                                            COST £26–£50

The Manor is incongruously tucked away on the fringes of a village that seems to court relentless development. It is a lovely eighteenth-century house, 'shielded from the reality of late twentieth-century existence by mature trees and acres of parkland'; it also boasts a croquet lawn, grotto and castellated walled kitchen garden. The interior is grand without seeming awesome – 'old England' at its most civilised and gracious: it comes as no surprise to hear tapes of Elgar playing in the stunning Music Room. Ian McAndrew has departed, a new regime has moved in and former chef Duncan Poyser is back in the kitchen. It is early days yet, but first reports suggest that the set-up is moving into top gear. This is up-to-the-minute, ambitious cooking with the confidence to handle unfashionable ingredients such as tongue and catfish. Menus are fixed-price. Two consecutive dinners produced some top-draw dishes: triumphant red mullet soup with perfectly toasted croûtons, grilled tuna served on cracked wheat with a gazpacho sauce, lobster en papillote with Sauternes, tender medallions of pork with spinach and a sticky reduced sauce laced with armagnac, and custardy crème brûlée with caramelised oranges. Simpler lunches almost keep pace, with stir-fried squid cooked with ginger and coconut milk, and hot-smoked chicken glazed with red wine and tarragon. The ancillaries are spot-on: excellent appetisers and petits fours, brilliant bread rolls, beautifully handled vegetables. Service is generally amicable and courteous without seeming stuffy. The wine list is 'dull and dear', according to one reporter: France is the main source of supply, with clarets and burgundies to the fore. House wine is £9.75.

CHEF: Duncan Poyser   PROPRIETORS: Mazard Hotel Management   OPEN: all week; 12.30 to 1.45, 7 to 9.30   MEALS: Set L £15.50 (2 courses) to £18.50, Set D £28 (2 courses) to £32.50   SERVICE: not inc   CARDS: Access, Amex, Visa   DETAILS: 50 seats. 4 tables outside. Private parties: 60 main room, 14, 16 and 60 private rooms. Car park. Vegetarian meals. Children's helpings. Smart dress preferred. No smoking in dining-room. No music ACCOMMODATION: 15 rooms, all with bath/shower. B&B £78 to £190. Children welcome. Baby facilities. Pets welcome in bedrooms. Afternoon teas. Garden. Tennis. TV. Phone. Doors close at midnight. Confirm by 4. Fax: (0525) 712242

---

**FOLKESTONE Kent**                                                                    map 3

## Paul's

2A Bouverie Road West,
Folkestone CT20 2RX                                                          COOKING 1
FOLKESTONE (0303) 259697                                                 COST £23–£28

Enter the house on the other side of the road to a giant Sainsbury's and the riot of colour and curtaining will hit you fair and square between the eyes. The Haggers have run this popular local restaurant for many years, keeping it up to the decorative mark, polishing madly, putting up more pictures, and cooking dishes that have moved somewhat with the times ('We use less cream than we used to,' remarks Paul Hagger) but include old favourites like crab gratin, mussels with a Parmesan crust, and fish from day-boats as well as game in season. Puddings tend to be a serious deal. Skip the Gallo on the wine list and look at the 1982 and 1983 clarets. House wines are £7.95.

CHEFS/PROPRIETORS: Paul and Penny Hagger   OPEN: all week; 12 to 2.30, 7.30 to 9.30 (7 to 10 Sat)   CLOSED: few days Christmas   MEALS: alc (main courses £10)   SERVICE: not inc CARDS: Access, Visa   DETAILS: 60–100 seats. 5 tables outside. Private parties: 100 main room. Car park D. Vegetarian meals. Children's helpings on request. Wheelchair access (2 steps; also WC). No music

---

**FORTON Lancashire**                                                                  map 5

## El Nido                                                    NEW ENTRY

Whinney Brow Lane, Forton PR3 0AE
FORTON (0524) 791254                                                       COOKING 1
on A6, 1m S of M6 junction 33                                             COST £15–£37

'A little piece of Iberia in the verdant farmland of the Fylde, and on the edge of the Forest of Bowland,' say the owners of this place that looks like a country pub but is strewn with Spanish ornaments, and where even the 'My Way' on the Muzak machine is Hispanic. The cooking has Spanish aspirations, though the garlic content is reduced for British palates, vegetables are served in

Lancastrian quantities, and the shellfish salad is not exactly Mediterranean. For all that, materials can be good and fresh, and some of the sauces 'rich and fulsome' – for instance, that of garlic, ham, onions, peppers and sherry with fillet of pork – rather than over-sweet, as was the worrying pineapple and curry sauce with a grilled plaice. Desserts come off a trolley and coffee out of a communal pot. A score of Spanish wines are the main attraction of the list. House wines are £7.50.

CHEFS: L. Kenny and T. Pool   PROPRIETORS: René and Tracey Mollinga   OPEN: L Wed to Fri (May to Oct) and Sun, D Tue to Sun; 12 to 2, 7 to 10.15   MEALS: alc (main courses £7 to £13). Set L £7.95   SERVICE: not inc   CARDS: Access, Visa   DETAILS: 55 seats. 3 tables outside. Private parties: 40 main room. Car park. Vegetarian meals. Children's helpings. Smart dress preferred. Wheelchair access (2 steps; also WC). Music. Air-conditioned

---

**FOWEY** Cornwall                                                                                    map 1

## *Food for Thought*

Town Quay, Fowey PL23 1AT                                                    COOKING 2
FOWEY (072 683) 2221                                                        COST £23–£49

'Fowey was flooded. Unable to explore much of the town centre, we spotted Food for Thought. We vaulted in over the sandbags keeping out the estuary and were lucky enough to find a table for two, as – surprise, surprise – some diners were unable to make it. Every English summer cloud has a silver lining.' Where the sea comes as close as this, you would expect an emphasis on fish and you find it here. The lobster tank is a welcome arrival; fish soup is 'well flavoured, a peppery homogenous bisque'; turbot, gravlax and a smoked salmon and cucumber parcel with cream and herb dressing have all satisfied expectation. Medallion of prime beef fillet was 'cooked perfectly medium rare and set on a bed of latticed potatoes crowned by oyster mushrooms'; pink duck breast was thinly sliced and well matched by a red wine and honey sauce. Some sauces make two appearances, in first- and second-course guise, which reduces choice, main ingredient notwithstanding; and the hollandaise which coats the vegetables is still felt to be a sauce too far, muting the flavour of, say, a delicate carrot mousse and acting as a dessert deterrent. You need appetite for dessert, since Cornish clotted cream is the near-ubiquitous accompaniment. Strawberries nested in meringue then caged in sugar indicate a love of artful presentation, also reflected in careful table dressings (large white napkins and Wedgwood 'Insignia' china). Service is generally liked, though meal endings can be abrupt if more customers are waiting. The wine list is unambitious but genuinely inexpensive, with house wines at £6.95.

CHEF: Martin Billingsley   PROPRIETORS: Martin and Caroline Billingsley   OPEN: Mon to Sat, D only; 7 to 9.30   CLOSED: Jan, Feb   MEALS: alc (main courses £10 to £19). Set D £16.95   SERVICE: not inc, card slips closed   CARDS: Access, Visa   DETAILS: 38 seats. Private parties: 24 main room. Vegetarian meals. No children under 10. Smart dress preferred. Wheelchair access. No music

---

*See the back of the Guide for an index of restaurants listed.*

## FRAMPTON ON SEVERN Gloucestershire · map 2

# Saverys

The Green, Frampton on Severn GL2 7EA
GLOUCESTER (0452) 740077
2½m NW of M5 junction 13

COOKING 2*
COST £30–£47

Frampton on Severn boasts the longest village green in England; ducks swim
on the pond, cricket is played in summer. It makes the perfect setting for a
personally run country restaurant. Saverys is a pretty cottage with white
railings and green-painted criss-cross windows with ornamental ducks on the
sills. The interior has a cosy atmosphere with pot plants, spindle-back chairs
and ruffled pink curtains. Patricia Carpenter is a polite, pleasant and
unflustered hostess. The handwritten menu changes regularly and offers a
well-balanced choice of three courses (plus cheese) at a fixed price. This is self-
assured, confident cooking that relies on good raw materials and gives effete
high fashion a wide berth. Mousse of crab and prawns comes as a 'sandcastle'
timbale with a purée of red and green peppers; warm salad of black pudding
and perfectly timed quail's eggs receives a sprinkling of Dijon dressing.
Typically good main courses have included roast rack of lamb with a glossy,
tangy, piquant sauce and well-hung fillet of beef sitting on a cake of rösti with
green peppercorn, cream and brandy sauce. Spot-on vegetables are served in
separate dishes. Desserts such as home-made prune and armagnac ice-cream
with brandy sauce or dark chocolate and amaretto marquise are executed with
impeccable skill. The wine list is short, with plenty of good drinking for
around £15. House French is £7.95.

CHEF: John Savery  PROPRIETORS: John Savery and Patricia Carpenter  OPEN: Tue to Sat,
D only; 7 to 9  MEALS: Set D £21.95  SERVICE: not inc, card slips closed  CARDS: Access,
Visa  DETAILS: 25 seats. Private parties: 25 main room. Vegetarian meals with prior notice.
No children under 14. Smart dress preferred. No pipes in dining-room. Wheelchair access.
Music

## FRESSINGFIELD Suffolk · map 6

# Fox and Goose ▮

Fressingfield IP21 5PB
FRESSINGFIELD (037 986) 247
on B1116, 3½m S of Harleston

COOKING 3
COST £19–£40

What the urban middle classes consider to be country living and what actual
country-town dwellers do are two very different things. Some reports of this
pub-cum-restaurant express well the dilemma. 'A skilful retention of pub
atmosphere preserves the urban fiction of rural England', wrote one; 'Its
unique ex-guildhall building and setting in an unspoilt village between a
remarkable church and the duck-pond, miles off any main road, make for an
important atmosphere,' contributed a second. But, 'tatty' was a counter-offer;
'We hoped for tangible proof of our expenditure in terms of service and
surroundings' was a final reproof. The Fox and Goose is relaxed, the food is not
meant to be full dress in the way of some five-star hotel, and the casual

ambience derived from 'a ragbag of bar furniture, good pictures and jokey notices, plus a dining-room with log fire, and closely arranged tables with paper cloths over linen' is intentional. Some good food has been enjoyed: various tempuras, a substantial Tuscan bean soup (more minestrone than bean), invigorating bruschetta (even if the tomatoes were bland on one occasion), salmon fish-cakes, rabbit with prunes and chocolate sauce, plain entrecôte, lemon-curd tart, Afghan rice-pudding and warm treacle tart are among things mentioned. Though the menu seems to borrow from every nation, English cooking – as in sausages and mash, cod and parsley mash, serious roast beef and potted shrimps from Morecambe – is still a strong point. There are cheaper bar snacks, and a new package: dinner at the Fox and Goose, bedrooms at village B&Bs. There seems to have been a slight glitch to proceedings over last autumn, but things have settled down once more. Ruth Watson's gardening has become very keen, and the salads and vegetable plates show the benefit. The 'short wine list' is easier to read this year; it offers a range by the glass and a good catholic selection which is modestly and fairly priced. This is complemented by a 'serious' list long enough to occupy an enthusiast for half an evening; it provides a remarkable balance of maturity and quality at commensurate prices, but also many excellent halves. Prices are not all high, and a search around the list will repay with excellent Alsaces and Italians. House wines start at £7.95 for one from their own French vineyard.
CELLARMAN'S CHOICE: Bordeaux, Ch. Valade 1990, £11.90; Bordeaux, Ch. Thieuley (rosé) 1990, £12.50.

CHEFS: Ruth Watson, Brendan Ansbro and James Perry   PROPRIETOR: Ruth Watson
OPEN: Wed to Sun (winter Sun D by arrangement); 12 to 2, 7 to 9.15   CLOSED: 1 week
Christmas, 2 to 3 weeks summer   MEALS: alc. Set L £9.95 (2 courses)   SERVICE: not inc
DETAILS: 50 seats. 4 tables outside. Private parties: 24 main room, 24 private room. Car
park. Vegetarian meals. Children's helpings on request. No cigars/pipes in dining-room.
No music. Fax: (0379) 868107

---

GATESHEAD Tyne & Wear                                                    map 7

▲ *Eslington Villa Hotel* ⅝✳

8 Station Road, Low Fell,
Gateshead NE9 6DR
091-487 6017
on A6127, 2m S of Newcastle city centre

COOKING 2
COST £20–£52

The view across the Team valley may no longer enchant as it did in less developed days, but competent cooking continues to please both hungry locals and travellers crossing the gastronomic tundra of Tyne & Wear. Art nouveau ceramics and Edwardian furniture lend tone to the comfortable but otherwise unexceptional lounge in which drinks are taken; the dining-room is darker and smarter. You can eat well and cheaply from the lunch and dinner set-price menus; you can eat slightly better but rather less cheaply from the *carte*. Warm salad of duck breast interleaving hot, freshly seared meat with avocado crescents around a hazelnut-dressed hummock of salad leaves proved 'conventional but satisfying'; the multiple-choice salad might reappear in quail's egg, bacon and chicken-liver guise. Rolling and wrapping are popular:

scallops in bacon, chicken breast in bacon and cabbage, or pork fillet in oatmeal served with a mushroom and whisky sauce. Vegetable accompaniments have brought stir-fried pepper, onion, cauliflower, baby corn and bacon together – with sauté potatoes. Cheeses come pursued by a pastry mousse; desserts range from the mildly exotic (peach and almond cream tart with a bitter chocolate sauce) to the frankly populist (brandy cream and chocolate-chip crunch served with chocolate chip ice-cream). 'Outstandingly pleasant, efficient and knowledgeable' service is matched by a sound, working wine list. House wines (at £8.95) are from Burgundy's largest négoçiant, though that does not mean they are from Burgundy, and there is a litre of Bornheimer Adelberg for the thirsty for only £9.95.

CHEF: Ian Lowery   PROPRIETORS: Mr N. and Mrs M. Tulip   OPEN: Mon to Sat, exc Sat L; 12 to 2, 7 to 10.45   MEALS: alc. Set L £13.95 to £15, Set D £21.95 to £25   SERVICE: not inc CARDS: Access, Amex, Diners, Visa   DETAILS: 55 seats. Private parties: 40 main room, 16 private room. Car park. Vegetarian meals. Children's helpings. Smart dress preferred. No smoking in dining-room. Wheelchair access (2 steps; also WC). Music   ACCOMMODATION: 12 rooms, all with bath/shower. Rooms for disabled. B&B £39.50 to £79.50. Children welcome. Small dogs welcome. Afternoon teas. Garden. TV. Phone. Fax: 091-482 2359

## Fumi £

| | |
|---|---|
| 248 Durham Road, Gateshead NE8 4JR | COOKING 1 |
| 091-477 1152 | COST £18–£41 |

Behind the elaborate façade is a dining-room that seems more like a café than a restaurant. Pictures of sushi hang above the Formica-topped tables, and a serving bar is set up at the far end. Newcomers to Japanese food are either instantly hooked, slightly wary or simply bemused. And so it is at Fumi. Sometimes the staff provide helpful guidance, but diners have been left to fend for themselves despite a typically courteous welcome. Delicate appetisers such as ikura oroshi (salmon roe with grated white radish) or natto isobeage (fermented soya beans wrapped in seaweed) precede more substantial dishes highlighting different cooking techniques: deep-fried sardines with 'plum taste', grilled chicken teriyaki, sunomono specialities with savoury rice vinegar, vegetable tempura, then raw sashimi and sushi. Meals finish authentically with soup noodles. Dishes arrive sporadically. Warm saké is a suitable accompaniment. House wine is £6.50.

CHEF: Akio Konno   PROPRIETOR: Akihiko Mori   OPEN: Tue to Sun, D only; 6 to 10.30 CLOSED: 10 to 14 days from Jan 1, 4 days summer   MEALS: alc (main courses £3.50 to £12) SERVICE: not inc, card slips closed   CARDS: Access, Visa   DETAILS: 52 seats. 20 tables outside. Private parties: 40 main room, 15 private room. Vegetarian meals. Children's helpings. No-smoking area. Wheelchair access. Music. Air-conditioned. Fax: 091-276 2951

---

*'While we were there a male strippogram arrived and the birthday girl removed the rest of the clothing with her teeth.'*  On eating in Avon

*'The bill took so long to arrive that I went off to brush my teeth by way of passing the time.'*  On eating in Avon

---

## GEDNEY DYKE Lincolnshire

map 6

## *Chequers* £

NEW ENTRY

Main Street, Gedney Dyke, PE12 0AJ
HOLBEACH (0406) 362666
just off B2359, from Gedney roundabout
on A17, 3m E of Holbeach

COOKING 1
COST £15–£30

Set in a 'peaceful and verdant fenland backwater', this is the local pub – a villagers' place, not a bistro. It is also, in the words of one reporter, 'a place to treasure and return to again and again'. Landlord Rob Marshall dispenses real ales in the beamed bar and snacks are available at all times. The pub also has a simple, uncluttered dining-room with bare tables and few frills, while a note on the menu acknowledges local suppliers and helpers. Judith Marshall heads the kitchen and offers a straightforward, unshowy menu backed up by blackboard specials including 'oodles of fish' (monkfish, wild salmon, sole with asparagus). Dishes are satisfying, generous and presented with care. Seafood pancakes, pretty noisettes of lamb with powerful Cajun spicing, and Gressingham duck with orange impressed an inspector, who also praised the locally grown, perfectly cooked vegetables. Intense chocolate and chestnut gâteau and hazelnut meringue have been good sweets. The sensibly chosen list of around 40 wines will not break the bank. House wine is £5.95.

CHEFS: Judith Marshall and Paul Murphy  PROPRIETORS: Judith and Rob Marshall
OPEN: all week, exc Sat L and Sun D; 12 to 1.45, 7 to 9 (9.30 Thur to Sat)  CLOSED: 25 to 27 Dec  MEALS: alc (main courses £5.50 to £11)  SERVICE: not inc, card slips closed  CARDS: Access, Amex, Diners, Visa  DETAILS: restaurant 32 seats, bar 36 seats. Private parties: 30 main room. Car park. Vegetarian meals. Children's helpings. Smart dress preferred. Wheelchair access (1 step; also WC). Music

## GILLINGHAM Dorset

map 2

## ▲ *Stock Hill* ⁵⁄✳

Gillingham SP8 5NR
GILLINGHAM (0747) 823626
off B3081, 1½m W of Gillingham

COOKING 3*
COST £26–£42

The Doberman is 'fairly friendly', the wooden prancing horses in the hall are astounding. Both set the tone for this late-Victorian house, which is decorated with verve, passion and comfort. The Hausers have put their all into the hospitality and fabric of Stock Hill (with a little time left over for the impressive gardens) and the result is very personal. Peter's Austrian background is inescapable in his concise fixed-price menu, which offers classical technique allied to great generosity and an affection for slow cooking (there is an Aga in the house). He flits from home-grown nettle soup to zuppa pavese as easily as he does from turbot topped with crab mousseline to long-poached shin of beef in a horseradish glaze with a bread dumpling.
Occasionally the broad gesture gets in the way of direct and attacking flavours, but there was small complaint for a crab and prawn sausage on ratatouille or king scallop ravioli with mushrooms. The cooking style is 'robust for modern

tastes'; this may not be a criticism, especially if the breakfast sets you up for the whole of the day. Desserts, when sugar and chocolate get employed, are seriously considered. And the spiced bread (but not the sliced bread for toast) is much appreciated. The amazing thing here is the intensity of the welcome. The food will ensure a spirit strong enough to enjoy it. The wine list has always been good on Rhônes and Loires from Gillingham's dentist-turned-wine merchant, Robin Yapp. Some useful New World choices flesh it out and the prices will not perturb. House wines are a Lirac and a Muscadet at £9.95.

CHEF: Peter Hauser and Lorna Connor   PROPRIETORS: Peter and Nita Hauser   OPEN: Tue to Sun (and bank hol D), exc Sat L and Sun D; 12.30 to 1.45, 7.30 to 8.45   MEALS: Set L £18.50, Set D £26.50   SERVICE: not inc, card slips closed   CARDS: Access, Diners, Visa DETAILS: 24 seats. Private parties: 12 main room, 15 private room. Car park. Vegetarian meals. Children's helpings. No children under 7. Smart dress preferred. No smoking in dining-room. Wheelchair access (2 steps). No music   ACCOMMODATION: 9 rooms, all with bath/shower. D,B&B £85 to £210. Deposit: £50. No children under 7. Garden. Tennis. TV. Phone. Doors close at midnight. Fax: (0747) 825628 (*The Which? Hotel Guide*)

---

**GLASTONBURY Somerset**                                                        map 2

## ▲ *No.3* ✻

3 Magdalene Street, Glastonbury BA6 9EW
GLASTONBURY (0458) 832129                                          COOKING 1
on A39 Wells to Bridgewater road                                   COST £36–£50

Not far from the Abbey gardens, No. 3 is a pleasant Georgian house that is lovingly tended by John and Ann Tynan. Across the hall from the 'absolutely charming' lounge is a red and white dining-room with bright, impressionistic oil paintings on the walls, floral curtains and roses on the tables. John Tynan is a friendly host, while Ann cooks. The menu is fixed price, with around six choices at each stage. Roquefort and walnut 'parcels' with fresh watercress sauce and Cornish scallops in shrimp sauce have been agreeable starters. An 'entirely natural' sorbet, enlivened with rose petals picked from the walled garden, provides refreshment before main courses such as high-quality fillet steak with green peppercorn sauce, rich navarin of lamb and red mullet baked in the Aga and served with provençale sauce. Lobster specialities carry a £5 supplement. 'Inventive' sweets might include mixed berries in yogurt, cream and Cointreau sauce, and pear frangipane with apricot sauce. The wine list is substantial and several ports are also available. House French is £9.50.

CHEF: Ann Tynan   PROPRIETORS: John and Ann Tynan   OPEN: Tue to Sat, D only; 7.30 to 9   CLOSED: Dec and Jan   MEALS: Set D £26   SERVICE: not inc   CARDS: Access, Visa DETAILS: 20 seats. 2 tables outside. Private parties: 20 main room. Car park. Vegetarian meals. Children's helpings with prior notice. Smart dress preferred. No smoking in dining-room. No music   ACCOMMODATION: 6 rooms, all with bath/shower. Rooms for disabled. B&B £50 to £75. Children by arrangement. Garden. TV. Phone. Doors close at 11.30. Confirm by 6 (*The Which? Hotel Guide*)

---

*The* Guide *is totally independent, accepts no free hospitality, and survives on the number of copies sold each year.*

## GLOUCESTER Gloucestershire
map 2

# Yeung's £

St Oswalds Road, Cattle Market,
Gloucester GL1 2SR
GLOUCESTER (0452) 309957

COOKING 1
COST £14–£39

The garden-centre analogy still holds good for this country Chinese restaurant, with all the trellises and greenery on a spacious site. Even if the kitchen does not hold the promise of the rare or unfamiliar ingredients available in big-city chinatowns, it does manage very direct and fresh-tasting mostly Peking- and Szechuan-inspired food. An acceptable wine list starts with house wine at £7.

CHEF: P.S. Lok   PROPRIETORS: Peter Lee and S.C. Chung   OPEN: Mon to Sat, exc Mon L;
12 to 2.15, 6 to 11.15   MEALS: alc (main courses £4.50 to £6). Set L and D £12 to £22.50.
Minimum £8   SERVICE: 10%   DETAILS: 100 seats. Private parties: 60 main room.
Vegetarian meals. Children welcome. Smart dress preferred. Wheelchair access (also WC).
Music. Air-conditioned

## GOLCAR West Yorkshire
map 5

# Weavers Shed

Acre Mill, Knowl Road, Golcar HD7 4AN
HUDDERSFIELD (0484) 654284
on B6111, 2½m W of Huddersfield from A62

COOKING 2
COST £17–£40

As a restaurant, Weavers Shed is 21 years old; as an industrial monument (with bale barrow in the garden, shuttles on the walls, lots of old stone walls and flagstoned floors to prove its cloth mill ancestry), it is much older. Stephen Jackson remarks, 'We would have been unlikely to last this long if we had not offered good value' – and fair cooking into the bargain as local residents would confirm. Careful interpretation of well-tried favourites may be a leitmotif: roundels of smoked salmon filled with smoked trout pâté, a cucumber and dill mayonnaise to one side, is one choice; roast Lunesdale duck with a bitter orange and lemon sauce is a second. The cooking of meat is particularly satisfactory: in first courses such as kidneys with a madeira and mustard sauce under a puff-pastry crust, or in main dishes like collops of beef with a watercress sauce (a reader was unsure whether the light sauce and hearty beef formed a true marriage), or tender, well-flavoured venison served with a shallot and caper sauce. British, indeed North Country, cheeses are served with 'Old Peculier' cake in the Yorkshire fashion, but many are loath to sacrifice their desserts – perhaps a lemon tart with good edge to the flavour, or a light sticky toffee pudding – to try them. The wine list has a little bit of everything to give range, and a slate of Duboeuf Beaujolais, Bruno Paillard champagnes and a handful of good clarets should give confidence in the soundness of its other choices. Prices are fair. House wines are £8.95.

*See inside the front cover for an explanation of the symbols used at the tops of entries.*

CHEFS: Peter McGunnigle, Ian McGunnigle and Stephen Jackson  PROPRIETOR: Stephen Jackson  OPEN: Tue to Sat, exc Sat L; 12 to 1.45, 7 to 9 (9.15 Sat)  CLOSED: first 2 weeks Jan, last 2 weeks July  MEALS: alc (main courses L £5 to £9, D £11 to £14). Set L £10.95  SERVICE: not inc  CARDS: Access, Amex, Visa  DETAILS: 70 seats. Private parties: 40 main room, 30 private room. Car park. Vegetarian meals with prior notice. Children's helpings. Smart dress preferred. Wheelchair access (2 steps). Music

---

## GORING Oxfordshire

map 2

# Leatherne Bottel

Goring RG8 0HS
GORING-ON-THAMES (0491) 872667
on B4009 out of Goring, 5m S of Wallingford

COOKING 2*
COST £29–£47

River, flowers, view, natural stone textures, old beams: this inn has much going for it. 'In the summer it's delightful to sit out by the river without hordes of people looking for crisps and a pint. In winter, there's always a log fire burning and a friendly welcome,' wrote one man who found that in wintertime the heating did not extend to the loos, but everything else was tickety-boo. Keith Read's natural style of cooking eschews cream and butter in favour of the materials themselves, and enlivens them with herbs and spices. Salmon chargrilled and served with fried ginger, capers, coriander and pleurotte mushrooms, and a fish soup/stew with lemon leaves, ginger, green horseradish and samphire are two examples of his production. Another is fresh pasta served with a nasturtium and chilli butter and grilled red pimento. The style fits the location. 'No peanuts, no crisps, but freshly baked bread, British cheese and a menu from local and home-grown produce' is how Keith Read puts it. There have been some ups and downs, but this year's reports have been mainly positive. The wine list is fair, with a better slate of clarets than anything else. House wines are £10.50. If the sun shines, hire the 34-foot Edwardian river launch.

CHEFS: Keith Read and Clive O'Connor  PROPRIETORS: Keith Read and Annie Bonnet  OPEN: all week; 12.15 to 2 (2.30 Sat and Sun), 7.15 to 9.15  CLOSED: 25 Dec  MEALS: alc (main courses £10.50 to £15)  SERVICE: not inc, card slips closed  CARDS: Access, Amex, Visa  DETAILS: 60 seats. 20 tables outside. Private parties: 20 main room, 12 private room. Car park. Vegetarian meals. Smart dress preferred. Wheelchair access. No music. Air-conditioned

---

## GRAMPOUND Cornwall

map 1

# Eastern Promise ⅝✳ £

1 Moor View, Grampound TR2 4RT
ST AUSTELL (0726) 883033

COOKING 1
COST £17–£39

A Cornish cottage converted into a Chinese restaurant sounds unlikely, but the fact that this place now has three car parks says a great deal about its popularity. The setting is a long, low dining-room dominated by a fish tank; the atmosphere is happily relaxed and Philip Tse's *bonhomie* is infectious. The menu stays with a varied assortment of mostly Peking and Szechuan dishes along the lines of Kung Po chicken, stir-fried beef in oyster sauce, twice-cooked pork and Hong Kong-style spare ribs. Crispy aromatic duck – marinated, steamed, then deep-fried – is the best seller. Seafood is regularly endorsed: 'juicy wholesome' scallops served on a sizzling platter, and sizzling king prawns with green peppers have been mentioned. The availability of fresh local fish also enables the kitchen to create specialities such as stir-fried salmon with fresh mango. Do not expect Chinatown café prices, although the food is generous and reckoned to be good value. No tips are accepted. The wine list offers some acceptable drinking, otherwise go for saké or Tsing Tao beer. House French is £7.

CHEF: Lisa Tse PROPRIETOR: Philip Tse OPEN: Thur to Tue, D only; 6 to 11 MEALS: alc (main courses £7 to £12). Set D £17.50 SERVICE: card slips closed CARDS: Access, Amex, Diners, Visa DETAILS: 70 seats. Private parties: 40 main room, 30 private room. Car park. Vegetarian meals. No children under 3. Smart dress preferred. No smoking in dining-room. Wheelchair access. Music. Air-conditioned

---

**GRASMERE Cumbria**                                                        map 7

## ▲ Michael's Nook ♀ ⅙✳

Grasmere LA22 9RP                                                    COOKING 3*
GRASMERE (053 94) 35496                                              COST £37–£70

'As Londoners, we found no locks on the doors a bit difficult to cope with,' remarked a couple who were expecting a restaurant-with-rooms but found instead a full-blown country-house hotel. They enjoyed the Russian Blue cat pottering about, and the Great Danes in the office; they enthused about the furnishings, 'almost too like a private home'; and they found the food tip-top: wild mushroom mousse, rillettes of smoked halibut, fillet of beef with a parsley and mustard crust, local cheeses, and an almond pastry with vanilla and chocolate ice-creams and a calvados sauce. Comments have been favourable about the cooking this year; dishes are quite complicated, but skilfully executed. Examples have been a clever stew of artichoke and salsify with trompettes-de-mort; a plateful of wild mushrooms done as an aspic, as tortellini and as a mousse; fillet of beef that is poached, then topped with a hollandaise and served with lardons and a madeira sauce; liver with a brioche crust, with lentils and wild mushrooms; and hot soufflés or perhaps a peach on champagne sorbet for dessert. The price is fixed and quite high. There is also a seven-course gourmet special. The trouble comes not from the food, but from aspects of the service. This occasionally has lapses, either of performance or in planning and original conception. It is then that the price begins to seem high. If the food can be dear, the correction comes with the wine list. Every effort has been made to give a good range of inexpensive bottles, and from decent growers too. Margins are reasonable throughout and there are some gems to be had, whether a 1982 Hermitage from Jaboulet, a Breaky Bottom Seyval Blanc, or a Collard Bros Chardonnay. House wines are £11.70.

---

🍾 *denotes an outstanding wine cellar;* ♀ *denotes a good wine list, worth travelling for.*

CHEFS: Kevin Mangeolles, Michael Penny and Gary Pennington   PROPRIETORS: Mr and Mrs R.S.E. Gifford   OPEN: all week; 12.30 to 1, 7.15 to 8.30   MEALS: Set L £27.50, Set D £39.50 to £46.50   SERVICE: not inc   CARDS: Access, Amex, Diners, Visa   DETAILS: 50 seats. Private parties: 35 private room. Car park. Vegetarian meals with prior notice. Children's high tea. No children under 10. Jacket and tie. No smoking in dining-room. Wheelchair access. No music   ACCOMMODATION: 14 rooms, all with bath/shower. Rooms for disabled. D,B&B £108 to £290. Deposit: £50. No children under 10. Garden. Swimming-pool. Sauna. Fishing. Golf. TV. Phone. Doors close at 11.45. Fax: (053 94) 35765

---

## ▲ White Moss House 🍷 ⁵⁄✳

Rydal Water, Grasmere LA22 9SE
GRASMERE (053 94) 35295                                              COOKING 3*
on A591, at N end of Rydal Water                                     COST £34–£41

Certain people say of this small yet distinguished hotel that it is not the place for the gin-and-Jag set. It hardly has the facilities; it appeals to those who want peace, who are happy left to their own devices. What the kitchen does, however, is cook superlative food and offer wine at knock-out prices. You may stay in the house itself, which may be a trifle noisy on the road side, or in Brockstone cottage on the hill behind. Dinner is served to everyone at the same time, from a menu that offers no choice till puddings – and pudding means what it says here. The formula might be said to read soup, soufflé (fish), meat and four vegetables, sweet, cheese, then coffee in the drawing-room. Variation occurs within those limits, though good ideas are not squandered after one outing, and change there is (if not radical development). 'We simply have never been disappointed' is the firm conclusion of a couple who return most years. These visitors applaud the depth of flavour in soups such as celeriac, cauliflower and chive, and the delicacy of the fish course such as a trout soufflé with Sancerre matched with local smoked salmon. They remember fondly the adventure of chicken stuffed with lime and lovage, and cooked in vin jaune de Jura and yogurt, and the vegetables: potatoes roasted with duck fat, courgettes with lemon, glazed carrots and crisp stir-fried mange-tout. The desserts provoke atavism with a steamed carrot and almond pudding, a cabinet pudding, a perfumed sorbet, and a chocolate hazelnut cream slice, while cheeses are patriotically British and local. The accuracy is very fine. Some people take issue with the quiet seriousness of the set up, or perhaps the style, and claim misfires that are sometimes hard to distinguish from a criticism of the ambience. The wine list never stops growing or enquiring. The bottles from beyond France are very distinguished, even if claret must still take the bouquets. Prices are exemplary; just on their own, they make the journey worthwhile. There is much by the glass and the personal choice usually starts at about £7.95 a bottle.

---

CHEFS: Peter Dixon and Colin Percival   PROPRIETORS: Susan and Peter Dixon   OPEN: Mon to Sat, D only; 8   CLOSED: Dec to end Feb   MEALS: Set D £27   SERVICE: not inc, card slips closed   CARDS: Access, Visa   DETAILS: 18 seats. Private parties: 20 main room. Car park. Vegetarian meals with prior notice. Older children welcome. No smoking in dining-room. Wheelchair access. No music   ACCOMMODATION: 6 double rooms, all with bath/shower. D,B&B £79 to £190. Older children welcome. Garden. Sauna. Fishing. TV. Phone. Doors close at 11. Confirm by 5 (*The Which? Hotel Guide*)

317

## GRAYSHOTT Hampshire

map 2

# *Woods Place*

Headley Road, Grayshott GU26 6LB
HINDHEAD (0428) 605555

COOKING 1
COST £23–£35

Though this bistro, run very much as a family affair, is on the site of a former butcher's shop, fish is given a fair outing, offering north Hampshire a taste of Scandinavia. Eric Norrgren does not restrict himself, however, to marinated herrings, gravlax, Jansson's 'temptation' (sliced potatoes baked with cream and fish), or cloudberry ice-cream: there is a touch of the Deep South (with salmon in Cajun spices), France (skate with black butter), and current taste (pigeon marinated in port, served with a plum and mustard sauce). Bread is charged separately, but people find it moreish. The wine list is pleasantly short and sweet, and prices are reasonable. House wines are £7.90.

CHEF: Eric Norrgren   PROPRIETORS: Eric and Dana Norrgren   OPEN: Tue to Sat; 12.30 to 2, 7 to 11   MEALS: alc (main courses £8.50 to £12)   SERVICE: 10%, card slips closed   CARDS: Access, Amex, Diners, Visa   DETAILS: 36 seats. Private parties: 16 main room. Vegetarian meals with prior notice. Children's helpings. Wheelchair access (also WC). Music

---

## GREAT DUNMOW Essex

map 3

# ▲ *The Starr* ❢ ⁂

Market Place, Great Dunmow CM6 1AX
GREAT DUNMOW (0371) 874321
off A120, 9m E of Bishop's Stortford

COOKING 2
COST £22–£47

Don't start counting beams at this sixteenth-century restaurant (with rooms in the stable block) – a calculator is needed. The Jones' formula has not changed a lot over the years – 'They've been making cheese straws ever since I started going there; they could try something different' was a plaint – but it seems to work (especially now that lunch is à la carte during the week). Menu choice is wide, still wider when all the day's specials have been explained, but the repertoire appears firmly based in popular notions such as smoked ham and melon, gazpacho, smoked salmon and scrambled egg, guinea-fowl in red wine, olives and thyme, duck breast with orange, and escalope of veal. A winter dinner began with a bang after mussels with lashings of cayenne, and a salad of avocado and smoked trout. A main dish of sea bream with tomato topping, prawns and a garlic bourride-style sauce 'had the appearance of a dish that the chef enjoyed cooking', just as the diner enjoyed eating from the good British cheeseboard, before succumbing to a temptation of white- and milk-chocolate mousses each served on the other's sauce. Well fed, well served and well chosen were the verdicts. It is wise not to break a pattern proved acceptable to so wide an audience. Listed by style and in price order, the wine selection is intelligently balanced, with marked enthusiasms for New World bottles. Prices are considerate with much below £15, but the range of halves could perhaps be extended. French house wines are from £9.95. CELLARMAN'S CHOICE: Stirling Hills, Chardonnay 1991, £11.95; Lay & Wheeler claret 1989, £10.50.

CHEF: Mark Fisher  PROPRIETOR: Brian G. Jones  OPEN: all week, exc Sat L and Sun D; 12 to 1.30, 7 to 9.30  MEALS: alc weekday L (main courses £7 to £15). Set Sun L £21.50, Set D £21.50 to £35  SERVICE: not inc  CARDS: Access, Amex, Visa  DETAILS: 60 seats. Private parties: 60 main room, 14 and 34 private rooms. Car park. Vegetarian meals. Children's helpings. Smart dress preferred. No smoking in dining-room. Wheelchair access. Music ACCOMMODATION: 8 rooms, all with bath/shower. Rooms for disabled. B&B £55 to £110. Children welcome. Baby facilities. TV. Phone. Confirm by 4. Fax: (0371) 876337 (*The Which? Hotel Guide*)

---

**GREAT GONERBY Lincolnshire** map 6

## Harry's Place ❖✳

17 High Street, Great Gonerby NG31 8JS
GRANTHAM (0476) 61780                               COOKING 3
on B1174, 2m NW of Grantham                     COST £40–£68

While at one end of the country Sir Terence Conran reopens a pleasure-dome for 400 at Quaglino's, at the other in a Georgian house opposite the Social Club Harry Hallam cooks a menu of six dishes for between two and eight customers at not dissimilar prices. All parties seem satisfied. 'The food is as fresh as it possibly can be; we had the impression it was totally cooked to order and served at its peak,' wrote a couple who minded not the wait, the expense, or the lack of choice. Harry gets up of a morning, drives all round the East Midlands to buy the makings of his evening's meal, gets home and starts work. Preparation apart, not a thing sees the heat until the customers are sitting and waiting. This impressive and single-minded formula is all Harry's own. Appetising smells greet the traveller as the front door opens to show a charming dining-room of stripped pine, warm colours and dainty displays. Here, Caroline Hallam keeps the party trotting on, whether there be one table or three. The menu hints at the serious style, as do the canapés that are used to while away the cooking time. Substantial pieces of meat or fish are cooked straightforwardly, with many herbs and real sauces. Flavours are obvious, though sometimes slightly out of balance if a herb (for instance, coriander) is used with too much enthusiasm. One evening's choice of onion soup and a pancake that enveloped chicken, Parma ham, lemon thyme and coriander was followed by Scottish salmon softened with lemon juice and white wine, cooked with butter and olive oil and again flavoured with lashings of herbs, together with fillet of beef with red wine and cognac, served with a horseradish béarnaise. To finish, hot soufflés are the thing, among other choices. Allow the whole evening for the meal. The wine list is very short and has no truck with rubbish. The range is almost too restricted unless you come with a bulging wallet.

---

CHEF: Harry Hallam  PROPRIETORS: Harry and Caroline Hallam  OPEN: Tue to Sat (Sun and Mon by arrangement); 12.30 to 2, 7 to 9.30  CLOSED: 25 and 26 Dec, bank hols MEALS: alc (main courses £14 to £20)  SERVICE: not inc  CARDS: Access, Visa  DETAILS: 10 seats. Private parties: 10 main room. Car park. Vegetarian meals with prior notice. Children's helpings. No children under 5. No smoking in dining-room. Wheelchair access (1 step). No music

## GREAT MILTON Oxfordshire

map 2

▲ *Le Manoir aux Quat'Saisons* 🍷 ❋

Church Road, Great Milton OX9 7PD
GREAT MILTON (0844) 278881
off A329, 1m from M40 junction 7

COOKING 5
COST £40–£100

When he has time for reflection, it must strike Raymond Blanc as remarkable that in less than 20 years he has gone from not knowing much about cooking and (for the purposes of this comment) penniless, to owning a giant operation that employs more staff than anything the village of Great Milton has ever seen. All this on the drive, ambition, skill and brilliance of one man. He has, of course, gathered a team around him that he has, to use modern cant, empowered to work to the same ends; it is also true that an individual's experience of Le Manoir may not always reach a bliss sublime; but the achievement should be celebrated. You do not get as far as this on lackadaisical habits or relaxed generosity, yet the very act of eating out and enjoying yourself demands that the providers of the service should seem relaxed and generous. The customer almost begins to think that M. Blanc should give the food away. When a sight of the bill brings it home that the opposite has been done, some people recoil. This contradiction lies at the very heart of the business of expensive restaurants. It may seem wrong to pay so dearly for pleasure, yet pay we must, and the question is whether the payment is ultimately resented. This year, many have delighted in paying, and seem almost to want to pay more. It is yet another mark of the achievement. The house is indeed a manor, just as we dream of, all Cotswold coloured stone, lawns and walls. There has been redecoration of the dining-rooms – bolder and more expressive – and the conservatory that holds the most people is still an unexpected (most unmanorial) colour scheme and setting. There are crowds of waiters, mainly French, while the kitchen staff is mainly English. They perform their tasks with the necessary rituals, but people often respond only to Raymond Blanc's own presence, or comment on the skill of Alain Desenclos, the restaurant manager, or that of the young sommelier. The cooking has attracted very little criticism. Sometimes portions are thought small; sometimes people have found the short lunch menu less interesting or ambitious than it should be. But dishes like a ravioli of spinach and quail's egg, flavoured with Parmesan, truffle and truffle oil, given a wonderful sauce of poultry stock, or a pot au feu franc-comtois where the belly, leg and shoulder of sucking pig with saucisse de Morteau are served with crusty bread and vegetables and a deep dish of the broth (topped up in this instance by Alain Desenclos with red wine), or the cider and calvados mousse with caramelised apples and a glaze of apple and apricot syrup, set in an apple stock speckled with vanilla seeds, with wafer-thin slices of dried apple around it and an apple sorbet to provide a little contrast, are impressive creatures, capable of using tradition, modern skills and good taste to their ultimate. There is a cheaper lunch menu (though not on Sundays, one disconsolate visitor discovered), or there is the *carte* or the menu gourmand. Their range is great, indulging more than most in a taste for offal – for instance, oxtail with wild mushrooms and red wine sauce, or a plate of 'abats' on the winter menu, with not a fillet steak in sight. The use of herbs and flavourings is imaginative and exact – for instance, the barbary duck with a maize syrup, ginger and lemon sauce – and the vegetable cookery is superb. There are occasional slips, as in one person finding the bread less than satisfactory – i.e. not fresh – for dinner, though fine for lunch. But many will console themselves with dessert: the long running café crème, or the apple and quince tart with cinnamon ice-cream or even the brochette of exotic fruits with a rice pudding – items that have entered the lingua franca of modern British cooking. If you can reconcile youself to the mark-ups, the wine list is among the best for its exploration of the French provinces. The classics too are brilliantly covered and the sommelier is a true enthusiast. Unfortunately, the percentage rules throughout, and there is nothing available by the glass if you want to change colour through a meal. The list is laid out so that it is easy to get lost. CELLARMAN'S CHOICE: Arbois Blanc, Cuvée de Luran 1979, £22.50; Fronsac, Ch. La Vieille Curé 1986, £20.

CHEFS: Raymond Blanc and Clive Fretwell PROPRIETOR: Raymond Blanc OPEN: all week; 12.15 to 2.30, 7.15 to 10.30 MEALS: alc (main courses £21.50 to £32.50). Set L £29.50 (exc Sun) to £59.50, Set D £59.50 SERVICE: net prices CARDS: Access, Amex, Diners, Visa DETAILS: 95 seats. Private parties: 62 main room, 6, 18 and 45 private rooms. Car park. Vegetarian meals. Children's helpings on request. Smart dress preferred. No smoking in 1 dining-room. Wheelchair access (1 step; also WC). No music. Air-conditioned ACCOMMODATION: 19 rooms, all with bath/shower. Rooms for disabled. B&B £165 to £375. Deposit: £150. Children welcome. Baby facilities. Afternoon teas. Garden. Swimming-pool. Tennis. Fishing. TV. Phone. Fax: (0844) 278847 (*The Which? Hotel Guide*)

---

**GREAT MISSENDEN Buckinghamshire**                                          map 3

## *La Petite Auberge*

107 High Street,
Great Missenden HP16 0BB                                          COOKING 1*
GREAT MISSENDEN (0494) 865370                                    COST £31–£42

The tiny dining-room of this modest village restaurant is tiny on two levels, with prints of the old French 'counties' on the walls, pale blue curtains at the windows, and a rust-coloured carpet. Tables are packed close together, which does not make for privacy. The lack of space can cause problems: just one person smoking may affect the whole restaurant, and one diner was irritated by 'intrusive kitchen smells'. The cooking is consistently good, but the short, patriotically French menu rarely changes. Many dishes have pleased: strongly flavoured fish soup with rouille; asparagus in chervil butter sauce; breast of duck with caramelised onions; fillet of veal with lemon. Sea bass might be garnished with celeriac or served on a bed of tomatoes. 'Foie gras' of duck is made on the premises. Thin slices of hot apple with cinnamon ice-cream, crème de menthe chocolate gâteau and lemon tart have been good finales. Service generates a mixed response: some find it attentive, unobtrusive and 'beyond reproach'; others have considered it to be slow and lacking professionalism. There is no house wine, but the short list provides acceptable drinking from the major French regions.

CHEF: H. Martel   PROPRIETORS: Mr and Mrs H. Martel   OPEN: Mon to Sat, D only; 7.30 to 10.30   CLOSED: Christmas, bank hols   MEALS: alc (main courses £13 to £15.50)   SERVICE: not inc   CARDS: Access, Visa   DETAILS: 30 seats. Private parties: 30 main room. Vegetarian meals with prior notice. Children welcome. Smart dress preferred. Wheelchair access (also WC). Music

---

**GREAT YARMOUTH Norfolk**                                                          map 6

## *Seafood Restaurant*

85 North Quay, Great Yarmouth NR30 1JF                                  COOKING 2
GREAT YARMOUTH (0493) 856009                                           COST £22–£53

'Old pub, done up; next to the railway station; small bar; fresh fish in tanks and on slab; all fresh.' Thus run the notes of one summer visitor who sighed at finding this haven where the lobsters are live not frozen; there are Loch Fyne oysters, and a seafood platter for those with appetite. If you cannot see what you want on the menu, then amble to the counter and pick your cut from there. The conversion of the pub is very comfortable, full of plush, and the kitchen copes well with getting fine produce on the table with little intrusion. The wine list should not be sniffed at: it is an upper-class set that includes Dry Creek from California, Cloudy Bay from New Zealand, Luc Sorin's Irancy, some fair-value clarets like Ch. Caronne-Ste-Gemme, and Hennessy's Paradis cognac at half the price you would pay in London's West End. House wines are from £8.70.

---

CHEFS: Mark Chrisostomou and Chris Kikis   PROPRIETORS: Chris and Miriam Kikis   OPEN: Mon to Sat, exc Sat L; 12 to 1.45, 7 to 10.45   CLOSED: 3 weeks Christmas, bank hol Mons   MEALS: alc (main courses £7 to £19.50)   SERVICE: not inc   CARDS: Access, Amex, Diners, Visa   DETAILS: 40 seats. Private parties: 40 main room. Vegetarian meals. No children under 8. Smart dress preferred. Music. Air-conditioned

---

**GRIMSTON Norfolk**                                                                map 6

## ▲ *Congham Hall* ⁵⁄ ✱

Grimston PE32 1AH
HILLINGTON (0485) 600250                                                COOKING 2
off A148 or B1153, 7m E of King's Lynn                                  COST £18–£55

Speed over the Norfolk flatlands to this brick-built Georgian manor house set in 40 acres of grounds close to King's Lynn. The view is no more exciting than the landscape, but the Forecasts have made the best of it with a fine English garden, and the devoted plantsman can while away an hour or two in the herb gardens behind. Inside the house itself an overpowering aroma of pot-pourri serves to reinforce the country-house image. Of a summer's evening, drinks on the terrace followed by dinner in the orangery-style dining-room is a pleasing experience. There are several fixed-price menus, each with its own level of choice and complexity; simple light snacks are also available at lunch-time. The herb garden figures in the menus – sometimes, as in a herb sauce with a piece of braised fillet, to very good effect indeed. Murray Chapman's cooking does not want for ambition, though execution occasionally shows lapses or lack of flavour balance. 'My vegetables made al dente seem soft' was one comment, while another person felt that pork tenderloin with melted cheese and a crisp pancake with parsley hollandaise was difficult to identify through all its parts, not helped by an extra and intrusive sweetish stock sauce. Main dishes have generally been more successful than first courses, and they in turn were better than sweet dishes. There is undoubted skill in this kitchen, but it does not always come to the fore. The wine list has a wide range and some fair choices, either from the classic regions or from the New World. House wines are £11.50.

CHEF: Murray Chapman   PROPRIETORS: Christine and Trevor Forecast   OPEN: all week, exc Sat L; 12 to 2, 7.30 to 9.30   CLOSED: bank hol Mon L   MEALS: alc light L (main courses £4.50 to £10.50). Set L £13.50 (2 courses) to £15, Set D £19.50 to £36   SERVICE: not inc, card slips closed   CARDS: Access, Amex, Diners, Visa   DETAILS: 50 seats. 5 tables outside. Private parties: 50 main room, 16 private room. Car park. Vegetarian meals. No children under 12. Jacket and tie. No smoking in dining-room. Wheelchair access (2 steps; also WC). No music   ACCOMMODATION: 14 rooms, all with bath/shower. B&B £72 to £170. Deposit: £20. No children under 12. Dogs in kennels. Afternoon teas. Garden. Swimming-pool. Tennis. TV. Phone. Doors close at 11. Confirm by 6. Fax: (0485) 601191 (*The Which? Hotel Guide*)

---

HALFORD Warwickshire                                                               map 2

## Sykes House ⅝✳

Queen Street, Halford CV36 5BT                                          COOKING 2
STRATFORD-UPON-AVON (0789) 740976                            COST £37–£44

The form at David and Peggy Cunliffe's sixteenth-century stone house is to ring at least 24 hours in advance, have the set menu explained and turn up any time between 7.30 and 8.15pm. 'It's almost like arriving at a friend's house for a dinner party; the ground floor is brightly lit and you're not entirely sure whether to use the front or back door,' reported a couple who dined in May. Three separate rooms open out on to the kitchen where it is possible to observe David Cunliffe's every move. The atmosphere is jolly and never rarified, with questions eagerly answered. The style of the six-course dinner is innovative without being outlandish and is executed with keen attention to detail. A typical November meal kicked off with a marvellously concentrated wild celery and rabbit consommé accompanied by home-baked buttermilk rolls, before terrine of beef with horseradish vinaigrette. The centrepiece was turbot hotpot, the fish sitting on a layer of sliced potatoes and leeks and topped with shredded celeriac. Then came a Caesar salad, a palate-refreshing sorbet of Marc de Gewurztraminer, and finally ginger-poached pear in butterscotch sauce. Meals begin with 'welcoming appetisers' and end with coffee and 'small fancies'. 'A haze of intricate flavours' was one reporter's overall verdict after three hours of unremitting pleasure. Gratuities are neither expected nor solicited. A glass of champagne laced with home-made elderflower cordial makes a fragrant aperitif, and the wine list is carefully considered, wide-ranging and knowledgeably described. House vin de pays is £8.25.

CHEF: David Cunliffe  PROPRIETORS: David and Peggy Cunliffe  OPEN: Wed to Sat D (reservations only), Mon and Tue D and L by arrangement for 8 or more; 7.30 to 8.15 MEALS: Set D £32.50  SERVICE: card slips closed  CARD: Visa  DETAILS: 24 seats. Private parties: 12 main room, 12 in 2 private rooms. Car park. Vegetarian meals with prior notice. Children welcome. Smart dress preferred. No smoking in dining-room. No music

---

**HAMBLETON** Leicestershire
map 6

## ▲ *Hambleton Hall* 🍾

Hambleton LE15 8TH
OAKHAM (0572) 756991
COOKING 4
off A606, 3m SE of Oakham
COST £35–£82

Hambleton, a late-Victorian gem, has class: there is an understated elegance to most of the decoration (which is not so understated in the bar) that gives it an 'inhabited' feel, while never allowing you to forget that everything is perfect. The flowers, reading matter and small details are very good indeed. So is the setting – (man-made) lakeside – which cuts you off from the hurly-burly and is just the recipe for a country weekend. Aaron Patterson has continued to impress locals and visitors alike with his cooking. Aficionados of the Ram Jam Inn (Tim Hart's transport version of Hambleton on the Great North Road) have been surprised at the prices; they have also taken issue with the ornate style of service – but they like the food. Luxuries are common, as are the tics of current stove-top practice: foie gras, shellfish and wild mushrooms are everywhere, pasta of some sort is often found, thin strips of vegetables are frequent accompaniments, a mixture of old- and new-wave herbs and spices dominates the flavour combinations, and offal inevitably appears. A deeply expensive gourmet menu in the spring showed something of the tilt: it took in tartare of salmon with spring vegetables and dill, a fricassee of wild mushrooms and foie gras with tarragon, loin of lamb with apricots and more spring vegetables served with a lemon grass-infused gravy, good cheeses and home-baked walnut bread; these were followed by a hot passion-fruit soufflé with its sorbet (always recommended). Presentation is seemly yet imaginative; ancillaries such as varied canapés, excellent little appetisers (lobster sometimes, if you strike lucky), and *tour de force* petits fours make the experience a definite 'oasis in the desert of the East Midlands'. There are, of course, cheaper alternatives on a menu that has changed its arrangement and slightly extended its choice, but there is little modesty when it comes to price. The service pleases far more than it displeases: 'courteous yet welcoming', it makes most people feel a bit like a lord, which is half the battle for a place of this character. Surprisingly the wine list offers opportunities for relatively modest drinking with decent bottles below £15 and a good range of halves, although there has been comment about bad stock-keeping in this department. If extravagance drives you, and few customers could arrive here with economy in mind, then the range and quality will delight no less; everywhere gets a toehold and there are fine representatives from Italy and Australia as well as the expected classics. There is, thankfully, not too much of anything; all is restrained and terribly superior. House wine is £16. CELLARMAN'S CHOICE: Jurançon, Dom. Castera 1990, £13.50; St-Emilion, Clos des Jacobins 1983, £29.

CHEF: Aaron Patterson  PROPRIETORS: Timothy and Stefa Hart  OPEN: all week; 12 to 2, 7
to 9.30  MEALS: alc (main courses £22 to £29). Set L and D £26.50, Set Sun L £29.50, Set L
and D 'Gourmet Menu' £50 to £60  SERVICE: net prices, card slips closed  CARDS: Access,
Amex, Visa  DETAILS: 60 seats. 4 tables outside. Private parties: 60 main room, 15 and 20
private rooms. Car park. Vegetarian meals. Children's helpings. Smart dress preferred. No
cigars/pipes in dining-room. Wheelchair access (also WC). No music  ACCOMMODATION:
15 rooms, all with bath/shower. Rooms for disabled. Lift. B&B £95 to £250. Children
welcome. Baby facilities. Pets by arrangement (not in public rooms). Afternoon teas.
Garden. Swimming-pool. Tennis. TV. Phone. Doors close at 1am. Fax: (0572) 724721
(*The Which? Hotel Guide*)

---

**HAMPTON WICK  Greater London** map 3

# Dijonnais

35 High Street, Hampton Wick,
Kingston upon Thames KT1 4DA COOKING 2
081-977 4895 COST £17–£40

'This is how one's local should be,' observes a Surrey reporter. M. and Mme
Jolivet run this as a family affair – he in the kitchen, she maintaining a homely
presence out front. The setting is an impeccable, cottagey dining-room that has
its counterparts in many French towns. M. Jolivet's cooking is sound, generous
and loyal to tradition; he has no truck with fancy modern fashions. Daily
specials supplement the short printed menu, which is dyed-in-the-wool
French provincial: witness excellent salade Alésia with crispy bacon, frogs'
legs in mustard sauce, chicken forestière, and a version of civet of duck in a
creamy cider and apple sauce. Juicy, well-hung fillet steak is served with a
sauce of mushrooms gathered from the wild. Vegetables are ample and
perfectly cooked, and the extra dish of pommes dauphinois draws unanimous
praise. Desserts such as apricot clafoutis or a tart of Reine Claude plums are
highlighted by exemplary pastry-work. The quality of the bread seems to
disappoint most reporters. The wine list is minimal; most people opt for the
house Duboeuf at £8.50.

---

CHEF: Lionel Jolivet  PROPRIETORS: Lionel and Jan Jolivet  OPEN: Mon to Sat, exc Sat L
(Sun L by arrangement); 12 to 2.30, 6 to 10  MEALS: alc (main courses £7 to £12.50). Set L
£8.95 to £10.95 (Sun), Set D £15.95. Cover £1  SERVICE: not inc  CARDS: Access, Amex,
Visa  DETAILS: 26 seats. 1 table outside. Private parties: 30 main room. Vegetarian meals.
Children's helpings. Wheelchair access (1 step). Music

# Le Petit Max

97A High Street, Hampton Wick,
Kingston upon Thames KT2 5NB COOKING 3
081-977 0236 COST £23–£45

**NEW ENTRY**

A few editions of the *Guide* ago there was a restaurant in Kew called Chez Max,
run by the same brothers. After an enforced interregnum, they have reopened
in a surreal little room called Bonzo's – because by day it is indeed Bonzo's
Café. In the shadow of the railway bridge over the Hampton road, this bare-
brick space has red gingham cloths, small chairs and little space for the

tables, while remarkable food is served in very much the same image as at the last venture. It is French – so French that Max seems ever keen to speak the language to all comers – but not so French that the menu is untranslatable and indecipherable, as it used to be. The brothers delight in materials, presented directly, with proper accompaniments. Eat crevettes here, eat foie gras, eat beef or gravlax. Proper, complicated cooking is also worth pursuing, be it cassoulet, scallops with crayfish sauce, or one of the exquisitely simple tartes à la crème, or tarte Tatin with pears rather than apples. Cheese will be one cheese, properly bought. There is no licence, but wine can be got from a shop next door. The meal price is fixed, but with supplements for luxuries – the temptation is to try them. An awful lot of trouble seems to surround the booking process. It may be coincidence, but we have had several reports of difficulties and error. Perhaps true enthusiasts, and the Renzlands are that, have to be permitted their eccentricities.

CHEFS: Marc Renzland and Matthew Jones  PROPRIETORS: Marc and Max Renzland
OPEN: all week D, and Sun L; 12.30 to 4, 7 to 11  CLOSED: 4 days at start of each month
(telephone to check)  MEALS: Set L and D £18. Unlicensed, but bring your own: corkage
£1.50  SERVICE: 10%  DETAILS: 34 seats. Private parties: 34 main room. Vegetarian meals
with prior notice. Children's helpings Sun L. No children under 8. No pipes in dining-
room. Wheelchair access. No music

---

**HARROGATE North Yorkshire**                                                    map 5

## La Bergerie                                              | NEW ENTRY |

11 Mount Parade, Harrogate HG1 1BX                              COOKING 1
HARROGATE (0423) 500089                                         COST £22–£29

Cream and green awnings mark out Jacques and Juliet Giron's modest restaurant in a quiet terrace off one of Harrogate's main thoroughfares. Inside, it feels like 'someone's home', with comfortable armchairs in the lounge and photographs of French provincial life on the walls. The atmosphere is 'serious, provincial France and very relaxing'. Jacques Giron pitches his menu towards the cuisine of the south-west and changes his output every eight weeks. Menus are fixed-price for three or four courses and meals are at a sensible cost. On a typical evening you might find pigeon breast with walnut and shallot vinaigrette, fillet of bream with brunoise of vegetables and fennel, and best end of lamb in pastry with provençal herbs. Cassoulet toulousaine is the speciality of the house. The cooking is generally on target and dishes look very pretty – for example, tartare of salmon surrounded by a pale green coulis, pan-fried duck breast with caramelised turnips and port sauce, and bavarois of white and dark chocolate. The all-French wine list has plenty of fair-priced drinking across the range. House wine is £9.

CHEF: Jacques Giron  PROPRIETORS: Jacques and Juliet Giron  OPEN: Mon to Sat, D only
(L by arrangement); 7.30 to 11  MEALS: Set D £13.50 to £15.50  SERVICE: not inc  CARDS:
Access, Visa  DETAILS: 30 seats. Private parties: 22 main room, 12 private room. Vegetarian
meals. Children's helpings. Wheelchair access (1 step; also WC). Music

## Drum and Monkey £

5 Montpellier Gardens, Harrogate HG1 2TF
HARROGATE (0423) 502650

COOKING 2
COST £13–£41

Frequenters of antique shops can spend a happy morning in the immediate vicinity of this converted pub – wine bar-cum-restaurant on the ground floor and busy dining-room with gold and dark-green wallpaper on the first – but it is only a geriatric skip from the spa itself. The abiding popularity of low prices (lower at lunch than at dinner), friendly and familiar service, good materials and straightforward cooking is attested by the difficulty in finding a slate-topped and bench seating table without prior booking. Either go early, or plan the day. It is certainly worth eating oysters and lobster here, and the flat fish is fresh as a daisy. Meat is not on offer. The menu does not change or develop to any great extent: the formula is well tried. Best to stick to the direct rendering of good ingredients, although the 'made' dishes, if not always à la mode, are not badly done. Some details – for example, the butter – might be improved, but in the enjoyment of the entire show, such small matters sink to insignificance. The wine list is emphatically good value, though there is not a lot of detail to the entries. House wines are £6.55.

CHEF: Keith Penny   PROPRIETOR: William Fuller   OPEN: Mon to Sat; 12 to 2.30, 7 to 10.15
CLOSED: 24 Dec to 2 Jan   MEALS: alc (main courses L £4 to £14.50, D £6 to £14.50)
SERVICE: not inc   CARDS: Access, Visa   DETAILS: 64 seats L, 48 seats D. Private parties:
8 main room. Children's helpings on request. Wheelchair access (3 steps; also WC). No
music

## Millers, The Bistro

1 Montpelier Mews, Harrogate HG1 2TG
HARROGATE (0423) 530708

COOKING 3
COST £23–£47

Had this entry been written a month before going to press, it would have been Millers, The Restaurant. The site is the same (part of a dinky mews redevelopment), so is the cook, so are the prices (more or less), but not the package. Whether this is viewed as a cynical manipulation of the market (note that a cover charge has been introduced as part of the repositioning) is by the way, because it seems to have worked. Early witnesses have stressed the change in atmosphere. Where once everything was a trifle claustrophobic, now the bare walls and floor fairly hum with chatter and crowds. There are signs of the influence of Marco Pierre White and his venture, the Canteen (see entry, London): jean-clad waiters, some White dishes, the cover charge, the phraseology of the menu itself. This may have connections with the rumours that Simon Gueller was to combine with his mentor in a Leeds brasserie, but events will be the proof of speculation. For the time being, until Simon Gueller's attention is perhaps diverted to larger horizons, take a chance at this place, where dishes such as rump of lamb with red peppers, aubergines and courgettes and an oil emulsified jus, or a mosaic of salmon with green peppercorns and a gazpacho sauce have combined flavour with direct appeal. The wine list is longer than the place might demand, and is a useful set of moderately priced moderns, including Oxford Landing Chardonnay and

Cabernet Sauvignon/Shiraz, Bruno Paillard champagne and Duboeuf Brouilly. House wines are £8.50.

CHEF: Simon Gueller   PROPRIETORS: Rena and Simon Gueller   OPEN: Tue to Sun, exc Sun D; 12 to 2 (3 Sun), 6.30 to 10.30   CLOSED: bank hols   MEALS: alc (main courses £7.50 to £18). Cover £1   SERVICE: not inc   CARDS: Access, Amex, Visa   DETAILS: 40 seats. 6 tables outside. Private parties: 40 main room. Vegetarian meals. Children's helpings. Wheelchair access (1 step; also WC). Music

---

**HARVINGTON Hereford & Worcester**                                        map 2

## ▲ Mill at Harvington ⁵⅄

Anchor Lane, Harvington WR11 5NR
EVESHAM (0386) 870688
S of B439 Evesham to Bidford-on-Avon                          COOKING 2
road, avoid village                                          COST £16−£36

Well off the beaten track at the end of a no-through road, this hotel restaurant is peaceful and calm, neat and tidy, even when the River Avon decides to clamber over the lawns, as it may do in the spring. 'Rabbits and swallows were visible in the gloaming from the dining-room,' noted one summer diner, as she set about Jane Greenhalgh's disarmingly simple, tasty dishes. 'The produce, much of it local, is incredibly fresh and of the highest quality. We had duck and chicken for our main courses, both of which were sensational – for flavour and the taste of freshness,' enthuses another. Duck may come with an orange and ginger sauce; chicken breast with avocado, bacon-wrapped, then served with a creamy white wine sauce. Occasionally ideas are taken from further afield – king prawns served, say, with a curried cream sauce and garnished with apple – but most dishes are carefully prepared English, as in game pie 'containing identifiable pigeon, guinea-fowl, rabbit and pheasant in a good crust'. Breakfasts are champion. The service is exemplary and thoughtful in every respect. This year sees a much improved wine list, sensibly organised by style and containing useful information on grape varieties. The selection is improving, as the smaller, more assiduous producers (like Vieux Télégraphe) replace some of the larger merchants (like Jaboulet-Vercherre, Reine Pédauque or Boisset). A different fine wine is opened weekly for guests to try by the glass – a much-appreciated idea. House wines are £8.50.

CHEFS: Jane Greenhalgh, Bill Downing and John Hunter   PROPRIETORS: Simon and Jane Greenhalgh   OPEN: all week; 11.45 to 1.45, 7 to 9   CLOSED: 24 to 28 Dec   MEALS: alc light L (main courses £4.50 to £6.50). Set L £10.95 (2 courses) to £13.95, Set D £19.50 to £23 SERVICE: not inc, card slips closed   CARDS: Access, Amex, Visa   DETAILS: 45 seats. 12 tables outside. Private parties: 40 main room, 14 private room. Car park. Vegetarian meals. Children's helpings on request. Smart dress preferred. No smoking in dining-room. Wheelchair access (1 step; also WC). No music   ACCOMMODATION: 15 rooms, all with bath/shower. Rooms for disabled. B&B £54 to £85. No children under 10. Garden. Swimming-pool. Tennis. Fishing. TV. Phone. Fax: (0386) 870688 (*The Which? Hotel Guide*)

---

*All entries in the Guide are rewritten every year, not least because restaurant standards fluctuate. Don't trust an out-of-date Guide.*

---

**HARWICH** Essex                                                                map 3

## ▲ *Pier at Harwich* ♀

| The Quay, Harwich CO12 3HH | COOKING 1 |
|---|---|
| HARWICH (0255) 241212 | COST £19–£49 |

Fresh fish is the name of the game at the Pier – a converted Victorian building
on the quayside, overlooking the twin estuaries of the Stour and the Orwell.
Supplies come straight from the local boats, or from local markets and
wholesalers. Prices are 'restaurant' rather than 'chippie' (a kid's portion of fish
and chips will not leave much change from £5), but reporters generally approve
of the quality. Cold and hot starters such as dressed crab and baked mussels
precede the centrepiece attractions – fish pie, whole plaice or Dover sole on the
bone as well as flashier ideas, including gâteau of cod, crabmeat and spinach
with chive butter sauce. Meat-eaters might opt for home-smoked chicken
breast, steak or a brochette of three fillets with three sauces. Interesting ice-
creams, such as gin and lavender, stand out among the sweets. Service may
falter, judging by reports. Lay & Wheeler provides the wines, always an
encouraging sign, and the restaurant passes them on at fair prices. Whites
predominate, with an impressive range that encompasses classic burgundies
from Leflaive, excellence from the New World and a strong showing from the
Loire. The Pier house selection makes for speed and ease without loss of
interest. Halves are good. House wines are from £7.95. CELLARMAN'S CHOICE:
Frog's Leap, Sauvignon Blanc 1991, £15.95; Vin de Pays d'Oc, Merlot, Dom.
Andrieu 1991, £7.95.

CHEF: C.E. Oakley   PROPRIETORS: G.M.W. Milsom and J.R. Wheeler   OPEN: all week; 12
to 2, 6 to 9.30   MEALS: alc (main courses £7 to £16). Set L £9 (2 courses) to £11.75, Set D
£16   SERVICE: 10%, card slips closed   CARDS: Access, Amex, Diners, Visa   DETAILS: 80
seats. Private parties: 90 main room, 60 private room. Car park. Vegetarian meals.
Children's helpings. Smart dress preferred. No cigars/pipes in dining-room. Music. Air-
conditioned   ACCOMMODATION: 6 rooms, all with bath/shower. B&B £45 to £72.50.
Children welcome. TV. Phone. Doors close at midnight. Fax: (0206) 322752 (*The Which?
Hotel Guide*)

---

**HASLEMERE** Surrey                                                           map 3

## *Morels* ▮ ⁙✳

| 25–27 Lower Street, Haslemere GU27 2NY | COOKING 4 |
|---|---|
| HASLEMERE (0428) 651462 | COST £27–£51 |

'A few paces from the municipal car park,' a reader who had had some trouble
locating the set of cottages on the high pavement above the main road reminds
us. It's a question of park and walk. The changing levels, corners and turns,
and quite low ceilings of the original houses are brought together by a cool
blue and white colour scheme that unites curtains and coffee cups. This
successful piece of design moves the locale several squares from a cottage, as
does Jean-Yves Morel's cooking, which is more sophisticated than any
peasant's, yet retains a hook of flavour. A set-price lunch began with a bonne
bouche tartlet before fish soup, tartare of smoked haddock and a terrine of
confit of duck with provençal sauce for first courses, then moved on to a

'lasagne' of pigeon with red wine sauce and leg of chicken stuffed with spinach and served with a tarragon sauce. French cheeses, a crème brûlée served in a flat dish, not a little ramekin, and a plate called 'chocolate happening' were followed by good coffee and petits fours. The trimmings here are enjoyed as much the meal itself. A dinner at the beginning of the year started with a triple-decker sandwich of blinis, smoked salmon, sour cream and caviare, and another sandwich, but this time of confit of duck and potato galette with caramelised onions. 'The second was the winner.' Oxtail with grapes and onions, gelatinous and deep-flavoured, was one main choice, duck with green and pink peppercorns and stuffed cabbage was another, lamb stuffed with basil mousse was a third. Dessert was assiette du chef – a prime favourite. The repertoire is settled, not without change, but only gradual. Blinis and oxtail, for instance, are long-runners. The balance of sauce to prime ingredient is particularly impressive. Service has good points (the captains) and not always so good (the foot soldiers). It is not unwilling, but sometimes uninformed. The wine list is very fine and has spread its wings this year beyond the earlier French boundaries. Spain and Australia are admitted, but only a few pretty classy bottles; standards are demanding here and the Italians have either failed to qualify or have remained ignored. It is a very good, classic French list, with safe rather than interesting Alsaces, and clarets and burgundies excelling in provenance and maturity. The halves are fine. House wine is £11.50.

CHEF: Jean-Yves Morel   PROPRIETORS: Jean-Yves and Mary Anne Morel   OPEN: Tue to Sat, exc Sat L; 12 to 2, 7 to 10   MEALS: alc (2 courses £24). Set L £16.50, Set D £19.50
SERVICE: not inc   CARDS: Access, Amex, Visa   DETAILS: 50 seats. Private parties: 50 main room. Vegetarian meals. Children's helpings. Smart dress preferred. No smoking in dining-room. Wheelchair access (1 step; also WC). No music

---

HASLINGDEN Lancashire                                                          map 5

## Hazel Tree                                              [NEW ENTRY]

32 Manchester Road, Haslingden BB4 5ST
ROSSENDALE (0706) 211530                                           COOKING 1
on A56, 7m SE of Blackburn                                         COST £20–£27

There is an intended Danish angle to this converted shop-restaurant on the main road, though reporters who tell of the menus chalked on boards (the Danes must have good eyesight) would accord more Scandinavian influence to the spare but satisfactory setting than to the cooking of dishes such as chicken livers with red wine and (a little) cream and brandy, filo parcels of Brie and Stilton with a garlic cream sauce, halibut with a lime and herb butter sauce, and roast leg of lamb with mint and red wine sauce. All of these came with good potatoes and acceptable greens (but very good red cabbage). Bread-and-butter pudding and a lemon tart were reasonable desserts. One comment was that some of the advertised flavours are fugitive (not enough lime in the halibut's sauce, for instance), though the materials and methods are sound. The welcome is unforced and pleasing. The reasonably priced wine list is short enough to be chalked on a blackboard. House wines are £7.25.

CHEFS/PROPRIETORS: Andrew Lyzniak and Noel Scarry  OPEN: Tue to Sun, exc Tue D; 10 (10.30 Sun) to 1.30, 7 to 9.30 (5.30 to 8.30 Sun)  MEALS: alc (main courses £9 to £9.50) SERVICE: not inc, card slips closed  CARDS: Access, Visa  DETAILS: 40 seats. Private parties: 40 main room. Vegetarian meals. Children's helpings. Smart dress preferred. Wheelchair access (1 step; also WC). Music

---

## HAWORTH West Yorkshire
map 5

## ▲ *Weavers* ✱ £

15 West Lane, Haworth BD22 8DU
HAWORTH (0535) 643822
beside car park for Brontë Parsonage Museum

COOKING **2**
COST £19–£40

It is possible the Rushworths were surprised to find their style of cookery in fashion come the '90s when the old ways came back into favour and artsy slices of this and that on top of a mousse or two were put on the blacklist. This trio of converted weavers' cottages offers 'Yorkshire Pud wi' Onion Gravy' as well as a 'turban' of sole with crabmeat, 'Old School Pud' as well as carrot and coriander soup. As one reporter put it, cheese and spinach flan might have been 'a reminder of school dinner, but the school canteen never put a crust of filo pastry on top'. It is not really school dinners, rather a happy meld of things with some alert flavours and welcome lightness; just as the cottages retain their period feel yet manage to offer space and comfort. The Rushworths, and their young helpers, have not lost any enthusiasm, which makes for a happy atmosphere, and the good value (Sunday lunch and early-bird menu especially) contributes full houses. 'No nonsense' has been offered as a short-hand description of the cooking, but that should not disguise the generosity of, for example, a fish pie of smoked and fresh haddock and salmon, or 'Cow Pie', the favourite beefsteak and onion pie, or the accurate flavourings deployed to make parsnip and cashew roast palatable for one vegetarian. The wine list continues the emphasis on value and quality with some useful South African and Australian choices, as well as a sound range of burgundies. Bruno Paillard champagnes and Brunello di Montalcino from Tenuta Caparzo make welcome appearances. House wines start at £8.25.

---

CHEFS/PROPRIETORS: Colin and Jane Rushworth  OPEN: Tue to Sat D, and Sun L (Oct to Easter); 12 to 1.30, 6.45 to 9  CLOSED: 2 weeks end July, 2 weeks after Christmas  MEALS: alc (main courses £6.50 to £13). Set Sun L £13.50, Set D £13.50 ('early doors menu' before 7.15 pm)  SERVICE: not inc  CARDS: Access, Amex, Diners, Visa  DETAILS: 45 seats. Private parties: 16 main room. Vegetarian meals. Children's helpings on request. Smart dress preferred. No smoking in dining-room. Music. Air-conditioned  ACCOMMODATION: 4 rooms, all with bath/shower. B&B £45 to £65. Deposit: £25. TV. Phone. Doors close at midnight. Confirm by 6 (*The Which? Hotel Guide*)

---

*Not inc in the details at the end of an entry indicates that no service charge is made and any tipping is at the discretion of the customer.*

*All letters to the* Guide *are acknowledged with an update on latest sales, closures, chef changes and so on.*

---

## General Havelock Inn

Radcliffe Road, Haydon Bridge NE47 6ER　　　　　COOKING 1
HEXHAM (0434) 684376　　　　　　　　　　　　COST £16–£35

The name suggests a pub, but the General Havelock is more a restaurant with bar. Although the dining-room has glass doors opening on to the terrace overlooking the river, it can feel inhospitable. 'There was only one portable radiant gas heater, which was off. Being so cold, I put my coat over my legs' was one reader's experience. Others have had happier experiences. Lunch is a modest *carte*, dinner a fixed-price affair running to four courses. Fresh herbs enliven many dishes on the handwritten menu: breast of chicken stuffed with cream cheese pâté, fillet of pork with Dijon mustard, poached salmon with lemon and dill. To start you might find tomato soup and spinach pancakes; to finish the choice could include date and treacle pudding with butterscotch sauce. The wine list is short, fairly priced and has a good showing of halves. House wine is £8.

CHEF: Angela Clyde　PROPRIETORS: Ian and Angela Clyde　OPEN: Wed to Sun, exc Sun D; 12 to 1.15, 7.30 to 8.30　CLOSED: first 2 weeks Jan, first 2 weeks Sept　MEALS: alc (main courses £5.50 to £6.50). Set L £9 to £12, Set Sun L £11, Set D £18　SERVICE: not inc
DETAILS: 28 seats. 1 table outside. Private parties: 28 main room. Vegetarian meals. Children's helpings. Smart dress preferred. No cigars/pipes in dining-room. Wheelchair access (1 step). No music

## ▲ Bridge End

7 Church Street, Hayfield SK12 5JE　　　　　　COOKING 2*
NEW MILLS (0663) 747321　　　　　　　　　　COST £22–£41

This is not merely a fuelling stop for walkers off Kinder Scout; culture gets thrown into the soup as well: reports have told of musical interludes from the Hallé Orchestra (live) to aid the digestion of customers. The Tiers were newcomers to the business (though Barbara Tier was an environmental health officer, which must have given her some acquaintance with its pitfalls) when they opened so successfully a few years back. Thus Jonathan Holmes was allowed the chance to express his very catholic view of world cookery – none of the chauvinism of *grande cuisine* here. The enthusiasm comes through in dishes such as lamb with a ginger butter sauce and fresh figs, or home-smoked fillet of beef with red wine, served with a tartlet of steak and kidney, or even apple and rhubarb crumble with a kirsch custard and an apple sorbet. Vegetarian cookery is given a fair outing on every menu – for instance, with an aubergine dish that comes with tomatoes, cumin, coriander and fennel, bound with Greek yogurt. Praise comes for the ancillaries of the meal – for example, the breads – and for the 'Unabridged' dessert, which comprises a grand selection. Service is enjoyed, though the very popularity of the restaurant has caused the odd delay. The policy towards wine pricing that favours the more expensive end is commendable. House wines are £9.

CHEFS: Jonathan Holmes and Joanne Winch  PROPRIETORS: Geoffrey and Barbara Tier
OPEN: Tue to Sat D, and Sun L; 12.20 to 2.30, 7 to 10   MEALS: alc (main courses £9.50 to
£14). Set Sun L £15   SERVICE: not inc   CARDS: Access, Amex, Diners, Visa   DETAILS: 56
seats. Private parties: 36 main room, 20 private room. Car park. Vegetarian meals.
Children's helpings. Smart dress preferred. Music   ACCOMMODATION: 4 rooms, all with
bath/shower. B&B £29 to £46. Children welcome. Baby facilities. TV. Fax: (0663) 742121
(*The Which? Hotel Guide*)

---

## HELFORD  Cornwall  map 1

## ▲ *Riverside* ♥

Helford TR12 6JU
MANACCAN (0326) 231443                                      COOKING 2
off B3293, 6m E of Helston                                  COST £25–£44

This is a cottage restaurant sitting above the village creek, that in turn leads
down to the broad-flowing Helford River just round the corner. If people have
memories that go back as far as 'cottage hotels' – the English version of chalets
– Riverside meets some of those requirements: the main cottage houses the
restaurant and kitchen, then there are a couple of other small buildings and one
other cottage that have bedrooms for guests. Steps rise vertiginously up the
hillside; it is atmospherically Cornwall. The Darrells have taken advantage of
their position to major on fish, and have kept eyes and ears open enough to
cook it in rather modern style. Monkfish is done with peppers and saffroned
oil, sea bass with asparagus and broad beans on a honey butter sauce, scallops
with a red pepper mousse and a rosemary butter sauce. A spring visitor
remarked that prime ingredients were more expressive than the sauces that
accompanied them and, modern manners notwithstanding, that portions were
reminiscent of 'nouvelle'. Desserts shown an enjoyment of pastry-work, and
the cheeseboard is local, British, and a help to drinking from the good wine list.
This has some impressive names: Baumard's Clos du Papillon and Coltassala
from Volpaia for example. A wide range of halves is now augmented by 10
wines of some individuality, all offered by the glass. House wine is £9.50.
CELLARMAN'S CHOICE: Redwood Valley, Sauvignon Blanc 1989, £12.70;
Châteauneuf-du-Pape 1990, Père Caboche, £17.65.

---

CHEFS: Susan Darrell and Alyn Williams   PROPRIETORS: Edward and Susan Darrell
OPEN: all week, D only; 7.30 to 9.30   CLOSED: mid-Nov to mid-Feb   MEALS: Set D £18 to
£28   SERVICE: 10%   DETAILS: 35 seats. 4 tables outside. Private parties: 35 main room.
Car park. Vegetarian meals with prior notice. Children's helpings. No children under 13.
Smart dress preferred. Wheelchair access (1 step; also WC). No music   ACCOMMODATION:
7 rooms, all with bath/shower. Rooms for disabled. B&B £60 to £95. Deposit: £75. Children
welcome. Baby facilities. Garden. TV. Confirm by 6. Fax: (0326) 231103 (*The Which? Hotel
Guide*)

---

*All details are as accurate as possible at the time of going to press, but chefs and owners
often change, and it is wise to check by telephone before making a special journey. Many
readers have been disappointed when set-price bargain meals are no longer available.
Ask when booking.*

---

**HERSTMONCEUX East Sussex**                                                        map 3

## Sundial ⚡✳

Gardner Street, Herstmonceux BN27 4LA                                    COOKING 2
HERSTMONCEUX (0323) 832217                                               COST £26–£66

The sun shows no sign of setting on Giuseppe Bertoli's long-established 'auberge country style' restaurant. His cooking continues to delight a loyal brigade of followers. 'We have been going here for years and always enjoy our meals' is one typical comment; 'a very pretty restaurant with a good sense of occasion' is another. The atmosphere is peaceful and unhurried, service is invariably friendly and attentive. The kitchen works to a long *carte* written in French with English translations, backed up by fixed-price menus, plats du jour and a five-course 'menu surprise gourmandise'. The food is classically entrenched but spiked with touches of modern invention. Many dishes have found favour this year: 'delectable' scallop mousse, sliced melon with strawberry coulis, Mediterranean fish soup, crisp duck in fruits of the forest sauce, game pie. Vegetables are reckoned to be 'outstanding'. Most reports also praise the sweets. Appetisers, a generous supply of breads and biscuits, plus plentiful petits fours are extra delights. Fresh peach juice is a favourite aperitif and the restaurant has a good stock of armagnacs and cognacs. Enthusiasm for wine is confined mostly to the classic areas; the detour to Italy is treated with inconsistent detail and the New World receives barely a mention. There are though some very good bottles, clarets especially, with good age and listed methodically; prices are not unreasonable. House wine is £11.50.

CHEF: Giuseppe Bertoli   PROPRIETORS: Laure and Giuseppe Bertoli   OPEN: Tue to Sun, exc Sun D; 12 to 2 (2.30 Sun), 7 to 9.30 (10 Sat)   CLOSED: 3 weeks from 1 Aug, 25 Dec to 20 Jan   MEALS: alc (main courses £14.50 to £25). Set L £15.50 to £19.50, Set D £26.50
SERVICE: 10%, card slips closed   CARDS: Access, Amex, Diners, Visa   DETAILS: 60 seats. 8 tables outside. Private parties: 60 main room, 20 private room. Car park. Vegetarian meals. Children's helpings. Smart dress preferred. No smoking in dining-room. Wheelchair access (1 step; also WC). Music

---

**HETTON North Yorkshire**                                                         map 5

## Angel Inn ▮ ⚡✳ £

Hetton BD23 6LT
SKIPTON (0756) 730263                                                    COOKING 3
off B6265, 5m N of Skipton                                               COST £15–£36

The seventeenth-century Angel sits astride most forms of public eating in this country. It is the village pub ('it preserves its pubby atmosphere well'), a brasserie or modern eating-place ('I like to go to Italy for lunch'), and a serious restaurant. Some of these activities are physically separated, but the same kitchen inspires all the food (with economic variations). While some of its *very* long-running favourites are kept, such as little moneybags of seafood in filo pastry, new things continually crop up on the menus. Italy, France, England and Thailand are among the acknowledged influences, and the Angel again drives home the fact that all you need to be is good, and the dreaded English conservatism falls away as if by magic. 'The atmosphere is jolly, bright and stimulating,' wrote one who marvelled at the fish soup with aïoli before going on to salmon with white wine and red peppers. Fish is a very strong suit: 'My baby codling (well, adolescent really) had a herb and mushroom topping and a white wine and leek sauce', and shellfish, such as scallops, are often enjoyed. Something of the multilingual nature of the cooking is seen in a menu that has duck Normandy-style, Scotch beef with horseradish, venison with celeriac, oxtail with Guinness and chicken with Thai spices. Puddings stay at home with summer pudding or sticky toffee, but also take off to the tropics for mango with vanilla cream and passion-fruit sauce. Prices are very competitive, especially given the quality of the cooking, and service is friendly and knowledgeable – 'so much so it verges on the sassy'. The wine list remains reticent when it comes to New World wines and it is the classic areas and a strong collection of Italians that really excite. Buying is intelligent, the balance of maturity and youth well maintained, and prices fair with much below £15 and many good halves. House wines are £8.95. CELLARMAN'S CHOICE: Chablis 1991, Jean Collet, £15.05; Givry 'En Choué' 1990, Lespinasse, £15.75.

CHEFS: Denis Watkins and John Topham   PROPRIETORS: Denis and Juliet Watkins, and John Topham   OPEN: restaurant Mon to Sat, D only, and Sun L; 12 to 1.30, 7 to 9. Bar/brasserie all week; 12 to 2, 7 to 10   MEALS: bar/brasserie alc (main courses £4.50 to £12.50). Set Sun L £16, Set D £21.90   SERVICE: not inc, card slips closed   CARDS: Access, Visa   DETAILS: restaurant 53 seats, bar/brasserie 65 seats. 10 tables outside. Private parties: 40 main room. Car park. Vegetarian meals with prior notice. Children's helpings Sun L. Smart dress preferred in restaurant. No smoking in 1 dining-room. No-smoking room in bar/brasserie. Wheelchair access (1 step). No music. Fax: (0756) 730363

---

**HEXHAM Northumberland**                                                   map 7

## Black House ⅸ

Dipton Mill Road, Hexham NE46 1RZ
HEXHAM (0434) 604744                                          COOKING 2*
on Whitley Chapel road, S of Hexham                          COST £26–£46

This country restaurant is set in converted out-buildings attached to a large stone farmhouse with a 'landscaped' car park. Through a big oak stable door is the relaxing, draught-proof sitting area where drinks and first-rate home-made canapés are served. The split-level dining-room is all bare stone walls, and there are original oak beams swathed in bunches of dried flowers, heavy oak tables and sideboards, fine china and country prints. Chris Pittock is a pleasant host, Hazel Pittock and Dawn Aston run the kitchen. Pastry is outstanding: witness a 'very delicate' tart of warm tomatoes on a base of mascarpone, mozzarella and Parmesan or a sweet tart of caramelised oranges. The mood is pleasant and unfussy, although the synchronised lifting of silver domes suggests a fondness for theatrical formality. Approved dishes from the short, monthly-changing menu have included warm smoked salmon with watercress sauce and tiny cheese shortbreads, beef olives with hazelnut stuffing, Northumbrian spring lamb in mustard sauce, and kebabs of monkfish and scallops with tarragon hollandaise. Vegetarians have also endorsed grilled parsnip, red pepper and mozzarella kebabs glazed with honey and ginger. The almost exclusively French wine list is not always easy to read. Why tuck the two very decent house wines at the bottom of a page of vintage champagnes? With fine Alsace and Rhônes and a generous sprinkling of half-bottles there is evidence of enthusiasm and knowledge. House wines are £8.50.

CHEF: Hazel Pittock   PROPRIETORS: Chris and Hazel Pittock   OPEN: Tue to Sat (and Suns before bank hols), D only; 7 to 9.30   MEALS: alc (main courses £10 to £16.50)   SERVICE: not inc, card slips closed   CARDS: Access, Visa   DETAILS: 26 seats. Private parties: 30 main room. Car park. Vegetarian meals. No children under 10. Smart dress preferred. No smoking in dining-room. Wheelchair access. Music

---

HIGH ONGAR Essex                                                          map 3

## The Shoes

The Street, High Ongar CM5 9ND
ONGAR (0277) 363350                                      COOKING 1*
off A414, between Harlow and Chelmsford                  COST £18–£38

Once you have separated High Ongar from Chipping Ongar, there is no mistaking this piece of half-timbering for Shoes. A pair of red ones hang over the door; china ones adorn every nook and cranny. New chef Jonathan Siddle carries on where Paul Spry left off and has received approval for straightforward roast beef and vegetables, home-made Cumberland sausages on a compote of onions and blackberries served with a Cumberland sauce, calf's liver on a bed of spinach with a madeira sauce, and duck with cabbage, bacon and green peppercorns. Passion-fruit crème brûlée and pear tarte Tatin are two desserts mentioned in dispatches. A new two-course set-price lunch is an especial bargain. The wine list is a very fair united nations of a collection with ample choice of halves. Martinborough Pinot Noir, Berberana Rioja 1980 and Jean Musso's Hautes Côtes de Beaune in particular are worth noting. House wines are £8.95.

CHEF: Jonathan Siddle   PROPRIETORS: Lynton Wootton, and Peter and Doreen Gowan   OPEN: Wed to Sun, exc Sat L and Sun D; 12 to 2.30, 7 to 9.30   CLOSED: 1 week after Christmas   MEALS: Set L £7 (2 courses) to £14, Set D Wed to Fri £15, Set D Sat £24   SERVICE: not inc, card slips closed   CARDS: Access, Amex, Visa   DETAILS: 50 seats. Private parties: 35 main room, 20 private room. Car park. Vegetarian meals. Children's helpings L. Smart dress preferred. Wheelchair access (1 step). Music

---

HINTLESHAM Suffolk                                                       map 3

## ▲ Hintlesham Hall ♥ ⅗⚹

Hintlesham IP8 3NS
HINTLESHAM (0473) 652268                                 COOKING 3
off A1071, 4½m W of Ipswich                              COST £30–£68

The Hall rests like gossamer on the pillow of the landscape, its Tudor brick smokestacks like so many power-points plugged into heaven. This vision, however, is anchored firmly to the earth by the strong style of hospitality presented by staff and management. The course set over the past 10 years has not faltered, as the country-house experience – set off by a magnificent series of

Caroline interiors – has been modified by the accretion of a greater hotel function, a golf course and clubhouse. The number of fine paintings may have been reduced, but the decoration and furnishings are still sumptuous: 'Our room was the whole floor of one wing' was one satisfied report. That same reader felt that Alan Ford's cooking over a long seasonal menu that does not stint on choice 'occupies the browns and beiges of the taste spectrum'. This may be a way of saying that there is little roughness here (vegetables may still be tied in faggots) and sometimes a blandness; but when a meal is closely described the cooking has many fine qualities of accuracy and discretion. The canapés, often little brochettes, start the event well; the appetiser, perhaps a scallop on cucumber with a lemon mayonnaise, augurs even better. What followed, therefore, was no surprise: fricassee of fish round a timbale of wild rice with a green coriander cream, foie gras in a puff-pastry box with various pulses, some lime-marinated salmon dressed with olive oil, before a classic piece of lamb with a white wine and sage sauce, helped by a goodly dose of creamed spinach, and finished by a good tarte Tatin. Another meal that drew on lobster with mustard and cream, foie gras cooked to the right second, and a chocolate mousse with fresh figs showed that Alan Ford is no stranger to the richest of ingredients. Service is always enjoyed, even if the long message on the menu about tipping (which used to be discouraged here) is so convoluted that 'you don't know what to do with yourself'. The wine list is very good: three pages of house recommendations followed by a page of country wines at moderate prices are reassuringly friendly and helpful to the customer. Elsewhere the prices appear inconsistent, with little discernable pattern. Quality remains high throughout, and at the lower end some prices are very fair. House French is £12.50. CELLARMAN'S CHOICE: Quincy 1991, Mardon et Fils, £17.65; Ch. Cissac 1986, £21.75.

---

CHEF: Alan Ford  PROPRIETORS: Hintlesham Hall Ltd  OPEN: all week, exc Sat L; 12 to 1.45, 7 to 9.30  MEALS: alc (main courses £14.50 to £21). Set weekday L £18.50, Set Sun L £19.50, Set Sun to Thur D £22  SERVICE: not inc, card slips closed  CARDS: Access, Amex, Diners, Visa  DETAILS: 120 seats. Private parties: 81 main room, 14, 42 and 81 private rooms. Car park. Vegetarian meals. Children's helpings L. No children under 10 D. Smart dress preferred. No smoking in dining-room. Wheelchair access (1 step; also WC). Music ACCOMMODATION: 33 rooms, all with bath/shower. B&B £85 to £300. Children welcome. Pets welcome (not in public rooms). Garden. Swimming-pool. Sauna. Tennis. Fishing. Golf. Snooker. TV. Phone. Doors close at midnight. Confirm 1 day ahead. Fax: (0473) 652463 (*The Which? Hotel Guide*)

---

**HINTON CHARTERHOUSE** Avon                                            map 2

▲ *Homewood Park Hotel* ♥ ⁵⁄⁴✳              NEW ENTRY

Hinton Charterhouse BA3 6BB
BATH (0225) 723731                                          COOKING 3
off A36, 6m SE of Bath                                   COST £31–£57

'It avoids stuffiness while being elegant' was a comment from someone who went on to stress that the 'total deal' was essential to a proper assessment of the success of the cooking: the rooms, the breakfast, the careful touches enjoyed by guests staying here. Homewood has long been in the *Guide* since its first beginnings as a country-house hotel (called Rosses) in the hands of Stephen and Penny Ross, now at the Olive Tree in Bath (see entry). Their successors, elegant products themselves of long professional training in Switzerland, have managed to put the house back on the visiting-lists of the well-travelled. The decoration of this Georgian house – there is a new wing, but no one would know it – steers a course between over- and under-ornate. 'Good taste' is a terrible phrase, but the owners manage to avoid offence on almost every count, and the atmosphere of slight hush is never too reverent or oppressive. Tim Ford's cooking seems equally *à point*, though prices are by no means shy. Several people mention nouvelle cuisine in their reports. In part this is a reflection of small details, like meeting with baby sweetcorn and mild, if not tasteless, baby turnips among the vegetables, in part it is the general approach of not overloading plates, and seeking to arrange them slightly artfully, and perhaps it just notes that the repertoire seeks no grand gestures of brutal or over-bold flavours. One Sunday lunch produced an excellent meal including a seafood terrine with subtle lobster sauce, brill fried with a beurre noisette, and a notable plate of hare with baby turnips (this time appreciated) and a light gravy. English cheeses and an apple tart were a fine finish. Sauces are not mere exercises in blandness: that accompanying brill with some mussels and a pile of linguine gave all the buttery richness needed; a madeira and truffle sauce with chargrilled fillet steak demonstrated that skills ranged beyond slapping meat near heat. Fish is often recommended, for instance a ragoût of seafood with a piquant sauce. Desserts carry on the good work, whether a bread-and-butter pudding laced with Grand Marnier, a chocolate and strawberry soufflé or something as regular as a nougatine parfait. It is often pleasant to hear of an old favourite being cared for. The intelligent, not overlong wine list offers good range and carefully edited choices from the New World. There are halves and a decent spread of bottles below £15, but the mark-up on the better bottles can be severe. House wine is £14. CELLARMAN'S CHOICE: Graves, Ch. Rahoul white 1989, £25; Graves, Ch. Rahoul red 1985, £27.

CHEF: Tim Ford  PROPRIETORS: Mr F. and Mrs S. Gueuning  OPEN: all week; 12 to 1.30, 7 to 9.30  MEALS: Set L £18.50, Set D £29.50  SERVICE: not inc  CARDS: Access, Amex, Diners, Visa  DETAILS: 50 seats. Private parties: 40 main room, 15 private room. Car park. Children's helpings (6 to 7 D). Smart dress preferred. No smoking in dining-room. Wheelchair access (also WC). No music  ACCOMMODATION: 15 rooms, all with bath/shower. Rooms for disabled. B&B £80 to £130. Children welcome in some rooms. Baby facilities. Afternoon teas. Garden. Tennis. TV. Phone. Doors close at 11. Confirm by 6. Fax: (0225) 723820 (*The Which? Hotel Guide*)

---

## HOLDENBY Northamptonshire                                      map 3

## ▲ *Lynton House*

Holdenby NN6 8DJ
NORTHAMPTON (0604) 770777
between A50 and A428, E of Holdenby                    COOKING 2
towards Church Brampton                                COST £19–£40

Carol Bertozzi continues to deliver a distinctive brand of Anglo-Italian cooking in this substantial Northamptonshire rectory. Her style is neither old trattoria nor new-wave, but sits happily between the two. Lunch is fixed-price; dinner is a lengthy *carte* that might take in poached scallops with nutmeg-flavoured risotto, osso buco, skewers of monkfish and squid with pizzaiola sauce, and rack of lamb with caramelised mint sauce. Reporters have spoken well of scampi on a bed of raw mushrooms with olive oil, chargrilled veal with rosemary and lemon, and steamed sea bream. Vegetables are creditably handled. The list of puddings might feature tiramisù and semifreddo as well as hot black cherries with ice-cream and brandy, and walnut roulade. Occasional mishaps such as 'tired' seafood platter and rabbit that was, according to one rabbit-fancier, 'definitely an old beast' can mar the picture. 'Service charge is neither included nor expected.' The wine list is heavily tilted towards Italy, although some pricey clarets are also on offer. House wine is £9.75.

CHEF: Carol Bertozzi   PROPRIETORS: Carlo and Carol Bertozzi   OPEN: Mon to Sat, exc L Mon and Sat; 12.15 to 1.45, 7.30 to 9.45   MEALS: alc (main courses £12 to £17). Set L £13.75. Minimum £19.75 Sat D   SERVICE: card slips closed   CARDS: Access, Amex, Visa DETAILS: 45 seats. 4 tables outside. Private parties: 60 main room, 18 private room. Car park. Vegetarian meals. Children's helpings. No children under 5. Smart dress preferred. No cigars/pipes in dining-room. Wheelchair access (also men's WC). No music ACCOMMODATION: 5 rooms, all with bath/shower. B&B £49 to £55. No children under 5. Garden. TV. Phone. Doors close at midnight. Confirm by 9am (*The Which? Hotel Guide*)

---

**HOLT Norfolk**                                                        map 6

## Yetman's ✸✗

| 37 Norwich Road, Holt NR25 6SA | COOKING 2 |
| CROMER (0263) 713320 | COST £24–£42 |

'Only last Sunday one of our local fishermen arrived during lunch with sea bass – still kicking – which solved the problem of what to cook for supper.' So writes Peter Yetman. On another occasion, the plumber turned up with a pike when he came to fix the boiler. This is a restaurant driven by the search for local produce, and the owners have tapped into the food network, procuring organic vegetables from nearby market gardens, and exchanging ideas and ingredients with other restaurants in the area. The place stands next to a supermarket at the edge of town – look out for the old cottage-style houses with window boxes. The dining-room is 'absolutely spotless', with sweeping bright yellow curtains, fresh flowers and carved wooden pigs which are everywhere. But do not expect much standing on ceremony: the waiters wear jeans and children are often to be seen at play. The menu is short (some say 'restricted') but it continues to delight most visitors: artichoke soup, 'divine' twice-baked cheese soufflé, grilled sardines, guinea-fowl with game sauce and turbot in white wine sauce have all been endorsed. Home-made breads are first-rate, as are the vegetables. Top-drawer sweets have included blackcurrant and vanilla bombe and ever-popular crème brûlée. Peter Yetman points out that Saturday lunch is slightly cheaper. The wine list is not vast, but takes the New World seriously and pinpoints pedigree growers. Prices are fair and halves show up strongly. Ten house wines are from £7.

---

*A report form is at the back of the book; write a letter if you prefer.*

---

CHEF: Alison Yetman   PROPRIETORS: Alison and Peter Yetman   OPEN: Wed to Sun D, Sat and Sun L (Mon D summer); 12.30 to 2, 7.30 to 9 (7 to 9.30 summer)   MEALS: alc (main courses £13.50 to £15.50 – around £10 Sat L). Surcharge on main course alone £3.75 SERVICE: not inc   DETAILS: 32 seats. Private parties: 20 main room, 12 private room. Vegetarian meals. Children's helpings. No smoking in dining-room. Wheelchair access (1 step). No music

---

## HORNCASTLE Lincolnshire

map 6

# Magpies £

73–75 East Street, Horncastle LN9 6AA   COOKING 1
HORNCASTLE (0507) 527004   COST £14–£36

The resolutions of the Common Market have not yet done away with local slaughterhouses here, so the Lee family can draw on local supplies for meat, on Grimsby for fish, and on the dark soils of the fens for good vegetables. They are served up in a row of converted cottages on the road to Skegness: comfortable and well lit, somewhat cosy, but welcoming. Plenty of food is on offer (Lincolnshire develops big appetites), but so too are competence and a certain adventure, seasoned with a steady eye on well-tried favourites: rare commodities in the district. French onion soup, tagliatelle with mussels, snails with garlic butter, followed by a composite dish of roast breast and casseroled leg of duck with blackberry sauce and an apple galette, or simply fresh whiting, made a spring meal of conspicuous value, especially with surefire stickies such as apple and blueberry pancakes with maple syrup, or butterscotch and almond sundae. Nor is a ransom asked for the improved wine list, with sound choices in most sections. There are eight house selections dotting round the globe, all at £7.50.

CHEFS: Matthew and Simon Lee   PROPRIETORS: Joan, Matthew and Caroline Lee   OPEN: Tue to Sat, D only, and Sun L; 12.30 to 2, 7.15 to 10   CLOSED: 2 weeks Sept/Oct, restricted opening early Jan   MEALS: alc (main courses £9 to £13). Set L £8.95 to £9.50, Set D £13.95 to £14.95. Minimum £11.50   SERVICE: not inc   CARDS: Access, Visa   DETAILS: 45 seats. Private parties: 45 main room. Children's helpings Sun L. No children under 4. Smart dress preferred. Wheelchair access. Music

---

## HORTON Northamptonshire

map 3

# French Partridge 🍴

Horton NN7 2AP
NORTHAMPTON (0604) 870033   COOKING 3
on B526, 5m SE of Northampton   COST £25–£33

This particular bird has the stamina of the highest-bred racing pigeon and shows no sign of exhaustion. Its cage is a former coaching-inn: Georgian seemliness decked up with no particular flummery. Two generations of Partridges deal with all aspects. 'Mrs P. junior is very efficient; Mrs P. senior is still a delight, and manages the wine, the menus, the experiments and the customers very firmly,' writes a local habitué. The menu continues to be a set price, with a short choice at each of the four courses (just one alternative for the second – fish or vegetable). The style of 'French provincial' that so captivated David Partridge when he dreamed of cooking for a living still rules, even if other wider influences have made themselves felt in dishes like couscous or taramasalata and pitta bread. Consistency matters, helped by understatement and good value. Mackerel marinated with white wine and vinegar, a quiche of mushroom and Swiss chard, boiled home-cured pork with broad beans and a parsley sauce, and then brown-sugar meringues is an exemplary meal that has pleased literally generations. But there are new converts: 'I tended to avoid this restaurant; however, we called on the off-chance and found Mrs Partridge bubbly and welcoming, and the food matching her mood.' Penetrating the disarming modesty of the wine list reveals not only the reliable petits châteaux, good Alsaces and a decent, now standard, run of antipodeans, but also some remarkable wines such as Rousseau Gevrey-Chambertin, Guigal's 1985 Hermitage, and a more modest trawl through south-west France. There is much enthusiasm here and the prices are generous to a T. House wines are from £9.50. CELLARMAN'S CHOICE: Pouilly-Fuissé 1990, Forest, £21; St Chinian, Berloup 1990, £11.

CHEFS: David Partridge and Justin Partridge  PROPRIETORS: David and Mary Partridge OPEN: Tue to Sat, D only; 7.30 to 9  CLOSED: 2 weeks Christmas and Easter, 3 weeks end Jul to Aug  MEALS: Set weekday D £21, Set Sat D £22  SERVICE: net prices  DETAILS: 50 seats. Private parties: 20 main room. Car park. Vegetarian meals with prior notice. Children welcome. No smoking during meals. Wheelchair access (1 step). No music

---

HUDDERSFIELD  West Yorkshire                                           map 5

## ▲ Lodge Hotel

48 Birkby Lodge Road, Birkby,
Huddersfield HD2 2BG                                         COOKING 1
HUDDERSFIELD (0484) 431001                                   COST £21–£36

The art nouveau decoration by Manchester architect Edgar Wood survives intact among the encumbrances of soft furnishings necessary to pamper customers of this *fin de siècle* hotel. It is a country-house image that is sought among the leafy suburbs of Huddersfield and, by and large, it is achieved. The Birley brothers' menus are elaborate in the way of country-house cooking of the last decade, but despite the fanciful presentation and mould-breaking combinations they often please. Indicative dishes are chicken breast with scallops, wild mushrooms and a mild curry sauce, pork with blue cheese, spinach and grapes on a herb sauce, or beef with crayfish and green peppercorns. Mixtures of fish and meat, and a certain sweetness in the sauces, are enjoyed. Tradition reasserts itself in Sunday lunch and desserts. The fully annotated wine list has good suppliers and very prices are very reasonable. House wines are £8.95.

---

*The text of entries is based on unsolicited reports sent in by readers, backed up by inspections conducted anonymously. The factual details under the text are from questionnaires the* Guide *sends to all restaurants that feature in the book.*

CHEFS: Richard Hanson, Kevin and Garry Birley  PROPRIETORS: Kevin and Garry Birley
OPEN: all week, exc Sat L (by arrangement) and Sun D; 12 to 2, 7.30 to 9.45  MEALS: alc
(main courses £5.50 to £7). Set D £20.50. Minimum £6.75 L  SERVICE: not inc, card slips
closed  CARDS: Access, Amex, Visa  DETAILS: 62 seats. 4 tables outside. Private parties:
62 main room, 10 and 24 private rooms. Car park. Vegetarian meals. Children's helpings.
Smart dress preferred. No-smoking area. Wheelchair access (1 step; also WC). Music
ACCOMMODATION: 11 rooms, all with bath/shower. Rooms for disabled. B&B £50 to £60.
Children welcome. Baby facilities. Pets welcome. Afternoon teas. Garden. Snooker. TV.
Phone. Doors close at 1am. Fax: (0484) 421590 (*The Which? Hotel Guide*)

---

| HUNSTRETE Avon | map 2 |
|---|---|

## ▲ *Hunstrete House* ❋

| | NEW ENTRY |
|---|---|

Hunstrete, Chelwood BS18 4NS
MENDIP (0761) 490490                                          COOKING 2
off A368, 4m S of Keynsham                                    COST £23–£58

'They should have a notice in the kitchen that states: "Do not use tomato as a
garnish",' remarked someone who felt that had she added together all the wild
mushrooms and tomatoes littering her plates they would have made a dinner
for one. Hunstrete, a slightly squat Georgian house with atmospheric
courtyard, a fine parkland setting, and a cosy suite of public rooms with
furniture on a substantial scale and some decent pictures to while away idle
moments, runs trippingly along under corporate ownership, with Darren Bott
in the kitchen. Prices are aimed at the squirearchy, or higher, but lunch tosses
crumbs of comfort to the masses. Disregard the garnish and the cooking has
skill. Sauces have been praised for themselves, though not necessarily for their
matching to the main ingredient. A rosemary beurre blanc would have been
happier with a starter of artichokes, lentils and spinach mousseline than it was
with the noisettes of lamb, while the aforementioned delicate spinach dish was
drowned out somewhat by its companions' earthy juices. The repertoire shows
a smidgeon of adventure in a soy-sauce velouté with scallops and Chinese
vegetables, and a light touch with salmon with roast vegetables and red pepper
oil, and consommé of shellfish fired up with a rouille. Puddings seem well
composed and capable of exploration, though trial and error was not the
method chosen by a table that plumped wholesale for the mulled apple and
pear crumble with cinnamon custard. Cheeses are British and listed, but petits
fours may vary in quality. The wine list has names to conjure with and a price
range that hardly favours those with disadvantaged incomes. A champagne
below £32.50 would help, and a more interesting choice below £20 is
suggested. House claret is £12.

CHEF: Darren Bott  PROPRIETORS: Clipper Hotels  OPEN: all week; 12 to 2, 7.15 to 9.30
MEALS: alc (main courses £14 to £20). Set L £15, Set D £29.50  SERVICE: not inc, card slips
closed  CARDS: Access, Visa  DETAILS: Terrace restaurant 36 seats, Garden restaurant 14
seats. 4 tables outside. Private parties: 50 main room, 8 and 20 private rooms. Car park.
Vegetarian meals. No children under 9. Jacket and tie. No-smoking in 1 dining-room.
Wheelchair access (also WC). No music  ACCOMMODATION: 24 rooms, all with bath/
shower. Rooms for disabled. B&B £90 to £195. No children under 9. Afternoon teas.
Garden. Swimming-pool. Tennis. TV. Phone. Confirm by 11am. Fax: (0761) 490732
(*The Which? Hotel Guide*)

# ▲ *Esseborne Manor* ♀

Hurstbourne Tarrant SP11 0ER
HURSTBOURNE TARRANT (0264) 76444                          COOKING 2
on the A343, 1½m N of Hurstbourne Tarrant                 COST £26–£47

This country manor was once the estate farmhouse. Now it is a snug but
handsome hotel and restaurant. New chef Andrew Norman has settled in
quickly and is carrying on where his predecessor left off. Very little seems to
have changed: there is still an 'incredible value' fixed-price three-course menu
as well as a short *carte*, plus the option of a two-course 'quickie' at lunch-time.
One reporter thought the dish descriptions rather prosaic – 'individual
shepherd's pie, provençal beef stew, three kinds of fish cooked in a paper bag'
– but the results were reckoned to be more exciting than that. The repertoire
takes in plain and elaborate, classic and modern ideas, ranging from
minestrone soup and game casserole with dumplings to mille-feuille of herring
roes with leeks, and home-made ravioli filled with savoury vegetable purée.
Local specialities, such as Chilbolton asparagus, watercress and air-cured
Dorset ham, also appear from time to time. High points have been warm diced
black pudding with apple and celeriac salad pointed up with a 'heavenly',
slightly sweet dressing, poached salmon with spinach purée and tomato coulis,
and a pot of baked chocolate cream topped with sliced strawberries. Service is
excellent throughout. Bread is good, but nibbles and petits fours could be
improved. Happily, prices at the upper end of the wine list have seen some
dramatic reductions. The wines themselves are sourced from some of the best
and most imaginative merchants and the range is catholic. There are good half-
bottles and the list here is beginning to look good value. House wine is £12.
CELLARMAN'S CHOICE: Menetou-Salon 1990, Clément, £15.70; Médoc, Ch.
Potensac 1985, £21.80.

CHEF: Andrew Norman   PROPRIETORS: Michael and Frieda Yeo, and Simon Richardson
OPEN: all week; 12.30 to 2, 7.30 to 9.30   CLOSED: 28 to 30 Dec   MEALS: alc (main courses
£14 to £18.50). Set L £14 (2 courses) to £17.50, Set D £19.50   SERVICE: not inc, card slips
closed   CARDS: Access, Amex, Diners, Visa   DETAILS: 35 seats. 5 tables outside. Private
parties: 20 main room. Car park. Vegetarian meals. No children under 12. Smart dress
preferred. No cigars/pipes in dining-room. Wheelchair access (also WC). No music
ACCOMMODATION: 12 rooms, all with bath/shower. Rooms for disabled. B&B £84 to £125.
No children under 12. Garden. Tennis. TV. Phone. Doors close at midnight. Confirm by 6.
Fax: (0264) 76473 (*The Which? Hotel Guide*)

---

# ▲ *Barton Cross*                                      NEW ENTRY

Huxham EX5 4EJ
EXETER (0392) 841245 and 841584                          COOKING 1*
½m E of A396 at Stoke Canon, 5m N of Exeter             COST £31–£39

This hotel in the Devon countryside was originally three seventeenth-century
thatched cottages, with modern bedrooms added in 1987. The interior
is beamed and cottagey. An attractive gallery is the main feature of the

dining-room, which has pretty floral tablecloths, high-backed chairs and classical music on disc. Stuart Fowles offers a modern menu with some intriguing ideas; meals are fixed-price for two or three courses (including a sorbet). Slices of venison sausage and boar sausage on nettle tagliatelle with sauce Robert has been an excellent starter. Main courses might range from honey-glazed breast of Lunesdale duckling with lime and ginger syrup to roast rack of lamb with minted yogurt. Fish from the local boats is given simple, effective treatment. Desserts such as coffee cheesecake or kiwi and pineapple mille-feuilles come with local clotted cream. Mrs Ball and staff maintain an agreeable, unfussy atmosphere conducive to civilised enjoyment. 'Gratuities should be earned, not expected,' says the menu. The wine list of 100 bins has been thoughtfully put together by Christopher Piper Wines: descriptions are helpful, prices are fair. House wines are from £8.25.

CHEF: Stuart Fowles   PROPRIETORS: Mr and Mrs R. Ball   OPEN: Mon to Sat (Sun residents only); 12.15 to 1.30, 7 to 9.30   MEALS: Set L and D £18.50 (2 courses) to £22.50   SERVICE: not inc, card slips closed   CARDS: Access, Amex, Diners, Visa   DETAILS: 32 seats. 10 tables outside. Private parties: 40 main room, 10 private room. Car park. Vegetarian meals. Children's helpings. Wheelchair access. Music   ACCOMMODATION: 7 rooms, all with bath/shower. B&B £63.50 to £85. Children welcome. Baby facilities. Pets welcome in bedrooms. Afternoon teas. TV. Phone. Fax: (0392) 841942

---

## ILKLEY West Yorkshire                                                           map 5

## *Box Tree*

35–37 Church Street, Ilkley LS29 9DR
ILKLEY (0943) 608484                                                    COST £31–£47

*As the* Guide *went to press, changes in staff at this
establishment made our review invalid.*

---

PROPRIETORS: The Box Tree Restaurant (Ilkley) Ltd   OPEN: Tue to Sun, exc Sat L and Sun D; 12 to 2, 7 to 10   CLOSED: 27 to 30 Dec, 21 to 31 Jan   MEALS: Set L £22.50, Set D £29.50   SERVICE: net prices, card slips closed   CARDS: Access, Visa   DETAILS: 50 seats. Private parties: 34 main room, 14 and 34 private rooms. Vegetarian meals. Children's helpings. Smart dress preferred. No cigars/pipes in dining-room. Wheelchair access. No music. Fax: (0943) 607186

## ▲ *Rombalds* ⁜✱ £　　　　　　　　　　　　 NEW ENTRY

West View, Wells Road, Ilkley LS29 9JG　　　　　　　　　COOKING 2
ILKLEY (0943) 603201　　　　　　　　　　　　　　　　　COST £17–£43

'We are the only restaurant in Ilkley to have remained under the same ownership since we began in 1981' is Ian Guthrie's proud claim, based, he would say, on providing what the customer wants. The site is a terrace of Victorian houses, well and truly decorated, shining like a new pin. While the lunch offering pays homage to the virtues of speed and economy, allowing full play to businessmen's conservatism, dinner-time is much more fun – and there may be an organist to jolly it along. Reports have praised the ancillaries and the evident concern of the Guthries that everything should be just right. They have also applauded the main attraction: dishes like scallops and leeks with a cheese topping and white wine sauce; brill with oysters and champagne; brill again, with ratatouille; fillet of beef with shallots, lentils and bacon; orange and lemon tart; hazelnut and pistachio parfait; and apple in filo pastry with honey ice-cream. Tastes stand up; methods are genuine. The enthusiasm brought to bear by Ian Guthrie is just as apparent in his wine list. The prices are genuinely fair, the choices extemely sensible and interesting. The New World grabs some of the attention, for instance Simon Hackett and Geoff Merrill wines, but France is well covered too, both with smaller appellations and in the classic regions. House wines are from £7.60, but this sort of list repays exploration.

CHEFS: Ian Guthrie and Jonathan Nicholls　PROPRIETORS: Ian and Jill Guthrie　OPEN: all week; 12 to 2 (9 to 1.30 Sun brunch), 7 to 9.30　CLOSED: 28 to 30 Dec　MEALS: alc (main courses £9.50 to £17). Mon to Sat Set L £9.95, Mon to Fri Set D £10 (2 courses) to £12.95, Set Sun brunch £10.25 to £13.35, Set Sun D £15 (2 courses) to £18.50　SERVICE: not inc, card slips closed　CARDS: Access, Amex, Diners, Visa　DETAILS: 35 seats. Private parties: 50 main room, 20 and 50 private rooms. Car park. Vegetarian meals. Children's helpings. No smoking in dining-room. Wheelchair access (also WC). Music　ACCOMMODATION: 15 rooms, all with bath/shower. B&B £72 to £84. Deposit: £30. Children welcome. Baby facilities. Pets welcome (not in public rooms). Afternoon teas. TV. Phone. Doors close at 1am. Fax: (0943) 816586 (*The Which? Hotel Guide*)

---

£ *indicates that it is possible to have a three-course meal, including coffee, a half-bottle of house wine and service, at any time the restaurant is open (i.e. at dinner as well as at lunch, unless a place is open only for dinner), for £20 or less per person.*

*The* Guide *office can quickly spot when a restaurateur is encouraging customers to write recommending inclusion – and sadly, several restaurants have been doing this in 1993. Such reports do not further a restaurant's cause. Please tell us if a restaurateur invites you to write to the* Guide.

*The 1995 Guide will be published before Christmas 1994. Reports on meals are most welcome at any time of the year, but are extremely valuable in the spring. Send them to* The Good Food Guide, *FREEPOST, 2 Marylebone Road, London NW1 1YN. No stamp is needed if posted in the UK.*

## Kwok's Rendezvous £ | NEW ENTRY |

23 St Nicholas Street, Ipswich IP1 1TW
IPSWICH (0473) 256833

COOKING 1
COST £17–£31

Thomas Kwok pioneered Szechuan cooking in Suffolk. Today, though advertising himself as offering Peking cuisine, he still cooks Szechuan and Cantonese dishes. That said, Peking duck is probably the big seller here, 'and it is very, very tasty too. I am not surprised it elicits enthusiasm,' adds a constant visitor. He was also moved to praise the sweet-and-sour wun-tun, the beef in black-bean sauce, and the glazed toffee-apples. The place has the virtue of consistency, pleasant family service and a rather good wine list including Alsaces from Trimbach, some white burgundies from Oliver Leflaive, and a Moulin-à-Vent from Loron. Though Pacific wines might be more suitable, Kwok's does not include them. The house wines, however, are Australian, at £7.30.

CHEF: Thomas Kwok PROPRIETORS: Lucia and Thomas Kwok OPEN: Mon to Sat (Sat L by arrangement only); 12 to 2, 7 to 10.30 CLOSED: bank hols MEALS: alc (main courses £4.50 to £6). Set L and D £13.95 to £15.95 (minimum 2 people). Minimum £9.95 SERVICE: not inc CARDS: Amex, Access, Visa DETAILS: 50 seats. Private parties: 50 main room. Vegetarian meals. Children welcome. Smart dress preferred. Wheelchair access (2 steps; also WC). Music. Fax: (0473) 256833

## Mortimer's on the Quay

Wherry Quay, Ipswich IP4 1AS
IPSWICH (0473) 230225

COOKING 1
COST £18–£40

Situated on the water-front by the wet dock, this restaurant is the younger sister of Mortimer's in Bury St Edmunds (see entry). Visitors have found parking a problem, although one couple noted that it would 'probably be better at the weekend when the Ipswich Port Authority reserved car parking is available to the public'. Thomas Mortimer seascapes line the walls, there are oilcloths on the tables and the menu takes its cue from the local catch. The freshness of the fish is impressive, and the repertoire changes daily. Moules marinière, chargrilled tuna provençale, steamed fillet of halibut florentine and brill with hollandaise sauce are typical offerings. Sweets might include chocolate pot, crème caramel and home-made sorbets. Coffee comes with Belgian 'fish' chocolates. Service is 'discreet but attentive'. Whites dominate the short, good-value wine list. House wine is £7.65.

CHEF: Kenneth Ambler PROPRIETORS: Kenneth Ambler and Michael Gooding OPEN: Mon to Sat, exc Sat L; 12 to 2, 7 to 9 (6.30 to 8.15 Mon) CLOSED: 25 Dec to 6 Jan, last week Aug, first week Sept MEALS: alc (main courses £7 to £16) SERVICE: not inc CARDS: Access, Amex, Diners, Visa DETAILS: 60 seats. Private parties: 12 main room, 20 private room. Vegetarian meals. Children's helpings. Smart dress preferred. No-smoking area. Wheelchair access (also WC). No music

## Singing Chef

| | |
|---|---|
| 200 St Helen's Street, Ipswich IP4 2LH | COOKING 1 |
| IPSWICH (0473) 255236 | COST £22–£40 |

'Unremittingly French,' observed reporters about the Toyés' long-standing
bistro near Suffolk College; but they added: 'The standard of cooking and the
prices they charge should command more than slightly spartan surroundings,
hard chairs, paper-covered tables, inadequate serviettes and outside loos.'
Kenneth Toyé is a character, still prepared to compose and sing ditties for
special parties. His cooking is pure Elizabeth David, with its roots deep in the
French provincial tradition. Fish soup with rouille, pissaladière and baked
shoulder of lamb stuffed with aromatic herbs are typical of the repertoire, as
was an outstanding version of boeuf en daube du Rhône. To finish, there might
be crêpes with orange and brandy and home-made sorbets. However, the high
enthusiasm of some reports is tempered by occasional complaints, including
'amateurish' service. Kenneth Toyé also offers a take-away service (telephone
orders only) and cooks in customers' own homes on Sundays and Mondays.
The modest wine list plunders France for good-value drinking. House wine
is £9.75.

CHEF: Kenneth Toyé   PROPRIETORS: Cynthia and Kenneth Toyé   OPEN: Tue to Sat, D only
(other times by arrangement); 7 to 11   MEALS: alc (main courses £9 to £12.50). Set D £13.95
SERVICE: not inc, card slips closed   CARDS: Access, Visa   DETAILS: 36 seats. 4 tables
outside. Private parties: 36 main room. Vegetarian meals. Children's helpings. Smart dress
preferred. Wheelchair access (also WC). Music

---

**IXWORTH Suffolk**                                                          map 6

## Theobalds ✸✱

| | |
|---|---|
| 68 High Street, Ixworth IP31 2HJ | COOKING 2 |
| PAKENHAM (0359) 31707 | COST £23–£42 |

Theobalds' high-street frontage is a matter-of-fact shop conversion, but inside
it is well fitted out with fine china, Suffolk beams, atmospheric fireplace and
all. Plastic flowers were allegedly spotted by one visitor, but they hardly
detracted from the pleasure of a dish of lamb with rosemary served on a bed of
aubergine, pimento and tomato. Nor did they spoil the gentle, even service
from Geraldine Theobald and the consistency of the performance in the kitchen
of her husband, Simon. Theobalds thrives on regulars, people who are fond of
an outing that can be relied upon and the food that offers sound ingredients
matched by enjoyable, flavourful sauces: for example, juniper, gin and
blackcurrant sauce with hare; white wine, English mustard and anchovy sauce
with skate; and white port sauce with brill. Finish up with a dessert such as
chocolate truffle cake or mandarin nougat mousse. The wine list here is
serious. Makers such as Leflaive, Couly-Dutheuil, Guigal and Bava are among
the world's best, and prices are not outrageous. The range is wide and there
are enough unfamiliar bottles to pique the most jaded curiosity. House French
is £9.75.

CHEF: Simon Theobald  PROPRIETORS: Simon and Geraldine Theobald  OPEN: Tue to Sun, exc Sat L and Sun D; 12 to 1.30 (2 Sun), 7 to 9.30 (10 Sat)  MEALS: Set L £11.95 (2 courses) to £14.95, Set Sun L £15.95, Set D £18.50 to £26.50  SERVICE: not inc  CARDS: Access, Visa  DETAILS: 36 seats. Private parties: 36 main room. Vegetarian meals. Children's helpings. No children under 8 D. Smart dress preferred. No smoking in dining-room. No music

---

## JEVINGTON  East Sussex

map 3

## *Hungry Monk* ⚡✳

Jevington BN26 5QF
POLEGATE (0323) 482178
off A22/A259, between Polegate and Friston

COOKING 2
COST £29–£34

This popular cottage restaurant celebrated its silver jubilee in the ownership of the Mackenzies in 1993. It continues to demonstrate that continuity from the '60s and the '70s in its cooking and style of service. One party spent the day walking the Downs, rolled up an hour late, were greeted with enthusiasm, shown to one of the small reception rooms for drinks and noted how the furniture glowed in the soft light, and how the crowds packed the building tight. These diners proceeded to eat a terrine of chicken livers with vegetables in aspic, a tomato and basil mousse, calf's liver with cream and pepper sauce, goujons of sole, and vegetables that 'took the admirable fashion of cooking greens lightly a little too far; al dente broccoli could not have been tackled were the dente not your own.' The dessert of 'rich, back-to-childhood, runny, juicy knickerbocker glory' was a fine finish. There is an attempt to suit at least two sorts of culinary style in the set-price menu (which usually has a couple of dishes at a supplement). On the one hand terrines, mousses and filo-wrapped parcels get their outing – for instance three cheeses in filo with a cranberry sauce or a platter of fish mousses and terrines; on the other, simpler affairs like wild mushrooms on polenta or squid stuffed with pine-kernels and spinach are on offer. Try the English wines from Breaky Bottom or Kingley. Otherwise, there is a good set of clarets supported by the wider world for range of price; the French classics draw on long-established négociants and names. Prices are set by calculator to the nearest penny; no rounding down or up here. House wines start at £8.50.

---

CHEFS: Clare Burgess and Thai La Roche  PROPRIETORS: Nigel and Susan Mackenzie
OPEN: all week, D only, and Sun L; 12.15 to 2, 7 to 10  CLOSED: 24 to 26 Dec  MEALS: Set Sun L and D £19.90  SERVICE: not inc (12.5% for 8 or more)  CARDS: Amex  DETAILS: 40 seats. 2 tables ouside. Private parties: 40 main room, 10 and 16 private rooms. Car park. Vegetarian meals. Children's helpings. No children under 3. Smart dress preferred. No smoking in dining-room. Music. Fax: (0323) 483989

---

*See the inside of the front cover for an explanation of the 1 to 5 rating system for cooking standards.*

⚡✳ *indicates that smoking is either banned altogether or that a dining-room is maintained for non-smokers. The symbol does not apply to restaurants that simply have no-smoking areas.*

KELSALE Suffolk        map 3

## Hedgehog Hall ✼       NEW ENTRY

Kelsale IP17 2RF
SAXMUNDHAM (0728) 602420        COOKING 1
on W side of A12, 1m N of Saxmundham        COST £16–£34

Sara Fox and Peter Hill, late of the Regatta restaurant in Aldeburgh, have
'really surpassed themselves' at this thatched Tudor building, says a reporter.
The setting is delightful: outside is a lovely garden with all kinds of artefacts
including a Normandy cider press and an Indian gazebo. The interior consists
of uneven floors, thresholds and beams: it feels cottagey, cosy and refreshingly
informal. At lunch there are bar snacks and simple dishes with a British
regional flavour, while in the evening guests are offered a fixed-price menu
with plenty of choice. Good intentions and enterprise are evident, even if the
results are sometimes 'from the book rather than from the heart'. Rabbit and
duck terrine is served with home-made pickles, carpaccio is paired with
Parmesan and black olives. Typical main courses might include roast salmon
fillet with pepper and basil, pan-fried chicken fillet with Roquefort, and
stuffed field mushrooms and red peppers with sun-dried tomatoes and pesto.
To finish, the bread-and-butter pudding 'is worth breaking any diet for'. The
short international wine list changes almost by the week, but prices are fair.
Adnams bitter is on draught. House wine is £7.95.

CHEF: Sara Fox   PROPRIETORS: Sara Fox and Peter Hill   OPEN: Tue to Sun, exc Sun D;
12.30 to 2.30, 7 to 10.30 (later during Aldeburgh Festival and Snape Proms)   MEALS: alc
(main courses £5 to £11). Set Sun L £10.75, Set D £13.50 (2 courses) to £15.75   SERVICE:
not inc   CARDS: Access, Visa   DETAILS: 60 seats. 6 tables outside. Private parties: 30 main
room. Car park. Vegetarian meals. Children's helpings. Smart dress preferred. No smoking
in dining-room. Wheelchair access (1 step; also WC). Music

---

KENDAL Cumbria       map 7

## Duffins £

54 Stramongate, Kendal LA9 4BD        COOKING 1
KENDAL (0539) 720387        COST £11–£32

Andrew Duffin describes his popular business as 'a small lock-up restaurant'
in a row of terraced shops. It is an asset to the community, an industrious
enterprise producing everything from bread rolls and truffles to pigeon
sausages. At lunch-time, the tablecloths come off and the place functions as a
café, serving local office workers and shoppers with cakes, snacks and simple
dishes such as beef stew with mushroom and onion dumplings. A touch of
good-natured formality returns in the evening, when Andrew cooks to a short,
well-balanced menu of more elaborate dishes with distinct French overtones.
Confit of duck on a bed of lentils, steamed chicken with avocado and tarragon
sauce, and rabbit with Dijon mustard sauce are typical offerings. Fish is at
market price. Main dishes come with plentiful vegetables and two kinds of
potato. On the dessert menu you might find poached pears in red wine,
steamed ginger pudding with cinnamon anglaise, and lemon and passion-fruit

mousse. The wine list is well spread and cosmopolitan, with the virtue of offering 14 wines for 'under a tenner'. House wine is £7.50.

CHEFS: Andrew Duffin and Will Ginnelly   PROPRIETOR: Andrew Duffin   OPEN: Mon to Sat, exc Mon D; 11.30 to 2.30, 7 to 9.30   MEALS: alc (main courses L £3 to £5, D £8.50 to £12)   SERVICE: not inc   CARDS: Access, Diners, Visa   DETAILS: 32 seats. Private parties: 32 main room. Vegetarian meals. Children welcome. Wheelchair access. Music

## Moon ✳ £

129 Highgate, Kendal LA9 4EN   COOKING 1
KENDAL (0539) 729254   COST £17–£26

Val Macconnell's informal bistro-style restaurant opposite the Brewery Arts Centre is an ever-popular pit-stop for show-goers. From the outside it looks like a narrow-fronted shop, while the attractive, casual and bright interior has green-painted chairs and gingham tablecloths. The food is an equally colourful mix of eclectic dishes, half meat and fish, half vegetarian. A regularly changing repertoire has some long-standing favourites, such as warm Camembert with rye bread and pesto, honey-roast chicken breast, haddock fillet in yoghurt, red peppers and turmeric sauce, vegetable bake topped with hummus, and stuffed peppers. The food has a keen following, although reports of rough edges and overdosed spicing in items such as lamb and apricot bobotie or Cajun-style vegetables suggest that the kitchen does not always get things right. But this is low-cost cooking, not a rarified sybaritic experience. Sweets include sticky toffee or rhubarb, apple and orange suet pudding. The wine list has nine bottles all at £9.75; house wine is £7.25 a litre. Belgian fruit beers, Chimay, Duvel and French Jenlain bière de garde add some drinking interest.

CHEFS: Sharon Moreton and Val Macconnell   PROPRIETOR: Val Macconnell   OPEN: all week, D only; 6.30 to 10 (6 to 10.30 Fri and Sat)   CLOSED: 24 and 25 Dec, 1 Jan, last 2 weeks Jan to second week Feb   MEALS: alc (main courses £6.50 to £8)   SERVICE: not inc CARDS: Access, Visa   DETAILS: 35 seats. Private parties: 40 private room. Vegetarian meals. Children's helpings. No smoking downstairs. Wheelchair access (also WC). Music

---

**KENILWORTH Warwickshire**   map 5

## Restaurant Bosquet ☙

97A Warwick Road, Kenilworth CV8 1HP
KENILWORTH (0926) 52463

COUNTY OF THE YEAR RESTAURANT

COOKING 3*
COST £30–£49

'Monsieur Lignier seems uncharacteristically cheerful for a Frenchman,' reported one traveller who makes a point of stopping here *en route* for less satisfactory pastures. Perhaps the chef is happy because he cooks good food. The house seems almost insignificant in its terrace, flanked by two competitors, fading net in the windows, and a simple conversion from domestic use once you are through the door. The food, however, is a step up from domestic, as may be seen from a meal of boudin of sea bass and lobster with stewed fennel, saffron and tomato, followed by veal sweetbreads on a bed of asparagus and chervil with a madeira sauce, before a raspberry mille-feuille. This impressed particularly for its balance between seasoning, strength of saucing and the flavours of the main ingredients. Another dinner started with pâté de foie gras and chicken with caramelised apple, before wild salmon with wild mushrooms. These dishes come either from a *prix fixe* or a *carte* that both show Bernard Lignier's affection for his heritage. A repertoire that includes guinea-fowl with truffle butter and a madeira sauce, duck with cherries, or veal with wild mushrooms and a cream sauce is high French indeed. Many enjoy the consistency and the small scale of the enterprise – with Jane Lignier to be found cleaning the front step in the morning as well as doing the honours at table come dinner. The wine list may seem short, but it has length in clarets and some very sound choices throughout a wholly French selection. The Madirans from A. Brumont head some good regional wines and the Rhônes from Dom. Chave are worth exploring. Prices are fair in most departments. House wines start at £11.80.

CHEF: Bernard Lignier   PROPRIETORS: Bernard and Jane Lignier   OPEN: Tue to Sun (L by prior reservation only); 12 to 1.15, 7 to 9.30   MEALS: alc (main courses £14.50). Set L and D (exc Sat) £19.80   SERVICE: not inc   CARDS: Access, Amex, Visa   DETAILS: 26 seats. Private parties: 30 main room. Vegetarian meals with prior notice. Children's helpings on request. Smart dress preferred. Wheelchair access (2 steps). No music

---

**KESWICK** Cumbria                                                                map 7

▲ *Swinside Lodge*

COUNTY OF THE YEAR RESTAURANT

Newlands, Keswick CA12 5UE
KESWICK (076 87) 72948
off A66 Penrith to Cockermouth road, turn                    COOKING 2
left at Portinscale and follow Grange road for 2m            COST £22–£32

Graham Taylor has room only for residents at this gem of British hospitality. However, outsiders may dine if the house is not full, so telephone beforehand. 'Luxury at affordable prices' is his description, roundly endorsed by those happy to receive the little extras in the room, the well-furnished house, and the carefully constructed dinners, served at once to the dining-room so that the mood is very much of living at home, but no washing up. There is praise for the balance, the understated skill and the fine materials presented in a meal which might consist of a smoked cheese soufflé, then carrot and artichoke soup, before roast loin of pork cooked with mustard, rosemary and cider, and a goodly raft of vegetables. A trio of sweet dishes – rhubarb pie, a roulade, a meringue and ice-cream item – come before English cheese and coffee. Bread, biscuits, either with cheese, or those awaiting you in the bedroom, and fudge – all the little things – are produced on site. Breakfasts are good too. There is no alcohol licence and no corkage charge.

CHEFS: Irene Dent and Graham Taylor   PROPRIETOR: Graham Taylor   OPEN: all week, D only; 7.30   CLOSED: mid-Dec to mid-Feb   MEALS: Set D £22 to £24. Unlicensed, but bring your own: no corkage   SERVICE: not inc   DETAILS: 20 seats. Private parties: 10 main room. Car park. Vegetarian meals with prior notice. No children under 12. Smart dress preferred. No smoking in dining-room. No music   ACCOMMODATION: 9 rooms, all with bath/shower. B&B £38 to £76. Deposit: £20. No children under 12. Afternoon teas. Garden. TV. Doors close at 11. Confirm by 4 (*The Which? Hotel Guide*)

## KEYSTON Cambridgeshire

map 6

# Pheasant Inn ♥ £

Keyston P18 0RE
BYTHORN (080 14) 241
on B663, 1m S of junction with A604

COOKING 1*
COST £16–£41

The village is matchless as a type: handsome architecture, a sense of wealth, and little intrusion of latter-day eyesores. The pub keeps up the standard with thatch and whitewash on the outside and a rationalised, yet still atmospheric, set of beams, fires and easy chairs indoors. There is a restaurant section but it is a matter of location rather than food – the same menu is offered throughout the building. Coincidence would have it that more satisfactory meals have been served to people in the dining-room than in the pub at large. The menu runs to some length and is certainly more with-it than that in most pubs. Bruschetta with sun-dried tomatoes, aubergine and basil, chargrilled tuna, pigeon with celeriac, and wild boar sausages with mash are some of the items, and these can be well executed. Criticisms have been heard, which seem to indicate inattention in the kitchen and a certain brusqueness of service. The wine list may salve some wounds: it is put together by the same hands as that of the George at Stamford (see entry) and displays identical characteristics of intelligence and canny choice of up-to-the-minute names and properties. Age is not ignored, but who needs to pay for it when you can have Big House Red from Bonny Doon, or Chianti from Isole e Olena? House wines start at £7.75.

CHEF: Roger Jones   PROPRIETORS: Poste Hotels   OPEN: all week; 12 to 2, 6 (7 Sun) to 10
MEALS: alc (main courses £6 to £14)   SERVICE: not inc, card slips closed   CARDS: Access,
Amex, Diners, Visa   DETAILS: 110 seats. 4 tables outside. Private parties: 30 main room.
Car park. Vegetarian meals. Children's helpings. Smart dress preferred. Wheelchair access
(1 step). Music (31 Dec only). Fax: (080 14) 340

## KINGSBRIDGE Devon

map 1

# ▲ Buckland-Tout-Saints Hotel, Queen Anne ⁵⁄₊×

Goveton, Kingsbridge TQ7 2DS
KINGSBRIDGE (0548) 853055
1½m off A381, 2m NE of Kingsbridge

COOKING 2*
COST £22–£43

The house has much to recommend it. Standing four-square on terraced lawns, it is tucked away down a Devon valley far from intrusion or disturbance. Victorian improvements to the main public rooms have overlaid some of the essential Queen Anne character so evident from the outside. The Taylors have completed their first year of ownership, having learned the ropes in Scotland, and have wisely maintained continuity with the earlier regime, especially in the person of chef Alastair Carter. A nightly menu is fixed in price, with four alternatives at each course. Its character is restrained yet correct, not very adventurous, but reliant on decent materials and careful techniques. Something will usually be wrapped in filo or other pastry in the first two courses, whether it be scallops and leeks with a tomato butter sauce or pork fillet with tapénade and a tomato and basil sauce or, a south-western peculiar, salmon with ginger and currants. But the cooking in combination with the setting make this place a natural for a posh night out which should convince by the efforts towards quality yet avoid offence by any straying into wayward tastes and flavours. It is worth waiting a moment for the hot dessert, be it hot chocolate soufflé or maybe plum and apple pancakes with cinnamon ice-cream. The wine list shows well in clarets and has an excellent classic French base – note the Hermitage 1983 from Jaboulet, or the white Châteauneuf from Font de Michelle. Other countries are admitted to give some broader price range. House wines start at £7.50.

CHEFS: Alastair Carter and Angela Mace   PROPRIETORS: John and Tove Taylor   OPEN: all week; 12.30 to 1.45, 7 to 9.30   MEALS: Set L £14.50, Set D £25   SERVICE: not inc, card slips closed   CARDS: Access, Amex, Visa   DETAILS: 56 seats. 5 tables outside. Private parties: 30 main room, 10 and 18 private rooms. Car park. Vegetarian meals. Children's helpings. Smart dress preferred. No smoking in dining-room. No music   ACCOMMODATION: 12 rooms, all with bath/shower. D,B&B £75 to £190. Deposit: £50. Children welcome. Pets by arrangement. Afternoon teas. Garden. TV. Phone. Doors close at midnight. Confirm by 6.30. Fax: (0548) 856261

---

KING'S LYNN Norfolk                                                                    map 6

## Riverside

27 King Street,King's Lynn PE30 1HA                          COOKING 1
KING'S LYNN (0553) 773134                                     COST £14–£37

The Arts Complex – a collection of ancient wharf buildings and courtyards – not only houses a 'subterranean' coffee-shop, but this airy restaurant with original timbers and elegantly laid tables. From the picture windows you can watch the boats on the River Ouse or enjoy the view from the terrace. 'This is a smashing place,' noted a traveller, who found the owners disarmingly friendly. The kitchen does not indulge in culinary fireworks or high fashion, but the food is honest and excellent value. Michael and Sylvia Savage care about ingredients, which include local fish and superb vegetables from their own garden: a slab of sweet-tasting poached cod with leeks was accompanied by earthy new potatoes, cauliflower and brilliantly fresh runner beans. Lunch-time fixtures feature omelettes, seafood pasta, lasagne and ratatouille pancakes, while evening heralds a touch more ambition, with medallions of beef in puff pastry and noisettes of lamb with glazed vegetables and chive sauce. A thick wedge of blackberry and apple pie has been a pleasant choice from the sweets trolley. The short wine list has some eminently drinkable stuff from reputable makers. House wines are £7.95.

CHEFS: Dennis Taylor and Pat Isbill   PROPRIETORS: Michael and Sylvia Savage   OPEN: Mon to Sat; 12 to 2, 7 to 10   MEALS: alc (main courses L £4 to £10, D £12 to £14.50). Set D £15.95   SERVICE: not inc, card slips closed   CARDS: Access, Visa   DETAILS: 80 seats. 12 tables outside. Private parties: 60 main room. Car park. Vegetarian meals. Children's helpings. Smart dress preferred. Music

---

*The* Guide *always appreciates hearing about changes of chef or owner.*

# Rococo ▼

11 Saturday Market Place,
King's Lynn PE30 5DQ
KING'S LYNN (0553) 771483

COOKING 2
COST £20–£44

'Lucky Lynn!' exclaimed a visitor about this 'cracking modern restaurant' close by the Town Hall (follow directions to the Old Town). The building is discreetly signed with an unobtrusive black frontage. The small, welcoming lounge area is done out in green and white, with comfortable sofas and wine books to read. Beyond is the primrose-yellow dining-room, with a skylight above, lovely fresh flowers and large modern canvases painted by co-proprietor Anne Anderson. Subdued classical music plays in the background. Service is well paced, informal and suited to the setting. Nick Anderson's cooking has come of age. His menus bristle with up-to-the-minute ideas as well as classical variations, and he takes account of local produce: goats' cheese is made by a customer and ducks are specially reared for the restaurant. Influences from the Mediterranean and the Far East are obvious in dishes such as aubergine charlotte filled with spicy bean ragoût, and baby squid in coriander, garlic and ginger butter on a bed of rice noodles. Otherwise there might be rabbit and hare with crisp shallots, halibut and monkfish en croûte with tarragon sauce, and soufflé omelette with raspberry sauce. Light lunch-time snacks (from £2.25) and fixed-price meals offer excellent value. Information is sometimes lacking or inaccurate on the wine list, but the bottles are well chosen and show nicely balanced enthusiasms. It is a shame that last year's listing by style has been dropped in favour of the geographical: somehow a bit of spark seems to have gone. House wine starts at £9.50. CELLARMAN'S CHOICE: Coonawarra, Chardonnay 1991, Hollick, £17.50; Bordeaux, Ch. La Rivière 1979, £26.50.

CHEF: Nicholas Anderson  PROPRIETORS: Anne and Nicholas Anderson  OPEN: all week, exc Mon L and Sun D (by arrangement only); 12 to 2, 7 to 10  MEALS: Set L £9 (2 courses) to £12, Set D £15 to £23.75  SERVICE: not inc, card slips closed  CARDS: Access, Visa
DETAILS: 40 seats. Private parties: 40 main room. Vegetarian meals. Children's helpings. Smart dress preferred. No cigars/pipes in dining-room. Wheelchair access (also WC). Music

KINGSTON UPON THAMES Surrey                                    map 3

# Ayudhya

14 Kingston Hill,
Kingston upon Thames KT2 7NH
081-549 5984 and 546 5878

COOKING 1*
COST £21–£42

This is an unchanging fixture of the Kingston eating scene and local reporters confirm that it remains on course. The three floors have been redecorated (exotic Thai embellishments join forces with wood panelling and deep red carpets), but the waterfall in the basement still trickles and the menu is constant. What impresses is the quality of the ingredients, the delicacy of touch (no 'heavy-footed sauces' here) and the fact that 'you come away feeling sated but not stuffed'. The menu runs to more than 80 dishes and includes some interesting specialities such as green papaya salad with minced shrimps, curried seafood mousse steamed in a ramekin, and stir-fried water spinach in black-bean sauce. Diners have spoken well of the mixed hors d'oeuvre – 'startlingly flavoursome' satays, prawn toasts, chicken wrapped in pandanus (screw pine) leaf, pork 'in a sarong' – as well as stir-fried beef with chillies and sweet basil, pork with lemon grass and Thai herbs and jungle curry, which tasted innocuous until it hit the throat. Vegetables, fragrant rice and noodles are up to the mark, although desserts have been 'disappointing'. Singha Thai beer is a good accompaniment; otherwise explore the wine list which offers a concise, fairly priced selection that matches the food quite well. House wine is £6.95.

CHEF/PROPRIETOR: Somjai Thanpho   OPEN: Tue to Sun; 12 to 2.30 (12.30 to 3 Sun), 6.30 (6 Sun) to 11 (11.30 Fri and Sat)   CLOSED: 25 Dec, 1 Jan, Easter Sun   MEALS: alc (main courses £5.50 to £9)   SERVICE: not inc   CARDS: Access, Amex, Diners, Visa   DETAILS: 80 seats. Private parties: 42 main room, 30 private rooms. Vegetarian meals. Children's helpings on request. Smart dress preferred. Wheelchair access (1 step). Music

---

**KINGTON** Hereford & Worcester                                                    map 4

## ▲ *Penrhos Court* ⅚✳

Kington HR5 3LH
KINGTON (0544) 230720                                              COOKING 1*
on A44, 1m E of Kington                                           COST £17–£46

The restoration and conversion of the medieval cruck hall by Martin Griffiths, with Daphne Lambert supplying the food, have been a saga of some years standing. The view that hits the visitor, fresh out of his car after a long drive through marcher country, of this half-timbered house with high gables rearing above an old horse pond encapsulates much of the allure of these parts. Conversion has got so far now as to provide a wing of modern rooms in former agricultural ranges so that the whole affair slowly edges towards the status of hotel, though corners to the concept still need to be rounded and finished off. Daphne Lambert's serious side takes in a permanent interest in medieval food and cookery, which can be tried, in the flesh so to speak, at one of her special events. Cooking for everyday is more modern than that, with at best a nicely direct approach to protein and something to make it taste better. Examples might be calf's liver with seed mustard, king prawns with ginger and coriander, or grilled queen scallops with a simple herb crust. The wine list is short and sharp, much of it from Bibendum in London which makes a fashionable surprise deep in the wilds of Herefordshire. House wines are £10.50.

CHEF: Daphne Lambert   PROPRIETORS: Daphne Lambert and Martin Griffiths   OPEN: all week, D only, and Sun L; 12.30 to 2, 7.30 to 9.30   MEALS: alc (main courses £14 to £16). Set Sun L £10 to £15.50, Set D £18.50 to £21.50   SERVICE: not inc, card slips closed   CARDS: Access, Amex, Diners, Visa   DETAILS: 60 seats. 20 tables outside. Private parties: 80 main room, 20, 60 and 80 private rooms. Car park. Vegetarian meals. Children's helpings. No smoking in dining-room. Wheelchair access (also WC). Music   ACCOMMODATION: 19 rooms, all with bath/shower. Rooms for disabled. B&B £40 to £120. Children welcome. Baby facilities. Garden. TV. Phone. Doors close at midnight. Confirm 1 week ahead. Fax: (0544) 230754

## KINTBURY Berkshire map 2

# ▲ *Dundas Arms* 🍾

53 Station Road, Kintbury RG15 0UT
KINTBURY (0488) 58263 and 58559      COOKING 1
1m S of A4, between Newbury and Hungerford      COST £23–£48

Those delighted by transport will find trains, cars and barges much in evidence
at this water-bound, hence relatively peaceful, pub. Prompt arrivals for dinner
may not always be greeted with warmth, but at least you get a chance to sit at
the window table with its views of gently patrolling ducks. The food is
unfussy, yet there is variety of register: vegetable terrine, sweetbreads, grilled
bread and vegetables, lamb shank and sea bass. One reporter's 'excellent-
quality meat cooked to pink perfection' might be another's 'undercooked and
dull', but most agree on the quality of starters and puddings, and wine. There
are a few New World, new-wave interlopers like Bonny Doon and Leeuwin,
but this is basically a burgundy and claret list. The high-class names (among
them Leflaive, Ducru-Beaucaillou and Chasse-Spleen) mean that, for between
£20 to £50, you can give the Old World the fairest of hearings – though take a
pocketbook to look things up in, since the list tells you little beyond name, age
and rank. House wines are from £9.50. CELLARMAN'S CHOICE: Chablis, La
Vallée aux Sages 1991, Gallois, £17; Chambolle-Musigny 1987, Roumier, £29.

CHEFS: David Dalzell-Piper, Sue Bright and Stuart Hall   PROPRIETORS: D. and W.E.
Dalzell-Piper   OPEN: Mon to Sat, exc Mon D; restaurant 12.30 to 1.30, 7.30 to 9.30; bar 12
to 2, 7 to 9.15   CLOSED: Christmas to New Year   MEALS: alc (main courses £12 to £18). Set
L £16.50. Bar menu   SERVICE: not inc   CARDS: Access, Amex, Diners, Visa   DETAILS: 50
seats. 15 tables outside. Private parties: 22 main room. Car park. Vegetarian meals.
Children's helpings. Smart dress preferred. No-smoking area. Wheelchair access (2 steps;
also WC). No music   ACCOMMODATION: 5 double rooms, all with bath/shower. Rooms for
disabled. B&B £55 to £65. Children welcome. Pets welcome. TV. Phone. Doors close at 11.
Confirm by 6. Fax: (0488) 58568 (*The Which? Hotel Guide*)

## KIRKHAM Lancashire map 5

# *Cromwellian* 🍷

16 Poulton Street, Kirkham PR4 2AB      COOKING 2
KIRKHAM (0772) 685680      COST £29–£39

Peter and Josie Fawcett have never been content to rest on their laurels, and
each year brings changes to their admirable restaurant in a narrow
seventeenth-century house in Kirkham's main street. 'What a pleasant and
different little place,' noted one visitor. Improvements continue. In particular,
the dining area is confined to the ground floor, while the upstairs now
functions as a private lounge. Similarly, Josie's monthly-changing menus
feature a number of new dishes: broccoli, pear and tarragon soup, spinach and
green pepper tart with walnut pastry, casserole of pork 'Pays Basque' (with
tomatoes, peppers and haricot beans), and choux pastry filled with smoked
trout and water-chestnuts in Pernod sauce are listed among the new arrivals.
Other items, such as koulibiac of salmon in filo pastry, and fillet steak stuffed
with Roquefort and served with Roquefort and port sauce (charged extra),

remain fixtures, and vegetarians are not neglected. Over the years the wine list has gained in stature and clarity. Good names abound, showing as much strength in the antipodes, Spain and Italy as in the classic areas. Rhônes from the post-1986 Chapoutier generation encourage, as does the well-judged range of clarets. Prices are fair. House wine is £8.95. CELLARMAN'S CHOICE: Chardonnay 1990, Villa da Capezzana, £17.95; St-Aubin, premier cru 'Sentier du Clou' 1989, Prudhon, £19.95

CHEF: Josie Fawcett   PROPRIETORS: Peter and Josie Fawcett   OPEN: Tue to Sat, D only; 7 to 9   CLOSED: first week Apr, 2 weeks Aug   MEALS: Set D £19.95   SERVICE: not inc, card slips closed   CARDS: Access, Amex, Visa   DETAILS: 16 seats. Private parties: 10 main room, 8 and 10 private rooms. Vegetarian meals. Children's helpings on request. Smart dress preferred. Wheelchair access. Music

---

**LANGAR** Nottinghamshire                                        map 5

## ▲ Langar Hall

Langar NG13 9HG
MARBY (0949) 60559                                          COOKING 2
between A46 and A52, 4m S of Bingham                        COST £21–£51

'Civility as well as comfort' might be a motto for this handsome Regency house beyond the church at Langar – itself only a mile from England's best Stilton at Colston Bassett. Imogen Skirving succeeds in making a private house public, without creating that uncomfortable feeling of intrusion on someone else's space, yet drawing every advantage from furnishings and objects that were always more than just the whim of an unidentifiable designer. This makes for a fine sense of relaxation. Add to that the developed sense of hospitality in Mrs Skirving herself, the public performances – dramatic or musical – of Crispin Harris, who seconds as head waiter, and the unexpectedly metropolitan output of the kitchen – Toby Garratt has worked in many places around London, and Dan Evans, a regular visitor, was last tasted at 192 (see entry, London) – and the cocktail may indeed be heady. It does not always work; perhaps too many personalities are involved. When it does, it is a great antidote to Nottingham. Where else in these parts would you get a menu promising salt-cod pancakes with a leek vinaigrette and truffle dressing, or Moroccan hotpot with cumin and lemon, or toasted scallops, asparagus, Parma ham and salsa verde? Imogen Skirving has returned to the kitchen to take charge of sweet things – this should be celebrated with a trial of tarte Tatin, rhubarb fool or Yankee bourbon truffle cake. The wine list changes but uses some proper makers – Hugel, Jaboulet and Antinori among others. House wines are £8.50.

CHEFS: Imogen Skirving, Dan Evans and Toby Garratt   PROPRIETOR: Imogen Skirving OPEN: all week, exc Sun D; 12.30 to 2.30, 7.30 to 9.30   MEALS: alc (main courses £7.50 to £20)   SERVICE: not inc (10% for 6 or more)   CARDS: Access, Amex, Visa   DETAILS: 30 seats. 6 tables outside. Private parties: 30 main room, 6, 18 and 30 private rooms. Car park. Vegetarian meals. Children's helpings. No- smoking area. Music   ACCOMMODATION: 12 rooms, all with bath/shower. B&B £57.50 to £120. Deposit: £20. Pets by arrangement. Afternoon teas. Garden. TV. Phone. Doors close at midnight. Confirm by 4. Fax: (0949) 61045 (*The Which? Hotel Guide*)

**LANGHO** Lancashire map 5

## ▲ *Northcote Manor*

Northcote Road, Langho BB6 9BB
BLACKBURN (0254) 240555 COOKING **2***
on A59, 9m E of M6 exit 31 COST £18–£49

Renovation is complete: after an extensive programme of refurbishment and
rebuilding, the Victorian red-brick Northcote Manor is entering a new phase.
The elegant 'well-shaped' dining-room with its yellow and gold colour
schemes, navy-blue carpet and deep-red chairs has a 'nice aura'. Service is
attentive without being servile. Some fine cooking goes on here, according to
reporters. The lunch-time menu is simpler, cheaper and more flexible than the
evening *carte*. Nigel Haworth works to a menu backed up by seasonal
specialities, with the emphasis firmly on fish and game. Some traditional ideas
have crept into the overall repertoire, such as eighteenth-century collared pork,
chump of lamb on purée potatoes, and baked knuckle of ham in pastry with
pea butter, although the cooking generally inhabits more modern, inventive
territory. Flavour and consistency are the key words. Salmon fish-cakes
('singing of salmon') come with a perfect match of melted butter, capers and
parsley; risotto of leeks and mushrooms topped with steamed grey mullet
'evoked sun and light on a drizzly day,' commented a lunch-time visitor who
thought the result was 'simple but soigné'. Fillet of beef dressed with garden
herbs, shallots and mustard with vegetable crudités is a speciality. Desserts
range from sugared brioche with rhubarb and blood oranges to brown bread-
and-butter pudding with home-made custard. The wine list covers a lot of
ground, prices are fair and halves are much in evidence. House French is £8.10.

CHEF: Nigel Haworth   PROPRIETORS: Craig J. Bancroft and Nigel Haworth   OPEN: all
week; 12 to 1.30 (2 Sun), 7 to 9.30 (10 Sat)   CLOSED: 1 Jan   MEALS: alc (main courses L
£7.50 to £14, D £12 to £17)   SERVICE: 10%, card slips closed   CARDS: Access, Amex,
Diners, Visa   DETAILS: 80 seats. Private parties: 100 main room, 40 private room. Car park.
Vegetarian meals. Children's helpings. Smart dress preferred. Wheelchair access (2 steps;
also WC). Music   ACCOMMODATION: 14 rooms, all with bath/shower. Room for disabled.
B&B £54 to £64. Children welcome. Baby facilities. Afternoon teas. Garden. TV. Phone.
Doors close at 1am. Confirm by 6. Fax: (0254) 248965 (*The Which? Hotel Guide*)

**LANGLEY MARSH** Somerset map 2

## ▲ *Langley House Hotel* ♟ ✻

Langley Marsh TA4 2UF
WIVELISCOMBE (0984) 23318,
changes to (0984) 623318 autumn 1993 COOKING **3**
½m N of Wiveliscombe COST £32–£44

The stencilled frieze to the warm apricot tones of the dining-room (with its few
beams that add historic colour) help towards the description 'pretty'. Other
rooms have bolder colour schemes, and the accent is on comfort with
informality. Their decoration belies the outside of the place, which seems more
farmhouse than Georgian manor house to the roving eye. The garden is
groomed to the last blade. Peter Wilson offers a set dinner menu, almost austere

in style, with a smidgeon of choice at the end. A simple cold beginning, soup, fish, then meat is the normal progression. Fanned dessert pear marinated in walnut oil seems the inevitable starter. Turbot with a crust of crab, tomato coulis and a mixture of spring onions and courgettes is an oft-reported fish dish; John Dory with ginger and soy is another. Duck with honey in an apple and thyme sauce, lamb with onions and Cassis, and beef with rosemary, mustard and lemon are some of the meats. Portions are 'well judged' – for some that means scanty. Desserts may be on the rich side: after choosing between strawberry and Drambuie crème brûlée, chocolate bavarois or elderflower syllabub one diner yearned for a sorbet or fruit salad. Cheeses are good and local: eat walnut and banana bread with them. Anne Wilson makes sure she looks after you, to most people's delight – this is 'a perfect country house' – though 'the excess of anxiety to please creates in the customer a corresponding anxiety to be pleased'. On the wine side, the half-bottles demand particular attention; like the bottles, they offer range in price and geography. But under-representation beyond France – notably Spain and Italy – is surprising in a list that otherwise shows such consideration and intelligence. The mark-up shows no favours at the high reaches; lower down, it is reasonable. House wine is £7.75. CELLARMAN'S CHOICE: Victoria, Fumé Blanc 1989, Taltarni, £16.75; Médoc, Ch. La Cardonne 1981, £27.50.

CHEF: Peter Wilson  PROPRIETORS: Peter and Anne Wilson  OPEN: all week, D only; 7.30 to 8.30  CLOSED: Feb  MEALS: Set D £22.50 to £26.50  SERVICE: not inc, card slips closed  CARDS: Access, Amex, Visa  DETAILS: 18 seats. Private parties: 18 main room, 18 private room. Car park. Vegetarian meals. Children's helpings. Smart dress preferred. No smoking in dining-room. Wheelchair access (also WC). No music  ACCOMMODATION: 8 rooms, all with bath/shower. B&B £58 to £104.50. Children welcome. Baby facilities. Pets welcome (not in public rooms). Afternoon teas. Garden. TV. Phone. Doors close at midnight. Confirm by 6. Fax: (0984) 24573, changes to (0984) 624573 autumn 1993 (*The Which? Hotel Guide*)

---

**LAUNCESTON Cornwall**                                                                      map 1

## *Randells* £

Prospect House, 11 Western Road,
Launceston PL15 7AS                                                             COOKING 1
LAUNCESTON (0566) 776484                                                      COST £14–£31

'Proprietors: Patrick Randell and Debbie Hutchings; chefs: Patrick Randell and Debbie Hutchings; waiting staff: Patrick Randell and Debbie Hutchings.' They keep it in the family at this small restaurant in a Victorian house next to the town hall. The repertoire is sensibly scaled and conservatively constructed. Starters of chicken liver pâté, Caesar salad or deep-fried pieces of cheese with a cherry sauce are matched by main dishes of chicken Maryland, scallops Mornay or paupiettes of sole with crab. These classical recipes are interpreted in a steady fashion. Desserts would win over anyone wanting to put on weight, and locals would applaud the plate of south-western cheeses. A baker's dozen of bottles supplies the wine list. House wines are from £7.20.

CHEFS/PROPRIETORS: Patrick Randell and Debbie Hutchings OPEN: Tue to Sat, D only; 7 to 9 (9.30 Sat) MEALS: alc (main courses £7.50 to £11) SERVICE: not inc CARDS: Access, Visa DETAILS: 32 seats. Private parties: 20 main room. Vegetarian meals. Children's helpings. Smart dress preferred. Wheelchair access (3 steps; also WC). Music

---

## LAVENHAM Suffolk
map 3

# ▲ *Great House*

Market Place, Lavenham CO10 9QZ
LAVENHAM (0787) 247431

COOKING 2
COST £26–£51

Lavenham itself may be quintessential England, but the Great House, a fine piece of Lavenham architecture (medieval encased by the eighteenth century), represents, in the main, unreconstructed France. This is the charm of Regis Crépy's cooking, and the allure of the resolutely Gallic service. Some concession is made to current tastes in a dish such as tiger prawns with soy sauce and Chinese spices, but in the main the menu reads like a list of restaurant/bistro classics: pigeon with red wine and ceps, duck with a pimento sauce, chateaubriand béarnaise, venison chasseur. People enjoy the ambience and the steady character of the kitchen's production. House wines are £14 (there are cheaper bottles on the list).

CHEF: Regis Crépy PROPRIETOR: John Spice OPEN: Tue to Sun, exc Sun D; 12 to 2.30, 7 to 9.30 MEALS: alc (main courses L Tue to Sat £6.50 to £8, D £12.50 to £17). Set Sun L £14.95, Set Tue to Fri D £14.95 SERVICE: not inc CARDS: Access, Amex, Visa DETAILS: 45 seats. 7 tables outside. Private parties: 50 main room. Vegetarian meals. Children welcome. Smart dress preferred. No smoking during meals. Wheelchair access (2 steps; also WC). Music ACCOMMODATION: 4 rooms, all with bath/shower. B&B £45 to £80. Deposit: £25. Children welcome. Baby facilities. Pets welcome. Afternoon teas. Garden. TV. Phone. Doors close at midnight. Confirm by midday. Fax: (0787) 248080 (*The Which? Hotel Guide*)

---

## LEAMINGTON SPA Warwickshire
map 2

# *Les Plantagenêts*

15 Dormer Place,
Leamington Spa CV32 5AA
LEAMINGTON SPA (0926) 451792

COOKING 2
COST £21–£49

Regular comments about a full dining-room suggest that this restaurant in the basement of a terraced house is well on course. The entrance is through a leafy courtyard which leads into a magnolia-coloured eating area with pointed arch patterns painted black as the prevailing theme. In the spaces are 'simplistic heraldic images'. The style of the place has been described as 'all big plates and presentation' and the atmosphere is defined by the thoroughly professional, thoroughly French waiters. 'Horrible' pop music seems totally out of keeping. As the restaurant name suggests, the cooking is classic French with the emphasis on Anjou. There is butter and cream aplenty. Chef/proprietor Rémy Loth (who acts as maître d' from time to time) offers a short *carte* and a fixed-price menu backed up by specials. Fish shows up well: scallops with hollandaise, avocado salad garnished with prawns and crayfish, sea bass, steamed squid with a sharp warm vinaigrette and loads of diced garlic, bouillabaisse and sea bass have been mentioned. Elsewhere there have been endorsements for smoked duck salad, roast fillet of lamb with garlic and baby onions, and fillet of beef in puff pastry. Chateaubriand in red wine sauce spiked with garlic is a Saturday-night speciality. Vegetables are 'firm' but minuscule. To finish, Cointreau soufflé has been 'fabulous'. The substantial cheeseboard is worth exploring.

CHEF/PROPRIETOR: Rémy Loth   OPEN: Mon to Sat, exc Sat L; 12 to 2, 7 to 10   MEALS: alc (main courses £12.50 to £16). Set L £12.50, Set D £18.50   SERVICE: not inc, card slips closed   CARDS: Access, Amex, Visa   DETAILS: 42 seats. Private parties: 45 main room. Vegetarian meals with prior notice. Children welcome. Smart dress preferred. Music

---

**LECK Lancashire**                                                          map 7

## ▲ *Cobwebs* ▮ ✻

Leck, Cowan Bridge LA6 2HZ
KIRKBY LONSDALE (052 42) 72141
2m SE of Kirkby Lonsdale on                                        COOKING 3
A65, turn left at Cowan Bridge                                   COST £31–£44

The location of this small Victorian country-house hotel is splendidly rural: its windows overlook the Pennines and the Lune Valley, and it is but a short drive to two National Parks, the Lake District and the Yorkshire Dales. Indeed, enthusiasm runs the risk of turning to effusion here, both decoratively ('very fussy Sanderson style') and in a slightly overwrought cooking idiom. Two soups in one bowl are pretty, but when one is warm and the other cold, the dish's appeal stops at the metaphysical. But even those who take against 'dinkiness' agree that there is much in these five-course menus to praise: superb smoked fish, 'beautifully moist' breast of guinea-fowl 'adroitly carved and laid out, the lustrous sauce giving character and interest to the meat', and a lattice of halibut and salmon 'cooked to perfection'. Local farm cheeses enjoy a reputation of their own, and the dessert is always well executed, be it simple apple and raspberry crumble or a complex trio of choux swan on crème anglaise, meringue fruit nest on raspberry coulis and three-flavour ice-cream in a tulip-shaped biscuit basket on butterscotch sauce. Paul Kelly is admired for being an enthusiastic host, and his vinous enthusiasm has spawned a splendid wine list. Here is one of the largest Alsace ranges of any restaurant in Britain, and intelligent selections appear from everywhere else. Prices are never less than reasonable, and £35 puts really fine and curious drinking within reach – vintage champagne, Vouvray from the '60s, three vintages of Mas de Daumas Gassac, five classed-growth '82s, Musar '70 and '66, and so on. Adam and David Wynn's organic Eden Ridge begins the list at £8, and it ends with pages of spirits, liqueurs and fortified wines by the glass. House wines are from £8. CELLARMAN'S CHOICE: Wairau River, Sauvignon Blanc 1992, £14; Corbières, Dom. des Pensées Sauvages Reserve 1990, Nick Bradford £12.

---

▮ *denotes an outstanding wine cellar;* ▼ *denotes a good wine list, worth travelling for.*

---

CHEF: Yvonne Thompson   PROPRIETOR: Paul Kelly   OPEN: Tue to Sat, D only; 7.30 for 8
CLOSED: Jan to mid-Mar   MEALS: Set D £24   SERVICE: not inc, card slips closed   CARDS:
Access, Visa   DETAILS: 25 seats. Private parties: 25 main room. Car park. Vegetarian meals
with prior notice. No children under 12. Smart dress preferred. No smoking in dining-
room. Wheelchair access (2 steps; also WC). Music   ACCOMMODATION: 5 rooms, all with
bath/shower. B&B £40 to £65. Deposit: £20. Garden. TV. Phone. Doors close at midnight.
Confirm by 6. Fax: (052 42) 72141 (*The Which? Hotel Guide*)

---

**LEDBURY  Hereford & Worcester**                                             map 2

## ▲ *Hope End* ♥ ⁵⁄ᵪ

Hope End, Ledbury HR8 1JQ
LEDBURY (0531) 633613
2m N of Ledbury, just beyond                                    COOKING 3
Wellington Heath                                               COST £34–£41

This long lozenge of a house, its many eccentricities crowned by the elegant
minaret to the rear, is 'lost in richest countryside' according to the brochure,
and some have lost themselves in trying to track it down. Simplicity and
spaciousness, almost spareness, are the interior keynotes: modern pine tables
are laid without cloths, and plain walls and curtains are 'more characteristic of
an Islington bistro than a country-house hotel'. From 1994, dinner itself will be
simplified down from five courses to three in response, the Hegartys say, to
guests' wishes; a wider choice of starters, and the possibility of taking cheese as
an extra course for £4 (or substituting dessert with cheese), will also be offered
then. 'The essence of the cooking, to me, is subtlety with simplicity,' reports
one; for another 'the main thing about Patricia Hegarty's cooking is that it is so
*tasty*'. The garden continues to maraud the kitchen: lovage gives potato soup its
style, and tarragon does the same for mushroom soup; a little gem pumpkin
might be stuffed with walnuts and red peppers; the hollandaise served with
John Dory is flavoured with sage, and roast Herefordshire duckling comes with
Blaisdon plum relish; dressings call on parsley, savoury sauces on perry,
sorbets on elderflower. Some feel that novelty is pursued for its own sake: 'My
father, a musician, has said that there is a very good reason why some musical
works are seldom played. I have concluded there is a very good reason why
some vegetables are rarely served, and cardoon [here creamed with chestnuts]
falls into this category.' Others find 'perfection'. Everyone nominates a
different cheese (Llandboidy, Devon Oak, Shropshire Blue) as favourite.
Gratuities are not expected. The wine list is less adventurous than some of the
dishes, but will please claret and burgundy drinkers with its good range, fair
prices and talented producers; half-bottles swarm. House wines are £8.

---

CHEF: Patricia Hegarty   PROPRIETORS: John and Patricia Hegarty   OPEN: all week, D only;
7.30 to 9   MEALS: Set D £30   SERVICE: card slips closed   CARDS: Access, Visa   DETAILS:
24 seats. Private parties: 8 main room. Car park. Vegetarian meals. No children under 12.
Smart dress preferred. No smoking in dining-room. Wheelchair access (2 steps; also WC).
No music   ACCOMMODATION: 9 rooms, all with bath/shower. B&B £87 to £143. Deposit:
£60. No children under 12. Garden. Phone. Doors close at 11. Confirm by 4. Fax: (0531)
636366 (*The Which? Hotel Guide*)

LEEDS West Yorkshire                                                                          map 5

## Brasserie Forty Four £

42–44 The Calls, Leeds LS2 8AQ                                                     COOKING 1
LEEDS (0532) 343232                                                                 COST £17–£41

The converted grain mill on the River Aire that contains this modern brasserie
seems an ocean away from the Tetley brewery opposite. The décor is
successfully intriguing: it encompasses swings that dangle from metal beams,
colourful abstract paintings by local art students, and a mechanical player-
piano. But the wide range of straightforward, clean-tasting, mainly
Mediterranean dishes priced to the nearest five pence provides a firmly drawn
bottom line. Yorkshire pud jostles dim-sum and warm aubergine terrine;
steakburger or rib of beef provides reassurance for those threatened by roast
cod à la basquaise or confit of duck. Standards vary: garlic prawns were
ungarlicky, but turbot fillet (gobsmacked to find itself in a raspberry sauce)
was grilled to perfection. The wine list is good, keenly priced and
intercontinental. House white, a Venetian Chardonnay, is £8.75, and
Dalwood's jolly Shiraz/Cabernet is £8.75.

CHEF: Jeff Baker   PROPRIETORS: Martin Hodgson, Michael Gill and Jonathan Wix
OPEN: Mon to Sat, exc Sat L; 12 to 2.30, 6.30 to 10.30 (11 Fri and Sat)   CLOSED: bank hols
MEALS: alc (main courses £4 to £13). Set L £7.50 (2 courses) to £11.25   SERVICE: 10%, card
slips closed   CARDS: Access, Amex, Visa   DETAILS: 130 seats. 7 tables outside. Private
parties: 50 main room. Vegetarian meals. Children's helpings. Smart dress preferred. No
cigars/pipes in dining-room. Wheelchair access (also WC). Music. Air-conditioned. Fax:
(0532) 343332

## ▲ Haley's

NEW ENTRY

Shire Oak Road, Headingley,
Leeds LS6 2DE                                                                      COOKING 2
LEEDS (0532) 784446                                                                 COST £25–£51

The name Haley apparently refers to a master stonemason prominent in Leeds
at the turn of the century. There is no mistaking the architectural
distinctiveness of this country-house hotel a couple of miles from the city
centre: notice the light stonework, the mock-Tudor half-timbering, the red roof
tiles and the pointed turrets at each corner of the building. No expense has been
spared in redesigning the interior: the restaurant has long draped curtains,
'really comfortable' upholstered chairs and well-spaced, beautifully set tables.
Pillars and alcoves allow for intimacy. Smart and correct sum up the service.
The short 'menu du chef' makes easy reading and is priced according to the
number of courses taken. By contrast, the *carte* veers into French with intricate
English translations: chilled gazpacho is served with tartare of salmon and
cucumber; breast of Barbary duck is accompanied by broad beans, port sauce
and crispy spätzlis. Reporters have applauded the immaculate presentation and
freshness of rendezvous of seafood with vegetable noodles, timbale of smoked
haddock with marinated scallops, and roast saddle of lamb – 'just still pink' –
with a gratin of provençal vegetables and a sauce scented with rosemary.
Desserts can seem exceedingly rich and are not always successful. The wine list

runs to around 70 bottles from many countries and prestigious names are prominent. House wines start at £8.50.

CHEF: Chris Baxter  PROPRIETOR: John Appleyard  OPEN: all week, exc L Mon and Sat and Sun D; 12.30 to 2, 7.15 to 9.45  MEALS: alc (main courses £10.50 to £19.50). Set L £13.95 to £16.95, Set D £18.95 to £23.95  SERVICE: not inc, card slips closed  CARDS: Access, Amex, Diners, Visa  DETAILS: 45 seats. Private parties: 45 main room, 14 and 25 private rooms. Car park. Vegetarian meals. Children's helpings Sun L. Smart dress preferred. No cigars/pipes in dining-room. Wheelchair access (2 steps). Music. Air-conditioned  ACCOMMODATION: 22 rooms, all with bath/shower. B&B £95 to £112. Children welcome. Baby facilities. Afternoon teas. TV. Phone. Confirm by 6 on day before arrival. Fax: (0532) 753342 (*The Which? Hotel Guide*)

---

## Leodis ♀ £

| | |
|---|---|
| Victoria Mill, Sovereign Street, | |
| Leeds LS1 4BJ | COOKING 1 |
| LEEDS (0532) 421010 | COST £18–£49 |

**NEW ENTRY**

Leeds is on the up. One of the latest arrivals is this brasserie in a converted red-brick mill on the banks of the River Aire. The interior – a low, iron-columned room with exposed brickwork and vaulted ceilings – has echoes of the past, but modern flourishes, such as polished wood floors and etched glass screens, have been grafted on to the original. The cooking tips its hat to most current fashions: bangers and mash and steak and kidney pudding line up with roast guinea-fowl with morels, chargrilled vegetable and basil salad, and mille-feuille of goats' cheese. Fish specialities, such as monkfish with oyster mushrooms, bacon and samphire, are listed on a separate menu. Reports suggest that the kitchen performs unevenly: excellent black pudding with potato and apple cake and 'seriously good' loin of lamb in filo pastry with spinach mousse and cranberry sauce, but also on one occasion disappointing vegetables, sweets and vegetarian options. 'Very young things' provide friendly service. Fashionable and helpful listing by price eschews geographical classification of the wines. House wines (from £7.95) and bubblies apart, the wines are sorted into the basics and the 'expensive'. The list is very good, with fine range and, if the top end is avoided, value that matches quality closely, with much below £12. CELLARMAN'S CHOICE: Washington State, Ch. Ste Michelle, Sauvignon Blanc 1991, £13.45; Argentina, Coleccion Privada 1985, Bodega Navarro Correas, £14.95.

CHEFS: Steven Kendell and Simon Shaw  PROPRIETORS: Martin Spalding and Steven Kendell  OPEN: Mon to Sat, exc Sat L; 12 to 2, 6 to 10 (11 Fri and Sat)  MEALS: alc (main courses £6 to £13). Set L and D (6 to 7.30 Sat) £10.95  SERVICE: not inc, card slips closed  CARDS: Access, Amex, Visa  DETAILS: 148 seats. 16 tables outside. Private parties: 180 main room. Car park. Vegetarian meals. Children's helpings on request. Smart dress preferred. Wheelchair access (also WC). Music. Air-conditioned. Fax: (0532) 430432

---

*Restaurateurs justifiably resent no-shows. If you quote a credit card number when booking, you may be liable for the restaurant's lost profit margin if you don't turn up. Always phone to cancel.*

---

## Olive Tree £

Oaklands, 55 Rodley Lane,
Leeds LS13 1NG
LEEDS (0532) 569283
on A6120, by Rodley roundabout

COOKING 1
COST £17–£36

George Psarias holds the world record for the longest kebab and is proud that his loos have won awards. His food is also a talking point. The action takes place in a converted Victorian house some five miles out of the city. A huge brass fan, a chandelier and a statue of Aphrodite dominate the scene in the dining-room. Loudspeakers blast out *Zorba the Greek* tunes and musicians play bouzouki music every Tuesday evening. The menu moves beyond the Greek-Cyriot standards and embraces regional specialities from the islands and the mainland. One reporter's mixed meze yielded excellent hummus and other dips, dolmades, keftedes (meatballs with fresh herbs) and tyropitakia (filo pastries filled with feta cheese and mint) before a delicate little vegetarian moussaka, skewered chicken and beef stifado. Baklava is a good version with an 'uncloying' honey sauce. Prices are not bargain-basement, but the ingredients are of good quality and the cooking hits the target. Service is unfailingly polite. The wine list has a few Greeks among the French, German and New World representatives, although mark-ups can seem high for what is offered. House wine is £7.95.

CHEFS: George Psarias and Andreas Iacovou   PROPRIETORS: George and Vasoulla Psarias
OPEN: all week, exc Sat L; 12 to 2, 6.30 to 11.30   CLOSED: 25 and 26 Dec, bank hols
MEALS: alc (main courses £7.50 to £11). Set L and D £9.95   SERVICE: 10%, card slips
closed   CARDS: Access, Amex, Visa   DETAILS: 140 seats. Private parties: 60 main room,
20 to 60 private rooms. Car park. Vegetarian meals. Children's helpings. Smart dress
preferred. Wheelchair access (also WC). Music

## Paris

36A Town Street, Horsforth,
Leeds LS18 4RJ
LEEDS (0532) 581885

COOKING 1*
COST £15–£36

It pays to be cheerful and that quality is one of the good things about Paris: the staff seem pleased to see customers. Customers seem to like the staff, the low prices (super-economy with the 'early bird' menu), the lack of fuss and the speedy service. Paris is not Parisian – the food is more English than French, but it is fresh and has some taste. It is also more ambitious than the price might lead you to suppose. One autumn dinner that satisfied on most counts of taste and presentation included warm salad of pigeon (which had a liverish texture but better flavour), grey mullet with deep-fried spring cabbage and a butter sauce, chicken stuffed with aparagus and basil mousse on a tomato sauce ringed by an asparagus cream sauce, loin of pork with smoked sausage and spring onion, roast lamb with leek and mustard glaze, banana mousse with a raspberry coulis, and a fine version of apple crumble. The menu is large, but business keeps the food turning over. The 'light and airy' upstairs room has wooden floors, rag-rolled walls and wooden tables. The wine list is good on range and fair on price. Vacheron Sancerre, Borgogno Barolo 1985, Hochar Ch.

Musar and Paillard champagnes mean that many of the bins are from excellent makers. House wines are £7.50.

CHEF: Thomas Mulkerrin PROPRIETORS: Martin Spalding and Steven Kendell OPEN: all week, D only; 6 to 10.30 (11 Fri and Sat) CLOSED: 25 and 26 Dec, 1 Jan MEALS: alc (main courses £6 to £10.50). Set D 6 to 7.30pm £12.95 (inc wine) SERVICE: not inc CARDS: Access, Amex, Visa DETAILS: 76 seats. Private parties: 76 main room. Vegetarian meals. Children's helpings with prior notice. Smart dress preferred. Music. Fax: (0532) 430432

## *Sous le Nez en Ville* 🍾 £

The Basement, Quebec House,
Quebec Street, Leeds LS1 2HA
LEEDS (0532) 440108

COOKING 1
COST £16–£47

A hop and a skip from the railway station, this basement offers a whole range of options, from tapas to a full meal, reflecting its use by the families, businesses and the streetwise of Leeds. The menu is a giant, with the printed choice supplemented by a blackboard full of fish. It pursues the same line as a number of its competitors in this field – Leeds has embraced the concept of large modern bistros with enthusiasm – with dishes such as grilled tuna with bean sprouts, brochette of king prawns with wild rice, black pudding with braised cabbage, lamb with provençal vegetables, veal with pesto noodles and sun-dried tomatoes, and (you can almost guarantee it in this day and age) puddings such as crème brûlée and sticky toffee pudding. Cheerful, competent and a service – exactly what this sort of place should be about. Enthusiasm and a well-informed tenacity has assembled an extremely good wine list. The sense that recognises the limited demands of lunch-time imbibers and provides a dozen-plus house wines by the glass is balanced by the idiosyncratic trawl through recent novelties such as the incredible Syrah from Isole e Olena and a superlative red Chinon. Otherwise there are Paillard champagne, Fleurie from Chignard, carefully chosen petits châteaux and up-to-date Italians and antipodeans. Prices are very reasonable. House wines are from £6.95.
CELLARMAN'S CHOICE: Marlborough, Oyster Bay, Chardonnay 1992, £13.40; Corbières, Dom. du Grand Crès 1991, £12.60.

CHEF: Andrew Carter PROPRIETORS: C.R.C.R. Partnership OPEN: Mon to Sat, exc Sat L; 12 to 2.30, 6 to 10.30 (11 Fri and Sat) CLOSED: bank hols (exc Good Fri) MEALS: alc (main courses £5.50 to £13.95). Set D (6 to 7.30pm) £12.95 (inc wine). Bar menu SERVICE: not inc, card slips closed CARDS: Access, Amex, Visa DETAILS: 70 seats. Private parties: 80 main room, 10 and 28 private rooms. Vegetarian meals. Children's helpings. No children under 11 D. No pipes in dining-room. Music D. Fax: (0532) 450240

*The Guide is totally independent, accepts no free hospitality, and survives on the number of copies sold each year.*

*Prices quoted in the Guide are based on information supplied by restaurateurs. The prices quoted at the top of each entry represent a range, from the lowest meal price to the highest; the latter is inflated by 20 per cent to take account of likely price rises during the year of the Guide.*

map 5

## Bobby's £

154 Belgrave Road, Leicester LE4 5AT                         COOKING 1
LEICESTER (0533) 660106 and 662448                           COST £9–£21

Belgrave Road, north of the city centre, is the hub of Leicester's Asian
community. Bobby's has been in business since 1976 and continues to offer
some of the most authentic and best-value vegetarian food in the
neighbourhood. Mrs Lakhani runs the kitchen, and her menu is a wide-ranging
blend of Gujarati and south Indian dishes bolstered by one or two Punjabi
specialities such as chana masala and bhatura bread. Ingredients are fresh,
spices are ground on the premises and no onions or garlic appear in the recipes.
A brilliant array of farsan savoury snacks, from kachori and bateta wada to pani
puri and masala dosa, are always available, along with thalis, vegetable curries
and impeccable breads and rice – look for thepla with green chillies and
khichri (the ancestor of kedgeree). Go at the weekend, when more esoteric
dishes are available. Wine is not served, but customers can bring their own;
otherwise there is a choice of lassi, falooda, juices and masala tea.

CHEF: Mrs M.B. Lakhani   PROPRIETORS: Mr B.A. and Mrs M.B. Lakhani   OPEN: Tue to
Sun; 11am to 10pm (10.30 Fri to Sun)   CLOSED: day after bank hols   MEALS: alc (main
courses £2 to £6.50). Set L and D £5.25 to £6.50. Cover 40p. Unlicensed, but bring your
own: no corkage   SERVICE: not inc   CARDS: Access, Amex, Visa   DETAILS: 84 seats.
Private parties: 60 main room, 22 and 40 private rooms. Vegetarian meals only. Children
welcome. No-smoking area. Music. Air-conditioned

## Welford Place

9 Welford Place, Leicester LE1 6ZH                           COOKING 1
LEICESTER (0533) 470758                                      COST £17–£37

Ceilings are high and settings grand but never opulent in this former
gentlemen's club. The place is well sited, allowing the survey of professional
and juridical Leicester. It is run by the same family that is reponsible for the
Wig & Mitre in Lincoln (see entry), and there are similar principles of 'can-do'
and a general wish to oblige. Motivation is high. A series of menus changes
daily or weekly and offers almost any combination to breakfasters, city
lunchers, casual drop-ins, serious diners, or whatever. The intentions are very
good, with dishes such as rillette of rabbit with green peppercorns and a date
chutney, a warm salad of chicken livers and black pudding with hazelnuts and
green beans, followed by quail served with couscous and flavoured with lemon
and basil, or calves' kidneys with tarragon mustard and wild rice. Performance
does not always hit the mark, though many legal gents have found lunches that
may consist of a mushroom, cream and bacon tart followed by lemon sole with
lemon butter (and bacon again) sufficient to win the case. Bread-and-butter
pudding or cold rice-pudding are better bets than the tiramisù. This is a brave
venture that deserves to succeed as it improves. The wine list is a rather safe
affair. Perhaps some of the verve and directness found in metropolitan
establishments whose aims it is trying, very laudably, to emulate would not
come amiss. Prices are fair, with house wines at £9.40.

CHEFS: Lino Poli and Paul Vidic  PROPRIETORS: Valerie and Michael Hope  OPEN: all week; 8am to 11.30pm  MEALS: alc (main courses £7.50 to £13). Set L £8.25 (2 courses) to £9.50, Set Sun L £12.50  SERVICE: not inc, card slips closed  CARDS: Access, Amex, Diners, Visa  DETAILS: 216 seats. Private parties: 60 main room, 16 to 50 in private rooms. Vegetarian meals. Children's helpings. Wheelchair access. No music. Fax: (0533) 471843

---

LEWDOWN Devon                                                                 map 1

# ▲ *Lewtrenchard Manor* ♀ ⅍

Lewdown EX20 4PN
LEWDOWN (056 683) 256 and 222
off A30 Okehampton to Launceston road,
turn left at Lewdown for ¼m
                                                                      COST £22–£49

The grouping of house, dovecote, garden house, church and fine gardens with giant trees is impressive indeed. The original building is Elizabethan, but the Victorian parson, hymn-writer and historian Sabine Baring-Gould left his restoring mark very heavily on everything. The result is a quirky pastiche, with some impressive public rooms, good bedrooms and frightening examples of country-copyists' art. The Murrays have taken well to their new profession of squire-like hoteliers, after coming here in 1988 from southern Africa. With a succession of chefs, the latest taking up the ladle at the very moment of the *Guide* going to press (hence no cooking mark above), the Murrays have offered a careful and attentive version of modern country-house cooking, at none too low a price – more reports, please. The wine list is not just a satisfactory generalist collection of good growers, but has perhaps the most interesting set of South African wines for many miles. These include Klein Constantia whites, Rustenberg Chardonnay and 1982 Cabernet Sauvignon, as well as a pair from Thelema. Unfortunately, the stockpile is not long enough to have anything with great age. House Penedès from Barbier is £8. CELLARMAN'S CHOICE: Victoria, Frenchman's Vineyard, Sauvignon 1991, Taltarni, £15; Kanonkop, Pintotage 1990, £12.50.

CHEF: Anthony Pierce  PROPRIETORS: James and Sue Murray  OPEN: all week, D only, and Sun L (Mon to Sat L by arrangement); 12.15 to 2, 7.15 to 9.30  MEALS: alc (main courses £16 to £19). Set Sun L £16, Set D £24.50  SERVICE: not inc, card slips closed  CARDS: Access, Amex, Diners, Visa  DETAILS: 35 seats. Private parties: 8 main room, 16 and 26 private rooms. Car park. Vegetarian meals with prior notice. Children's helpings on request. No children under 8. Smart dress preferred. No smoking in dining-room. Wheelchair access (1 step; also WC)  ACCOMMODATION: 8 double rooms, all with bath/shower. B&B £75 to £130. No children under 8. Pets by arrangement. Afternoon teas. Garden. Fishing. TV. Phone. Doors close at midnight. Confirm by 6. Fax: (056 683) 332 (*The Which? Hotel Guide*)

---

CELLARMAN'S CHOICE: *Wines recommended by the restaurateur, normally more expensive than house wine.*

Net prices *in the details at the end of an entry indicates that the prices given on a menu and on a bill are inclusive of VAT and service charge, and that this practice is clearly stated on menu and bill.*

---

## LICHFIELD Staffordshire map 5

## ▲ *Swinfen Hall Hotel* ⁵✳

Swinfen, nr Lichfield WS14 9RS
LICHFIELD (0543) 481494                          COOKING 1
just off A38, 2m S of Lichfield                  COST £21–£48

The Hall makes much of its history. It was constructed as a manor house in
1755 under the direction of local architect Benjamin Wyatt and now ranks as a
listed building. Paintings by famous and unknown artists adorn the public
rooms. Chef Chris Morrall worked at several pedigree restaurants, including
The Elms, Abberley (see entry), before moving here and his cooking
deliberately aspires to the setting. Boudin of seafood with saffron noodles and
tomato coulis, fillet of brill with timbale of scallops and crayfish on vermouth
sauce, and whole boned poussin served on glazed leeks with truffles and
tomatoes are typical of his style. Elsewhere, reporters have praised simpler
offerings such as celery and Stilton soup, gravlax, perfectly cooked tournedos
of beef, and chocolate mousse. Service is knowledgable. The wine list does not
venture far beyond France, but it is peppered with good names. House wine
is £9.50.

CHEF: Chris Morrall   PROPRIETORS: Mr V.J. and Mrs H.L. Wiser   OPEN: all week, exc Sat
L and Sun D; 12 to 2.30, 7.30 to 9.30   MEALS: alc (main courses £9 to £16). Set L £12.95
(2 courses) to £14.95, Set Sun L £13.95 to £17.95, Set D £15.50 (2 courses) to £18.50
SERVICE: not inc, card slips closed   CARDS: Access, Amex, Visa   DETAILS: 60 seats. Private
parties: 60 main room, 28 and 150 private rooms. Car park. Vegetarian meals. Children's
helpings. Smart dress preferred. No smoking in dining-room. Wheelchair access. Music
ACCOMMODATION: 19 rooms, all with bath/shower. B&B £65 to £125. Children welcome.
Baby facilities. Afternoon teas. Garden. TV. Phone. Confirm by 6. Fax: (0543) 480341

## LIFTON Devon map 1

## ▲ *Arundell Arms* ⁵✳

Lifton PL16 0AA
LIFTON (0566) 784666                             COOKING 1*
just off A30, 3m E of Launceston                 COST £23–£45

Most fly-fishermen have heard of the Arundell Arms; water is its life-blood and
fisherfolk its aficionados. In addition to the 20-odd miles of river, there is the
new Roadford reservoir to explore, and peace and quiet after a good day's
casting is now assured with Lifton being bypassed by the new A30. Sport was
ever in the blood of this old inn, for the cock-pit survives, in use as a tackle
room. All this sport – there is shooting come winter – gives rise to large
appetites, and Philip Burgess' menus are built to satisfy carnivorous taste with
grills of beef, fowl and salmon, as well as a few more dainty dishes like
sweetbreads with a bacon and thyme sauce, or a vegetable croustade. The
intentions are not complicated, though the slightly pedestrian *carte* is
supplemented by a daily menu with some fancy dishes, be it sweet pepper
salad, a turbot and crab tart with a béarnaise, or roast hake with herbs. For
dessert, try the bread-and-butter pudding. Bar snacks are available both at

lunch-time and in the evening. The wine list is well founded, with much taken from Christopher Piper and house wines starting at £8.75.

CHEF: Philip Burgess   PROPRIETOR: Anne Voss-Bark   OPEN: all week; 12 to 2 (2.30 bar), 7.30 to 9.30   MEALS: alc (main courses £15 to £16.50). Set L £11.75 (2 courses) to £14.75, Set D £22. Bar menu   SERVICE: not inc   CARDS: Access, Amex, Diners, Visa   DETAILS: 70 seats. Private parties: 80 main room, 30 private room. Car park. Vegetarian meals. Children's helpings on request. No smoking in dining-room. Wheelchair access (2 steps). Music   ACCOMMODATION: 29 rooms, all with bath/shower. B&B £37 to £88. Children welcome. Baby facilities. Dogs welcome. Afternoon teas. Garden. Fishing. TV. Phone. Doors close at 11.30. Fax: (0566) 784494 (*The Which? Hotel Guide*)

---

**LINCOLN Lincolnshire**                                                    map 6

## Jew's House

15 The Strait, Lincoln LN2 1JD                                   COOKING 2
LINCOLN (0522) 524851                                            COST £23–£45

Lincoln Cathedral stands at the top of Steep Hill, while at the bottom this restaurant inhabits one of the oldest houses in the city. The Gibbs offer an amiable welcome (save one winter's night when inexplicably they refused service to a benighted, yet booked, couple half an hour before the advertised closing time), and some sound cooking. 'Moules marinière started the meal after an amuse-bouche of filo-wrapped prawns, and came with a very creamy, yet balanced, sauce that made several rolls disappear in the mopping-up procedure. A main course of noisettes of lamb served with dijonnaise potatoes, high on onions, left room enough for a lemon tart as good as most.' As this reader commented, the food was distraction enough on a quiet night. The repertoire here is mainstream but not tired: two first courses are avocado and mozzarella salad with basil, chives and sun-dried tomatoes, and oyster mushrooms in puff pastry with thyme; exemplary main dishes include a mixed plate of venison and duck with pink peppercorns, and beef with shallots and garlic. A blackboard is posted for daily additions of fish. There is an almost audible sigh of anticipation for the list (longer than many) of puddings that runs the gamut of bread-and-butter pudding soufflé, tarte Tatin and banana and brandy pancake: they like things hot in Lincoln. The wine list has some excellent makers from France and elsewhere. It manages a fair range of prices, though there could be more half-bottles. House wines are Australian, French or German and start at £8.75.

CHEF: Richard Gibbs   PROPRIETORS: Richard and Sally Gibbs   OPEN: Tue to Sat; 12 to 1.30, 7 to 9.30   CLOSED: bank hol Mons   MEALS: alc (main courses £9.50 to £13.50). Set L and D £16.50   SERVICE: not inc   CARDS: Access, Amex, Diners, Visa   DETAILS: 28 seats. Private parties: 30 main room. Vegetarian meals. Children's helpings. No pipes in dining-room. Music

---

*All details are as accurate as possible at the time of going to press, but chefs and owners often change, and it is wise to check by telephone before making a special journey. Many readers have been disappointed when set-price bargain meals are no longer available. Ask when booking.*

---

## Wig & Mitre £

29 Steep Hill, Lincoln LN2 1LU
LINCOLN (0522) 535190 and 523705

COOKING 2
COST £16–£38

Steep Hill is surely steep. One man short of puff recommended the Wig & Mitre because it was at the top of the slope – and that is where he started. There are other reasons for a visit: as a pub it is open all hours, it serves food all day, and offers menus that twist this way or that according to your wants. (It is also in one of the oldest parts of Lincoln, and is a short stroll from the cathedral.) 'Waitresses drift into the pub bearing perfectly presented meals,' noted one visitor, who twigged that the top of the house contains the restaurant section of the enterprise, among the rafters, beams and old partitions. The Wig & Mitre is managed by the Hopes, who also run Welford Place in Leicester (see entry), and the mix of daily and weekly menus, as well as the wine list, indicates the family link. Here, satisfactory cooking shows in dishes like a first course of cheese soufflé with ham followed by scallops parcelled up in filo pastry, calves' kidneys with green peppercorns and cream, or fresh pasta with wild mushrooms and cream. Some of the details, like the new potatoes tossed with garlic or the decent vinaigrette, impress more than the coffee or the occasionally overcooked vegetables. They certainly do better than an avocado and lentil pâté that may please a vegan but resembled lake-bottom sludge to eyes not used to that sort of texture. People enjoy their puddings (there is often a hot one), and the cheese is also given fair praise. When a place like this sets out so transparently to oblige, people respond. In Lincoln, people rejoice. The wine list resorts too readily to the safety of big reliable names and draws surprisingly little from the New World or the exciting wines now coming from the small appellations of France. Prices are generally fair; house wines cost £9.40.

CHEFS: Paul Vidic, Peter Dodd and Simon Shaw  PROPRIETORS: Valerie and Michael Hope  OPEN: all week; 8am to 11.30pm  CLOSED: 25 Dec  MEALS: alc (main courses £4 to £13)  SERVICE: not inc, card slips closed  CARDS: Access, Amex, Diners, Visa DETAILS: 120 seats. 6 tables outside. Private parties: 60 main room, 40 private room. Vegetarian meals. Children's helpings. Wheelchair access (1 step; also WC). No music. Fax: (0522) 532402

---

LIVERPOOL Merseyside                                                    map 5

## Armadillo ♟

20–22 Mathew Street, L2 6RE
051-236 4123

COOKING 2*
COST £21–£33

Never think that places like the Armadillo are going to produce food of entirely even quality every day and all day, or that people will all react in the same way to its pleasantly idiosyncratic manner. For some it is heaven; for others it is a mite messy and uncomfortable – even dilapidated. It is important to stress that the Armadillo is in Liverpool (not a lot else is) and that Martin Cooper cares and knows what he does with food. Vegetarians find this converted warehouse (sit by a window and watch Liverpool life) always has something to offer them, from excellent soups to filo parcels with different fillings and leek and Cheddar pasties. The general approach to food and recipes would in any case encourage inventive vegetarian cookery. The Middle East and its flavours inform much of what is done here – stuffed vine leaves and even salt pork with spiced lentils are instances of generic influence – and some diners have commented that too much food gets complicated treatment when simplicity would be best. Fish, however, is excluded from these remarks, for Martin tends to hang back on overloading its gentle tastes. Yet fish is better here than in most of the rest of the city. There are deficiencies in technique, but value is high and the relaxed amiability of the staff will please old and young alike (but not the stuffy). A snack menu is available between 5 and 6.30 pm Tuesday to Friday. The wine list is admirable; it explores nooks and crannies – and growers – that are not always familiar, and the prices are indeed fair. House wines are £6.95 a litre.

CHEFS: John Scotland and Martin Cooper   PROPRIETORS: Martin and Angela Cooper
OPEN: Tue to Sat; 12 to 2.45, 7.30 to 10.30   CLOSED: bank hols, few days after Christmas
MEALS: alc (main courses £10 to £14)   SERVICE: not inc, card slips closed (10% for 10 or
more)   CARDS: Access, Visa   DETAILS: 65 seats. Private parties: 65 main room. Vegetarian
meals. Children welcome. Music

---

## LIVERSEDGE West Yorkshire                                                                 map 5

## ▲ Lillibet's

64 Leeds Road, Liversedge WF15 6HX
HECKMONDWIKE (0924) 404911,
changes to (019 24) 404911 April 1994

COOKING 1
COST £26–£37

The downstairs of this substantial stone house with outbuildings, done out in powder blue and sunshine yellow, shines like a new pin. The cooking rejoices in Yorkshire generosity, with portions to match. Even the garlic bread of old has become garlic and herb bread topped with mozzarella cheese. Dishes are topped and tailed: deep-fried mushrooms are stuffed with bacon, cream cheese and garlic, a tomato and feta salad has a garlic 'mini-pitta', and mousses and fillings adorn main dishes. It works. There has been a lightening of the cost as well as a shortening of the meal this year (down from four courses to three) – perhaps slimmming is catching on in Yorkshire. The Australasian section in the well-spread wine list is the one to look at. House wines are £8.95.

CHEFS: Liz Roberts and Simon Gomersal   PROPRIETORS: Martin and Liz Roberts
OPEN: Mon to Sat, D only (L by arrangement for 12 or more); 7 to 9.30   CLOSED: 1 week
Christmas, 2 weeks end Aug, bank hols   MEALS: Set D £17.25 to £21.95   SERVICE: not
inc   CARDS: Access, Amex, Visa   DETAILS: 60 seats. Private parties: 70 main room. Car
park. Vegetarian meals. Children's helpings. No babies. Smart dress preferred. No cigars/
pipes in dining-room. Wheelchair access (3 steps; also WC). Music   ACCOMMODATION: 13
rooms, all with bath/shower. Rooms for disabled. B&B £49 to £70. Children welcome.
Baby facilities. TV. Phone. Doors close at midnight. Fax: (0924) 404912, changes to (019 24)
404912 April 1994 (*The Which? Hotel Guide*)

---

Card slips closed *in the details at the end of an entry indicates that the total on the slips
of credit cards is closed when handed over for signature.*

LONG CRENDON Buckinghamshire                                          map 2

## ▲ *Angel Inn* ✠ £                                         NEW ENTRY

Bicester Road, Long Crendon HP18 9EE
LONG CRENDON (0844) 208268                              COOKING 1
on B4011, 2m NW of Thame                               COST £19–£36

'On an incandescent May evening, the drive through green Chiltern lanes was
enchanting,' recalls a traveller seeking out this substantial, seventeenth-
century roadside inn. Inside is a curious mix of pub and restaurant. The bar,
with Brakspear on handpump, feels more like someone's sitting-room, with
plush settees and a wood-burning stove at one end. Beyond is a maze of eating
areas in different styles. The printed monthly-changing menu is a selection of
up-market pub/restaurant dishes ranging from up-to-the-minute Italian
specialities to old favourites such as bangers and mash. In addition, daily
specials are chalked up around the bar: fish is the main attraction, with
anything from chargrilled squid with roasted peppers and chilli oil to baked
cod with spinach and tomato fondue. Reporters have been impressed by
carpaccio of salmon with honey vinaigrette, intense fish soup, and rack of lamb
with roasted shallots and honey glaze. Olive bread and anchovy bread are like
variations on bruschetta. The staff are generally amiable. The wine list is a
better-than-average selection with a strong showing from the New World.
Monthly house wines are from £8 to £10.

CHEF: M.E. Jones   PROPRIETORS: Mr and Mrs M.E. Jones   OPEN: all week, exc Sun D;
12 to 2.30, 7 to 10 (11 to 4.30 Sun)   MEALS: alc (main courses £5 to £11)   SERVICE: not inc
CARDS: Access, Visa   DETAILS: 80 seats. 4 tables outside. Private parties: 40 main room,
10, 15 and 40 private rooms. Car park. Vegetarian meals. Children welcome. No smoking in
conservatory. Music   ACCOMMODATION: 4 rooms, all with bath/shower. B&B £35 to £50.
Children welcome. Baby facilities. Pets by arrangement. TV. Phone. Doors close at 1am

LONG MELFORD Suffolk                                                 map 3

## *Scutchers Bistro* £

Westgate Street, Long Melford CO10 9DP                 COOKING 1*
SUDBURY (0787) 310200 and 310620                       COST £19–£34

Take a boring pub, rip out the partitions but keep the beams and split levels,
furnish brightly with pictures, tiles on the floor and pine furniture and, hey
presto, a country bistro which many say serves bright-coloured and sprightly
food, though others have recorded the odd languid night. The printed menu
does change, but more rapid adjustments are made on a blackboard (for wines
too) – just to keep the bistro image. Mushrooms sautéed with garlic butter,
deep-fried Brie with a strawberry coulis, cod with chips and lemon
mayonnaise, and breast of duck with a pear and ginger sauce made, for one
party, a 'perfect bistro meal', finishing in style with a hot coconut soufflé.
Rabbit with pears and a mustard sauce and salmon with a herb crust and a
ginger and lemon grass sauce show the will to invent and adapt. Service is
personable, and the wine list surpasses most bistro efforts. Good growers and

fair prices make choice difficult. House wines from the Producteurs Plaimont are £6.75.

CHEF/PROPRIETOR: Nicholas Barrett OPEN: Mon to Sat; 12 to 2, 7 to 9.30 CLOSED: bank hols MEALS: alc (main courses £6 to £11) SERVICE: not inc, card slips closed CARDS: Access, Visa DETAILS: 75 seats. 6 tables outside. Private parties: 75 main room. Car park. Vegetarian meals. Children's helpings. No cigars/pipes in dining-room. Wheelchair access (also WC). Music. Fax: (0787) 310157

---

**LONGRIDGE Lancashire** map 5

## *Heathcote's*

COUNTY RESTAURANT OF THE YEAR

Higher Road, Longridge PR3 3SY COOKING 4
PRESTON (0772) 784969 COST £31–£65

The address has some of the details: this treble-cottage restaurant is towards the town end of a hill-crest lane out of Longridge. The interior is so cottagey that you can hardly believe that you are sitting in the midst of late-Victorian wasteland development on the outskirts of Preston. The cooking is still further out of character with the slightly flouncy interior, and the suave jacketed service is so couth as to summon up images of vast country houses. The venture, therefore, is unlikely for its ambition and achievement, within so relatively humble a framework. Paul Heathcote is a very good cook. He has the ability to season dishes so that they taste of something, as well as the wish to render them into forms that are a long way from the slapdash trendiness of many of today's favourites. He can, however, do a shank of lamb as well as anyone, and he can cook a cheap lunch that would compete with several big-city smarts. A gourmet menu of mid-winter exemplifies some of his skills. Mosaic of duck terrine with foie gras was served with apple and fig chutney; ravioli were filled with chicken and mushrooms and served on a madeira sauce; a ballottine of fresh salmon was wrapped in parsley, served with a parsley mayonnaise and some crème fraîche; lamb was stuffed with a chicken and basil mousse and served with a confit of shallots, beans and pulses with a slight perfume of lavender to the sauce; a hot and cold cocktail of raspberry sorbet and hot raspberry soufflé was an alternative to a plate of British cheeses in good condition, before strong coffee and fine petits fours. Apart from a sorbet before the meat course, there was no superfluity. The recipes are fairly conventional but executed with enough variation in detail to make them live in the memory. Best of all, the seasoning and balance of flavours is carefully thought about and consistent. The removal of last year's notes from the wine list is applauded. There remains though an unevenness in selection: genuine strength in Spain and the antipodes and Alsace is balanced by a Rhône selection that lacks weight and a surprisingly limited range of Italians and over-cautious burgundies. There are good half-bottles and prices are firm. House wine is from £13. CELLARMAN'S CHOICE: Mâcon-Fuissé, Dom. du Fussiacus 1991, J. Paquet, £17; Chiroubles, Dom. de la Grosse Pierre 1990, A. Passet, £18.50.

---

The Good Food Guide *is a registered trade mark of Consumers' Association Ltd.*

CHEFS: Paul Heathcote and Andrew Barnes  PROPRIETOR: Paul Heathcote  OPEN: Tue to Sun D, Fri and Sun L; 12 to 2, 7 to 9  CLOSED: some days Jan  MEALS: alc (main courses £17 to £19). Set L £20, Set D £32.50 to £40  SERVICE: 15%, card slips closed  CARDS: Access, Amex, Visa  DETAILS: 60 seats. Private parties: 60 main room, 60 private room. Car park. Vegetarian meals. Children welcome. Smart dress preferred. No smoking in dining-room. Wheelchair access. Music. Fax: (0772) 785713

---

**LONGSTOCK** Hampshire  map 2

## *Peat Spade Inn* £

Longstock, Stockbridge SO20 6DR
ANDOVER (0264) 810612  COOKING 1*
off A3057, 1m N of Stockbridge  COST £18–£34

Julie Tuckett is both head cook and landlady of this red-brick Victorian inn. She points out that the premises are 'not very pubby'; in fact, the place reminds some people of a neat and tidy private residence. Visitors appreciate the quiet, comfortable surroundings and the good-value, well-cooked food. The flexible set-up means that meals can be eaten anywhere in the bar, dining-room or garden; dishes can also be mixed and matched from the two blackboards or the fixed-price menu. Julie's cooking is quick, simple and perfectly tuned: meats are sauté or chargrilled, fish is roasted and vegetables are steamed. It also reflects the seasons: light fish dishes and salads in summer, meaty pies in winter. The three-course set menu is short and to the point, with centrepieces such as roast fillet of salmon with white truffle sauce, sauté suprême of guinea-fowl 'maison' (flamed in calvados and finished with cider and cream), and wild boar sausages with tiny boiled potatoes. Reporters have raved about the lemon cheesecake and sticky toffee pudding. A dozen admirable house wines are served by the glass or bottle. Prices go from £9.10 to £11.85, and the well-spread list has plenty of affordable drinking. Beer from Gale's and Boddingtons is on draught.

---

CHEF: Julie T. Tuckett  PROPRIETORS: T.P.M. Inns Ltd  OPEN: all week, exc Sun D; 12.15 to 2, 7.15 to 10  CLOSED: 25 Dec, 3 weeks Jan to Feb  MEALS: alc (main courses £5.50 to £11). Set L and D £15.75  SERVICE: not inc, card slips closed  CARDS: Amex, Diners  DETAILS: 30 seats. 6 tables outside. Private parties: 24 main room, 14 private room. Car park. Vegetarian meals. Children's helpings. Smart dress preferred in dining-room. Wheelchair access (also WC). No music. Fax: (0264) 810612

---

**LOUTH** Lincolnshire  map 6

## *Alfred's* £

Upgate, Louth LN11 9EY  COOKING 2
LOUTH (0507) 607431  COST £20–£42

Lamb shank with flageolet beans has got to Louth. Not all Lincolnshire is stuck in cooking's dim distant days. Rosemarie Dicker has espoused the modern cause at this plain, red-brick building and people appreciate it – for variety as much as anything. Grilled tuna with oil, lemon and garlic, and chicken with fennel, shallots, saffron and cream are two exemplary main courses, and saffron

375

may get another outing in an inventive first course of carrot and coriander cakes with mussels. A Lincolnshire ploughboy would hardly know his working day if it ended with puchero, a Spanish stew of pork, beans and saveloy, but a devotee of 'modern British' might soon recognise escalopes of monkfish with a courgette chutney, and there is always a chargrilled steak for conservatives. The menus are kept sensibly short, the tone is very even. The wine list offered to all keeps well below a £20 ceiling, but the plutocrats can ask to see the 'reserve du patron' and be greeted by annotated sheets of superior stuff indeed. Cheap or dear, decent makers are raided for supplies, be it the house Mas de Gourgonnier at £8.95 or Cape Mentelle Cabernet Sauvignon at £23.50.

CHEFS: Rosemarie Dicker and Diane White   PROPRIETORS: Paul and Rosemarie Dicker
OPEN: Tue to Sat D (Tue to Fri L by arrangement); 12 to 2, 7 to 9 (9.30 Sat)   CLOSED: 26
Dec   MEALS: alc (main courses £7 to £15.50). Set L and D £15   SERVICE: not inc, card slips
closed   CARDS: Access, Diners, Visa   DETAILS: 45 seats. Private parties: 55 main room.
Vegetarian meals. Children's helpings with prior notice. Wheelchair access (3 steps). Music

---

**LOWER BEEDING West Sussex**                                                    map 3

## Jeremy's at The Crabtree ⁵⁄₄✳

Brighton Road, Lower Beeding RH13 6PT                              COOKING 2
HORSHAM (0403) 891257                                              COST £18–£34

The pub sits on the Brighton road and is very much a front and a back, or two sides – Jeremy's being the right-hand side, through to the back where there are handsome oak settles, a big fireplace and flagged paving. The room apart, atmosphere is at a premium, but Jeremy Ashpool makes up for it with some expressive cooking that comes as a surprise in a country pub, at prices that do not shock. Starters have included mussel and leek tart with ginger and grilled goats' cheese with pesto. Some of the main dishes on the menu may, however, have less clear flavours than the written note implies, due to too many extraneous elements. This has sometimes been the case with lamb with red onions, courgettes and a garlic and tarragon sauce, or venison in puff pastry on a celeriac purée served with a thyme sauce. But the basic cooking, for instance of meat, is excellent and invention is high. Puddings, too, as in lemon on brioche dough, chocolate biscuit cake or home-made ice-creams, have their supporters. Lunch is simpler in style, and cheaper, though obviously from the same hand. The wine list is sensibly short and quite adequate. House wines are £7.95.

CHEFS: Jeremy Ashpool, James Boardman and Pia Waters   PROPRIETORS: Jeremy's
Restaurant Ltd   OPEN: all week, exc Sun D; 12.15 to 2, 7.30 to 9.45   CLOSED: 25 Dec
MEALS: alc L (main courses £6 to £8). Set Sun L £13.50. Set D £8.95 to £18.95   SERVICE: not
inc L, 10% D and Set Sun L, card slips closed   CARDS: Access, Visa   DETAILS: 40 seats.
Private parties: 22 main room. Car park. Vegetarian meals. Children's helpings on request.
No smoking in 1 dining-room. Wheelchair access. Music

---

'My milkman tells me that it (the restaurant) is spotlessly clean behind the scenes as well as out front!' On eating in Northamptonshire

---

## ▲ South Lodge ✸

Brighton Road, Lower Beeding RH13 6PS
LOWER BEEDING (0403) 891711      COOKING 3
on A281, 6m SE of Horsham      COST £26–£76

All toilers in the garden of horticulture must pass the South Lodge gates at least once in their lives because there are so many famous gardens (by Jekyll and Lutyens, for example) within spitting distance. The eye at South Lodge will be seduced by the country's largest rhododendron, interesting Victorian gardens lit by a veritable forest of lanterns at night, and much ornate woodwork (plus de Morgan tiles) and dull paint in the house itself. The original builder was a collector of Islamic pottery. His cabinets have been given over to depressing displays of objects for sale, or modern Chinese plates. There is, however, nothing cheerless about the food and no doubting Tony Tobin's assurance in dishes such as salmon escalope with a pizza-style topping, and duck with olives and mashed potato. His repertoire extends through a range wider than that of many modern country houses: salade niçoise with proper tuna, veal chop with spinach and a rosemary sauce, sea bass with tomatoes and spices, a mousseline version of piedmontese peppers, and beef with a cassis sauce, plus puddings such as fruits in a champagne jelly, hot soufflés, and strawberry tarts with a saffron ice-cream. Though the service is as professional as you would expect, there have been comments about uneven standards and flavours that should jump out at you, cowering on the lip of the plate. The wine list might be funding a transfer fee for a football club: it runs to money, though the names are steady enough and the range is certainly adequate. House French is £12.75 and £13.

CHEF: Anthony Tobin   PROPRIETORS: Exclusive Hotels   OPEN: all week; 12.30 to 2.30 (3 Sun), 7.30 to 10 (11 Fri and Sat)   MEALS: alc (main courses £18 to £28). Set L £15, Set Sun L £17.50, Set D £25 to £32   SERVICE: not inc, card slips closed   CARDS: Access, Amex, Diners, Visa   DETAILS: 40 seats. 4 tables outside. Private parties: 80 main room, 8, 10, 24, 60 and 80 private rooms. Car park. Vegetarian meals. Children's helpings. Jacket and tie. No smoking in dining-room. Wheelchair access (1 step; also WC). No music ACCOMMODATION: 39 rooms, all with bath/shower. Rooms for disabled. B&B £100 to £275. Children welcome. Baby facilities. Afternoon teas. Garden. Tennis. Fishing. Snooker. TV. Phone. Confirm by 6. Fax: (0403) 891766 (*The Which? Hotel Guide*)

---

**LOWER BRAILES** Warwickshire      map 2

## ▲ Feldon House ♥ ✸

Lower Brailes OX15 5HW
BRAILES (060 885) 580,
changes to (0608) 685580 autumn 1993      COOKING 2
on B4035, between Banbury and Shipston on Stour      COST £24–£36

This Victorian house near the village church is as immaculate within as without, where a walled garden stretches down to the road. 'This is not a "normal" restaurant in any sense,' reports one, taken aback at the single dining-table – though a conservatory and terrace (in summer) are also available. 'We are,' say the Withericks, 'a very personal restaurant with rooms.' Concern for bodily wellbeing extends to those caught short by sugar-lust in the loo, where wrapped toffees await. You will be asked, when booking, for likes and dislikes, since the four-course dinner and three-course lunch menus offer no choice. Great efforts go into the dishes, and some feel a slightly plainer approach would be preferable: Evesham asparagus, for example, with a plain pool of butter rather than chopped eggs and rollmop herring. On another occasion 'rather dry' fillet of lamb lacked balance when served with carrots, red cabbage and rhubarb chutney, all more or less sweet. But pink saddle of lamb surprised pleasantly with a purée of carrots with sherry and cream, as did halibut in a gentle butter sauce with mango slices (alongside potatoes, Swiss chard, red cabbage and tomato-filled courgette); and a beef and herb dumpling stew was felt to be 'a culinary masterpiece'. Dessert meringue is good, whether in the form of chocolate meringue cake, strawberry ice-cream and meringue, or meringue with poached apricots. Breakfasts are champion, and service charms. The short wine list (chosen 'con amore', sensed one) is generously annotated for full bottles, though not for halves and bin-ends. It is as well-balanced as any list this succinct could be; prices begin at £8.50 for house French. CELLARMAN'S CHOICE: Pouilly-Fumé, Vieilles Vignes 1990, Caves de Pouilly-sur-Loire, £18.50; Ch. La Tour Saint-Bonnet, 1986, £15.75.

CHEF: Allan Witherick  PROPRIETORS: Allan and Maggie Witherick  OPEN: all week, exc Sun D; 12.30 to 1.30, 7 to 8.30  CLOSED: 2 weeks autumn  MEALS: Set L £17.95, Set D £22.95  SERVICE: not inc, card slips closed  CARDS: Access, Amex, Visa  DETAILS: 16 seats. Private parties: 16 main room. Car park. Vegetarian meals with prior notice. No children under 12. Children's helpings with prior notice. No smoking in conservatory. No music  ACCOMMODATION: 4 rooms, all with bath/shower. B&B £30 to £60. No children under 12. Pets by arrangement in annexe. Garden. TV. Phone (*The Which? Hotel Guide*)

---

**LOWER SLAUGHTER** Gloucestershire                                        map 2

▲ *Lower Slaughter Manor* ⅟✷                          | NEW ENTRY |

Lower Slaughter GL54 2HP
COTSWOLD (0451) 820456                                        COOKING 3
off A429, at sign 'The Slaughters'                        COST £31–£53

The Slaughters manage two manor houses, and now two country-house hotels (see also Lords of the Manor, Upper Slaughter). The son of the builder of this one was chief stonemason of St Paul's Cathedral under Sir Christopher Wren. Bits of the architectural grand manner have rubbed off, especially in the plastered saloon and dining-room, as well as a taste for geometrical gardens. Other parts are less grandiose, but as a whole the setting is impressive, even if the furnishing classifies as luxurious rather than creative. Audrey and Peter Marks have served their apprenticeship in this particular sector of the market – at Rookery Hall near Nantwich – and old hands have welcomed their reappearance. The four-course dinner presents cooking of technical proficiency (except petits fours and nibbles) that is surprisingly substantial and, in some cases, ornate. Sometimes the skill overtakes the impact so that a savarin of salmon and Cotswold trout with its centre filled with diced scallops in a buttery sauce, an extra sorrel and cream sauce surrounding the whole, actually failed to make much impression save richness. On the other hand, a confit of duck leg was 'completely what a confit should be'. The wintry menu, even in high summer, will present the trencherman with problems: fat-on breast of duck and confit of leg, with lashings of spätzli, saddle of lamb with 'gone wrong' potatoes, pig's trotter, fillet of beef with mashed potato and smoked bacon, or scallops and crayfish with ginger sauce are some of the options. Bread from a French bakery in Chipping Campden has received much praise. Wine prices are neither high nor low, range is catholic, but distribution is perhaps uneven with safety overcoming excitement in Alsace, Italy notably absent but a predominance of posh bottles from Burgundy. Halves there are, but they are shown unhelpfully with little to differentiate them from the bottles. House wine is £14.50.

CHEF: Julian Ehlers  PROPRIETORS: Audrey and Peter Marks  OPEN: all week; 12.15 to 2 (2.30 Sun), 7 to 9.30 (10 Fri and Sat)  MEALS: Set L £17.95, Set D £29.50  SERVICE: not inc, card slips closed  CARDS: Access, Amex, Visa  DETAILS: 30 seats. Private parties: 30 main room. Car park. Vegetarian meals. No children under 10. Jacket and tie D. No smoking in dining-room. No music  ACCOMMODATION: 15 rooms, all with bath/shower. Rooms for disabled. D,B&B £145 to £250. Deposit: 50%. No children under 10. Afternoon teas. Garden. Swimming-pool. Sauna. TV. Phone. Doors close at midnight. Fax: (0451) 822150 (*The Which? Hotel Guide*)

---

**LOW LAITHE** North Yorkshire                                                          map 7

## Dusty Miller

NEW ENTRY

Low Laithe HG3 4BU
HARROGATE (0423) 780837
on B6165, 2m SE of Pateley Bridge

COOKING 3
COST £29–£52

The drive down narrow lanes to the Dusty Miller is scenic, and the views of Nidderdale from the lounge and the dining-room are wonderful. This stone-built house has been in the hands of the Dennisons for the last 10 years and they have built up a considerable local following, as well as drawing people from the conference and exhibition honeypot of Harrogate. Here is a fine example of doing things simply, yet well. A short *carte*, a set meal and a late-night one-course dinner menu employ the finest materials, and methods are direct but never crude. Hence a warm salad of scallops benefited from great scallops and a tremendously expressive dressing heavy with the fragrance of extra-virgin olive oil. Again, a duck was roasted whole, then taken off the bone and wrapped in skin before being finished off again to give crispness and dryness. It was served with almost syrupy juices and calvados – 'an intense and yet incredibly complementary sauce'. Lamb was also blessed with a great sauce. This meal was finished with a treacle sponge that was light yet had lots of taste, and bread-and-butter pudding that may have suffered from too much cream. This sort of cooking puts a good shine on the image of Britain. House wines change a lot, but a good burgundy from Parent or La Serre Chardonnay were summer choices at £12.90 and £9.90.

---

*Dining-rooms where live and recorded music are never played are signalled by* No music *in the details at the end of an entry.*

---

CHEFS: Brian Dennison and Ben South  PROPRIETORS: Mr and Mrs Brian Dennison
OPEN: Tue to Sat, D only (L, Sun and Mon D by arrangement); 6.30 to 11  CLOSED: 25 and
26 Dec, 1 Jan, 2 weeks Aug  MEALS: alc (main courses £17 to £20). Set D £24  SERVICE:
not inc, card slips closed  CARDS: Access, Amex, Visa  DETAILS: 40 seats. Private parties:
32 main room, 14 and 32 private rooms. Car park. Vegetarian meals. No children under 9.
Smart dress preferred. Wheelchair access. Music. Fax: (0423) 780065

---

**LYMPSTONE Devon**                                                       map 1

## ▲ *River House* ✸✖

The Strand, Lympstone EX8 5EY                                    COOKING 1*
EXMOUTH (0395) 265147                                             COST £18–£61

The house does more than look out on the river – some of it is built on stilts
directly over the estuarial sand. Take binoculars for a flash at the waders before
the soup. Meanwhile, Shirley Wilkes can be seen at the stove through a glass
screen dividing kitchen from dining-room, so observation of two kinds is
available to diners. A core menu costed according to the number of courses
eaten is bolstered by a *carte* with small supplements to the fixed prices, offering
a wide range of options for so small a restaurant. By and large, it works, though
exigencies of supply may mean that what is offered on the night bears little
resemblance to the listing on the menu. Methods are kept fairly simple. A salad
of anchovy, tomato, goats' cheese, olives and leaves was well enough dressed
to satisfy; prawns with mayonnaise and smoked ham kept it good company.
Fish dishes like red gurnard with a red pepper sauce, or sole stuffed with
prawns in a herb and cream sauce showed discretion in the flavourings and
good fresh produce, while a rump steak braised to dissolution in port and
Guinness was good enough to have the diner try it out in her own home the
next week. Puddings revolve around ice-cream, cheeses around Long Clawson.
Bread can be good or, out of season perhaps, bad. Michael Wilkes is a host
much in evidence – some may prefer gentler handling. The wine list is
serviceable. House wines are £8.50.

CHEF: Shirley Wilkes  PROPRIETORS: Michael and Shirley Wilkes  OPEN: Tue to Sun, exc
Sun D (D Mon and Sun for residents – telephone to check for non-residents); 12 to 1.30, 7
to 9.30 (10 Sat)  CLOSED: 25 and 26 Dec, bank hol Mons (exc for residents)  MEALS: alc L
(main courses £4.50 to £8.50). Set Sun L £16 (2 courses) to £21, Set L and D £18.50 (2
courses) to £28  SERVICE: not inc  CARDS: Access, Amex, Visa  DETAILS: 34 seats. Private
parties: 42 main room, 14 private room. Vegetarian meals. Children's helpings. No children
under 6. Smart dress preferred. No smoking in dining-room. No music  ACCOMMODATION:
2 rooms, all with bath/shower. B&B £55 to £74. No children under 6. TV

---

*The text of entries is based on unsolicited reports sent in by readers, backed up by
inspections conducted anonymously. The factual details under the text are from
questionnaires the* Guide *sends to all restaurants that feature in the book.*

*The* Guide *office can quickly spot when a restaurateur is encouraging customers to write
recommending inclusion – and sadly, several restaurants have been doing this in 1993.
Such reports do not further a restaurant's cause. Please tell us if a restaurateur invites you
to write to the* Guide.

---

## Le Petit Canard

Dorchester Road, Maiden Newton DT2 0BE — COOKING 2*
MAIDEN NEWTON (0300) 20536 — COST £29–£36

The little duck is a much-travelled bird: Canadian Geoff Chapman trained in France before working alongside cleaver-wielding Chinese, and rural England seems neither to have cramped nor calmed his style. Regulars come to this small restaurant for East-meets-West invigoration: spring rolls split to reveal goats' cheese and roasted red pepper; chargrilled smoked salmon is drizzled with a sour cream, caper and onion dressing; leek-stuffed chicken breast lounges on toasted macadamia-nut sauce. Puddings, such as a chocolate and raspberry terrine and an 'excellent' basket of spiced oranges and Grand Marnier ice-cream, have been praised. Definition (not volume) of flavour is noted, and customers are surprised to find that the combinations work, and work well. Lin Chapman's wine list reflects the food perfectly, in that it is also a walk-on-walk-off roundabout of world flavour, thoughtfully compiled and informatively annotated with updates as often as every two or three days. The enthusiasm that shines out of the list is refracted on through the service. 'This restaurant is a jewel,' declares a Dorchester diner. House wine is £9.95.

CHEF: Geoff Chapman  PROPRIETORS: Geoff and Lin Chapman  OPEN: Tue to Sat, D only; 7 to 9  MEALS: Set D £20  SERVICE: not inc  CARDS: Access, Visa  DETAILS: 28 seats. Private parties: 34 main room. Vegetarian meals. No children under 7. No cigars/pipes in dining-room. Wheelchair access. Music

## Croque-en-Bouche ▮ ⁵⚹

221 Wells Road, Malvern Wells WR14 4HF
MALVERN (0684) 565612 — COOKING 4
on A449, 2m S of Great Malvern — COST £38–£52

The strong, direct colours of the bar and restaurant chime well with the strong late-Victorian lines of the house itself, as does the single, huge aspidistra. Niches in the dining-room, stripped of brown and green paint by Marion Jones herself, once housed the produce shelves of a baker and grocer devoted to Malvern's middle classes. Visitors now come from further afield. Marion Jones' cooking is an object of pilgrimage, Robin Jones' wine cellar the subject of hushed wonder. They have developed a system to cope with the crowds. A short menu has three choices for entrée and main dish, prefaced by soup, then salad, cheese and a slate of six desserts before 'possibly the best cafetière I have had' and a giant's set of petits fours. This is cooked by Marion and served by Robin. The real point of all this is that the food is extremely good. Two people enjoyed – an understatement – a summer meal that consisted of soup of salt cod, leeks, dill and sorrel; skate with a hot pesto sauce and grilled vegetables marinated in olive oil; a salad of artichoke and asparagus with a relish of sun-dried tomatoes and capers; roast guinea-fowl with pancetta, served with braised red cabbage; grilled venison with a madeira sauce infused with porcini, and served with a pilaff of rice, wild rice and mushrooms; a fine gratin of potatoes wafting nutmeg through the room; a salad dressed with sesame oil; a board of British cheeses; and a rice caramel custard flanked by tropical fruits. Marion Jones becomes more expressive, her flavours bolder, as the years roll by. For some people, Robin Jones mellows; for others, he still has prickles. Turn up on time. Perhaps even turn up early for perusal of the wine list. This is sensational with no overcharging. A straightforward differentiation is made between 'great winemaking' and 'good value', which is as intelligent as it is helpful since it recognises that occasions and customers have different demands. The wines remain extraordinarily catholic in range and are presented with an informed but unpompous enthusiasm. But, oenophiles be warned, allow time or risk terminal frustration. House wines are from £7. CELLARMAN'S CHOICE: Wairau River, Sauvignon Blanc 1992, £14.50; Rosemount Show Reserve, Syrah 1990, £15.50

CHEF: Marion Jones   PROPRIETORS: Robin and Marion Jones   OPEN: Wed to Sat, D only; 7.30 to 9.30   MEALS: Set D £33.50   SERVICE: net prices, card slips closed   CARDS: Access, Visa   DETAILS: 24 seats. Private parties: 6 main room, 6 private room. Children welcome. No smoking in dining-room. Wheelchair access (1 step). No music

# Planters

191–193 Wells Road,
Malvern Wells WR14 9HB
MALVERN (0684) 575065
on A449, 3m S of Great Malvern

COOKING 2
COST £21–£41

Planters by name, planters by prospect – the plants 'provide a lovely splash of colour to the Victorian frontage,' observed one who was as much taken by the gardening as by the cooking skills. These latter are by no means lacking. Chicken and beef satay with peanut, plum and hot chilli sauces served with deep-fried king prawns so light it was hard to credit they had seen fat, chicken breasts grilled with garlic and coriander, egg murtaba (a flatbread cooked with egg) and a Thai salad with tofu, broccoli, onion, tomato and cucumber were the components of one meal that impressed for its flavours as well as for its unfamiliarity to local denizens. Chandra de Alwis seems able to marry sauces to the main ingredients without drowning them. Malaysian, Indonesian, South-East Asian and Sri Lankan dishes are on offer and may be taken from a short *carte* or a 'feast' menu. Watch the specials board, where really unfamiliar items such as wild boar or pheasant may be listed, or perhaps fresh Cornish crab cooked with chillis in the Singapore style. Puddings are European and elicit opposing views: 'Not worth the bother,' says one who found the crème brûlée floury; 'Superb' said another who had gone a bundle on white chocolate and mocha ice-creams with hot chocolate sauce. One-plate meals from around £6 to £10 are a new introduction. The wine list may be short, but it encompasses a big range of flavours and some fine makers such as Guigal from the Rhône, Hochar from the Lebanon and Marqués de Cáceres from Rioja. House wines are £6.75.

CHEF: Chandra de Alwis  PROPRIETOR: Sandra Pegg  OPEN: Tue to Sat, D only, L bank hol
Mons and L Sun (summer only); 6.30 (7 winter) to 9.30  MEALS: alc (main courses £6.50 to
£7.50). Set D £18.95 (minimum 2 people)  SERVICE: 10%, card slips closed; net prices, card
slips closed L Sun and bank hol Mons  CARDS: Access, Visa  DETAILS: 40 seats. Private
parties: 40 main room. Vegetarian meals. Children welcome. No cigars/pipes in dining-
room. Wheelchair access (1 step). No music

---

**MANCHESTER  Greater Manchester**                                        map 5

## Gaylord £                                              NEW ENTRY

Amethyst House, Spring Gardens, M2 1EA                     COOKING 1*
061-832 6037 and 4866                                     COST £13–£26

The sight of the menu brings total recall,' says a reporter, revisiting after a long
gap, who has known this Indian restaurant for decades. The setting is the first
floor of a modern terrace and inside is a long, split-level dining-room with
traditional prints and paintings on the walls, and smart, closely packed tables.
Light comes from brass filigree lampholders, and strings of brass bells act as
window blinds. Service is smooth and unfailingly efficient. The cooking is
'sensitive', the food assertive. Do not expect new-wave/brasserie fireworks
here: this is simply old-school, curry-house cuisine of a high order. The
tandoori chef can be seen at work through a glass wall panel (the mixed grill
has been distinctively spiced), and the repertoire extends to chicken dupiaza,
lamb pasanda, prawn bhuna and a handful of birianis. Visitors have
commented favourably on karahi chicken, rogan josh and promising vegetable
dishes such as spinach with lotus roots. Breads are first-class – try the onion
kulcha. House wine is £7.95.

CHEF: V.K. Wadhera  PROPRIETORS: Tandoori Catering Consultants Ltd  OPEN: all week;
12 to 2.45, 6 to 11.30  CLOSED: 25 Dec, 1 Jan  MEALS: alc (main courses £5 to £9). Set L
Mon to Sat £5.95 (2 courses), Set D £10.95  SERVICE: 10%  CARDS: Access, Amex, Diners,
Visa  DETAILS: 90 seats. Private parties: 90 main room. Vegetarian meals. Children
welcome. Smart dress preferred. Music. Air-conditioned

---

## ▲ Granada Hotel, Armenian £

404 Wilmslow Road,
Withington, M20 9BM                                        COOKING 1
061-434 3480                                              COST £14–£31

'This place has an authenticity which transcends fashion – a small oasis of
Armenia within Manchester,' observed a reporter. The setting is the basement
of one of Withington's many hotels and the interior is done out in taverna style
with archways, heavy rustic chairs and fancy plates and prints on the walls.
Taped oriental music plays; service is very correct 'but nice with it'. The menu
begins with a standard showing of Middle Eastern meze – crisp falafel, stuffed
vine leaves, baba-ganouge (commendably mashed, rather than puréed
aubergine), garlicky sausage, fried spinach and lemony tabbouleh. Main
courses have included immense portions of fluffy couscous with 'lethal' chilli
sauce and Tbilisi kebab (an excellent mix of kofta and shish kebab). Bread,

pickles and salads are perfectly acceptable. The coffee is first-rate. A few Greek wines plus Ch. Musar are dotted among the short list. House wine is £7.95 a litre.

CHEFS: Mrs Minto and Mr Hovnanian  PROPRIETORS: Hanni Al-Tarabously and Mr Jajoo  OPEN: all week, D only; 6 to 10.30 (11 Fri and Sat)  MEALS: alc (main courses £6 to £10.50). Set D £7.95 (Mon to Thur 6 to 8)  SERVICE: not inc, card slips closed  CARDS: Access, Amex, Diners, Visa  DETAILS: 65 seats. Private parties: 65 main room. Vegetarian meals. Children's helpings. Music  ACCOMMODATION: 11 rooms, all with bath/shower. B&B £35 to £50. Children welcome. Baby facilities. TV. Phone. Confirm by 5

## Koreana £

| Kings House, 40 King Street West, M3 2WY | COOKING 1 |
| 061-832 4330 | COST £11–£40 |

'Our somewhat jaded palates never fail to be invigorated by the food here,' observe two serious Mancunian eaters. 'This is real food, cooked with skill, offering freshness and intensity of flavour.' Koreana, a basement restaurant bedecked with Korean memorabilia, holds a special place in the central Manchester scene and it continues to evolve. The 'make your own' set meals offer intriguing possibilities, and there are five-course banquets, including one for vegetarians. Recent recommendations have included many fixtures of classic Korean cooking: fried pork dumplings, chilli-hot cakes of minced pork and pickled kim-chee, gu jul pan (an assortment of morsels served in a sectioned box), bindae tok (a bean-flour pancake), and sauté pork with water-chestnuts and a 'chilli-hot, garlic-laden sauce'. Bulgogi, cooked at the table, is up to scratch, and rice is authentically sticky. Service is sensitive and helpful. Ginseng tea and saké are available; otherwise the wine list is a commendable well-chosen selection. House French is £7.90.

CHEFS: Hyun K. Kim and Hyun-Suk Shin  PROPRIETORS: Koreana Restaurant Ltd  OPEN: Mon to Sat, exc Sat L; 12 to 2.30, 6.30 to 11  CLOSED: bank hol L  MEALS: Set L £4.95 to £7.30, Set D £12.50 to £19.50  SERVICE: not inc (10% for 8 or more)  CARDS: Access, Amex, Diners, Visa  DETAILS: 60 seats. Private parties: 80 main room. Vegetarian meals. Children welcome. Smart dress preferred. No music. Fax: 061-832 2293

## Kosmos Taverna £

| 248 Wilmslow Road, M14 6LD | COOKING 1 |
| 061-225 9106 | COST £15–£28 |

'I enjoy the Kosmos – the Greek Muzak, the jokes the waiter makes,' begins a typically lively report about this bustling venue near the university. Expect noise, a young crowd, lots of Greek families and light-hearted casual service. But do not expect plate-smashing. The crowds pour in because Loulla Astin delivers some of the most authentic and best-value Greek-Cypriot cooking in Manchester. The trio of impressive mezes (meat, fish and vegetarian) draw most praise and many items are nominated: brilliant hummus, tender, crispy squid, spanakopitakia, halloumi and revithia ('a wonderful concoction of chickpeas in a sauce redolent of cumin'). Elsewhere, reporters have voted for rosto (baked lamb on the bone) and chicken kebabs marinated in olive oil and lemon juice. The weekly specials are undoubtedly tempting: sikoti krassado (pan-fried calf's liver in a rosemary sauce served with cracked wheat pilaff), and rollo (belly-pork with herb and garlic stuffing), while one visitor's meal ended memorably with oven-fresh filo pastry rolls filled with home-made custard. The wine list has a decent clutch of Greek-Cypriot wines at bargain prices. House Italian is £7.50.

CHEF: Loulla Astin PROPRIETORS: Stewart and Loulla Astin OPEN: all week, D only, and Sun L; 6.30 (1 Sun) to 11.30 (12.30 Fri and Sat) MEALS: alc (main courses £5 to £9.50). Set D £10 to £12 SERVICE: not inc CARDS: Access, Visa DETAILS: 90 seats. Private parties: 40 main room. Vegetarian meals. Children's helpings. No cigars/pipes in dining-room. Wheelchair access. Music. Air-conditioned. Fax: 061-256 4442

## Lime Tree

8 Lapwing Lane, West Didsbury, M20 8WS        COOKING 1
061-445 1217        COST £17–£33

'Seriously good food' was the verdict of a reporter who attended a wedding lunch for 55 people at this Didsbury bistro. The dining-room with its light, bright conservatory makes a pleasant setting for a good-value menu that acknowledges the seasons. Typical dishes might include veal and rabbit terrine with apple chutney and Cumberland sauce, roast duckling with kumquat and mango sauce, and loin of spring lamb with cherry tomatoes and basil. Fish shows up well: quenelles of crab are served with fresh tomato sauce, halibut comes with a warm red and green pepper dressing, and fillet of salmon is cooked in white wine with dill, lemon and cucumber. There is always something for vegetarians. The wine list consists of around 30 French bottles from the major growing regions; prices are fair. House wine is £8.50.

CHEFS/PROPRIETORS: Patrick Hannity and Robert Williams OPEN: all week, D only, and Sun L; 12 to 2.30, 6.30 to 10.30 MEALS: alc (main courses £8.50 to £12.50). Set Sun L £10.50 SERVICE: not inc CARDS: Access, Amex, Visa DETAILS: 80 seats. Private parties: 45 main room. Vegetarian meals. Children's helpings Sun L. Wheelchair access. Music

## Little Yang Sing | NEW ENTRY

17 George Street, M1 4HE        COOKING 2
061-228 7722        COST £17–£52

Over the years, the Yeung dynasty has set a particular style of Cantonese cooking in several high-ranking Manchester restaurants, although one aficionado feels that too many of its former innovations are today's clichés. However, this restaurant in a slightly cramped but light basement behind the Piccadilly Hotel is capable of delivering the goods. As a reporter put it, 'This is very much the positive face of adaptation.' Staff are knowledgeable and are prepared to advise, assist and guide customers through the repertoire. Set banquets are a feature, but the place also has a long *carte*, a full vegetarian menu and the promise of a forthcoming children's menu. Casseroles, barbecued dishes and a big showing of one-plate rice and noodle specialities show the kitchen's authentic roots. The selection of dim-sum and appetisers has been impressively handled: first-rate crabmeat balls, beef dumplings with ginger and spring onion, steamed Chinese mushrooms with meatballs and seaweed special with prawn toasts and coconut-cream balls have all been excellent. Roast duck is served correctly cold and on the bone. Other good dishes have included salt and chilli bean curd and prawns with crunchy bo-bo beans and aromatic sauce. The short list of around 30 wines makes familiar reading and prices are reasonable. House wine is £8.25.

CHEFS: Au Ting Chung and G. Huang  PROPRIETOR: Kui Keung Yeung  OPEN: all week; 12 to 3, 5 to 11.15  CLOSED: 25 Dec  MEALS: alc (main courses £6.50 to £9). Set L £10 to £16, Set D £12 to £13 (minimum 2 people)  SERVICE: 10%  CARDS: Access, Amex, Visa DETAILS: 90 seats. Private parties: 120 main room. Vegetarian meals. Children's helpings L. Smart dress preferred. No music. Air-conditioned. Fax: 061-237 9257

## Market Restaurant

Edge Street/104 High Street, M4 1HQ                                        COOKING 2
061-834 3743                                                              COST £22–£36

This aptly named place is in the lively old market area of Manchester, still dominated by the rag-trade. Here, you may buy the 'dukkah' salad topping – a spicy mixture here of groundnuts, other nuts in other places – used by the jar, so popular has it proved; likewise the marinated olives. There is a long-standing team here and it has hammered out a style all of its own: drawing on our own heritage (the Pudding Club), India and the Middle East (cf. the afore-mentioned dukkah) as well as a wider Europe. Reluctant to restrict customers to wine, the staff urge you to a choice of beers from a fine slate of Belgian and German examples – and will as readily cook carbonade à la flamande with Chimay beer as coq au vin with Beaujolais. But as many go for the Bury black pudding, the potted fish or the whitebait that may be offered at a special English evening of the Starters Society as for the remarkable whole-world range of the nightly menu. 'We always eat something different here, and it will be discussed intelligently by any of the team,' wrote one who likes the slightly bookish adventure of it all. 'It really is a winner,' he went on, disregarding the slightly spartan surroundings because it always comes up trumps. Vegetarians get a fair deal, children even fairer: this is a user-friendly establishment. The beers are more interesting than the wines, inasmuch as they are rarely found elsewhere. But prices for both are scrupulous; house wine is 'du patron' and £4.50 for a half-litre.

CHEFS: Mary-Rose Edgecombe, Paul Mertz and Dawn Wellens  PROPRIETORS: Peter O'Grady, Anne O'Grady and Mary-Rose Edgecombe  OPEN: Wed to Sat, D only (other times private parties by arrangement); 6 (7 Sat) to 9.30  CLOSED: 1 week Christmas, 1 week Easter, Aug  MEALS: alc (main courses £8 to £13)  SERVICE: not inc, card slips closed  CARDS: Access, Amex, Diners, Visa  DETAILS: 42 seats. Private parties: 42 main room, 28 private room. Vegetarian meals. Children welcome. Wheelchair access. Music. Air-conditioned

---

*The text of entries is based on unsolicited reports sent in by readers, backed up by inspections conducted anonymously. The factual details under the text are from questionnaires the* Guide *sends to all restaurants that feature in the book.*

## ▲ Moss Nook

Ringway Road, M22 5NA
061-437 4778
on B5166, 1m from Manchester         COOKING 3
Airport, M56 junction 5         COST £23–£66

'The most under-rated restaurant in the north-west – excellent standard, friendly service,' writes a supporter. The number of descriptions that come to the *Guide* of the surroundings of this restaurant make it an object of some interest. 'The food has to be good to compensate for the airport-wasteland-suburban location and the ex-show house architecture,' ventures one person who goes on to qualify this with 'The interior is more like a Mike Leigh movie-set of a French bordello than French restaurant.' If this sounds damning, it isn't. Nor are the comments about the food which itself shies away from the current fashions and tends to produce good examples of classic cooking. This may sometimes appear tedious, and it is then that people strike out for the multi-course menu surprise. When it starts with lamb bolognese tarts so good that 'we now do this at home for guests', the auguries are good. The menu may go on to salmon and brill with passion-fruit and honey sauce, or venison with sorrel sauce – all these in tiny portions, but maybe up to seven of them. The *carte* itself shows an enjoyment of sweetness and fruit, and sticks quite closely to prime cuts and relatively safe ideas. It is also highly priced but sets a standard that is most unlikely in such a location. The adequate, not overlong wine list shows most allegiance to the classic areas; New World wines are decent, but areas like the Rhône and Alsace are weakly represented. Italy is ignored. House wine is from £8.90.

CHEF: Kevin Lofthouse   PROPRIETORS: Pauline and Derek Harrison   OPEN: Tue to Sat, exc Sat L; 12 to 1.30, 7 to 9.30   CLOSED: 2 weeks Christmas   MEALS: alc (main courses £18 to £19). Set L £16.50, Set D £28   SERVICE: not inc, card slips closed   CARDS: Access, Amex, Diners, Visa   DETAILS: 65 seats. 6 tables outside. Private parties: 50 main room. Car park. Vegetarian meals. No children under 8. Smart dress preferred. No music
ACCOMMODATION: 1 room in cottage, with bath/shower. D,B&B £140. No children under 8. Garden. TV. Phone. Fax: 061-498 8089

## *Pearl City* £             **NEW ENTRY**

33 George Street, M1 4PH         COOKING 1*
061-228 7683         COST £10–£45

Pearl City may have a scruffy stairway approach, but the dining-room is acceptable at this Cantonese restaurant where the one-plate meals and dim-sum are especially recommended, and seafood has gained the most praise of all. Sesame-seed prawns with lemon sauce elicited the comment, 'I have rarely had fresher, tastier prawns than these, and though the sauce was rather sweet and jammy, the prawns were sufficiently good on their own for this not to matter.' Braised fish with mushroom and sliced brisket was another contender for the word 'outstanding', even if the char siu did not impress. But salt and pepper ribs make no concession to Western tastes and are as lip-numbing as they might be. House wines are £7.90.

CHEF/PROPRIETOR: Mr Cheung   OPEN: all week; noon to 2am (noon to midnight Sun)
MEALS: alc (main courses £6 to £19). Set L £4.50 to £7.50, Set D £15 to £25   SERVICE: 10%,
card slips closed   CARDS: Access, Amex, Visa   DETAILS: 500 seats. Vegetarian meals.
Children welcome. Smart dress preferred. Music. Air-conditioned. Fax: 061-237 9173

## Quan Ju De  £

| | |
|---|---|
| 44 Princess Street, M1 6DE | COOKING 1* |
| 061-236 5236 and 228 7270 | COST £11–£43 |

A resident pianist plays on most evenings in this swish city-centre restaurant,
which offers a creditable version of Peking cuisine in contrast to its mostly
Cantonese neighbours in Chinatown. The original Quan Ju De in Beijing
specialises in duck and this shows up strongly on the Manchester menu – not
only classic Peking duck, but in crispy duck wings, fried breast of spiced duck,
and stir-fried duck web with mange-tout. Some of the most interesting
specialities appear among the hot and cold appetisers: dry orange peel-
flavoured beef, marinated jellyfish, grilled prawns with rice wine, pan-fried
dumplings with ginger vinegar. Otherwise the repertoire moves between the
familiar and the esoteric for double-cooked pork and seafood hotpot to pot-
cooked shin of beef with mooli. Hot buffet lunches provide fair value for dishes
such as sweet-and-sour chicken, mixed vegetables and egg-fried rice. The
well-spread wine list is not overpriced and offers some appropriate drinking –
especially among the whites. Saké, bottled beers and tea are also available.
House wine is £8.20.

CHEF: Jian Ping Ma   PROPRIETOR: Hoo Man Lau   OPEN: all week; 12 to 2.15, 6 to 11
CLOSED: bank hols   MEALS: alc (main courses £6 to £12.50). Buffet L £4.80 to £9.50, Set D
£14.50 to £24.50   SERVICE: not inc; net prices set meals   CARDS: Access, Amex, Visa
DETAILS: 110 seats. Private parties: 85 main room, 40 private room. Vegetarian meals.
Children welcome. Smart dress preferred. No-smoking area. Music. Air-conditioned

£ *indicates that it is possible to have a three-course meal, including coffee, a half-bottle of*
*house wine and service, at any time the restaurant is open (i.e. at dinner as well as at*
*lunch, unless a place is open only for dinner), for £20 or less per person.*

*The 1995* Guide *will be published before Christmas 1994. Reports on meals are most*
*welcome at any time of the year, but are extremely valuable in the spring. Send them to*
The Good Food Guide, *FREEPOST, 2 Marylebone Road, London NW1 1YN. No stamp*
*is needed if posted in the UK.*

*Prices quoted in the* Guide *are based on information supplied by restaurateurs. The prices*
*quoted at the top of each entry represent a range, from the lowest meal price to the highest;*
*the latter is inflated by 20 per cent to take account of likely price rises during the year of*
*the* Guide.

*All details are as accurate as possible at the time of going to press, but chefs and owners*
*often change, and it is wise to check by telephone before making a special journey. Many*
*readers have been disappointed when set-price bargain meals are no longer available.*
*Ask when booking.*

## Siam Orchid £

54 Portland Street, M1 4QU
061-236 1388 and 9757

COOKING 1
COST £12–£41

This Thai restaurant is a prominent feature in Manchester's Chinatown. Opinions vary wildly on whether this or its sister restaurant, the Royal Orchid, is the better, but casual visitors have found some satisfaction with the Siam Orchid's Thai Muslim curry of chicken, heavy on coconut cream and with mild spicing, from a menu that seems more weighted with curries than those of most Thai restaurants. In part this impression comes from the fact that the menu has no transliterations. Other dishes endorsed have been beef with basil and chilli, king prawns with broccoli, and some of the noodle dishes. Set lunches are cheap, though not everyone has been so impressed. House wines start at £7.50.

CHEF: C. Sirisompan   PROPRIETORS: C. Sirisompan and K. Sirisambhand   OPEN: all week; 11.30 to 2.30, 6.30 (6 Fri) to 11.30 (11.30am to 11.30pm Sat, noon to 11pm Sun) CLOSED: bank hols, 25 Dec   MEALS: alc (main courses £6 to £9.50). Set L £5 (2 dishes) to £27, Set D £16 to £27   SERVICE: 10%   CARDS: Access, Amex, Visa   DETAILS: 60 seats. 14 tables outside. Private parties: 65 main room. Vegetarian meals. Children welcome. Smart dress preferred. Music. Air-conditioned. Fax: 061-236 8830

## Sonarga £

269–271 Barlowmoor Road,
Chorlton cum Hardy, M21 2GJ
061-861 0334 and 860 6363

NEW ENTRY

COOKING 1
COST £15–£38

'Three large windows framed by ritzy swagged curtains give Mancunians a clear view of their probable final resting place' is the lugubrious observation of someone who finds the curries here rather good, giving every reason to avoid pushing up the daisies prematurely: Sonarga faces Manchester's Southern Cemetery. The menu strikes a different note, even if there are familiar tandooris, bhunas and vindaloos. House specialities include things not always offered, such as 'beef mustard' (braised beef with English mustard) which must have links with the Raj, 'fish chop' (battered fish-cakes with chilli and parsley and a mint raita), and a satisfactory khas khas chicken, with green peppers, coriander and methi leaves. 'The food was full of fresh herbs, subtly hot and butter-rich' was one verdict. Breads have also been approved, though the vegetables, often one of the best things about Indian restaurants, have not seemed particularly full of impact. There is a one-page list of wines; house French is £8 a litre.

*The text of entries is based on unsolicited reports sent in by readers, backed up by inspections conducted anonymously. The factual details under the text are from questionnaires the* Guide *sends to all restaurants that feature in the book.*

*Restaurateurs justifiably resent no-shows. If you quote a credit card number when booking, you may be liable for the restaurant's lost profit margin if you don't turn up. Always phone to cancel.*

CHEFS: M.F. Haque and M. Khan    PROPRIETORS: M.F. Haque and M.M. Haque    OPEN: all week, D only; 5.30 (3.30 Sat) to midnight (12.30am Fri and Sat)    CLOSED: 25 and 26 Dec    MEALS: alc (main courses £4.50 to £10). Set D £15 (minimum 2)    SERVICE: not inc    CARDS: Access, Visa    DETAILS: 80 seats. Private parties: 80 main room. Car park. Vegetarian meals. Children welcome. Smart dress preferred. Wheelchair access (1 step; also WC). Music. Air-conditioned

## *That Café* £

|  |  |
|---|---|
| 1031 Stockport Road, Levenshulme, M19 2TB 061-432 4672 | COOKING 1 COST £17–£35 |

The Café is situated in a pair of converted shops and stands out like a beacon in this part of suburban Manchester. Redecoration has given the dining-room a 'classier' feel, but it has lost none of its delightfully idiosyncratic atmosphere with its wooden floors and closely packed tables. Everyone seems to love the jumble of old teapots, plants and pictures which are cluttered about the place. Meals are excellent value, and you can choose from one of the set menus or opt for the monthly *carte*. The repertoire is 'enticing', fish is fresh each day and the kitchen takes vegetarianism in its stride. Deep green spinach soup with chunky bread is often mentioned; other recommendations have included salmon kedgeree, lamb en croûte, chicken breast stuffed with asparagus, and chestnut and vegetable strudel in filo pastry. Vegetables are good and fresh. Puddings have included 'superb' raspberry pavlova as well as apple crumble with vanilla custard. The staff manage to balance unobtrusiveness with charm and efficiency. Around two dozen well-spread wines will not break the bank. House wine is £6.95.

CHEF/PROPRIETOR: Joe Quinn    OPEN: Mon to Sat, D only, and Sun L; 12 to 3, 7 to 10.30    CLOSED: 1 week Jan, 1 week Aug    MEALS: alc (main courses £8 to £13). Set Sun L £10.95, Set D Mon to Thur £12.95    SERVICE: not inc    CARDS: Access, Amex, Visa    DETAILS: 80 seats. Private parties: 55 main room, 35 private room. Vegetarian meals. Children's helpings. Wheelchair access (1 step). Music

## ▲ *Woodlands*

|  |  |
|---|---|
| 33 Shepley Road, Audenshaw, M34 5DL 061-336 4241 | COOKING 2* COST £23–£38 |

The realism that has suffused the British catering industry recently has had its effect on Woodlands, a pleasing red-brick suburban villa on the outskirts of Manchester, where some prices seem to have come down, not gone up. There have been no reports of a parallel slippage in the service, the welcome or William Jackson's steady cooking. A menu that was once bilingual has gone native, shedding the French version, though not the largely French influence; a repertoire that was familiar with the odd luxury item has perhaps trimmed its extravagance to match the more sensible prices. A competent technique is plain for all to witness: instances are seen in the taste for wrapping things such as fillets of trout or a sandwich of brill and salmon, and an enjoyment of stuffings, such as avocado mousse in chicken breast or apricot and thyme in lamb.

Reporters have enjoyed no less than six different vegetables served in crescent-shaped dishes that accompanied the main course, and a light sticky toffee pudding was strongly recommended in a contest with a brandy-snap basket filled with coffee cream and home-made ice-cream. The short, almost wholly French and German wine list holds some good names, few surprises and acceptable prices. House French is £8.25.

CHEF: William Jackson  PROPRIETORS: Mr and Mrs Dennis Crank  OPEN: Tue to Sat, exc Sat L; 12 to 2, 7 to 9.30 (10 Sat)  CLOSED: 1 week after Christmas, 1 week at Easter, 2 weeks mid-Aug  MEALS: alc. Set L and D £15.65 (exc Sat D)  SERVICE: not inc, card slips closed CARDS: Access, Visa  DETAILS: 38 seats. Private parties: 22 main room, 17 private room. Car park. Vegetarian meals on request. Children's helpings. No children under 10 D. Smart dress preferred. No cigars/pipes in dining-room. Wheelchair access (3 steps; also WC). Music  ACCOMMODATION: 3 rooms, all with bath/shower. Rooms for disabled. B&B £40 to £60. Children welcome. Baby facilities. Garden. TV. Phone

## Yang Sing £

34 Princess Street, M1 4JY     COOKING 2
061-236 2200     COST £16–£37

A knowledgeable student of the Manchester Chinese scene considers that the Yang Sing wears two different hats. At lunch-time it delivers probably the finest selection of dim-sum in the land (especially on Sunday, when families pack in and special dishes are on offer). But the weekly selection is mightily impressive and few items are less than excellent: woo kok (yam croquettes), thin wrapped prawns in rice paper, fish-cakes with coriander, shredded duck-meat roll and 'definitive' bat col sui mai (steamed Chinese mushroom with meatball) are regularly cited. The full menu is a massive tome with traditional Cantonese specialities looming large. Harry Yeung is a chef who can handle goose webs, ducks' tongues, chickens' feet, jellyfish and sea slug with dexterity, but can also conjure up new-wave dishes such as stuffed steak roll in black pepper sauce. Diners have enjoyed duck in black-bean sauce, beef with ginger and spring onion, prawns with chilli and salt, and king prawns with cashews and broccoli. One-plate rice and noodle dishes are gargantuan affairs. The place is invariably full and queues are frequent even though there are now two dining-rooms (one on the ground floor, another in the basement). A short wine list offers a decent selection of bottles appropriate to the food. House wines start at £8.40

CHEF: Harry Yeung  PROPRIETORS: Yang Sing Restaurant Ltd  OPEN: all week; noon to 11.30  CLOSED: 25 Dec  MEALS: alc (main courses £6 to £9). Set L and D £13.25 (minimum 2)  SERVICE: 10%  CARDS: Access, Amex, Visa  DETAILS: 140 seats. Private parties: 200 main room, 30 and 70 private rooms. Vegetarian meals. Children welcome. Smart dress preferred. Wheelchair access (via goods lift). Music. Air-conditioned. Fax: 061-236 5934

*All letters to the* Guide *are acknowledged with an update on latest sales, closures, chef changes and so on.*

*All entries in the* Guide *are rewritten every year, not least because restaurant standards fluctuate. Don't trust an out-of-date* Guide.

---

**MANNINGTREE** Essex                                                    map 3

## Stour Bay Café ⁙*

39–43 High Street,
Manningtree CO11 1AH                                          COOKING 1
COLCHESTER (0206) 396687                                     COST £21–£35

'Beautiful building, superb menu – I felt I could have chosen with a pin' was
the initial reaction to this unlikely outpost of Californian cooking deep in
Essex. It must keep the Department of American Studies at the nearby
university from falling homesick. Though Sherri Singleton, the American half
of the partnership, manages to offer dishes such as chargrilled rib steak with
tobacco onions and caramelised onion butter, and beer and black-bean chilli
with tomato salsa, as well as a raft of daily fish that adds plenty of variety to the
slate, there is not always a capacity to live up to the promise of the menu:
dishes have been on occasions 'tepid', 'lacking in taste', and pastry has been
unsatisfactory. The short wine list is entirely New World and includes an aged
Mondavi Cabernet Sauvignon, Australians from Henschke, and the remarkable
Mark West Gewurztraminer from Russian River Valley. House wines are Fetzer
from £8.35.

CHEF: Sherri Singleton   PROPRIETORS: David McKay and Sherri Singleton   OPEN: Tue to
Sun, exc Sun D; 12 to 2.15, 7 to 9.30 (10 Sat)   MEALS: alc (main courses £8.50 to £13)
SERVICE: not inc   CARDS: Access, Amex, Visa   DETAILS: 75 seats. Private parties: 60 main
room, 15 private room. Vegetarian meals. Children's helpings. No smoking in 1 dining-
room. Wheelchair access. Music. Fax: (0206) 395462

---

**MARSTON MORETAINE** Bedfordshire                                       map 3

## Moreteyne Manor

Woburn Road,
Marston Moretaine MK43 0NG                                   COOKING 2*
BEDFORD (0234) 767003                                        COST £26–£60

Keep your eyes peeled for the 'very small sign which is easy to miss,' warns a
visitor. Expect a quirky, off-beat experience in Jeremy Blake O'Connor's
kingdom, where booking is essential. You are likely to be greeted by the man
himself, regaled with stories and conversation, even used as 'guinea-pigs' for
new culinary ideas. After the fire of 1992, the fifteenth-century moated manor
house seems to have regained most of its vigour. The interior is all genuine
beams, cool pale-blue colour schemes and handsome flower arrangements –
although one observer felt the place needed 'a woman's touch'. O'Connor
cooks with gusto and serves up massive portions ('not for the faint-hearted,'
commented one diner who ate alone at lunch-time). A variety of menus,
changed weekly, are rooted in the French tradition, with influences from the
Mediterannean and the Orient grafted on as inspiration. Calf's liver with
Cassis and blackcurrant vinegar sauce, rack of local lamb with herb juice and
ratatouille of vegetables, fillets of red mullet and daurade with celery and
fennel on a basil and tomato coulis, and chocolate marquise with home-made
caramel ice-cream are typical of the repertoire. Reporters have been impressed

by chicken liver mousse with cognac and sultanas, fillet of beef in a 'basket' of crisp cabbage, and brandy-snap basket of red fruits. The wine list was about to be revamped as we went to press, but it is certain to be keenly chosen. House wines start at £10.50.

CHEF: Jeremy Blake O'Connor  PROPRIETORS: Pridelocal Ltd  OPEN: Tue to Sun, exc Sun D (Sun D and Mon by arrangement for parties); 12.15 to 2, 7.15 to 9.45  CLOSED: first week Jan  MEALS: Set L £12 (2 courses) to £18.50, Set D £22.50 (Tue to Fri only) to £40 SERVICE: not inc, card slips closed  CARDS: Access, Amex, Visa  DETAILS: 70 seats. 5 tables outside. Private parties: 30 main room, 20 and 80 private rooms. Car park. Vegetarian meals. Children's helpings. Smart dress preferred. No cigars/pipes in dining-room. Wheelchair access (also WC). Music. Fax: (0234) 765382

---

**MARY TAVY Devon**                                                         map 1

## ▲ *Stannary* 🍴

Mary Tavy PL19 9QB
MARY TAVY (0822) 810897
on A386 Tavistock to Okehampton                              COOKING 1
road, 4m NE of Tavistock                                     COST £37–£52

Those who went vegetarian because it was cheaper are in for a shock at this handsome restaurant-with-rooms (which the owners describe as 'part-sixteenth-century and part-Victorian'). Prices are kept high for the extended-choice but fixed-price dinner menus – justifiably so, many will maintain, for Alison Fife's cooking is skilled and dedicated, and the quality of materials and the work required to garner them are impressive. The food avoids the stodge and heavyweight flavours of much vegetarian cooking and uses ingredients intelligently to provide seasoning and balance and reduce reliance on sugar and salt. Examples of such dishes might be figgy con chilli, where figs marinated in blackberry wine are served with beans and vegetables and a thick chilli sauce, or pistachio pie, in which the nuts are bound with a pesto mix flavoured with bay leaves in a wholemeal cheese pastry. The sauce in this instance is a gravy infused with vanilla. Many people get worked up at the prospect of dessert, and the owners are enthusiasts for teas and coffees. The wine list shows the enthusiasm again, with bins marked vegetarian and organic where applicable. The range is impressive, with some high-grade classic makers as well as English and New World choices. House wines are £9.20.

CHEF: Alison Fife  PROPRIETORS: Michael Cook and Alison Fife  OPEN: Tue to Sat, D only (by arrangement winter for non-residents); 7 to 9.30  MEALS: Set D £24 (2 courses) to £35  SERVICE: not inc, card slips closed  CARDS: Access, Visa (4% surcharge)  DETAILS: 20 seats. 4 tables outside. Private parties: 50 main room. Car park. Vegetarian meals only. Healthy eating options. No children under 12. Smart dress preferred. No smoking in dining-room. Music  ACCOMMODATION: 4 rooms, 1 with bath/shower. D,B&B £70 to £120. Deposit: £20. No children under 12. Garden. TV. Doors close at midnight. Confirm by 6. Fax: (0822) 810898

---

▲ *This symbol means accommodation is available.*

---

| MASHAM North Yorkshire | map 7 |
|---|---|

## *Floodlite* ✦ £

| 7 Silver Street, Masham HG4 4DX | |
|---|---|
| RIPON (0765) 689000 | COOKING 3 |
| off A6108, 9m N of Ripon | COST £15–£40 |

'Floodlit it is not,' punned one visitor, referring to this restaurant's maroon bistro-style exterior and modest interior, 'more like a special front room only used for guests.' But tables are spacious, linen is starched, flowers are fresh – and anyway, most are here to enjoy simple, sound dishes at keen prices (super-keen at Sunday lunch). It remains a 'something-for-everyone' sort of menu, though game-lovers are particularly well cared for: hare terrine contained discernible chunks of flesh, and was 'gamey but not overstrong'; grouse was good if a little unmanageable (since uncarved and served whole); and roast hare with wild mushrooms 'was perfectly cooked with an excellent rich dark sauce'. Asparagus comes with an unfussy hollandaise; wonderful king scallops ('best I have tasted') were cooked with ginger and spring onions and served in a cream sauce; salmon is fresh, bone-free, flavoursome and 'beautifully cooked'. The fruited bread-and-butter puddings are much applauded, and tarts are all they should be: lemon tart, for example, had 'crisp short-crust pastry and a thick lemony filling with strips of lemon rind mixed in', and apple and almond tart was neatly fashioned and served with an 'excellent (not too sweet) butterscotch sauce'. Generosity is in evidence with offers of more vegetables and endless coffee refills, and service is friendly if sometimes stretched. There is a sound, short wine list. House wines are £7.50, though spending a little more will bring a lot more flavour.

CHEF: Charles Flood   PROPRIETORS: Charles and Christine Flood   OPEN: Tue to Sun D, Fri to Sun L (other days by arrangement); 12 to 2, 7 to 9.30   CLOSED: 3 weeks Jan   MEALS: alc (main courses £8.50 to £16.50). Set Sun L £9.50   SERVICE: not inc, card slips closed   CARDS: Access, Visa   DETAILS: 36 seats. Private parties: 28 main room, 10 private room. Vegetarian meals. Children's helpings. Smart dress preferred. No smoking in 1 dining-room. Wheelchair access (2 steps). Music

| MATLOCK Derbyshire | map 5 |
|---|---|

## ▲ *Riber Hall*

| Matlock DE4 5JU | |
|---|---|
| MATLOCK (0629) 582795 | COOKING 2 |
| 1m off A615 at Tansley | COST £24–£46 |

One scarred reporter observed that the shaving mirror was only useful if you climbed on the washbasin, but, having completed his ablutions by touch, he was happy enough with the dinner that awaited him. Riber Hall is atmospheric ('my room was a trifle dark') but immaculate. The Elizabethan manor house – all small stone courts, mullions and gables – is perched high above Matlock, well out of day-trippers' reach. The cooking remains 'country house' and so do the prices, but few grumbles are heard about value. A parcel of smoked trout mousse wrapped in smoked salmon with a herb yogurt sauce or ravioli of wild mushrooms with a madeira cream are two first courses that exemplify the light yet conventional approach. A fillet of salmon with oyster mushrooms and a sherry and basil cream, and a trio of grilled fish with a Riesling sauce and a charlotte of prawns and baby vegetables are a pair of main courses that had one weekend visitor reaching for superlatives. Vegetarians have also reported well of their treatment – a mushroom soufflé and a nut ('to the fore') quiche were fully approved. Pastry work is good – better than the sorbets – and the trimmings are well cared for. This is a place that knows its market and nurtures it. The wine list provides solid grounding, with a few flights to the financial heavens. Choice all round is pukka, from the petits châteaux to makers such as Brocard in Chablis, Millérioux in Sancerre, Cloudy Bay in New Zealand and Oak Knoll in Oregon. House wines are £10.80 for Villa Montes wines from Chile.

CHEF: Jeremy Brazelle  PROPRIETORS: Alex and Gill Biggin  OPEN: all week; 12 to 1.30, 7 to 9.30  MEALS: alc (main courses £13 to £17). Set L £14.50 to £20  SERVICE: not inc, card slips closed  CARDS: Access, Amex, Diners, Visa  DETAILS: 50 seats. Private parties: 34 main room, 16 and 34 private rooms. Car park. Vegetarian meals. Children's helpings. No children under 12 D. Smart dress preferred. No music  ACCOMMODATION: 11 rooms, all with bath/shower. B&B £78 to £137. Deposit: £35. No children under 12 D. Afternoon teas. Garden. Tennis. TV. Phone. Doors close at 11. Fax: (0629) 580475 (*The Which? Hotel Guide*)

---

MAWGAN Cornwall                                                        map 1

## Yard Bistro  £

Trelowarren, Mawgan TR12 6AF
MAWGAN (0326) 22595                                           COOKING 1
off B3293, 3m SE of Helston                                  COST £18–£30

The setting is a converted carriage house in the stable yard of Trelowarren Manor, and it has been lovingly nurtured by the Vyvyan family over the years. At lunch-time it is a café pure and simple, with a cheap, colourful menu taking in the likes of Cornish seafood broth, chicken liver rillettes, stir-fried tofu, lamb 'cobbler', grilled goats' cheese salad, and rhubarb and apple crumble. According to one satisfied reporter, this was 'so good that we returned for dinner the next night and again the following night'. The evening menu moves up a gear for bistro-style dishes such as twice-baked crab soufflé with tomato and chive dressing, warm salad of stir-fried oysters and chillies, roast breast of chicken with ravioli of calabrese, and paupiette of pork stuffed with brandied prunes. Ingredients are fresh, the cooking is exact and the welcome is warm. The short wine list has been put together with an eye on quality and price. House wines are £7.50.

CHEF: Trevor Bayfield  PROPRIETOR: Ferrers Vyvyan  OPEN: Tue to Sun, exc D Sun and Tue (also Mon bank hols and high season); 12 to 2, 7 to 9 (9.30 Fri and Sat high season) CLOSED: Jan, Feb  MEALS: alc (main courses £7 to £11). Light L menu  SERVICE: not inc CARDS: Access, Diners, Visa  DETAILS: 50 seats. 6 tables outside. Private parties: 70 main room. Car park. Vegetarian meals. Children's helpings. Wheelchair access (also WC). Music

---

MAWNAN SMITH Cornwall  map 1

## ▲ *Nansidwell Country House*

---

Mawnan Smith TR11 5HU
FALMOUTH (0326) 250340
off A394 Helston road, take                                    COOKING 2
left fork at Red Lion in village                               COST £22–£51

---

You can see the sea 'even on a foggy anticyclonic February day' from this
Edwardian mansion built at the head of a small valley looking out towards
Falmouth Bay. In winter any fog outside is amply combatted by blazing logs,
expressive decoration, handsome pictures and a good collection of hanging
plates for the antiquarian-minded. 'The whole "bit" is better than the cooking'
was a comment that intended no disrespect to Tony Allcott's work, which is
offered to guests as a daily set-price menu, with a *carte* tacked to one side
offering a further set of choices at a supplement. Without breaking the bounds
of convention, there is a lightness of touch that pleases in dishes such as
kidneys with a mustard sauce, stir-fried king prawns with ginger and red
pepper, fillets of red mullet with strips of root vegetables, and breast of chicken
with prawns and a mild curry sauce. The home-smoker is used to good,
sometimes strong, effect with salmon, fish, chicken and bacon. This settled
version of 'modern British' cooking has many successes, not least the pan-fried
bananas with lemon sabayon and baby figs. Service, just like the flowers, the
welcome and the ambience, is cheerful and appreciated. The wine list is not as
long as customary country-house offerings. It is not badly chosen, however, or
overpriced. House wines start at £10.

---

CHEF: Tony Allcott  PROPRIETORS: Jamie and Felicity Robertson  OPEN: all week; 12.30 to
1.45, 7 to 9  CLOSED: Jan  MEALS: Set L £14.75, Set D £20 to £23  SERVICE: not inc
CARDS: Access, Visa  DETAILS: 38 seats. Private parties: 70 main room. Car park.
Vegetarian meals. Children's helpings with prior notice. No children under 8 D. Smart
dress preferred. No cigars/pipes in dining-room. Wheelchair access. No music
ACCOMMODATION: 12 rooms, all with bath/shower. Rooms for disabled. D,B&B £90 to
£186. Deposit: £100. Children welcome. Pets welcome. Garden. Tennis. TV. Phone. Fax:
(0326) 250440 (*The Which? Hotel Guide*)

---

MELBOURN Cambridgeshire  map 3

## *Pink Geranium* 🍴✖    | NEW ENTRY |

---

Station Road, Melbourn SG8 6DX
ROYSTON (0763) 260215                                          COOKING 2
just off A10, 2m N of Royston                                  COST £25–£63

---

'Our restaurant has been visited frequently by royalty and many celebrities
including Cabinet Ministers,' states the menu of this pink, pink, pink cottage
plus conservatory that has been cleverly converted to hold lots of people, yet
never seems too crowded. Perhaps that is the reason for the surprising prices.
'This seems to be in the gin 'n' Jag belt, so late arrival at the car park will leave
you no room' was one slightly bitter remark from a reader otherwise impressed
by the technical deftness of the cooking. His meal took in a perfectly risen
soufflé of shiitake mushrooms, scallops and a mousseline sauce that could not

have been faulted for timing, and a brilliant almond tart and palmiers that could rank with the best. These come from a menu that rings bells of recognition for people whose experience was founded in the '70s. Adventurous it is not, but nor is it unskilled. A problem, for instance in that soufflé, or in the vegetables, is that seasoning may be forgotten in the rush. Tastes, therefore, can be muted. All is not always so smooth, especially considering the cost. Fortunately, wine prices are not so steeply calculated, and the selection is 'up to date with world events and top producers'. Quality is spread throughout, so choice may be difficult. House wine is £10.95.

CHEF: Steven Saunders   PROPRIETORS: Mr and Mrs Steven Saunders   OPEN: Tue to Sun, exc Sat L and Sun D; 12 to 2.30, 7 to 10   MEALS: alc (main courses £14 to £20). Set L £14.95 (2 courses) to £17.95, Set D £24.95   SERVICE: not inc   CARDS: Access, Amex, Visa DETAILS: 70 seats. Private parties: 30 main room, 16 private room. Car park. Vegetarian meals. Children's helpings. No smoking in dining-room. Wheelchair access (1 step). Music. Fax: (0763) 262110

---

**MELKSHAM** Wiltshire                                                                          map 2

▲ *Toxique* ⁵✳

187 Woodrow Road, Melksham SN12 7AY                                       COOKING 2
MELKSHAM (0225) 702129                                                           COST £23–£38

*(badge: COUNTY OF THE YEAR RESTAURANT)*

At Melksham's town-centre roundabout take the Calne road for a third of a mile, turn left into Forest Road and, down on the left, you will find eventually a garden, a farmhouse and a seriously wild interior. Such is the mixture, and no one finds it poisonous. A plum and dark-blue colour scheme, pine-cone cornice, flower-pots that double as candle-holders, table-top moss gardens and a 'particularly appealing painting of a banana' are but some of the features. The venture is a relaxed conjunction of architect and dress designer, some explanation at least of the setting, but people also approve how the sense of adventure carries through to the cooking. Galingale, saffron, lemon grass, coriander, basil, chilli, ginger and sage are some of the flavourings listed in a single spring menu, so the presumption of a catholic, relaxed approach to what tastes good may be assumed. And if a meal that took in a salad of marinated duck with rösti and toasted pine-kernels, venison with juniper and port sauce served with lentils and spring greens, then a Toxique cassata can be taken as typical, then it is worth pursuing Helen Bartlett's tastes. The bedrooms are as characterful as the restaurant. The wine list is soundly based and fairly priced. Ochoa's Tempranillo, Happ's Vineyard's Cabernet Sauvignon/Merlot, Firestone's Cabernet Sauvignon and Mathias' Pouilly-Fuissé are decent names from a range that dots all over the world leaving space for but four clarets. House wines are £9.50.

CHEF: Helen Bartlett   PROPRIETORS: Peter Jewkes and Helen Bartlett   OPEN: Wed to Sat, D only, and Sun L (Wed to Fri L by arrangement); 12.30 to 2, 7 to 10   MEALS: Set L £13.50 (2 courses) to £16.50, Set D £24   SERVICE: not inc, card slips closed   CARDS: Access, Visa DETAILS: 40 seats. 5 tables outside. Private parties: 24 main room, 24 private room. Car park. Vegetarian meals. Children's helpings. Smart dress preferred. No smoking in dining-room. Wheelchair access (1 step). Music   ACCOMMODATION: 4 rooms, all with bath. B&B £50 to £80. Children welcome. Baby facilities. Garden (*The Which? Hotel Guide*)

MELMERBY Cumbria                                                                map 7

## Village Bakery ✝✱ £

Melmerby CA10 1HE
LANGWATHBY (0768) 881515                                          COOKING 1
on A686, between Penrith and Alston                              COST £15–£22

Andrew and Lis Whitley's remarkable village bakery is an ecologically minded
system in full swing. Organic flour comes from the local watermill at Little
Salkeld, as well as from Shipton Mill; a five-acre smallholding provides
organic produce for the kitchen; but the set-up revolves around the wood-fired
brick oven. A daytime business, emphatically committed to wholesome natural
food, the Bakery does not promise high cuisine, but is in a different league to
the 'pick and shovel' school of wholefood cookery. Breakfast brings raspberry
porridge, oak-smoked kippers, Cumberland sausage sandwiches and chocolate
croissants, not to mention mighty carnivorous *and* vegetarian fry-ups.
Substantial lunches feature home-made soups, jugged rabbit, tomato tart,
North Country cheeses and sweet Cumberland Rum Nicky. Afternoon tea
sounds tempting. Freshly squeezed orange juice, scented teas, organic cider,
beers and lagers back up the short organically biased wine list. House wine
is £6.40.

CHEF: Diane Richter  PROPRIETORS: Andrew and Lis Whitley  OPEN: all week, daytime
only; 8.30am (9.30 Sun) to 5pm  CLOSED: 8.30am to 2.30pm Jan and Feb  MEALS: alc
(main courses £5.50 to £7)  SERVICE: not inc  CARDS: Access, Diners, Visa  DETAILS: 40
seats. Private parties: 25 main room. Car park. Vegetarian meals. Children's helpings. No
smoking in dining-room. Wheelchair access (1 step). No music. Fax: (0768) 881848

MERLEY Dorset                                                                   map 2

## Les Bouviers ✝✱                                            [ NEW ENTRY ]

Oakley Hill, Merley,
nr Wimborne BH21 1RJ                                              COOKING 1*
WIMBORNE (0202) 889555                                            COST £18–£54

Though the address proclaims this place to be near Wimborne, memories of
country are buried beneath several layers of sub-suburbia. The location may
explain some of the style of the place. James Coward is a talented chef, an
inveterate entrant of competitions and a cup winner. His restaurant manager
also picked up the gold medal for napkin folding at the 1993 Bournemouth
International Culinary Festival. A background in haute cuisine, French at that,
leaks into a menu that is an impossibly complicated read: each dish gets four
lines of bilingual description. The end result may be as elaborate as its
announcement. That does not mean, however, that it is bad, just that
simplification would sometimes help, in the same way that a less fussy
approach to decoration and furnishings might increase the impact. The fashions
pursued closely reflect those of a few years ago: meat is often partnered with
fruit, though not always as sweetly as chicken breast stuffed with mango; there
is a complementary sorbet after the main course; tomato decorations abound.
Yet something like a pigeon with red wine and juniper sauce and a garnish of

pearls of beetroot was excellent, so was an oval platter (for fish) with seared scallops with ginger (light to undetectable) finished with a vermouth and saffron sauce. A dessert of blackcurrant mousse on a lemon curd sauce was brilliant, and ice-creams and sorbets have impressed. The wine list will do very well for a start, and the bottle of Haut Brion 1970 at £55 is a bargain.

CHEF/PROPRIETOR: James Coward  OPEN: all week, exc Sat L and Sun D; 12 to 2 (2.30 Sun), 7 to 10  MEALS: alc (main courses £13 to £17.50). Set L £8.95 (2 courses) to £16.75, Set D £19.95  SERVICE: not inc, card slips closed  CARDS: Access, Amex, Visa  DETAILS: 50 seats. Private parties: 50 main room, 12 private room. Car park. Vegetarian meals. Children's helpings. Smart dress preferred. No smoking in 1 dining-room. Music. Air-conditioned

---

**MIDDLE WALLOP  Hampshire**                                              map 2

## ▲ *Fifehead Manor*

Middle Wallop SO20 8EG                                            COOKING 2*
ANDOVER (0264) 781565                                          COST £24–£42

The restaurant in this imposing hotel set in spacious grounds continues serenely on its way, continuing to surprise and please by its consistency: one reporter, on five separate occasions, found standards 'never less than excellent'. Simplicity, tellingly, is not scorned here: chicken liver parfait with toasted brioche is smooth and distinctively flavoured; roast loin of lamb with tarragon draws very complimentary remarks. A provençale vegetable soup with saffron mayonnaise was 'hot and spicy with all the flavours shining through', and guinea-fowl in lemon and garlic sauce showed the same adaptive intelligence at work on Mediterranean themes. Yet old England lives on, too, in Middle Wallop: Scottish beef sirloin with Yorkshire puddings and a port sauce, pork fillet in a caraway beer sauce with herby dumplings, or variations on a theme of duck with capers furnish the proof. Pear mincemeat and hazelnut tart with poire William cream was 'warm and light', while the lemon bavarois with raspberry sauce succeeded admirably. The wine list draws deeply on France. Prices are modest, and the range (founded on sound, middle-ground négoçiants like Labouré-Roi and Delas Frères) is fair. House wines, sensibly, are French country wines at £8.50.

CHEF: Mark Robertson  PROPRIETOR: Margaret Van Veelen  OPEN: all week; 12.30 to 2, 7 to 9.30 (10 summer)  MEALS: alc (main courses £12.50 to £16). Set L £17.50, Set D £24 SERVICE: not inc  CARDS: Access, Amex, Diners, Visa  DETAILS: 40 seats. 4 tables outside. Private parties: 40 main room, 14 and 20 private rooms. Car park. Vegetarian meals. Children's helpings. Wheelchair access (also WC). No music  ACCOMMODATION: 16 rooms, all with bath/shower. Rooms for disabled. B&B £50 to £95. Children welcome. Baby facilities. Pets welcome. Afternoon teas. Garden. TV. Phone. Doors close at 11. Fax: (0264) 781400 (*The Which? Hotel Guide*)

---

'We were driving a new ''K''-reg car and wanted to keep an eye on it, so we sat in the café window. For about seven minutes, four youths eyed the car, but an independent, unshaven cigarette-smoking gent was the first to try the door. We left our tea, quite quickly.'
On eating in Scotland

---

MIDHURST West Sussex map 3

## ▲ *Angel Hotel* 🍷

North Street, Midhurst GU29 9DN COOKING 2*
MIDHURST (0730) 812421 COST £21–£45

Peter Crawford-Rolt converted this eighteenth-century hotel on Midhurst's broad main street at double-quick speed. The result is handsome, in keeping and comfortable. The level of welcome is a comfort, too, with no hint of false proprieties or mad convention, just a wish that people enjoy themselves. The main restaurant occupies a large room with a charcoal grill stretched altar-like across one end. A small brasserie – with some emphasis on shellfish when the boats come in – hinges on the bar. The menus to both places are quite long, developing every day, and do not show unhealthy reliance on grilling as might be inferred from the set-up. Spices are added enjoyably: try black pudding with spinach and a Creole sauce, or a vegetarian dish of aubergine and pimento with spiced lentils, or half a lobster served with a caponata. When on form, the cooking is expressive. It can sometimes be more complicated (not to good effect) than expected, but dishes such as skate with caper sauce, grilled rib steak, marinated anchovies with avocado and prawns, or a warm salad of lamb's kidney with bacon and croûtons have shown much skill in handling simpler elements. Choose mango cheek with coconut ice-cream over any of the other sweets. The hotel is a good place to stay at, tempering luxury to cost without a sense of penny-pinching. The wine list has a feeling of the temporary, which is no bad sign; it can show not inefficiency but enthusiasm. A rather random house selection and no apparent mention of the house wines, however, do not put the customer at ease. But the wines lack neither interest nor quality, with a well-aged 1979 Léon Cabernet and the excellent Alsace of Rolly-Gassmann. House wines are £9.25. CELLARMAN'S CHOICE: Tuscany, Bianco, 1991, Avignonesi, £17; Chile, Los Vasos, Cabernet Sauvignon 1986, £12.50.

CHEF: Peter Crawford-Rolt PROPRIETORS: Peter Crawford-Rolt and Nicholas Davies
OPEN: restaurant all week; 12 to 2.30, 7 to 9.30 (10 Fri and Sat). Brasserie all week; 12 to 2.30, 6.30 to 10 MEALS: alc (main courses £8 to £12.50). Set L £13.50 to £14.50, Set L brasserie £16.50 SERVICE: not inc, card slips closed CARDS: Access, Amex, Diners, Visa
DETAILS: 100 seats. 6 tables outside. Private parties: 90 main room, 40 and 80 private rooms. Car park. Vegetarian meals. Children's helpings on request. Smart dress preferred restaurant. No cigars/pipes in dining-room. Wheelchair access (also WC). Music brasserie
ACCOMMODATION: 17 rooms, all with bath/shower. B&B £50 to £105. Deposit: 50%. Children welcome. Baby facilities. Afternoon teas. Garden. TV. Phone. Doors close at midnight. Confirm by 6. Fax: (0730) 815928 (*The Which? Hotel Guide*)

## *Maxine's*

Red Lion Street, Midhurst GU29 9PB COOKING 2
MIDHURST (0730) 816271 COST £17–£38

'When I checked on the number of visits in the last 12 months (30), I was amused to see we were within one of the previous year. So [here are] two customers as consistent as the proprietors' cooking and service.' The reporters in question use the de Jagers' restaurant as a local home from home. Others, from further afield, are also happy to endorse its virtues. Maxine's is a modest establishment in a half-timbered house next to the Swan Inn in mid-Midhurst; it offers excellent value for money, especially in its set menus. The bedrock of the repertoire seldom changes, although specials are regularly available and there is always a daily fish dish. Baked monkfish with thyme and honey, lambs' sweetbreads with mushrooms in white wine sauce, and fillet of lamb with madeira typify the kitchen's output. Sunday lunch is well reported – a fine roast flanked by spicy Singapore salad and 'featherlight' hot treacle pudding. Marti de Jager's qualities as a thoughtful, attentive hostess are never in doubt and are one of the enduring attractions of the place. The 50-strong wine list centres on France, with a few forays into the New World. Prices are fair, with plenty of very acceptable drinking to be had for under £15. House wine is £7.95.

CHEF: Robert de Jager  PROPRIETORS: Robert and Marti de Jager  OPEN: Wed to Sun, exc Sun D; 12 to 1.30, 7 to 9.30  MEALS: alc (main courses £9 to £16.50). Set L and D £11.95, exc Sat D  SERVICE: net prices, card slips closed  CARDS: Access, Visa  DETAILS: 24 seats. Private parties: 30 main room. Vegetarian meals. Children's helpings. No smoking during meals. No music

MILFORD ON SEA  Hampshire                                            map 2

## Rocher's

69–71 High Street,
Milford on Sea SO41 0QG
LYMINGTON (0590) 642340
on B3058, 3m SW of Lymington

COOKING 3
COST £20–£39

'I like this place. True, it's simple. True, it's cheap. However, the *tastiness* of the food is wonderful. It's not fussy, but classical French,' wrote one reader: several reasons, then, for recommendation. Most people also hasten to add to these Rebecca Rocher's enthusiastic description of the dishes on the menu, and her unfussed but warm hospitality. The cost is not dear, particularly at lunch, and though the setting is no more than a converted former shop in the centre of the village, the place performs its function admirably; refurbishment has given it a certain gloss. Eggs florentine, gazpacho, Charentais melon with Cassis, feuilleté of mushroom with garlic: these are mainstream French first courses. Main dishes spotlight a single prime ingredient, plus a sauce. Indeed, sauces are what catch the attention – the complexities of 'old' nouvelle or the jumbles of some new-wave cooking are not found here; nor, on the whole, is much offal. Desserts major on crèmes brûlées – listed as 'of the day', these are perhaps coffee and whisky-flavoured, or fruit-based – but people also speak kindly of the lemon tart and the sorbets. The wine list has a good section on the Loire (Alain Rocher hails from thence), but its clarets are better than ever with a useful choice of *crus bourgeois* (and none-too-wayward prices). France is the subject; the New World is excluded. House wines start at £8.50.

*A report form is at the back of the book; write a letter if you prefer.*

CHEF: Alain Rocher   PROPRIETORS: Alain and Rebecca Rocher   OPEN: Wed to Sat and Sun bank hols, D only, and Sun L (parties other times by arrangement); 12.15 to 1.30, 7 to 9.30   CLOSED: first 2 weeks June   MEALS: Set L £13.50, Set D £16.50 (Wed to Fri) to £21.90   SERVICE: not inc, card slips closed   CARDS: Access, Visa   DETAILS: 30 seats. Private parties: 30 main room. Vegetarian meals with prior notice. No children under 10 L, under 13 D. Smart dress preferred. No cigars/pipes in dining-room. Wheelchair access. No music

---

## MOLLINGTON Cheshire
map 5

## ▲ *Crabwall Manor*

Parkgate Road, Mollington CH1 6NE
CHESTER (0244) 851666
off A540, 3m N of Chester

COOKING 2*
COST £21–£57

The older core of this large red-brick manor has been wrapped and extended by modern additions to give lots more bedrooms and working space than were ever envisaged. To that extent, the place represents the 'hotel in the country' movement rather than the 'country-house hotel', although luxury in rooms ancient or modern is never in doubt and the grounds are extensive. This year set-price menus seem to have been abandoned: on offer is a long *carte* with remarkable price range. Always praised for value – the Sunday lunches have been a case in point – the menu's worth remains evident in economical dishes such as sauté lambs' kidneys with chorizo and vegetables or chicken escalope with tomatoes and Gruyère. Buy venison, however, and prices rise at speed. Michael Truelove's cooking is well able to cope with every kitchen skill, though it is less certain that every skill can be extended equally to a full dining-room. Unevenness comes through in reports. None the less, plaudits have been given for a whole pickled pear stuffed with chicken liver parfait, a salmon and leek terrine, a hot mousseline of salmon and sole, chicken breast with calvados sauce, lamb with ratatouille, a Sunday joint of beef, and pheasant with chestnuts. Desserts have been satisfactory, as have most of the trimmings: 'They have improved the bread and strengthened the coffee.' The wine list is a bit of a tease; there are many wonderful bottles at prices that are not at all bad, given the surroundings. But interspersed with these are wines of less certain provenance. Perhaps some newer, better merchants hover in the wings awaiting the clearance of old stock. House wines are from £9.90.

CHEF: Michael Truelove   PROPRIETOR: Carl Lewis   OPEN: all week; 12.30 to 2, 7 to 9.45   MEALS: alc (main courses £6.50 to £18.50). Set Sun L £14.50   SERVICE: not inc, card slips closed   CARDS: Access, Amex, Diners, Visa   DETAILS: 100 seats. 6 tables outside. Private parties: 100 main room, 30, 40 and 100 private rooms. Car park. Vegetarian meals. Children's helpings. Jacket and tie. Wheelchair access (3 steps; also WC). Music. Air-conditioned   ACCOMMODATION: 48 rooms, all with bath/shower. Rooms for disabled. D,B&B £98.50 to £125. Children welcome. Garden. Snooker. TV. Phone. Confirm 1 day ahead. Fax: (0244) 851400 (*The Which? Hotel Guide*)

---

*Restaurateurs justifiably resent no-shows. If you quote a credit card number when booking, you may be liable for the restaurant's lost profit margin if you don't turn up. Always phone to cancel.*

---

## MONTACUTE Somerset                                              map 2

## ▲ *Milk House* ₅⨯

The Borough, Montacute TA15 6XB                          COOKING 1
YEOVIL (0935) 823823                                     COST £16–£38

The Milk House derives its name from its fifteenth-century function as a dairy.
The house now extends into two ancient cottages around a courtyard garden,
complete with a creeper-covered terrace. Inside is a grand mix of antique
furniture, original paintings, open fires and low arching doorways. Service is
generally sincere. Lee Dufton's cooking relies heavily – some might say
obsessively – on organic produce, wild fish, free-range eggs and home-grown
vegetables. The results have not impressed everyone ('I could have cooked it all
myself at home' was one verdict), but there is honest intent here and some
creditable food that takes account of vegetarians, vegans and weight-watchers.
Soups, such as walnut or dark-green watercress, have been enjoyed, and the
home-made walnut bread is reckoned to be particularly good. Spiced garlic
mushrooms topped with chopped nuts, stuffed sorrel pancakes, grilled sole
and guinea-fowl with herb sauce have also pleased reporters. Chocolate
mousse and refreshing apple and lemon sorbet have been more convincing
than 'soggy' brown bread ice-cream. Organic wines loom large on the
affordable wine list. House wines are from £8.90.

CHEF: Lee Dufton   PROPRIETORS: Bill and Lee Dufton   OPEN: Wed to Sat, D only, and Sun
L (Wed to Sat L by arrangement for 6 or more); 12.30 to 1.30, 7.30 to 9.30   CLOSED: 25 and
26 Dec   MEALS: alc (main courses £8 to £14). Set L £12.50, Set D £19.80. Minimum £12.50
SERVICE: not inc, card slips closed   CARDS: Access, Visa   DETAILS: 30 seats. 3 tables
outside. Private parties: 30 main room, 30 private rooms. Vegetarian meals. Children's
helpings on request. No children between 9 months and 3. Smart dress preferred. No
smoking in dining-room. Wheelchair access. No music   ACCOMMODATION: 2 rooms, all
with bath/shower. B&B £40 to £48. Deposit: £20. Children under 9 months and over 12
years welcome. Garden. Doors close at midnight. Confirm by 4

## MORETON-IN-MARSH Gloucestershire                     map 2

## *Annie's*

3 Oxford Street,
Moreton-in-Marsh GL56 0LA                                COOKING 1*
MORETON-IN-MARSH (0608) 651981                           COST £23–£48

Hanging baskets bedeck the outside walls of this little Cotswold cottage just off
Main Street, while the interior is a homely mix of original beams, exposed
stonework, flagstone floors and chintzy fabrics. Dried flowers and pictures
adorn the walls, and almost everyone approves of the background music. The
atmosphere is very warm and cosy. David and Anne Ellis run the place as a
team: he cooks, she attends to the front-of-house. They describe the food as a
mixture of English and French country cooking based around short menus that
take account of the seasons. Warm salads and roulades are favourite starters,
while main courses might feature saddle of venison with port wine and juniper
sauce, duck breast with orange and Noilly Prat sauce garnished with orange
and almond dumplings, and salmon with white wine sauce. Puddings are old

favourites: spotted dick with custard, toffee pudding, treacle tart. The wine list is a creditable selection of around 50 bottles at reasonable prices. House wines are £9.50.

CHEFS: David Ellis and Milly Kent   PROPRIETORS: David and Anne Ellis   OPEN: Mon to Sat, D only, and Sun L; 12 to 2, 7 to 10   MEALS: alc (main courses £13.50 to £17.50). Set Sun L £16, Set D £19   SERVICE: not inc, card slips closed   CARDS: Access, Amex, Diners, Visa   DETAILS: 32 seats. Private parties: 32 main room, 12 private room. Vegetarian meals. Children's helpings. Smart dress preferred. No smoking while others eat. Wheelchair access. Music

## Marsh Goose ⁝✻

High Street, Moreton-in-Marsh GL56 0AX          COOKING 3
MORETON-IN-MARSH (0608) 52111                   COST £22–£46

The stone floors and walls of this former stable block and coach-house shape a series of pleasing, skylit rooms – though their size means that conversational space may be subject to invasion by the loud neighbour. In the rather cramped bar, a giant avocado tree alludes to the tropics; in the kitchen, Barbados-born Sonya Kidney provides dishes inspired more by her land of adoption than her birth: mallard in a rich, liver-based sauce, venison with a 'finely judged' green pepper sauce, and lemon sole on a bed of crab meat in saffron butter, in which 'every flavour was distinct yet made a wonderful whole – a masterpiece'. Desserts, soufflés, game and lamb are all first-rate; quibbles include a tendency to herb overkill ('my cauliflower and rosemary soup was really cream of rosemary') and lily-gilding ('terrine of guinea-fowl came laden with melon, orange, strips of leek and pine-kernels'), while bread is not always to hand when you want it, and some find portions small. The skill and attentiveness of the youthful staff continue to impress. The wine list is serviceable; it begins at £8.05 for Ochoa's reliable and beautifully labelled Navarra wines, and provides good choice for under £15. Drinkers of sweet wines are spoiled by a range of six, five of them available by the glass (£4.50 to £5.20).

CHEF: Sonya Kidney   PROPRIETORS: Sonya Kidney, Leo Brooke-Little and Gordon Campbell-Gray   OPEN: Tue to Sun, exc Sun D; 12.30 to 2.30, 7.30 to 9.45   MEALS: alc L (main courses £9.50 to £12). Set Sun L £16, Set D £21.50   SERVICE: not inc   CARDS: Access, Visa   DETAILS: 60 seats. Private parties: 22 main room, 6 and 14 private rooms. Vegetarian meals. Children's helpings on request. Smart dress preferred. No smoking in dining-room. Wheelchair access (also WC). No music

---

**MORSTON Norfolk**                                          map 6

## ▲ Morston Hall

Morston, nr Holt NR25 7AA
CLEY (0263) 741041                              COOKING 2
2m W of Blakeney, on A149                       COST £19–£34

The Blackistons and Justin Fraser, a young team full of enthusiasm, have built up an admiring following in a very few months at this brick-and-flint house on the north Norfolk coast. It is not grand, but very seemly, and well decked out into the bargain. After his stint with John Tovey in the Lake District, Galton Blackiston has exported the Miller Howe dinner formula: four courses, no choice until pudding, lots of vegetables with surprising flavours ranged in little piles round the plate, and the undoctrinaire Tovey approach to combinations and tastes. This has suited Norfolk well. A spring-time dinner proffered warm Roquefort cheesecake with a pear and lemon vinaigrette; cod in a beer batter with parsley sauce; duck breast on rhubarb and ginger purée with a liver stuffing and thick gravy; carrots, parsnips, swede, leeks and potato gratin with lemon; coffee rice pudding brûlée, or lemon banana gâteau, or apple charlotte with custard. There have been days when the savoury courses have triumphed over the sweet, and the thrust of the cooking seems aimed more at hearty appetites than sensitivity. The wine list is arranged by grape variety and makes no bones about buying from all over the world. It also keeps its prices at reasonable levels and runs to an adequate number of halves. House wines are £8.50.

CHEF: Galton Blackiston   PROPRIETORS: Tracy and Galton Blackiston, and Justin Fraser
OPEN: all week, D only, and Sun L; 12.30 for 1, 7.30 for 8   CLOSED: Jan to early Mar
MEALS: Set L £13, Set D £21   SERVICE: not inc, card slips closed   CARDS: Access, Amex,
Visa   DETAILS: 30 seats. Private parties: 55 main room. Car park. Vegetarian meals.
Children's helpings. Smart dress preferred. No smoking during meals. Wheelchair access
(also WC). No music   ACCOMMODATION: 4 rooms, all with bath/shower. B&B £60 to £140.
Children welcome. Baby facilities. Pets welcome in bedrooms. Afternoon teas. Garden. TV.
Phone. Confirm by 6. Fax: (0263) 741041 (*The Which? Hotel Guide*)

---

**MOULSFORD Oxfordshire**                                                          map 2

## ▲ *Beetle & Wedge* ▮

Moulsford, OX10 9JF
CHOLSEY (0491) 651381                                              COOKING 3
off A329, turn down Ferry Lane to river                        COST £25–£66

The Beetle & Wedge, on the River Thames, is 'idyllic' on a fine summer's day, when you can eat in the Water Garden and watch coots scooting in and out of the reeds on the opposite bank; snug in winter, when you are ensconced in either the beamed Boathouse or more soigné Dining Room. The experience is 'very English', most agree; the menus have patriotic patches and a foundation of common sense, but look out to the world beyond often enough to excite. It is best to bring plenty of appetite, since cream comes in ladlefuls and portions can be generous. The Boathouse features a brasserie-style menu with on-the-spot chargrilling to add atmosphere. Duck and pork rillettes, warm sauté aubergine, mixed peppers and tomatoes with warm goats' cheese, or venison medallions with fresh figs and port strike a fair balance between informality and treat-eatery. In the Dining Room, the same basic ingredients are embroidered more lavishly; the Boathouse's hare casserole with creamy mashed potato becomes fillet of hare with foie gras and wild mushrooms; fillet of turbot waves goodbye to its baby leeks and saffron sauce to reappear arm-in-arm with spinach and langoustines. Some feel starters and desserts are keener in price than execution; for others, the cost is 'expensive but worth every penny'. The kitchen shows a laudable desire to please; one customer was asked for comments 'for the benefit of the lads in the kitchen' concerning sweetbreads on toasted brioche ('mushy and granular' was the not-entirely-favourable verdict). Service is variable: 'We were extremely well looked after' one lunch, yet things were 'chaotically incompetent' the following night (though 'very well-meaning and actually very entertaining'). The cooking for the Boathouse comes in for some criticism. Expense is noted again of the wine list, and some lament its French orientation; the best policy, though, is to sit back and enjoy it, particularly the fine Alsace wines from Trimbach and Schlumberger, and a good Rhône range (including four different wines from St-Joseph). More wines deserve annotation than the present handful, especially since wine advice from the waiting staff seldom matches the clear descriptions of the dishes. House wines are well selected and offer fair value at £10.25 per bottle. CELLARMAN'S CHOICE: St-Veran, Ch. Fuissé 1991, Vincent, £20; Chambolle Musigny, premier cru 1987, Felettig, £36.

CHEF: Richard Smith    PROPRIETORS: Richard and Kate Smith    OPEN: Dining Room Tue to Sun, exc Sun D; Boathouse all week; 12.30 to 2, 7.30 to 10    MEALS: alc (main courses Dining Room £19.50 to £25, Boathouse £8.50 to £14). Set Sun L Dining Room £24.50
SERVICE: not inc    CARDS: Access, Amex, Diners, Visa    DETAILS: Dining Room 35 seats, Boathouse 50 seats. 12 tables outside. Private parties: 12 main room, 65 private room. Car park. Vegetarian meals. Children welcome. Smart dress preferred in Dining Room. No cigars/pipes in Dining Room. Wheelchair access (also WC in Boathouse). No music
ACCOMMODATION: 10 rooms, all with bath/shower. Rooms for disabled. B&B £70 to £125. Children welcome. Baby facilities. Pets by arrangement. Garden. Fishing. TV. Phone. Fax: (0491) 651376 (*The Which? Hotel Guide*)

---

## MOULTON North Yorkshire
map 7

# Black Bull Inn

Moulton DL10 6QJ
DARLINGTON (0325) 377289
1m SE of Scotch Corner, 1m from A1

COOKING 2*
COST £20–£53

Readers continue to endorse the virtues of this long-established North Country pub/restaurant. The place has a number of different eating areas, all of which attract positive reports. The beamed bar offers excellent value at lunch-time, and there is no doubting the quality of the smoked salmon, 'creamy smooth' leek and potato soup and pan-fried fish-cakes in tomato sauce. There is praise, too, for roast pheasant with brandy-soaked prunes and burnt sugar ice-cream with toffee sauce ('fairly zinging on the taste-buds'). Other reports mention the conservatory with its fantastic collection of railway coats of arms, although one visitor focused on the indoor vine 'occasionally loosing a greenfly on to the passing service'. Formal meals are served in 'Hazel' – a renovated Pullman carriage which provided an occasion to remember for one satisfied customer. The menu divides equally between meat and fish: roast rack of lamb, grilled sirloin with red wine and shallots, poached turbot with hollandaise, lobster thermidor. Chateaubriand has been cooked to perfection. Service is reckoned to be amiable rather than professional. The owners are also wine merchants and offer a comprehensive, mostly French, list with house Duboeuf from £7.25, a good showing of half-bottles and plenty of clarets and burgundies for around £20. Theakston Bitter is on handpump in the bar.

CHEF: Stuart Birkett   PROPRIETORS: G.H. and A.M.C. Pagendam   OPEN: Mon to Sat;
12 to 2, 6.45 to 10.15   CLOSED: 24 to 26 Dec   MEALS: alc (main courses £11 to £20). Set L
£12.75   SERVICE: not inc   CARDS: Access, Amex, Visa   DETAILS: 100 seats. 4 tables
outside. Private parties: 36 main room, 12 and 36 private rooms. Vegetarian meals. No
children under 7. Wheelchair access. No music. Air-conditioned. Fax: (0325) 377422

---

## NAILSWORTH Gloucestershire

map 2

# William's Bistro

NEW ENTRY

3 Fountain Street, Nailsworth GL6 0BL
NAILSWORTH (0453) 835507

COOKING 2
COST £21–£36

It is all change at William's. The excellent delicatessen remains, but the
restaurant at the back has reverted to the simple bistro style that was once its
hallmark. Chef Gary Flynn has gone and the décor has lost its cool, designer
look. 'Cottagey' sums up the new mood of the place. Roller blinds hang at the
windows, the tables are laid with paper cloths, and paintings adorn the
powder-pink walls. The kitchen's reputation hinges on top-class supplies of
fresh fish and the short menu reflects daily deliveries. Robust fisherman's stew
is a fixture; other dishes might include scallops with thinly shredded leeks,
squat lobster tails with saffron and skate with capers. Meat-eaters might be
offered 'juicy' fat-free duck breast with ginger and spring onions, and rack of
lamb. Vegetables consist of a healthy jumble of fresh, well-timed items.
Puddings may disappoint: lemon tart with 'stodgy' pastry, summer pudding
that lacked texture and identity. The quality of the raw materials and value for
money are features of the place; these are reinforced by the short unpretentious
wine list, which offers the prospect of interesting drinking at fair prices. House
wine is £7.

CHEFS: Clive Gawlick and William Beeston   PROPRIETORS: William and Rae Beeston
OPEN: Tue to Sat, D only; 7 to 9.45   CLOSED: Christmas, Good Fri, Tue following bank hol
Mons   MEALS: alc (main courses £8.50 to £14.50)   SERVICE: not inc, card slips closed
CARDS: Access, Visa   DETAILS: 45 seats. Children's helpings. No music. Fax: (0453) 835950

---

## NANTWICH Cheshire

map 5

# Churche's Mansion

COUNTY
OF THE
YEAR
RESTAURANT

NEW ENTRY

Hospital Street, Nantwich CW5 0RY
NANTWICH (0270) 625933

COOKING 2*
COST £18–£41

This was a rich merchant's house built in 1567 and still shows plenty of the
original (one reporter focused on the 'exposed old oak beams, lovely oak doors
and open fireplaces'), albeit now decked in seemly modern clothing. Amanda
Latham has made an auspicious start in reviving the restaurant's fortunes,
asking a variety of non-greedy prices for meals of varying length depending on
the time of day. Graham Tucker and many of his team seem to have worked
at Rookery Hall (see entry in England round-up, Worleston) up the road, and
are therefore well trained in the art of pleasing Cheshire. The repertoire they
have put on view has many resonances of 'modern British': its tendency is
light, there is a certain degree of mix and match, and something unusual is

bound to meet the eye. Two perfect examples of this came from a spring menu: a main course of duck on deep-fried couscous with raspberry and star-anise sauce topped with fried celeriac, and a first-course feuilleté of broccoli mousse and asparagus with a lemon and chervil sauce. In point of fact little fault has been found so far with the execution of either the principals or the peripherals such as vegetables or midway sorbet. Nor are potentially outlandish flavours so wayward as they sound. 'This is a gem,' enthused our first report of the new regime, and praise was given for ambience, service, sauces, furnishings and menu range by another hard on its heels. The wine list comes from Haughton Fine Wines, and covers a wide slate of flavours in short compass: the growers are good, with a fine showing of organics and none-too-high prices. House wines cost from £7.75.

CHEF: Graham Tucker   PROPRIETORS: Robin Latham and Amanda Latham   OPEN: Tue to Sun, exc Sun D; 12 to 2.30, 7 to 9.30   MEALS: alc light L (main courses £3.50 to £6). Set L £9.50 (2 courses) to £12.50, Set D £20   SERVICE: not inc, card slips closed   CARDS: Access, Diners, Visa   DETAILS: 50 seats. 4 tables outside. Private parties: 48 main room, 21 and 48 private rooms. Car park. Vegetarian meals. Children's helpings. No children under 10 D. Smart dress preferred. No cigars/pipes in dining-room. Wheelchair access. Music

---

NAYLAND Suffolk                                                                                          map 3

## Martha's Vineyard ♀ ⁵✳

18 High Street, Nayland CO6 4JF
COLCHESTER (0206) 262888                                                               COOKING 3
off A134, 6½m N of Colchester                                                     COST £21–£31

Last year's chef was Larkin Warren, this year's is Larkin Rogers: 'same person, same cooking, different name.' Visitors regularly enthuse about the unpretentious informality of this converted high street shop and are won over by the cheery, welcoming service. Tables are closely packed and the noise level can be high – especially on a busy Saturday night – but this adds to the buzz of the place. The cooking is fiercely fashionable, although the kitchen has no facilities for chargrilling. It looks west to California for inspiration (Larkin's transatlantic lineage) and also east to the Mediterranean, and can deliver anything from Chesapeake crab-cakes with lemon and herb mayonnaise, cioppino (California-style fish stew) and pork loin marinated in bourbon, molasses and mustard with mango and black-bean salsa to open buckwheat ravioli with shiitake mushrooms, goats' cheese and lentil sauce or roast haddock fillet with fennel and black olives. Ideas abound. This is food that challenges and enlivens the palate without resorting to extravagant flights of fancy. The owners have tapped into the local network of growers and producers who are thick on the ground in Suffolk, which has meant seeking out sources of anything from quinces to old varieties of pear. Herbs and fruit are home-grown and daily breads are baked with serious intent. Reporters have enjoyed 'rainbow' summer soup (green basil and red tomato), corn puddings with crab sauce, ratatouille risotto with Parmesan shavings, and chicken 'jerk' with lime and peppers. Desserts occasionally disappoint, although bread-and-butter pudding flavoured with lemon and coriander has been given the thumbs-up. As the name Martha's Vineyard denotes, wine is big here, but this, mercifully, does not extend to the length of the list. Within the 45 bins on offer is packed as eclectic and enjoyable a range as could be desired, plundered from some of the best merchants in East Anglia and beyond. California predominates, but canny selections from New Zealand, Italy and even France – half-bottles of 1970 Ch. Cissac – make for fair balance of the classics and the quirky. There are good halves and reasonable prices. House wines are from £8.75. CELLARMAN'S CHOICE: Gavi, Bava 1991, £14.50; Napa, Clos du Val, Zinfandel 1989, £16.50.

CHEFS: Larkin Rogers and Denise Woolsey   PROPRIETORS: Christopher Warren and Larkin Rogers   OPEN: Tue to Sat, D only; 7 to 9 (9.30 Fri and Sat)   CLOSED: 2 weeks winter, 2 weeks summer   MEALS: alc (main courses £8 to £10)   SERVICE: not inc (10% for 6 or more)   CARDS: Access, Visa   DETAILS: 41 seats. Private parties: 8 main room. Vegetarian meals. Children's helpings. No smoking in dining-room. Wheelchair access. No music

---

**NEAR SAWREY Cumbria** map 7

## ▲ Ees Wyke ⁵✱ | NEW ENTRY

Near Sawrey, Ambleside LA22 0JZ
HAWKSHEAD (053 94) 36393                                         COOKING 2
on B5286 road from Hawkshead                                   COST £23–£28

The house has tip-top views over Esthwaite Water. Beatrix Potter used to stay here in the summer months, before the place was turned into a hotel. Margaret Williams is an assiduous hostess, drawing outsiders and residents into an impromptu house-party by introducing all and sundry while they sip their sherries in the drawing-room. The building has the decent proportions of a late-Georgian house in the country, though decoration has stopped short of embellishing this. John Williams was 'classically trained' and has stuck to his guns, producing a menu that will not amaze for its adventure but will satisfy for its technique. Thus a dinner that started with asparagus soup with good stock and 'at least 12 crunchy asparagus tips', went on to veal cordon bleu that was correct in every way, and even included 'pommes Byron', which is a 'sort of mash with a cheese crust'. Blackcurrant bavarois was not as good as rhubarb fool. The third dessert that night was, surprise, surprise, sticky toffee pudding. This is steady cooking that is ideal after a day's walking on the Lakeland hills, and it does not cost a fortune. The wine list is short. House wine is £8.50.

CHEF: John Williams   PROPRIETORS: Margaret and John Williams   OPEN: all week, D only; 7 for 7.30   CLOSED: Jan, Feb   MEALS: Set D £12 to £17 (non-residents)   SERVICE: not inc   DETAILS: 18 seats. Car park. Vegetarian meals with prior notice. Children's helpings. No children under 10. Smart dress preferred. No smoking in dining-room. Wheelchair access. No music   ACCOMMODATION: 8 rooms, all with bath/shower. B&B £34 to £68. Deposit: £50. No children under 10. Pets welcome (not in public rooms). Garden. Fishing. TV (*The Which? Hotel Guide*)

---

⁵✱ *indicates that smoking is either banned altogether or that a dining-room is maintained for non-smokers. The symbol does not apply to restaurants that simply have no-smoking areas.*

---

---

**NETHERFIELD East Sussex** map 3

## ▲ *Netherfield Place* | NEW ENTRY |

Netherfield TN33 9PP
BATTLE (0424) 774455 COOKING 2*
off B2096, 2m W of Battle COST £16–£44

Set in the wooded Wealden landscape not far from Battle Abbey, this mock-Georgian, 1920s country house is a thoroughly civilised retreat. A drive through parkland, past rhododendrons and azaleas leads to the place itself, while beyond is the garden, with secluded pockets of lawns and shrubbery. The Colliers have been in residence since 1985 and have given the interior a comfortable, 'reassuring' atmosphere without resorting to flashiness. At one end of the warm, convivial dining-room is a sturdy granite fireplace, tables are well spaced and a door opens out into the garden. Michael Collier offers a well-balanced *carte* with plenty of choice, as well as a good-value four-course set menu. Dishes are elaborate and floridly described ('turbans of Dover sole filled with spinach mousse passed through the oven and presented basking in a saffron butter sauce'), but the results on the plate are impressively good. One particularly fine meal featured spot-on salad of pigeon breast with lightly dressed green leaves, interleaved fillets of salmon and brill with hollandaise and herb-crusted loin of lamb, carefully filleted and served with sherry and rosemary sauce, and tart of fresh fruit with excellent crisp shortcrust pastry and butterscotch sauce. Incidentals such as nibbles, good white rolls, unsalted butter and vegetables from the kitchen garden and home-made chocolates suggest that this is a serious enterprise. As an introduction to the wine list, the Netherfield Place Reserve – several pages of the fine and ancient at commensurate prices – is a little deceptive since the intention is to provide a broad and reasonably priced list. There are good half-bottles and a reasonable strength beyond the classics. House wine is £8.95.

CHEF: Michael Collier PROPRIETORS: Michael and Helen Collier OPEN: all week; 12 to 2, 7 to 9.30 (9 Sun) CLOSED: 2 weeks Christmas and New Year MEALS: alc (main courses £15 to £16.50). Set L £14.95 to £15.95 (inc wine), Set D £22.50 SERVICE: not inc CARDS: Access, Amex, Diners, Visa DETAILS: 50 seats. Private parties: 75 main room, 24 and 40 private rooms. Car park. Vegetarian meals. Children's helpings L. Smart dress preferred. Wheelchair access (1 step; also WC). Music ACCOMMODATION: 14 rooms, all with bath/shower. B&B £56 to £120. Young children welcome. Baby facilities. Afternoon teas. Garden. Tennis. TV. Phone. Doors close at midnight. Fax: (0424) 774024 (*The Which? Hotel Guide*)

---

**NEW ALRESFORD Hampshire** map 2

## ▲ *Hunters* | NEW ENTRY |

32 Broad Street, New Alresford SO24 9AQ COOKING 2*
WINCHESTER (0962) 732468 COST £17–£46

As the name gives warning, it is hunting – memorabilia and pictures – that dominates the décor. But not at the expense of the food. Since his arrival in the summer of 1992, young chef Michael Greenhalgh has made New Alresford sit up and take notice. His cooking bears marks of the nouvelle revolution in its complexity and relative lightness, but accuracy and attention to flavour skirt any incipient problems. The *carte* is priced more keenly than most country places serving this sort of food, and the economically minded find that lunch is a bargain as is the week-night set-price menu chalked on a blackboard. A summer dinner of hot cheese and seafood soufflé with a hollandaise, terrine of leek and prawn wrapped in smoked salmon with a basil vinaigrette, roast woodpigeon on lentils with a garlic confit, shallots and baby onions, lamb with a port sauce and filo parcels of Stilton, finished with a hot chocolate soufflé and a 'symphony' of chocolate proved satisfactory in many ways. The Stilton parcels sounded worryingly strong but were in fact nicely gauged; the cheese might have overpowered the seafood, but was also kept in check; the sauces enhanced the principals; and even the terrine, perhaps a fad of yesteryear, was much complimented. Service comes with a smile and the wine list is shared with the sister establishment in Winchester (see entry). The list is short but fine, with prices in line with the cost of the rest. House wines are £8.25.

CHEF: Michael Greenhalgh  PROPRIETORS: David and Martin Birmingham  OPEN: all week, exc Sun D; 12 to 2, 7 to 10  CLOSED: 25 to 28 Dec  MEALS: alc (main courses L £5 to £8, D £9 to £15). Set Mon to Fri D £11.95 (2 courses) to £13.95  SERVICE: 10%, card slips closed  CARDS: Access, Amex, Diners, Visa  DETAILS: 110 seats. 8 tables outside. Private parties: 30 main room, 80 private room. Vegetarian meals. Children's helpings. No cigars/pipes in dining-room. Wheelchair access (1 step; also WC). Music  ACCOMMODATION: 3 rooms, all with bath/shower. B&B £32.50 to £47.50. Deposit: £10. Children welcome. Afternoon teas. Garden. TV. Doors close at 11. Confirm by 11am

---

**NEWARK Nottinghamshire**                                              map 5

## Gannets Bistrot ⁑✳ £

35 Castlegate, Newark NG24 1AZ                                COOKING 1
NEWARK (0636) 702066 and 610018                            COST £17–£32

The daytime café on the ground floor is open from 10am to 4.30pm and deals in light snacks, cakes, salads and simple dishes. Upstairs is the 'bistrot' proper with its mahogany bar, bare floorboards, greenery and ornate brass lamps. Generally the place (opposite the castle) pleases with its friendliness and good value, but on occasion mishaps occur: a loyal supporter was saddened by indifferent food and 'an air of complacency and arrogance'. The Bowers respect ingredients, buy wisely and use organic produce where possible. The result is a repertoire that embraces bistro classics such as garlic mushrooms, prawn and cod gratin and beef bourguignonne, as well as Roquefort and onion soufflé, chargrilled lamb's liver and bacon with gin and lime sauce and daily specials such as fish with Noilly Prat. Salads are 'leafy'. The menu also has a strong vegetarian presence: for instance, spinach, hazelnut and aubergine bake and vegetable croustade. Sticky toffee pudding tops the list of sweets. The wine list is short, sharp and affordable; home-made lemonade is also recommended. House wine is £7.95 a litre.

---

*The* Guide *relies on feedback from its readers. Especially welcome are reports on new restaurants appearing in the book for the first time.*

---

CHEFS: Hilary Bower and Paul Godfrey   PROPRIETORS: Hilary and David Bower   OPEN: café all week; 10 to 4.30. Bistrot Wed to Sat; 12 to 2, 6.30 to 9.30   CLOSED: 25 and 26 Dec   MEALS: alc (main courses £6.50 to £13). Set L £7.95 (2 courses)   SERVICE: bistrot 10%, card slips closed   CARDS: Access, Visa   DETAILS: 40 seats. Private parties: 40 main room. Vegetarian meals. Children's helpings. No smoking in dining-room. Music

## Le Gourmet

| NEW ENTRY |

14 Castle Gate, Newark NG24 1BG                        COOKING 1
NEWARK (0636) 610141                                   COST £16–£43

The chef at this French restaurant is an Englishman whose previous job was at Les Artistes Gourmands in Nottingham. Does Mark Ashmore have a thing about France? Is a gourmet better than a gourmand? Le Gourmet is surely French: down to its Louis XVI chairs, a pleasant terrasse over the Trent, a gingham and candle bistro next door, and Piaf on the Muzak machine. Whether in French or English (and desserts get introduced as 'Our hand-crafted desserts'), the food is exactly what you might expect of a vaguely French restaurant operating in Midland England. No prizes are awarded, then, for imaginative adventure with items like sole and salmon paupiettes with leeks and a Chablis sauce, or carré of lamb with herbes de Provence. On the other hand, there are signs of fair cooking: excellent meats are properly treated, even if the Roquefort sauce with a carré of lamb was a hammer to crack a nut; desserts may be as good as one person's pavé of chocolate filled with a chocolate and coconut mousse; the coffee and the petits fours are very decent. Service is assiduous. The wine list stretches out beyond France, but choice is not enormous. Prices are fair enough. House wines are £9.

CHEF: Mark Ashmore   PROPRIETORS: Allez Manger Ltd   OPEN: Tue to Sun, exc Sun D; 12 to 2, 7 to 10   MEALS: alc (main courses £13 to £15). Set L £9.95, Set D £19.95   SERVICE: not inc   CARDS: Access, Amex, Diners, Visa   DETAILS: restaurant 35 seats, bistro 30 seats. 7 tables outside. Private parties: 40 main room, 10 and 20 private rooms. Vegetarian meals. Children's helpings. Smart dress preferred. Wheelchair access (3 steps). Music

## NEWCASTLE UPON TYNE  Tyne & Wear                                    map 7

## Courtney's

5–7 The Side, NE1 3JE                                  COOKING 2*
091-232 5537                                           COST £21–£39

Below Tyne Bridge and near Newcastle's bustling Quayside area lies Courtney's. 'Returning a daughter from Eastbourne to Newcastle in a day means that there has to be some kind of evening reward. Courtney's is mine,' wrote one exhausted parent. 'We like it,' added a local, 'because it gives "informality with tablecloths", enough space between tables for privacy, and interested service.' That big-city sense of things done properly, yet not overweighting the flounce, is aided by soothing jazz classics and is usually hit to a T at Courtney's. The tone matches the brasserie-style cooking, which displays nice judgement ('My scallop mousse was delicate-to-bland but the basil vinaigrette assailed the nostrils and lifted it, the lemon zest being a finishing touch'), proper technique and thoroughly modern manners – for instance, the salmon fish-cakes with salmon and sorrel sauce. A printed menu is supplemented by blackboard specials – often tropical fish, often grilled or blackened, often with a salsa of some sort – but rumours of satisfaction occur across the range. Breast of pheasant in brandy sauce, pot-roast sailfish with red wine and sun-dried tomatoes, noisettes of lamb with green peppercorns, and salmon with herbs and wild mushrooms are some other examples. Vegetables are praised, especially potatoes, and the desserts are pronounced steady, on the evidence of chocolate marquise, an orange-coloured chocolate-orange mousse, or a Lindisfarne mead posset on an apple purée base. The wine list is sensibly short and non-chauvinist; the recurrent theme is the enjoyable house wines from River Run, Australia, at £9.50 a bottle.

CHEF: Michael Carr  PROPRIETORS: Michael and Kerensa Carr  OPEN: Mon to Sat, exc Sat L; 12 to 2, 7 to 10.30  CLOSED: 1 week Christmas, 2 weeks May, bank hols  MEALS: alc (main courses £7 to £14). Set L £11.95 (2 courses) to £13.95  SERVICE: not inc  CARDS: Access, Amex, Visa  DETAILS: 27 seats. Private parties: 27 main room. Vegetarian meals. Children's helpings on request. Smart dress preferred. No cigars/pipes in dining-room. Music

## Fisherman's Lodge ⁵⁑✳

Jesmond Dene, NE7 7BQ  
091-281 3281

COOKING 3  
COST £31–£66

People remark on the setting of the Lodge: Jesmond Dene is an impressive park with steep wooded slopes and burn, and the restaurant occupies a house at its edge. The vibrant pattern of the carpets, the swags of the curtains, the padding on the bar itself and the strong shades of pink that glow in the night air mark the place with 'richly vulgar' comfort, designed for a good night out. The same might be said of the cooking. There is a goodly bit of display, and many elements often mark a dish. A trio of lamb – ragoût, fillet and en croûte – was resoundingly successful for its choice of materials and enjoyed for flavour and composition (even if the vegetables were not up to par). Sauces bulk large (perhaps too large when the sole is impossible to taste through the samphire) but they do contribute another building-block to the image. Fish is not the only speciality but it remains the chief attraction, both for luxury items such as salmon, oysters and lobster and for a more general run of daily purchases from North Shields. A new-wave thread has been running here over the last two years, taking in dishes such as lamb shank, oxtail with saffron noodles and black pudding with an onion marmalade. Desserts can end on the high note of the grand selection, may surprise when the hot lemon soufflé seems more like lemon meringue, but emerge again with credit after a taste of the baked apple strudel. The whole operation flows smoothly; it is a family business run with professional flair. The wine list has some interesting red Italian choices and a couple of clarets – Chasse Spleen and Fombrauge – that will not break the bank and will please. White burgundies, which should perhaps be the strongest section to complement the menu, are not as exciting as they could be. House wines are £9.50 a litre.

CHEF: Steven Jobson   PROPRIETORS: Franco and Pamela Cetoloni   OPEN: Mon to Sat, exc Sat L; 12 to 2, 7 to 11   MEALS: alc (main courses £16.50 to £25). Set L £16 to £17   SERVICE: not inc   CARDS: Access, Amex, Diners, Visa   DETAILS: 65 seats. 8 tables outside. Private parties: 14 main room, 14 and 40 private rooms. Car park. Vegetarian meals. Children's helpings. No children under 10. Smart dress preferred. No smoking in dining-room. Wheelchair access (1 step). Music (only in private rooms). Fax: 091-281 6410

## Leela's

20 Dean Street, NE1 1PG
091-230 1261

COOKING 1
COST £16–£41

Not far from the Theatre Royal and Quayside, this restaurant offers the prospect of intriguing south Indian cooking with a strong vegetarian bias in pleasant surroundings. Service is efficient, but noticeable rumblings of discontent have surfaced in reports. A cold atmosphere and jarring Muzak have not helped to convince some visitors of the restaurant's merits. Also, the cooking has shown signs of unevenness: 'mini-portions of carelessly spiced food' is one unhappy comment. On the plus side, the kitchen has delivered some fine dishes. Appam and lamb pappas (marinated lamb in a rich coconut sauce pointed up with curry leaves and mustard seeds and served with a lightly raised spongy pancake) have been excellent. Among good vegetables are cheera varalan (spinach and potatoes 'beautifully flavoured' with cardamom) and kathrikai thengapal (aubergines cooked with coconut). The thali on one occasion was no more than a couple of vegetable dishes plus basmati rice and salad, while bread – a benchmark of good Indian cuisine – can be far from exact. House vin de pays is £8.50.

CHEF: Kuriakose Paul   PROPRIETORS: Kuriakose and Leela Paul   OPEN: Mon to Sat; 12 to 2.30, 6 to 11.30   MEALS: alc (main courses £8 to £13). Set L £9.95   SERVICE: not inc CARDS: Access, Amex, Diners, Visa   DETAILS: 50 seats. Private parties: 25 main room. Vegetarian meals. Children's helpings. Smart dress preferred. Wheelchair access (3 steps). Music

## 21 Queen Street ▼

19–21 Queen Street, Princes Wharf,
Quayside, NE1 3UG
091-222 0755

COOKING 3*
COST £23–£63

This venue lies east of the Tyne bridges, in the bustling area of wharves and buildings bunched steeply below the railway station, down by the riverside. Unlike so many places seeking character, the Laybournes' restaurant eschews dark atmospherics for a modern interior. It has style and comfort, space and light. A relatively stable *carte* is given its own light and bounce by a daily selection of both fish and meat dishes. The regulars can still feast on Kielder Forest venison with sour cherries, grapes and walnuts and a grand veneur sauce, or they can vary the intake with lamb with basil and provençal vegetables. After eating four meals, someone commented that the last was as good, perhaps better, than the first. Someone else expressed dissatisfaction with portion size and 'chewy' duck. The kitchen has consistency; also style with dishes such as thin tomato tart with pistou and crisp fried herbs, boned oxtail with wild mushroom stuffing, roast lobster with herbs and olive oil, and Shanghai shellfish risotto with ginger. Trimmings – canapés and appetisers, petits fours on tiered silver stand – are all to the point. Service is occasionally unctuous, usually spot-on. A tendency to avoid the uncertain makes the wine list long on big obvious names. On the whole, choices are decent enough; do we detect a slight easing in the pricing policy? 21 Queen Street continues to impress on the strength of sound clarets and antipodeans, but this must be weighed against unexciting Alsaces and Beaujolais. There are some halves. House wine is from £9.60. CELLARMAN'S CHOICE: Montagny, premier cru, Les Vignes sur le Clou 1990, Dom. A. Roy, £18.60; Sancerre Rouge 'Cuvée Prestige' 1989, Crochet, £23.70.

CHEF: Terence Laybourne  PROPRIETORS: Susan and Terence Laybourne  OPEN: Mon to Sat, exc Sat L; 12 to 2, 7 to 10.45  CLOSED: public and bank hols  MEALS: alc (main courses £15.50 to £23.50). Set L £16  SERVICE: not inc  CARDS: Access, Amex, Diners, Visa SEATS: 50. Private parties: 50 main room. Vegetarian meals with prior notice. Children's helpings on request. Smart dress preferred. No pipes in dining-room. Wheelchair access. No music. Fax: 091-261 9054

---

**NEW HAW Surrey**                                                      map 3

## L'Ecluse £                                                    NEW ENTRY

10 Woodham Lane, New Haw KT15 3NA                           COOKING 1
WEYBRIDGE (0932) 858709                                      COST £16–£32

The good news is that Bernard Dumonteil is back at the stoves, after a stint in the homeland doing his national service. L'Ecluse (French for 'lock', one of which is just opposite on the River Wey) is nothing fancy, the comfort is limited, and the look of it reminded one person of the sort of place that you might have found in the backstreets of a French provincial town 20 years ago. The cooking, too, remains resolutely French mainstream, with excellent value for money and a nice line in cheap alternatives with the crêpe menu. Reports have contrasted the rather lackadaisical duck salad and its scanty dressing with the very acceptable mushrooms in a vol-au-vent with a port and red wine sauce, and the 'fat and juicy' moules farcies. Main dishes such as steak au poivre with a cognac cream sauce and salmon with a chive sauce and a beurre blanc were workmanlike, even if a potato cake served with a fillet steak with Pinot Noir sauce needed more study to get it right. French apple tart is perfectly acceptable. Understandably, the place is often packed: not too demanding, pleasant service and a pleasant location. New this year are the authentic Brittany crêpes, savoury and sweet, served with a glass of wine. The wine list is also fairly priced – all French, it has some choices from the south-west that do not strike as altogether hackneyed. House wines are £7.50.

CHEF: Bernard Dumonteil  PROPRIETOR: Francesca Duval  OPEN: Mon to Sat, D only (L by arrangement); 7 to 10.30  MEALS: alc (main courses £8.50 to £11.50). Set D £13.50 to £15.50. Menu express £9.50  SERVICE: not inc  CARDS: Access, Visa  DETAILS: 30 seats. 2 tables outside. Private parties: 30 main room. Vegetarian meals. Children's helpings. Wheelchair access. Music

## NEW MILTON Hampshire

map 2

# ▲ *Chewton Glen,*
# *Marryat Room* ❦ ✻

Christchurch Road, New Milton BH25 6QS
HIGHCLIFFE (0425) 275341
from A35 follow signs to Walkford and
Highcliffe, take second turning on left
after Walkford down Chewton Farm road

COOKING 3*
COST £28–£66

Chewton Glen is a most polished English country-house hotel in the New Forest. It caters for the chauffeur-driven classes, and pampers their bodies in the health and leisure centre as well as looking after their every whim in the hotel and the dining-room. Most people applaud the training and attitude of the staff who are much in evidence. Pierre Chevillard's cooking seems willing to mix dishes that can be termed venturesome with the definitely unexciting. Thus the range of meats offered on the restaurant *carte* is not going to offend, or even challenge, anyone's eating skills – there is not a bone in sight. But the fish includes turbot with an unctuous and brilliant garlic and foie gras sauce and roasted red peppers. Then again, chicken (which has flavour) is dolled up with truffles and leeks and given zing by a cashew-nut vinaigrette. Promise may not always be fulfilled: one especially disconsolate couple found the brochettes of 'exotic' fruits with rice pudding and raspberry sorbet consisted of apple, pineapple and banana. There are various types of menu: a lengthy *carte*, a dinner table d'hôte, a fixed-price lunch, and a *carte* that offers 'salads and light luncheon fare'. The wine list, which wins awards time and time again, most recently got a gong from the French for offering the best representation of their wine regions. This just goes to show that competitions never find out the whole truth, for there are several lists in Great Britain alone that do this far better. Chewton manages breadth without depth, as shown, for example, in the sections on Beaujolais, Loire reds and Rhônes. Taken as a whole, however, the list is a balanced gathering of worldwide wines. There are plenty of expensive first growths for the super-rich, but also extensive and reasonably priced choices from Australia, USA and Italy, not to mention Russia and Germany – to counter any charges of French chauvinism. House wine is from £11.95.
CELLARMAN'S CHOICE: Condrieu, Clos Chanson 1990, Perret, £38; St-Julien, Ch. Talbot 1983, £25.

CHEF: Pierre Chevillard  PROPRIETORS: Martin and Brigitte Skan  OPEN: all week; 12.30 to 2, 7 to 9.15  MEALS: alc (main courses £14 to £21.50). Set L £22.50 to £25, Set D £39. Light L menu  SERVICE: net prices  CARDS: Access, Amex, Diners, Visa  DETAILS: 110 seats. 10 tables outside. Private parties: 90 main room, 8, 24 and 120 private rooms. Car park. Vegetarian meals. Children's helpings. No children under 7. Jacket and tie. No smoking in dining-room. Wheelchair access (3 steps; also WC). Music  ACCOMMODATION: 58 rooms, all with bath/shower. Rooms for disabled. B&B £178 to £345. No children under 7. Afternoon teas. Garden. Swimming-pool. Sauna. Tennis. Golf. Snooker. TV. Phone. Confirm by 6. Fax: (0425) 272310 (*The Which? Hotel Guide*)

---

▲ *This symbol means accommodation is available.*

---

**NORTH CHEAM Surrey**　　　　　　　　　　　　　　　　map 3

## *Partners Brasserie* £　　　　　　　　　| NEW ENTRY |

---

23 Stonecot Hill, North Cheam,
nr Sutton SM3 9HB
081-644 7743　　　　　　　　　　　　　　　　　COOKING 1
on A24, 1m S of Morden (nr Woodstock pub)　　　　COST £17–£32

This is the cut-price version of Partners West Street, Dorking (see entry). It is
set, inauspiciously, among a row of suburban shops but, as a reporter pointed
out, the place succeeds because it has got the fundamentals right. The interior is
cheerfully done out in 'primary shades' with arty posters on the walls and
brightly coloured paper napkins on the tables. The well-trained staff fit in
perfectly. The menu is a jauntily presented affair backed up by daily specials
and the value for money is excellent. At the centre are one-bowl dishes such as
cassoulet of crispy duck leg with white beans and beef stew with herb
dumplings; elsewhere you will find moules marinière 'enlivened with cream',
fresh pasta with tomatoes, garlic and mozzarella, chargrilled calf's liver, and
sweets such as lemon tart with raspberry sauce and crème fraîche. Set menus
offer two choices at each course, with main dish examples being chicken or
salmon, and are affordably priced. The short wine list follows suit and the
Lupé-Cholet burgundy at £7.95 was 'the best house wine in years', according
to one expert.

---

CHEF: Timothy Franklin　PROPRIETORS: Partners Restaurants plc　OPEN: Tue to Sat, exc
Sat L; 12 to 2.30, 7 to 10　MEALS: alc (main courses £6.50 to £11.50). Set L and D £7.45 (2
courses) to £9.95　SERVICE: 10%, card slips closed　CARDS: Access, Amex, Diners, Visa
DETAILS: 30 seats. Private parties: 30 main room. Vegetarian meals. Children's helpings.
Wheelchair access. Music. Air-conditioned

---

**NORTHLEACH Gloucestershire**　　　　　　　　　　map 2

## *Old Woolhouse*

---

Market Place, Northleach GL54 3EE　　　　　　　　COOKING 3
COTSWOLD (0451) 860366　　　　　　　　　　　　COST £43–£56

High on the square of this little gem of a Cotswold town, on the church side, is
a house that seems to have been equipped once upon a time with plate-glass
shop windows. Now they are blanked out by lace curtains, and behind them
Jacques and Jenny Astic produce their very characterful and classic French
food. 'We both chose turbot and scallops with white wine and cream, followed
by noisettes of lamb with a red wine sauce and compote of peppers, onions and
courgettes and dauphinois potatoes. Then a simple green salad, St Marcellin
cheese and a raspberry tart. Each course was perfect in its way, the lamb
superlatively so.' The calm assurance, simplicity of choice, steady nature of the
repertoire and level of achievement appeal greatly to many people. Others find
the undoubted individuality of the place unsettling: it does not resound to the
toing and froing of the everyday world. We have not seen the wine list this
year, but it comes dear and French. House wines are from £14.

417

CHEF: Jacques Astic  PROPRIETORS: Jacques and Jenny Astic  OPEN: Tue to Sat, D only (L and Sun and Mon D by arrangement); from 8.15  CLOSED: 1 week Christmas  MEALS: Set D £32  SERVICE: not inc  DETAILS: 18 seats. Private parties: 18 main room. Vegetarian meals with prior notice. Children welcome. Smart dress preferred. No music

## Wickens ♥ ⁵⁄✳

Market Place, Northleach GL54 3EJ
COTSWOLD (0451) 860421

COOKING 3
COST £21–£37

The Square at Northleach is a positive haven for the stomach. On one side is this personal cottage restaurant where the Wickens promote home-grown and English-inspired cooking. Opposite is the new Windrush Wines shop, formerly at Cirencester, where Mark Savage offers a fine list – a fact not missed by the Wickens. Over towards the church is the Old Woolhouse (see previous entry), as French as Wickens is English. Wickens offers the best form of Anglicism: an intelligent adaptation of the old house, and use of local materials in ways that are open to outside influence, yet no history-book reconstruction. Hence salmon is grilled with olive oil and lemon, and 'Englishman's cassoulet' is made with pork, veal and lamb, not the goose products of Toulouse. Sometimes the past is ransacked, for instance in a first course of spiced beef done according to a Staffordshire recipe. The Britishness continues into sweets; here Joanna is paramount, producing puddings that Eliza Acton might recognise. Lunch-times see 'bumper open sandwiches' and light savouries. The wine list, peppered with almost as many exclamation marks as bottles, deals in the main with wines from English-speaking countries. The notes give some idea of the enthusiasm and names indicate the quality, whether a run of varieties from Three Choirs or a show of Stag's Leap, Brokenwood or Esk Valley in Hawkes Bay. Prices are very keen. House wines are £8.75.

CHEFS/PROPRIETORS: Christopher and Joanna Wickens  OPEN: Tue to Sat (L Nov to Apr by arrangement); 12.15 to 1.45, 7.20 to 9  MEALS: alc D (main courses £8.50 to £15). Light L menu  SERVICE: net prices  DETAILS: 36 seats. Private parties: 22 main room. Vegetarian meals. Children welcome. No smoking in dining-room. Music

---

**NORWICH Norfolk**

map 6

## Adlard's ▮

79 Upper St Giles Street, Norwich NR2 1AB
NORWICH (0603) 633522

COOKING 4
COST £21–£51

All is restful, calming and verdant inside. The table settings and green candles please; the pictures and prints intrigue; flowers are profuse and fresh; and you may enjoy the distraction of a mildly erotic screen as you lick curry butter sauce off your Morston oyster. The main push this year has been to emphasise unstuffiness and accessibility: enthusiastic participation in the *Financial Times* 'Lunch for a fiver' initiative has brought the legacy of a permanent two-course 'Lunch for a tenner', with an option on three courses at £13. Dinner, meanwhile, may be priced any way you want, from £32 for four courses down to £4.50 for cheese and salad alone, with canapés and rolls thrown in. Starters win most praise: 'superb' mussels with a pillow of puff pastry on spinach with a lightly curried lentil sauce; wild mushrooms in choux; and salmon with thin green beans and goujon of Dover sole, the excellence of each being accentuated by 'elegant presentation' and delicate saucing (a dill beurre blanc, a vanilla vinaigrette, a lobster fumet, a vanilla jus, a red pepper coulis). Main courses show a similar level of expertise but a slight dimming of inspiration: venison sausages and pan-fried escalopes of lamb in red wine sauce 'were expertly cooked but weren't quite as tasty as they promised to be', while the vegetable selection, although well cooked, has been felt 'unenterprising'. Cooked fruit (roast pears, poached peaches, hot cherries and fooled rhubarb), in tandem with ices and sorbets, dominates dessert. It is service that lets the side down most regularly: 'We were met with long faces, no welcome smile and throughout the evening we felt that we, the customers, were really quite a nuisance.' The balance between creating a relaxed atmosphere and one where service lags is a fine one, since every table wants to be served at a different pace, but 'three dishes served at hourly intervals' is a little languid for most. 'No music – hooray!' was counterpointed by 'nowhere to take coffee and cigar to – unhooray'. The wide-ranging wine list consoles, with a first-rate New World selection combined with no less unbridled an enthusiasm for France. Other restaurateurs would do well to study the annotations, which enable every diner to order knowingly rather than stabbing in the dark; and the choices more than justify a taxi-ride home. House wine is £9.10. CELLARMAN'S CHOICE: Rosemount, Chardonnay 1992, £16; Côtes du Rhône, Parallele 45 1986, Jaboulet, £16.

CHEF: David Adlard   PROPRIETORS: David and Mary Adlard   OPEN: Tue to Sat, exc Sat L; 12.30 to 1.45, 7.30 to 10.30   MEALS: alc (main courses £17). Set L £10 (2 courses) to £13, Set D £29 to £32   SERVICE: not inc, card slips closed   CARDS: Access, Amex, Visa DETAILS: 40 seats. Private parties: 40 main room. Vegetarian meals. Children's helpings. No smoking until after main course. Wheelchair access. No music

## By Appointment

**NEW ENTRY**

27–29 St Georges Street, Norwich NR3 1AB   COOKING 2
NORWICH (0603) 630730   COST £27–£42

The two adjoining shops have undergone many changes in the last four or five hundred years. But none more than this final conversion to a restaurant. The result is that you go in through the back door, via the kitchen, and are faced with innumerable nooks and crannies for tables, in one shop, and a veritable antique shop in the next, where coffee and drinks are taken. A performance from the architecture is matched by the menu's recitation by Robert Culyer, who chalks it up on the blackboard earlier in the day. The repertoire may include fresh sardines with garlic and parsley, mussels out of their shells with leeks, Pernod and cream, turkey with apricots and sour cream, duck with sweet-and-sour lime and redcurrant sauce, and lamb stuffed with prunes and walnuts. It joins, perhaps, to the British love of mixing sweet and sour, fruit and meat. People have approved the production, however, though cavilling sometimes at the scanty sizing of the meat, made up for at the finish by a plateful of spotted dick, or a baked chocolate cheesecake with a rich chocolate sauce. The experience is much enjoyed for a night out. The wine list comes in large part from T & W Wines of Thetford. The Dom. La Grave from Peter Vinding Diers is a sign that not all the interest lies in bottles costing over £20 and there is much to debate in a choice that does not go overboard for length. House wines start at £10.30.

CHEF: Timothy Brown   PROPRIETORS: Timothy Brown and Robert Culyer   OPEN: Mon to Sat, D only; 7 to 9.30   MEALS: alc (main courses £12 to £14.50)   SERVICE: not inc   CARDS: Access, Visa   DETAILS: 30 seats. Private parties: 30 main room, 6 to 25 in private rooms. Car park. Vegetarian meals. No children under 12. Smart dress preferred. No smoking during meals in dining-room. Wheelchair access (also WC). Music

## Marco's � ⚜

| | |
|---|---|
| 17 Pottergate, Norwich NR2 1DS | COOKING 1 |
| NORWICH (0603) 624044 | COST £28–£50 |

A slight interruption of service occurred in the winter months while Marco Vessalio was reconditioned for extended service; but otherwise, this long-runner motors on. Ring the bell for access, note the cleanliness of kitchen as you pass and enjoy the soft colours of the dining-room, resplendent with swagged Georgian windows and heavy linen on every surface. Home-made pasta, gnocchi and bresaola link hands across the menu with scampi, Dover sole and chicken breast with prawns, ginger and pimento. It is not the usual list of a Britalian trattoria, though the clichés of the Cal-Ital new-wave have not seeped as far as Pottergate either. Reactions vary, which may indicate that performance does also. The wine list does not always give the growers' names, but when they are provided they show a steady eye for quality with Isole e Olena Chianti and the wonderful caramel orange Moscato di Pantelleria. Champagnes excepted, all bins are Italian. Prices are fair and house wines are £9. CELLARMAN'S CHOICE: Torbato Terre Bianche 1990, Sella & Mosca, £16; Schioppettino di Garmigliano 1985, Collavini, £15.

CHEF/PROPRIETOR: Marco Vessalio   OPEN: Tue to Sat; 12 to 2, 7 to 10   CLOSED: last 2 weeks Sept, first 2 weeks Oct   MEALS: alc (main courses £12 to £16). Set L and D £19 SERVICE: not inc, card slips closed   CARDS: Access, Amex, Diners, Visa   DETAILS: 22 seats. Private parties: 10 main room. Vegetarian meals. Children's helpings. Smart dress preferred. No smoking in dining-room. Wheelchair access. No music

## St Benedicts Grill £

| | |
|---|---|
| 9 St Benedicts, Norwich NR2 4PE | COOKING 2 |
| NORWICH (0603) 765377 | COST £19–£33 |

The Raffles have grown. Not only have they bought out their initial partners, the Mabeys of Sudbury, but they have also grafted on Pinocchio's next door. The intention is to keep the two places separate, and St Benedicts continues to plough its own furrow of good value, spare comfort (you sit on pews) and modern cooking. Reports of Pinocchio's have not been as satisfactory as those for St Benedicts. The cooking at St Benedicts, however, has received much praise for dishes like spinach, mushroom and artichoke gratin, smoked goose and bacon salad, halibut and asparagus fricassee, and a duo of bass and halibut marinated in olive oil and balsamic, served warm with new potatoes. Grilled calf's liver with red onions and mash was thought a perfect rendering of this standard. Big chips are also appreciated, and when desserts include simplicities like blackcurrant mousse or a chocolate sorbet, both of which taste intensely of what they are meant to, then reporters feel happy in their choice. The place fairly buzzes. A dissenting voice remarked that the food, which seems clear and simple, in fact ends up less full of impact than it should and that, under a mask of modernity there lurked a '60s bistro. The sound wine list is sensibly priced and draws from plenty of sources, including some good makers like Marqués de Cáceres, Bailly-Reverdy and Roger Luquet in Mâcon. House wines are from £6.95.

CHEF: Nigel Raffles  PROPRIETORS: Nigel and Jayne Raffles  OPEN: Tue to Sat; 12 to 2, 7 to 10 (10.30 Fri and Sat)  CLOSED: 25 to 31 Dec  MEALS: alc (main courses £7 to £9.50) SERVICE: not inc  CARDS: Access, Amex, Visa  DETAILS: 42 seats. Private parties: 42 main room, 25 private room. Vegetarian meals. Children welcome. No cigars/pipes in dining-room. Wheelchair access. Music

---

**NOTTINGHAM Nottinghamshire**                                                      map 5

## *Saagar* £

473 Mansfield Road, Sherwood,
Nottingham NG5 2DR
NOTTINGHAM (0602) 622014 and 692860                                    COOKING 1
on A60, 2½m from city centre                                             COST £12–£37

Readers continue to endorse this comfortable, friendly restaurant opposite Sherwood Public Library. The interior is unobtrusively decorated, with tables not too close together. The chef is from Kashmir, so the main thrust of the cooking is north Indian. Tandooris, kebabs and karahi dishes line up alongside Kashmiri aubergines cooked with mint, yogurt and cashews, and Kashmiri kurma. The menu also shows a south Indian presence in the shape of kaallan specialities cooked with mango, yogurt and coconut. The repertoire is extensive and many specialities are peculiar to the restaurant; the range of breads and accompaniments is also impressive. The cost of most main courses includes rice, poppadum and chutney. Reporters describe the service as 'relaxed and civilised'. Lager is probably the most appropriate drink, although the Indian tea has been 'excellent'. House wine is £7 a litre.

CHEF: Amjaid Habib  PROPRIETOR: Mohammed Khizer  OPEN: all week; 12 to 2.30, 5.30 to 12  MEALS: alc (main courses £6 to £9). Set L £6, Set L and D £12.50 (minimum 2) SERVICE: not inc  CARDS: Access, Amex, Visa  DETAILS: 40 seats. Private parties: 40 main room. Car park. Vegetarian meals. Children's helpings before 7pm. No children under 6. Smart dress preferred. Music. Air-conditioned

---

*See the inside of the front cover for an explanation of the 1 to 5 rating system for cooking standards.*

£ *indicates that it is possible to have a three-course meal, including coffee, a half-bottle of house wine and service, at any time the restaurant is open (i.e. at dinner as well as at lunch, unless a place is open only for dinner), for £20 or less per person.*

---

## Sonny's

3 Carlton Street, Hockley,
Nottingham NG1 1NL
NOTTINGHAM (0602) 473041

COOKING 1
COST £18–£37

'I am not keen to let it be known that I spent £44.95 sitting in an empty shop window eating bangers and mash' was a rueful comment of one who failed to see the value of giant sausages and an even bigger lump of bubble and squeak that had carrots, not cabbage, as its character builder. Sonny's, in a white-painted converted shop near the Lace Market, may go in for such 'peasant' fare. The cooking is in the modern mode of its Barnes parent (see London entry), and light starter dishes such as grilled salmon and chervil vinaigrette, and grilled aubergine and courgette with mint and pistachio pesto are also found. Experiment is tempered to Nottingham tastes come the main dishes, which revolve round chicken with tomatoes, beef and calf's liver, a ratatouille and goats' cheese sandwich made with rösti potatoes, and prawn and chorizo gumbo. The service is relaxed. The café serves light snack meals and pasta. The wine list is a short but useful set that keeps prices mostly below £20, though margins are by no means wafer-thin. House wines are £7.95.

CHEF: A. Poole   PROPRIETORS: Rebecca Mascarenhas and Vernon Mascarenhas   OPEN: all week; restaurant 12 to 2.30, 7 to 10.30 (11 Fri and Sat), café 11 to 4   CLOSED: 25 Dec MEALS: alc (main courses café £3 to £4.50, restaurant £7 to £12). Set L £9.95 (2 courses) to £12.95, Set D £12.95   SERVICE: not inc   CARDS: Access, Amex, Visa   DETAILS: restaurant 70 seats. Private parties: 70 main room. Vegetarian meals. Children welcome. Smart dress preferred. Wheelchair access. Music

## Truffles

43 Broad Street,
Nottingham NG1 3AP
NOTTINGHAM (0602) 526116

COOKING 2
COST £19–£35

This city-centre restaurant on the fringe of the Lace Market is variously described as 'low-key', and 'sparse', with bare boards, minimal tables and background music. However, most people accept that this informal place serves its purpose, with helpful and intelligent waitresses, and the good cooking of Anthony Scott. When you think of the cultural influences, and transport costs, that have gone into a dish of brill (North Sea) served with pak choi (China) and a sauce of sun-dried tomatoes (Apulia) and vermouth (Piedmont), you realise that to designate a restaurant like Truffles 'French' is wide of the mark. Such far-flung influences are accepted gratefully in further instances such as merguez sausages with peperonata, mussels with honey and curry sauce, scallops and monkfish with oyster mushroom sauce, or calf's liver with coconut, cardamom and coriander sauce – dishes to which the customer responds with enthusiasm. Game, offal and 'luxury' fish such as sea bass are specialities. It helps that the chef is not frightened to make a dish taste of the advertised ingredients. Puddings are also popular, be they sticky toffee or a terrine of four chocolates with coffee-bean sauce. The wine list has enough to be going on with, at prices that seem reasonable. House wines are £7.75.

CHEF: Anthony Scott  PROPRIETORS: Anthony and Firooze Scott  OPEN: Tue to Sat, D only;
7 to 10.45  MEALS: alc (main courses £9 to £13). Set D Tue to Fri £10.95 (2 courses)
SERVICE: not inc  CARDS: Access, Amex, Diners, Visa  DETAILS: 45 seats. Private parties:
45 main room. Car park. Vegetarian meals with prior notice. Children welcome. Smart
dress preferred. Wheelchair access (1 step; also WC). Music

---

## OLD BURGHCLERE Hampshire

map 2

# Dew Pond ✷

Old Burghclere RG15 9LH
BURGHCLERE (0635) 278408
off old A34, 3m W of Kingsclere

COOKING 2*
COST £28–£44

Newbury has its stockbroker-belt, and this somewhat rambling cottage
restaurant (with rural charms helped along courtesy of Laura Ashley) hangs,
just, by its southern hem. Beyond the car park fence, however, is grassland –
pilgrims to Watership Down can lunch here. Whether made up of Newbury
residents or rabbit fanciers, there are full houses at weekends. A hit of the
summer was chilled melon soup flavoured with mint and served with a
strawberry purée. A meal at the same season consisted of a warm salad of quail
dressed with walnut oil, medallions of venison with apples and mushrooms,
poached sole and brill with coriander, cucumber and spring onions in a
vermouth sauce, and desserts of nougat parfait and strawberry shortcake. This
captures quite well the classical tilt to the cooking, with sauces often a
centrepiece (as is game), which seems to fit the image of a serious country
restaurant that showcases enduring fashions with a hint of a modern touch.
What may be intended as delicate may sometimes be vapid; what can be skilled
can sometimes misfire. But the constituency is large for this style of competent,
conventional cooking that shows much craftsmanship and plenty of
commitment. The family atmosphere of service and presentation is appreciated.
The wine list has adequate choices of half-bottles and a range of items under
£15 to keep the bill in check. House Duboeuf is £8.

CHEF: Keith Marshall  PROPRIETORS: Keith and Julie Marshall  OPEN: Tue to Sat, exc Sat
L; 12 to 2, 7 to 10  CLOSED: first 2 weeks Jan, 2 weeks mid-Aug  MEALS: Set L £16 (2
courses) to £19.50, Set D £23  SERVICE: not inc  CARDS: Access, Visa  DETAILS: 45 seats.
Private parties: 50 main room, 25 private room. Car park. Vegetarian meals. Children's
helpings on request. No children under 12. Smart dress preferred. No smoking in dining-
room. Wheelchair access (also WC). No music

---

## OSWESTRY Shropshire

map 4

# Sebastian

| NEW ENTRY |

45 Willow Street, Oswestry SY11 1AQ
OSWESTRY (0691) 655444

COOKING 2
COST £17–£53

A French flag flies outside this converted shop in the town centre. None the
less, the place sports its full Shropshire complement of beams and panelling,
though the decorative touches continue the French theme (etchings of
châteaux, Perrier bottles as vases), and the French (language) menu endlessly

reinforces it (this has to be the reason for serving flambéed snails). In fact, Mark (Sebastian) Fisher is a good cook: 'The flavours were clear and strong, raw materials were good' was one positive comment. A terrine of salmon wrapped in leeks, the fish layered with an aspic containing sun-dried tomatoes and chives, with strips of asparagus and some peeled fresh prawns was really good to eat. A tournedos with a horseradish crust was generous, extremely well kept, exactly cooked and well seasoned. Its stock sauce flavoured with tarragon was similarly *à point*. The accuracy continued through to the vegetables and only petered out with the pudding, when the gratin of fruits seemed slightly lacklustre, even if Mark manages to put the kirsch where the menu says it is (so many restaurants don't). There are gestures towards local tastes: for example, a midway sorbet, elaborate canapés and fancy petits fours. People have applauded the cheaper set-price menu, just as they have the hospitality of Michelle Fisher at the front-of-house. A minimum of six people may like to try the Grande Bouffe menu at £16.50 a head. The wine list is another bit of francophilia: it keeps the prices down, is strong on Duboeuf, has a good group of regionals, and has Bruno Paillard champagne. House wines are from £8.25.

CHEF: Mark Sebastian Fisher   PROPRIETORS: Michelle A. and Mark S. Fisher   OPEN: Tue to Sat, D only (L by arrangement for 6 or more); 6.30 to 10.30   CLOSED: 25 and 26 Dec   MEALS: alc (main courses £12.50 to £18). Set D £9.95 (Tue to Thur) to £13.95 (Tue to Fri)   SERVICE: not inc, card slips closed   CARDS: Access, Visa   DETAILS: 32 seats. 3 tables outside. Private parties: 20 main room. Vegetarian meals. Children's helpings. Wheelchair access. Music

---

## OXFORD Oxfordshire                                                     map 2

# *Al-Shami* £

| | |
|---|---|
| 25 Walton Crescent, Oxford OX1 2JG | COOKING 1 |
| OXFORD (0865) 310066 | COST £17–£29 |

Al-Shami continues to offer good value and 'refreshing, interesting flavours'. The dining-room may seem cramped, but the atmosphere is pleasant and the mood is warm and comfortable. A few Middle Eastern pictures adorn the bare brick walls. The cooking is authentically Lebanese and meals kick off with a cornucopia of raw vegetables and olives. Hot and cold starters continue to receive endorsements: kibbeh nayeh (spiced raw lamb mixed with crushed wheat), fatayer (spinach patties) and hummus topped with slivers of lamb and pine-nuts have been successes. Most main dishes, such as spicy marinated lamb, koftas, and chicken with lemon and garlic, rely on animal protein and the chargrill. Moussaka is the genuine article, 'bursting with flavours'. Lightly dressed salads demonstrate 'excellent knifework' and Lebanese-style mixed vegetables have been given the thumbs-up. Superbly light paklava is a good way to round off a meal. Iryan yogurt drink and Almaza beer supplement the short wine list, which is dominated by Lebanese Araks, Ksara and Ch. Musar. House wine is £9.99.

CHEF/PROPRIETOR: Mimo Mahfouz   OPEN: all week; noon to midnight   MEALS: alc (main dishes £5 to £7). Cover £1   SERVICE: not inc (10% for 6 or more)   DETAILS: 60 seats. Private parties: 65 main room. Vegetarian meals. Children's helpings. Smart dress preferred. Wheelchair access (also WC). Music. Fax: (0865) 311241

## ▲ Bath Place Hotel ♀ ⁵⁄₊✳

| 4–5 Bath Place, Oxford OX1 3SU | COOKING 2 |
| OXFORD (0865) 791812 | COST £21–£60 |

Tucked down an alleyway off Holywell Street, this hotel is an agglomeration of tiny houses that may at first seem like toytown, but serve up bags of atmosphere: would that they were better heated and the breakfasts were less standardised, commented some who have stayed the night. The restaurant continues to serve a useful purpose in a city that has wavered in culinary direction for some years now. Peter Cherrill is a 'modern' cook, his recipes and presentation bear reminders of the revolutionary '70s and, when all the details are equally considered, his product is good. Unfortunately, consistency across the whole meal is not always achieved. However, people still speak warmly of rabbit with tagliatelle and armagnac, of pigeon with savoy cabbage and cinnamon, and of chicken with blewit mushrooms and truffle juices. Vegetables do not get a good press, though the apple and almond pithiviers redressed the balance, even if a mille-feuille of bitter chocolate and raspberries would have benefited from greater bitterness. This year has seen a switch from set-price to *carte* menu, though Sunday lunch remains unchanged. The wine list stand out as much for succinct no-fuss approach as for the quality of the bottles, and the few but carefully chosen halves. Growers of the quality of Basedows in the Barossa valley, Ch. Lanessan in the Médoc and Juillot in Burgundy pepper the list. Prices are fair, with house wines at £10.50. CELLARMAN'S CHOICE: Napa Valley, Hawk Crest, Chardonnay 1991, £13.25; Rully Rouge, La Chatelienne 1989, Juillot, £18.25.

CHEF: Peter Cherrill  PROPRIETORS: Mrs Kathleen Fawsitt and Miss Yolanda Fawsitt OPEN: Tue to Sun, exc Tue L and Sun D; 12 to 2, 7 to 10 (10.30 Fri and Sat)  MEALS: alc (main courses £7.50 to £17.50). Set Sun L £19.50. Light L £9.50  SERVICE: not inc (10% for 6 or more)  CARDS: Access, Amex, Visa  DETAILS: 32 seats. Private parties: 30 main room. Car park. Vegetarian meals. Children's helpings with prior notice. Smart dress preferred. No smoking in dining-room. Wheelchair access (2 steps). Music. Air-conditioned ACCOMMODATION: 10 rooms, all with bath/shower. B&B £70 to £100. Deposit: £25. Children welcome. Pets by arrangement. TV. Phone. Fax: (0865) 791834

## Cherwell Boathouse ♪

| Bardwell Road, Oxford OX2 6SR | COOKING 2 |
| OXFORD (0865) 52746 | COST £19–£29 |

'Although our arrival coincided with that of a party of 20 revellers, I was served courteously and quickly' was the relieved comment of someone who recognised that the Boathouse is well placed for an outing – there are river banks, dappled sunlight by day or evening when the weather is fine, none too many cars and charas, an affordable menu and good cooking. Weekly menus do not give a lot of choice, perhaps three items per course, but most people find something to their liking. Curried parsnip soup, rabbit and pistachio terrine with a port and lemon jelly, or mussels à la crème might be followed by hare with a vinegar and pepper sauce, grilled red snapper with sorrel, and potatoes and chanterelles with cream. Puddings are not exactly luxurious but carry on the victory roll: there is usually something hot and stodgy, something cold and something fruity. The house wine selections, including good half-bottles, are intelligently chosen and priced generously: a decent white Blanc de Blancs from Gascony starts the bidding at £6.50. The remainder of the long and serious list, which is well balanced between the classics and the new, also has fine value. Isole e Olena Chianti at £10.50 or the excellent Crozes-Hermitage of Jaboulet at £12.50 will please most, and the profligate should be quite happy with first-growth clarets and mature burgundies. Half-bottles are absent from the main list. CELLARMAN'S CHOICE: Ch. Cos d'Estournel 1983, £24; Meursault, Clos de la Barre 1986, £29.

CHEF: Gerard Crowley  PROPRIETOR: Anthony Verdin  OPEN: Tue to Sat D, Wed to Sun L (Sat and Sun L only mid-Sept to mid-Apr); 12 to 2 (2.15 Sun), 6.30 to 10 (10.15 Sat) MEALS: alc L (main courses £8 to £11). Set L and D £16  SERVICE: not inc (10%, card slips closed, for 6 or more)  CARDS: Access, Amex, Diners, Visa  DETAILS: 50 seats. 5 tables outside. Private parties: 50 main room, 120 boathouse. Car park. Vegetarian meals. Children's helpings. Wheelchair access (1 step; also WC). No music. Fax: (0865) 391459

## 15 North Parade

15 North Parade Avenue, Oxford OX2 6LX  
OXFORD (0865) 513773

COOKING 2  
COST £21–£43

North Parade Avenue is a narrow one-way street off the Banbury Road and is considerably further *south* than South Parade. Owner Georgina Wood is very much in charge of the front-of-house, ably supported by a team of efficient waiters. New chef Colin Gilbert spent two years at Gray d'Albion in Cannes before coming here and his cooking has a strong provençal accent. In addition to a *carte* (not offered Saturday night or Sunday lunch), there are now fixed-price Sunday lunch and Saturday dinner menus. A new feature is a special bargain two-course lunch. The kitchen specialises in colourful ideas, visual excitement, light sauces and spot-on dressings: parfait of chicken livers with pickled kumquats, baked goats' cheese with provençal vegetables, roast breast of duckling with lentils and a subtle citrus sauce, pigeon with courgette and maize blini, and marinated lambs' kidneys with onion jus have all been recommended. Mosaic of leeks with creamed Jerusalem artichokes and sun-dried tomato sauce has also been singled out. Cornish fish such as black bream is a daily special. As a finale, an 'elegant' version of crème brûlée, with mangos and sultanas marinated in whisky with maple essence, has generated favourable comments. The global list of around 40 wines offers fair-priced drinking and halves show up well. House wine is £9.50.

CHEF: Colin Gilbert  PROPRIETOR: Georgina Wood  OPEN: all week, exc Sun D; 12 to 2, 7 to 10 (11 Sat)  CLOSED: last 2 weeks Aug  MEALS: alc (main courses £8 to £15). Set L £10 (2 courses), Set Sun L £12.95, Set Sat D £19.50  SERVICE: not inc  CARDS: Access, Visa DETAILS: 60 seats. 4 tables outside. Private parties: 60 main room. Vegetarian meals. Children's helpings. Wheelchair access (1 step; also WC). Music. Air-conditioned

*Several sharp operators have tried to extort money from restaurateurs on the promise of an entry in a guidebook that has never appeared.* The Good Food Guide *makes no charge for inclusion and does not offer certificates of any kind.*

# ▲ Old Parsonage, Parsonage Bar ♟

NEW ENTRY

1 Banbury Road, Oxford OX2 6NN
OXFORD (0865) 310210

COOKING 1*
COST £24–£46

It seems strange to relate that some of the most appetising food in Oxford is not found in a restaurant but in this attractively converted hotel hard by St Giles's church, where resident and visitor alike can take a meal in the Parsonage Bar. It has no formal tables and no frills; merely comfortable seats, a decent wine list, a motivated staff, lots of interesting pictures and a pleasing atmosphere – a model hostelry indeed. The historic building is delightful and blends perfectly with the surrounding colleges; a walled garden and roof garden offer seclusion from city bustle. The food is simple, direct and fresh. Examples include asparagus, salmon cakes with mayonnaise, tagliatelle with chicken and pesto, grilled steak, and perhaps calf's liver. This is a sort of middle-class version of the Eagle and the Lansdowne in London (see entries), cleaned up round the edges. The wine list displays intelligence and care in selection and consideration for the customer. Prices are fair, half-bottles very adequate, and a range of a dozen wines by the glass augment the pleasure, with Bruno Paillard champagne and Teruzzi Puthod among them. Altogether, this place is good news for Oxford. House wines are from £10. CELLARMAN'S CHOICE: Ca' del Solo, Malvasia Bianca 1991, Bonny Doon, £16.50; Barossa Valley, Cabernet Sauvignon, Stewart Point 1988, £13.

CHEF: Alison Watkins   PROPRIETOR: Jeremy Mogford   OPEN: all week; 12 to 3, 6 to 11
MEALS: alc (main courses £7 to £14.50)   SERVICE: not inc, card slips closed   CARDS: Access, Amex, Diners, Visa   DETAILS: 35 seats. 11 tables outside. Car park. Vegetarian meals. Children's helpings. Smart dress preferred. No cigars/pipes in dining-room. Wheelchair access. Music. Air-conditioned   ACCOMMODATION: 30 rooms, all with bath/ shower. Rooms for disabled. B&B £97.50 to £195. Children welcome. Pets welcome (bedrooms only). Afternoon teas. Garden. TV. Phone. Doors close at 12.30am. Confirm by 4. Fax: (0865) 311262 (*The Which? Hotel Guide*)

# Restaurant Elizabeth ♟

82 St Aldate's, Oxford OX1 1RA
OXFORD (0865) 242230

COOKING 1*
COST £22–£43

There are times when this restaurant seems to change as little as the ancient monument in which it is housed. Disregard the unlikely entrance, and reserve your oohs and aahs for the plasterwork and panelling and the views over Christ Church. Conservative cooking and choice of dishes for the menu are allied to traditional service – Dover sole is filleted at the table and coffee is served in a chemistry-set Cona. This suits several parties down to the ground, though others may find the old-fashioned way of making sauces, for instance, a little surprising. If game is available, it is well worth ordering, beef is cooked accurately and dauphinois potatoes are delicious. The speciality of the house is crème brûlée. The wine list is replete with treasures, with some old bottles worth thinking about. The Riojas, German beerenauslesen and sweet Bordeaux sections are impressive. House wines are £8.25.

CHEF: Salvador Rodriguez  PROPRIETOR: Antonio Lopez  OPEN: Tue to Sun; 12.30 to 2.30, 6.30 to 11 (7 to 10.30 Sun)  CLOSED: 24 to 30 Dec, Good Fri  MEALS: alc (main courses £13 to £17). Set L £15. Cover £1. Minimum £12  SERVICE: net prices  CARDS: Access, Amex, Diners, Visa  DETAILS: 40 seats. Private parties: 40 main room, 20 and 40 private rooms. Vegetarian meals. Children's helpings. Smart dress preferred. No music

## Whites ⅝✳

| | |
|---|---|
| | **NEW ENTRY** |

16 Turl Street, Oxford OX1 3DH  COOKING 1*
OXFORD (0865) 793396  COST £21–£50

This restaurant and wine merchant is on a narrow street between Broad Street and the High. The vaults (as old as the city walls) deal with the drinking side; then comes the restaurant; then, on the floor above, is the Taj Mahal Indian restaurant – a tower of good living. Whites is nearly as collegiate as its street and has offered a spirited welcome to many lost souls since its opening. Pass by the bar with lines of home-made vinegars, descend a few steps into the restaurant (Dali prints on the walls) and be offered a series of menus to fit pockets as varying as those of students and more affluent parents. The thrust of the cooking is similarly broad: traditionalist values in onion soup, chicken liver pâté and grills; more modern touches in a seafood sausage with parsley pesto, foie gras with brioche and citrus fruits, or fish with pasta, leeks and chives. All these come with lots of intelligent wine recommendations and plenty of advice from the owners, if needed. The cooking has pleased, though sometimes the advertised flavours have been more muted than might be expected from the description. Desserts are seriously enjoyed. The wine list benefits from regular changes directed by the vault-master, and the prices are not greedy. House wine is £7.90.

CHEFS: Christopher Bland, John Martin and David Owens  PROPRIETORS: M. Llewellyn-White and R.M.A. Patterson  OPEN: all week, exc Sun D; 12.30 to 2, 6.30 to 10.15
CLOSED: 1 week Christmas, L bank hols  MEALS: alc (main courses £12 to £18). Set L and D £11.50 (2 courses) to £13.95, Set L and D (inc wine) £21 to £26.95  SERVICE: not inc (10% for 10 or more)  CARDS: Access, Amex, Diners, Visa  DETAILS: 48 seats. Private parties: 30 main room. Vegetarian meals. Children's helpings. No smoking in 1 dining-room. Music. Fax: (0865) 200303

---

**PADSTOW** Cornwall  map 1

## ▲ Seafood Restaurant 🍾

Riverside, Padstow PL28 8BY  COOKING 4
PADSTOW (0841) 532485  COST £28–£75

'We meant to try some more places in Cornwall, but perhaps after the Seafood, they would have been a let down.' Thus the postcard from people reconciled to life at a table looking out over the estuary (bedrooms upstairs for the somnolent have even better views) in a restaurant that does not flag. Rick Stein is still an inventive cook making inroads on the prejudices of English people when it comes to eating fish. Try the plaice with steamed cucumber and coriander, or cod baked in salt, with aoïli and butter beans, or scallops with mange-tout and

butter beans. This is fish cooking that takes notice of the seasons, marries fresh
foods sensibly without the heaviness and encumbrances of old-style sauces,
and is not afraid of reality being left ungarnished if that is best for it. Hence
moules marinière, grilled sole, seafood platter or simple oysters or langoustines
are allowed their space. People who are mad for meat can always have
something fleshy for first course – for instance, pigeon with potatoes, lentils
and leaves – and there is usually a steak. The set-price meals are a good deal
and fairly costed if you have fewer courses than expected. What is such a
pleasure here is that the room is bright and colourful, the chairs are comfortable
without being ornate, and the atmosphere buzzes at almost any time of year.
Desserts are not afterthoughts. The lemon tart had 'the crispest pastry I have
ever eaten', the cheeseboard is respectable, the tarte Tatin well loved. Some
people raise voices at the prices, but they may have never bought fresh fish in
their lives. Those who have see the reason. For the wines, 'Our Selection'
continues to offer a clever and interestng range that will suit most customers.
The emphasis throughout is on white as might be expected, and quality is high;
reds are not outdone and selection remains as secure. Prices are all very fair
with much under £15. House wine is from £8.95. CELLARMAN'S CHOICE:
Bourgogne Aligoté de Bouzeron 1992, A. de Villaine, £14.95; Poggio alle Gazze
1991, Antinori, £22.50.

CHEF: Richard Stein  PROPRIETORS: Richard and Jill Stein  OPEN: Mon to Sat; 12.30 to
2.15, 7 to 9.30 (10 Easter to Sept)  CLOSED: 20 Dec to early Feb, 1 May  MEALS: alc (main
courses £12.50 to £30). Set L £19.25, Set D £26.50  SERVICE: not inc  CARDS: Access,
Amex, Visa  DETAILS: 70 seats. Private parties: 15 main room. Vegetarian meals.
Children's helpings. Music. Air-conditioned  ACCOMMODATION: 10 rooms, all with bath/
shower. B&B £32 to £102. Deposit: 25%. Children welcome. Baby facilities. Pets welcome.
TV. Phone. Fax: (0841) 533344 (*The Which? Hotel Guide*)

---

PAINSWICK Gloucestershire                                              map 2

## Country Elephant

New Street, Painswick GL6 6XH
PAINSWICK (0452) 813564                                        COOKING 3
on A46 Cheltenham to Stroud road                              COST £18–£43

The cooking here is unexpectedly good, and Mark Edwards, the Gibsons' son-
in-law, should take the credit. This Elephant is slap-bang in the middle of
Painswick's elegant Cotswold-stone main street, the house imparting its own
grace to the dining-room (though some have said service can be less graceful
than functional). While keeping his eye upon the possibilities of better value
(by virtue of a set-price evening menu alongside the *carte* and by no longer
offering weekday lunch), Mark Edwards combines deft lightness and intensity
with the need to fuel people's expectations of country cooking. Thus a Sunday
lunch consisted of eggs stuffed with tuna mayonnaise, followed by roast lamb
with onion gravy and a bread-and-butter pudding to close. A weekday dinner
might include an avocado and fresh pear salad with rocket and Parmesan
croûtons or a small hotpot of Cornish fish with a lemon cream sauce, followed
by sand sole with chive butter sauce or venison with black-bean sauce,
finishing with classic modern desserts such as lemon tart or a rhubarb and

ginger pudding. Recommended are fish cookery, duck brought down from Herefordshire, and the hot chocolate pudding. The wine list is a reasonable selection, with house claret or white burgundy at £8.75.

CHEFS: Mark Edwards and Marril Gibson   PROPRIETORS: Kenneth and Marril Gibson
OPEN: Tue to Sun, D only, and Sun L; 12.30 to 2, 7 to 10   CLOSED: 25 to 31 Dec   MEALS: alc (main courses £10 to £16.50). Set Sun L £12.50 to £14.50, Set D £13 to £15   SERVICE: 10% (not inc Sun L), card slips closed   CARDS: Access, Diners, Visa   DETAILS: 40 seats. 4 tables outside. Private parties: 20 main room. Vegetarian meals. Children's helpings. No children under 7. Smart dress preferred. No cigars/pipes in dining-room. Wheelchair access (2 steps; also WC). Music

---

**PAULERSPURY Northamptonshire**                                            map 2

# ▲ Vine House

100 High Street, Paulerspury NN12 7NA
PAULERSPURY (032 733) 267                                          COOKING 2
off A5, 2½m SE of Towcester                                       COST £21–£40

This 300-year-old converted farmhouse built out of limestone is on the road that leads out of Paulerspury. Marcus Springett has caught the British culinary bug with a vengeance. 'Auntie Hilda's traditional recipe for fresh lamb rissoles: we serve this dish with proper sauté potatoes and rosemary gravy,' reads the menu (for gravy, read sauce). Yet the recipes are not standard British either: for example, wild nettle soup with sweetbread dumplings, or oxtail pie braised with Guinness and thyme, served with orange-flavoured mashed potato. Beef gets a more-than-average outing; some would prefer a more balanced menu. On the whole, cooking is adventurous and has often been reported as satisfactory. Julie Springett is a cheerful hostess, though the service has not always run smoothly. The wine list is a general canter with some serviceable choices, though readers have on occasion reported several items out of stock at the same time. House wine is £8.95.

CHEF: Marcus Springett   PROPRIETORS: Marcus and Julie Springett   OPEN: all week, exc L Mon and Sat, and Sun D; 12 to 2.30, 7 to 10   MEALS: Set L £13.95, Set D Mon to Thur £19.50, Set D Fri and Sat £23.50   SERVICE: not inc   CARDS: Access, Visa   DETAILS: 45 seats. Private parties: 25 main room, 12 private room. Car park. Vegetarian meals with prior notice. Children's helpings. Smart dress preferred. No cigars/pipes in dining-room. No music   ACCOMMODATION: 6 rooms, all with bath/shower. B&B £39 to £61. Children welcome. Garden. TV. Phone. Doors close at midnight. Confirm by 6. Fax: (032 733) 309 (*The Which? Hotel Guide*)

---

Net prices *in the details at the end of an entry indicates that the prices given on a menu and on a bill are inclusive of VAT and service charge, and that this practice is clearly stated on menu and bill.*

*Prices quoted in the* Guide *are based on information supplied by restaurateurs. The prices quoted at the top of each entry represent a range, from the lowest meal price to the highest; the latter is inflated by 20 per cent to take account of likely price rises during the year of the* Guide.

---

**PITTON** Wiltshire                                                                                    map 2

## *Silver Plough*

Pitton SP5 1DZ
FARLEY (072 272) 266                                                          COOKING 1
off A30, 5m E of Salisbury                                                 COST £22–£30

Michael Beckett insists that the Silver Plough is 'first and foremost a pub'. But it is a hostelry valiantly trying to change the way pub food is perceived. In the heavily beamed bars you will find a range of hearty basic dishes – fresh pasta, cassoulets, pies, salads and ploughman's. Sometimes the set-up scores – an Indonesian fish hotpot was thoroughly enjoyable – but sometimes there are mishaps as in: 'tasteless' soup, and 'a gigantic slab of fatty roast belly pork that would have suited a docker'. The restaurant concentrates on more eclectic offerings: menus are fixed-price for two or three courses and the repertoire might take in crab-cakes with sweet chilli and coriander sauce; grilled red mullet with minted tabbouleh; and poached boudin blanc with lentils, garlic and shallots. Service is congenial. Real ale is served in the bar and the wine list roams interestingly around the globe; prices are fair. Eight house wines start at £8.95.

CHEF: Joanne Dockerty  PROPRIETOR: Michael Beckett  OPEN: all week; 12 to 2, 7 to 10 CLOSED: Dec 25, Sun D Jan, Feb  MEALS: alc (main courses £9.50). Set L £13.95, Set D £12.95 (2 courses) to £15.95  SERVICE: not inc, card slips closed  CARDS: Access, Amex, Visa  DETAILS: 50 seats. 10 tables outside. Private parties: 40 main room. Car park. Vegetarian meals. Children's helpings. Smart dress preferred. No pipes in dining-room. Music

---

**PLUMTREE** Nottinghamshire                                                      map 5

## *Perkins Bar Bistro* ⁵✳ £

Old Railway Station, Plumtree NG12 5NA
PLUMTREE (0602) 373695                                                      COOKING 2*
off A606, 2m S of Nottingham                                             COST £19–£35

After 11 years in business, Tony Perkins' bistro continues to steam ahead and visitors are seldom disappointed. The novel setting in a converted Victorian country railway station is one of the attractions, and the mature trees and shrub borders help to make the exterior very appealing. The spot is generally tranquil, although the rumble of an occasional test train can disturb the peace. The interior still feels deliberately old-fashioned, with copies of French impressionist paintings, gas-lamp fittings and a traditional French wood-burning stove. The central bar is the focal point, and a non-smoking conservatory extension adds light relief. The menu has a strong Gallic accent and scores heavily on freshness and consistency, even if some reporters reckon that prices are beginning to move out of the bistro bracket. Everything, apart from bread and ice-cream, is made on the premises. The repertoire has many fixtures such as moules marinière, baked eggs with duxelles gratinée, herb-crusted rack of lamb and braised woodpigeon breasts in red wine. Good dishes have also included avocado, apple, celery and chicken salad, Scotch salmon with herb mayonnaise and freshly baked plum frangipane tart. The affordable list of around 50 wines has half a dozen good-value French country wines and a clutch of halves. House wines from Georges Duboeuf are £7.60.

CHEF: Tony Perkins   PROPRIETORS: Tony and Wendy Perkins   OPEN: Tue to Sat; 12 to 2, 7 to 9.45   CLOSED: 4 days Christmas   MEALS: alc (main courses £7 to £10)   SERVICE: not inc   CARDS: Access, Amex, Diners, Visa   DETAILS: 73 seats. 6 tables outside. Private parties: 30 main room, 30 private room. Car park. Vegetarian meals. Children welcome. Smart dress preferred. No smoking in conservatory. Wheelchair access (1 step). Music

---

**PLYMOUTH Devon**                                                             map 1

## Chez Nous ▼

13 Frankfort Gate, Plymouth PL1 1QA                                   COOKING 3*
PLYMOUTH (0752) 266793                                                COST £37–£69

Jacques and Suzanne Marchal's small restaurant is on a depressing pedestrianised square and usefully close to a giant car park in the centre of reconstructed Plymouth. The bold shutters on the windows may cause the observer to expect something dashingly modern within. Wrong: décor and ambience are seriously French bistro. The food, however, is not; nor, with the odd hiccup, is the service. The watchwords here are 'la cuisine spontanée', but this may be taken with a pinch of salt: it does not mean that helter-skelter, rag-bag approach of some English chefs who are anxious to try anything and everything in whatever combinations fit their pocket or fancy. Nor is it that spontaneity that may come from country living and gardening (if there is a glut, cook it). In fact, the approach is rooted in French method and a fairly settled repertoire; the shopping is done in markets and also pursues a pattern. There is variation and immediacy, particularly in the fish (though Plymouth's market is a shadow of its former self). A light touch with vegetables, and some well-judged sauces, give the place an edge. Certainly everything tastes very good, even if it may take some time to decipher the blackboard menu. Dishes such as scallops with a light ginger butter sauce, sweetbreads with lentils, ox tongue with madeira sauce, and simple lamb with tarragon sauce are fine examples of exact technique and sensitive seasoning. Also, this is a restaurant where offal gets its proper due. Desserts may extend to serious chocolate cake with two sauces or home-made ice-creams, and the Turkish delight that may come with coffee should be savoured. The wine list has a wealth of halves and a good slate of clarets and burgundies, old and new. There are eight wines from other countries for those who do not want classic region prices. House wines are from £9.50.

CHEF: Jacques Marchal   PROPRIETORS: Suzanne and Jacques Marchal   OPEN: Tue to Sat; 12.30 to 2, 7 to 10.30   CLOSED: first 3 weeks Feb and Sept   MEALS: alc (main courses £17 to £19). Set L and D £26.50   SERVICE: not inc   CARDS: Access, Amex, Diners, Visa DETAILS: 28 seats. Private parties: 32 main room. Vegetarian meals with prior notice. Children's helpings. No children under 8. Smart dress preferred. Wheelchair access (1 step; also WC). Music. Air-conditioned

---

▲ denotes an outstanding wine cellar; ▼ denotes a good wine list, worth travelling for.

## *Yang Cheng* £

| 30A Western Approach, Plymouth PL1 1TQ | COOKING 1 |
|---|---|
| PLYMOUTH (0752) 660170 | COST £12–£36 |

Yang Cheng is a friendly, family operation popular with Plymouth residents as well as with Chinese sailors working for the Royal Navy. The largely Cantonese menu holds few surprises and changes little, though some variation comes from shopping in the fish markets, making steamed whole sea bass, for instance, a good bet when available. The restaurant is one of the few in the region to offer a dim-sum selection, especially useful at lunch-time. The chef's special banquet is available for four or more people. Drink saké or house French wine at £6.30.

CHEF: K.Y Wong  PROPRIETORS: K.Y. Wong, Mrs K.S. Ling and Mrs Y. Lee Wong  OPEN: Tue to Sun; 12 to 2.30 (3 Sun), 6 to 11 (6.30 to 10.30 Sun)  MEALS: alc (main courses £5.50 to £15). Set L £6.50 to £8.50, Set D £9 to £33  SERVICE: not inc  CARDS: Access, Visa DETAILS: 70 seats. 13 tables outside. Private parties: 70 main room. Vegetarian meals. Children's helpings. Smart dress preferred. Music. Air-conditioned

---

**POLPERRO Cornwall**                                                          map 1

## *Kitchen*

| The Coombes, Polperro PL13 2RQ | |
|---|---|
| POLPERRO (0503) 72780 | COOKING 1 |
| on A387, 3m SW of Looe | COST £22–£37 |

The pink cottage chimes well with the 'little fishing village' image Polperro would like to promote. In fact, it is between the car park and the harbour, and a long walk on a rainy night. The Batesons develop their repertoire slowly, though it covers a lot of ground, happily offering oriental or spiced recipes alongside those which appeal to a British love of sweet and sour. Fish is their pride and joy, though simplicity is not, except when it comes to the vegetables, which are often singled out for praise. The multitude of flavours advertised is sometimes lost in the cooking: basil in a tomato sauce being mere threads of the herb added later, oranges with not a lot of Grand Marnier 'but delicious anyway'. The intentions seem to outrun the achievement. The merchant's wine list, with a tendency to Mommessin, is reasonably priced. House wines are from £8.

CHEFS/PROPRIETORS: Ian and Vanessa Bateson  OPEN: Wed to Mon, D only (in winter D Fri and Sat only); 7 to 9.30  MEALS: alc (main courses £8.50 to £13). Minimum £8.50 SERVICE: not inc, card slips closed  CARDS: Access, Visa  DETAILS: 24 seats. Vegetarian meals. No children under 7. Smart dress preferred. No cigars/pipes in dining-room. Wheelchair access. Music

---

*The 1995 Guide will be published before Christmas 1994. Reports on meals are most welcome at any time of the year, but are extremely valuable in the spring. Send them to* The Good Food Guide, *FREEPOST, 2 Marylebone Road, London NW1 1YN. No stamp is needed if posted in the UK.*

---

| POOLE  Dorset | map 2 |

## ▲ *Mansion House* [NEW ENTRY]

Thames Street, Poole BH15 1JN
POOLE (0202) 685666

COOKING 1
COST £23–£61

The late Georgian house by the harbour at Poole has long been a dining club
where non-members paid a £5 surcharge if they wanted to join for a day. The
principles of operation are changing this year so that the place is to become a
conventional hotel and restaurant, but members (or hotel guests) will be
entitled to a discount. It has been decorated to accommodate every taste known
to Poole, with panelling and plush cosseting the diner, while members drink
in bare-brick neo-Jolly Jack Tar. The menu takes the same line of a little bit of
everything, so that conservative palates are handsomely dealt with off a carving
trolley, plus plenty of duck liver pâté, a mixed hors d'oeuvre, fillet with green
peppercorns, grilled sole, or lobster thermidor. With the other hand chef can
work in a mode nearer to modern fashions, and a meal that included scallops
on a bed of lentils with horseradish sauce, rack of lamb with herb crust and a
tarragon sauce and a pudding of pear poached in champagne set in a chocolate
cup with a dark chocolate mousse showed that he had the will to do this sort of
cooking with skill and judgement. Where the restaurant has fallen down is in
the trimmings and extras like vegetables, coffee, petits fours and the hard
bullet of strawberry sorbet offered between courses. The wine list is split
between the over- and under-£20 and arranged by weight or strength. At heart,
it is a conventional, but decent, French selection, with a bit of the other added
in to give variety and range. House wines are from £9.75.

CHEF: Gerry Godden  PROPRIETOR: Robert Leonard  OPEN: all week, exc Sat L and Sun D;
12.30 to 2, 7.30 to 9.30  MEALS: alc (main courses £12.50 to £28). Set L £13.45 (2 courses)
to £15.75, Set D £19.25  SERVICE: not inc  CARDS: Access, Amex, Diners, Visa  DETAILS:
100 seats. Private parties: 100 main room, 14, 31 and 40 private rooms. Car park. Vegetarian
meals. Children's helpings L. No children under 5. Smart dress preferred. Music. Air-
conditioned  ACCOMMODATION: 28 rooms, all with bath/shower. B&B £50 to £110.
Children welcome. Baby facilities. Pets by arrangement (not in public rooms). Afternoon
teas. TV. Phone. Doors close at midnight. Confirm by 6. Fax: (0202) 665709 (*The Which?
Hotel Guide*)

| POOL IN WHARFEDALE  West Yorkshire | map 5 |

## ▲ *Pool Court* ▮

Pool Bank, Pool in Wharfedale LS21 1EH
LEEDS (0532) 842288
on A658, 3m N of Leeds/Bradford Airport

COOKING 3*
COST £33–£59

Michael Gill, whose Pool Court restaurant has been operative since 1966,
subsequently became involved in other places, but he has never ignored his
original project. This – a creeper-clad classical Georgian house set in grounds
near the main road – has recently received some attention. One change is that
the dining-rooms have been redecorated in cool greys and whites, and
ornamented with architectural prints. Another addition is that after your order
has been taken a personal menu is rapidly printed (such are the glories of

modern technology). Armed with this little card you have no excuse for thinking you were eating venison when in fact you ordered duckling. One old hand maintains that the cooking has lightened along with the decoration. His confit of duck in a pastry case 'belied its ingredients by its lightness', just as a mousseline of sole had impressed by its flavour on so insubstantial a body. The Pool Court format offers either a 'traditional menu' of several choices, but a set price; or the 'Signature Menu' (price £37.50) of no choice, but a slate of wines served to complement the food; or a new short *carte* which enables people to eat a one- or two-course meal at lower cost than hitherto. The £10 set menu, a loved but perhaps inadequately supported institution, has been deleted. Ideas are not lacking: a first course of smoked and chargrilled salmon is layered with potato cakes, spring greens and horseradish cream; fish-cakes are made with scallops and lobster and served with spinach, leeks and shallots; and a saddle of hare is chargrilled, the leg is jugged, and a sauce made with celeriac and pepper. One man's meal that had started inauspiciously with a paillard of salmon with tapénade and mashed potato ('not as tasty as it could have been'), was redeemed by fillet of beef topped by perfectly salted spinach above 'a thick syrupy oxtail and root vegetable stew, and a "sauce" of mashed potato ladled into the gravy at the table. For me, a lover of potatoes, this was a masterstroke.' While the choice presented is often beguiling, and the ancillaries of bread, petits fours and canapés can hardly be bettered, there are occasional notes to the effect that flavours are not quite as upstanding as they should be. If you like sweet things, 'and Pool Court desserts are so good that we didn't want to miss them', then avoid the slice of fruitcake with the piece of Wensleydale cheese. Service 'is less stiff and intimidating than it used to be; perhaps familiarity eases the slightly mannered formality which can awe newcomers,' remarked one who also suggested that the redecoration has lightened the spirits as well as the rooms. A lively interest in wine manifests itself in an intelligent wide-ranging list. Those who are nostalgic will remain relatively unsatisfied since the wholly admirable concern here is with what is current. An everyday selection of wines, all at £8.95, plus a good range of half-bottles save the day for customers daunted by a list that rarely dips below £16. CELLARMAN'S CHOICE: Jurançon, Dom. Cauhapé Sec 1991, £24.95; Bourgogne, Hautes Côtes de Nuits 1987, Dom. Jean Gros, £19.50.

CHEF: David Watson  PROPRIETORS: Michael and Hanni Gill  OPEN: Tue to Sat, D only (L by arrangement for 10 or more); 6.30 to 9.30  CLOSED: 2 weeks Christmas  MEALS: alc (main courses £7.50 to £14). Set D £25.50 (2 courses) to £33.50  SERVICE: not inc  CARDS: Access, Amex, Diners, Visa  DETAILS: 65 seats. Private parties: 85 main room, 30 and 36 private rooms. Car park. Vegetarian meals. Healthy eating options. Children's helpings with prior notice. Smart dress preferred. No cigars/pipes in dining-room. Wheelchair access (1 step). No music. Air-conditioned  ACCOMMODATION: 6 rooms, all with bath/shower. B&B £70 to £120. Children welcome. Garden. TV. Phone. Doors close at midnight. Fax: (0532) 843115 (*The Which? Hotel Guide*)

Healthy eating options *in the details at the end of an entry signifies that a restaurant marks on its menu, in words and/or using symbols, low-fat dishes or other healthy eating choices.*

## PORTHOUSTOCK Cornwall

map 1

## *Café Volnay*

Porthoustock, nr St Keverne TR12 6QW
ST KEVERNE (0326) 280183
off B3293, 1½m E of St Keverne

COOKING 2
COST £22–£37

A beamed, whitewashed room given over one-third to open kitchen and two-thirds to simple seating in what was once a row of fishermen's cottages now houses a restaurant (opposite the telephone box) that took the fancy of East Anglians on 'a simply foul, rain-soaked, thick foggy night'. Despite the weather they went on to call it 'an experience and something of an exploration'. Mark the maps well and depart. Messrs Rye and Chapman devise a short, sensibly priced menu with refreshing ideas such as a large field mushroom filled with tomato and garlic, served with a tossed salad, or a Mediterranean tartlet of tomatoes, olives, anchovies and cream, before main courses like duck with plums, red mullet with capers, red wine and anchovies, or scallops wrapped in Parma ham. The staff's enthusiasm is catching, the clientele is younger than often seems to hug the British coastline and people have fun at the Volnay. Come dessert, there may be an Italian feel to offerings like bukkarram and biscotti, Taleggio cheese with pears and passito, or even grape and almond tart; but those with sweeter teeth can try chocolate decadence or a strawberry and hazelnut meringue cake. More places like this would raise the status of Cornwall. The wine list is brief, but the makers are reliable and prices very fair. House wine is £6.95.

CHEFS/PROPRIETORS: S.A. Chapman and C.N. Rye   OPEN: Tue to Sun (Thur to Sat winter),
D only, and Sun brunch winter; 7.30 to 9 (Sun brunch 11 to 2)   CLOSED: day after bank
hols   MEALS: alc (main courses £9 to £15)   SERVICE: not inc   DETAILS: 24 seats. Private
parties: 18 main room. Vegetarian meals with prior notice. Children welcome. No cigars in
dining-room. Music

## PORT ISAAC Cornwall

map 1

## ▲ *Slipway* ✣

**NEW ENTRY**

Harbour Front, Port Isaac PL29 3RH
BODMIN (0208) 880264

COOKING 1
COST £19–£40

The main car park for the village is the harbour at low water. What happens at high tide is another matter, but the young team at this hotel by the slipway would be sure to tell you. The Bishop brothers make no bones about their maritime setting (a sixteenth-century building, once a chandlers) and the menu is full of fish and shellfish. A good thing, people have said, for it is fresh and capably dealt with. Try sole with scallops and a lobster sauce, or John Dory with herb butter. There is also a strong vegetarian line, though this has not met the same praise: it wins no converts, even if performing a service. A summer visit confirmed the fish side, soft-pedalled the puddings, and spoke warmly of the welcoming atmosphere. At lunch-times, bar snacks and light meals are served. The wine list is a mix of the humdrum and acceptable. House wines are £7.95.

CHEFS: Karen Smith and Eden Osabofu   PROPRIETORS: S.D.R. Bishop, P.J.A. Bishop and J.J. Bishop   OPEN: all week; 12 to 2.30, 6.45 to 9.30   CLOSED: Nov to 20 Dec, 3 Jan to 21 Mar   MEALS: alc (main courses bar L £4 to £6, restaurant D £9 to £15.50). Set D Mon to Wed £16.50   SERVICE: not inc, card slips closed   CARDS: Access, Amex, Visa   DETAILS: 40 seats. 6 tables outside. Private parties: 40 main room. Car park. Vegetarian meals. Children's helpings L. No smoking on top floor. Wheelchair access ground floor. Music   ACCOMMODATION: 10 rooms, 6 with bath/shower. B&B £19 to £52. Deposit: £15. Children welcome. Baby facilities. Afternoon teas. Garden. Phone (*The Which? Hotel Guide*)

---

POULTON-LE-FYLDE Lancashire                                          map 5

## ▲ *River House* ▼

Skippool Creek,
Thornton-le-Fylde FY5 5LF                                        COOKING 2
POULTON-LE-FYLDE (0253) 883497 and 883307                        COST £21–£69

Built in 1830 for a gentleman farmer, the River House has been in the Scott family since 1958. It stands peacefully 'up the creek' with only the call of seabirds and the sound of boats to disturb the peace. The full *carte* is a substantial affair, with very little to suggest pandering to current fashion. Here is a kitchen that delivers medley of seafood with wine and cream sauce, beef Stroganov, grilled Dover sole and sauté chicken with tarragon sauce and saffron rice. Desserts continue the same theme, with ticky tacky pudding (the original hot date and walnut pudding with butterscotch sauce), chocolate mille-feuille and brandy-snap baskets filled with sorbet. Light lunches – crab mousse, sauté chicken livers, salmon fish-cakes, sandwiches and so on – are a new feature. Wine is taken seriously: an on-site 'off-licence' provides bottles for customers to purchase and the list is an impressive tome – even if details are minimal. Look for the weighty clarets, Bandols from Provence and the German contingent. English fruit wines are also on show. House wine is £12.50.

CHEFS: Bill and Carole Scott   PROPRIETORS: the Scott family   OPEN: all week, exc Sun D; 12 to 2, 7 to 9.30   MEALS: alc (main courses £16 to £25). Set Sun L £12.75, Set L and D £18.50   SERVICE: not inc   CARDS: Access, Visa   DETAILS: 40 seats. Private parties: 40 main room, 14 private room. Car park. Vegetarian meals. Children's helpings. Smart dress preferred. Music   ACCOMMODATION: 4 rooms, all with bath/shower. B&B £55 to £100. Children welcome. Baby facilities. Pets welcome. Garden. TV. Phone. Confirm by 6. Fax: (0253) 892083 (*The Which? Hotel Guide*)

---

POWBURN Northumberland                                              map 7

## ▲ *Breamish House* ⅚✳

Powburn NE66 4LL                                                 COOKING 1
POWBURN (066 578) 266 and 544                                    COST £18–£31

This one-time Georgian farmhouse set in five acres of well-kept gardens at the foot of the Cheviots is for many a model of a country hotel: comfortable and welcoming, it uses local materials and offers straightforwardly prepared food. A set-price dinner brings perhaps four choices of first course and a pair of main courses, with soup in between, and sweets from the trolley. Saturday may produce a bigger menu, but at the same price. A rough pâté with Cumberland sauce, melon with passion-fruit sorbet, loin of pork with mustard sauce and salmon with cucumber sauce are examples of the style. Game is enjoyed in its season. Vegetables are copious and may come from the Johnsons' garden; puddings are British. Reports have had it that organisation may break down under weight of numbers. A service charge is not made or expected. The wine list has a sensible range and some very good names, among them Luc Sorin, Penfolds, Billecart-Salmon and Stag's Leap. House wines are £10.90.

CHEFS/PROPRIETORS: Doreen and Alan Johnson OPEN: all week, D only, and Sun L (light L Mon to Sat by arrangement); 12 to 1, 7 to 8 CLOSED: Jan to first week Feb MEALS: Set Sun L £12.95, Set D £19.95 SERVICE: card slips closed CARDS: Access, Visa DETAILS: 30 seats. Private parties: 30 main room, 12 private room. Car park. Vegetarian meals with prior notice. Children under 12 by arrangement. Children's high tea. Smart dress preferred. No smoking in dining-room. Wheelchair access (also WC). No music ACCOMMODATION: 11 rooms, all with bath/shower. B&B £36 to £96. Deposit: £25. Children under 12 by arrangement. Pets by arrangement. Afternoon teas. Garden. TV. Phone. Doors close at 11. Confirm by 6. Fax: (066 578) 500 (*The Which? Hotel Guide*)

---

POWERSTOCK Dorset                                                              map 2

## ▲ *Three Horseshoes* ⅝✳ £

Powerstock DT6 3TF
POWERSTOCK (0308) 485328                                            COOKING 2
off A3066 at Gore Cross, 4m NE of Bridport                          COST £15–£43

'Tapas night' at the Three Horseshoes seems about as far from the image of a country pub in Hardy country as you can get, and casual visitors have noted the existence of 'the green-wellie brigade' here as at every other part of this fabled coastline. However, the outsiders will be on the way to eat fish rather than tapas, for it is the catches from the Weymouth boats that are the main attraction – unless, in winter, you fancy game. The bar is the seat of much action, including the blackboards from which choice must be made, but a degree of peace and quiet can be had in the dining-room beyond. Matters can get hectic on busy nights, and service may suffer. But a slate full of sea bass, turbot, salmon, red mullet or John Dory is tempting, especially when accompanied with something from a well-founded yet short wine list. The cooking has come under the hand of Will Longman, once owner of his own restaurant in Bridport. He has deftness allied to good sense and a fine way with fish. House wines are £7.90.

CHEF: Will Longman PROPRIETORS: Pat and Diana Ferguson OPEN: all week; 12 to 2, 7 to 10 MEALS: alc (main courses £4 to £17). Set Sun L £12.50 SERVICE: not inc, card slips closed CARDS: Access, Amex, Diners, Visa DETAILS: 100 seats. 15 tables outside. Private parties: 75 main room, 25 and 75 private rooms. Car park. Vegetarian meals. Children's helpings. No smoking in restaurant. Wheelchair access (also WC). Music ACCOMMODATION: 4 rooms, 2 with bath/shower. B&B £24 to £45. Deposit: 50%. Children welcome. Baby facilities. Pets welcome. Afternoon teas. Garden. TV. Doors close at 11 (*The Which? Hotel Guide*)

map 5

## ▲ White House

New Road, The Village,
Prestbury SK10 4DG
PRESTBURY (0625) 829376                    COOKING 1
on A538, 4m N of Macclesfield              COST £20–£52

The catalogue of 'fancy drapes, cane chairs, dragged walls, subtle lighting' gives some hint that this is an attractive old house done up to the nines. The same could be said of the menu – it promises much, then delivers it in a style that confirms the intentions, though underneath it all it might be better undressed and simple. This was the opinion of someone who deemed lunch acceptable, but found that spiced fruit sponge with custard and a citrus reduction sauce was the simplest and the best item of the meal. Melon as a first course is guaranteed a full kit of garnish. The range of the menu ensures happiness for a wide body of people, offering old standards like grilled sole, steak with onion rings, duckling two ways and liver and bacon, but also extending the options to more adventurous pairings like salmon fish-cakes with pineapple salsa, and tagliatelle with monkfish and chicory. 'I had a rotten headache when we came here after a hectic morning, and it says a lot that I enjoyed the meal enormously' was one recommendation encompassing the food, the welcome and the service (although this can be slow if they are very busy). The wines are divided between New World and others. The list uses sound sources and the prices are not out of the way. House wines are £10 a litre and several others are offered by the glass.

CHEFS: Ryland Wakeham and Mark Cunniffe   PROPRIETORS: Ryland and Judith Wakeham   OPEN: all week, exc Mon L and Sun D; 12 to 2, 7 to 10   CLOSED: first week Jan   MEALS: alc (main courses £9 to £18.50). Set L £10.95   SERVICE: not inc, card slips closed   CARDS: Access, Amex, Diners, Visa   DETAILS: 75 seats. 3 tables outside. Private parties: 28 main room, 28 and 40 private rooms. Car park. Vegetarian meals. Children's helpings. Smart dress preferred. No cigars/pipes in dining-room. Wheelchair access. Music   ACCOMMODATION: 9 rooms, all with bath/shower. Rooms for disabled. B&B £62 to £104. Children welcome. Baby facilities. Pets welcome. Garden. TV. Phone. Doors close at midnight. Confirm by noon. Fax: (0625) 828627 (*The Which? Hotel Guide*)

map 3

## Stane Street Hollow ♥ ⚒

Codmore Hill, Pulborough RH20 1BG
PULBOROUGH (0798) 872819                    COOKING 3
on A29, 1½m NE of Pulborough               COST £19–£43

A reader who finds the food here tip-top, questions the 'third-class railway-carriage seating of the bar and the music which consists of brass instruments, cowbells and peasants slapping their leather shorts'. The dining-room, he avers, is much better: it is cosy, especially in winter, and the music does not penetrate. The Hollow is set among duck-pond and vegetable garden and is a cross between cottage and farmhouse. René Kaiser cooks in tune with the Swiss music, but his wife Ann casts a spell of good humour on visitors. Some measure of this skill is taken from one who went to try the bargain lunch but who was tempted to plunge into the *carte* instead: he enjoyed scallops parisienne, escalopes of venison with bacon and mushroom and a hollowed apple filled with quince preserve, leeks with cream and sauté potatoes, then a dessert that topped all desserts. 'On tasting the chocolate cake, I realised there was a serious chef in the kitchen,' he finally admitted, before embarking upon the Assiette René – blackcurrant sorbet in a meringue swan, citrus parfait, and a light cheesecake with raspberry sauce. People pronounce on the qualities of the vegetable cookery (seasonal) and enjoy the Swiss or German outings they are sometimes offered with dishes such as fish knödels with caper sauce, or a Jaegertopf (game casserole). The chocolate cake, of course, is Black Forest. The wine list is surprisingly cheap. A Morey St-Denis 1982 from Dujac at £27 is very fair, and the choices of maker and growth are generally upper crust. A more aggressive salesman would pronounce every bottle 'a steal'. At these prices there is no need for 'house wines'. CELLARMAN'S CHOICE: Valais, Oeil de Perdrix 1990, £13.55; Rioja Reserva 1983, Ondarre, £13.65.

CHEF: René Kaiser   PROPRIETORS: René and Ann Kaiser   OPEN: Wed to Sun, exc Sat L and Sun D; 12.30 to 1.15 (12 to 1.30 Sun), 7.30 to 9   CLOSED: 2 weeks May and Oct   MEALS: alc (main courses £10 to £12.50). Set L £8.50 (2 courses)   SERVICE: not inc   DETAILS: 32 seats. Private parties: 24 main room, 14 private room. Car park. Vegetarian meals. Children's helpings. Smart dress preferred. No smoking in dining-room. Wheelchair access (3 steps). No music

---

**RAMSBOTTOM  Greater Manchester**                                           map 5

## *Ramsbottom Victuallers Company Ltd, Village Restaurant* ▮ ⁵✳

16 Market Place, Ramsbottom BL0 9HT
RAMSBOTTOM (070 682) 5070                                    COOKING 3
off A56/M66, 4m N of Bury                                    COST £16–£53

This year's entry reflects a time of turmoil and change in the affairs of Chris Johnson and Ros Hunter. It is not gossip-column material, but reflection of their attempts to adjust their business to different times and local tastes. As the Ramsbottom Victuallers they have opened a food and wine shop, drawing on the 800 bins (and rising) of the old restaurant wine list, and offering ingredients not usually available in the Bury supermarkets. This extends to a coffee-shop and supper room that has taken over most of the business from the Village Restaurant, which now functions only for dinner on Saturdays (unless there is a party booking). Supper is served in two sittings, a three-course meal with a brace of choices for each course. Ros Hunter's style – good ingredients, not too complicated – comes through even in this more populist mode. Carrot, orange and cinnamon soup, Lancashire hot-pot and summer fruit soup was one set of alternatives for the end of June; smoked lamb with a mango and onion salad, pork with prunes, and rhubarb crumble was another, from the middle of the month. 'This bistro – church pews and hang on to your cutlery – is so good, I've been four times,' reports someone who was pleased with her reception, even when eating alone. British cooking needs such a lift, particularly in this region. There is a short wine list, but you can buy from the shop and pay a

£4.70 corkage charge. The Village Restaurant continues to operate in its inimitable manner. Efforts should be made to sample the experience, even in its new phase of truncated opening. 'It is not really a restaurant, but a church, complete with priest and priestess, a temple dedicated to the adoration of food. Those admitted are expected to take an active part in the service, in particular paying strict attention to the frequent sermons about the next course from the high priest, and, for those deemed sufficiently reverent, by taking part in call-and-response sessions with him. There is a collection at the end.' One slightly agnostic reporter, who none the less 'would have paid more, for less', was served a meal of game terrine, Stilton, onion and parsley soup, baby halibut with sea urchin mousseline sauce, pork prepared two ways and served with seasonal vegetables, unpasteurised British cheeses, and a choice of crème brûlée, apple amber, marquise au chocolat or exotic fruit salad. Coffee will be a named blend (as it is in the supper room, where it changes every so often). Agnostic, perhaps, but he was impressed – 'the eight slivers of cheese, graded perfectly from bland to sharp, provided a memorable interlude' is a measure of the care and attention invested. The pork and the terrine were less impressive than the soup, fish and cheese. Puddings? Pretty good. The wine list is remarkable, though there are some changes in the making due to the shift in business. It is one of the great encyclopaedias of the country. There is no stock list at present, but Chris Johnson will afford you close guidance.

CHEF: Ros Hunter   PROPRIETORS: Ros Hunter and Chris Johnson   OPEN: Ramsbottom Victuallers Tue to Sat, exc Sat D; 12 to 2.30, 6.30 and 9 (2 sittings). Village Restaurant Sat D only; 8 for 8.30   MEALS: Ramsbottom Victuallers alc L (main courses £4.50 to £6), Set D £9.50. Village Restaurant Set D £29.50   SERVICE: not inc, card slips closed   CARDS: Access, Amex, Visa   DETAILS: 20 seats. Private parties: 14 main room, 8 and 14 private rooms. Vegetarian meals with prior notice. Children welcome. Smart dress preferred. No smoking. Wheelchair access. No music

---

REDLYNCH Wiltshire                                                                          map 2

## ▲ *Langley Wood*

Hamptworth Road, Redlynch SP5 2PB
ROMSEY (0794) 390348                                                            COOKING 2
off A338, then B3080, 7m SE of Salisbury                              COST £17–£36

'We felt very happy and contented,' remarked a couple who visited this small country house on the edge of the New Forest for Sunday lunch. Part of the appeal of the place is its homely domesticity. Some reporters see it as 'primarily a reasonably priced B&B in a far better-than-average setting', which is not intended to demean. Sylvia Rosen's cooking is a generous version of traditional British with a few modern overtones and plentiful use of local produce. Old English potted Cheddar followed by collops of beef with pickled walnuts line up alongside mussels with vermicelli, then chicken breast stuffed with courgettes and served with sweet pepper sauce. Vegetarians might be offered spinach and walnut pudding with onion marmalade. Careful buying from the local butcher ensures that roasts and steaks are reliable bets. Sweets are from the trolley and the chocolate count can be high. Changes to the wine list have added depth to the range of clarets and seen judicious New World additions.

Half-bottles are also worth investigating. Prices are fair throughout. House wine is £7.20.

CHEF: Sylvia Rosen   PROPRIETORS: David and Sylvia Rosen   OPEN: Wed to Sat, D only, and Sun L; 12.30 to 2, 7.30 to 11   CLOSED: 2 to 3 weeks Jan to Feb   MEALS: alc (main courses £10 to £13.50). Set Sun L £12.75   SERVICE: not inc   CARDS: Access, Amex, Diners, Visa   DETAILS: 30 seats. Private parties: 30 main room. Car park. Vegetarian meals. Children's helpings Sun L. Smart dress preferred. No cigars/pipes in dining-room. Wheelchair access (also WC). Music   ACCOMMODATION: 3 rooms. B&B £17.50 to £35. Children welcome. Pets welcome. Afternoon teas. Garden

---

RICHMOND Surrey                                                                                    map 3

## ▲ Petersham Hotel, Nightingales

NEW ENTRY

Nightingale Lane, Richmond TW10 6UZ                                          COOKING 2
081-940 7471                                                                       COST £26–£50

Perched on Richmond Hill, the building is a distinctive mid-Victorian mansion in French Gothic style with the topmost section looking like some kind of folly. Its grand, high-ceilinged dining-room overlooks one of the most famous stretches of the River Thames. As one reporter observed, 'The food now goes a long way towards matching the acclaimed view.' Tim Richardson is a chef with real talent and an eye for exquisite presentation, and he is capable of producing some quite exceptional dishes. His menu is in the modern British idiom, veering between medallions of venison with red cabbage, blueberries and a pumpkin and potato cake, and steamed skate with tarragon and red wine vinegar, to resurrected stalwarts such as fish-cakes, omelette Arnold Bennett, and liver and bacon with bubble and squeak. Reporters have heartily endorsed delicate crab and guacamole gâteau with champagne dressing, a 'fantastic' latticework pithiviers of chicken livers with fennel and tomato sauce, and roast breast of duck glazed with honey, coriander and cumin, which 'cut like a dream'. Vegetables are cooked to perfection, while desserts are examples of classics such as crème brûlée and summer pudding. Meals progress at a leisurely pace and service can sometimes seem a little 'disorganised'. The wine list is extensive and includes some excellent bin-ends; prices are fair. House wine is £12.50.

CHEF: Tim Richardson   PROPRIETOR: C.S. Dare   OPEN: all week; 12.15 (12.30 Sun) to 2.15, 7 to 9.45 (8.30 Sun)   MEALS: alc (main courses £9.50 to £18). Set Sun L £20, Set D for 8 or more Mon to Sat £20   SERVICE: not inc   CARDS: Access, Amex, Diners, Visa DETAILS: 80 seats. Private parties: 12 main room, 20 and 36 private rooms. Car park. Vegetarian meals. Children's helpings. Smart dress preferred. No-smoking area. Music ACCOMMODATION: 54 rooms, all with bath/shower. Lift. B&B £72 to £130. Children welcome. Baby facilities. Afternoon teas. Garden. TV. Phone. Confirm by noon. Fax: 081-940 9998

---

*If a restaurant is new to the* Guide *this year (did not appear as a main entry in the last edition)* NEW ENTRY *appears opposite its name.*

---

RICHMOND  North Yorkshire                                                   map 7

## ▲ *Howe Villa* ╬✳

Whitcliffe Mill, Richmond DL10 4TJ
RICHMOND (0748) 850055
take A6108 Richmond to Leyburn road
for ½m, turn left at ATS tyre service                          COOKING **2***
station, keep left following sign                             COST £20–£24

'I have just returned from a four-night break at Howe Villa and marvel afresh at
Mrs Berry's standards, which, if not perfect – an unattainable state in this
imperfect world – are as near to it as human endeavour can manage.' This is
enthusiasm of an uncommon order, but it is echoed by others visiting this
elegantly furnished Georgian mill-owner's home (paper, not flour: enter
through the old papermill yard) hidden away by the River Swale on the edge of
Richmond. There is no wine list (but no corkage either for your own bottle
buys) and the menu offers little choice. This changes nightly, and everybody
seems to find everything 'delicious': for example, a first-course cucumber and
herb mousse looked 'so colourful and attractive with its various trimmings that
one was tempted to take a photo', and a mousseline of sole and smoked salmon
was 'really delicious, wonderfully light'. Menus are five courses, and soups
(watercress, asparagus, pea and mint) follow first courses. Main-course dishes
might include breast of chicken sliced at an angle, served around a potato
galette sandwiched together with spinach and cheese, or pink roast beef slices
with vegetables, 'done in all sorts of interesting ways'. A choice is always
available at dessert ('we were persuaded to try each'), and might include lemon
pudding, chocolate and strawberry roulade, or a rum and ratafia cream ('a
triumph, quite beautiful, one felt totally happy afterwards'). Swaledale cheese
produced in Richmond then plugs any remaining gaps. Housekeeping and
breakfasts match dinner; Anita Berry serves as well as cooks; and all leave
marvelling at the 'perfect British cooking'.

CHEF: Anita Berry   PROPRIETORS: Tom and Anita Berry   OPEN: Tue to Sat, D only; 7.30
CLOSED: Dec to 1 Mar   MEALS: Set D £20. Unlicensed, but bring your own: no corkage
SERVICE: not inc   DETAILS: 12 seats. Private parties: 12 main room. Car park. Vegetarian
meals. Children's helpings. No children under 12. No smoking in dining-room. Music
ACCOMMODATION: 5 rooms, all with bath/shower. D,B&B £65 to £110. Deposit: £10. No
children under 12. Garden. TV. Doors close at 11.30. Confirm by 6 (*The Which? Hotel Guide*)

---

RIDGEWAY  Derbyshire                                                        map 5

## *Old Vicarage* ▮ ╬✳

Ridgeway Moor, Ridgeway S12 3XW
SHEFFIELD (0742) 475814
off A616, on B6054 nearly opposite                            COOKING **4**
village church                                               COST £26–£45

Economics do have practical effect. Here at the Old Vicarage, a Victorian house
and garden most of the way down the hill which constitutes the village of
Ridgeway, a drive for greater financial accessibility has led to the creation of a

bistro where meals can be eaten at a cheaper price. Meanwhile, the original dining-room (the bistro is in the conservatory part) continues to offer characterful food cooked by Tessa Bramley. Her son, Andrew, remains the major-domo. It is not, however, just economics that induce change. Tessa Bramley has curiosity and its consequences are shifts in emphasis, alterations in taste. This year an exemplary lunch began with a timbale of peppers with a chive sabayon and a tomato and tarragon sauce. Then there were Thai-style fish-cakes coated in sesame, flavoured with lemon balm rather than lemon grass, given a spaghetti of vegetables and a definitely Chinese glossy sauce, and partnered by some tiger prawns wrapped in filo, with lots of five-spice and texture from onions and green peppers. An intermediate course was a raviolo of goats' cheese flecked with red pimento, with a pesto dressing, before a real medley of fish cooked with cream, fennel and chives. This stew was dressed with croûtons topped with rouille, some broccoli and beans and a dish of potato gratin with leeks and lovage – a mixture of culinary messages if ever there were one. The finish was rhubarb strudel with sweet cicely. Tessa Bramley has struck out through the world for ideas and she is unwilling to let a good thing alone. It is not fussed to death, but she enjoys embellishing the message. Hence fillet steak is served with a ramekin of steak and kidney pie; pork fillet with cardamom and honey gets Chinese-style pancakes. It is great fun. Sometimes people find the place serious and wish that it was generally *more* fun. Perhaps this is mere reflection that everyone is not on the same wavelength, for many find it bubbling over with jollity. Pastry-work is good, garden work is excellent. The techniques of grande cuisine are never forgotten and it has much to offer. The wine list is always good with plenty of curiosity here, too, and a pricing policy that is not too painful. House wines are from £9.

CHEFS: Tessa Bramley and Rupert Staniforth   PROPRIETORS: Tessa Bramley and Andrew Bramley   OPEN: Tue to Sun, exc Sat L and Sun D; 12.15 to 3, 7 to 10.45   CLOSED: 26 to 30 Dec   MEALS: Set bistro L and D £17.50, Set restaurant L and D £27.50   SERVICE: not inc, card slips closed   CARDS: Access, Amex, Diners, Visa   DETAILS: 50 seats. 5 tables outside. Private parties: 40 main room, 12, 26 and 40 private rooms. Car park. Vegetarian meals. Children's helpings. No smoking in 1 dining-room. Wheelchair access (2 steps). Music. Fax: (0742) 477079

---

**RIPLEY** Surrey                                                                               map 3

## *Michels'* ▮

13 High Street, Ripley GU23 6AQ
GUILDFORD (0483) 224777                                                       COOKING 3
off A3, 4m SW of Cobham                                                    COST £27–£57

This individual building with old walled garden, swags and furbelows of fabric, lots of flowers and elephants and cockerels dotted around the place is the product of many generations of builders who have added to the Georgian beginnings. Erik Michel's cooking is individual too. Presentation counts for much, and there are as many layers to recipes used here as to the architecture. None the less the modern shift to bolder flavours has resulted in dishes like a cassoulet of bacon, and smoked eel and salt cod with scallops, and the fad for offal comes up in something like a daube of ox cheek with kidneys, vegetables and herb dumplings. People speak with affection of the three fillets of beef, pork and veal – an old conceit, but done well with three sauces tasting of something. A reader's comment was 'excellent, exquisite, exquisite, too filling' as he went through the courses. 'Too filling' was for a hot soufflé, though he had already registered a gap in that vegetables were scanty. His only gripe was not with the food but the inattentive service. There are few restaurants in mid-Surrey that try so hard at the stove, whatever happens to the service. The wine list is intelligent and not overlong, with enough to please the profligate, but essentially aimed at the middle ground with prices to match, and careful selection throughout. House wines are from £8.75. CELLARMAN'S CHOICE: Margaret River, Chardonnay 1990, Cullen, £24.95; Vacqueyras, Dom. la Monordière 1989, £12.95.

CHEFS: Erik Michel and Paul Warner   PROPRIETORS: Erik and Karen Michel   OPEN: Tue to Sun, exc Sat L and Sun D; 12.30 to 1.45, 7.30 to 9 (9.30 Sat)   MEALS: alc (main courses £12 to £16.50). Set L £18, Set D Tue to Fri £20 to £27 (inc wine)   SERVICE: not inc   CARDS: Access, Amex, Visa   DETAILS: 50 seats. Private parties: 10 main room, 12 private room. Car park. Vegetarian meals. Children welcome. Smart dress preferred. Wheelchair access (2 steps). Music

---

**RIPLEY North Yorkshire**                                                                    map 7

## ▲ *Boar's Head*

Ripley HG3 3AY                                                    COOKING 2
HARROGATE (0423) 771888                                           COST £21–£41

Three miles north of Harrogate, this hotel (once a coaching-inn) is another to add to a list of stop-overs for travellers between north and south: it is comfortable, well appointed and welcoming. The village is a model, rebuilt in the 1830s by the owners of Ripley Castle. Visitors may regret that the castle is not their destination, but rest consoled that many of the furnishings started life in the family pile, and that guests have free run of the grounds and may fish in the lakes. The food at the Boar's Head may mop up any lingering resentment. David Box has not trimmed his grand-hotel style, so many dishes are quite elaborate to the eye, if not in the cooking. The set-price menu has gained approvals for dishes such as salt cod fish-cakes with parsley sauce, pigeon with green lentils and a light pepper sauce, pheasant casserole with herb dumplings, fillet of beef with creamed potato and shallots, turbot and salmon with chive butter sauce, a warm plum duff with ice-cream and custard, caramelised apple with honey and cinnamon cream, and 'the best Christmas pudding I have tasted'. Grand-hotel style, therefore, but a noticeable attempt to produce food – lamb hotpot with red cabbage, for example – that will appeal to appetites honed by northern winds. The kitchen is not afraid of doing everything for itself, from canapés and petits fours to the bread. Somehow the mixture of posh hotel, serious restaurant and pleasant bar for beer and skittles has been achieved effortlessly in a very short time. The wine list takes in a bit of everything, but is better for reds and best for clarets. Half-bottles are not stinted and the house wines, at £8.95, are a trio of French that include a Gaillac from Dom. de Bosc-Long.

CHEF: David Box   PROPRIETORS: Sir Thomas and Lady Ingilby   OPEN: all week; 12 to 2, 7
to 9.45   MEALS: Set L £9.95 (2 courses) to £14.50, Set D £26.50   SERVICE: not inc   CARDS:
Access, Amex, Visa   DETAILS: 50 seats. Private parties: 60 main room, 15 private room. Car
park. Vegetarian meals. Children welcome. Smart dress preferred. No cigars/pipes in
dining-room. Wheelchair access (also WC). Music   ACCOMMODATION: 25 rooms, all with
bath/shower. Rooms for disabled. B&B £80 to £98. Children welcome. Baby facilities. Pets
by arrangement. Afternoon teas. Garden. Tennis. Fishing. TV. Phone. Fax: (0423) 771509

---

**RIPON  North Yorkshire**                                                    map 7

## ▲ *Old Deanery* ⅜               | NEW ENTRY |

Minster Road, Ripon HG4 1QS                                   COOKING 2
RIPON (0765) 603518                                            COST £20–£52

The deans had good living quarters, conveniently located hard by the north
face of the cathedral, with space and the patina of centuries. The Dooleys have
an equally ornamental restaurant, though some old hands remember the
studied mix-and-match furnishing of their predecessors with fondness.
Daphne Dooley is a self-taught cook who none the less manages to juggle a *carte*
that is long for these parts, especially as there are vegetarian and daily menus in
addition. She produces food very much to Ripon's taste. Mushrooms à la
Deanery are wrapped in smoked salmon and puff pastry, baked and sauced
with mushrooms and white wine and a fair dollop of caviare; Wensleydale
croissant is a home-made crescent filled with cheese and given a red berry
sauce; Gressingham duck comes pink, with a honey and lemon sauce; a
'symphony' of fish can be tasted in all its notes; dauphinois potatoes are
seductive. Fish is considered a strong point. Debate simmers about the overall
atmosphere: many say cheerful, a few say glum. A new addition is La Brasserie,
offering cheaper meals Monday to Friday – reports, please. The wine list offers
a few New World producers; the French choice is on the dear side, solid rather
than exciting. House wines are from £9.

---

CHEF: Daphne Dooley   PROPRIETORS: Graham Dooley, Daphne Dooley and Jon Dooley
OPEN: restaurant Tue to Sun, exc Sat L and Sun D; 12 to 2, 7 to 9.30 (10 Sat). La Brasserie,
Mon to Fri; 12 to 2, 7 to 10   CLOSED: last 2 weeks Jan   MEALS: restaurant alc (main courses
£15 to £18). Set Sun L £11.50, Set D £15.95. La Brasserie alc (main courses £7 to £8)
SERVICE: not inc, card slips closed   CARDS: Access, Amex, Diners, Visa   DETAILS: 60 seats.
7 tables outside. Private parties: 80 main room, 15, 25 and 35 private rooms. Car park.
Vegetarian meals. Children's helpings Sun L. Smart dress preferred. No smoking in dining-
room. Wheelchair access. No music   ACCOMMODATION: 2 rooms, both with bath/shower.
B&B £60 to £100. Children welcome. Baby facilities. Garden. TV. Doors close at midnight.
Confirm by 6

---

⅜ *indicates that smoking is either banned altogether or that a dining-room is maintained
for non-smokers. The symbol does not apply to restaurants that simply have no-smoking
areas.*

*The text of entries is based on unsolicited reports sent in by readers, backed up by
inspections conducted anonymously. The factual details under the text are from
questionnaires the* Guide *sends to all restaurants that feature in the book.*

ROADE Northamptonshire                                    map 3

## Roadhouse Restaurant

16 High Street, Roade NN7 2NW
NORTHAMPTON (0604) 863372                          COOKING 3
off A508, 4m S of Northampton                      COST £20–£37

At five minutes from junction 15 (turn left at the George), the Roadhouse is
almost near enough to the M1 to serve as a stand-in service station. Don't be
fooled: the competence, consistency and imagination of Christopher Kewley's
cooking are a world away from the edible platitudes offered to those at the
wheel. The last year has seen expansion; table settings continue to please more
than décor, 'but one does not go there to admire the wallpaper'; and the only
music you will catch is a drift of Wagner from the kitchen. 'The food, value and
the occasion were so good that I am in danger of using too many superlatives
and losing credibility,' worried one, left beaming by a pre-Christmas carol
service lunch of hot terrine of crab with tomato and chive sauce, breast of
mushroom-stuffed pheasant with a cabbage parcel of minced legmeat,
chocolate marquise with Drambuie custard, fine coffee and mince pies – all for
£15. A regular visitor has relished variations on a theme of bacon-wrapped
chicken breast – once stuffed and sauced with leek, cream and herbs, and once
with garlic and orange. Crisp pastry cases are always appreciated, filled either
with asparagus and lemon sole in a cream sauce, with spinach and a curried
vegetable stew, or with smoked haddock and a poached egg. Daubes and stews
are the usual main-course anchors. Desserts metamorphose with less regularity
than the savoury dishes, though they are no less reliable. Susan Kewley leads
informal and efficient service. Australia plays an increasingly important role in
the wine list (from £8.50 up), though it is sad to see the loss of the short tasting-
descriptions for each wine. As most will be driving here, a selection of
grown-up non-alcoholic drinks would be welcome.

CHEF: Christopher Kewley   PROPRIETORS: Christopher and Susan Kewley   OPEN: Tue to
Sun, exc Sat L and Sun D; 12.30 to 1.45, 7 to 9.30 (10.30 Sat)   CLOSED: 2 weeks summer
MEALS: alc (main courses £10 to £16). Set L £14, Set Sun L £15   SERVICE: net prices, card
slips closed   CARDS: Access, Amex, Visa   DETAILS: 45 seats. Private parties: 50 main
room. Car park. Vegetarian meals with prior notice. Children's helpings on request. Smart
dress preferred. No music

---

ROMALDKIRK Co Durham                                     map 7

## ▲ Rose and Crown ✳ £                          NEW ENTRY

Romaldkirk DL12 9EB
TEESDALE (0833) 50213,
changes to (0833) 650213 October 1993              COOKING 1
on B6277, 6m NW of Barnard Castle                  COST £13–£38

This imposing stone building dominating the manicured village green still
functions as a local pub, although it is becoming increasingly popular for its
accommodation and restaurant. Considerable improvements have been noted
of late: willing, friendly service, copious amounts of polished woodwork, a

roaring fire and more lighting have greatly improved the feel of the place. The restaurant is an oak-panelled room with an elegant, relaxed atmosphere. Dinner is a four-course, fixed-price menu (with a couple of supplements) that changes daily. The cooking can be accomplished, although sometimes the results are a mixed bag. Home-baked bread and vegetables are cooked with real flair and imagination, but some other aspects are less reliable. On the plus side, reporters have enthused about quenelles of crab with dill sauce, hot kipper, apple and calvados salad, and mussels with Muscadet and cream. Main courses have ranged from veal with oysters mushrooms in Cinzano and halibut in Gruyère and grain mustard sauce, to roast poussin with a bright blackberry-coloured red wine sauce. Puddings are similarly uneven, although home-made ice-creams have been praised. The place also has a good reputation for its adventurous bar menu and real ale. The comprehensive wine list runs to over 160 bins and has plenty of decent drinking for around £12. House wine is £7.95.

CHEF: Christopher Davy  PROPRIETORS: Christopher and Alison Davy  OPEN: restaurant Mon to Sat, D only, and Sun L; 12 to 1.30, 7.30 to 9. Bar all week; 12 to 2, 6.30 (7 Sun) to 9.30  CLOSED: 25 and 26 Dec  MEALS: alc bar (main courses £3 to £10). Set Sun L £10.75, Set D £22  SERVICE: not inc, card slips closed  CARDS: Access, Visa  DETAILS: 24 seats. 6 tables outside bar. Private parties: 18 main room. Car park. Vegetarian meals with prior notice. Children's helpings Sun L. No children under 6 D. Smart dress preferred. No smoking in dining-room. No music  ACCOMMODATION: 12 rooms, all with bath/shower. Rooms for disabled. B&B £52 to £74. Deposit: £20. Children welcome. Pets welcome (not in public rooms). Afternoon teas. TV. Phone. Doors close at 11. Confirm by 4. Fax: (0833) 50828, changes to (0833) 650828 Oct 1993 (*The Which? Hotel Guide*)

---

**ROMSEY** Hampshire                                                                                map 2

## *Old Manor House* ▮

21 Palmerston Street, Romsey SO51 8GF                              COOKING 3*
ROMSEY (0794) 517353                                                     COST £23–£56

Around and about this half-timbered, jettied building with diamond panes, giant fireplaces, heavy beams and all the accoutrements of age is modern Romsey. Ignore it; keep to the old and good. Mauro Bregoli has been cooking for many years and has an eye for quality, technique and flavour. 'I feel that there is a clash between two sides of his personality, one wanting to cook native, even earthy, Italian, the other producing adoptive creations from France and international cuisine,' commented one who was impressed by examples of the latter in a lunch of mussels in saffron cream sauce on a bed of leeks, followed by duck with quinces in a light black-bean sauce, then a chocolate fondant with satisfyingly bitter apricot sauce. For one diner, Italian dishes like cotechino sausage with lentils had 'far more taste than usual'; so did tagliolini with crisp wild mushrooms and 'a perfect carbonara-type sauce' for another reporter, who felt the best came at the end – an outstanding mille-feuille of strawberries. As these comments reveal, the repertoire is very wide over a variety of set menus (which are good value at lunch), culminating in a long set-price *carte* at dinner. Service is old-fashioned in its ornateness, though not always capable of dealing with emergencies. The setting is grandly old world, though tables are too closely set. The performance varies, as if attention has slipped, or the pressure of major events – for instance, New Year's Eve – is too great to allow the best potential to be realised. 'The Choice of the House', a page of interesting wines that makes allowances for the less knowledgeable, would on its own make a more careful, considerate and exciting list than many restaurants can muster. For the enthusiast with time and money the 20-odd pages that follow are a wonder; there are mature clarets and burgundies from the top echelons, decent bourgeois Médocs, eight fine Hermitages, as many Barolos and a page of half-bottles. To complain of high prices misses the point: Mauro Bregoli is a collector who wishes to share his treasures, although the collection comes expensive. The list is a wise balance that must please most people. House wine is £9.50. CELLARMAN'S CHOICE: Barossa Valley, Stewart Point, Semillon/Chardonnay 1990, £14.50; Barossa Valley, St Hallett, Cabernet/Merlot 1990, £15.

CHEF/PROPRIETOR: Mauro Bregoli   OPEN: Tue to Sun, exc Sun D; 12 to 2, 7 to 9.30
CLOSED: 24 to 31 Dec   MEALS: Set L £14.50 to £25, Set D £35   SERVICE: not inc   CARDS:
Access, Amex, Visa   DETAILS: 45 seats. Private parties: 12 main room, 24 private room. Car park. Vegetarian meals. Children welcome. Smart dress preferred. No cigars/pipes in dining-room. No music

---

**ROSS-ON-WYE** Hereford & Worcester                                              map 4

▲ *Pheasants* ❢                                    NEW ENTRY

52 Edde Cross Street,
Ross-on-Wye HR9 7BZ                                                      COOKING 2*
ROSS-ON-WYE (0989) 65751                                               COST £18–£47

An unprepossessing shop-front to this former pub in an out-of-the-way street belies an unusual and excellent interior. The mood is mellow: walls have been ragged and sponged a deep, soft red; idle jazz dissolves in the air; battered books invite inspection. The food here reconciles two widely divergent culinary seams – old English and modern Californian – with remarkable success, thanks to 'neat, loving care' in the kitchen. The menus intrigue, though choices are limited (Eileen Brunnarius cooks alone); California is more evident in the lunch-time brasserie-style blackboard menu; inventive archaeology in the dinner *carte*. Nibbles are generous to a fault – two nutmeggy ricotta and spinach tortellini and a blue-cheese-filled filo pouch arrived for a single diner. A starter of meaty rabbit and hazelnut terrine was served with an ideally contrastive orange chutney relish; one of three dollops of well-flavoured smoked haddock mousse was wrapped in thickly sliced Cornish smoked salmon, with a rustic vinaigrette dribbled around its pleasing forms. Old England is recalled by pike with anchovy gusto ('a successful dish, though a little strange'), its legacy by three thick, large slices of 'utterly fatless' beef served tenderly rare with a 'really top-class pool of rye-whiskey sauce, very creamy, and subtly yet clearly flavoured'. Vegetarian options (such as potato and celeriac pancakes with wild mushrooms and water-chestnuts in a brandy cream sauce) are always included on the menus. Bread-and-butter pudding, a staple, is 'absolutely delicious, soft inside, crisp outside'. Service, from New Zealander Adrian Wells, is keen, 'professional yet personal – a decided plus'. He has also compiled the first-rate wine list. It is frantically inventive (seven

449

aperitifs by the glass range from Sercial madeira via Lillet to King Offa All-Apple Aperitif) and has exemplary organisation and annotation: all the wines are divided into stylistic groups, then listed by grape variety, with clear descriptions for most. There is an extensive range of wines by the glass to encourage adventurous drinking. House wines are from £8.

CHEF/PROPRIETOR: Eileen Brunnarius    OPEN: Tue to Sat (winter L by arrangement only); 12.30 to 2.30, 7 to 10    CLOSED: 24 Dec to 2 Jan, bank hol Sun and Mon    MEALS: alc (main courses L £4 to £7, D £11 to £16.50). Set D £18.50    SERVICE: not inc, card slips closed CARDS: Access, Amex, Diners, Visa    DETAILS: 22 seats. Private parties: 24 main room. Vegetarian meals. No children under 10. Smart dress preferred. Wheelchair access. Music ACCOMMODATION: 2 rooms. B&B £25 to £40. Confirm by 6

---

**ROWDE** Wiltshire                                                                           map 2

## George & Dragon  £

High Street, Rowde SN10 2PN                                               COOKING 3
DEVIZES (0380) 723053                                                      COST £17–£37

Something of a battle, it is felt, is being waged between the set-up of this ordinary village pub – complete with bar fruit-machine flashing and burbling – and kitchen achievement, as embodied by the 'unbelievable delight' of sea bream in a mustard sauce, or the 'excellent combination of flavours' found in spicy chicken grilled with yogurt. Dining-room and garden are more congenial. 'Are there many places offering a better-value set lunch?' questioned a traveller, replete after grilled brandade, chicken savoyarde ('a casserole of good chicken in a powerful, creamy tarragon sauce, mash and four veg') and crème brûlée – all for £10. 'Strong and fresh' watercress and spinach soup and 'excellent' fish soup ('not too heavy and creamy') typify Tim Withers' straightforward but clear-headed cooking. A sense of adventure is cultivated, as when salmon in pastry is given the sweet cosseting of raisins and ginger, or in immos – lamb in yogurt with coriander and garlic ('quite delicate, no flavours overpowering'). Access to good, fresh fish supplies is reflected in roast hake with aïoli and grilled red mullet with orange and anchovy, cooked with the respect they merit. Not every meal succeeds: wild duck was tough enough to take to the air under pressure from knife and fork, and gristly calf's liver was partnered by an over-sharp sauce. 'Brilliant local vegetables', though, show commendable attention to detail, and desserts (prune and armagnac tart, pecan pie, 'perfectly crisped' rhubarb crumble) are carefully composed enough to satisfy without sating. One report described service as 'pleasant and amateur; the dress and earrings of the two males also slightly off-putting (me being stuffy)'. The wine list, which begins at £7.50 (or £1.25 by the glass), is better than it looks at first glance.

CHEF: Tim Withers    PROPRIETORS: Mr and Mrs T. Withers    OPEN: Tue to Sun, exc Sun D; 12 to 2, 7 to 10    CLOSED: 2 weeks Christmas    MEALS: alc (main courses £5 to £17.50). Set L £10    SERVICE: not inc, card slips closed    CARDS: Access, Visa    DETAILS: 35 seats. 5 tables outside. Private parties: 35 main room. Car park. Vegetarian meals. Children's helpings. No children after 9pm. No music

RYE  East Sussex                                                      map 3

## Landgate Bistro ▼ £

| 5–6 Landgate, Rye TN31 7LH | COOKING 2* |
| RYE (0797) 222829 | COST £18–£33 |

Landgate was once the entrance to Rye and this well-established restaurant is
outside the old town at the end of the High Street. Do not expect cosseted
luxury: 'I wish they'd sack the plastic cloths and some of the chairs are less
comfortable than others,' remarks a regular who values the place for its
consistently honest cooking rather than its fittings. A short fixed-price menu
(Tuesday to Thursday) supplements the *carte*, which boasts bistro prices but far
from prosaic ideas. This is serious, potent and generous cooking by any
standards. Many dishes have found favour: white boudin with fried apples;
salmon and smoked haddock fish-cakes; juicy braised squid with white wine,
tomatoes and garlic; leek and Roquefort tart; hare 'as high as it should be'.
'Very fishy' stew is an old favourite. Local fish, well-handled vegetables and a
brilliant assemblage of salad leaves show the owners' commitment to quality.
Desserts draw paeans of praise: crème caramel, apple and almond tart and
chocolate marquise have received rave reviews but, for one reporter, ice-creams
steal the show: they are 'redolent of deep, simple goodness'. As a finale, visitors
are offered a plate of excellent English cheeses. Prices on the wine list remain
eminently fair and this year has seen better house-wines, such as the Touraine
Sauvignon of Marcadet and a basic Pinot from Jadot. The list as a whole has
been spiced up with notable burgundies and clarets of fair age. It is mercifully
not over-long and the choices offered are intelligent. House wines are from
£7.40. CELLARMAN'S CHOICE: Marlborough, Sauvignon 1992, Montana Estate,
£9.20; Ardèche, Les Collines de Laure, 1991, Jean-Luc Colombo, £13.

CHEF: Toni Ferguson-Lees   PROPRIETORS: Nick Parkin and Toni Ferguson-Lees   OPEN:
Tue to Sat, D only; 7 to 9.30 (10 Sat)   CLOSED: 1 week Christmas, 1 week June, 1 week
Oct   MEALS: alc (main courses £7.50 to £11). Set Tue to Thur D £14.50   SERVICE: net
prices, card slips closed   CARDS: Access, Amex, Diners, Visa   DETAILS: 30 seats. Private
parties: 10 main room. Vegetarian meals. Children's helpings. Wheelchair access (2 steps).
Music

SAFFRON WALDEN  Essex                                                map 3

## Old Hoops £

| 15 King Street, Saffron Walden CB10 1HE | COOKING 1 |
| SAFFRON WALDEN (0799) 522813 | COST £17–£38 |

Shoppers, businessmen and family parties unite in applauding this as Saffron
Walden's most useful neighbourhood restaurant, on the first floor of a former
coaching-inn, just off the market square. The number of portions of
'musselcress' soup that have been served must total six figures since Don Irwin
and Ray Morrison made it their hallmark from day one in 1984. Its regular
appearance is matched by other favourites such as lamb with spinach and
bacon wrapping served with a Dijon mustard sauce, and veal chop portugaise,
with a sauce of tomato and garlic. Favourite desserts include pancakes filled

with apple and cinnamon, roulade of chocolate and crème brûlée. The wine list will not surprise or shock. House wines are £6.95.

CHEF: Ray Morrison   PROPRIETORS: Don Irwin and Ray Morrison   OPEN: Tue to Sat; 12 to 2.15, 7 to 10   MEALS: alc (main courses £5 L to £11.50)   SERVICE: not inc   CARDS: Access, Amex, Diners, Visa   DETAILS: 40 seats. Private parties: 40 main room. Vegetarian meals. Children's helpings. Smart dress preferred. Music

---

ST IVES  Cornwall                                                                         map 1

## Pig 'n' Fish

Norway Lane, St Ives TR26 1LZ                                              COOKING 2*
ST IVES (0736) 794204                                                          COST £24–£40

More fish than pig here, this is essentially a place to eat seafood. St Ives' new Tate Gallery has brought the town to the notice of an even greater number of trippers and visitors; this restaurant should be used to restore the flagging spirits at the end of a long day's art appreciation. The underlying intention is informality (with some good art to show intelligence) coupled with serious cooking – no stuffed shirts here, but lots of sensitive palates. An appreciative fellow-restaurateur found dining on an unctuous bourride of crayfish, gurnard, John Dory and mussels, fresh and inexpensive oysters, fillet of mackerel with a Catalan romescu sauce, carpaccio of salmon with fennel, olive oil and basil vinegar, roast tronçon of turbot and desserts that certainly kept up the standards (chocolate and hazelnut tart, crème brûlée, strawberries with red wine sauce and mascarpone) was an experience worth repeating. Others have confirmed that the personal cookery – occasioning sometimes a bit of delay – the friendly service and welcome from Debby Wilkins, and the attractive yet unpretentious surroundings are a welcome find in an area with little to offer the greedy traveller. The wine list is very short and sound rather than exciting. It does not, however, cost a lot. House wines are £7.50.

CHEF: Paul Sellars   PROPRIETORS: Paul Sellars and Debby Wilkins   OPEN: Mon to Sat, D only; 7 to 9.30   CLOSED: Christmas to mid-Feb   MEALS: alc (main courses £9.50 to £14.50)   SERVICE: not inc   CARDS: Access, Visa   DETAILS: 30 seats. Private parties: 30 main room. Vegetarian meals with prior notice. Children's helpings on request. No pipes in dining-room. Music

---

ST KEYNE  Cornwall                                                                        map 1

## ▲ Well House

St Keyne PL14 4RN
LISKEARD (0579) 342001                                                        COOKING 3
on B3254, 3m S of Liskeard                                                   COST £28–£45

This 'gem' of a country house built in 1894 is close to St Keyne's well – hence the name. The place draws special praise and its attractions are addictive: the food was so good that one enthusiast ate there four times in one week. Light and fixed-price lunches are available, but the serious business takes place in the evening. The price depends on the number of courses taken, with generally five choices at each stage, plus canapés. A light lunch can also be taken from around £13. David Woolfall is a seeker-out of ingredients: wild boar is 'the real thing – not feral pig from Australia'. From the sea there might be anything from brill and langoustines to red bream and barracuda (cooked with olives, capers, onions and Gruyère cheese). Up-to-the-minute lightness marks out dishes such as crisp fillet of salmon with cucumber spaghetti and tomato coulis, or breast of chicken with sherry vinegar sauce, while hot tartlet of duck confit and breast of guinea-fowl with crépinette of leg and port sauce suggest that old-style richness lives on. Desserts are in similar vein: bitter chocolate and orange marquise with coffee sauce, iced praline and armagnac parfait with raspberry coulis. Farmhouse cheeses are served with walnut bread. One sumptuous meal took in fish soup with a strong rouille, 'fantastic' pink duck with Cassis sauce, crisp vegetables, and fresh fruit salad full of 'wonderful exotica' with mango sorbet. To enjoy the Well House to the full, stay overnight. The bedrooms have received high praise and breakfast is worth waiting for, although one reporter warns that it might be something of a challenge. 'But', she adds, 'there's a tennis court and swimming-pool to work it off!' The list of around 80 wines is restricted to Europe, with France as the major supplier. Prices are reasonable although weighty clarets will send the bill soaring. The choice of halves was being revised as we went to press. House wine is £8.50.

CHEF: David Woolfall   PROPRIETOR: Nicholas Wainford   OPEN: all week; 12.30 to 1.45, 7.30 to 9   MEALS: Set L £21, Set D £19.95 (2 courses) to £29.70   SERVICE: not inc, card slips closed   CARDS: Access, Visa   DETAILS: 36 seats. 5 tables outside. Private parties: 32 main room. Car park. Vegetarian meals. Children's helpings. No children under 8 D. Smart dress preferred. No cigars/pipes in dining-room. Wheelchair access (1 step; also men's WC). No music   ACCOMMODATION: 7 rooms, all with bath/shower. B&B £60 to £105. Deposit: £50. Children welcome. Baby facilities. Pets welcome. Garden. Swimming-pool. Tennis. TV. Phone (*The Which? Hotel Guide*)

---

**ST LEONARDS** East Sussex                                                map 3

## Röser's ▮

64 Eversfield Place, St Leonards TN37 6DB                    COOKING 3*
HASTINGS (0424) 712218                                        COST £20–£51

*COUNTY OF THE YEAR RESTAURANT*

'I ate here the first time because of advice from guidebooks; I returned on the next two nights because I was so delighted with the food, service and wine list.' When you are marooned opposite Hastings pier, Rösers comes as a serious and godsent lifebelt. On a January morning to be able to lunch on pike mousseline, rösti of wild mushrooms, and Belgian chocolate mousse is a delight. Gerard Röser is a dedicated chef, a fact made plain by the serious tone of the restaurant itself, the steady – in a sense single-minded – repertoire, and the evident skill of the cooking. This comes out not just in the fairly elaborate presentation and willingness to tackle techniques that require adept handling, but also in the intensity of flavours in dishes such as game sausages with wild boar bacon and choucroute, chicken marinated in red wine and served with lardons and shallots, a dish of scallops with saffron sauce and grilled vegetables, and succulent desserts like the mille-feuille of apples with butterscotch sauce. The largely safe, big names wine list strongly features Jadot, Hugel and Jaboulet; small producers, say from Alsace or the Rhône, still fail to attract the Rösers' attention. It is, though, a wonderful list, with an abundance of mature clarets, Chablis from the best years, fine Mosels, nicely aged Italians and canny choices from the New World. Prices, even at the upper reaches, are fair, with much enjoyable drinking at and well below £15. Half-bottles show equal range and consideration. Non-drivers are urged to ponder the modestly priced spirits list. House wines are from £8.95. CELLARMAN'S CHOICE: Pouilly Fumé, Les Loges 1990, Saget, £15.20; Penfolds, Bin 389 Cabernet Sauvignon/Shiraz 1987, £17.95.

CHEF: Gerald Röser   PROPRIETORS: Gerald and Jenny Röser   OPEN: Tue to Sat, exc Sat L; 12 to 2, 7 to 10   CLOSED: first week Jan, last week Aug   MEALS: alc (main courses £10 to £15). Set L £10.95 (2 courses) to £15.95   SERVICE: net prices, card slips closed   CARDS: Access, Amex, Diners, Visa   DETAILS: 30 seats. Private parties: 20 main room, 30 private room. Vegetarian meals. Children welcome. No cigars/pipes in dining-room. Wheelchair access (2 steps; also WC). No music

---

## ST MARGARET'S AT CLIFFE Kent                                             map 3

## ▲ Wallett's Court ⁵✳

West Cliffe,
St Margaret's at Cliffe CT15 6EW
DOVER (0304) 852424                                              COOKING 2
on B2058, off A258 Dover to Deal road, 3m NE of Dover           COST £27–£37

The manor house was recorded in the Domesday Book, and over the centuries it has been home to many dignitaries, from Queen Eleanor and the Black Prince to William Pitt the Younger. Today it is a slice of living history, thanks to the efforts of the Oakley family, who have restored it to a state of grace. 'No showing-off, but style and simplicity,' commented guests who enjoyed a three-night stay and the chance to sample the full range of Christopher Oakley's cooking. Specialist game terrines and pâtés are his forte, and dishes are generously pointed up with robust cream sauces. Fish is from the quayside at Folkestone. Approved dishes have included chicken, leek and potato soup, gratin of seafood, pork tenderloin with Tewkesbury mustard sauce and oyster mushrooms, and pan-fried steak with marmalade of shallots and pan juices. Rack of lamb, served on a purée of Bramley apples, is cooked to exact pinkness. Among the desserts, reporters have mentioned chocolate mousse with whisky and lemon cream, bread-and-butter pudding and a fine version of fresh fruit salad. Service is friendly without being oppressive. The list of 79 wines concentrates on France and a few halves are on offer. Prices are very fair. House wines start at £8.50.

CHEF: Christopher Oakley   PROPRIETORS: Christopher and Leonora Oakley   OPEN: Mon to Sat, D only; 7 to 9   CLOSED: 24 to 28 Dec   MEALS: Set D £18.50 to £22.50 (Sat only) SERVICE: not inc, card slips closed   CARDS: Access, Visa   DETAILS: 50 seats. Private parties: 40 main room. Car park. Vegetarian meals. Children's helpings. Smart dress preferred. No smoking in dining-room. Wheelchair access (2 steps; also WC). No music ACCOMMODATION: 7 rooms, all with bath/shower. B&B £30 to £65. Children welcome. Baby facilities. Afternoon teas summer. Garden. Tennis. Snooker. TV. Phone. Doors close at midnight. Confirm by 4. Fax: (0304) 853430 (The Which? Hotel Guide)

ST MICHAEL'S ON WYRE Lancashire                                        map 5

## Mallards

Garstang Road,
St Michael's on Wyre PR3 0TE                                       COOKING 1
ST MICHAEL'S (099 58) 661                                        COST £16–£38

Two cottages knocked into one provide the homely setting; the black tables are beautifully laid and warmth trickles out slowly, both from the radiators and the staff, though in spite of the sometimes languid service, a gently mellow mood usually prevails by the end of the meal. Certainly the value, particularly the four-course Sunday lunch, merits smiles. Simple, carefully prepared meals are what John Steel does well: poached egg on a pikelet coated with hollandaise may be followed by two pieces of pork in a cream and mushroom sauce; a little pudding mound of rice filled with prawns in a creamy curried sauce makes way for a plump, whole breast of chicken, its skin butter-and-honey-crisped, stuffed with mild cheese and lean bacon; cream of onion soup is pleasantly cidery and chocolate and orange tart is well made. The wine list is longer than one might expect, and an excellent choice of half-bottles provides further incentive for the fiscally challenged to dine here. There are 12 bottles at under £10, with house French at £8.50.

CHEF: John Steel   PROPRIETORS: John and Ann Steel   OPEN: Mon to Sat, D only, and Sun L; 12 to 2.30, 7 to 9.30   CLOSED: 2 weeks Aug, 1 week Jan   MEALS: alc (main courses £10 to £13). Set Sun L £9.95, Set D £15.50   SERVICE: not inc, card slips closed   CARDS: Access, Visa   DETAILS: 24 seats. Private parties: 36 main room. Car park. Vegetarian meals. Children's helpings. Smart dress preferred. No smoking during meals. Wheelchair access. Music

---

SALISBURY Wiltshire                                                     map 2

## Harper's £

6–7 Ox Row, The Market Square,
Salisbury SP1 1EU                                                  COOKING 1
SALISBURY (0722) 333118                                          COST £13–£31

The world and his wife trek to Harper's both because it has been going long enough to have its supporters and for the enviable value. A large, airy room on the first floor overlooks the old market place, and a window seat gives those having lunch something to watch. Tradition has its way with items such as tarragon chicken, pork with sage, orange, mustard and honey, or lamb with rosemary and apricot stuffing; one-plate lunchers can solve the problem with a vegetarian lasagne or pasta with chilli and ginger; sausage freaks can eat locally made pork and turkey sausages with potato cakes and ratatouille; and fish lovers can see what is on the blackboard fresh from Poole. Plenty of sweet things console the addicted. A sound neighbourhood place, with enough enthusiasm to comfort, yet not so much art as to want to break the bounds of what it does well. The wine list continues the theme of fair value and fair quality. Jaboulet's Côte Rôtie les Jumelles 1976 is £30. House wines are £7.50.

CHEFS: Adrian Harper and Sam North   PROPRIETORS: Adrian and Ann Harper   OPEN: all week, exc Sun L; 12 to 2, 6.30 to 10 (10.30 Sat)   CLOSED: Sun Oct to Easter   MEALS: alc (main courses £4 to £11). Set L £7.30, Set D £13.50   SERVICE: not inc   CARDS: Access, Amex, Diners, Visa   DETAILS: 60 seats. Private parties: 60 main room. Vegetarian meals. Children's helpings. No-smoking area. Music. Air-conditioned

---

**SANDIWAY  Cheshire**                                                                          map 5

## ▲ *Nunsmere Hall* £✳

Tarporley Road, Sandiway CW8 2ES
NORTHWICH (0606) 889100                                                         COOKING 3*
off A49, 4m SW of Northwich                                                    COST £20–£44

As you bowl down the drive to this Edwardian house, the fact that it is on a promontory rising sheer above a lake (once a quarry or gravel pit) is not immediately obvious. The setting is remarkable, and all the better for its element of surprise. The best news about Nunsmere is that the prices have come down. Paul Kitching's cooking was always worth a try, but was very dear. Lunch is now a bargain, dinner is an understandable set price and the only pity is that Sunday has turned into brunch. The style of the food tends towards the ornate and is still busy with add-ons that do not always seem essential; but the happy truth is that flavour is thought paramount and makes the jump from kitchen to dining-room. Disregarding this year's preoccupation with lentils – which seem to crop up at every turn – there are lots of ideas at work. Lamb comes with a lemon pancake stuffed with vegetables, salmon with lobster and some saffron noodles, duck with a beetroot and chive sauce and a bit of black pudding, and beef as a sandwich with a potato cake as the filling. As a first course a poached breast of pigeon is given some edge by Parma ham, softened by green beans and moistened by a rosemary cream sauce. And even when the options looked dull, 'sauces and conception produced a first-class meal'. Service in the elaborately decorated dining-room is definitely keen, young and competent. The wine list has plenty of range, though the prices seem designed for the richer classes of Cheshire. House Duboeuf is £9.90.

CHEF: Paul Kitching   PROPRIETORS: Malcolm and Julie McHardy   OPEN: all week; 12 to 2 (11.30 to 2.30 Sun brunch), 7 to 9.30 (10.30 Sat)   MEALS: Set L £14.95 (2 courses) to £17.50, Set D £22 to £28.50. Sun brunch £13.95   CARDS: Access, Amex, Diners, Visa   SERVICE: not inc, card slips closed   DETAILS: 48 seats. 6 tables outside. Private parties: 60 main room, 24 to 42 in private rooms. Car park. Vegetarian meals. Children's helpings. Smart dress preferred. No smoking in dining-room. Wheelchair access (3 steps; also WC). Music   ACCOMMODATION: 32 rooms, all with bath/shower. Rooms for disabled. Lift. B&B £95 to £120. Deposit: 25%. Children welcome. Afternoon teas. Garden. Snooker. TV. Phone. Fax: (0606) 889055 (*The Which? Hotel Guide*)

---

*The* Guide *is totally independent, accepts no free hospitality, and survives on the number of copies sold each year.*

*Restaurateurs justifiably resent no-shows. If you quote a credit card number when booking, you may be liable for the restaurant's lost profit margin if you don't turn up. Always phone to cancel.*

---

SCARBOROUGH  North Yorkshire                                    map 6A

# Lanterna

33 Queen Street, Scarborough YO11 1HQ                    COOKING 1
SCARBOROUGH (0723) 363616                                COST £22–£33

Italian restaurants are on the up, but genuine family-run trattorias will not be
extinguished by bruschetta and balsamic vinegar. Twenty years on, the
Lanterna still holds its ground – even though the menu sounds like a culinary
rendition of 'O Sole Mio'. Gianluigi and Janet Arecco offer customers
minestrone, spaghetti carbonara, pollo pizzaiola and bistecca Barolo, but ring
the changes with more interesting daily specials which have a bias towards
fish. Queenies (scallops) provençale with rice are regularly endorsed. Service is
full of Mediterranean warmth. The wine list is a minimal collection of familiar
names with a mainly Italian accent. House wine is £9.50.

CHEF: Gianluigi Arecco  PROPRIETORS: Gianluigi and Janet Arecco  OPEN: Tue to Sat,
D only; 7 to 9.30  MEALS: alc (main courses £9.50 to £12)  SERVICE: not inc, card slips
closed  CARDS: Access, Visa  DETAILS: 40 seats. Private parties: 40 main room. Vegetarian
meals. Children welcome. Wheelchair access. Music

---

SCARISBRICK  Lancashire                                          map 5

# Master McGraths  £                              NEW ENTRY

535 Southport Road, Scarisbrick L40 9RF
SCARISBRICK (0704) 880050                                COOKING 1*
on A570, Ormskirk to Southport road                      COST £13–£31

The success of this team at High Moor (see entry, Wrightington) should be
preparation for what is to come here. They know their clientele, and they know
how to cook. The setting may raise many strangers' eyebrows, so may the disco
and the music and the furnishings, but the food is surprisingly good. A dinner
that took in salmon fish-cakes with ginger hollandaise, rack of lamb with a
mint and blackcurrant sauce, stir-fried chicken with mange-tout and cashew-
nuts, crisp vegetables, a pineapple cream torte with mango coulis and a sweet
chocolate truffle bavarois was hard to fault. The menu shows many Eastern
influences and a love of fruit flavours. The service is cheerful and cares about
contentment. Small wonder the place is a success. The wine list is not so
interesting. House wines cost from £8.75.

CHEFS: James Sines and Stephen Smith  PROPRIETORS: James Sines and John Nelson
OPEN: all week; 12 to 2, 5.30 to 10  CLOSED: 1 Jan  MEALS: alc (main courses £8 to £11.50).
Set D £7.50 (2 courses) to £9.50. Bar menu (main courses £3 to £5.50)  SERVICE: not inc
CARDS: Access, Amex, Diners, Visa  DETAILS: 130 seats. 8 tables outside. Private parties:
130 main room. Car park. Vegetarian meals. Children's helpings. Smart dress preferred.
No-smoking area. Wheelchair access (also WC). Music. Air-conditioned

---

*The* Guide *relies on feedback from its readers. Especially welcome are reports on new
restaurants appearing in the book for the first time.*

---

**SEAFORD** East Sussex                                          map 3

## Quincy's

| | |
|---|---|
| 42 High Street, Seaford BN25 1PL | COOKING 1* |
| SEAFORD (0323) 895490 | COST £27–£36 |

The garden at the rear of Quincy's gives a bosky outlook to this wooden bow-fronted shop conversion. The Dowdings have been very successful in creating a bright, warm domestic atmosphere with generous curtains, bookshelves in the back dining-room (once the parlour), and pictures everywhere. As years go by, repertoires move away from the mousses and stuffings beloved of the '80s and Ian Dowding is no exception. He offers stir-fried squid with ginger and garlic, hot crab tart with red pimento sauce, lamb with mint coriander and garlic, and beef with rösti potatoes, aubergines, peppers and tomatoes. Fish is a good point here, especially given the location, but many people also comment on the puddings (such as hot chocolate soufflé) and the pleasant touch in offering a savoury at the end as well as sweets. The fixed-price menus of two or three courses offer some dishes at a supplement (notably Beluga caviare on pancakes). Service is gentle and appealing. The wine list is in scale with the restaurant – none too large – and prices are sensible. House wines are £8.25.

CHEF: Ian Dowding   PROPRIETORS: Ian and Dawn Dowding   OPEN: Tue to Sat, D only, and Sun L; 12 to 2, 7 to 10   MEALS: Set Sun L and D £16.95 (2 courses) to £18.95. Minimum £16.95   SERVICE: not inc   CARDS: Access, Amex, Visa   DETAILS: 30 seats. Private parties: 30 main room, 10 and 20 private rooms. Vegetarian meals. Children's helpings. Music

---

**SEATON BURN** Tyne & Wear                                      map 7

## ▲ Horton Grange ⅌                          | NEW ENTRY |

| | |
|---|---|
| Seaton Burn NE13 6BU | |
| PONTELAND (0661) 860686 | |
| off A1, at Stannington, 3m N | COOKING 2* |
| of Newcastle upon Tyne | COST £38–£46 |

'Do not be fooled by the address – Horton Grange is far from Seaton Burn,' started our inspection report: allow plenty of time to arrive. The Newcastle area has done better with restaurants than hotels, so the addition of this country house to the repertoire in the last three years is welcome. Once a farmhouse, this place retains the comfortable aura associated with solid stone buildings. The Shiltons have furnished it with discretion and comfort: themes are pastoral, shades are pastel. A very sound chef offers daily menus of good materials and proper technique. The meal is designed along North Country lines: a set price, an intermediate course of soup or sorbet, and cheeses after the dessert. Although there can sometimes be an affection for moulds or shapes – for instance, a herby mould of courgette and tomato, or a little mousse of brown crab meat to go with the excellently fresh white meat topped with a lime mayonnaise – the cooking is no more overstated than the surroundings. One diner questioned whether collops of chicken were a necessary accompaniment to venison steaks with a finely balanced redcurrant and port sauce and some fried apple 'pearls', but could not suggest any improvement to medallions of beef with pleurottes and a red wine sauce. Nor could he remove from his memory the flavours of a rum baba of apricot and cinnamon filled with Chantilly cream and served with buttery pears. The wine list is short, but the wines evidently have been tasted; the notes are quite useful. For some reason, the vintages are supplied by word of mouth; none the less the range of growers and properties is very sound and quite gentle on the pocket. House wines are from Ochoa and cost £9.90.

CHEF: Steven Martin   PROPRIETOR: Andrew P. Shilton   OPEN: all week, D only; 7 to 8.45
CLOSED: 25 and 26 Dec   MEALS: Set D £29.90   SERVICE: not inc, card slips closed
CARDS: Access, Visa   DETAILS: 30 seats. Private parties: 32 main room, 8 private room. Car park. Vegetarian meals with prior notice. Children's helpings on request. Smart dress preferred. No smoking in dining-room. Wheelchair access (also WC). Music
ACCOMMODATION: 9 rooms, all with bath/shower. Rooms for disabled. B&B £59 to £80. Children welcome. Baby facilities. Pets welcome. Garden. TV. Phone. Doors close at 2am. Fax: (0661) 860308

---

**SETTLE** North Yorkshire                                              map 7

## *Blue Goose*                                          | NEW ENTRY |

Market Place, Settle BD24 9EG
SETTLE (0729) 822901
on B6479, just off A65 Kirkby Lonsdale                          COOKING 1
to Skipton road                                            COST £16–£36

The setting is a three-storey stone building with dark blue woodwork and a small terrace overlooking the market square. 'Every town should be able to support this quality of cooking,' notes a reporter. Inside are two beamed rooms with dark green and striped wallpaper and craft displays in the windows. This is an industrious set-up: it functions not only as a restaurant, but also as a wine bar with a cookery school attached; demonstrations and special events are regular attractions. Chef/proprietor Willi Rehbock hails from Germany and the menu has some Teutonic touches: Goose served in blueberry sauce – 'a true Blue Goose' – is the eponymous speciality of the house. The wine bar menu and the *carte* are interchangeable and you can mix and match. Among dishes that have found favour are rich Breton fish soup with home-baked walnut and raisin bread, black pudding with warm potato salad and mustard sauce, chicken, leek and herb mousse and medallions of beef with creamed mushrooms and red wine sauce. Sweets are less exciting. Service is relaxed and children are well catered for. Afternoon teas are also available in the summer. Twenty reasonably priced wines help to keep the bill within limits. House wine is £8.95.

CHEF/PROPRIETOR: Willi Rehbock   OPEN: Mon to Sat; 11 to 2, 7 to 9.30   CLOSED: Jan
MEALS: alc (main courses restaurant £8.50 to £10.50, wine bar £4.50 to £7). Set L £4.95
(2 courses)   SERVICE: not inc   CARDS: Access, Visa   DETAILS: 36 seats. 4 tables outside. Private parties: 36 main room, 14 and 20 private rooms. Vegetarian meals. Children's helpings. Music

---

*See the back of the* Guide *for an index of restaurants listed.*

---

**SHAFTESBURY Dorset** map 2

## La Fleur de Lys ♟

25 Salisbury Street, Shaftesbury SP7 8EL
SHAFTESBURY (0747) 53717

COOKING 2
COST £25–£44

This first-floor restaurant is well clear of the nostalgia of Gold Hill (made famous by a Hovis ad): you pass through a covered passage off Salisbury Street to a small cobbled courtyard, overlooked by the kitchen. The downstairs reception room, where drinks can be taken, is too much of a thoroughfare to be relaxing – better to move straight to table, up the narrow stairs to the darkish, candle-lit restaurant room. Day-time views feature Blackmoor Vale. Ingredients are good. 'Probably the best lamb I've ever had,' declared one diner, to whom it was served in a 'cobweb of delicious pastry and with a passion-fruit and thyme sauce in which both fruit and herb components were exactly right.' Salmon pan-fried with lemon butter, duck with blackcurrant sauce, orange soufflé beignets and a chocolate box containing fresh fruit and pistachio ice-cream have all won praise, though other reports have been checked by over-discreet flavourings, 'soggy fried potatoes' and a mania for the presentational flourish. Service, sometimes 'fine, unobtrusive', can on other occasions lack gaiety. The wine list is both informed and informative; the cheapest bottles are a red and white from Penedès at £7.95, but £11.50 would bring you the excellent Ch. Bonnet white Entre-Deux-Mers or £11 the Stoneleigh Vineyard Marlborough Sauvignon Blanc. The list is stronger in whites than reds. House wines are from £7.95.

CHEFS: David Shepherd and Marc Preston  PROPRIETORS: David Shepherd, Mary Griffin and Marc Preston  OPEN: Tue to Sun L, Mon to Sat D (Sun D by arrangement); 12 to 3, 7 to 10  MEALS: alc (main courses L £10 to £11.50, D £13.50 to £15.50). Set D £18.50. Minimum £8 L  SERVICE: not inc  CARDS: Access, Visa  DETAILS: 40 seats. Private parties: 35 main room, 12 private room. Vegetarian meals. Children's helpings. Smart dress preferred. No cigars/pipes in dining-room and restricted smoking before 10pm. Music. Air-conditioned

---

**SHEFFIELD South Yorkshire** map 5

## Greenhead House ※

84 Burncross Road, Chapeltown,
Sheffield S30 4SF
SHEFFIELD (0742) 469004

COOKING 2*
COST £33–£43

Some might call Chapeltown a suburb to the north of Sheffield. Some might call Greenhead House a cottage, which would serve the purpose of warning people that the atmosphere is pleasingly domestic and that not too much fuss, pomp and circumstance surround the act of dining. Cottagey, however, is not the right term for the expressive cooking, which is sensibly limited in the number of dishes that are offered on any one night, yet makes every attempt to pack some sort of substantial punch into tastes and flavours. A pigeon pie with truffle and madeira sauce has the breast of pigeon wrapped in a cabbage leaf with a slice of foie gras mousse, then a thin wrapping of puff pastry; calf's liver has pasta to accompany it and a luxurious sauce of cream, mushrooms and sherry; vegetables such as artichokes, asparagus and mushrooms are cooked à la grecque and served with a pungent romescu sauce of hazelnuts, pimento, garlic and tomato; venison terrine comes layered with prunes and apple with a hazelnut dressing on a French bean salad to one side. Save space for the desserts, or look at the British cheeses. The menus change monthly, the price is determined by choice of main course, and there is a soup course interpolated after the entrée. The wine list is sensibly priced: the choices rarely go above £25, and the bulk are well under £15. Yet the sources are perfectly respectable. House wines are £9.

CHEFS: Neil Allen and Christine Roberts   PROPRIETORS: Neil and Anne Allen   OPEN: Tue to Sat, D only; 7 to 9   CLOSED: Christmas to New Year, 2 weeks Easter, 2 weeks mid-Aug   MEALS: Set D £25.50 to £27.95   SERVICE: not inc, card slips closed   CARDS: Access, Visa   DETAILS: 34 seats. Private parties: 34 main room. Car park. No children under 6. No smoking in dining-room. Wheelchair access (also WC). No music

## Le Neptune  £

NEW ENTRY

141 West Street, Sheffield S1 4EW
SHEFFIELD (0742) 796677

COOKING 1
COST £20–£34

The style here is chic; the décor is cool and smart (lemon-yellow walls, pink and green pastel prints, cream floor, and many large plants). What strikes the casual visitor is the keenness of the team. The staff whip around at tremendous pace, subject no one to French curls of lip, and genuinely seem to want you to enjoy yourself. As the name may imply, Le Neptune is a fish restaurant (though meat does get cooked), which takes the rather unexpected line of having a fixed printed seasonal menu with only small daily additions. What this says about the fish supplies is difficult to tell, yet people who have eaten there do not accuse them of being anything less than fresh. The place also pursues a line of fish cookery deeply embedded in classic traditions of messing everything about, giving the fish cream or velouté sauces, even stuffing it even with mousses. Add this tendency to the uninspiring list of first courses and one has to be surprised Simon Wild has not taken a leaf out of the books of the more go-ahead chefs further south and offered something simple and bold. The wine list is as chauvinist as you would expect a French restaurant's to be. House wines are £8.65.

CHEF: Simon Wild   PROPRIETORS: West Hill House Ltd   OPEN: Mon to Sat; 12 to 1.45, 6 to 10.30 (post-theatre D by arrangement)   MEALS: alc (main courses £6.50 to £11). Set L and D £12.25   SERVICE: 10%, card slips closed   CARDS: Access, Amex, Visa   DETAILS: 70 seats. Private parties: 50 main room, 20 private room. Vegetarian meals. Children's helpings. No cigars/pipes in dining-room. Wheelchair access (also WC). Music

*If a restaurant is new to the* Guide *this year (did not appear as a main entry in the last edition)* NEW ENTRY *appears opposite its name.*

£ *indicates that it is possible to have a three-course meal, including coffee, a half-bottle of house wine and service, at any time the restaurant is open (i.e. at dinner as well as at lunch, unless a place is open only for dinner), for £20 or less per person.*

# Blostin's

29 Waterloo Road,
Shepton Mallet BA4 5HH
SHEPTON MALLET (0749) 343648

COOKING 2
COST £22–£34

Some new pictures now decorate the walls, otherwise the style and mood of this friendly, straightforward bistro-style restaurant remain unchanged. Returning regulars suggest that Nick Reed's cooking has 'settled down to an assured pattern', but he is always prepared to introduce new ideas and takes his cue from the seasons. Most people come for the excellent-value set menus, although specialities are equally enticing and vegetarians get plenty of choice. A dinner of moules marinière, casseroled venison with wine and mushrooms, rich chocolate and walnut cake with crème anglaise, and brandy-snap basket filled with orange parfait was thoroughly enjoyed. Other dishes offered are brochette of scallops with braised fennel and pastis, fillet of beef in puff pastry, loin of smoked pork with ratatouille, and spinach and cream cheese filo parcels with saffron sauce. Lynne Reed runs the front-of-house with cheerful good humour. The wine list is not long, but it offers fair-priced drinking, plenty of halves and a blackboard selection chosen for its for 'exceptional quality and value'. House French is £7.95.

CHEF: Nick Reed　PROPRIETORS: Nick and Lynne Reed　OPEN: Tue to Sat, D only (L by arrangement); 7 to 9.30 (10 Sat)　CLOSED: 2 weeks Jan, 2 weeks June　MEALS: alc (main courses £11 to £12). Set D £13.95 (2 courses) to £14.95　SERVICE: not inc, card slips closed　CARDS: Access, Visa　DETAILS: 32 seats. Private parties: 32 main room. Vegetarian meals. Children's helpings. No cigars/pipes in dining-room. Wheelchair access (1 step). Music

# ▲ Bowlish House ▼

Wells Road, Shepton Mallet BA4 5JD
SHEPTON MALLET (0749) 342022
on A371, on outskirts of town

COOKING 1
COST £19–£35

The Wells road may run close to this handsome Georgian merchant's house, but the traffic does not obtrude; there is peace to be found in the garden for a digestive stroll, and a happy mix of formality in the dining-room and relaxed comfort in the bar. That goes for Bob Morley as well. 'He was relaxed, willing to chat, but did not hover,' reflected one couple who went on to enjoy a light mushroom soufflé, duck with a pepper and raspberry sauce, plain vegetables and a simple salad, before sticky toffee pudding and a passable strawberry meringue. 'The whole enterprise struck us as a model of its kind, particularly as regards the integrity and dedication of its modest owners,' they concluded, though wishing for some of the savoury flavours to be a little more stand-up. Mr Morley knows his wines and maintains an undemanding price regime. A list of clarets founded on a range of decent bourgeois growths always encourages, as does the realism that eschews the premium first growths. That may be a point to argue, but what is incontestable is the insistence here on quality at whatever level. There is much under £10, an especially careful selection of halves, and 10 interesting house wines are offered by the glass – hard to beat. House wine is £7.95. CELLARMAN'S CHOICE: Cabernet Sauvignon 1989, Villa Montes, £8.25; Dry Muscat Blanc 1989, Brown Brothers, £10.25.

CHEF: Linda Morley   PROPRIETORS: Bob and Linda Morley   OPEN: all week, D only, and Sun L first Sun of the month (other L by arrangement); 1.30 for 2, 7 to 9.30   CLOSED: 1 week spring, 1 week autumn   MEALS: Set Sun L £12.95, Set D £22.50   SERVICE: not inc, card slips closed   CARDS: Access, Visa   DETAILS: 24 seats. Private parties: 36 main room. Car park. Vegetarian meals. Children's helpings with prior notice. Smart dress preferred. No smoking while others eat. No music   ACCOMMODATION: 3 rooms, all with bath/shower. B&B £48. Children welcome. Baby facilities. Pets welcome (bedrooms only). Garden. TV. Doors close at midnight. Confirm by 6 (*The Which? Hotel Guide*)

---

**SHINFIELD Berkshire**                                                                    map 2

# L'Ortolan

The Old Vicarage, Church Lane,
Shinfield RG2 9BY
READING (0734) 883783
off A33, S of M4 junction 11

COOKING 5
COST £45–£75

The best time to go, we were advised by someone who knows, is Saturday lunch. There is no financial distinction between lunch and dinner, but there are two concurrent menus: one keenly priced, one very dear. The scope and scale of the cooking at this restaurant are almost larger than the building permits. It is a pleasant enough brick vicarage, balanced to each side by conservatories – one where you drink aperitifs, the other where you may eat – and the setting is by no means humble. Yet the food needs space, perhaps even grandeur, and more anticipation than the drive through the hinterland of Reading will supply. John Burton-Race gets down to business with a will, his style throws the book at you and holds nothing back. A summer birthday lunch might give some sense of what he is doing. It began with a few insubstantial nibbles: radishes, olives stuffed with olives, a barquette of ratatouille with fromage frais, a tart of onion marmalade with a quail egg on top, black pudding with apples, some foie gras mousseline with truffle. The first course was a big raviolo made with rye flour filled with wild mushrooms served on a truffle cream. Then came a plate of salmon marinated with dill and lemon juice with a warm potato salad and a caviare cream, and a spoonful of caviare on top. This was a prelude to a pig's trotter stuffed with sweetbreads, tongue and ham, 'glazed rich brown and glossy, looking too life-like for the daughter who picked at it rather'. To cut the richness, there was a sauce gribiche, a salad dressed with walnut oil and a pot of mashed potato. It could almost have done with a little more acidity. Respite was found in a tulip of wild strawberry sorbet before launching into a little 'casserole' made with nougatine, lined with slices of banana and filled with a passion-fruit mousse. A lid was formed with spun sugar and there was a mandarin orange coulis. Petits fours were as good as could be imagined. No stinting on luxuries, a wish to tackle difficult bits of the body as well as prime cuts, and an ability to dress things up are some of the hallmarks. The dressing is not just cosmetic – it all works together. It does, however, make a meal here quite rich – 'although I had not eaten a lot, I felt that I had,' someone concluded. The range of the menu is impressive; the kitchen does not hold back for fear of offending a rich and conservative clientele, nor is there that insistence on shellfish that is often the case in other luxury places. Desserts still get the loudest cheers, and the largest brickbats are reserved for the service. Somehow, there is less of a sense of relaxation than there should be. This is a restaurant still in full evolution, which makes it rather exciting to watch. The wine list may be impressive, and it certainly has lots of range. But the only sensible thing to do is to stick with the first page. The mark-ups are high and rising for most of the rest, which does give some unlikely prices. House wines are from £15.50.

CHEF: John Burton-Race   PROPRIETORS: Burton-Race Restaurants plc   OPEN: Tue to Sun, exc Sun D; 12 to 2.15, 7 to 10   CLOSED: last 2 weeks Feb, last 2 weeks Aug   MEALS: Set L and D £21.50 (2 courses) to £44   SERVICE: not inc   CARDS: Access, Amex, Diners, Visa   DETAILS: 60 seats. Private parties: 40 main room, 30 private room. Car park. Vegetarian meals with prior notice. Children's helpings. Smart dress preferred. Wheelchair access (3 steps). Music. Fax: (0734) 885391

---

**SHIPTON GORGE Dorset**                                                          map 2

## ▲ Innsacre 🍷 ✳

Shipton Gorge DT6 4LJ
BRIDPORT (0308) 56137                                                    COOKING 2
2m E of Bridport, S of A35                                            COST £28–£44

This handsome converted farmhouse with terrace, fine views and good location could be said to be 'full o' beams', and full of country too – which may mean it is not too warm in winter. There has been applause for dishes such as a soup flavoured with Ricard containing warmed oysters encased in spinach leaves and oriental vegetables wrapped in filo, followed by venison with beetroot and cabbage, and salmon with scallop ravioli and a lemon-flavoured sauce, then an old English pudding such as apple tansy (not such a high-flavoured affair as it used to be, more of a soufflé on a caramel sauce). But the cooking is a mix of inspirations, often ambitious, sometimes not quite worked out. The routine of the house and the production of the meals (the form is to start in the bar then move to the restaurant) and so on, can sometimes intrude. The short wine list includes many good names: Deiss from Alsace, Lafon Meursault and Grgich Hills, for example. Prices are fair and the half-bottle list offers especial interest. House wines start at £9. CELLARMAN'S CHOICE: Hermitage, Chante-Alouette 1990, Chapoutier, £22; Rouge Homme, Cabernet/Shiraz 1988, £14.

CHEFS: Tim Emberley and Anthony Sutch   PROPRIETORS: Sydney Davies   OPEN: Tue to Sat, D only, and most bank hols (L by arrangement for 10 or more); 7 to 9   CLOSED: 2 weeks Nov, 25 and 26 Dec   MEALS: Set D £19.80 to £24.80   SERVICE: not inc, card slips closed   CARDS: Access, Visa   DETAILS: 36 seats. 8 tables outside. Private parties: 65 main room. Car park. Vegetarian meals. Children's helpings. No smoking in dining-room. Wheelchair access (1 step; also WC). Music   ACCOMMODATION: 6 rooms, all with bath/shower. B&B £45 to £66. Deposit: £25. Children welcome. Baby facilities. Pets welcome. Garden. TV. Doors close at midnight. Confirm by 5. Fax: (0308) 27277 (*The Which? Hotel Guide*)

SHOTLEY Suffolk                                                              map 3

## Old Boot House ✦✕                                             [NEW ENTRY]

Main Road, Shotley, Ipswich IP9 1EY
IPSWICH (0473) 787755                                          COOKING 1
10m SE of Ipswich on B1456                                      COST £17–£37

On the Shotley Peninsula, close to the River Orwell, this redundant country pub now functions as a country restaurant, with beams, wildlife pictures on the walls and views of fields from the windows. Ian Chamberlain trained in Suffolk, travelled, and then returned to embark on what he calls 'British free-style cookery': in other words dishes such as steamed Norfolk venison pudding and oriental spiced duck and coriander sausages. The menu is 'hand scribbled' each day and reporters have endorsed chicken liver and bacon salad with honey and lavender sauce, breast of chicken with a cinnamon and pecan crust drizzled with maple sauce, baked guinea-fowl with thyme mousse and wild mushroom sauce, and steamed 'figgy' pudding. A special provençal menu yielded excellent mushrooms stuffed with snails, and rillettes of pork with kumquat marmalade, as well as fricassee of chicken with wild mushrooms, and crêpes suzette. Around 40 wines include some classy halves and a mixed bag of bottles from reputable sources. House wine is £7.25.

CHEF: Ian Chamberlain   PROPRIETORS: Ian and Pamela Chamberlain   OPEN: Tue to Sun, exc Sun D; 12 to 2, 7 to 9 (9.30 Sat)   MEALS: alc (main courses L £6 to £8, D £9 to £16). Set Sun L £10.95   SERVICE: not inc, card slips closed   CARDS: Access, Visa   DETAILS: 40 seats. Private parties: 40 main room. Car park. Vegetarian meals. Children welcome. Smart dress preferred. No smoking in dining-room. Wheelchair access (1 step; also WC). No music

---

SHURDINGTON Gloucestershire                                    map 2

## ▲ Greenway

Shurdington GL51 5UG
CHELTENHAM (0242) 862352                                      COOKING 2*
on A46, 2½m S of Cheltenham                                    COST £22–£45

Best make your way slowly up the 'seriously ramped' drive to this old stone house in the peaceful sequestration of the Cotswold hills. You are likely to leave still more slowly, ballasted by the rib-sticking opulence of Chris Colmer's cooking – though a change of philosophy regarding pricing and menus allows the selection of just one dish from the à la carte menu 'for a light supper'. That dish may consist of an enormous whole pig's trotter, 'stuffed with really inordinate amounts of sliced morel and truffle', beached on a no less enormous, truffle-charged rösti 'in a pool of heavy, dark, stock-based sauce, heavily scented with madeira and truffle and morels'. The raw materials are first-rate, and lighter alternatives (brioche buns baked with Somerset Brie, pistachios, spring onions and tomato coulis, or timbale of sole and seared scallops with cucumber pickle and a light fish sauce, for example) appear for the faint-hearted. Timing is good, too – three chunks of new-season lamb were 'tender, pink and juicy'. Lunch-times are simpler: a salmon, caper and parsley fish-cake or grilled goats' cheese and artichoke hearts, followed by steak and kidney pud or smoked haddock and cod bake. Desserts tend to come in threes, brocaded with over-elaborate saucing and piping. Ambition and talent are here, but they need calming a whit. Service is pleasant, and tipping is courageously discouraged. The wine list is long and expensive, distinguished only in its ports and German wines. The two vins de pays house wines are £10.75.

CHEF: Chris Colmer   PROPRIETOR: Tony Elliott   OPEN: all week, exc Sat L; 12 to 2, 7 to 9.30 (7.30 to 8 Sun)   CLOSED: L bank hol Mons, first week Jan   MEALS: alc (main courses £12.50 to £18.50). Set L £15 (2 courses) to £17, Set D £25   SERVICE: net prices, card slips closed   CARDS: Access, Amex, Diners, Visa   DETAILS: 50 seats. 6 tables outside. Private parties: 14 main room, 12 and 20 private rooms. Car park. Vegetarian meals. No children under 7. Smart dress preferred. No-smoking area. No cigars/pipes in dining-room. Wheelchair access (also WC). Music   ACCOMMODATION: 19 rooms, all with bath/shower. Rooms for disabled. B&B £75 to £175. No children under 7. Garden. TV. Phone. Doors close at 11.30. Fax: (0242) 862780 (*The Which? Hotel Guide*)

---

**SISSINGHURST Kent**                                                      map 3

## Rankins'

The Street, Sissinghurst TN17 2JH                             COOKING 1*
CRANBROOK (0580) 713964                                       COST £24–£41

'Reminiscent of a good, old-fashioned French family bistro,' observed a reporter about Hugh and Leonora Rankin's popular family restaurant: a narrow room with lots of worm-eaten beams and generously spaced dark wooden tables. The owners take care to buy selectively from good local sources. The menu has a strong Gallic accent, although exotic touches colour some dishes. Spinach, nutmeg and garlic terrine with red pepper and tomato salsa, a fine ceviche of haddock and prawns, steamed brill and salmon with tarragon beurre blanc have been skilfully executed. Stir-fries and English roasts add another dimension to the menu. Sweets, such as chocolate marquise with raspberry coulis, English toffee ice-cream with caramel orange sauce and mango and lychee sorbet, are in similar vein. Service can sometimes be slow and unwelcoming, although it generally pleases. Around 50 wines centre on France and the New World, with a good showing of reasonably priced halves. House French is £7.80.

CHEF: Hugh Rankin   PROPRIETORS: Hugh and Leonora Rankin   OPEN: Wed to Sat, D only, and Sun L; 12.30 to 1.30, 7.30 to 9   CLOSED: bank hol Mons, 25 Dec   MEALS: alc (main courses £10.50 to £15)   SERVICE: not inc   CARDS: Access, Visa   DETAILS: 30 seats. Private parties: 24 main room. Vegetarian meals with prior notice. Children's helpings Sun L. No children under 7 at D. Smart dress preferred. No smoking before 2 L, and 10 D. No music

---

*'They claimed they could not make French fries ''since the chip pan hasn't worked since the last power cut''.'* On eating in Cambridgeshire

*'I had roast pork – admittedly of the tasteless variety – but how many real pigs are there in Britain today?'* On eating in Sussex

---

## Madhu's Brilliant  £

39 South Road, Southall UB1 1SW — COOKING 2
081-574 1897 and 571 6380 — COST £13–£30

Southall is one of the centres of Asian culture in London, and this restaurant close to the station remains one of the most impressive and popular restaurants in the neighbourhood. Downstairs is beige and wooden, upstairs is blue, pink and trim, both areas linked by a spiral staircase. Service is unerringly friendly and helpful and the place brings in crowds of all ages. It is family by name and family by nature. The Anands describe their menu as short, featuring traditional Punjabi-style cooking, and many items have drawn favourable reports. Butter chicken with exciting home-made chutneys has been a good starter. Other specialities have included karai chicken, chicken tikka masala and 'superb' aloo chollay ('a perfect blend of heavy potato and pulse'). Dishes are served in brass pots, heated by candles, with their own brass ladles. Rice and breads are well up to the mark, and one visitor claimed the kulfi was 'in a class of its own'. House wine is £7; some might prefer to choose from the list of imported bottled lagers.

CHEFS: Sanjee Anand, Jagdish Kumar Anand and Satpal Singh Gill  PROPRIETORS: Jagdish Kumar Anand, Krishna Kumari Anand, Sanjay Anand and Sanjee Anand  OPEN: Wed to Mon, exc L Sat and Sun; 12.30 to 2.45, 6 to 11.30 (12 Fri and Sat)  MEALS: alc (main courses £3 to £7). Set L £8 to £12.50, Set D £10 to £15  SERVICE: 10%, card slips closed  CARDS: Access, Amex, Diners, Visa  DETAILS: 104 seats. Private parties: 60 main room, 60 private room. Vegetarian meals. Children welcome. Smart dress preferred. Wheelchair access. Music. Air-conditioned. Fax: 081-813 8639

## Browns Brasserie £✳ | NEW ENTRY |

Frobisher House, Nelson Gate,
Southampton SO1 0GX — COOKING 2
SOUTHAMPTON (0703) 332615 — COST £23–£51

The landmarks in this fairly bleak part of the city (off Commercial Road) are the station and the Mayflower Theatre. 'We had a wonderful time here,' commented a party impressed by the friendliness of the welcome, the fresh and uncluttered decoration, and the unexpected quality of the food. 'Brasserie' is not part of the equation; it is a restaurant, with the owners doing most of the work. Patricia Brown cooks a surprisingly upbeat menu with some ambitious aspects like, her own version of zampone, pot-roasted squab with herb and lentil dumplings, and chicken stuffed with crab, wrapped in pastry and served with a crab sauce. First courses, including such things as oysters poached in champagne and finished with cream, hot lobster soufflé, or duck livers with tarragon and cognac, live up to the principal dishes, though highest praise was received for the lemon and lime tart with caramel sauce and the bread-and-butter pudding with calvados and prunes that came at the end of one meal. The short wine list does not give much information about makers or origins. House wines are £8.95.

CHEF: Patricia Brown   PROPRIETORS: Mr R.F. and Mrs P.A. Brown   OPEN: Mon to Sat, exc Sat L; 12 to 2.30, 6.30 (5.30 pre-theatre) to 10.30   CLOSED: 24 to 30 Dec   MEALS: alc (main courses £13.95 to £19.95). Set L and D £14.95 to £22.50   SERVICE: not inc   CARDS: Access, Amex, Diners, Visa   DETAILS: 28 seats. Private parties: 50 main room. Car park (D and Sat). Vegetarian meals. No children under 12. Smart dress preferred. No smoking in dining-room. Music

---

**SOUTH MOLTON Devon**                                                    map 1

## ▲ *Whitechapel Manor* ♟ ⚡✳

South Molton EX36 3EG
SOUTH MOLTON (0769) 573377
1m off A361 at roundabout 1½m E of South Molton                    COST £34–£57

The low-key exterior hardly prepares the unknowing for the gem behind those grey walls. The Shaplands have engineered a brilliant conversion of a house full of character – and of original woodwork. Their welcome seems consistently gauged to make people feel at home: 'We felt like lords of the manor for two hours.' The surprise, even shock, at finding such good cooking in so remote a place may occasionally be tempered by the kitchen cutting its estimates too fine at the beginning of the day, thus leaving small choice for those who arrive at the end. That said, the menus – there are two set prices relating each to a short choice – offer a remarkable range of ingredients, and none of them those little chef-like confections that use up odds and ends. Thus an evening might bring confit of duck, wild mushroom soup, calves' sweetbreads, turbot, foie gras or scallops as alternatives for first courses, followed by pheasant, sea bass, monkfish, beef, venison, pork or lamb as main dishes. This is so much more enlivening than the usual country-house round. In the spring a dinner began with a plate of blini with salmon roe, cheese straws and croûtons topped with ratatouille. The meal itself included scallops with asparagus in an armagnac and orange sauce and brill with seed mustard sauce, then really good cheeses 'knowledgeably and enthusiastically explained by Della, the only full-time waitress', before an impressive finish of apple and walnut galette, and a mousse-like dark and white chocolate cake with an orange zest sauce. These comments were elicited by food from the hands of Thierry **Leprêtre-Granet** and Patricia Shapland. Since then, the former has moved on, leaving Mrs Shapland in sole charge after a year's tuition. It is too soon to gauge developments – her skills will be taxed to the full in the ensuing year. The wine list is no great volume suitable for browsing over, but a very intelligent generalist collection of good wines. Prices are not outrageous (£9 and up), and there is enough of the upper-crust yet unfamiliar to appease the pickiest drinker.

---

*All entries in the* Guide *are rewritten every year, not least because restaurant standards fluctuate. Don't trust an out-of-date* Guide.

---

CHEF: Patricia Shapland   PROPRIETORS: John and Patricia Shapland   OPEN: all week;
12 to 1.45, 7 to 8.45 (9 Fri and Sat)   MEALS: Set L and D £26 to £37   SERVICE: not inc,
card slips closed   CARDS: Access, Amex, Diners, Visa   DETAILS: 22 seats. Private parties:
60 main room, 48 and 60 private rooms. Car park. Vegetarian meals with prior notice.
Children's helpings before 7. Smart dress preferred. No smoking in dining-room.
No music   ACCOMMODATION: 10 rooms, all with bath/shower. B&B £65 to £160. Deposit:
£100. Children welcome. Baby facilities. Afternoon teas. Garden. TV. Phone. Doors close at
11. Confirm by 7. Fax: (0769) 573797 (*The Which? Hotel Guide*)

---

**SOUTHSEA Hampshire**                                                                      map 2

## *Bistro Montparnasse*

103 Palmerston Road, Southsea PO5 3PS                             COOKING 1*
PORTSMOUTH (0705) 816754                                              COST £20–£36

Most people have been delighted at Gillian Scott's assumption of the chef's hat
at this little bistro 'that would not discredit the 16me', and which aims 'to give
passengers on the ferry a good send-off'. She has succeeded in lending
imagination and eclecticism to a monthly fixed-price (and a cheaper weekday
special) menu that takes in osso buco, duck with soy and ginger, salmon with
blood orange sauce, and classic prime rib with a mushroom jus. First courses,
too, are arresting: a trio of aubergine dishes, or oriental shrimp cakes with
lemon grass, for example. Occasional faults, like skimpy amounts of sauce or a
slip in timing, are as nothing when compared to the resources found in the rest
of the city. A simple environment, shielded by full-length chintz from the
comings and goings of promenaders on the way to Southsea's pubs and clubs,
is well matched to the restaurant's intentions. The wine list is short (but has
Ch. Chauvin, St-Emilion and Pousse d'Or's Volnay, Les Caillerets) and fairly
priced. House Duboeuf is £8.50.

CHEF: Gillian Scott   PROPRIETORS: Peter and Gillian Scott   OPEN: Tue to Sat, D only; 7 to
10   CLOSED: 2 weeks Jan, Tues following bank hol Mons   MEALS: Set D £12.50 (Mon to
Fri) to £19.90   SERVICE: not inc   CARDS: Access, Amex, Visa   DETAILS: 36 seats. Private
parties: 30 main room. Vegetarian meals. Children welcome. Smart dress preferred. No
cigars/pipes in dining-room. Wheelchair access. No music

---

**SOUTHWOLD Suffolk**                                                                     map 6

## ▲ *Crown* 🍷 ✳ £

90 High Street, Southwold IP18 6DP                                 COOKING 2
SOUTHWOLD (0502) 722275                                              COST £18–£32

If you own two hotels in the same street, people are bound to ask about the
differences. Useful shorthand would have it that Adnams' Swan Hotel was
stuffy and the Crown relaxed. 'A pleasant cheerful atmosphere in contrast to
the wooden faces at the Swan' was one comment, so direct that it hurts. The
Crown makes the most of its image as a traditional eighteenth-century
coaching-inn. For sure, the long bar and restaurant at the back are happy,
bustling places, offering accessible, flavourful food such as fresh sprats with a
herb mayonnaise, couscous 'pithiviers' with tomato and basil, grilled plaice

with lemon and capers, and pork tenderloin with apple and peppercorn sauce. The restaurant lives up to its name by listing dishes like a smoked halibut cornet stuffed with avocado mousse or roulade of sole filled with a salmon mousse; these sound more elaborate (not necessarily better) than offerings from the bar. Because the place is busy there may be slips, but the impression given is so much better than it was a few years ago that it is good to record the recovery. No recovery, however, was necessary on the wine front; as always the cullings from Adnams' retail list are made with intelligence and generosity. A monthly selection, available by the glass, of two dozen wines divided neatly between house wines at amazingly low prices (from £6.50) and very fine classics will be sufficient for most. For the fastidious with time to spare, the main list of close to 300 bins is a joy. The Swan – Market Place, Southwold, Tel: (0502) 722186 – has had less satisfactory reports for its food this year, although it continues to merit attention as a place to stay.

CHEF: Andrew Mulliss  PROPRIETORS: Adnams plc  OPEN: all week; restaurant 12.30 to 1.30, 7.30 to 9.30; bar 12.15 to 1.45, 7.15 to 9.45  CLOSED: 1 week Jan  MEALS: bar menu (main courses £7 to £10.50). Set L £12.75 (2 courses) to £14.75, Set D £17.25 (2 courses) to £19.25  SERVICE: not inc, card slips closed  CARDS: Access, Amex, Visa  DETAILS: restaurant 22 seats, bar 34 seats. 3 tables outside. Private parties: 24 and 40 private rooms. Car park. Vegetarian meals. Children's helpings. Smart dress preferred restaurant. No smoking in dining-room. Wheelchair access (3 steps). No music. Air-conditioned  ACCOMMODATION: 12 rooms, all with bath/shower. B&B £37 to £57. Children welcome. Baby facilities. TV. Phone. Doors close at 11.30. Confirm by 6. Fax: (0502) 724805 (*The Which? Hotel Guide*)

---

**SPARK BRIDGE** Cumbria                                                      map 7

## ▲ *Bridgefield House*

Spark Bridge, Ulverston LA12 8DA
LOWICK BRIDGE (0229) 885239
4m N of Ulverston, off A5084 on back                          COOKING 2
road to Coniston, E of River Crake                            COST £26–£34

This is a pleasing Victorian house (slightly hard to find; go via Lowick Bridge, rather than Spark Bridge) and a herculean garden – all David Glister's own work. Rosemary Glister tends the kitchen, even on crutches as reported one autumn, and continues her well-tried style of six-course dinners with short choices either side of a fixed soup, main course and sorbet. Bridgefield maintains the after-dinner savoury: lambs' kidneys, Welsh rarebit, even sweetbreads. Her cooking is to the taste of many people, with its characterful soups, imaginative vegetables and puddings which show signs of welcome variation on the norm: two examples are gingerbread and stem ginger pudding (as in bread-and-butter pudding) and papaya in a lemon syllabub cream. Welcome, too, is the sense of Bridgefield's being the Glisters' own home, of guests being part of an adventure, now some years on. Some find the meal almost too long; perhaps they should do the garden to build up an appetite. The quality and range of drinking on the wine list is remarkable, and half-bottles remain abundant although their distribution lacks consistency. Spanish, antipodeans and Rhônes are exceptional, Alsaces and burgundies numerous but a little staid. CELLARMAN'S CHOICE: Waipara Springs, Chardonnay 1991, £16.35; Rioja Reserva, Contino 1986, £14.85.

CHEF: Rosemary Glister   PROPRIETORS: David and Rosemary Glister   OPEN: all week, D only; 7.30 for 8   CLOSED: L 25 Dec   MEALS: Set D £20   SERVICE: not inc, card slips closed   CARDS: Access, Visa   DETAILS: 30 seats. Private parties: 24 main room. Car park. Vegetarian meals with prior notice. Children's helpings. Smart dress preferred. No smoking in dining-room. No music   ACCOMMODATION: 5 rooms, all with bath/shower. B&B £30 to £60. Deposit: £20. Children welcome. Baby facilities. Pets welcome. Afternoon teas. Garden. Fishing. Phone. Doors close at 2am. Confirm by 3. Fax: (0229) 885379 (*The Which? Hotel Guide*)

---

**STADDLEBRIDGE  North Yorkshire**                                          map 7

## ▲ McCoy's ☻

The Tontine, Staddlebridge DL6 3JB
EAST HARLSEY (0609) 882671
at junction of A19 and A172,                                    COOKING 3*
6m NE of Northallerton                                        COST £25–£55

'I wandered into the bar to see if anything had changed and discovered Peter McCoy stretched out on a sofa taking an afternoon nap. This is a singular place and will not suit everyone – we like it enormously.' This warning is not heeded by a great number of people; in other words, McCoy's is popular. Even after a revamp in the dining-room (goodbye to all those parasols) it is still eccentric in every department: 'The springs on the sofas are liable to do serious damage to your backside'; the staff are laid-back, but professional and competent; the prices are high, but then the cooking is nearly always good – although not for one eager diner with fond memories of his last visit: 'Everything seemed burned, it was a truly dreadful performance.' Along with the redecoration the menu has developed more quickly than it usually does, though addicts may be assured that old favourites never die. The Tontine is a fine, stone-built late eighteenth-century inn on the side of the main road (double glazing mutes the roar of traffic) – once a stopover for those travelling between Newcastle and York. But the McCoy family are hooked on the 1930s, not the Augustans, so all the furniture and ambience (note the music) is tilted to deco. Some items may have come from a boot sale, other bits have beauty and everything has the charm of self-confidence and joie de vivre. The cooking in the restaurant is classic, sassy and reflects a love of expensive ingredients – truffles and other luxuries crop up at many turns. But the sauces are well made and discreet, and the techniques deliver light mousses, accurate meats and mouthwatering puddings. Chicken rolled in Parma ham and a cabbage leaf reminded some southerners of Alastair Little's version; pigeon on lentils gave them a true taste of peasantry. Ravioli of langoustines were finely made, the shellfish were excellent, and the stock was clean and strong. The supply lines for protein are very good indeed, but vegetables are less interesting. Desserts are sensational, even if occasionally sensationally horrible – 'the worst I have ever been served'. 'Choc-o-bloc Stanley', crêpe San Lorenzo, strawberry mille-feuille: these are the standards. Down below in the bistro people pile in for better value and simpler dishes. The mood, however, is not so different.

Pretension is kept in check at McCoy's, captivating strangers who expect a different approach in the far-flung provinces, and evidently convincing the locals. The unfussy wine list details 25 bottles plus an intelligently selected dozen halves. Do not come looking for familiar names; put your trust in the McCoys, whose aim is brevity and excellence, not 'a cellar-full of average wines'. Would that more restaurateurs stopped the pretence that length is a substitute for quality. Prices are fair. House wine is £10.25. CELLARMAN'S CHOICE: Chablis 1991, Boudin, £23.95; Châteauneuf-du-Pape 1990, Dom. St-Benoit, £20.50.

CHEF: Tom McCoy   PROPRIETORS: Peter, Tom and Eugene McCoy   OPEN: restaurant Tue to Sat, D only; 7 to 10. Bistro all week; 12 to 2, 7 to 10   CLOSED: 25 and 26 Dec, 1 Jan   MEALS: alc (main courses bistro £10.50 to £17, restaurant £13.50 to £18)   SERVICE: not inc, card slips closed   CARDS: Amex, Access, Diners, Visa   DETAILS: restaurant 60 seats, bistro 90 seats. Private parties: 60 main room, 30 private room. Car park. Vegetarian meals. Children's helpings on request. Music. Air-conditioned   ACCOMMODATION: 6 rooms, all with bath/shower. B&B £69 to £99. Children welcome. Baby facilities. Pets welcome. Garden. Air-conditioned. TV. Phone. Doors close at 2am. Fax: (060 982) 660

---

**STAITHES  North Yorkshire**                                                                                       map 6A

# ▲ *Endeavour*  £

1 High Street, Staithes TS13 5BH                                                              COOKING 1
WHITBY (0947) 840825                                                                          COST £20–£36

Lisa Chapman runs this converted shop a stone's throw from the front as a one-woman show and takes full advantage of the catch from the local boats. Her blackboard menu features an ever-changing repertoire of distinctive dishes such as salmon fish-cakes, crab with avocado, rock turbot au poivre, and grilled lobster with garlic butter. Smoked halibut with lime sauce has been particularly good. The piscatorial element is balanced with some spicy meat and vegetarian specialities, along the lines of feta and olive terrine, Goan pork with Basmati rice, and chicken breast stuffed with herb cheese pâté. Crème brûlée with raspberries is the speciality of the house and it gets its share of praise; fresh cherry and almond tart is also recommended. Thirty wines offer the prospect of decent drinking around the £10 mark. House French is from £7.75.

CHEF/PROPRIETOR: Lisa Chapman   OPEN: Mon to Sat, exc Sat L (Sun D July to Sept, and bank hol weekends); 12 to 2, 7 to 9.30 (later in high summer)   CLOSED: mid-Jan to mid-Mar   MEALS: alc (main courses £8 to £13.50)   SERVICE: not inc   DETAILS: 45 seats. Private parties: 25 main room, 14 and 20 private rooms. Vegetarian meals. Children welcome. Smart dress preferred. Music   ACCOMMODATION: 3 rooms, 1 with bath/shower. B&B £16.50 to £37. Children welcome. Doors close at 11

---

*All details are as accurate as possible at the time of going to press, but chefs and owners often change, and it is wise to check by telephone before making a special journey. Many readers have been disappointed when set-price bargain meals are no longer available. Ask when booking.*

STAMFORD Lincolnshire                                         map 6

## ▲ *George Hotel* ♦

71 St Martins, Stamford PE9 2LB                          COOKING **2\***
STAMFORD (0780) 55171                                     COST £24–£52

This hotel, once an inn, cannot be missed on a drive north through Stamford.
The inn sign – a gallows – straddles the old road on the approach to the town
and confirms the place's long history as a coaching stage. The complexity of the
architecture – long back courts for stables and accommodation (now all
converted to shops, meeting-rooms, car parks and handsome flower-filled
yards) – is another measure of former times. For some years the George has
been the flagship of Poste Hotels, a small family-run group that somehow
manages to be businesslike yet interested in the fate of its customers. This
approach contributes to a remarkably democratic mix of food styles, from
public bar through cheaper eating up to full-dress dining in a panelled,
heraldry-hung hall of a dining-room. Readers have suggested that we have
undervalued Chris Pitman's achievement in this last location. 'The calf's liver is
as good as I have ever tasted,' said one, though another detected some lack in
the trimmings. But there could be little fault found with the king prawns in
sesame-seed batter, lamb fillet with kidney and liver and a tomato and basil
sauce, saddle of hare with onion, bacon, and mushrooms, or an oft-appreciated
roast joint from the silver trolley that figures on the seasonal menu. This is
steady cooking with enough flair to carry the wine list and the prices. The
desserts have not always had the applause of the first two courses. People in a
hurry may eat in the less formal (and cheaper) Garden Lounge, where the food
has distinct Italian overtones, though standards may fluctuate with the press of
business. The nice thing about the George is that from breakfast onwards,
something is there for everyone, and the obliging staff are even happy to direct
you to the cookery bookshop in the premises beyond. A 'predominantly Italian
house list' of wines offers good range at modest prices. These bottles are
augmented by as happy a range as can be found anywhere: excellent Alsaces,
solid antipodeans and yet more Italians. Classic areas are peppered with fine
vintages, and new but exciting names. Here, buying is very good and prices
fair; for extra interest refer to the bin-ends. House wine is £8.45. CELLARMAN'S
CHOICE: South-East Australia, Semillon/Chardonnay 1992, Aldridge Estate,
£8.95; Barbera d'Asti 1990, Ceppi Storici, £10.95.

CHEFS: Chris Pitman and Matthew Carroll   PROPRIETORS: Poste Hotels Ltd   OPEN: all
week; 12.30 to 2.30, 7 to 10.30   MEALS: alc (main courses £13 to £18.50). Set L Mon to Sat
(restaurant) £15.50 to £18.50   SERVICE: not inc, card slips closed   CARDS: Access, Amex,
Diners, Visa   DETAILS: restaurant 90 seats, Garden Lounge 80 seats. 30 tables outside.
Private parties: 100 main room, 12 to 35 in private rooms. Car park. Vegetarian meals.
Children's helpings. Jacket and tie restaurant. Wheelchair access (also WC). No music
ACCOMMODATION: 47 rooms, all with bath/shower. B&B £66 to £154. Children welcome.
Baby facilities. Pets welcome. Afternoon teas. Garden. TV. Phone. Fax: (0780) 57070 (*The
Which? Hotel Guide*)

---

♦ *denotes an outstanding wine cellar;* ♟ *denotes a good wine list, worth travelling for.*

---

## STAPLEFORD Leicestershire

map 5

## ▲ *Stapleford Park* ❢ ✳

Stapleford, nr Melton Mowbray LE14 2EF
WYMONDHAM (057 284) 522
off B676, 9m W of A1 at Colsterworth,
turn left 1m past Saxby

COOKING 2*
COST £32–£58

This is one of the best country houses to have a hotel within its walls. Every style of architecture can be studied, and the modern restoration is impeccable. If the house is not enough, visit the stables or the Gothick church that you pass on entering the demesne. Bedrooms have been done out by various trendy designers (or, for less money, by Bob and Wendy Payton): they have novelty – one room has been kitted out in shirt fabric – and grandeur (with windows fit for a queen to wave from). 'We were taken on a guided tour' is a sign of the irrepressible American showmanship that contributes to the unlikely success of Bob Payton's style of doing things, which here is crossed with English shires restraint. In a room filled with Grinling Gibbons swags and carvings, or in a more austere but evocative subsidiary dining-room that was once the kitchen, experience the American manner of cooking things. Chilled, grilled vegetable salad with black pepper pesto, Caesar salad, and farfalle with smoked salmon, mange-tout and dill cream are three first courses. These may be matched at main course by lamb with sun-dried tomato pesto and red pepper cream, or chicken with spaghetti of vegetables and garlic and chive sauce, or lentil, bean and chickpea stew with polenta. Desserts, needless to say, carry the theme to its conclusion: well-worn favourites include pecan pie or blueberry ice-cream with a plum and almond tart. The cooking can be very successful, but there have been moments when the advertised flavours do not stand up as they should: this is a cause for concern, as the prices are for haute not street cuisine. Commitment to the experience, however, evinced by the really excellent staff makes up for any shortcomings. The short wine list interestingly eschews geography in favour of grape variety as the criterion for arrangement. Prices are on the high side, but decent house and other wines provide sufficient satisfaction below £15. Around a dozen half-bottles are also offered. House wine starts at £12. CELLARMAN'S CHOICE: Firestone, Chardonnay 1990, £18.50; Napa, Sanford, Pinot Noir 1990, £25.

CHEF: Mark Barker  PROPRIETORS: Bob and Wendy Payton  OPEN: all week; 12 to 2.30, 7 to 9.30 (10.30 Fri and Sat)  MEALS: alc (main courses £12 to £21.50)  SERVICE: not inc, card slips closed  CARDS: Access, Amex, Diners, Visa  DETAILS: 70 seats. 10 tables outside. Private parties: 150 main room, 20, 30 and 40 private rooms. Car park. Vegetarian meals. Children's helpings. Smart dress preferred. No smoking in dining-room. Wheelchair access (also WC). Music  ACCOMMODATION: 35 rooms, all with bath/shower. Rooms for disabled. Lift. B&B £125 to £285. Deposit: £50. Children welcome. Baby facilities. Pets welcome. Afternoon teas. Garden. Tennis. Fishing. TV. Phone. Fax: (057 284) 651 (*The Which? Hotel Guide*)

CELLARMAN'S CHOICE: *Wines recommended by the restaurateur, normally more expensive than house wine.*

STOKE BRUERNE Northamptonshire                                          map 3

## Bruernes Lock

**NEW ENTRY**

5 The Canalside, Stoke Bruerne NN12 7SB
ROADE (0604) 863654                                                COOKING 1
off A508, 3½m from A5 at Towcester                                 COST £23–£46

'On our way back from a rain-soaked day at the Grand Prix of Europe at
Donnington, a meal here turned a disastrous bank holiday into a delightful
relaxing experience,' reported a reader who might also use this place when
visiting Silverstone, or perhaps enjoying the relic of an Inigo Jones villa but a
short distance away. The restaurant is on the towpath of the Grand Union
Canal, at the summit of a flight of seven locks. 'Its position is its biggest
advantage' was one comment, but that does not count the great success of hosts
Gavin Caldwell and Nigel Hollick or the appreciation usually given the food
cooked by Nicholas Collingwood. He cooks energetically and often accurately
dishes that may include breast of pigeon on an apple galette with a port sauce, a
mixed hors d'oeuvre that had too many losers among its winners, John Dory of
impeccable quality, though married to a mixture of chinese-style vegetables
and a strong sauce that almost swamped the purity of the fish, and a dish that
was called ground lamb and herb dumpling but was in fact a meatball, and a
good one too. The repertoire, therefore, can be a bit more lusty than at many
country places, though some slips in execution can make a good thing less
spiffing. A caramelised and cold rice pudding got top marks, even if a vanilla
mousse was jellyish. The wine list offers fair range at fair prices. House wines
are £10.95.

CHEF: Nicholas Collingwood   PROPRIETORS: Gavin Caldwell, Nigel Hollick and Michael
Ross Collins   OPEN: Tue to Sun, exc Sat L and Sun D; 12.30 to 2, 7.30 to 9.30 (9.45 Sat)
MEALS: alc (main courses £11.50 to £17). Set L £15   SERVICE: not inc   CARDS: Access,
Amex, Visa   DETAILS: 30 seats. 4 tables outside. Private parties: 30 main room. Car park.
Vegetarian meals. Children welcome. Smart dress preferred. Wheelchair access (2 steps).
Music

---

STOKE-BY-NAYLAND Suffolk                                                map 3

## ▲ Angel Inn £

Stoke-by-Nayland CO6 4SA
NAYLAND (0206) 263245                                              COOKING 2
on B1068, 5m SW of Hadleigh                                        COST £17–£38

The Angel, which dates back to the sixteenth century, has had many warm
affirmations of quality, friendliness, good beer, comfort and character. 'The
main problem is timing your visit so that you can get a table,' warns one reader.
'You say the menu changes frequently, you didn't say that it changes all the
time, even during a meal,' exclaimed a second. 'After trying many things, and
assaying all the beers, we were still able to fill in the form to say how good the
place is' was the peroration of a third. It's first come, first served in the bar area
and the press of business occasionally means a wait in pleasant surroundings,
but the Well Room (containing a 52-foot-deep well) is fitted out as a restaurant

and takes bookings. There is, however, no longer a separate restaurant menu. Picking from gravlax, mushrooms stuffed with snails, pigeon with Cumberland sauce or grilled fresh sardines may take care of first courses, but a trio of grilled lamb cutlets, squid with oregano, chimney-smoked ham with asparagus and butter, or excellent fresh fish will tempt people on to the main dishes from the chalkboard, just as the vegetables (try the gratin of Jerusalem artichokes) will round off the experience well. Brown bread ice-cream with a caramel sauce was a welcome refresher, but German bread-and-butter pudding or steamed syrup pudding are there for those with ample room left. The wine list has little truck with anything over £15, but makes a decent fist of careful choices below that level. House wines are £7.

CHEF: Mark Johnson  PROPRIETORS: Richard Wright and Peter Smith  OPEN: all week; 12 to 2, 6.30 to 9  CLOSED: 25 and 26 Dec, 1 Jan  MEALS: alc (main courses £6 to £15) SERVICE: not inc  CARDS: Access, Amex, Diners, Visa  DETAILS: 90 seats. 4 tables outside. Private parties: 30 main room. Car park. Vegetarian meals. No children under 14. Smart dress preferred. No pipes in dining-room. Wheelchair access (1 step; also WC). Music ACCOMMODATION: 6 rooms, all with bath/shower. B&B £42 to £55. No children under 8. TV. Phone. Doors close at 11.30. Fax: (0206) 37324 (*The Which? Hotel Guide*)

---

## STOKE-ON-TRENT Staffordshire  map 5

# Ria £

61–67 Piccadilly, Hanley,
Stoke-on-Trent ST1 1HR                                    COOKING 1
STOKE-ON-TRENT (0782) 264411                      COST £10–£35

'More enjoyable than a tandoori,' observes a travelling reporter about this converted shop, which still rates as one of the few authentic Thai restaurants in the area. It is very much an 'ethnic place', despite some attempts at smartness in the décor. The menu runs to around 130 dishes and covers most of the major strands of Thai cuisine, including soups, curries, noodles and salads. A separate menu caters for vegetarians, with many promising items such as crispy crêpes filled with grated coconut, clear noodle salad with black fungus, and red bean curd curry. Soups are reckoned to be 'painfully hot'. Garlic and pepper king prawns with claypot rice have been successfully handled, and the main menu also offers a few unusual items such as sakoo sai moo (steamed tapioca seeds wrapped with minced pork and Thai stuffing) and larb neua (a northern Thai salad of finely chopped beef with lime juice, herbs and roasted rice). Rambutans and Thai palm seeds figure among the sweets, along with lemon sorbet and banana fritters. Drink Singha Thai beer. House wine is £6.95.

CHEF: Mrs Anong Sangpreechakul  PROPRIETOR: Charoon Sangpreechakul  OPEN: all week, exc L Mon and Sun; 12 to 2, 6.30 to 11.30 (7.30 to 10.30 Sun and bank hols) CLOSED: 25 and 26 Dec, 1 Jan  MEALS: alc (main courses £4 to £8.50). Set L £5 to £6.95, Set D £10.50 to £13.75  SERVICE: 10%, card slips closed  CARDS: Access, Amex, Diners, Visa  DETAILS: 100 seats. Private parties: 70 main room, 50 private room. Vegetarian meals. Children welcome. Wheelchair access (also WC). Music. Air-conditioned

---

*See inside the front cover for an explanation of the symbols used at the tops of entries.*

**STOKESLEY** North Yorkshire

map 7

## ▲ *Chapters* £

27 High Street, Stokesley TS9 5AD
MIDDLESBROUGH (0642) 711888

COOKING 2*
COST £15–£46

This three-storey former coaching-inn in Stokesley's main square continues to wring appreciation from both locals and travellers: 'It's nice to go to a proper restaurant again,' reported one, many miles from his Welsh home. The large, airy room with its high beams, white walls, green radiators and white Lloyd Loom-style chairs does not please everyone; it can seem 'barren and sterile', though friendly, knowledgeable service compensates. Alan Thompson is conscious of the nearby sea full of fish, and he makes as much use of them as possible: a vol-au-vent of scallops and asparagus was 'perfectly flavoured'; sole in filo was 'odd but successful'; while fillets of sole were diligently stuffed with shrimp and leek mousse, then lowered on to spinach around which lapped 'a deep orange sauce which was sweet and actually had some saffron flavour'. A dish of duck came in triptych form: slices of breast, a piece of leg roast and chopped liver in a filo parcel; venison medallions have been tender and well flavoured. 'Desserts are amusing: a strawberry dome – fresh strawberries beneath a light, fluffy meringue; cold amaretto crêpes with raspberry coulis; peach tartlet with butterscotch sauce. They are all so light with wonderful flavours.' The bistro, meanwhile, juxtaposes bangers and mash with stir-fry beef, paella with satays. The wine list is short and not particularly inventive, signing up wholesale for Duboeuf and Rosemount. House Duboeuf is £8.90.

CHEFS: Alan Thompson and Dominique Renaut  PROPRIETORS: Alan and Catherine Thompson  OPEN: restaurant Mon to Sat, D only; 7 to 9.30 (10 Sat). Bistro Mon to Sun, exc Sun L; 12 to 1.45, 7 to 9.30 (10 Sat and Sun)  CLOSED: 25 and 26 Dec, 1 Jan  MEALS: alc (bistro main courses L £4 to £6, D £7.50 to £9.50; restaurant £12.50 to £17). Set restaurant D £17.95  SERVICE: not inc  CARDS: Access, Amex, Diners, Visa  DETAILS: 40 seats. 10 tables outside. Private parties: 50 main room. Vegetarian meals with prior notice. Children's helpings on request. Smart dress preferred. No cigars in dining-room. Wheelchair access (2 steps; also WC). Music. Air-conditioned  ACCOMMODATION: 13 rooms, all with bath/shower. B&B £44 to £66. Children welcome. Baby facilities. Pets welcome. Afternoon teas. Garden. TV. Phone. Doors close at 2.30am. Fax: (0642) 711888 (*The Which? Hotel Guide*)

**STON EASTON** Somerset

map 2

## ▲ *Ston Easton Park*

Ston Easton BA3 4DF
MENDIP (0761) 241631
on A37, 12m S of Bristol

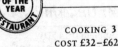

COOKING 3
COST £32–£62

People have extolled the grandeur of the Smedleys' Georgian house often enough, but it bears repetition. There are few country-house hotels that can match the scale of Ston Easton's saloon or entrance hall, the elegance of its plasterwork and its sensitive colour schemes. By contrast, the interior of the dining-room is modern in style, with dragged walls and bamboo chairs: the effect is pleasing, but some would prefer to dine in a full-dress location. The

477

grounds are being restored to Repton's original. The first thrill of Ston Easton sweeps over most visitors while they are still outside: you are met at your car. This is mere prelude to very good service indeed. 'I saw someone being served salmon with Yorkshire pudding. It can't have been the kitchen's idea, but was simply immediate accession to a customer's wishes,' coos one reporter who finds a meal here restores all faith in the idea of willingness (tips are not expected). Mark Harrington's cooking on a regularly changing menu is conservative by design. 'It is elegant food which avoids the trap of over-elaboration,' commented one, 'though flavours tend to be muted.' This may be no bad thing if, as is generally the case, the standards are consistent. 'Delicate' may be another description of dishes such as a two-layered timbale of crab with a champagne cream sauce, avocado and anchovies, a chargrilled noisette of veal with a sausage of forcemeat and Emmental cheese, and loin of lamb served with mushrooms and basil in cream. Pure-tasting stock sauces do not suffer from over-reduction. The same exactitude comes over well in something like a quenelle of sole with shredded leeks and baked scallops: 'They were so light they floated.' Lightness is also applauded in desserts. 'A torte with strawberry purée was far better than the 'cheesecake' description given it by the waiter.' Incidentals are well thought-out, though salted butter and undressed salad were noticed during the summer. Light *carte* lunches are a pleasure on the terrace (or indoors on a dull day) and breakfasts are as palatial in scale as the house. Quality and interest abound on the wine list, which includes a much-enjoyed Chianti Isole e Olena, and mature Spanish and New World wines, as well as sensibly wide-ranging clarets. Burgundies remain grand, not drawn strongly from smaller domaines. Prices dip rarely below £15, though half-bottles are generously provided. House wines are £14.50.
CELLARMAN'S CHOICE: Hunter Valley, Chardonnay 1991, Rothbury Estate, £22; Crozes-Hermitage, Dom. de Thalabert 1988, Jaboulet, £22.

CHEF: Mark Harrington   PROPRIETORS: Peter and Christine Smedley   OPEN: all week; 12.30 to 2, 7.30 to 9.30 (10 Fri and Sat)   MEALS: 'Terrace Menu' L alc (main courses £12 to £16). Set L £26, Set D £38   SERVICE: net prices, card slips closed   CARDS: Access, Amex, Diners, Visa   DETAILS: 40 seats. 4 tables outside. Private parties: 24 main room, 24 private room. Car park. Vegetarian meals. Children's helpings on Request. No children under 7. Jacket and tie. No smoking in dining-room. Wheelchair access (2 steps). No music
ACCOMMODATION: 21 rooms, all with bath/shower. B&B £75 to £320. No children under 7. Baby facilities. Pets by arrangement. Afternoon teas. Garden. Tennis. Snooker. TV. Phone. Doors close at midnight. Confirm by 6. Fax: (0761) 241377 (*The Which? Hotel Guide*)

---

**STONHAM Suffolk**                                                      map 3

# Mr Underhill's ⼁

Stonham IP14 5DW
STOWMARKET (0449) 711206
on A140, 300 yards S of junction with A1120

COUNTY OF THE YEAR RESTAURANT

COOKING 4
COST £27–£46

The Bradleys have created one of East Anglia's most distinctive restaurants out of this roadside house. This is clear enough from its looks: outside, sculpture on the front lawn; inside, pictures by Michael Chase and Norman Stevens, and odds and bobs on shelves and in corners – always worth a second look. This is a restaurant that shows the mark of its owners, not merely reflecting the expectations of its users. The same is true of the formula – a set, no-choice (except for the sweet course) meal discussed in advance. Such consultations will cause variation, so that Chris Bradley may cook a whole range of dinners for different tables, but each party will eat the same. The fact of real importance is that the cooking (by a self-taught chef on an Aga) is distinguished. It shows balance and discretion, careful purchasing, an attention to flavour and proper technique. It is not flamboyant, but nor is it stick-in-the-mud. A warm salad of moist and delicate smoked haddock with a cream sauce of tomato, white wine and chives, followed by a tender and succulent pot-roasted fillet with a wild mushroom sauce that was correctly described as essence, cheese if wanted, then a pear poached with vanilla and a sorbet made with the syrup was one such meal enjoyed this year. The subtle touches on the vegetables – snow peas with lemon oil, a mixed 'spaghetti' of vegetables with judicious addition of red pimento, and a bench-mark dauphinois – lifted an already satisfactory main course to something memorable. Judy Bradley knows everything there is to say about the food, the wine and the restaurant. Such small, individual places sometimes take the stranger aback – they fail to get on each other's wavelength – but this is a spot to savour. Wine enthusiasms here stretch from decent bourgeois clarets to rather more expensive Gaja in Piedmont; classics and antipodeans of character are nicely balanced, and prices throughout are fair. Half-bottles deserve more than a glance. House wine is £9.75. CELLARMAN'S CHOICE: Bourgogne Blanc de St-Bris 1990, Tabit, £13.25; Freycinet, Pinot Noir 1990, £23.95.

CHEF: Christopher Bradley  PROPRIETORS: Christopher and Judy Bradley  OPEN: Tue to Sat, D only, and Sun L (L Tue to Fri by arrangement); 12.30 to 1.45, 7.30 to 8.45  MEALS: Set Sun L £15 (2 courses) to £19.95, Set Tue to Fri L and D £19.95, Set D £18.95 to £29.50, Set Sat D £29.95  SERVICE: not inc  CARDS: Access, Diners, Visa  DETAILS: 30 seats. 6 tables outside. Private parties: 30 main room, 16 private room. Car park. Vegetarian meals with prior notice. Children's helpings with prior notice. No smoking during meals. Wheelchair access. No music

---

STONOR Oxfordshire                                                    map 2

## ▲ Stonor Arms ▼

Stonor RG9 6HE
HENLEY-ON-THAMES (0491) 638345                              COOKING 1
on B480, 5m N of Henley-on-Thames                          COST £22–£50

The antiques and pictures, all in impeccable Home Counties taste, continue to please without reservation. During the year the Blades bar has changed into a 'lounge area' for drinks and lunch-time snacks. The Blades brasserie menu continues to be served in the two conservatories ('fully heated', though reporters still advise a precautionary jacket) as well as in the Stonor restaurant at Sunday lunch-time (with the addition of a traditional roast). A fixed-price dinner menu is available in the restaurant (except on Sundays); however, gastronomic contentment as in 'marvellous lamb platter' or 'tender baked breast of chicken with a delicate yogurt dressing spiked with herbs' has been counter-balanced by 'shrivelled and dry duck livers on brioche' and 'tough' steak. Service has improved during the year. The wine list is wide-ranging, both geographically – with wine from the almost adjacent Old Luxter's vineyard – and historically with eight vintages of Ch. Batailley dating back to 1947. Sound burgundy from Leflaive is also a speciality. House vin de pays is £8.75.

CHEF: Stephen Frost  PROPRIETORS: Stonor Hotels Ltd  OPEN: Stonor restaurant Mon to Sat, D only, and Sun L, Blades brasserie all week; 12 to 2, 7 to 9.30  MEALS: brasserie alc (main courses £8 to £10.50). Restaurant Set D £27.50 to £31.50  SERVICE: not inc, card slips closed  CARDS: Access, Amex, Visa  DETAILS: 20 seats. 6 tables outside. Private parties: 24 main room, 12 and 24 private rooms. Car park. Vegetarian meals. Children's helpings on request. Smart dress preferred. No cigars/pipes in dining-room. Wheelchair access (also WC). Music  ACCOMMODATION: 9 rooms, all with bath/shower. Rooms for disabled. B&B £82.50 to £92.50. Children welcome. Baby facilities. Guide dogs only. Afternoon teas. Garden. Golf. TV. Phone. Doors close at 11. Fax: (0491) 638863 (*The Which? Hotel Guide*)

---

**STORRINGTON** West Sussex                                                 map 3

## ▲ *Manleys* ♥

Manleys Hill, Storrington RH20 4BT                                  COOKING 3
STORRINGTON (0903) 742331                                       COST £28–£56

The small Queen Anne house sits at the foot of the South Downs just before the village. Décor includes a large ersatz log fire set in an inglenook, beams in the small bar, and green carpeting in the dining-room. Manleys is a full-dress restaurant: domes are lifted, linen is crisp, service deferential. Karl Löderer reveals classical training, as well as an Austrian inheritance, in dishes such as lamb wrapped in a potato galette served with shallots, or three filets mignons of beef sauced respectively with a duxelles, a tomato concassée and a hollandaise. Austria may come through in spätzli or a love of cabbage, served sometimes with duck or as a bed to a tournedos of lamb. The Austrian influence is also evident in the desserts: the Salzburger Nockerln are paradise. There is a certain richness to the cooking: a lot of the sauces have butter or cream bases. Though prices may rise if the *carte* is ransacked, the lunch prices are not excessive for the quality of kitchen work involved, the degree of pukka service, and every conceivable ancillary. Sunday lunches are justifiably popular. The wine list reflects the same enduring values; clarets show intelligent range without resort to the ancient or misplaced emphasis on the grand. Rhônes are confined largely to Jaboulet, which is no bad thing. The halves or the careful choice of house wines are not too expensive. Prices are fair, albeit on the high side, because quality is commensurately fine. House wine is £12.80.
CELLARMAN'S CHOICE: Barossa Valley, Chardonnay 1989, Penfolds, £19.90; Haut Médoc, Ch. Villegeorge 1986, £19.50.

CHEF/PROPRIETOR: Karl Löderer  OPEN: Tue to Sun, exc Sun D; 12 to 2, 7 to 9.30 (10 Sat) CLOSED: first 2 weeks Jan  MEALS: alc £26 (2 courses). Set L £18.60, Set Sun L £22.50, Set D £25  SERVICE: not inc  CARDS: Access, Amex, Visa  DETAILS: 48 seats. Private parties: 30 main room, 22 private room. Car park. Vegetarian meals. Children's helpings on request. Smart dress preferred. No cigars/pipes in dining-room. Wheelchair access (also WC). No music  ACCOMMODATION: 1 apartment, with bath/shower. B&B £50 to £80. TV. Phone

## Old Forge

6A Church Street, Storrington RH20 4LA
STORRINGTON (0903) 743402

COOKING 1*
COST £20–£38

Clive Roberts strikes hard at the anvil of creativity in this sometime blacksmith's shop now a cottage restaurant. Lambs' sweetbreads braised with sherry and vinegar and layered in a puff pastry case with a yogurt sauce, or mousseline of chicken and avocado scented with rosemary and served with a cucumber vinaigrette, calf's liver with caramelised onions, cognac and lemon, or magret of duck stuffed with salami, orange and walnuts on a vermouth sauce show a full range of flavourings and counterpoint, executed with a fair degree of flourish and complexity. Visitors have been struck by the enthusiasm of both the Roberts, and by the lack of pretension allied to simple direct flavours in the cooking. Vegetables, sauces, materials (Southdown lamb and Sussex-landed fish are mentioned) and, most noteworthy of all, puddings get honourable mention. Strawberry and rhubarb strudel and a roulade of cinnamon sponge with caramelised walnut ice-cream and a Grand Marnier sabayon are two desserts that tasted as good as they sounded. Ancillaries are well thought out and the wine list is a model of concise yet considered choice. Each bottle is relevant to the concept of range and price, the makers and the vintages are enviable and the sources catholic. House wines are £7.50, and there is a fine range of sweet things to be had by the glass to accompany the excellent desserts.

CHEFS/PROPRIETORS: Clive and Cathy Roberts  OPEN: Tue to Sun, exc L Tue and Sat and Sun D; 12.30 to 1.30, 7.15 to 9  CLOSED: 1 week late spring, 3 weeks Oct  MEALS: alc (main courses £11 to £13.50). Set L £14, Set D to £19.50  SERVICE: not inc, card slips closed  CARDS: Access, Amex, Diners, Visa  DETAILS: 24 seats. Private parties: 16 main room. Vegetarian meals. Children's helpings. Smart dress preferred. No smoking while others eat. Wheelchair access (3 steps). Music

---

**STOW-ON-THE-WOLD** Gloucestershire

map 2

## ▲ *Wyck Hill House* ⁵⁄✳

Burford Road,
Stow-on-the-Wold GL54 1HY
COTSWOLD (0451) 831936
on A424, 2m SE of Stow-on-the-Wold

COOKING 2
COST £22–£59

The house, the views, the lawns, the furnishings, the attention to guests' needs are the stuff to write home about. Less convincing is the need to charge so much for the food, however competent the technique. There is more of interest in the first courses: for instance, squid and king prawns on a salad of artichoke, sun-dried tomatoes and basil, and a lobster and scallop minestrone that has pleased for its lightness combined with taste. The main dishes seem a less than imaginative set of meats: beef fillet, duck, lamb, chicken and turkey. The sorrel sauce with the lamb seems to have been the most exciting sauce. Light snacks are also available at lunch-time. The wine list gives scant attention to countries beyond France, where the most interesting section is the mature clarets (not all from the best years) though prices are high. House wines are £11.75.

CHEF: Ian Smith   PROPRIETORS: Lyric Hotels   OPEN: all week; 12.30 to 2, 7.30 to 9.30
MEALS: alc (main courses £12.50 to £22.50). Set L £11.95. Light L menu   SERVICE: not inc
CARDS: Access, Amex, Diners, Visa   DETAILS: 80 seats. Private parties: 80 main room, 40
private room. Car park. Vegetarian meals. Children's helpings. Jacket and tie. No smoking
in dining-room. Wheelchair access (also WC). Music. Air-conditioned   ACCOMMODATION:
30 rooms, all with bath/shower. Rooms for disabled. Lift. B&B £70 to £170. Children
welcome. Pets welcome (not in public rooms). Afternoon teas. Garden. TV. Phone. Doors
close at midnight. Confirm by 3. Fax: (0451) 832243 (*The Which? Hotel Guide*)

---

**STRATFORD-UPON-AVON Warwickshire**                                        map 2

## Sir Toby's

8 Church Street,
Stratford-upon-Avon CV37 6HB                                    COOKING 1
STRATFORD-UPON-AVON (0789) 268822                              COST £21–£35

People still have trouble eating in Stratford, so thank heaven for Sir Toby's.
Occupying a malt house dating back to 1682, the restaurant's seating is on
bench pews, the tables are none too large and the style is definitely bistro, but
welcomes are cheerful, smiles broad and people's treatment is 'civility
personified'. Evenings start early at Sir Toby's, with pre-theatre meals a
lynchpin of its success. First courses may include chargrilled turkey kebabs
with peanut sauce, spinach and sorrel roulade filled with smoked salmon,
home-made fish ravioli with prawn sauce, and herring roes with a light curry
flavour served on hot toast; main dish choices could be scallops and salmon
stir-fried with ginger and spring onions, chicken with olives, rosemary and
thyme with a wild mushroom sauce, and veal served with savoury rice and a
marjoram jelly. To finish, if bread-and-butter pudding or chocolate mousseline
with orange Curaçao do not suit, there are a couple of savouries. A simple wine
list gives adequate support at sensible prices. House wines are from £6.70.

CHEF: Joanna Watkins   PROPRIETORS: Carl and Joanna Watkins   OPEN: Wed to Sat,
D only; 5.30 to 9.30   MEALS: alc (main courses £9 to £11)   SERVICE: not inc, card slips
closed   CARDS: Access, Amex, Visa   DETAILS: 36 seats. Private parties: 36 main room,
16 private room. Vegetarian meals. Children's helpings. Smart dress preferred. No pipes
in dining-room. Wheelchair access. No music. Air-conditioned

---

**STREATLEY Berkshire**                                                     map 2

## ▲ Swan Diplomat,
## Riverside Restaurant                                    | NEW ENTRY |

High Street, Streatley RG8 9HR                                 COOKING 2
GORING-ON-THAMES (0491) 873737                                COST £27–£78

The hotel is a commercial pleasure-dome on the banks of the Thames (meetings
can be held in the magnificently restored Magdalen College barge) and the
restaurant overlooks the river. The private customer may sneer at the demands
of business and commerce, but the setting is magical – 'The only movement
was that of the bats in the darkening sky.' Within doors, touches reflect the

Swedish ownership and distance the treatment from the usual British pseudo-historical elegance. Do not expect great originality from the cooking – that would run counter to the market – but anticipate a degree of competence (and firm prices) for dishes such as pasta with ham, mushrooms and truffle; baked aubergine with ratatouille and Gruyère cheese and a suggestion of cardamom; and Dover sole cooked in three styles, salmon in two, or scampi with a curry sauce. There are Swedish touches in December, when a 'Julbord' Christmas buffet is offered, and in summer, when gravlax is served using wild salmon. The sweets come on a trolley. Service is keen, yet more Berkshire than West End, and the chef seems to like cream. The wine list is good, showing a lot of bins and good choices. Clarets are a strong point, but prices can be excruciating. House wines are from £10.50.

CHEF: Christopher Cleveland  PROPRIETORS: Diplomat Hotels of Sweden  OPEN: all week, exc Sat L and Sun D; 12.30 to 2, 7.30 (7 Fri and Sat) to 9.30  MEALS: alc (main courses £15 to £30). Set L £15.85 (2 courses) to £19.25, Set D £24  SERVICE: not inc  CARDS: Access, Amex, Diners, Visa  DETAILS: 75 seats. 7 tables outside. Private parties: 100 main room, 18, 32 and 100 private rooms. Car park. Vegetarian meals. Children's helpings. Smart dress preferred. No cigars/pipes in dining-room. Wheelchair access (3 steps; also WC). Music  ACCOMMODATION: 46 rooms, all with bath/shower. Rooms for disabled. B&B £96 to £134. Children welcome. Baby facilities by arrangement. Pets welcome (not in public areas). Afternoon teas. Garden. Swimming-pool. Sauna. TV. Phone. Confirm 1 day ahead. Fax: (0491) 872554

---

**STRETE** Devon                                                          map 1

## Laughing Monk  £

Strete TQ6 0RN
STOKE FLEMING (0803) 770639
5m from Dartmouth on coast road                          COOKING 1
to Kingsbridge                                                    COST £17–£34

Inside this ex-church school of the 1880s the feel is rustic – pine tables, a blackboard menu, high-backed settles to provide a measure of privacy, shaded lights and 'music so soft it was hardly discernible'. 'First the good things. The savoury apple starter (filled with herb-cheese pâté and coated with tarragon cream) was praiseworthy both for originality and flavour, while the poussin had the retina-appeal of a cookbook illustration.' It tasted good, too; as did attractively glazed duck, and fillet steak stuffed with a mushroom duxelles and garlic – though the requested medium erred towards rare. Salmon quenelles, however, were dryish, as was a rather dense crab soufflé. The dessert trolley is admired, especially since combinations are permitted, though some lament the disappearance of cheese as an option. Service is 'friendly and helpful'. The wine list is more extensive than the surroundings suggest, though quality is mixed. New World choices are good value and are generally better than the European wines, many of which are sourced from large négoçiants. House wines are £7.25.

---

*A report form is at the back of the book; write a letter if you prefer.*

---

CHEF: David Rothwell  PROPRIETORS: Mr and Mrs David Rothwell  OPEN: Tue to Sat D (exc Tue Nov to Mar), Sun L Oct to May; 12 to 1.30, 7 to 9.30  MEALS: alc (main courses £6.50 to £13). Set Sun L £7.25 (2 courses) to £9.95  SERVICE: not inc, card slips closed CARDS: Access, Visa  DETAILS: 50 seats. Private parties: 50 main room. Car park. Vegetarian meals with prior notice. Children's helpings. Smart dress preferred. No-smoking area. Wheelchair access (2 steps; also WC). Music

---

**STROUD Gloucestershire**                                                          map 2

## Oakes

169 Slad Road, Stroud GL5 1RG
STROUD (0453) 759950                                                    COOKING 4
on B4070, ½m NE of Stroud                                               COST £23–£50

This year has seen the addition of a bar next to the restaurant, but in other respects the scene is unchanged. 'At Oakes, you are only paying for the food, certainly not the surroundings,' reports one. Yet the informality (no tablecloths, no plush carpets) which prevails in this 'old stone building on a dull road' is deliberate: 'We are simple, honest people who try to run a simple (no-frills) honest restaurant,' state Caroline and Christopher Oakes. The plants are healthy; the tables and chairs are comfortable. The soups are good: a pea and ham was 'one of the best soups we have tasted', a lobster bisque 'v. v. v. good'. Other signs of the painstaking attention to detail which has won this restaurant so many friends are the 'superb bread' and 'faultless vegetables': rösti, chiffonade of green cabbage, quenelles of parsnip purée and a carrot/swede mixture with beurre blanc was a typical selection, typically appreciated. Those who opt for the salad alternative are no less taken with leaves and dressings. Piquant contrasts are an Oakes hallmark: turbot embedded on spinach responded enthusiastically to the bite of a café de France butter sauce; fillet of gurnard came with a slightly sharp chive sauce; and a ragoût of seafood, encased in puff pastry, was served with pickled samphire. Meat dishes are able to reflect local supplies more closely: superb breast of pigeon, for example, or pork sausages 'carefully flavoured' with sage, onion and green peppercorns. Desserts are predominantly comforting (steamed walnut pudding with a sultana and rum sauce, or prunes in custard sauce with almond and vanilla ice-cream), yet pistachio soufflé with cinnamon cream or iced cherry and hazelnut meringue parfait with a mango sauce show an exotic turn of speed when required. The proprietors say no gratuities are expected. The wine list is as no-frills as everything else. House wines begin at £7.25, and £15 procures a fair choice, including a slowly expanding collection of New World wines to match the solidly French base.

---

CHEF: Christopher Oakes  PROPRIETORS: Christopher and Caroline Oakes, and Nowell and Jean Scott  OPEN: Tue to Sun, exc Sun D; 12.30 to 1.45, 7.30 to 9.30  MEALS: Set L Tue to Sat £19, Set Sun L £22, Set D £36  SERVICE: card slips closed  CARDS: Access, Amex, Visa  DETAILS: 34 seats. Private parties: 34 main room. Car park. Vegetarian meals with prior notice. Children's helpings. Wheelchair access. No music

---

*The* Guide *always appreciates hearing about changes of chef or owner.*

---

## Three Lions 🍾

Stuckton Road, Stuckton, SP6 2HF
FORDINGBRIDGE (0425) 652489                                    COOKING 3
1m off A338 at Fordingbridge                                  COST £19–£47

The inn started life as part of Stuckton Farm. When a tavern, it was fairly basic, 'serving foresters and gypsies,' June Wadsack speculates. However, in the Wadsacks' hands, it has gradually developed. Karl Wadsack is a classically trained chef, once at Chewton Glen, and was hardly going to be content with serving pub food as a sideline. Today, the food has displaced the beer as the main attraction, though surroundings have never been so transformed that the original pub function is forgotten. This makes eating here much less constricted than it would be in a full-dress restaurant – one reason for its immense popularity. In addition, the fact that Karl's underlying technique is sound, his materials are properly sourced and his tastebuds are finely tuned puts his cooking into another stratosphere from pub food. This is not home cooking gone commercial, but professional cooking made available to a wide market. The repertoire is conservative in that it has not rushed to convert to the new-wave Mediterranean style. Beef Stroganov, chopped venison steak with venison sausage, pheasant and (always tender) pigeon breast grand veneur, fillet of pork with wood mushrooms and an armagnac sauce, and wiener schnitzel are marker dishes. Fish cookery, also well sourced, is perhaps lighter and more recognisably of the '90s – for instance, monkfish with a red pepper, mushroom and sherry cream sauce, and king prawns, scallops and other fish cooked with a curry and coriander sauce. Northern European origins surface with marinated herrings, Arbroath smokies and soups like duck and beetroot. Room should be made for desserts of the order of apple strudel, chocolate pots and meringue glacé . The wine list has some treasures. Perhaps the strongest or most interesting sections are the sweet wines, the German wines and those from Australia. The latter are a new enthusiasm and are showing well. Prices are not exorbitant. House wines are £8.95.

CHEF: Karl Wadsack   PROPRIETORS: June and Karl Wadsack   OPEN: Tue to Sat; 12.15 to 1.30, 7.15 to 9 (9.30 Sat)   CLOSED: 24 to 29 Dec, 4 to 5 weeks from 5 Feb (telephone to check), 2 weeks end July to Aug   MEALS: alc (main courses L £5 to £15 D)   SERVICE: not inc   CARDS: Access, Visa   DETAILS: 55 seats. Private parties: 20 main room. Car park. Vegetarian meals with prior notice. No children under 14. Smart dress preferred. Wheelchair access (1 step; also WC). No music. Air-conditioned. Fax: (0425) 656144

---

*Several sharp operators have tried to extort money from restaurateurs on the promise of an entry in a guidebook that has never appeared.* The Good Food Guide *makes no charge for inclusion and does not offer certificates of any kind.*

*The 1995* Guide *will be published before Christmas 1994. Reports on meals are most welcome at any time of the year, but are extremely valuable in the spring. Send them to* The Good Food Guide, *FREEPOST, 2 Marylebone Road, London NW1 1YN. No stamp is needed if posted in the UK.*

## STURMINSTER NEWTON Dorset

map 2

# ▲ *Plumber Manor*

Sturminster Newton DT10 2AF
STURMINSTER NEWTON (0258) 72507,
changes to (0258) 472507 late 1993
A357 to Sturminster Newton, take first left
to Hazelbury Bryan, on left-hand side after 2m

COOKING 1
COST £23–£38

English country living is the raison d'être of this manor house, still inhabited
by the family that built it in the first place. The living has expanded somewhat
over the years, as guests occupy premises formerly filled with hay or horses,
and one occasional visitor was heard to mutter 'motel' rather than 'paradise' as
he hauled his bags across the court. Cooking remains fairly plain, best for game
and roasts, and not keen to change a well-set formula. Come the weekend, it
can get fairly hectic as the place fills with those who come for their Sunday
sport, as well as with people from neighbouring towns out for the evening.
This may affect the care or complexity of the food preparation. Desserts still
come from a trolley, and the wine list continues to be a sound selection of good
names, though there has been a diminution of old clarets from the cellar. House
wines are £9.50.

CHEF: Brian Prideaux-Brune   PROPRIETOR: Richard Prideaux-Brune   OPEN: all week,
D only, and Sun L; 12.30 to 2, 7.30 to 9.30   MEALS: Set L £17.50, Set D £20 to £26.50
SERVICE: net prices, card slips closed   CARDS: Access, Amex, Diners, Visa   DETAILS: 60
seats. Private parties: 46 main room, 14 and 24 private rooms. Car park. Vegetarian meals.
Children by arrangement. Children's helpings Sun L. Smart dress preferred. No cigars/
pipes in dining-room. Wheelchair access (also WC). No music   ACCOMMODATION: 16
rooms, all with bath/shower. Rooms for disabled. B&B £60 to £110. Children under 12 by
arrangement. Pets welcome. Garden. Tennis. TV. Phone. Fax: (0258) 473370 (*The Which?
Hotel Guide*)

## SUDBURY Suffolk

map 3

# *Mabey's Brasserie* ⁵⊁ £

47 Gainsborough Street,
Sudbury CO10 7SS
SUDBURY (0787) 374298
next to Gainsborough House Museum

COOKING 2*
COST £19–£33

Refurbishment has given extra space and light to what was once a kitchen/
restaurant at the back of the site. It is a happy consequence of popularity. The
formula – for the concept was closely worked out – has not changed radically
with the furnishings: fresh food, cooked before your eyes, according to a
mixture of traditional and modern recipes, and charged at reasonable prices.
Breast of chicken on a bed of rice with red wine sauce, skate with caper sauce,
salmon with fresh pasta, grilled lamb with onion gravy are some examples of
straightforward cooking done well. Game is a strong point; fish runs it a close
second. Puddings are seriously enjoyed. Robert Mabey decided against *la
grande restauration* and has designed something that is accessible yet quality-
conscious. It has worked. The wine list stays short and international. The top

price is £16.50, but there are growers such as Schleret, St Hallett, Antinori and Leflaive that would be the envy of anywhere. House wines are £6.95.

CHEF: Robert Mabey   PROPRIETORS: Robert and Johanna Mabey   OPEN: Tue to Sat; 12 to 2, 7 to 10   CLOSED: 25 and 26 Dec   MEALS: alc (main courses £7 to £11.50)   SERVICE: not inc, card slips closed   CARDS: Access, Amex, Visa   DETAILS: 60 seats. Private parties: 30 main room. Vegetarian meals. Children's helpings. No smoking in main dining-room. Wheelchair access (2 steps). No music. Air-conditioned

---

**SURBITON Surrey**                                                                    map 3

# Chez Max

85 Maple Road, Surbiton KT6 4AW                                     COOKING 2
081-399 2365                                                                   COST £28–£40

There are exceptions to every rule, and Max Markarian's quiet, unfussy, pastel-hued restaurant questions the axiom that the easier a suburb is to get to, the less rewarding it is when you get there. People migrate inwards to eat, so most come to this terraced former shop in Surbiton from further out in Surrey – to enjoy sure-handed, French-accented cooking in surroundings more spacious than the frontage would suggest. The disappearance of the *carte* and a growing emphasis on homely ingredients are sources of regret to some; others are grateful for the value that the set-price lunches and dinners provide (but note that desserts cost extra). The repertoire sticks with popular perennials: spicy duck in filo with apricot sauce, a feuilleté of haddock with tomato and cream sauce, duck breast in a honey and clove sauce, and hazelnut meringue with its 'mountain' of strawberries. Service in general is friendly and unobtrusive. The French-only wine list has now grown too grand for the menu, and badly needs an infusion of mid-priced wines; house wines at £12.50 have been thought pricey, and those who request a greater choice of half-bottles are perplexed at being told there is no demand for them.

CHEF: Max Markarian   PROPRIETORS: Mr and Mrs Max Markarian   OPEN: Tue to Sat, exc Sat L; 12.30 to 2, 7.30 to 10   CLOSED: 24 to 30 Dec   MEALS: Set L £15.95 (2 courses), Set D Tue to Fri £15.95 (2 courses), Set D Sat £16.50 (2 courses)   SERVICE: 12.5%, card slips closed   CARDS: Access, Amex, Diners, Visa   DETAILS: 40 seats. Private parties: 45 main room. Vegetarian meals. Children's helpings with prior notice. No children under 5. Wheelchair access. Music

---

**SUTTON COLDFIELD West Midlands**                                          map 5

# ▲ New Hall ⁑

Walmley Road, Sutton Coldfield B76 8QX                          COOKING 2*
021-378 2442                                                                   COST £25–£61

Set in 26 acres of private gardens, New Hall is reputedly the oldest-surviving moated manor house in the country. It is a country hotel, serving the business community of the 1990s, but it guards its sense of history. Everywhere there are signs of the past in the old beams, oak panelling and mullioned windows. Glenn Purcell cooks with one eye on the old country-hotel repertoire and another on trendsetting fashion. His *carte* and daily set menus feature dishes such as crab tortellini with shellfish vinaigrette and crispy leeks, roast Gressingham duck breast on a Bramley apple compote with red cabbage ravioli, and lamb cutlets with sweet-pea mousse and grilled pleurottes on a tarragon sauce. Dover sole is grilled, and tournedos of salmon is set on a pool of vegetable and truffle butter. Puddings might include hot praline soufflé with Bailey's ice-cream, mango and kiwi délice, and mille-feuille of caramelised bananas. The 350-strong wine list takes some reading, but considered exploration will yield plenty of fine drinking at prices that will not empty the wallet. A page of house wines starts at £11.45.

CHEF: Glenn Purcell  PROPRIETORS: Ian and Caroline Parkes  OPEN: all week, exc Sat L; 12.30 to 2 (2.15 Sun), 7 to 10  MEALS: alc (main courses L £8.50 to £10.50, D £17 to £21). Set Sun L £16.50, Set D £24.95  SERVICE: not inc, card slips closed  CARDS: Access, Amex, Diners, Visa  DETAILS: 60 seats. 6 tables outside. Private parties: 12 main room, 10 and 40 private rooms. Car park. Vegetarian meals. Children's helpings. No children under 8. Jacket and tie. No smoking in dining-room. Wheelchair access (also WC). No music ACCOMMODATION: 62 rooms, all with bath/shower. Rooms for disabled. B&B £70 to £265. No children under 8. Baby facilities. Afternoon teas. Garden. Fishing. TV. Phone. Doors close at 11. Confirm by 6. Fax: 021-378 4637 (*The Which? Hotel Guide*)

---

### SUTTON COURTENAY  Oxfordshire                                    map 2

## *Fish at Sutton Courtenay* ✸✳

Appleford Road,
Sutton Courtenay OX14 4NQ                                     COOKING 2*
ABINGDON (0235) 848242                                       COST £27–£42

'It's taking its pub persona rather too seriously; things could be happily spruced up without loss of character' was the conclusion of one visitor who found the scanning of the blackboard *before* being able to sit down a touch irritating and had to discover the ritual for herself. Nevertheless, the food gets many plaudits and as we went to press the place was getting a new lick of paint. Bruce Buchan cooks more than fish, even if that gets star billing. Dishes such as gurnard with chickpeas and coriander or monkfish with a sauce containing sun-dried tomatoes are expressive and successful, while plain sole with lemon or whole Cornish crab with mayonnaise give the raw material a chance to shine. In fact, there are as many meat dishes: beef in puff pastry with green peppercorns, or more luxuriously with foie gras ('and a goodly slice'), and duck with a five-spice and plum sauce are some instances. Vegetables come crisply, all in a bowl. Sweet production may include sugar baskets or all three puds on a single plate for the greedy; the sticky toffee pudding is wicked. Service is invariably cheerful, if not suave. The fairly priced wine list is also on a board, with excellent range. House wine is £8.75.

CHEFS: Bruce Buchan and Jason Fretwell  PROPRIETORS: Bruce and Kay Buchan OPEN: all week, exc Tue D; 12 to 2.15, 7 to 9.30 (10 Fri and Sat)  CLOSED: 4 days between Christmas and New Year  MEALS: alc (main courses £11 to £14)  SERVICE: not inc, card slips closed  CARDS: Access, Amex, Diners, Visa  DETAILS: 55 seats. Private parties: 38 main room, 20 and 30 private rooms. Car park. Vegetarian meals. Children's helpings. Smart dress preferred. No smoking in 1 dining-room. Wheelchair access (1 step). Music. Fax: (0235) 848242

## SWANAGE Dorset
map 2

# Galley £

9 High Street, Swanage BH19 2LN
SWANAGE (0929) 427299

COOKING 1
COST £20–£30

The Storers had hoped to open a fish and chip shop in their high street premises near the pier, but failed to get planning permission. So they opted instead for an unassuming restaurant serving fresh food every evening throughout the tourist season. Fish is still the main attraction on the short, varied fixed-price menu (a few items are at a supplement): some is caught by a member of the family, the rest is from local boats. It appears in simply handled dishes such as grilled slip soles with dill butter, sauté John Dory fillets provençale, and hake baked in filo pastry with hollandaise. The owners grow herbs on their allotment, obtain smoked salmon from a local fishmonger who cures his own, and buy meat from local butchers. Consequently their repertoire also extends to cold watercress soup, sauté pigeon breast with mixed leaves and toasted hazelnuts, venison and red wine pudding, and braised chicken breast with leeks and sage dumplings. Sweets might include steamed fruit sponge with Muscat sauce. Around 40 affordable wines are bolstered by a few specials and bin-ends; whites naturally predominate. New World wines are from £8.50.

CHEF: Nick Storer   PROPRIETORS: N.D. and M.G. Storer   OPEN: all week, D only; 6.45 to 9.30 (10 Sat)   CLOSED: New Year to Easter (exc some weekends – telephone to check) MEALS: Set D £14.50   SERVICE: net prices, card slips closed   CARDS: Access, Amex, Diners, Visa   DETAILS: 32 seats. Private parties: 32 main room. Vegetarian meals. Children's helpings with prior notice. Music. Air-conditioned

## TADWORTH Surrey
map 3

# Gemini

**NEW ENTRY**

Station Approach, Tadworth KT20 5AH
TADWORTH (0737) 812179

COOKING 2
COST £19–£32

Tadworth is not a village noted for its fine restaurants, but the Fosters have taken this Tudorbethan shop unit and intend to prove otherwise. Robert was trained classically, his career culminating at Boulestin. The repertoire, therefore, is very much neo-classical French cuisine with an emphasis on sauces and finesse. A seasonal fixed-price menu is helped along by daily blackboard extras. Accuracy and refinement do seem to be on offer, evinced by a summer meal that consisted of a feuilleté of kidneys and calf's liver with port and garlic sauce, duck with a forestière sauce, and monkfish with herbs on a sauce Nantua. Fresh noodles were also sampled and were good. Whether gratin dauphinois was the correct accompaniment to monkfish was ignored by the person who ate it eagerly, along with a raft of beans, broccoli, carrots and cauliflower: West End classicism meets country insistence on plenty. Crème brûlée with rum and sultanas was outstanding, but a Beaumes de Venise mousse, lemon tart and hot bananas with cinnamon sauce offered strong competition. The wine list does not list much over £20, but gives fair choice at fair prices – even if details are scant. House wines are £7.

CHEF: Robert Foster   PROPRIETORS: Robert and Debbie Foster   OPEN: Tue to Sun, exc Sat L and Sun D; 12 to 2, 7 to 9.30   MEALS: Set L £9.50 (2 courses) to £13.50, Set D £17.50 (2 courses Tue to Thur) to £21   SERVICE: not inc   CARDS: Access, Visa   DETAILS: 38 seats. Private parties: 40 main room. Vegetarian meals. Children's helpings L. No children under 12 D. Smart dress preferred. No cigars/pipes in dining-room. Wheelchair access (1 step; also WC). Music

---

**TAUNTON Somerset**                                                                  map 2

## *Capriccio* ✂✳                                            `NEW ENTRY`

41 Bridge Street, Taunton TA1 1TP                                    COOKING  1
TAUNTON (0823) 335711                                                COST £16–£29

Italy has come to Taunton in the shape of this modest family restaurant in the centre of town. Owners Andrea and Kathy Zunino imported furnishings and fittings from their native land, including the floor in the conservatory, the glassware and the cutlery. The setting is comfortable, with neatly laid, well-spaced tables and staff get full marks for their manner and expertise. Andrea Zunino cooks an essentially north Italian menu that changes every six weeks. Pasta and ice-creams are made on the premises. The repertoire is a step up from Pavarotti trattoria and the value for money is reckoned excellent. Melanzane (baked aubergines with mozzarella and tomato sauce), pappardelle with chicken liver and peas, risotto with mushrooms, and calf's liver with Marsala are typical offerings. Savoury cheese profiteroles with mushrooms and cream has been a 'mouthwatering' starter before vitello alla piedmontese stuffed with Fontina cheese accompanied by a side dish of well-timed spaghetti. Sorbets make a delectable finale. Andrea makes a yearly trip to a small vineyard to procure a 'vino da tavola', otherwise the exclusively Italian list provides very affordable drinking. House wine is £6.75 a litre.

CHEF: Andrea Zunino   PROPRIETORS: Andrea and Kathy Zunino   OPEN: Mon to Sat, D only; 7 to 10   CLOSED: Christmas to mid-Jan, bank hols   MEALS: alc (main courses £5.50 to £11). Set D £9.95 (2 courses) to £12.95   SERVICE: not inc   CARDS: Access, Visa DETAILS: 48 seats. Vegetarian meals. Children's helpings. Smart dress preferred. No smoking in 1 dining-room. Wheelchair access (1 step). Music

---

## ▲ *Castle Hotel* ❢

Castle Green, Taunton TA1 1NF                                        COOKING  4
TAUNTON (0823) 272671                                                COST £22–£59

This bastion of British cooking sounds a latter-day trump for high standards in privately owned city-centre hotels at a time when most of the fancy have fled to country mansions to practise luxury hotel-keeping. The Castle is a smooth operation indeed, the bedrooms are given every trick of decoration and comfort, the public rooms are as suave as can be. Yet, atavistic urges to remain a place used by the community as a whole – definitely not a trait of country-house hotels – remain in the lunch menus that compete for price with the commonest city restaurants and trounce them for value. Phil Vickery has settled in to his responsibilities with panache. 'We had been to the Castle in February, and I think the food had greatly improved even since then' was the judgement of a family that took a suite for the weekend and voted the puddings the best thing of all. 'I had a generous slice of creamy egg custard tart with a spoonful each of clotted cream, and nutmeg ice-cream; my husband had a plateful of four chocolate puddings: a cup of chocolate orange cream, white chocolate chip ice-cream, rich chocolate cake and a little mousse.' Out of simplicity and firm intentions sometimes comes bliss. That inexpensive lunch might consist of a giant flat mushroom with an intense tomato compote and a glazing of hollandaise, followed by mild boiled bacon with some of the best mashed potatoes in England (not too oily, full of potato flavour, yet smooth and rich) and a properly made madeira sauce, then an almond blancmange with lemon grass syrup and candied lemon. The blancmange was what all children fear and adults fondly remember yet can never reproduce from a packet; the lemon grass syrup could have had more zing to it from the herb; the candied lemon gave the necessary point and edge. The enjoyment in some of the British-style cooking is the combination of relatively simple elements, like that boiled bacon, with techniques from upper-crust classical cooking, like the madeira sauce. The more expensive menus (set prices for three or four courses) will offer ideas drawn from traditions other than just British. A dish of artichoke heart filled with fresh crab and surrounded by strips of pan-fried squid with a light cream garlic sauce was one which impressed, as did saffron noodles, scallops and braised onions, or lobster sausage with couscous and a lobster and caviare dressing. Fine materials have always been a feature here, suppliers given a credit on the menu, seasonality always observed, butchers and fishmongers supplying the very best. Bread, strangely, is not a particularly strong suit. A virtual monopoly of supply for the Rhône by Jaboulet characterises the wine list. This remains good, but also stubbornly rooted in the safety of big names, which however excellent they may be denies access to fine, but smaller growers. House wines, 25 in all, perhaps provide the greatest excitement and are fairly priced (from £8.05). CELLARMAN'S CHOICE: Rouge Homme, Chardonnay 1987, £18.35; Châteauneuf-du-Pape, Les Cèdres 1985, Jaboulet, £22.40.

CHEF: Phil Vickery   PROPRIETORS: the Chapman family   OPEN: all week; 12.30 to 2, 7.30 to 9   MEALS: Set L £13.50 (2 courses) to £29.90, Set D £17.90 to £29.90   SERVICE: not inc, card slips closed   CARDS: Access, Amex, Diners, Visa   DETAILS: 65 seats. Private parties: 110 main room, 50 and 110 private rooms. Car park. Vegetarian meals. Children's helpings. Smart dress preferred. No smoking during meals. Wheelchair access (1 step; also WC). No music   ACCOMMODATION: 35 rooms, all with bath/shower. Rooms for disabled. Lift. B&B £59.50 to £90. Children welcome. Baby facilities. Dogs welcome (bedrooms only). Garden. TV. Phone. Doors close at 11.30. Confirm by 3. Fax: (0823) 272671 (*The Which? Hotel Guide*)

CELLARMAN'S CHOICE: *Wines recommended by the restaurateur, normally more expensive than house wine.*

*Prices quoted in the* Guide *are based on information supplied by restaurateurs. The prices quoted at the top of each entry represent a range, from the lowest meal price to the highest; the latter is inflated by 20 per cent to take account of likely price rises during the year of the* Guide.

TAVISTOCK Devon                                                                    map 1

## ▲ Horn of Plenty

Gulworthy, Tavistock PL19 8JD
TAVISTOCK (0822) 832528
3m W of Tavistock on A390,                                           COOKING 3
turn right at Gulworthy Cross                                        COST £25–£59

The odd upset aside, reports of the food and welcome at this former mine-
captain's house (with rooms in the stable block beyond), the dining-room and
terrace of which overlook the spectacular valley of the Tamar, have been
enthusiastic. The refurbishment programme has worked to great effect in the
dining-room, where the windows absorb the evening light or shield the diner
from buffeting storms. Peter Gorton's cooking has a certain consistency and
even tone; it is not flamboyant, but the pleasure gained from a small slice of
quiche with perfect pastry and a balance of sweet and salt in the light filling
may outweigh the consequences of many gastronomic pyrotechnics. A menu
formula of set price with many supplements is meant to combine the virtues of
a *carte* and table d'hôte, though it may give rise to muddle. It does, however,
enable luxuries to be mobilised, as in sea bass with buckwheat pasta and
caviare or truffles on top of goats' cheese on top of a breast of guinea-fowl with
port wine sauce. Lack of culinary fireworks may occasion blandness, though
not in a dinner that began with ravioli of smoked salmon, went on to a classic,
deeply flavoured new season's rack of lamb, and finished with a tart of
imported raspberries topped with chocolate. That lucky diner rated desserts a
great improvement over earlier practice. Elaine Gatehouse is considered very
attentive, a rock among pebbles. Her wine list has widened this year, taking in
more from far-flung territories. France is still the centrepiece, with some sound
clarets and rock-steady red Rhônes. House wines start at £9.50.

CHEFS: Peter Gorton and Karen Jones   PROPRIETORS: Elaine and Ian Gatehouse   OPEN: all
week, exc Mon L; 12 to 2.30, 7.15 to 9.30   CLOSED: 25 and 26 Dec   MEALS: Set L £14.50 (2
courses) to £17.50, Set D £25.50   SERVICE: not inc   CARDS: Access, Amex, Visa   DETAILS:
50 seats. 6 tables outside. Private parties: 50 main room, 20 private room. Car park.
Vegetarian meals. No children under 13, exc Sun L. Smart dress preferred. No-smoking
area. Wheelchair access (also WC). No music   ACCOMMODATION: 7 rooms, 5 with bath/
shower (2 with shower only). Rooms for disabled. B&B £51 to £90. Deposit: 10% or £20.
No children under 13. Pets welcome (not in public rooms). Garden. TV. Phone. Doors close
at 11.45. Confirm by 6. Fax: (0822) 832528 (*The Which? Hotel Guide*)

## Neil's ✴✻

27 King Street, Tavistock PL19 0DT                                   COOKING 2
TAVISTOCK (0822) 615550                                              COST £24–£38

'Food of this standard in London would be considered good value at twice the
price,' enthused weekenders from W14 who also appreciated the no-smoking
policy in the Neils' little beamed dining-room. Janet Neil's cooking is sharply
executed and follows the seasons. The keenly priced set menu in May offered
watercress pancakes filled with fresh crab, breast of chicken stuffed with
asparagus mousse, and iced elderflower and rhubarb mousse with rhubarb

compote. The *carte* has French overtones, but it also displays Mrs Neil's fondness for going her own way. Roast rack of lamb is given a rosemary and garlic crust, guinea-fowl is served with Meaux mustard sauce, but classic bourride is transmuted into a provençal fish tart – filo pastry is filled with fish and shellfish in aïoli sauce, plus black olives and sun-dried tomatoes topped with rouille. This was rated superb by a reporter who also enjoyed venison with oyster mushrooms and redcurrant sauce. Sweets such as iced plum soufflé with crème anglaise and plum coulis, and frangipane with caramelised apricots and toasted almonds have been appreciated, although the presence of only one 'slightly over the top' cheese has not. Occasionally the cooking has lacked sparkle, but generally this is an enterprise that pleases. Service is obliging, but sometimes a little timid. Murray Neil has some interesting malts in the bar and has put together a sharp little list with some fair-priced, lively drinking, especially among the Spanish and New World sections. House French is £9.75.

CHEF: Janet Neil   PROPRIETORS: Murray and Janet Neil   OPEN: Tue to Sat, D only; 7 to 9
CLOSED: 25 and 26 Dec   MEALS: alc (main courses £12 to £14). Set D £16. Minimum
£11.75   SERVICE: not inc   CARDS: Access, Visa   DETAILS: 20 seats. Private parties: 20
main room. Vegetarian meals. Children welcome. Smart dress preferred. No smoking in
dining-room. No music

---

**TEFFONT EVIAS** Wiltshire                                                        map 2

## ▲ *Howard's House Hotel*

Teffont Evias SP3 5RJ
TEFFONT (0722) 716392 and 716821                                    COOKING 1
off B3089, W of Dinton, signed Chicksgrove                           COST £24–£46

This was Catherine Howard's place, in the days of Good King Henry. She did not live to enjoy it. Today, the building is unusual yet comfortable, and the gardens are a delight ('I revelled in the peace'). Though it suffers from that English trick of cramming the world into a lounge before carting people off for dinner, guests respond to the welcome and to the enjoyment of an overnight stay ('breakfast was admirable'). An ambitious menu has alternately pleased and dissatisfied. Latest reports have not been as satisfactory, in that dishes that sound of interest – for example, a soufflé of arbroath smokies with a red pepper sauce, mullet with tomato and fennel, calf's liver with artichokes and a juniper and orange glaze, or guinea-fowl with a ballottine of apple, coriander and lime – have not lived up to expectations. Desserts, which had been impressive, have also showed some faltering. It is hoped that the hiccup is temporary. The wine list is more than adequate in geographical range, and delicate financing is considered too. North America fares less well than Australia (Wyndhams and Penfolds), and some useful Riojas are on offer. The strengths are burgundy and claret, albeit at a higher cost. House wines start at £8.95.

---

*Restaurateurs justifiably resent no-shows. If you quote a credit card number when booking, you may be liable for the restaurant's lost profit margin if you don't turn up. Always phone to cancel.*

---

CHEFS: Paul Firmin and Michael Fox  PROPRIETOR: Paul Firmin  OPEN: all week, D only,
and Sun L; 12.30 to 2, 7.15 to 10  MEALS: Set Sun L £17.50, Set D £25.50 to £27.50
SERVICE: not inc  CARDS: Access, Amex, Diners, Visa  DETAILS: 32 seats. 4 tables outside.
Private parties: 36 main room. Vegetarian meals. Children's helpings. No cigars/pipes in
dining-room. Wheelchair access (also men's WC). Music  ACCOMMODATION: 9 rooms, all
with bath/shower. B&B £70 to £90. Children welcome. Baby facilities. Pets welcome (not
in public rooms). Garden. TV. Phone. Doors close at midnight. Confirm by 6. Fax: (0722)
716820 (*The Which? Hotel Guide*)

---

TETBURY  Gloucestershire                                                     map 2

## ▲ Calcot Manor ❦ ✳

Beverston, Tetbury GL8 8YJ
TETBURY (0666) 890391                                              COOKING 2*
on A4135, 3½m W of Tetbury                                      COST £20–£40

This 'rambling farm' in the lovely, lonely heart of the Cotswolds is comfortable
and relaxed, the dining-room spacious and restful. The Ball family ('delightful
hoteliers') continue to oversee their collection of luxury cottages (once cow-
sheds) with charm and professionalism, yet reports from the dining-room
suggest wavering. On occasion meals pass swimmingly well, with 'delicious
and original combinations' such as a galette of Jerusalem artichokes and wild
mushrooms and perfectly cooked foie gras with whole shallots, or venison
with mushrooms and chestnuts. Ben Davies has an imagination and likes to
use it: marinated fish terrine brings together sea bass, monkfish and red mullet,
and comes with an 'excellent' dressing of confit fennel and red pepper; fillet of
brill has 'a most interesting topping' (a herb and garlic crust) and sits on an
aubergine terrine. Yet some dishes, or other ingredients, have seemed
unsympathetically handled: in one meal, both a starter of rabbit and main
course of duck were 'very tough, disappointing'; a 'most peculiar watercress
soup' was 'very dark green with three lumps of congealed something floating
on top'; and desserts, too, have been felt less inspired than the best of the rest.
Service is 'friendly but a little amateur', with speed still leisurely ('a service
charge is neither made or expected'). The wine list is mainly French, fairly
expensive, but contains wines from good producers such as Vatan in Sancerre
and the Cave Vinicole de Turckheim in Alsace. The notes are welcome, but all
the producers should be identified, layout could be improved, and there are
some sloppy mistakes which need ironing out. House wines are £11.95.

---

CHEF: Ben Davies  PROPRIETORS: Calcot Manor Hotel Ltd  OPEN: all week; 12.30 to 2, 7.30
to 9.30  MEALS: alc light L (main courses £5 to £6). Set L £13 (2 courses) to £18, Set D £18
to £26  SERVICE: card slips closed  CARDS: Access, Amex, Diners, Visa  DETAILS: 50
seats. 4 tables outside. Private parties: 50 main room, 14 private room. Car park. Vegetarian
meals with prior notice. Children's helpings on request. Smart dress preferred. No smoking
in dining-room. Wheelchair access (also WC). Music  ACCOMMODATION: 15 rooms, all
with bath/shower. Rooms for disabled. B&B £75 to £135. Children welcome. Baby
facilities. Afternoon teas. Garden. Swimming-pool. TV. Phone. Doors close at midnight.
Fax: (0666) 890394 (*The Which? Hotel Guide*)

---

▲ *This symbol means accommodation is available.*

---

THORNBURY Avon                                                          map 2

## ▲ *Thornbury Castle* ╬✳

Castle Street, Thornbury BS12 1HH
THORNBURY (0454) 281182                                          COOKING 2
off B4061, at N end of town                                      COST £26–£50

A spectacular setting, all agree – 'about as close as one can come to pretending
to be Anne Boleyn or Henry VIII'. Deep regal red dominates in the seven-sided
dining-room; the music, piped, is period. The dishes do not always quite rise to
the heights of the menu rhetoric ('Van Dyke of chilled Galia melon' seems
doomed to disappoint, and 'a symphony of sea fish' was presented with
chamber music resources), but there are much enjoyed successes, such as cream
of fennel soup; fillet of pork on a bed of truffle; pan-fried escalope of venison
with juniper and blackcurrant sauce; a strong, clearly flavoured mango soufflé;
and, of course, the now-almost-armorial treacle tart with clotted cream. Things
go right; things also go wrong: an Angus tournedos 'was not terrific', its red-
onion marmalade 'just slightly sweetish-tasting' and its horseradish and cream
sauce 'a huge pool of creamy, rather brown sauce, which tasted mostly of the
lots of chopped onion adrift in it'. Bread needs improvement; star-fruit was
meaningless with the treacle tart; and salads and vegetables can be a let-down.
Service is formal and courtly, and everyone admires the firmly worded refusal
of gratuities. The wine list is adequate, a larger-than-usual Californian section
reflecting transatlantic devotion to the 'Thornbury experience'; and the castle's
own Müller-Thurgau is reported 'most enjoyable'. House wines are from £12.

CHEF: Peter Brazill   PROPRIETORS: The Baron and Baroness of Portlethen   OPEN: all week;
12 to 2, 7 to 9.30 (10 Fri and Sat, 9 Sun)   CLOSED: 2 days early Jan   MEALS: Set L £17.75,
Set D £31   SERVICE: card slips closed   CARDS: Access, Amex, Diners, Visa   DETAILS: 60
seats. Private parties: 28 main room. Car park. Vegetarian meals. No children under 12.
Jacket and tie. No smoking in dining-room. Music   ACCOMMODATION: 18 rooms, all with
bath/shower. B&B £75 to £200. No children under 12. Afternoon teas. Garden. TV. Phone.
Fax: (0454) 416188 (*The Which? Hotel Guide*)

THORNTON-CLEVELEYS Lancashire                                          map 5

## ▲ *Victorian House*

Trunnah Road,
Thornton-Cleveleys FY5 4HF
BLACKPOOL (0253) 860619                                          COOKING 1
3m N of Blackpool                                                COST £17–£34

As you leave Thornton-Cleveleys, go past the windmill and turn right at the
church. Here is the appropriately named Victorian House, which *is* a Victorian
house. Inside, the Victorian theme is maintained in furniture and ornament.
Waitresses have also been decked in Victorian style. But Didier Guérin cooks a
late-twentieth century French repertoire: this may include old bourgeois
favourites like rabbit braised with prunes, but also shows a modern orientation
in dishes like the lamb stuffed with courgette, pesto and sun-dried tomatoes.
An English love of mild sweetness has infused the recipes at various points.

The short wine list stays firmly within French borders, but does not over-charge. House wines are £9.50.

CHEF: Didier Guérin  PROPRIETORS: Louise and Didier Guérin  OPEN: Mon to Sat, exc Mon L; 12 to 1.30, 7 to 9.30  CLOSED: last week Jan, first week Feb  MEALS: alc L (main courses £5.50). Set D £19.95  SERVICE: not inc, card slips closed  CARDS: Access, Visa  DETAILS: 60 seats. 4 tables outside. Private parties: 44 main room, 20 private room. Car park. Vegetarian meals with prior notice. Children's helpings on request. No children under 6. Smart dress preferred. Wheelchair access (3 steps). Music  ACCOMMODATION: 3 rooms, all with bath/shower. B&B £47 to £70. No children under 6. Pets welcome (not in public rooms). Garden. TV. Phone. Confirm by 6. Fax: (0253) 865350 (*The Which? Hotel Guide*)

---

**THUNDRIDGE Hertfordshire**                                              map 3

## ▲ *Hanbury Manor*

Thundridge SG12 0SD
WARE (0920) 487722                                                     COOKING 3
off A10, 1½m N of Ware                                             COST £28–£85

This is a giant clubhouse to a golf course and leisure centre. It also doubles as a hotel, though sometimes the amount of corporate activity – be it jolly rounds for customers, or consciousness-raising meetings – seems set to swamp the comings and goings of individual guests. An almost institutional air pervades the upstairs corridors, reminder that the house is not ancient history, merely a badge of success for some Victorian magnate. The Zodiac Room is the luxury restaurant; the golfers probably eat in the cheaper, more limited Vardon Grill. The menu is much better than that of most grand hotels for range and variety: there is not that constant reliance on shellfish and foie gras, and herbs are given their due prominence. English people often resort to the Sunday lunch of roast beef (consistently well reported), but most raise eyebrows at the practice of translating every menu entry into French. Some approval has been had for the elaborate, yet accurate, production of ravioli of quail and spinach with garlic and parsley butter, fillet of red mullet with orange and walnut, a bold rendering of turbot with ginger and wild mushrooms, and fillet of veal with artichokes, braised shallots and port. Desserts that have been mentioned include excellent summer pudding and banana and rum parfait. The service may be attentive but lacking ultimate finish. The wine list is a giant, with impressive prices like £27 for a Millérioux Sancerre. The mark-ups are bound to inhibit free choice, but perhaps the bourgeois clarets or the Beaujolais would be the safest areas. House wines start at £13.

---

*Not inc in the details at the end of an entry indicates that no service charge is made and any tipping is at the discretion of the customer.*

*All details are as accurate as possible at the time of going to press, but chefs and owners often change, and it is wise to check by telephone before making a special journey. Many readers have been disappointed when set-price bargain meals are no longer available. Ask when booking.*

CHEF: Rory Kennedy  PROPRIETORS: Poles Ltd  OPEN: all week, exc Sat L and Sun D;
12.30 to 2.30, 7.30 (7 Fri and Sat) to 10  MEALS: alc (main courses £18.50 to £31). Set L
£19.50 (Mon to Fri) to £35, Set D £25 (Mon to Sat) to £50  SERVICE: net prices, card slips
closed  CARDS: Access, Amex, Diners, Visa  DETAILS: 40 seats. 16 tables outside. Private
parties: 100 main room, 10 to 100 private rooms. Car park. Vegetarian meals. Children's
helpings. No children under 8. Jacket and tie. No cigars/pipes in dining-room. Wheelchair
access (1 step; also WC). Music  ACCOMMODATION: 96 rooms, all with bath/shower.
Rooms for disabled. B&B £95 to £385. Lift. Children welcome. Baby facilities. Pets
welcome (£15 per night). Afternoon teas. Garden. Swimming-pool. Sauna. Tennis.
Golf. Snooker. TV. Phone. Fax: (0920) 487692 (*The Which? Hotel Guide*)

---

**TORQUAY Devon**                                                    map 1

## *Capers*

7 Lisburne Square, Torquay TQ1 2PT                        COOKING 1
TORQUAY (0803) 291177                                     COST £25–£43

Ian Cawley is a man with a mission. This, he finds, is more readily understood
in Dartmouth and Totnes than in Torquay. He grows things for himself, he
buys only meat that has been reared organically, and he tries to cook naturally
and simply. Many of his ingredients come either from his own back allotment,
or from the like-minded shops and growers of the country beyond this English
Riviera. Owing to his feelings about modern farming methods, meat may be
venison, rabbit or pigeon rather than lamb or chicken; and fish will probably
get the better billing. Small wonder that he likes to cook soups. The
enthusiasm can be catching, and there is no stopping Mr Cawley in full flow.
Recipes, though ostensibly drawing on British tradition, are in fact quite up to
the minute; hence John Dory with mushrooms and spring onions, turbot with
lime and ginger, or entrecôte steak with a sauce zipped up with balsamic
vinegar. Desserts – often substantial – are another area of endeavour,
epitomised by lemon brioche, bread-and-butter pudding and sherry trifle. The
short wine list starts with house wines at £8.80.

CHEF: Ian Cawley  PROPRIETOR: Mr Burton  OPEN: Tue to Sat, D only; 7 to 9.30 (10 Sat)
CLOSED: Christmas week  MEALS: alc (main courses £10 to £15)  SERVICE: not inc, card
slips closed  CARDS: Access, Visa  DETAILS: 24 seats. Private parties: 10 main room.
Vegetarian meals. Children's helpings. Smart dress preferred. Music

---

## ▲ *Mulberry Room* ✸ £

1 Scarborough Road, Torquay TQ2 5UJ                       COOKING 2*
TORQUAY (0803) 213639                                     COST £14–£29

Lesley Cooper's Victorian guesthouse/tea-room/restaurant is hidden away 'in a
road full of the usual seaside resort boarding houses and unremarkable hotels'.
But it is easy to see the persuasive attractions of the place. One couple summed
it up perfectly: 'We like quiet and would prefer good food and good wine for a
reasonable price, rather than plush lounges, expensively printed menus and
waiters hovering around continually wanting to top up our glasses.' The place
is spotless, the food is remarkably affordable and it is the real thing; no
unnecessary bits and pieces clutter the plate or put up the bill. The consensus is

that the place is running on a high at the moment. Simple lunches are served in the old-fashioned Victorian dining-room, and on Friday and Saturday Lesley cooks dinner for all comers. A healthy vegetarian presence looms large on the menu with dishes such as baked avocado with mozzarella. Soups are regularly mentioned (leek and fennel, and carrot, parsnip and apple, for example), beef is from Devon beasts, cheeses are 'beautifully maintained', and vegetables are always a splendid assortment. Cheese and herb mousse, poached Scottish salmon, gratin of smoked ham and asparagus, and peppers stuffed with lamb and rice have been heartily endorsed. At other times, the blackboard might advertise grilled fillet of oak-smoked haddock with brown lentils, or clay-pot casserole of chicken, mushrooms and garlic. Bolstering this is a prodigious array of home-baked cakes, puddings and desserts laid out on a large side table. Few would complain about the cracking little wine list, which is a gem of its kind. House wine is £7.

CHEF/PROPRIETOR: Lesley Cooper  OPEN: Wed to Sun L, Fri and Sat D (Sun to Thur D residents only); 12.15 to 2, 7.30 to 9.30  MEALS: alc (main courses £5.50 L to £9.50 D). Set L £7.50 (2 courses) to £9, Set Sun L £11, Set D £13 (2 courses) to £16.50  SERVICE: not inc DETAILS: 30 seats. 2 tables outside. Private parties: 25 main room. Vegetarian meals. Children's helpings for 2 or more. No smoking in dining-room. Wheelchair access (also WC). Music  ACCOMMODATION: 3 rooms, all with bath/shower. B&B £21 to £37. Deposit: 10%. Children welcome. Afternoon teas. TV. Doors close at dusk. Confirm by dusk (*The Which? Hotel Guide*)

---

## ▲ *Osborne Hotel, Langtry's* 🎋

Hesketh Crescent, Meadfoot,
Torquay TQ1 2LL
TORQUAY (0803) 213311

COOKING 2
COST £25–£36

This place has a marketing wheeze: if you drink too much, then take a room at standby rates (overnight packs supplied), and enjoy a full breakfast with Buck's Fizz. Time on your hands may allow you the opportunity to appreciate the Regency crescent that houses hotel, restaurant, apartments, leisure centre and all. Here is old Torquay at its best. Chef Colin Liddy is more interested in startling modernity with no quaint revivalism, as seen in dishes such as terrine of smoked pork studded with prunes with a piccalilli, or gamba prawns on Thai-scented rice with a light curry sauce. He has a fondness for spices, which are sometimes misapplied, and an ability with fish – for instance, a mille-feuille of crab and lobster with lobster vinaigrette, grey mullet on leeks with a beurre rouge, and hake with samphire which was good enough to convert the unknowing. Desserts, which for one couple started with an exclamation ('Who would have thought of deep-frying strawberries?') may join old and new together with either bread-and-butter pudding or white chocolate truffle cake with a crème de menthe sauce for the really sweet-toothed. The wine list is largely from Eldridge Pope and thus soundly based. Prices are not excessive, and there is a chance to try four different grapes from the Yearlstone vineyard on the Exe. The provision of half-bottles is thoughtful. House wines start at £9.25.

CHEF: Colin Liddy  PROPRIETORS: Caparo  OPEN: all week, D only; 7 to 10  MEALS: Set D
£20.75 to £22.75  SERVICE: net prices, card slips closed  CARDS: Access, Visa  DETAILS:
60 seats. Private parties: 80 main room, 24 and 50 private rooms. Car park. Vegetarian
meals. Children's helpings. Smart dress preferred. No smoking in dining-room. Wheelchair
access (2 steps; also WC). Music  ACCOMMODATION: 23 rooms, all with bath/shower.
Rooms for disabled. Lift. B&B £55 to £158. Deposit: £50. Children welcome. Baby facilities.
Afternoon teas. Garden. Swimming-pool. Sauna. Tennis. Snooker. TV. Phone. Confirm
by 6. Fax: (0803) 296788

## Table ⅜✳

135 Babbacombe Road,
Babbacombe, Torquay TQ1 3SR                      COOKING 3*
TORQUAY (0803) 324292                            COST £32–£39

'We come to Torquay once a year and would not miss a visit to Table. The menu
always sounds a little down-to-earth, but what a revelation when the ordered
dish appears. For instance, rabbit, ham and yellow-pea terrine with watercress
mayonnaise consists of delicious, discreet slices of nuggets of saddle loosely
surrounded by the peas (how did they manage to slice it so perfectly?) with a
few dressed salad leaves touched with preserved lemon and a mayonnaise
green with cress. A sesame pancake with home-smoked salmon and
horseradish sauce – the crêpe, wafer-thin, grilled and cut into quarters,
standing up in a fan and the horseradish used with a very light hand, not
overpowering the salmon – turned out to be much more smoked salmon than
crêpe. For a main dish we had brill with chargrilled vegetables, the aubergine
much more digestible than usual, the sauce infused with the vegetable juices.
Side vegetables included broccoli with a tremendously tangy olive oil, beans,
and thin slices of celeriac with a touch of cheese. The apple strudel for dessert
sounds heavy, but not at Table; chocolate hazelnut torte with a passion-fruit
sorbet and vanilla custard was divine.' This little restaurant – hardly more than
a front room, with Jane Corrigan serving while Trevor Brooks cooks away –
gets serious praise for very genuine and good cooking. Torquay knows nothing
like it. Size ('small and intimate') and location (in an out-of-the-way suburban
street) mean that this is not the place for a grand occasion, unless food matters
more than fun and games. The level of achievement is unexpected. The
proprietors say that tipping is discouraged. The wine list has some good names
at very fair prices, including Avignonesi's Late Harvest Chardonnay/Semillon
mix which gets its sweetness in part from botrytis and also from the grapes
being semi-dried. House wines start at £8.50.

CHEFS/PROPRIETORS: Trevor Brooks and Jane Corrigan  OPEN: Tue to Sun, D only; 7.30
to 10  CLOSED: 1 to 18 Feb, 1 to 18 Sept  MEALS: Set D £26  SERVICE: card slips closed
CARDS: Access, Visa  DETAILS: 20 seats. Private parties: 20 main room. Vegetarian meals
with prior notice. Children welcome. Smart dress preferred. No smoking in dining-room.
Wheelchair access. No music

✳ *indicates that smoking is either banned altogether or that a dining-room is maintained
for non-smokers. The symbol does not apply to restaurants that simply have no-smoking
areas.*

---

**TRESCO** Isles of Scilly · map 1

## ▲ *Island Hotel*

Tresco TR24 0PU
SCILLONIA (0720) 22883

COOKING 1
COST £24–£56

Tresco has the advantage of a sub-tropical climate, the famous Abbey Gardens and no cars to pollute the atmosphere. It is no wonder that people return again and again. The Island Hotel has a rather nice idea for seating guests in the dining-room, notes a lady reporter, 'further back at the beginning of your stay and then nearer the sea-view each day, which causes amusement'. Service is friendly and thoughtful. Christopher Wyburn-Ridsdale offers a set five-course dinner menu as well as a *carte*, with modern aspirations and fish as the main theme. John Dory with raspberry dressing, salmon in a horseradish crust with sauté cucumber and escalope of veal with sauté peppers and vermouth are typical of his repertoire. Reporters have also enthused about the medley of fish ('a tuneful combination of four delicately steamed varieties'), sole on a cushion of spinach with saffron sauce, and bread-and-butter pudding. Lunches are available only in the bar and Sunday evening heralds a buffet. The creditable wine list has some promising offerings from the New World. House wine is £10.

---

CHEF: Christopher Wyburn-Ridsdale  PROPRIETOR: Robert Dorrien-Smith  OPEN: all week; 12 to 2.15, 7 to 9.30  CLOSED: last Fri Oct to end Feb  MEALS: alc (main courses £14 to £20). Set D £14.50 (2 courses) to £24. Bar menu L. Minimum £14.50 D.  SERVICE: not inc, card slips closed  CARDS: Access, Amex, Visa  DETAILS: 110 seats. 10 tables outside. Private parties: 70 main room. Vegetarian meals. Children's helpings. Smart dress preferred. Wheelchair access (also WC). Music  ACCOMMODATION: 40 rooms, all with bath/shower. D,B&B £80 to £240. Deposit: 20%. Children welcome. Baby facilities. Afternoon teas. Garden. Swimming-pool. Tennis. Fishing. TV. Phone. Fax: (0720) 23008 (*The Which? Hotel Guide*)

---

**TUNBRIDGE WELLS** Kent · map 3

## *Cheevers*

56 High Street, Tunbridge Wells TN1 1XF
TUNBRIDGE WELLS (0892) 545524

COOKING 2*
COST £23–£35

You do not have to walk far up the hill to come across this converted shop: home to some fair cooking. Decoration is on a shoestring – 'the grey carpet has seen better days,' someone observed – but it strikes a faint note of modernism that is not the usual vernacular of restaurants in these parts. The same might be said of the menu, which offers half a dozen choices at each course – priced individually at lunch, by the whole meal at dinner. The repertoire does not change radically and dishes that have been recommended before resurface in reports this year: examples include crab mousse wrapped in spinach with a dill sauce, rack of lamb with mint and almond crust, and guinea-fowl with fennel. Tim Cheevers is clearly a disciple of the school which advocates steady refinement of the master text rather than helter-skelter experimentalism. The wine list is gloriously generous in its provision of half-bottles. The range and choice of sources is done with an eye to keeping down the final bill and yet securing fair quality. Hence there are good names such as Ch. Larose-Trintaudon, Penfolds, Léon Beyer and Luc Sorin. House wines are £7.95.

CHEF: Timothy Cheevers  PROPRIETORS: Timothy Cheevers, Martin J. Miles and P.D. Tambini  OPEN: Tue to Sat; 12.30 to 2 (1.45 Sat), 7.30 to 10.30  MEALS: alc (main courses £8.50 to £10.50). Set D £22.50  SERVICE: not inc, card slips closed  CARDS: Access, Amex, Visa  DETAILS: 32 seats. Private parties: 24 main room. Vegetarian meals with prior notice. Children welcome. Wheelchair access (1 step). No music. Air-conditioned. Fax: (0892) 535956

## Sankey's ❧ £

NEW ENTRY

39 Mount Ephraim,
Tunbridge Wells TN4 8AA
TUNBRIDGE WELLS (0892) 511422

COOKING 1
COST £19–£44

An architectural mix of Victorian Gothic and 'Pont Street Dutch', Sankey's still thrives as an old-style seafood restaurant working to regular supplies of spanking fresh fish. As we went to press the restaurant was undergoing refurbishment. The full menu can seem pricey, although a good-value two-course dinner is served Monday to Thursday. Soupe de poissons is given a lift with a powerful rouille; elsewhere, fish is subjected to different techniques: Dover sole is grilled, fritto misto is deep-fried, monkfish is roasted with garlic, sea bass is steamed with soy, spring onions and ginger, and salmon is poached with spinach butter. Despite the undoubted quality of the fish and spot-on timing, other aspects of the cooking have caused problems: tiny portions of vegetables, dull 'freezing cold' salad and a crème brûlée that was 'powdery in texture' have marred otherwise good meals. The mainly British cheeseboard is worth exploring. The recently opened basement wine bar (entrance round the corner from the restaurant) has a loud, lively atmosphere and a range of cheaper dishes, taking in duck cassoulet, Moroccan lamb and leeks en croûte. King & Barnes Sussex Bitter, cidre bouchée and European beers back up the moderately priced wine list, which ranges from New World youngsters to mature clarets. House wines are £8.

CHEF: Eleutorio Lizzi  PROPRIETORS: Guy and Amanda Sankey  OPEN: all week; 12 to 2.30, 7 to 10  MEALS: alc (main courses £5 to £16)  SERVICE: not inc, card slips closed (10%, card slips closed, for 10 or more)  CARDS: Access, Amex, Diners, Visa  DETAILS: restaurant 60 seats, wine bar 30 seats. 10 tables outside. Private parties: 16 main room, 24 private room. Vegetarian meals. Children's helpings. No smoking in 2 dining-rooms. No music

## Thackeray's House ♥

85 London Road,
Tunbridge Wells TN1 1EA
TUNBRIDGE WELLS (0892) 511921

COOKING 3*
COST £18–£56

The house itself, which really was Thackeray's, stands close to the Conservative Association and is a distinguished piece of early classical vernacular. Bruce Wass has made an exceptionally attractive dining-room on the ground floor – a happy compromise between history (Victorian furniture)

and current function ('nice white table linen'). There can be few more sympathetic settings for eating in Kent. Down below, where servants once lurked, a bistro operates in the former kitchen. Both sides of the business receive much approval. The restaurant's short *carte* is bolstered by two set-price formulae – dishes are mixed and matched between them. Though training may come out, for instance, in the make-up of the sauces and the lightness of the bread, Bruce Wass is no hostage to excess of elaboration. Flavour is allied to proper classical techniques and careful assessment of raw materials. People write warmly of dishes as disparate as croustade of skate and scallops with pastis, fennel and orange, and boudin blanc of guinea-fowl with madeira and wild mushroom fumet (two preliminaries to a gourmet evening in the winter), followed by grilled skate with salsa verde, and saddle of rabbit with sun-dried tomatoes, basil and pine-kernels. The costing generally encourages people to take the fixed-price menu. One such meal began with a salad of artichoke hearts: this was simplicity itself, but successful contrasts of soft and crisp texture and bitter and unctuous flavours were achieved. The main dish was brill with tomato and saffron, the subtle sauce given added life by fresh herbs. The dessert of chocolate and armagnac loaf with coffee sauce was a chocolate mousse 'bombe' wrapped with a spirit-soaked sponge, laid on a rich and bitter-sweet sauce. The sauce won the day – the sponge was almost too dense for its own good. Downstairs at Thackeray's offers the wine bar 'snack' menu – but compare the snacks to most in the town – or an enterprising (for Tunbridge Wells) bistro *carte* that ranges from grilled fresh sardines, hearty zampone with lentils, and kidneys with grain mustard, to highly enjoyed puddings – the banana crème brûlée gets special mention. The service marries with the atmosphere of the place: quiet yet civilised. The wine list is very good. Bruce Wass takes trouble; he buys well and provides a wide-ranging house selection at modest prices and a very substantial list of halves. For the wine-buff there are old and famous names such as Krug 1973 and Jaboulet Châteauneuf from 1966. Well-chosen Spanish, Italian and Beaujolais wines make for balance, but Alsace could be pepped up. House wine prices start at £9.75. CELLARMAN'S CHOICE: Ardèche, Viognier 1992, Dom. des Terriers, £19.50; Barco Reale 1991, Capezzana, £15.90.

CHEF/PROPRIETOR: Bruce Wass   OPEN: Tue to Sun, exc Sun D (no Sun L bistro and wine bar); 12.30 to 2 (2.30 bistro and wine bar), 7 to 10   CLOSED: 5 days Christmas   MEALS: alc (main courses restaurant £11 to £17.50, bistro £7 to £9, wine bar £3.50 to £8). Set L £10 (2 courses) to £17, Set Sun L £17.50, Set D £19.85 (Tue to Thur) to £39   SERVICE: net prices, card slips closed   CARDS: Access, Visa   DETAILS: restaurant 40 seats, bistro 30 seats, wine bar 15 seats. 5 tables outside. Private parties: 50 main room, 12, 16 and 20 private rooms. Vegetarian meals. Children's helpings. No cigars/pipes in dining-room. Wheelchair access (1 step). No music

---

*Dining-rooms where live and recorded music are never played are signalled by* No music *in the details at the end of an entry.*

Net prices *in the details at the end of an entry indicates that the prices given on a menu and on a bill are inclusive of VAT and service charge, and that this practice is clearly stated on menu and bill.*

## McClements

12 The Green, Twickenham TW2 5AA                                   COOKING 3
081-755 0176 and 893 3089                                          COST £24–£49

The original small restaurant, a two up and two down at the apex of
Twickenham Green, has grown slightly over the years, has become brighter
and better appointed as a locale for eating, and demonstrates the virtues of true
grit. John McClements has hung in. Now, there is to be a bistro as well, at 2
Whitton Road, Twickenham, Tel: 071-744 9610 (opening just as the *Guide* went
to press) – reports, please. John McClements' cooking is very good indeed; it is
also quite expensive and sometimes may take the unfamiliar by surprise –
'Why does he not put more vegetables with his main course? If you can't afford
a first course, you are likely to leave the place hungry.' No matter how small the
scale, this is cooking in the grand manner, which demonstrates an ability to
season and bring out flavours that is not matched for some miles. Prices are
justified by the intense labour (mostly single-handed) and the willingness to
spend on luxury materials. Dishes that have found favour include a confit of
rabbit leg stuffed with foie gras, the rest of the rabbit rolled with bacon and
garlic; a brilliant, unctuous velouté of oysters and potato, turbot and lobster
with home-made noodles; a modern dish of shank of veal with the vegetables
that other reader craved; and a special mention for soufflés as desserts.
McClements is too small an operation for it not to be individual and sometimes
quirky. The wine list is classic and dear on the one hand, but has extended into
the New World for value. House wines are £10.

CHEF/PROPRIETOR: John McClements   OPEN: Mon to Sat; 12 to 2, 7 to 10.30 (11 Sat)
CLOSED: 1 week Christmas   MEALS: alc (main courses £13 to £15). Set L £17 to £19.50, Set
D £22 to £28   SERVICE: 10%, card slips closed   CARDS: Access, Visa   DETAILS: 35 seats.
Private parties: 28 main room, 15 private room. Vegetarian meals with prior notice.
Children's helpings on request. Smart dress preferred. Music. Air-conditioned. Fax:
081-890 1372

---

## ▲ Horsted Place ⅗✳

Little Horsted, nr Uckfield TN22 5TS
UCKFIELD (0825) 750581                                             COOKING 2
2m S of Uckfield, on A26                                          COST £24–£63

This Victorian Gothic mansion (Pugin) is worth a look. Beyond the windows
all is golf course, but the decoration is impressive, though where the expected
blazing fires were one dank winter's morning was a mystery to a casual lunch-
time visitor who felt the welcome was less than effusive. Prices are in line with
the level of curtaining but seem less justified by the country-house food.
Performance has been mixed this year in dishes like crab with cucumber and a
mustard dressing, and lamb with rosemary sauce and ratatouille that was
inexplicably spiked with lots of chilli. Much of this was redeemed by the sweet
course in a fixed-price menu when there arrived a plate of every dessert

produced by the kitchen, alongside another order of two parfaits – one coffee, one ginger – which were technically superior to the beginning of the meal, even if light in flavour. The wine list also suffers from high prices, even though it is an impressive set of bottles, drawing from all round the world for breadth, with the classic French regions giving depth. House wines are £12.50.

CHEF: Allan Garth   PROPRIETORS: Granfel Hotels   OPEN: all week; 12.30 to 2, 7.30 to 9.30
MEALS: alc (main courses £14.50 to £19.50). Light L menu (£6 to £12.50). Set L Mon to Fri
£14.95, Set L Sat and Sun £18.50, Set D £28.50   SERVICE: not inc, card slips closed
CARDS: Access, Amex, Diners, Visa   DETAILS: 40 seats. 8 tables outside. Private parties: 50
main room, 18 and 24 private rooms. Car park. Vegetarian meals. Children welcome. Jacket
and tie. No smoking in dining-room. Wheelchair access. No music   ACCOMMODATION: 17
rooms, all with bath/shower. Rooms for disabled. Lift. B&B £115 to £245. Deposit: 50%.
Children by arrangement. Pets by arrangement. Afternoon teas. Garden. Swimming-pool.
Tennis. Fishing. Golf. TV. Phone. Doors close at midnight. Confirm by 11. Fax: (0825)
750459 (*The Which? Hotel Guide*)

---

ULLSWATER Cumbria                                                                    map 7

## ▲ *Sharrow Bay* 🍴✳

Howtown Road, Ullswater CA10 2LZ
POOLEY BRIDGE (076 84) 86301 and 86483
2m from Pooley Bridge on E side of lake,                              COOKING 4
signposted Howtown and Martindale                                    COST £30–£55

'It is difficult to define its particular quality, but this restaurant produces such enjoyable food that I could not eat anywhere else locally; and the staff are so experienced and give everyone such a welcome that we look forward to our annual visit': this expresses a feeling shared by the thousands who have eaten at Sharrow Bay over the 46 years of its existence. Absolute devotion, which really does seem untiring, enthusiasm, skill and an innate sense of hospitality combine to make the place memorable. 'The service is honed to perfection; very, very friendly; even helping me break into my vehicle when I had locked myself out – large chef's knife to the rescue.' Most reports make mention of some small touch that improved the visit to this Italianate villa lapped by water (with an annexe of equal appeal further down the shore). The decoration gathers layer upon layer of ornament as years have passed. 'They surely must have a treasure who starts dusting at around two in the morning' was the conclusion of one who marvelled at the housekeeping, and was also impressed by the gentle methods of regimentation that kept the customers to time so that dinner could make its stately march across the evening. Settling at a table with views unfurling before your very eyes, dinner may take the form reported by one couple early in the summer. Gravlax with dill and light mustard dressing was on one side of the table, accurately cooked foie gras of duck with spinach and a madeira sauce (and oyster mushrooms and tiny herb gnocchi) was on the other. There was then a fillet of halibut with white wine sauce and a soufflé suissesse. The soufflé was 'light and springy, moist and redolent of Gruyère, the fish a splendid texture and good flavour, the sauce light enough not to overpower'. The fish course and the sorbet after it are the same for the whole dining-room. Choice returns with the main dish and one half of the aforementioned pair took the loin of lamb on a galette of leeks and potato, with turnips, mushrooms and glazed onions, while the other had turbot with spinach and a light curry sauce with a tangle of crisp fried vegetable 'hair' plus some small arrangement of carrot, courgette and basil. Vegetables, a myriad, are popped in little piles around the plate. Desserts of hot chocolate soufflé with hot chocolate sauce (and cream if you want it), and lemon tart with its sorbet were succeeded by slivers of cheese (all British). The scale of the cooking seems daunting: so much, so often, but no one complains of excess. There is a degree of fuss as well, but that is now a hallmark of the place and it is so well managed that even the most fervent admirer of new-wave brutalism will be converted. The menu, almost Connaught-like for length and range, has not changed its spots, but the wine list has got better and better. It now has range, fair prices and quality, including a German section that is worth investigation. House wines are £11.95.

CHEFS: Johnnie Martin, Colin Akrigg and Chris Bond   PROPRIETORS: Francis Coulson and Brian Sack   OPEN: all week; 1 to 1.45, 8 to 8.45   CLOSED: Dec, Jan, Feb   MEALS: Set L £24.50 to £29.50, Set D £39.50   SERVICE: net prices   DETAILS: 65 seats. Private parties: 10 main room. Car park. Vegetarian meals with prior notice. No children under 13. Jacket and tie. No smoking in dining-room. No music   ACCOMMODATION: 28 rooms, 24 with bath/shower. Rooms for disabled. D,B&B £90 to £300. No children under 13. Afternoon teas. Garden. TV. Phone. Doors close at midnight. Confirm by 10am. Fax: (076 84) 86349 (*The Which? Hotel Guide*)

---

**ULVERSTON** Cumbria                                                    map 7

## ▲ *Bay Horse Inn* ▾ ❀

Canal Foot, Ulverston LA12 9EL
ULVERSTON (0229) 583972
off A590, just before centre of                          COOKING 3
Ulverston, follow signs to Canal Foot                    COST £18–£38

The drive through the Glaxo factory car park continues to excite comment, but today's journey to this whitewashed pub is doubtless less of an adventure than it was in the past, when stagecoaches made their way here across the tidal Lancaster Sands. You can now gaze year-round at the watery views from the warmth and safety of the restaurant veranda grafted on to the pub. Most menu descriptions occupy between three and four lines, and the dishes are (as at the Miller Howe incarnation) furiously inventive: soups may bring together cauliflower, Stilton and Guinness; courgettes are stuffed with mushroom and onion pâté, then wrapped in local air-dried ham, baked on tomato, sauced with cheese and mustard and topped with breadcrumbs; and monkfish tails are bedded with king scallops then baked in yogurt, cardamom and ginger, shoehorned into puff pastry, and sauced with lemon and chive cream sauce. Even the Christmas turkey gets hit with mozzarella. Some have felt that the extra mile effort of the first five years has gone, but comments such as 'excellent', 'gorgeous' and 'very good' continue to fill reports; touches such as different cream patterns in a raspberry sauce for different diners provide frivolous delight. Service is accomplished, no matter how full the house, and the good-value inventive bar meals continue to attract attention. The separate New World wine list continues to lord it over what is a less imaginative Old

World selection. The cheapest bottles are two good £10 Germans, one of them a
Riesling from Karl Marx's old school (the Friedrich Wilhelm Gymnasium in
Trier). Most of the best drinking is antipodean, such as Martinborough's
expressive Chardonnay (at £22.75) or St Hallett's barnstorming Old Block
Shiraz from the Barossa Valley (at £17.75).

CHEFS: Robert Lyons and Esther Jarvis   PROPRIETORS: John J. Tovey and Robert Lyons
OPEN: restaurant Tue to Sat L, all week D; 12 to 1.30, 7.30 for 8. Bar Tue to Sun L; 12 to 2
(3 Sun)   MEALS: alc (main courses £12 to £14). Set L £13.50. Bar menu. Minimum £13.50
SERVICE: 10%, card slips closed   CARDS: Access, Visa   DETAILS: 50 seats. Private parties:
30 main room, 20 and 30 private rooms. Car park. Vegetarian meals. No children under 12.
Smart dress preferred. No smoking in dining-room. Wheelchair access (also WC). Music.
Air-conditioned   ACCOMMODATION: 6 rooms, all with bath/shower. B&B £80 to £140. No
children under 12. Pets welcome in guest rooms. Afternoon teas. TV. Phone. Doors close at
midnight. Confirm by noon. Fax: (0229) 580502

---

**UPPER SLAUGHTER** Gloucestershire                                    map 2

## ▲ *Lords of the Manor*

Upper Slaughter GL54 2JD
COTSWOLD (0451) 820243                                           COOKING 3
turn W off A429, 3m S of Stow-on-the-Wold                        COST £25–£59

Once a parsonage – but the rectors were squires – it makes a lordly Cotswold
picture of gables, stonework, mullions and archways, full of atmosphere, even
if some of the building is quite Victorian, and even if it has been firmly and
brightly decorated. The staff, one couple observed, displayed an assiduity that
verged on fuss, and this is without doubt a haven of luxury. Clive Dixon has
taken over the kitchens, after an auspicious start at the Old Swan at Minster
Lovell, but seems to be continuing aspects of style laid down by his
predecessor here. The tastes on offer are more robust and 'country' than the
ultra-smooth setting might indicate. A dinner taken early in his tenure started
with langoustine soup flavoured with coriander and Pernod, with sippets (an
accurate English equivalent of the French term – croûtons – usually used)
coated with Gruyère, and a light rouille. Main courses took in a grilled sirloin
with celeriac purée and onion sauce and lots of young broad beans, and a piece
of grilled calf's liver with red cabbage and rösti that handled sweetness very
well and had appealing texture contrasts. Pastry skills are in evidence in a very
fine apple tart with strong caramel sauce. The same adeptness came out in the
petits fours. The wine list lacks New World support and is marred by range
(upper-crust) and verbosity. House wines are £11.75.

CHEF: Clive Dixon   PROPRIETOR: James Gulliver   OPEN: all week; 12.30 to 2, 7.30 to 9.30
MEALS: alc (main courses L £7.50 to £8.50, D £17 to £19). Set Sun L £16.50   SERVICE:
12.5% D, not inc L, card slips closed   CARDS: Access, Amex, Diners, Visa   DETAILS:
60 seats. 8 tables outside. Private parties: 60 main room, 20 and 30 private rooms. Car park.
Vegetarian meals. Children's helpings. Smart dress preferred. No cigars/pipes in dining-
room. Wheelchair access (also WC). No music   ACCOMMODATION: 29 rooms, all with bath/
shower. B&B £80 to £185. Deposit: £50. Children welcome. Baby facilities. Afternoon teas.
Garden. Fishing. TV. Phone. Confirm by 6. Fax: (0451) 820696

VOWCHURCH Hereford & Worcester                                     map 4

## Poston Mill ✦✕

Vowchurch, HR2 0SF
GOLDEN VALLEY (0981) 550151
on B4348, between Vowchurch                              COOKING 2
and Peterchurch                                         COST £21–£33

'By local standards, truly astonishing' is the verdict on John Daniels' cooking.
This small, six-table restaurant in a Georgian flour mill by the River Dore is
fiercely championed by neglected locals, though tourists in this disarmingly
beautiful border region make up half the clientele. Drinks are taken upstairs in
the lounge, which is the only place where smoking is permitted; the restaurant
itself is roomy and music-free, and the tables are elegantly laid. Set-price
menus at £15 and £20.50 vary in choice and ingredients only, and change
monthly; cheese and semolina gnocchi served on salad leaves, salmon sausages
with dill and Trelough duck are repeatedly requested, and crisp filo pastry is
used inventively. A main course of rabbit with garlic and pearl barley or calf's
liver with lime and spring onions show a delicate sense of invention, and
vegetarians have left feeling cherished by dishes such as a tartlet of finely cut
vegetables set in nutmeg cream. 'Brown bread ice-cream in a caramel sauce was
both gritty in texture and creamy; simply delicious' marks a dessert
enthusiasm. A lunch-time snack menu is also available during the week.
Philippa Lydford's service is friendly and efficient, and the wine list contains a
modest but sound selection. House wines start at £8.

CHEF: John Daniels   PROPRIETORS: John Daniels and Philippa Lydford   OPEN: Tue to
Sun, exc Tue L and Sun D; 12 to 2, 7 to 9   CLOSED: 3 weeks from 25 Dec   MEALS: light L
menu Wed to Sat (£4 to £10). Set L and D £15 to £20.50   SERVICE: not inc, card slips
closed   CARDS: Access, Amex, Visa   DETAILS: 20 seats. 3 tables outside. Private parties: 20
main room. Car park. Vegetarian meals. Children's helpings. No smoking in dining-room.
No music

---

WADHURST East Sussex                                               map 3

## ▲ Spindlewood Hotel

Wallcrouch, Wadhurst TN5 7JG
TICEHURST (0580) 200430                                 COOKING 1
on B2099, between Wadhurst and Ticehurst                COST £21–£36

Not all country houses are the same. Some are for super-special occasions, or
need a Rolls or a helicopter to give your arrival sufficient style. Others are for
families: weddings, anniversaries and reunions. Spindlewood is such a house.
The gardens are decent, the dining-room cuts a bit of a dash, and the bar is not
uncomfortable. Harvey Lee Aram cooks savoury stuffed mushrooms, makes a
pork, pigeon and chicken terrine, and offers green pasta with salmon, scallops,
cream and paprika. These might be followed by pan-fried calf's liver; pork
with apricots; duck with ginger (the leg meat being stir-fried with lemon and
lime); or an often impressive set of fish. The result is country cooking, with
some style and enough variation to keep almost everyone happy. Service is

formal yet personal and the wine list is designed to avoid economic apoplexy. Sound makers such as Juillot, Pascal, Tollot-Beaut or Penfolds appear at fair prices. House wines are £7.50.

CHEF: Harvey Lee Aram  PROPRIETOR: R.V. Fitzsimmons  OPEN: all week; 12.15 to 1.30, 7.15 to 9  CLOSED: Christmas, L bank hols  MEALS: Set Sun L £14.95, Set L and D £23.20. Bar snacks  SERVICE: not inc, card slips closed  CARDS: Access, Visa  DETAILS: 40 seats. 4 tables outside. Private parties: 60 main room, 24 private room. Car park. Vegetarian meals. Children's helpings. Smart dress preferred. No cigars/pipes in dining-room. Music ACCOMMODATION: 9 rooms, all with bath/shower. B&B £47.50 to £77.50. Children welcome. Baby facilities. Garden. TV. Phone. Doors close at midnight. Confirm by 6. Fax: (0580) 201132

---

**WALKINGTON Humberside**　　　　　　　　　　　　　　　map 6

## ▲ *Manor House*　　　　　　　　　　　　　　　| NEW ENTRY |

Northlands, Walkington HU17 8RT
HULL (0482) 881645　　　　　　　　　　　　　　　COOKING 1*
off B1230 towards Beverley from Walkington　　　COST £22–£42

Derek and Lee Baugh's house is late-Victorian yellow brick set in rhododendron-filled gardens, with a handsome conservatory for dining set on one side. Though the Baughs intend, and get local support for, a full-dress country-house experience (one visitor regretted the mode of dressing the conservatory windows in 'knicker' curtains, however), it is occasionally vitiated by such details as 'the waitresses who haven't a clue what the cheeses are, and don't seek assistance from someone who does'. Derek Baugh can certainly cook, sometimes almost too much for the health of the dish. 'He has a compulsion to over-elaborate, to overfeed,' remarked a reader impressed by the sheer quality of the blackened beef served Cajun-style as a first course, the scallops served on too much pasta and cream sauce inside a pastry case, the halibut with a discreet vinaigrette sauce, the lamb with yet another tart (or potato) case filled with mashed peas, and a seafood fricassee that was generous to a fault. Six vegetables (including two in beignet style) nearly sank the boat. The wine list is commendable for its selection, range and fair prices. The Rhônes are particularly notable, in addition to some fine clarets, good Spanish and Beaujolais. House wine is £8.95.

CHEFS: Derek and Lee Baugh, and Shaun Jackson  PROPRIETORS: Derek and Lee Baugh OPEN: Mon to Sat, D only; 7.30 to 9.15  MEALS: Set D £15 (Mon to Fri only) to £27.50 SERVICE: not inc, card slips closed  CARDS: Access, Visa  DETAILS: 50 seats. Private parties: 24 main room, 24 private room. Car park. Vegetarian meals. No children under 12. Jacket and tie. No cigars/pipes in dining-room. Music  ACCOMMODATION: 7 rooms, all with bath/shower. B&B £70 to £100. No children under 12. Pets by arrangement. Garden. TV. Phone. Doors close at 12.30am. Confirm 1 day ahead. Fax: (0482) 866501 (*The Which? Hotel Guide*)

---

*Several sharp operators have tried to extort money from restaurateurs on the promise of an entry in a guidebook that has never appeared. The Good Food Guide makes no charge for inclusion and does not offer certificates of any kind.*

WALTON-ON-THAMES Surrey                                   map 3

## Le Pêcheur at the Anglers

Riverside, Walton-on-Thames KT12 2PG                      COOKING 1
WALTON-ON-THAMES (0932) 227423                           COST £18–£39

Situated on the first floor above the Anglers pub on the towpath overlooking the Thames, this restaurant offers the prospect of pleasant river views. Hanging baskets add a splash of colour and the walls are festooned with paintings by a local artist. Chef Stephen Read has moved on and has been replaced by Hervé Lainé who has given the cooking an even stronger bias towards fish. The short menu is written in French with English translations and features such dishes as home-made tagliatelle with salmon, pan-fried monkfish with cider sauce, gigot of lamb in rosemary sauce, and grilled fish of the day with basil butter. The seafood platter is a major event. Twice-baked cheese soufflé has been acceptable, while salmon dieppoise and duck breast with ginger and lime have been memorable for the quality of the sauces. Vegetables are nouvelle garnishes on the plate. Regulars note that 'desserts have gone downhill': the choice is prosaic and the results are inconsistent. This and other teething troubles should be ironed out as the new regime settles. The wine list is a short, reasonably priced assortment of familiar French names. House wine is £8.50.

CHEF: Hervé Lainé   PROPRIETOR: Jean-Jacques Fontaine   OPEN: Tue to Sun, exc Sun D; 12 to 2.15, 7 to 10 (10.15 Sat)   MEALS: alc (main courses £7 to £13). Set L £8.95 (2 courses) to £10.45, Set Sun L £11.95   SERVICE: not inc, card slips closed   CARDS: Access, Visa DETAILS: 60 seats. Private parties: 70 main room. Vegetarian meals. Children welcome. Music. Fax: (0932) 245962

---

WAREHAM Dorset                                            map 2

## ▲ Priory Hotel ▼

Church Green, Wareham BH20 4ND                            COOKING 1
WAREHAM (0929) 551666                                    COST £22–£58

The hotel, formerly the Priory of Lady St Mary, makes much of its seductive setting in four acres of gardens by the banks of the River Frome. On pleasant days the terrace is a perfect spot for drinks, coffee or cream teas with strawberries. Meals can be eaten in the upstairs Greenwood Dining-Room or the Abbots Cellar Restaurant – 'very cosy, very cool on a warm night,' noted two contented visitors. Chef Michael Rust makes good use of local ingredients for a repertoire that veers between the old-school theatricality of steak Diane and crêpes suzette and the modern invention of filo pastries of scampi and leeks with sweet red pimento sauce, or noisettes of lamb with lentil in truffled rosemary and onion jus. Dorset air-cured ham is put into a salad with almonds, mango and raspberry vinaigrette. A full menu is available for vegetarians. Reporters have noted particularly the quality of the sauces: mushroom sauce with sweetbreads, mustard sauce and herb crust with fillet steak, and raspberry sauce with bread-and-butter pudding. Everyone agrees that the surroundings are congenial, the welcome is friendly and the staff efficient. The wine list is lengthy and generally accurate and informative. For the knowledgeable it is a peach of a list, but with little help for the novice (minimal house wines, for example). Prices are fair but half-bottles are provided erratically. House wines are £8.50. CELLARMAN'S CHOICE: St Véran, Les Grandes Bruyères 1991, Luquet, £15.50; Médoc, Ch. la Tour Saint-Bonnet 1986, £17.50.

---

CHEF: Michael Rust PROPRIETORS: Stuart and John Turner OPEN: all week; 12.30 to 2, 7.30 to 10 MEALS: alc (main courses £15.50 to £19.50). Set L £11.95 (2 couses) to £13.95, Set D £22.50 to £26.50 (Sat) SERVICE: not inc, card slips closed CARDS: Access, Amex, Diners, Visa DETAILS: Greenwood 24 seats, Abbots Cellar 44 seats. 10 tables outside. Private parties: 44 main room, 22 and 44 private rooms. Car park. Vegetarian meals. Children's helpings on request. Smart dress preferred. Wheelchair access (also WC). Music ACCOMMODATION: 19 rooms, all with bath/shower. Rooms for disabled. B&B £70 to £175. Afternoon teas. Garden. Fishing. TV. Phone. Fax: (0929) 554519 (*The Which? Hotel Guide*)

---

WARMINSTER Wiltshire                                                      map 2

## ▲ *Bishopstrow House*                                   | NEW ENTRY |

Warminster BA12 9HH
WARMINSTER (0985) 212312                                       COOKING 2
on B3414, SW of Warminster                                    COST £22–£60

The Georgian ivy-clad house itself, a sister hotel to Reids of Madeira, is a welcome sight at the end of the drive with its honeyed stone, classical proportions and quiet prosperity. The same might be said of the main public rooms, though not unfortunately of the newer dining-room or the conservatory, where in the eyes of some people invention seems to have fled the coop. Chris Suter has been cooking here for the last five years and reports have been surprisingly mixed. On the one hand, asparagus salad with a Caesar dressing was 'a case of hunt the asparagus', and a confit of duck had neither much flavour, nor much added to it by a shallot and Cassis dressing that had been soaked up by the crisp potatoes, now soggy; a vanilla ice-cream in a basket had a ladleful of burning hot red berry sauce poured over it, 'so turning it into a pool of pinkish cream. The baked Alaska effect misfired.' The bad news may be balanced by rave reports of inexpensive lunches (given the comfort) of dishes like halibut in a puff pastry case with crab and dill sauce and morels, or poached salmon with lentils and a red wine sauce. One dinner included grilled red mullet and tapénade in a salad, three cutlets of lamb with sweetish gravy and a tarragon crust, cheese from the supplier Jereboam's (that had been kept too cold), and a gripping finale of a citrus terrine 'as refreshing as breakfast' with a passion-fruit sauce scattered with wild strawberries. Mixed fortunes, therefore, but the possibilities are great and Chris Suter is mercifully light on richness and nicely spare in decoration and ornament. The wine list is just short of expensive and has some excellent makers, including the Countess Guerrieri-Rizzardi, Castello Banfi, Jeff Clarke and Toni Stockhausen from Mount Helen and J-H Goisot from St-Bris. House wines are £12.50.

---

*If a restaurant is new to the* Guide *this year (did not appear as a main entry in the last edition)* NEW ENTRY *appears opposite its name.*

---

CHEF: Chris Suter   PROPRIETORS: Blandy Brothers and Co Ltd   OPEN: all week; 12.30 to 2,
7.30 to 9 (9.30 Fri and Sat)   MEALS: Set L £10.50 to £25, Set D £31 to £36   SERVICE: not
inc, card slips closed   CARDS: Access, Amex, Diners, Visa   DETAILS: 60 seats. 6 tables
outside. Private parties: 65 main room, 22 and 65 private rooms. Car park. Vegetarian
meals. Children's helpings. Smart dress preferred. Music   ACCOMMODATION: 32 rooms,
all with bath/shower. Rooms for disabled. B&B £98 to £123. Deposit: 50%. Children
welcome. Baby facilities. Pets welcome. Afternoon teas. Garden. Swimming-pool. Sauna.
Tennis. Fishing. TV. Phone. Conform by 6. Fax: (0985) 216769 (*The Which? Hotel Guide*)

---

## WATERHOUSES Staffordshire                                                map 5

## ▲ Old Beams

Waterhouses ST10 3HW
WATERHOUSES (0538) 308254                                   COOKING 3
on A523, 7m SE of Leek                                      COST £24–£45

A parallel is often drawn between this restaurant-with-rooms and a
professional yet family-run French country place. Of course, there is an explicit
intent on the part of the Wallises that guests should make the connection.
'Pass,' they say, 'from the old-world charm of the former inn [here be beams] to
the fantasy, reminiscent of Provence, of the conservatory', where most of the
dining goes on. Later, hop across the busy A523, eyes peeled, to the guest
bedrooms. Park the kids at Alton Towers and come here for lunch – much
cheaper than dinner but never stinted. Regulars approve of the refusal to cook
to a predictable pattern: changes keep them salivating, especially in the daily
fish dishes, which may include a langoustine soufflé or a jellied fish terrine, to
name but two first courses that impressed. Nigel Wallis' techniques are
classical, able both to deliver fine pastry for a box containing lamb sweetbreads
with a reduction of tarragon, tomato and madeira and to stop exactly in the
intensifying of a sauce for a fine pot-au-feu of oxtail beef, ham and lamb. He is
as good at soufflés as at pastry: eat the rhubarb one, or try the classic pithiviers
for something more solid. Output here is very consistent, and is well matched
by Ann Wallis' knowledgeable management at the front. If such a place can
survive with honour and success in Staffordshire, so evidently doing things
properly, why can't more? Also note the Wallises' firm views on tips: they are
definitely neither sanctioned nor expected. An absence of a grower's name
here, a misspelling there, are hardly going to dull our enthusiasm for the wine
list, which is reassuringly authoritative. With interesting wines by the glass
and equal regard given to the classics and the Californians, this is a generous-
hearted list, priced accurately and fairly. They know their wines here, so ask
Mrs Wallis for recommendations. House wines are from £14.55. CELLARMAN'S
CHOICE: Petit Chablis 1990, Delaunay, £16.95; St-Emilion, Ch. le Tertre
Rôteboeuf 1982, £29.50.

---

*The 1995 Guide will be published before Christmas 1994. Reports on meals are most
welcome at any time of the year, but are extremely valuable in the spring. Send them to
The Good Food Guide, FREEPOST, 2 Marylebone Road, London NW1 1YN. No stamp
is needed if posted in the UK.*

CHEF: Nigel Wallis   PROPRIETORS: Nigel and Ann Wallis   OPEN: Tue to Sun, exc Sat L and Sun D; 12 to 2, 7 to 10   CLOSED: 2 weeks Jan   MEALS: Set L £9.95 (weekdays only – 2 courses) to £16.50, Set D £18.50 (weekdays only – 2 courses) to £30   SERVICE: card slips closed   CARDS: Access, Amex, Diners, Visa   DETAILS: 50 seats. Private parties: 12 private room. Car park. Vegetarian meals. Children welcome. Smart dress preferred. No smoking in dining-room. Wheelchair access (also WC). Music   ACCOMMODATION: 6 rooms, all with bath/shower. Rooms for disabled. B&B £52 to £87. Children welcome. Baby facilities. Garden. Fishing. TV. Phone. Fax: (0538) 308157 (*The Which? Hotel Guide*)

---

**WATERMILLOCK Cumbria**                                                    map 7

## ▲ Rampsbeck Country House Hotel ♦✳

Watermillock CA11 0LP
POOLEY BRIDGE (076 84) 86442 and 86688                          COOKING 2*
on A592 Penrith to Windermere road                               COST £23–£49

The hotel is an eighteenth-century house standing on the edge of Ullswater: 'The views are magnificent,' comments one visitor. The kitchen takes care with ingredients and supplies: top of the list are Cumbrian farmed venison, spring lamb, free-range geese, and flour from the Watermill at Little Salkeld. This attentiveness is backed up by industrious enterprise, which yields home-smoked produce, home-baked bread, pasta, preserves and much more. The florid four-course dinner menu is peppered with a plethora of components: baked fillet of sea bass is served with a pimento sauce, warm timbale of smoked salmon is filled with Dublin Bay prawn mousse garnished with tiny prawn pizzas, and pan-fried loin of venison comes with wild mushroom and foie gras pithiviers and a game jus flavoured with green chartreuse. Desserts are equally flamboyant: one example is hot prune and armagnac crêpe soufflé served with white wine sabayon and prune and armagnac ice-cream. Vegetarians have been delighted to find a full menu of meatless specialities such as deep-fried goats' cheese with sultanas, plus a salad of winter greens with a hazelnut sauce. The cooking is generally sound, although some reporters have noticed an occasional heavy hand. Good-value bar lunches move into less heady territory. Note that weekday lunches must be booked in advance. The wine list is well spread but holds few surprises; wines are divided up into categories such as 'oaked', 'fruity', 'supple' and 'solid'. House wines are from £8.75 and there is plenty of reasonable drinking for under £15.

CHEF: Andrew McGeorge   PROPRIETORS: T.I. and M.M. Gibb   OPEN: all week; 12 to 1.30, 7 to 8.30   CLOSED: 4 Jan to mid-Feb   MEALS: alc bar L (main courses £9 to £10). Set L £19.95 to £22, Set D £24 to £32.50   SERVICE: not inc, card slips closed   CARDS: Access, Visa   DETAILS: 40 seats. Private parties: 60 main room, 15 private room. Car park. Vegetarian meals. Children's helpings. No children under 5. Smart dress preferred. No smoking in dining-room. No music   ACCOMMODATION: 19 rooms, all with bath/shower. B&B £48 to £140. Deposit: £30. No children under 5. Pets welcome (not in public rooms). Afternoon teas. Garden. Fishing. TV. Phone. Doors close at 11. Fax: (076 84) 86442 (*The Which? Hotel Guide*)

---

*The* Guide *always appreciates hearing about changes of chef or owner.*

---

WATH-IN-NIDDERDALE North Yorkshire                                    map 7

## ▲ *Sportsman's Arms* ▼ ⚒

Wath-in-Nidderdale HG3 5PP
HARROGATE (0423) 711306 and 712524
take B6165 or B6265 to Pateley Bridge, follow                    COOKING 2
signs by village, 2m NW of Pateley Bridge                     COST £18–£44

You would not expect flighty pretension at this old stone inn near Pateley
Bridge, nor do you get it – though one diner felt that inaccurate French (as in
'*prix fixe*') was unacceptable. 'Provides the goods very confidently' is the
general view: attractions include the set-price three-course dinner menu with
half a bottle of wine and coffee thrown in, use of local ingredients (such as
Scarborough woof – finned, not legged – and 'a huge Nidderdale trout'),
exemplary eggs ('I had forgotten that yolks like that even existed'), beautiful
floral displays, and a doughty refusal to take days off. Smoked duck has been
'succulent and flavourful', both lamb and fish well cooked, winter and summer
puddings alike win applause, and the choice of a savoury in their place is
appreciated. Locally made black pudding in a creamed apple and cider sauce,
though, was 'rather a gooey mess', and a smoked salmon parcel stuffed with
prawns was 'drowned in a poor-quality cheese sauce'. Portions, 'generous to a
fault', may include a 'small half-loaf of warm brown bread' with the first-
course dishes. The bar serves drinks and snacks. The wine list is good: wide-
ranging, imaginatively assembled, with particularly appealing value to be
found among the 'house selection' (nine wines at £7.95 to £10.70, with more on
request), and with a serious and well-merited look at France's Midi wines (like
the Faugères Resplandy at £9.45 or the Dom. du Révérend Corbières at £11.50).
CELLARMAN'S CHOICE: Chiroubles 1991, Ch. de Raousset, Duboeuf, £14.25;
Sancerre Pinot Rosé 1991, Lucien Crochet, £17.95.

CHEFS: Ray Carter, Chris Williamson and Penny Sollit  PROPRIETORS: Jane and Ray
Carter  OPEN: all week; 12 to 2.30, 7 to 10  CLOSED: 25 Dec  MEALS: alc (main courses
£10 to £16). Set L £12 to £15, Set Sun L £11.50, Set D £18.75  SERVICE: not inc, card slips
closed  CARDS: Access, Visa  DETAILS: 60 seats. 6 tables outside. Private parties: 60 main
room, 8 private rooms. Car park. Vegetarian meals. Children's helpings. Smart dress
preferred. No smoking in dining-room. Wheelchair access. No music  ACCOMMODATION:
7 rooms, 2 with bath/shower. B&B £28 to £50. Children welcome. Pets welcome. Afternoon
teas. Garden. Fishing. TV (*The Which? Hotel Guide*)

WATLINGTON Oxfordshire                                               map 2

## ▲ *Well House*

34–40 High Street, Watlington OX9 5PY                            COOKING 1
WATLINGTON (0491) 613333                                      COST £24–£48

The well in question is found in the small bar of this intelligent conversion of a
medieval brick and flint house, with bedrooms in a new extension. The success
of the menu can sometimes be mixed. Brickbats fly as well as affirmations of
good value and quality. Veal burgers with oyster mushrooms, lamb pie with
apricots and chicken with ginger are suggestions on a set-price menu, while

the *carte* dispenses the roasts, escalopes of veal with brandy and cream, rack of lamb with port and redcurrants, and mousseline of sole wrapped in smoked salmon. The style is familiar but steady. 'We were treated like real residents,' one pair of travellers remarked 'not just overnight stayers.' The wine list is a fair exposition of French skills, with the useful addition of a page of hocks and moselles. The New World gets more summary treatment. House wines are from £7.

CHEF: Patricia Crawford   PROPRIETORS: Patricia and Alan Crawford   OPEN: all week, exc L Mon and Sat and Sun D; 12.30 to 2, 7.15 to 9.15 (9.45 Sat)   MEALS: alc (main courses £9.50 to £16). Set L and D £12.90 (2 courses) to £16.40   SERVICE: not inc, card slips closed   CARDS: Access, Amex, Diners, Visa   DETAILS: 40 seats. 4 tables outside. Private parties: 50 main room. Car park. Vegetarian meals. Children's helpings. Smart dress preferred. Wheelchair access. No music   ACCOMMODATION: 10 rooms, all with bath/shower. Rooms for disabled. B&B £40 to £75. Children welcome. Baby facilities. Pets welcome. Afternoon teas. TV. Phone. Doors close at 11.30. Confirm by 6. Fax: (0491) 612025

---

WELLS Somerset                                                                                          map 2

## Ritcher's £

5 Sadler Street, Wells BA5 2RR                                                           COOKING 1
WELLS (0749) 679085                                                                   COST £18–£33

This is a useful local restaurant in the town centre, close to the cathedral. It offers everything from lunch-time snacks to full-blown fixed-price dinners. Nicholas Hart describes his cooking as 'classical French with a modern approach', and meals in the upstairs dining-room take in dishes along the lines of warm king prawn and chicken salad, veal, mushroom and chive fricassee, roast rack of lamb, and chocolate bavarois with fresh fruit. Simpler offerings can be had in the downstairs bistro, which provides anything from ploughman's, cold platters and bowls of spaghetti bolognese to steaks and deep-fried cod in breadcrumbs. A couple who enjoyed a meal in the cobbled courtyard were impressed by salmon with hollandaise sauce, breast of chicken in spicy tomato sauce, 'crisp, correct' vegetables and pear sorbet. Service is attentive 'in the right degree'. The wine list roams from France and Spain to the New World for some fair-priced drinking; also note the stock of vintage ports. House wines start at £7.85.

CHEF: Nicholas Hart   PROPRIETORS: Nicholas Hart and Kate Ritcher   OPEN: all week; 12 to 2.30, 7 (6 summer) to 9.30   CLOSED: 1 Jan   MEALS: alc bistro (main courses £6 to £13). Set L restaurant £12.50 (2 courses) to £14.50, Set D £14.50 (2 courses) to £17.50. Set L and D bistro £9.50 (2 courses) to £11.50   SERVICE: not inc, card slips closed   CARDS: Access, Visa   DETAILS: restaurant 14 seats, bistro 18 seats. 3 tables outside. Private parties: 25 main room. Vegetarian meals bistro, with prior notice restaurant. Children's helpings bistro. No children under 12 restaurant. Smart dress preferred restaurant. Wheelchair access bistro. No music

---

*All letters to the* Guide *are acknowledged with an update on latest sales, closures, chef changes and so on.*

---

## *Moorings* ▼ ⁵⅟✳

6 Freeman Street,
Wells-next-the-Sea NR23 1BA            COOKING 3
FAKENHAM (0328) 710949            COST £19–£31

'Bernard and Carla Phillips understand that there is more to a restaurant than
cooking,' writes a reporter, referring to the way in which this seaside restaurant
runs as a kind of community lightship, drawing on local people, local work
and the fruits of local hedgerows, woods and beaches. To some, the operation
may seem amateurish – the awkwardly typed wine list, the dense, handwritten menu (prices are set for one or more courses), the way supplies may run
out during the evening, and the food itself, where enthusiasm sometimes leads
to an overfashioning of basic ingredients. But for anyone who loves excitement
and exuberance in food – 'flavours buzzing, colliding, ricocheting everywhere'
– Moorings is a landmark. Soups are good and Carla Phillips' interest in
pickles and preserves was well realised by 'brilliant' home-smoked chicken
breast served with the 'perfect sweetish/sour foil' of a home-made chutney
vinaigrette. Fish is fresh or nothing; steamed sea bass, for example, was
'wriggling in the kitchen this morning', and by nightfall had been steamed
over coriander and served, elegantly, with threads of Japanese wakame
seaweed, slivers of red pepper and a niçoise vinaigrette. 'Deep orange-red in
colour, made from a puréed blend of olives, garlic, capers, tomatoes, peppers
and anchovies, plus some wine vinegar and olive oil, this was one of the best
things I've tasted for a long while.' Meat dishes of note include the Norfolk-
style pork brawn served with an orange vinaigrette and sweet-and-sour
pickled pumpkin, grilled ox tongue with a mustard, caper and herb sauce, and
pigeon breasts with port, wine and cream. Serious vegetables are 'nearly
always given an unexpected twist'. Cheeses continue to please more than
dessert. The smoke-free atmosphere 'improves the atmosphere and enjoyment
in this small dining-room'; yet the friendliness and informality of the service
can seem slow to city types. An exemplary selection of house wines (from
Australia, Portugal, Gascogne, Hérault, Roussillon, Quercy and the Loire) kicks
off the list at just £6.95 (or £1.60 a glass); the rest of the list is equally sparky
and equally keenly priced, despite looking a terrible mess. Beaujolais sourced
from Norfolkman Roger Harris is worth exploring, as are French country wines
in general (many from Adnams), since their unexpected, characterful flavours
are perfectly in tune with what is on the plate.

CHEFS: Carla Phillips and Jane Lee   PROPRIETORS: Bernard and Carla Phillips   OPEN:
Thur to Mon, exc Thur L; 12.30 to 2, 7.30 to 9   CLOSED: 2 weeks early Dec, 24 to 26 Dec,
2 weeks early June   MEALS: Set Mon and Fri L £9.95 (2 courses) to £12.95, Set Sat and
Sun L and Set D £12.95 (2 courses) to £17.45   SERVICE: not inc   DETAILS: 35 seats. Private
parties: 35 main room. Vegetarian meals. Children's helpings. No smoking in dining-room.
Wheelchair access (also WC). No music

Not inc *in the details at the end of an entry indicates that no service charge is made and
any tipping is at the discretion of the customer.*

**WEST BAY** Dorset                                                      map 2

## Riverside Restaurant and Café £

West Bay, Bridport DT6 4EZ
BRIDPORT (0308) 22011                                         COOKING 2*
off A35, ¾m S of Bridport                                    COST £16–£36

'I still think this is the most "French" restaurant I know in England. Not because it has any pretensions like most so-called French restaurants, but because it is a matter-of-fact place where people go, in families or couples or even alone to enjoy whatever food they fancy and when they fancy it.' So writes one astute reporter of this improbable seafood café-restaurant, which looks like a bungalow extension to West Bay post office and is sited implausibly on an island in the River Brit. The interior is pine-furnished, light and spacious; Arthur and Janet Watson try not to overfill the restaurant, yet admit that 'an intimate atmosphere *à deux* can be a problem during school holidays'. Attempts to create a non-smoking area have also so far been without success. Note seasonal variations on opening times between March and April, and October to November – telephone the restaurant for details. The food, based entirely on local catches, is ample compensation. 'My husband and I never agree about fish. We both like it but he insists it must be plain, while I like it dressed up.' Both were happy – he with plainly grilled plaice; she with John Dory in a wine, cream and onion sauce. Alternatives might include stuffed clams, local oysters, skate in black butter or baked brill Greek-style; lobsters and seafood platters await the modestly prodigal. Chips please connoisseurs, while salads are increasingly artful. The desserts of the day are often more extensive and exciting than those on the menu. A close look at the wine list reveals surprising catholicism: £6.95 will buy you a simple Australian dry white (Oakwood), but for less than double that price you could have one of New Zealand's very best Sauvignon Blancs, Jackson Estate's 1992 (£12.95). Muscadet (a choice of two) is practically the local wine.

CHEFS: Janet Watson and Natalie Ansell Green  PROPRIETORS: Janet and Arthur Watson  OPEN: Tue to Sun, exc Sun D; 11.30 to 2.30 (3.30 Sun), 6.30 to 8.30  CLOSED: Dec to early Mar  MEALS: alc (main courses £4.50 to £14)  SERVICE: net prices, card slips closed  CARDS: Access, Visa  DETAILS: 80 seats. 8 tables outside. Private parties: 70 main room. Vegetarian meals. Children's helpings. Wheelchair access (also WC). Music

---

**WEST BEXINGTON** Dorset                                               map 2

## ▲ Manor Hotel ⅓✳

Beach Road, West Bexington DT2 9DF
BURTON BRADSTOCK (0308) 897616                               COOKING 1
on B3157, 5m SE of Bridport                                  COST £19–£33

The breeze off the Chesil Beach is enough to freshen the most jaded appetites, and the team at this inn-cum-hotel, able to offer the widest range of price and elaboration, is happy to satisfy them. Whether eaten in restaurant or bar, the food is robust and substantial. In the dining-room there are two menus. Supper may offer you omelettes or skate wing while dinner rises to rack of lamb or breast of duck. Here, the style is mainstream – herb crust with rack of lamb, green peppercorn sauce with the duck – but this suits the crowds who find the cooking cheerful and fair value. Ample desserts are much gooier than anything that comes before; fish is an advisable choice at some stage. The wine list has broadened its scope to give better value and the sources remain reliable – for instance, Clos du Bois from California or some very sound bourgeois clarets like La Tour-de-By or Cissac. House wines are £6.95.

CHEFS: Clive Jobson and Rebecca Warbridge   PROPRIETORS: Richard and Jayne Childs
OPEN: all week; 12 to 2, 7 to 10   MEALS: Set L £12.50 to £14.50, Set D £15.95 to £19.95
SERVICE: not inc   CARDS: Access, Amex, Diners, Visa   DETAILS: 60 seats. 6 tables outside.
Private parties: 65 main room, 45 private room. Car park. Vegetarian meals. Children's
helpings. No smoking in conservatory. Music   ACCOMMODATION: 13 rooms, all with bath/
shower. B&B £44 to £71. Deposit: £10. Children welcome. Baby facilities. Afternoon teas.
Garden. TV. Phone. Doors close at midnight. Confirm by 6. Fax: (0308) 897035 (*The Which?
Hotel Guide*)

---

**WESTLINGTON Buckinghamshire**                                                    map 3

## La Chouette  £

Westlington Green, Dinton HP17 8UW
AYLESBURY (0296) 747422                                                  COOKING 1
on A418, 4m SW of Aylesbury                                            COST £19–£56

Last year's description is accurate, remarked one reader: 'pleasant, beamed ex-pub in a very pretty village'. He forgot to mention the owls – ornaments that celebrate the chef's ornithological enthusiasm. He then wondered if the chef should not spend more time in the kitchen than in the restaurant talking to the other guests. As Mr Desmette operates virtually single-handed, this might be a gain. The cooking is classically inspired and capable of great correctness. A spring menu of lobster and skate salad, turbot cooked with leeks, and breast of duck with elderberries, was finished with 'a surprise'. Most sweet surprises here are ice-creams with a sabayon. Asparagus à la flamande, cod with juniper berries or veal kidney with juniper may be indications of a Belgian background to the cooking. The wine list would benefit from greater range to offer some of the better products of the new wave of French makers. It does not, of course, recognise any other country. House wines are £10.

CHEF/PROPRIETOR: Frédéric Desmette   OPEN: Mon to Sat, exc Sat L (Sun L with reservation
1 day ahead); 12 to 2, 6.30 to 9   CLOSED: second week Jan   MEALS: alc (main courses £10
to £14). Set L and D £10 to £35   SERVICE: 12.5%, card slips closed   CARDS: Access, Visa
DETAILS: 40 seats. 4 tables outside. Private parties: 48 main room, 14 private room. Car
park. Vegetarian meals. Children's helpings. Smart dress preferred. No cigars/pipes in
dining-room. Wheelchair access (1 step; also WC). Music

---

*The* Guide *office can quickly spot when a restaurateur is encouraging customers to write
recommending inclusion – and sadly, several restaurants have been doing this in 1993.
Such reports do not further a restaurant's cause. Please tell us if a restaurateur invites you
to write to the* Guide.

**WEST MERSEA Essex** map 3

## ▲ *Blackwater Hotel,*
## *Le Champenois*

20–22 Church Road,
West Mersea CO5 8QH
COLCHESTER (0206) 383338 and 383038
just off B1025 from Colchester,           COOKING 2
turn right at West Mersea church           COST £21–£43

Outwardly it is unchanged, reports one reader with relief: an old coaching-inn in an out-of-the-way village all kitted up with French bistro touches. The menu changes little from month to month, unless you follow the daily dishes, which will strike a fuller chord of tastes and flavours. So there are plenty of moules marinière, oysters in season, onion soup and smoked mackerel pâté, followed by Stroganov, calf's liver and duck with orange. Chicken or fish couscous, and feuilleté of mussels, are dishes which keep the chef from getting bored and which customers find most enjoyable. The wine list is a positive tome of labels arranged scrap-book style, with most of the choice revolving round France. House wines are £7.95.

CHEF: R. Roudesli   PROPRIETOR: Monique Chapleo   OPEN: all week, exc Tue L and Sun D; 12 to 2, 7 to 10   CLOSED: first 3 weeks Jan   MEALS: alc (main courses £10 to £14.50). Set L £12.85 to £14.85   SERVICE: not inc, card slips closed   CARDS: Access, Amex, Visa DETAILS: 46 seats. 3 tables outside. Private parties: 55 main room, 25 private room. Car park. Vegetarian meals. Children's helpings. Smart dress preferred. No cigars/pipes in dining-room. Wheelchair access (1 step; also WC). No music   ACCOMMODATION: 7 rooms, 4 with bath/shower. B&B £31 to £68. Deposit: £10. Children welcome. Baby facilities. Pets by arrangement. Afternoon teas. Garden. TV. Doors close at 1am. Confirm by 7 (*The Which? Hotel Guide*)

**WETHERAL Cumbria** map 7

## *Fantails*

The Green, Wetheral CA4 8ET           COOKING 2
CARLISLE (0228) 560239           COST £19–£43

At the north end of a handsome green is an old blacksmith's shop with capacious lofts and back-buildings. This is the site of Fantails, called after the doves that still whirl above. The entrance is up a set of stone steps, which give on to a succession of rooms for dining or sitting (and sleeping) that make fair use of the stone walls and rafters for decorative effect. Large enough for the biggest local wedding, Fantails is also well sited for a quick lunge off the motorway for respite from noise and tedium. Dusty travellers have found the welcome beyond compare. A fairly conventional repertoire may include a hot cheese soufflé, a puff-pastry crescent with wild mushrooms and moules à la crème for first courses, then pheasant with cranberries or best end of lamb with a black grape sauce for main dishes: these are none the less cooked with care, an eye for the seasons and more imagination than appears at first sight. Thus a meal that took in duck breast steamed with green peppercorns and peaches was given a sauce of perfect balance; a lunch dish of curried 'Burmese' vegetables was exactly judged; milk bread baked on the premises was adjudged very good; and dauphinois potatoes were, for once, cooked properly. A 'light lunch menu' is also available with dishes for under £6. The wine list is general and very acceptable. House wines are £7.95: the white is from Ochoa, the red is a decent Côtes du Ventoux.

CHEF: Peter Bowman   PROPRIETORS: Robert and Jennifer Bowman, and Gill Tod   OPEN: Tue to Sun (Sun L by arrangement); 12 to 2, 6.30 to 9.30   MEALS: alc (main courses £10.50 to £16.50). Set L and D £18.50   SERVICE: not inc, card slips closed   CARDS: Access, Visa DETAILS: 100 seats. Private parties: 80 main room, 20 and 30 private rooms. Car park. Vegetarian meals. Children's helpings. Smart dress preferred. Music

---

**WETHERSFIELD Essex**                                                                    map 3

## Dicken's ♥

The Green, Wethersfield CM7 4BS                                        COOKING 3
GREAT DUNMOW (0371) 850723                                        COST £20–£34

'Worth a round trip of three hours,' suggested a reporter who made the pilgrimage to this 'gem in the wastelands of Essex'. The setting is a building more than 200 years old; inside, it can strike visitors as cramped, although 'if you are practically sitting on someone's lap' it is possible to admire dishes on different tables. 'John Dicken continues to delight us with the imaginative quality of his cooking,' admit a couple who single out the 'superb blend of flavours, the outstanding texture and the sheer visual attraction' of the food. There is plenty to admire and explore within his menus. He picks and chooses ideas with dexterity, pulling in influences from far and wide: venison and chestnut pudding, seafood tempura with summer leaf salad, rustic bruschetta, chargrilled steak with frites, Indian spiced chicken with aubergine and tomato chutney all make an appearance. The result is a perfect global balancing act. Carrot and chive soup sent one diner into 'ecstasies of delight'; others have enthused about Roquefort and spinach ravioli, fillets of red bream with courgettes and roasted peppers, and lamb marinated in provençale herbs and garlic. Even pure and simple dishes such as lobster salad and seafood platter have shone by virtue of freshness. Desserts such as strawberry délice are generally on target. Service is very professional and pleasant. The value for money is excellent, although charging extra for bread has raised a few eyebrows. The wine list is sound, clear and not so long as to cause indigestion on the brain. Prices are more than fair, and spread is wide enough to cope with whatever the kitchen cooks. House wine is £7.95. CELLARMAN'S CHOICE: Sancerre Cuvée François de la Grange de Montigny 1990, Natter, £22.95; Penley Estate Shiraz/Cabernet 1990, £17.65.

---

CHEF: John Dicken   PROPRIETORS: John and Maria Dicken   OPEN: Wed to Sun, exc Sun D; 12.30 to 2, 7.30 to 9.30   MEALS: alc (main courses £7 to £12.50). Set L £12.75 to £15.50, Set D £15 to £18   SERVICE: not inc   CARDS: Access, Amex, Visa   DETAILS: 45 seats. 5 tables outside. Private parties: 38 main room, 18 private room. Car park. Vegetarian meals. Children's helpings. Smart dress preferred. Wheelchair access (1 step; also men's WC). Music

---

**WEYMOUTH Dorset** map 2

## Perry's £ NEW ENTRY

4 Trinity Road, The Old Harbour,
Weymouth DT4 8TJ        COOKING 1*
WEYMOUTH (0305) 785799        COST £17–£40

New owners, the Hodder family, also run the Mock Turtle in Dorchester (see entry) and have quickly established a reputation in this restaurant by the harbour, where 'fishing boats, dinghies and the odd gin palace pootle in and out'. Perry's stands out in Weymouth – a town that seems to have more than its share of greasy spoons and scampi in the basket. The Hodders take care with details: black marble-topped tables with 'wonderful laundered napkins', displays of dried flowers and greenery, carved fishes dotted about the simply decorated dining-room. Fresh local fish such as Poole mussels, Abbotsbury oysters, bass, 'dived for' scallops and crab are chalked on a board; meat and game feature heavily on the printed menu. The cooking is sometimes uneven – thinly flavoured mushroom and tarragon soup, 'watery' monkfish, 'flavourless' kebabs – but these lapses are outweighed by some excellent dishes. Filo pastry parcel with scallops and John Dory, beef fillet (also in filo) with celeriac purée, salmon with sole, spinach and chive sauce (filo again!) and guinea-fowl in an 'unctuous' brown sauce with wild mushrooms have been notably good. Sorbets and very rich crème brûlée have been creditable sweets. Service is willing in this hardworking set up. The international wine list has a fair choice of reasonable drinking, with plenty under £15. House wine is £7.50.

CHEFS: Andy Pike and Sharon Robinson   PROPRIETORS: Raymond, Alan and Vivien Hodder   OPEN: all week, exc L Mon and Sat; 12 to 2, 7 to 10.15   CLOSED: Sun D Oct to Apr   MEALS: alc (main courses £7 to £17.50). Set L £8.95 (2 courses) to £10.95   SERVICE: not inc   CARDS: Access, Visa   DETAILS: 50 seats. 6 tables outside. Private parties: 40 main room. Vegetarian meals. Children's helpings on request. Music

---

**WHIMPLE Devon** map 1

## ▲ Woodhayes

Whimple EX5 2TD
WHIMPLE (0404) 822237        COOKING 2
off A30, 9m E of Exeter        COST £30–£36

'The welcome was enough to make the visit worthwhile,' wrote one happy to find this small country house (which resembles an over-sized rectory in scale) set among the apple orchards and garden centres to the east of Exeter. With but a few bedrooms and a small, Regency-inspired dining-room, the character of the hospitality counts for much, but the Rendles' cooking of a no-choice (until dessert), six-course dinner will help the cause of human warmth. An autumn meal may run through salmon mousse, leek and potato soup, fillet of sole filled with a trout mousseline on a saffron sauce, fillet of beef with red wine sauce, and crème brûlée before a final platter of Cheddar and Stilton. This, however, need not sink the diner: portions are considered, and the presence of two mousses is no more than characteristic of the dinner-party style. Care is paramount, and over-elaboration is avoided. A slate of good wine selections at £9.20 almost dispenses with the need for a longer list, but it exists and is of solid worth and fairly priced.

CHEFS: Katherine Rendle and Michael Rendle   PROPRIETORS: Katherine and Frank Rendle, and Michael Rendle   OPEN: all week, D only (L residents only); 7.30 to 9.30 MEALS: Set D £25   SERVICE: net prices, card slips closed   CARDS: Access, Amex, Diners, Visa   DETAILS: 16 seats. 3 tables outside. Private parties: 14 main room. Car park. Vegetarian meals. Children's helpings. No children under 12. Smart dress preferred. Music   ACCOMMODATION: 6 rooms, all with bath/shower. B&B £65 to £85. No children under 12. Afternoon teas. Garden. Tennis. TV. Phone. Doors close at midnight. Confirm by 7 (*The Which? Hotel Guide*)

---

## WHITBY North Yorkshire · map 6A

# *Magpie Café* £

| | |
|---|---|
| 14 Pier Road, Whitby YO21 3PU | COOKING 2 |
| WHITBY (0947) 602058 | COST £12–£32 |

'"Monkfish bites in batter" sounds awful, but were they served in a Japanese restaurant, people would rave and pay the earth' was the comment of one family that experienced this good-value, friendly and family-run café that concentrates on the freshest possible fish, the crispest possible batter and large yet digestible chips. A salad with crab may include strawberries and starfruit, but the crab is utterly wholesome and full of enough flavour to convince the most wavering of supporters of that taste. 'All that a café should be.' The tables are bare, there are queues, but the view is impressive and the puddings worth a visit on their own account. House wines are £5.95.

CHEF: Ian Robson   PROPRIETORS: Sheila and Ian McKenzie, and Ian and Alison McKenzie-Robson   OPEN: all week; 11.30 to 6.30   CLOSED: end Nov to mid-Mar MEALS: alc (main courses £4 to £11). Set meals £7.75 to £11.95   SERVICE: not inc, card slips closed   CARDS: Access, Visa   DETAILS: 100 seats. Private parties. 50 main room. Vegetarian meals. Healthy eating options. Children's helpings. No-smoking area. No music. Air-conditioned

---

## WHITLEY BAY Tyne & Wear · map 7

# *Le Provençale*

| | |
|---|---|
| 183 Park View, Whitley Bay NE26 3RE | COOKING 1 |
| 091-251 3567 | COST £25–£49 |

This is how restaurants used to be, in atmosphere and tone as well as in menu and cooking style – and it is much appreciated in Whitley Bay. Prices are firmer this year, but for this you get solid comfort, mothering service, and dishes from the book such as tournedos perigourdine, pheasant stuffed with its mousse with a bordelaise game sauce, beef Stroganov, chicken Dugléré and lashings of vegetables. The style is florid on occasion, but always generous. The short wine list is very reasonably priced. Ch. Lyonnat 1986 comes in at £12.95 and nothing apart from fizz is over £20. House wines are £7.90 a litre.

CHEF: Michael Guijarro   PROPRIETORS: Mr and Mrs M. Guijarro   OPEN: Mon to Sat D,
Thur and Fri L; 12 to 1.45, 7 to 9.45   CLOSED: first 2 weeks July   MEALS: alc (main courses
£13 to £20). Set Mon and Thur D £16.95   SERVICE: not inc   CARDS: Access, Amex, Diners,
Visa   DETAILS: 60 seats. Private parties: 60 main room. Children's helpings. No children
under 8. Smart dress preferred. Wheelchair access (also WC). Music. Air-conditioned

---

**WHITSTABLE Kent**                                                                    map 3

# ▲ Whitstable Oyster Fishery Co

Royal Native Oyster Stores,
The Horsebridge, Whitstable CT5 1BU                                    COOKING 1
WHITSTABLE (0227) 276856                                               COST £21–£35

One of Britain's few good indigenous restaurant forms is the place on the sea
coast that produces seafood and fish as plainly as possible. This warehouse
with rough brick walls and white-painted wooden beams but a stone's throw
from the shore is an example. The lobster is kept in live tanks, the fish is fresh
daily, the oysters are tip-top. Keep the order simple. Service can be chaotic,
especially when overrun by numbers. Some people, of course, like this aspect
of it, and do not want the thing to be 'tidied up and plasticised'. The wine list is
sensibly cheap, all white except one, and comes from Yapp Brothers. House
wines are £7.95.

CHEFS: Phil Colthup and Nikki Billington   PROPRIETORS: Whitstable Oyster Fishery Co
OPEN: Tue to Sun and bank hol Mons; 12 to 2.30, 7 to 9.30   MEALS: alc (main courses £8.50
to £14)   SERVICE: not inc   CARDS: Access, Amex, Diners, Visa   DETAILS: 125 seats. 15
tables outside. Private parties: 100 main room, 125 private room. Car park. Vegetarian
meals with prior notice. Children's helpings with prior notice. Wheelchair access (1 step;
also WC). Music   ACCOMMODATION: 6 self-catering fishermen's huts. £10 to £20 per
person per night. Children welcome

---

**WICKHAM Hampshire**                                                                  map 2

# ▲ Old House

The Square, Wickham PO17 5JG
WICKHAM (0329) 833049                                                 COOKING 2
2½m N of Fareham, at junction of A32/B2177                            COST £33–£43

Wickham is now prelude to Portsmouth, yet was once a market town in its own
right. The Old House fronts the market square and disguises behind its regular
Georgian brick façade a variety of rooms: original panelled chambers,
bedrooms with tall sash windows, and a clutch of beamed rooms in the former
servants' attic quarters. Diners are guided through the house to a room with
French doors to the garden. In homage to Annie Skipwith's French
background, the menu continues to nod towards the other side of the Channel:
a pleasing selection of dishes that are just the right side of conventional give
some interest without too much adventure. Turbot with pink and black
peppercorns has a sauce emulsified with olive oil; duck is moistened with a

sauce of veal stock sharpened with raspberry vinegar and given depth with some bitter chocolate; a slice of lamb is given some hearty presence by flageolets, tomatoes, garlic and cream. This settled repertoire is enjoyably finished with desserts like pear clafoutis and pineapple with more pink peppercorns and Grand Marnier. House wines are £10.

CHEF: Nicholas Harman PROPRIETORS: Richard and Annie Skipwith OPEN: Mon to Sat, exc L Mon and Sat; 12 to 1.45, 7 to 9.30 MEALS: Set L and D £25 to £28 SERVICE: net prices, card slips closed CARDS: Access, Amex, Diners, Visa DETAILS: 40 seats. Private parties: 40 main room, 14 private room. Car park. Vegetarian meals. Children's helpings. No cigars/pipes in dining-room. Wheelchair access (also WC). No music ACCOMMODATION: 12 rooms, all with bath/shower. B&B £60 to £85. Children welcome. Baby facilities. Garden. TV. Phone. Doors close at midnight. Confirm by noon. Fax: (0329) 833672 (*The Which? Hotel Guide*)

**WILLINGTON Co Durham** map 7

## *Stile* 🍷 $ ✱ £

97 High Street, Willington DL15 0PE
BISHOP AUCKLAND (0388) 746615 COOKING 1
on A690, 4m N of Bishop Auckland COST £20–£33

'A converted mine-owner's residence with conservatories' is how Mike Boustred describes his lively restaurant. The floors are polished stripped-pine, the walls are green, dried flowers abound, and a congenial, if slightly eccentric, mood prevails. No fancy nouvelle or post-modernistic touches intrude on to the menu. Steak is a fixture (Wellington, with green peppercorn sauce, and Stroganov); elsewhere, oriental ideas such as pakoras with cucumber dip, asparagus with spicy prawns and pork fillet with lime, ginger and sweet-sour sauce sit alongside Basque crab and Gressingham duck with blackcurrant sauce. Vegetables were a highlight for one reporter. Sweets have included a good slab of rich chocolate and brandy terrine with two sauces. The cooking does not always get rave reviews, but the value and sense of fun are good. The wine list has that giveaway look of randomness verging on chaos that the enthusiast is unable to control. Mike Boustred charges modestly for a range of wines that moves from Paillard champagne at £22.50 through a set of carefully chosen Loires,and some idiosyncratic Alsaces to mature clarets. The half-bottles are sparse but hardly need resorting to on economic grounds. House wine is £6.75.

CHEF: Jenny James PROPRIETORS: Mike Boustred and Jenny James OPEN: Tue to Sat, D only; 7 to 9.45 CLOSED: 2–3 weeks weeks Sept MEALS: alc (main courses £9.50 to £12.50). Set D £16.25 to £17.25 SERVICE: not inc, card slips closed CARDS: Access, Visa DETAILS: 45 seats. Private parties: 35 main room, 18 private room. Car park. Vegetarian meals. Children's helpings on request. No smoking in dining-room. Music

*Prices quoted in the* Guide *are based on information supplied by restaurateurs. The prices quoted at the top of each entry represent a range, from the lowest meal price to the highest; the latter is inflated by 20 per cent to take account of likely price rises during the year of the* Guide.

WILLITON Somerset                                          map 1

## ▲ *White House Hotel* 🍷

Williton TA4 4QW
WILLITON (0984) 632306 and 632777,                    COOKING 3
code changes to (019 84) April 1994                   COST £35–£51

'How do we exist from November to May when the restaurant is closed?' asks
an inveterate recidivist. We know that the Smiths, 26 years on, still retain their
enthusiasm and recharge their batteries with visits to competitors, 'the odd
ethnic cookery course' and exploratory drinking. Others must languish. Those
courses may be the cause of experiments in a sensible stable repertoire – for
instance, a chicken satay reported in the winter – but for the most part the
inspiration remains Elizabeth David and that ilk, the quality of the ingredients
themselves and true seasonality. The house is on the main road through the
village; 'low key' is one description though redecoration is in evidence. The
same words might apply to the service: modest, no flunkies, lots of peace and
quiet. The menu is short and is valued for its simplicity and occasional
voluptuous richness. Soufflé suissesse, pigeon breasts with hot beetroot, loin of
lamb with garlic and parsley cream sauce, wonderfully plain fresh vegetables
and serious puddings. May the place long prosper. There need be no apologies
for the 'idiosyncratic selection' of wines to which the Smiths wish to draw the
customer's special attention when these include a Crozes-Hermitage from
Graillot and the Tinto Pesquera offered at prices well below those of most
places. Rhônes are wonderful, but so are the burgundies, while Alsace is
perhaps a little safe. House wine is from £11. CELLARMAN'S CHOICE: Jurançon
Sec, Dom. Castera 1991, £14; Toro, Tinto Pesquera 1987, £17.90.

CHEFS/PROPRIETORS: Dick and Kay Smith  OPEN: all week, D only; 7.30 to 8.30
CLOSED: 1 Nov to 12 May  MEALS: Set D £25 to £31  SERVICE: not inc, card slips closed
CARDS: Access, Visa  DETAILS: 26 seats. Private parties: 12 main room. Car park.
Children's helpings. No smoking during meals. Wheelchair access. No music
ACCOMMODATION: 12 rooms, 10 with bath/shower. Rooms for disabled. B&B £32 to £78.
Deposit: £25. Children welcome. Baby facilities. Pets welcome. TV. Phone. Doors close at
11.30. Confirm by 6

---

WINCHCOMBE Gloucestershire                                 map 2

## ▲ *Wesley House*                              | NEW ENTRY |

High Street, Winchcombe GL54 5LJ
CHELTENHAM (0242) 602366                               COOKING 1*
on B4632, Cheltenham to Broadway road                 COST £19–£37

Wesley did not live here, but he visited. In fact, the house, dating from 1435,
was going long before the evangelist and is an attractively half-timbered
Cotswold merchant's dwelling. Messrs Brown and Lewis have only had it for a
year or so, but they spared no effort to bring the decoration up to the mark and
have worked a miracle on the cooking. The form this takes is a mite too fussy to
let all the flavours out. A preoccupation with effect, not first principles, was
detected – 'the bread was lots of different shapes, but one taste'. The set-price

menu is good value and offers half a dozen choices that have included a chicken parfait wrapped in Parma ham with shredded vegetables, venison fillet with wild mushrooms and a port sauce (with flavours that were somewhat muddied), and a very good lemon tart with a lemon-flavoured cream and tangy preserved kumquats. There aré daily specials in addition to the regularly changing menu: a dish of langoustines with a saffron vinaigrette was particularly recommended for its quality. A light lunch menu is also available in the bar. The wine list is inexpensive and has a useful set of house recommendations, starting with a Navarra red at £8.95.

CHEF: Johnathan Lewis  PROPRIETORS: Matthew Brown and Jonathan Lewis  OPEN: Wed to Mon, exc Sun D; 12 to 3, 7 to 10  CLOSED: last 2 weeks Jan, first week Feb  MEALS: alc L (main courses £6 to £7). Set L £12.50, Set D £19.50 (2 courses) to £22.50  SERVICE: not inc  CARDS: Access, Amex, Visa  DETAILS: 60 seats. Private parties: 60 main room. Vegetarian meals. Children's helpings. No-smoking area. Wheelchair access. Music ACCOMMODATION: 6 rooms, all with bath/shower. B&B £39 to £60. Children welcome. Afternoon teas. TV. Phone. Doors close at midnight. Confirm by noon

---

**WINCHESTER Hampshire**                                              map 2

## *Hunters*                                          | NEW ENTRY |

5 Jewry Street, Winchester SO23 8RZ                        COOKING 2
WINCHESTER (0962) 860006                                   COST £17 –£39

'We are in restaurant row in Winchester, with no less than seven places competing for the lunch-time trade,' writes David Birmingham of his second branch, which opened in the county town after the initial success of his New Alresford place (see entry). The theme here responds to the spirit of the place to reproduce a bistro-in-a-shop effect: the décor is all maroon, black and white, and cream; tables are plain wood on cast-iron legs. The cooking has displayed a passion for putting things in pastry, or on pastry or nestling in baskets, and for laying one ingredient on a bed of another. When this has happened with something slight the result has been less than intended: thus a smoked salmon and crab mash in a pithiviers was simply not strong enough. When the materials are allowed to speak for themselves, as they do in the main courses, then the cooking shows an adept hand. Seared red tuna with fennel and potato, a tomato rosemary coulis and bits of bacon was very good indeed. A dish of lamb's fillet, kidney and sweetbreads on mashed potato with onion sauce and stir-fried greens has also elicited praise, 'though the onion sauce somehow got lost between the mattress of potato and the duvet of meat'. A need for clarity and piercing taste was felt at the pudding stage and was provided by a really proper lemon tart. Service can be abstracted, but the value of the experience is considerable. The wine list is shared with the New Alresford branch. House wines are £8.25.

---

*Restaurateurs justifiably resent no-shows. If you quote a credit card number when booking, you may be liable for the restaurant's lost profit margin if you don't turn up. Always phone to cancel.*

---

CHEF: Paul Revill   PROPRIETORS: David and Martin Birmingham   OPEN: Mon to Sat; 12 to
2.30, 6.30 to 10.30   MEALS: alc (main courses L £5 to £10, D £6 to £15)   SERVICE: not inc
(10% for 6 or more)   CARDS: Access, Amex, Diners, Visa   DETAILS: 62 seats. Private
parties: 40 main room, 20 private room. Vegetarian meals. Children's helpings. Smart dress
preferred. No cigars/pipes in dining-room. No-smoking area. Wheelchair access. Music.
Fax: (0962) 860006

---

## ▲ Wykeham Arms ⅙✳                                    NEW ENTRY

75 Kingsgate Street, Winchester, SO23 9PE                      COOKING 1
WINCHESTER (0962) 853834                                       COST £23–£32

The Wykeham Arms is 'very hard to find without knowledge of the old part of
Winchester' – the best advice is to set a course for the College and the pub is
just round the corner by Kingsgate Arch. This fine old inn dates from the
middle of the eighteenth century and it breathes antiquity. The atmosphere is
lively in the bar, more civilised and peaceful in the dining area, which is filled
wall-to-wall with paintings and a collection of hats. The cooking is generally
on target and daily-changing menus provide an assortment of up-market pub
dishes, along the lines of sauté lambs' kidneys in puff pastry, Elizabethan pork
casserole and noisettes of monkfish with braised red cabbage. Steaks are
Aberdeen Angus. Mushroom, red pepper and tarragon tart, and collop of
venison with a light timbale of celeriac and smoked bacon have been
highlights. Vegetables and salads are excellent accompaniments. Sweets range
from chocolate marquise to almond and hazelnut tart. Sandwiches and cheaper
snacks are available in the bar. Service is unfailingly helpful and well paced.
The modest list of around 30 wines offers plenty of decent drinking for around
£10, and most are available by the glass. House French is £8.25.

CHEFS: Vanessa Booth, Belinda Watson, Nicola Jacques and Helen Brooks   PROPRIETORS:
Graeme and Anne Jameson   OPEN: Mon to Sat; 12 to 2.30, 6.30 to 8.45   CLOSED: 24 Dec to
1 Jan   MEALS: alc (main courses £10 to £11.50). Bar snacks   SERVICE: not inc, card slips
closed   CARDS: Access, Amex, Visa   DETAILS: 75 seats. 3 tables outside. Private parties:
8 main room. Car park. Vegetarian meals. No children under 14. No smoking in 3 dining-
rooms. Wheelchair access (1 step). No music   ACCOMMODATION: 7 rooms, all with bath/
shower. B&B £62.50 to £72.50. No children under 14. Pets welcome. Afternoon teas. Sauna.
TV. Phone. Doors close at midnight. Fax: (0962) 854411 (*The Which? Hotel Guide*)

---

**WINDERMERE  Cumbria**                                        map 7

## ▲ Gilpin Lodge ♈ ⅙✳

Crook Road, Windermere LA23 3NE                               COOKING 2
WINDERMERE (053 94) 88818                                     COST £17–£41

Set in 20 acres of gardens and woodland a couple of miles from Lake
Windermere, this turn-of-the-century lodge continues to thrive. A new wing
has recently been added, otherwise nothing changes. Christine Cunliffe's
cooking is modern French and she draws heavily on local produce. The
substantial five-course dinner menu might take in original creations such as
filo pastry tulip of queen scallops, walnuts and goats' cheese served on an
apple, Sauternes and orange coulis, or baked guinea-fowl in an ale sauce with

sage dumplings and smoked bacon spätzli, as well as classical dishes such as warm mousseline of sole with beurre blanc or roast rack of lamb in a herb crust with tarragon jus. A finely executed Sunday lunch yielded an attractive terrine of ham and chicken, a cutlet of salmon with saffron, chive and asparagus sauce, thick slices of roast sirloin, and strawberry bavarois ('rather cloying') filled with strawberry Romanoff on an excellent raspberry coulis, all rounded off with cafetière coffee and plenty of petits fours. During the rest of the week, more simple lunch dishes are served in the lounge. Four more than decent dessert wines offered by the glass and the suave provençal Dom. de Trevallon that features as a house wine are cause for encouragement. The remaining list displays intelligent and wide range, with a merciful absence of unnecessary display. Prices are very fair, and wine service is reported as correct. There are good burgundies and Rhônes, and serious effort is made to provide choice in half-bottles. House wines are from £9.95. CELLARMAN'S CHOICE: Pouilly Fumé, 'Les Loges' 1990, Guyot, £18.35; Maranges, Premier Cru Clos des Loyères 1990, Girardin, £24.

---

CHEFS: Christine Cunliffe and Christopher Davies  PROPRIETORS: John and Christine Cunliffe  OPEN: all week; 12 to 2, 7 to 8.45  MEALS: alc light L (main courses £4.50 to £6.50). Set Sun L £12.75, Set D £24  SERVICE: not inc  CARDS: Access, Amex, Diners, Visa  DETAILS: 45 seats. 4 tables outside. Private parties: 22 main room, 12 and 16 private rooms. Car park. Vegetarian meals. Children's helpings Sun L. No children under 9, exc Sun L. Smart dress preferred. No smoking in dining-room. Wheelchair access (1 step). No music  ACCOMMODATION: 9 rooms, all with bath/shower. B&B £40 to £110. No children under 9. Afternoon teas. Garden. TV. Phone. Doors close at midnight. Fax: (053 94) 88058

---

## ▲ Miller Howe  ▼ 🍴

Rayrigg Road, Windermere LA23 1EY
WINDERMERE (053 94) 42536
on A592, between Windermere and Bowness

COOKING 3
COST £43–£52

As the years pass, and John Tovey's creation has attained its majority, Miller Howe becomes more of a problem to many readers. The lakeside house, set amid crowding fells and hills, has run on similar lines since its inception, and newcomers to the experience find it out of step with their version of reality. Even the decoration may be condemned as 'sixties', the music as 'package airline departure lounge' stuff, and the style of cooking a long way from accepted norms. To others, however, consistency is a virtue, and if they have followed John Tovey from his first venture at the Windermere Hydro, they still like what he does. His recipe is group theatre: gather for drinks, canapés and music, progress to dinner, be served in a Mexican wave of dishes rolling out of the kitchen to dimmed lights and circumstance, pay up and leave. The food served has not changed a lot either: it still enjoys complexity of tastes, flavours and arrangement; it still rejoices in putting sweet next to sour; it still offers no choice to the five-course meal until desserts; it still puts five or so vegetables round the central mound of meat and sauce. If a dish such as breast of chicken with corn and peanut butter served on beetroot orange purée plus sweetcorn with honey, glazed carrots with Pernod, swede with dill, leeks in white wine, celeriac purée with pine-kernels, and minted new potatoes is your style, then this place is for you. If complexity means mess and turgid flavours, then it is not. Witnesses differ as to the success of the venture this year, whatever their taste. Some suggest that supervision is lacking so that standards go up and down; others that the excessively thick and glazed sauces with the main dish are always over the top; then some have not found the service as courtly as it might be, with too much of the production line to it; and others find the chef's tour embarrassing. There have been rather too many criticisms this year to make such points merely the product of one-night hiccups, though the drift of taste may account for many people's essential point of view. The abbreviated and much-improved style of the wine list is retained. It is, a little cheekily, all New World and the result of the sterling tasting work of Mr Tovey and his staff. New World does not, be warned, mean low prices, although the wines by the glass – two each evening – assist economy. House wine is £12.

CHEFS: Ian Dutton and Chris Blaydes PROPRIETOR: John J. Tovey OPEN: all week, D only; 8.30 CLOSED: Dec to Mar MEALS: Set D £32 SERVICE: 12.5%, card slips closed CARDS: Access, Amex, Diners, Visa DETAILS: 70 seats. Private parties: 40 main room. Car park. Vegetarian meals. No children under 12. Smart dress preferred. No smoking in dining-room. Wheelchair access (also WC). Music. Air-conditioned ACCOMMODATION: 13 rooms, all with bath/shower. B&B £70 to £230. No children under 12. Pets welcome (not in public rooms). Afternoon teas. Garden. TV. Phone. Doors close at 11. Confirm by 6. Fax: (053 94) 45664 (*The Which? Hotel Guide*)

## Miller Howe Café ⁑✳ £

Lakeland Plastics Ltd, Alexandra Buildings,
Station Precinct, Windermere LA23 1BQ      COOKING 1
WINDERMERE (053 94) 46732      COST £14–£21

By 12.30pm a long queue is to be expected. Once a seat is available, you order your food at the counter, wait for it to arrive, and thereafter get waitress service for puddings and coffee. 'We had delicious beef and tomato soup, jacket potatoes with two fillings, and toothsome sticky toffee pudding with butterscotch sauce,' reported one family that makes a point of visiting out of season, when the queues are shorter. A café in a plastics factory may sound unlikely, but John Tovey's experiment has many supporters. The food – for example, a meal of leek and potato soup, bobotie, then crème de menthe mousse – will sustain and appeal for value, but it, like the service, can be seriously affected by popularity and the crowds. We have had many comments about the brusque service and chaotic organisation of the operation this year. When these are not redeemed by decent food, which sometimes happens, the sin is the greater. House wine is £7.50.

CHEFS: Ian Dutton and Patrick Dacre PROPRIETORS: Ian and Annette Dutton, and John J. Tovey OPEN: all week; 9am to 5pm (10am to 4pm Sun) MEALS: alc (main courses £5 to £6.50) SERVICE: not inc, card slips closed CARDS: Access, Diners, Visa DETAILS: 45 seats. 6 tables outside. Private parties: 50 main room, 50 private room. Car park. Vegetarian meals. Children's helpings. No smoking. Wheelchair access (also WC). No music. Air-conditioned

*See the back of the* Guide *for an index of restaurants listed.*

## Roger's

4 High Street, Windermere LA23 1AF
WINDERMERE (053 94) 44954

COOKING 2*
COST £21–£42

Number four is at the top of the town near the railway station; it's a small house
that contains two small dining-rooms and a Lilliputian bar. The intense
decoration makes the space appear even smaller and Saturday nights can have
that feeling of 'all aboard the coach, please', or 'move along there'; this reaction
is not helped by deafening (at first) music in the upstairs room. There is a
steady pattern to the cooking: an enjoyment of good materials, the manufacture
of light yet interesting sauces, an acceptance of glorious classics such as
hollandaise, and usually a good finish with desserts that combine intensity
(damson sorbet), serious sweetness (hazelnut meringue with bananas, cream
and butterscotch sauce), and some good cooking (pancakes, baked puddings).
While discretion can produce satisfactory understatement in a simple salad of
seared scallops (often good here), or manipulation of textures to make
something bland seem interesting (a parsnip mousse with pine-kernels and a
hollandaise), there can also be misfires in technical performance and in
composition, with too many elements to a dish that have little sense of
togetherness. First and last courses may be better than the centrepiece. The
wine list is built on solid foundations with good French growers and classic
names, and a helpfully cheaper superstructure from the New World, Latin
America, South Africa and Eastern Europe. House wines are £9.95 a litre.

CHEF: Roger Pergl-Wilson   PROPRIETORS: Roger and Alena Pergl-Wilson   OPEN: Mon to
Sat (Sun bank hols), D only; 7 to 9.30 (10 Sat)   CLOSED: Christmas   MEALS: alc (main
courses £7.50 to £11.50). Set D £14.50   SERVICE: not inc, card slips closed   CARDS: Access,
Amex, Diners, Visa   DETAILS: 44 seats. Private parties: 26 main room, 26 private room.
Vegetarian meals. Children's helpings. Smart dress preferred. Wheelchair access. Music

---

**WINKLEIGH Devon**                                                    map 1

## ▲ London House ❧

**NEW ENTRY**

Winkleigh EX19 8HQ
WINKLEIGH (0837) 83202

COOKING 1
COST £7–£25

That there should be two characterful eating-houses in this Devon village is a
quirk of fate for which the traveller should be grateful. London House is more
nearly on the square and is run by the Jamesons, old hands at the game from
East Anglian days, but Devonians by adoption. London House, doubtless once
a shop – the window survives – has been converted sympathetically and is
green outside and in. Pleasing touches in the china and cutlery, country-style
furnishings and an overall warmth (both spirit and reality) make it happily
relaxed and natural, though Peter Jameson's manner imparts a little avuncular
formality. The menu may take a theme, for instance Normandy cooking, and
offer a couple of alternatives in the first two courses (garlic sausage in brioche
or fruits de mer to begin, lamb with flageolet beans or pork with apples for
seconds), then a sequence of salad, cheese and fruit tarts to end. The price is
all-in, aperitif too. One visitor extolled the cooking as 'Edwardian English
haute cuisine' (he had game pie); another recommended English puddings;

a third applauded the natural simplicity. There is enthusiasm and a certain art, which is not overplayed. The wine list may be short, but Peter Jameson is pretty keen on it and does not overcharge. House wines are £5, which may be some indication of that.

CHEF: Barbara Jameson  PROPRIETORS: Barbara and Peter Jameson  OPEN: all week, exc Sun D; 12 to 2, 7 to late  CLOSED: last 2 weeks Jan  MEALS: Set L £7, Set Sun L £10, Set D £18  SERVICE: net prices, card slips closed  CARDS: Access, Visa  DETAILS: 16 seats. 2 tables outside. Private parties: 16 main room. Vegetarian meals with prior notice. Children's helpings. Smart dress preferred. No smoking in dining-room. Wheelchair access (1 step). Music  ACCOMMODATION: 2 rooms, both with bath/shower. B&B £35 to £70. No children under 12

## Pophams 🍴✸ £

| Castle Street, Winkleigh EX19 8HQ | COOKING 2* |
|---|---|
| WINKLEIGH (0837) 83767 | COST £11–£22 |

Pophams has a very English charm. Imagine a densely built Devon village, once a town, with two castles, a fine church, a straggling central square and, at one extreme end, a small delicatessen or cooked-food shop that has, come lunch-time, two completely dressed tables that seat eight or ten people. Behind the shop counter (and in truth the shop has taken second place to the restaurant) Melvyn Popham practises his cookery in a kitchen open to all. At the front, Dennis Hawkes tends to every wish. The menu is short; the food has more ambitions than the scale of the place warrants. Good soups, excellent chicken-liver terrine, and a fair stab at fish terrine with proper hollandaise are some of the first courses. Main dishes of good repute are country bulk-builders such as the steak and kidney or the fish pie, but a more delicate chicken breast with herbs and goats' cheese has also pleased, and a duck breast marinated with ginger, soy, sherry vinegar and orange was impressive for its texture and deep flavour. Vegetables are not ignored, nor is the sweet extravaganza for the finale. Hold back some space for sticky toffee pudding, home-made ice-creams or rum nicky. This is the sort of place you like or loathe, and most people love it. It is unlicensed; there is no corkage.

CHEF: Melvyn Popham  PROPRIETORS: Melvyn Popham and Dennis Hawkes  OPEN: Mon to Sat, L only; 11.30 to 3  CLOSED: Feb  MEALS: alc (main courses £5 to £9). Unlicensed, but bring your own: no corkage  SERVICE: not inc, card slips closed  CARDS: Access, Visa  DETAILS: 10 seats. Private parties: 10 main room. Vegetarian meals. No children under 14. Smart dress preferred. No smoking in dining-room. Music. Air-conditioned

---

| WINTERINGHAM Humberside | map 6 |
|---|---|

## ▲ Winteringham Fields 🍷 🍴✸

| Winteringham DN15 9PF | COOKING 4 |
|---|---|
| SCUNTHORPE (0724) 733096 | COST £25–£63 |

The Schwabs have had an eventful year. Annie Schwab got sick and it seemed as if the couple would have to sell up. She got better and they have remained. In the interim they had a visit from Mark Wilkinson (a young chef whose absence from the Wirral was regretted very much last year) who was nicely mentioned on the menu during his stay, but who has now left for Canada. So, although the roller-coaster of survival has had its ups and downs, all is back on course. Everyone should try and come here. You may pass through purgatory en route ('It looked as if the Flixborough disaster had happened only yesterday'), but the goal is a very old house 'with surprising modern additions', where Victoriana of the sort that leaves no naked chair-legs and puts antimacassars here, there and everywhere seems to rule. The bedrooms, though, are less emphatic and considered comfortable and restful. Unlikely though the location may be, the Schwabs run a full-scale restaurant producing food of the highest order and invention. A seasonal menu is given daily injections of change from a short set meal, a varying menu surprise and regular 'specialities'. Flavours are intense, techniques are assured and combinations excite. A 'cappuccino' of fennel and clams with a glazing of saffron is a frothy start, but consider too John Dory with beetroot and capers and wild rice, or hot mousse of foie gras with elderflower sauce and black truffle. Being Swiss and working in Britain, gives the Schwabs licence to experiment with sweet flavours joined to savoury, and Germain Schwab manages to give them sufficient presence and balance. The sweet and sour approach is often tempered come the main course so that while a meal contained foie gras with a blackcurrant sauce, the main dish was pheasant with a tarragon mousse and vermouth sauce. Again, he is not afraid to revitalise old fashions with things like mousses and stuffings, but succeeds in giving them taste-attack so that they count for more than just elaboration. Desserts are good, but perhaps because of the excitement of what came before they may seem not as spectacular. However, there are good mentions of a fine apple tart with a praline custard, a cristalline of apples with green apple sorbet in a mint syrup and a lemon ice-cream as well, and a really fine deep-flavoured hot chocolate soufflé. Service is as proper as the cooking, and Annie Schwab humanises the whole operation. House wine is £10.50.

CHEF: Germain Schwab   PROPRIETORS: Annie and Germain Schwab   OPEN: Mon to Sat, exc L Mon and Sat; 12 to 1.15, 7.15 to 9.15   CLOSED: 2 weeks from 24 Dec, first week Aug   MEALS: alc (main courses £17 to £18.50). Set L £14.75, Set D £29 to £39   SERVICE: not inc, card slips closed   CARDS: Access, Visa   DETAILS: 38 seats. 2 tables outside. Private parties: 8 main room, 10 private room. Car park. Children's helpings L. Smart dress preferred. No smoking in dining-room. Wheelchair access (2 steps). Music   ACCOMMODATION: 7 rooms, all with bath/shower. Rooms for disabled. B&B £60 to £90 No children under 8. TV. Phone. Doors close at midnight. Confirm by 6. Fax: (0724) 733898 (*The Which? Hotel Guide*)

---

*All details are as accurate as possible at the time of going to press, but chefs and owners often change, and it is wise to check by telephone before making a special journey. Many readers have been disappointed when set-price bargain meals are no longer available. Ask when booking.*

*The 1995 Guide will be published before Christmas 1994. Reports on meals are most welcome at any time of the year, but are extremely valuable in the spring. Send them to* The Good Food Guide, *FREEPOST, 2 Marylebone Road, London NW1 1YN. No stamp is needed if posted in the UK.*

## ▲ Old Vicarage 🍷 ⁵⚔

Witherslack LA11 6RS
WITHERSLACK (053 95) 52381
off A590, take first left in village
to church and continue for ¾m

COOKING 3
COST £21–£40

This Victorian vicarage houses two pairs of incumbents: there are four partners who split the days between them. The hotel has been characterised as 'unpretentious', for which read 'comfort without too much fuss' and, just occasionally, ham-fisted service. An amalgam of Victoriana and Liberty prints, spacious grounds and peaceful location often proves seductive, though the public sitting-rooms could have been more comfortable for one couple. The cooking works to a certain routine. The menu normally has a single centrepiece – usually roast – and a pair of choices to either side (one of these is almost invariably a soup); after the pudding, a plate of British cheeses, lovingly resourced and described, is available at a £3 supplement (as are a second pudding and additional starter). Few voices are ever heard against this circumscription. Flavours may often be complex and true: 'A timbale of vermicelli with rosemary was held together by the milkiness of young Lancashire cheese, offset but not overcome by a freshly pungent salsa verde,' remarked one diner of a vegetarian dinner cooked during the summer. Dessert normally takes in a British hot tart or pudding: 'The gooseberry and apple amaretti-crisp pudding tasted recognisably of both fruits,' and there was added excitement from the bitter almond flavour in the topping. If damsons figure, they come from the hotel's own tree. The style of cooking is connected to the 'Lakeland School', exemplified in a dinner of smoked haddock, Lancashire cheese and fennel pancakes or apple, carrot and coriander soup with sweet brown bread, followed by fillet of beef with bordelaise and tarragon sauces and a raft of vegetables that included new potatoes, parsnips, stir-fried cabbage, and carrot and swede purée, and finishing with a marquise au chocolat, before the cheese and coffee with Kendal mint cake. The flavours risk being muddied by too many ingredients or insensitive handling, but this criticism is not often made. Some good beers at the end of the wine list deserve attention, as do the wines by the glass at the front. Taking in mature classics as well as carefully chosen antipodeans, the main list puts great stress, typographically, on the country of origin. For the customer this is perhaps less than helpful. Increasingly it is the style of wine that is of interest, and geographical differentiation is becoming less significant. Prices here are fair, with many bottles costing around £12. CELLARMAN'S CHOICE: St Véran, Dom. des Deux Roches, Vieilles Vignes 1990, £20; Pomerol, Clos Toulifant 1985, £23.50.

CHEFS/PROPRIETORS: Roger and Jill Burrington-Brown, Irene and Stanley Reeve OPEN: all week, D only, and Sun L; 12.30 for 1, 7.30 for 8 MEALS: Set Sun L £15, Set D £19.50 SERVICE: not inc, card slips closed CARDS: Access, Visa DETAILS: 35 seats. Private parties: 18 main room, 12 private room. Car park. Vegetarian meals with prior notice. Children's helpings on request. No smoking in dining-room. Wheelchair access (3 steps). Music ACCOMMODATION: 15 rooms, all with bath/shower. Rooms for disabled. B&B £59 to £138. Pets welcome (not in bedrooms). Afternoon teas. Garden. Tennis. TV. Phone. Doors close at 11.30. Confirm by 6. Fax: (053 95) 52373 (*The Which? Hotel Guide*)

**WOBURN Bedfordshire**                                                    map 3

## *Paris House*

Woburn Park, Woburn MK17 9QP
WOBURN (0525) 290692                                          COOKING 3
on A4012, 1¾m E of Woburn in Abbey grounds            COST £29–£57

Père David's deer graze in the grounds of Woburn Park, which adds to the
novelty of embarking on a trip to this black and white timbered house. The
building was erected in 1878 for the Paris Exhibition, then dismantled,
brought piece by piece to England and reconstructed on the Duke of Bedford's
estate. Peter Chandler celebrated 10 years in residence in 1993 and continues
to deliver some of the best food in the area. The *carte* has many fixtures,
including fisherman's soup, salmon in champagne sauce, and rib of beef
forestière. Most reporters single out the quality of the ingredients and fine
saucing as high points: escalope of salmon with sorrel and crisp breast of duck
with green peppercorns are examples. Other diners have endorsed the 'menu
gastronomique', a five-course affair that might run as follows: salad of smoked
salmon and artichokes, then medallions of monkfish in a rich, intense sauce
armoricaine ('which a weaker fish would not stand up to'), an 'exact'
elderflower sorbet before roast guinea-fowl with a heavily reduced tarragon
sauce and, to finish, hot fruit soufflés that have remained a star attraction since
the restaurant opened. ('How can you get so much raspberry flavour into such a
small pot?' mused one reporter.) There is little doubt that Peter Chandler can
cook to a high level, but the place has drawn some criticism. Prices and
questionable value for money are cited, the food is sometimes reckoned to be
'dull', and service comes in for some abrasive comments: 'rubbish', 'rather
brusque' and 'a good maître d' would work wonders' are examples. 'Extensive
and expensive' is one way of summing up the wine list, which has precious
little below £20. House wine is £10.

CHEF/PROPRIETOR: Peter Chandler   OPEN: Tue to Sun, exc Sun D; 12 to 2, 7 to 9.30
CLOSED: Feb   MEALS: Set L £21.50, Set D £32 to £38   SERVICE: not inc, card slips closed
CARDS: Access, Amex, Diners, Visa   DETAILS: 40 seats. 6 tables outside. Private parties: 40
main room, 16 private room. Car park. Vegetarian meals. Children's helpings on request.
Smart dress preferred. Wheelchair access (3 steps; also WC). No music. Fax: (0525) 290471

---

**WOODSTOCK Oxfordshire**                                                map 2

## ▲ *Feathers Hotel*

Market Street, Woodstock OX20 1SX                            COOKING 2*
WOODSTOCK (0993) 812291                                      COST £29–£58

Many people feel that this hotel in the centre of Woodstock has pitched itself
exactly: 'a maze of small rooms, corridors and stairs; every country hotel should
be like this' was one comment. 'Decent pictures and furniture; a welcome like
old friends' was another. The cooking here is expressive, more robust and
creative than much of what is on offer in England's country-house hotels.
'Essence' of Cornish mussels singed with cumin and coriander may sound
unlikely, but it tastes fine. Oak-smoked wild boar with balsamic vinegar and

walnut oil (also often served with ewes' milk cheese) is popular and, though oily, often satisfactory. Fillet of beef with deep-fried potatoes may be difficult to eat out of the large soup bowls that pass for meat plates, and the vegetables may be scanty and greasy, but the meat is good. This year many people have complained of the lack of proper vegetables. While lamb stuffed with apricots, flavoured with mint and served with ratatouille and new potatoes in their skins may be utterly unseasonal in November, the tastes were well handled and the meat was of generosity and quality. Other aspects of the hotel's way of doing business, however, meet with less approval, such as a 'voluntary' gratuity of 15 per cent noted on the menu, which becomes 'suggested' when the bill arrives. Bar charges and wine prices are thought to be high; so is the extra cost of two bowls of cereal – £5.90 plus service. Service can be perfect, but it can also be pressing: 'We were offered bread four times during our first course, twice by the same waitress.' The selection of house wines starts at £9, and rapidly escalates.

CHEF: David Lewis  PROPRIETORS: Andrew Leeman, Simon Lowe and Howard Malin
OPEN: all week; 12.30 to 2.30, 7.30 to 9.30  MEALS: alc (main courses £12 to £18). Set L £14.50 (2 courses) to £17.50, Set Sun L £19.50, Set D £19.50 to £23.50  SERVICE: 15%, card slips closed  CARDS: Access, Amex, Diners, Visa  DETAILS: 60 seats. 14 tables outside. Private parties: 60 main room, 25 private room. Vegetarian meals with prior notice. Children's helpings. Music. Air-conditioned  ACCOMMODATION: 17 rooms, all with bath/shower. B&B £75 to £170. Children welcome. Baby facilities. Dogs by arrangement. Afternoon teas. Garden. TV. Phone. Doors close at 11. Fax: (0993) 813158 (*The Which? Hotel Guide*)

---

**WOOLTON HILL Hampshire**                                              map 2

## ▲ *Hollington House Hotel* ♈              | NEW ENTRY |

Church Road, Woolton Hill RG15 9XR
HIGHCLERE (0635) 255100                                    COOKING 3
off A434, 3m S of Newbury                                  COST £30–£50

This is a big house (and gardens) in the southern Newbury hinterland. Though planning permission has finally been granted for a roadsign, the best advice if you want to avoid hours of Berkshire lanes is to follow the trail to the Hollington Herb Garden (no relation). People speak of impressive bedrooms, done up with style. Those who do not get as far as the upstairs report some pretty surprising paintings on the walls that not everyone will agree with, and an interior of muted but deep British comfort. The Guys are British-born but spent their working life in Victoria, Australia, where their Burnham Beeches Hotel – very much along the lines of a European country-house show – was a great success. On return to the homeland, idleness was not an option, so the Guys have built up this hotel from scratch. Their first months were greatly helped by the cooking of Richard Lovett, an Australian who had worked at Burnham Beeches. He has now departed, leaving the stoves to his British deputy, Stephen Astley. The menu is not distinguished by any outward mark of originality – very much the modern country-house norm – but it works much better in the eating and in the small touches such as the nibbles with the drinks, the baking and the home production of almost every element. The cooking is matched by a wine list of perfectly acceptable bottles from France and beyond, and a scintillating set of mature Australian reds from Penfolds, Trennert, Redgum and Seaview among others. Prices are not high. House wines are French and cost £11.50 and £12.50.

CHEF: Stephen Astley  PROPRIETORS: John and Penny Guy  OPEN: all week; 12.30 to 2.30, 7 to 9.30  MEALS: alc (main courses £11.50 to £14.50). Set L £13.50 (2 courses) to £19.50, Set D £18.50 (2 courses) to £25  SERVICE: not inc  CARDS: Access, Amex, Visa  DETAILS: 48 seats. 8 tables outside. Private parties: 48 main room, 46 private room. Car park. Vegetarian meals. Children's helpings. Smart dress preferred. No cigars/pipes in dining-room. Wheelchair access (also WC). Music  ACCOMMODATION: 20 rooms, all with bath/shower. Rooms for disabled. Lift. B&B £80 to £250. Children welcome. Baby facilities. Afternoon teas. Garden. Swimming-pool. Tennis. TV. Phone. Doors close at midnight. Confirm by 6. Fax: (0635) 255075 (*The Which? Hotel Guide*)

---

**WORCESTER** Hereford & Worcester                                    map 2

## *Brown's*

The Old Cornmill, 24 Quay Street,
Worcester WR1 2JJ                                         COOKING 2
WORCESTER (0905) 26263                                     COST £20–£42

The Tansleys' spacious, colourful warehouse conversion by the river is a much-loved building. The food is in keeping with the modernity of the place – witness chargrilled Mediterranean vegetables with caponata dressing, roast baby guinea-fowl with sun-dried tomatoes and mushrooms and duck with a confit of its legs and lentils. Most reporters continue to endorse the fixed-price three-course lunch: a party of four worked their way enthusiastically through much of the repertoire and spoke favourably of pigeon breast and chicken liver salad, chargrilled tuna with tomatoes and fennel, roast grouse, juicy langoustine and bacon kebabs with curry mayonnaise and plum ice-cream with plum sauce. Prices double in the evening, when the menu might also feature Moroccan lamb with couscous and lambs' kidneys provençale. The cheeseboard is extensive, although it seems to be a mixed bag, embracing some prosaic offerings and more interesting samples from England and France. The reasonably priced wine list has a strong Gallic presence, although it also ventures into the New World. Half-bottles are much in evidence. House wine is £9.50.

CHEF: W.R. Tansley  PROPRIETORS: W.R. and P.M. Tansley  OPEN: all week, exc Sat L and Sun D; 12.30 to 1.45, 7.30 to 9.45  CLOSED: Christmas week, bank hol Mons  MEALS: Set L £15, Set D £30  SERVICE: net prices, card slips closed  CARDS: Access, Amex, Diners, Visa  DETAILS: 100 seats. Private parties: 120 main room. Vegetarian meals. No children under 10. Smart dress preferred. Wheelchair access (also WC). Music (New Year's Eve and private parties only)

---

*Prices quoted in the* Guide *are based on information supplied by restaurateurs. The prices quoted at the top of each entry represent a range, from the lowest meal price to the highest; the latter is inflated by 20 per cent to take account of likely price rises during the year of the* Guide.

---

## Il Pescatore

34 Sidbury, Worcester WR1 2HZ          COOKING 1
WORCESTER (0905) 21444          COST £16–£43

An Italian restaurant in a listed, timber-framed building sounds quite novel, and a regular full house testifies to the popularity of Giuliano Ponzi's friendly establishment near the cathedral. Inside is a cosy dining-room with exposed beams and bare brickwork. Fresh fish and home-made pasta are the mainstays of a menu that encompasses cannelloni, salmon in cucumber sauce, saltimbocca and steak pizzaiola. Reporters have also spoken favourably of more enterprising daily specials: squid with ginger and spring onion, pasta parcels filled with spinach and ricotta in basil butter, seafood ragoût and breast of mallard in wine sauce with apple purée have all been first-rate. Vegetables are cooked crisp, and sweets include a fine version of crème brûlée. Ingredients are fresh, portions are generous and the bill is likely to be realistic. The wine list has around 50 fair-priced Italian bottles. House wine is £7.25.

CHEF: Kevin Capper   PROPRIETOR: Giuliano Ponzi   OPEN: Mon to Sat, exc Mon L; 12 to 2, 6 to 10   CLOSED: first 2 weeks Aug   MEALS: alc (main courses £6 to £14). Set L £9.50 to £11.50, Set D £14.50 to £16.50   SERVICE: not inc   CARDS: Access, Visa   DETAILS: 40 seats. Private parties: 40 main room. Vegetarian meals. Children welcome. Smart dress preferred. No-smoking area. Wheelchair access (1 step). Music. Fax: (0905) 21444

---

**WORFIELD Shropshire**          map 5

## ▲ Old Vicarage Hotel ⁵✳      NEW ENTRY

Worfield WV15 5JZ
WORFIELD (074 64) 497          COOKING 1
1m N of A454, 3m E of Bridgnorth          COST £18–£41

The rather stark red-brick house on the edge of the village ('left past the church, sharp right at the top of the hill') is anything but bare inside: 'Every available inch of the dining-room walls was covered with pictures (whose merit we debated).' The place is full of music too (with different tapes for different spaces) which set one reporter's teeth on edge. Peter Iles converted his own residence in an '80s career change, and since then has carried the hotel into the farthest corners of the coach-house to give extra accommodation. John Williams carries the kitchen, offering a menu with many resonances of the country-house revolution in train at about the time the hotel was converted – in arrangement and decoration, if not materials and flavours. These latter can sometimes be less emphatic than the description of the dish would warrant: this is cuisine of the eye, not of the tongue. Hence a sausage of turbot and basil with spinach and a wash of light cream sauce wobbled to perfection but masked its original materials by artfulness. Glazed suprême of Loomswood duckling with a light aubergine gâteau and essence of rosemary and sun-dried tomatoes had more ethereal wobble in the gâteau (very delicate), and a much bolder sauce which cut through most of the other tastes on the plate. Sausages, timbales, gâteaux and soufflés are very much on the agenda. Vegetables are not always well judged. British cheeses, however, are much appreciated. There is evidence of enthusiasm and knowledge in the wine department. Good merchants support the list with a fine range of Rhônes, mature Spanish and intelligent range of clarets and burgundies. Prices are fair, starting at about £8.

CHEF: John Williams   PROPRIETORS: Peter and Christine Iles   OPEN: all week, exc Sat L; 12 to 2, 7 to 9   MEALS: Set L £16.50, Set Sun L £11.50, Set D £19.50 to £27.50   CARDS: Access, Amex, Diners, Visa   SERVICE: not inc   DETAILS: 50 seats. Private parties: 30 main room, 14 private room. Car park. Vegetarian meals. Children's helpings. No children under 8 D. Smart dress preferred. No smoking in dining-rooms. Wheelchair access (2 steps; also WC). Music   ACCOMMODATION: 14 rooms, all with bath/shower. Rooms for disabled. B&B £63.50 to £100. Deposit: £40. Children welcome. Baby facilities. Pets welcome. Garden. TV. Phone. Doors close at 11. Fax: (074 64) 552 (*The Which? Hotel Guide*)

---

**WRIGHTINGTON Lancashire**                                             map 5

## *High Moor* ✱

High Moor Lane, Wrightington WN6 9QA
APPLEY BRIDGE (0257) 252364
off A5209, between M6 junction 27 and
Parbold, take Robin Hood Lane at crossroads                    COOKING 2
W of Wrightington Hospital, then next left                      COST £19–£46

It stands only three minutes' drive from the M6, but reporters warn that this restaurant is tricky to locate. The converted seventeenth-century building is high up on the moors, with views all around. Inside, the past has been preserved intact: low ceilings, original beams, a roaring fire in winter. Stephen Sloan offers a flamboyant *carte* focusing on elaborately described dishes with multinational influences tossed into the culinary melting pot: home-made cannelloni of Tay salmon, crab and Japanese ginger is served with a basil and chive fromage frais; fillet of beef comes with buttered haggis and pesto-flavoured noodles; breast of corn-fed chicken is accompanied by Indonesian spiced sauce and quince chutney. Most reporters, however, tend to settle for the more affordable table d'hôte, which has produced many favourable comments. 'Beautiful tasting' wild mushroom soup and excellent home-made ice-creams have been singled out. There is no doubt that the cooking is sound, although some dishes have lacked zing: an average warm salad of chicken livers, 'relatively tasteless' salmon with beurre blanc, 'slimy' dauphinois. New World wines and serious clarets dominate the 100-strong list. House wines are from £8.90.

CHEF: Stephen Sloan   PROPRIETOR: John Nelson   OPEN: Tue to Sat, D only, and Sun L; 12 to 2, 7 to 10   MEALS: alc (main courses £13 to £16). Set Sun L £12.95, Set D £15.95 SERVICE: 10%, card slips closed   CARDS: Access, Amex, Diners, Visa   DETAILS: 90 seats. Private parties: 75 main room, 18 private room. Car park. Vegetarian meals. Children's helpings. Smart dress preferred. No smoking in dining-room. Wheelchair access (also WC). Music. Air-conditioned. Fax: (0257) 255210

---

*All details are as accurate as possible at the time of going to press, but chefs and owners often change, and it is wise to check by telephone before making a special journey. Many readers have been disappointed when set-price bargain meals are no longer available. Ask when booking.*

## ▲ *Wife of Bath*

4 Upper Bridge Street, Wye TN25 5AW
WYE (0233) 812540 and 812232
just off A28, Ashford to Canterbury road

COOKING 1
COST £20–£43

This former doctor's residence has been a restaurant for 30 years and visitors still take it to their hearts. As we went to press, John Morgan had just converted the stables behind the building into two bedrooms for travellers looking for 'a stopping-off place near Dover and the Channel Tunnel'. Menus are changed every two weeks and the kitchen makes creditable use of local produce: game from the Brabourne estate, salads from Appledore, asparagus and soft fruit from Wye farmers. At lunch-time, the menu is a short *carte* with dishes such as rabbit casserole with fennel and mustard and roast rack of lamb with ratatouille. In the evening a more elaborate fixed-price menu is the order of the day: mousse of scallops with cucumber and saffron butter sauce, duckling with green chartreuse or pan-fried fillet steak with parsley and chive jus. Vegetables are good and fresh. Well-reported sweets have included poached pear on butterscotch sauce, meringues with strawberries and syllabub. The sensible wine list has plenty of halves and the bin-ends are worth exploring. House wine is £8.95.

CHEF: Robert Hymers   PROPRIETOR: John Morgan   OPEN: Tue to Sat; 12 to 2.30, 7.30 to 10.30   CLOSED: 2 weeks early Sept   MEALS: alc (main courses £9 to £14). Set L £11.50, Set D £19.75   SERVICE: not inc   CARDS: Access, Visa   DETAILS: 50 seats. Private parties: 55 main room, 20 private room. Car park. Vegetarian meals. Children's helpings. Smart dress preferred. Wheelchair access. No music   ACCOMMODATION: 2 rooms, both with bath/shower. Rooms for disabled. B&B £30 to £45. Garden. TV

---

## ▲ *Laburnum House*

Wylam NE41 8AJ
WYLAM (0661) 852185

COOKING 1
COST £32–£44

Laburnum House has plenty going for it: a delightful setting in a village by the River Tyne, reasonably priced accommodation and reliable cooking. The house (a converted shop) is caringly run. The short blackboard menu does not go in for gastronomic fireworks, but it does offer a good variety of dishes such as artichoke hearts provençale, sweet-and-sour king prawns, guinea-fowl breasts with Dijon mustard, grilled lemon sole with lime butter, and roast loin of lamb with rosemary and lavender jelly. The concise wine list has around 20 fairly priced bins from around the world. House wine from Boisset is £9.

CHEF: Kenneth Elliott   PROPRIETORS: Rowan Mahon and Kenneth Elliott   OPEN: Mon to Sat, D only; 6.30 to 10   CLOSED: 26 Dec, 1 Jan   MEALS: alc (main courses £14 to £15.50)   SERVICE: not inc   CARDS: Access, Amex, Visa   DETAILS: 46 seats. Private parties: 30 main room. Vegetarian meals with prior notice. Children welcome. Smart dress preferred. Wheelchair access (2 steps). Music   ACCOMMODATION: 4 double rooms, all with bath/shower. B&B £40 to £50. Children welcome. Baby facilities. Pets by arrangement. TV

## Kites £

| | |
|---|---|
| 13 Grape Lane, York YO1 2HU | COOKING 1 |
| YORK (0904) 641750 | COST £18–£33 |

Kites is something of a pilgrimage for visitors to York who want to eat in a place that takes a lateral view of life and still retains a bit of the old hang-loose spirit. They put up with the irritations or the ups and downs, and enjoy the steep climb up the stairs to try something of the order of best end of lamb with lavender, confit of duck with butter beans, tomato and basil, or chicken breast stuffed with coriander, parsley, pickled lime, olives and garlic, with a saffron sauce. Boo Orman battles through a changing hand of chefs and staff, but her approach wins many hearts. The wine list is cheap, but has some sounder new wines like Ochoa Tempranillo or Candido's Salente Rosso. House wines are £8.50.

CHEFS: T.J. Drew and Pauline Hornby   PROPRIETOR: Boo Orman   OPEN: Mon to Sat, D only, and Sat L; 12 to 1.45, 7 to 10.30 (6.30 to 11 Sat)   CLOSED: Christmas and New Year MEALS: alc (main courses £5 to £11)   SERVICE: not inc   CARDS: Access, Visa   DETAILS: 45 seats. Private parties: 25 main room. Vegetarian meals. Children's menu. No-smoking area. Music

## Melton's ▼

| | |
|---|---|
| 7 Scarcroft Road, York YO2 1ND | COOKING 3* |
| YORK (0904) 634341 | COST £18–£39 |

'Taste and flavour dominated the meal': how rarely that is written of a restaurant. The Hjorts have their priorities – and prices – right. The restaurant's decoration is described as 'simple and low key, an excellent foil for the food', the location as 'a nondescript row of shops' 10 minutes' walk from Clifford's Tower. A less charitable assessment might be that the lights are a bit bright, the furnishings occasionally 'suburban' and the tables can be cramped. But when you find on offer oysters on a bed of steamed cucumber, beetroot surmounting blinis, a platter of grilled vegetables with olive oil, celery and capers, breast of pheasant stuffed with ginger and pheasant mousse, wrapped in a cabbage leaf and served with straw potatoes and Jerusalem artichokes, roast goose with roasted onion filled with garlic purée, a platter of six British and Irish cheeses, all finished off with a poached orange with orange coulis and chocolate ice-cream, do you really care how characterful the adjacent shops are? As one chap confirmed: 'This is the business – personable, self-contained, as formal or informal as you wish to make it, classy without pomposity, with a respect for the freshness and seasonality of the ingredients, cooked without wayward modishness.' Tuesdays, Wednesdays and Thursdays highlight seafood, puddings and vegetarian dishes respectively; this gives welcome variety and added interest to an already resourceful menu. When, one evening, a traveller coincided with a truffle evening and was treated to an antipasto of York ham and preserved mushrooms, scrambled eggs and truffles, poached smoked haddock with ceps, chicken with morels and a chocolate truffle cake, you can imagine the pleasure. There are range and elaboration to the cooking, but little fussiness or missed targets through lack of practice. Lucy Hjort's control of the sharp end of the business also comes in for praise, as does the wine and beer list for its lack of greed and for its range of interest. Wines are treated with intelligence as well as generosity. Described by style rather than provenance and printed clearly and accurately, the list is amongst the friendliest. Careful choices among Italians and antipodeans feature Villa di Capezzana and Redwood Valley Riesling. Prices start below £9 and are contained at the upper end by the Hjorts' policy of holding the money mark-up at a maximum of £10. There are some halves, some decent offerings by the glass and a helpful page of recommendations, but no house wines. CELLARMAN'S CHOICE: Menetou-Salon, 'La Charnivolle' 1990, Fournier, £12.25; Fleurie 1991, Chignard, £20.40.

CHEF: Michael Hjort   PROPRIETORS: Michael and Lucy Hjort   OPEN: all week, exc Sun D and Mon L; 12 to 2, 5.30 to 10   CLOSED: 1 week end Aug, 3 weeks from 25 Dec   MEALS: alc (main courses L £3.50 to £13, D £9 to £14). Set L and early D £12.50   SERVICE: net prices, card slips closed   CARDS: Access, Visa   DETAILS: 40 seats. Private parties: 30 main room, 12 private room. Vegetarian meals. Children's helpings L and early D. Wheelchair access (1 step). Music. Fax: (0904) 629233

---

## ▲ Middlethorpe Hall ♥

Bishopthorpe Road, York YO2 1QB                             COOKING 2
YORK (0904) 641241                                          COST £17–£58

'Middlethorpe goes from strength to strength,' claims a supporter of this lavishly restored William and Mary house surrounded by manicured grounds not far from York race course. Few would dispute the allure of the setting or the sheer classiness of the service. Verdicts on the cooking are less unanimous. At his best, chef Kevin Francksen can deliver an elaborate, keenly executed version of Anglo-French cooking, but occasionally the results are disappointing. His repertoire encompasses pheasant, rabbit and venison pudding and Welsh rarebit, as well as haddock tartare and medallions of beef with amaretto and walnuts. Complex artistry is the key to desserts such as tangerine soufflé with caramelised oranges, orange tuile and Cointreau sauce. Details such as excellent nibbles with cocktails, fine vegetables, cheeses with walnut bread, and petits fours are those of a kitchen that takes its work seriously. One reporter's set lunch of warm fish terrine in horseradish and cream sauce, grilled mackerel balanced by sharp tomato chutney, and treacle tart with 'scoops of solid cream' was reckoned to be the best meal he had ever eaten at Middlethorpe. House wine at £11 apart, there is little on the wine list below £15. Quality is generally good, and some effort has been made to provide halves. The unremitting multiplier, though, makes most bottles very pricey. CELLARMAN'S CHOICE: Montagny, premier cru 1990, Leflaive, £24; Washington State, Merlot, Hogue Cellars 1990, £19.75.

---

Net prices *in the details at the end of an entry indicates that the prices given on a menu and on a bill are inclusive of VAT and service charge, and that this practice is clearly stated on menu and bill.*

---

CHEF: Kevin Francksen  PROPRIETORS: Historic House Hotels Ltd  OPEN: all week; 12.30 to 1.45, 7.30 to 9.45  MEALS: alc (main courses £16 to £20). Set L £14.90 (2 courses) to £16.90 (inc wine), Set D £29.95  SERVICE: net prices, card slips closed  CARDS: Access, Amex, Diners, Visa  DETAILS: 60 seats. Private parties: 50 main room, 14 and 50 private rooms. Car park. Vegetarian meals. No children under 8. Jacket and tie. No music  ACCOMMODATION: 30 rooms, all with bath/shower. Room for disabled. Lift. B&B £93 to £209. No children under 8. Afternoon teas. Garden. TV. Phone. Confirm by 6. Fax: (0904) 620176 (*The Which? Hotel Guide*)

## 19 Grape Lane ¦✗

| | |
|---|---|
| 19 Grape Lane, York YO1 2HU | COOKING 2 |
| YORK (0904) 636366 | COST £21–£45 |

'Creep down a side alley off Grape Lane to reach the restaurant door.' Inside is a tiny room with head-cracking beams and a window looking out on to the cobbled street. The cramped conditions lend the place a certain 'odd-ball individuality', the owners are chatty and everyone talks to everyone else. The printed menu has some perennial favourites, but blackboard specials provide seasonal variety. The cooking is light modern British, ingredients are well chosen and results generally hit the target. At lunch-time the kitchen deals in light dishes and sandwiches; in the evening it moves up a gear with a *carte* and a three-course fixed-priced menu. Terrines are regularly endorsed: game with Cumberland jelly, duck and lentil with tarragon jelly, and chicken and vegetable. Fish also stands out: North Sea medley, steamed halibut with saffron and ginger, and baked cod with lime and chive sauce have been mentioned. Other reports have praised broccoli and almond soup, fricassee of hare and stuffed guinea-fowl in pastry. Puddings look to the nursery for much of their inspiration. The wine list continues to evolve, offering range and variety from France and the New World. Halves are aplenty. House Duboeuf is £8.95.

CHEF: Michael Fraser  PROPRIETORS: Gordon and Carolyn Alexander  OPEN: Tue to Sat; 12 to 1.45, 7 to 10.30  CLOSED: 25 and 26 Dec, first 2 weeks Feb, last 2 weeks Sept  MEALS: alc (main courses L £7.50 to £8, D £12 to £15.50). Set D £18.95  SERVICE: not inc  CARDS: Access, Visa  DETAILS: 34 seats. Private parties: 22 main room. Vegetarian meals. No children under 5 D. Smart dress preferred. No smoking in 1 dining-room. No cigars/ pipes in dining-rooms. Wheelchair access (1 step). Music

# England round-ups

All the eating-places below have been recommended by readers but for one reason or another have not graduated to the main listing. They are not places that simply failed at inspection. All reports on these places would be most welcome.

## Avon

**Bristol** *Arnolfini* 16 Narrow Quay, (0272) 279330. Arts-complex café with interesting, inexpensive menu. Good cappuccino, sometimes loud music.
*Bistro Twenty One* 21 Cotham Road South, Kingsdown, (0272) 421744. 'Very French' revamped bistro; the regularly changing menu keeps faith with Alain Dubois' Gallic roots and takes account of the market.
*Glass Boat* Welsh Back, nr Bristol Bridge, (0272) 290704. Anglo-French cooking on a smartly converted barge, theatre menus useful for Old Vic visitors.
**Chelwood** *Chelwood House* (0761) 490730. Georgian country house with extensive views and conservatory dining-room. Bavarian influences; acceptable desserts and vegetables, sometimes unacceptable coffee.
**Combe Hay** *Wheatsheaf* nr Bath, (0225) 833504. Whitewashed pub atop wooded hillside; lovely garden with seating. Lots of choice including local game and seafood.
**Paulton** *Somerset Inn* Bath Road, Paulton, nr Bristol, (0761) 412828. Simple country pub with superb views; some organic produce and an eclectic menu; traditional Sunday lunch.
**Stanton Wick** *Carpenters Arms* Stanton Wick, nr Pensford, (0761) 490202. Stylish stone inn offering quality bar food and excellent wines.
**Wellow** *Fox and Badger* Railway Lane, Wellow, nr Bath, (0225) 832293. Popular and friendly local with a good choice of bar food. Well-kept real ales and decent wines by the glass.

## Bedfordshire

**Woburn** *Black Horse* 1 Bedford Street, (0525) 290210. Popular pub for steaks; garden.

## Berkshire

**Cookham** *Bel and the Dragon* High Street, (062 85) 21263. Fifteenth-century inn with a long-standing reputation. Bar and restaurant meals include some Swiss dishes.
**Hungerford** *Just William's* 50 Church Street, (0488) 681199. Bar and restaurant with a short menu boosted by blackboard specials; good moules marinière, sticky toffee pudding with a butterscotch sauce.
**Inkpen** *Swan Inn* Lower Inkpen, nr Hungerford, (0488) 668326. Wonderful contradiction of an old, beamed English pub serving Singaporean and Indonesian food, well-kept real ales.
**Taplow** *Cliveden* (062 86) 68561. Fabulous stately home, with several hundred acres of National Trust grounds, housing two terrifically expensive restaurants.
**West Ilsley** *Harrow* West Ilsley, nr Newbury, (0635) 281260. Quietly smart pub on the edge of the Berkshire Downs. Well-reported bar food takes in daily specials and inventive puddings.
**Windsor** *Cody's* 4 Church Street, (0753) 858331. Pleasing cooking and a varied menu; nice atmosphere.
**Yattendon** *Royal Oak* The Square, (0635) 201325. New chef and manager as the *Guide* went to press at this popular pub/restaurant. Reports, please.

# Buckinghamshire

FAWLEY *Walnut Tree* (049 163) 8360. Remote Chiltern inn offering traditional pub favourites plus more adventurous specials; good wines by the glass.

HIGH WYCOMBE *Blue Flag* Cadmore End, (0494) 881183. Pub and restaurant for home-style cooking, duck a speciality.

SKIRMETT *Old Crown* (0491) 638435. Unusual pub – no bar, machines or draught lager – for fresh, home-cooked food. Children not allowed.

SPEEN *Old Plow Inn* Flowers Bottom Lane. Flowers Bottom, (0494) 488300. Fifteenth-century beams, country location, satisfying bar food and a restaurant (booking recommended).

# Cambridgeshire

CAMBRIDGE *Browns* 23 Trumpington Street, (0223) 461655. Favourite student hang-out for fun Euro-style food and informal atmosphere.

*King's Pantry* 9A Kings Parade, (0223) 321551. Upbeat, opposite King's College, vegetarian restaurant where the food is light rather than heavy, and well presented.

*Tai Cheun* 12 St John's Street, (0223) 358281. Agreeable Chinese with a good selection of dishes and efficient service.

ELY *Dominique's* 8 St Mary's Street, (0353) 665011. Small, unpretentious place providing light lunches, teas and also dinners Thursday to Saturday.

FOWLMERE *Chequers* High Street, (0763) 208369. Ancient pub that's strong on wines; bar food may be more variable.

MADINGLEY *Three Horseshoes* 1 High Street, (0954) 210221. Popular thatched pub with both conservatory restaurant and brasserie-style bar food.

SUTTON GAULT *Anchor Inn* Bury Lane, Sutton Gault, nr Ely, (0353) 778537. Old ferry inn in remote Fens location. Inspired bar food is recommended as is an excellent wine list; espresso coffee, glorious views.

WANSFORD *Haycock Hotel* London Road, Wansford, nr Peterborough,

(0780) 782223. Former coaching-inn serving food throughout the day; perfectly kept real ales and decent wines by the glass, attractive gardens.

WITCHFORD *Needhams Farm Restaurant* Main Street, (0353) 661405. Not as rustic as the name might suggest but home to mostly fish and seafood cooking, let down by poor ancillaries.

# Cheshire

BICKLEY MOSS *Cholmondeley Arms* Cholmondeley, nr Bickley Moss, (0829) 720300. Country pub-cum-brasserie in a converted Victorian schoolhouse; lots of choice on interesting menus, fair cooking, comfortable rooms for the night.

CHESTER *Franc's* 14A Cuppin Street, (0244) 317952. Lively French brasserie with plenty on offer.

COTEBROOK *Alvanley Arms* Forest Road, (0829) 760200. Charming pub in prosperous horse-breeding and farming area; first-class bar food, cosy interior, separate restaurant.

KNUTSFORD *Dick Willett's* The Toft, Toft Road, (0565) 632603. Vegetarian restaurant and B&B in 400-year-old barn conversion. Interesting menus, intimate atmosphere; more reports, please.

NESTON *Vineyards* 10 Parkgate Road, 051-336 2367. Lovely building, eclectic menu; a change of ownership has led to mixed reports.

WILMSLOW *Stanneylands Hotel* Stanneylands Road, (0625) 525225. Caters for conferences and a captive Cheshire audience. Uneven cooking but still liked by some; expensive.

WORLESTON *Rookery Hall* (0270) 610016. Fine country-house setting, but management appears to be undergoing change.

# Cleveland

NEWTON UNDER ROSEBERRY *King's Head* (0642) 722318. Stone pub noted for its double-decker toasted sandwiches, creditable wines, set lunch and Sunday lunch (dining-room booking recommended).

# Cornwall

**CHAPEL AMBLE** *Maltsters Arms* (0208) 812473. Pleasant old pub for both bar and restaurant food. Expect local fish, perennial lemon tart and chocolate fudge cake.

**GWEEK** *Mellanoweth* (032 622) 271. Charming cottage inn providing good bar food and indulgent puddings.

**MULLION** *Polurrian Hotel* Polurrian Cove, (0326) 240421. Quiet, friendly clifftop site with delightful views. Fresh fish, marvellous breakfasts, children welcome.

**NANCENOY** *Trengilly Wartha Inn* nr Constantine, (0326) 40332. Hard to find, lovely location; friendly hosts, pleasing restaurant, bar meals not always so successful.

**PORT GAVERNE** *Port Gaverne Hotel* (0208) 880244. Old smugglers' haunt built high into the cliffs; gets very busy, best for soups, fresh seafood, imaginative vegetables.

**TREGONY** *Kea House* 69 Fore Street, (087 253) 642. Friendly place for fair English cooking and cream-laden desserts.

**VERYAN** *Nare Hotel* Carne Beach, (0872) 501279. A little difficult to find but a splendid situation for an old-fashioned dining experience. Brilliant desserts, plentiful coffee; relaxing.

# County Durham

**BARNARD CASTLE** *Blagraves House* The Bank, (0833) 37668. Monthly-changing menu and fresh ingredients.
*Market Place Teashop* 29 Horse Market, Market Place, (0833) 690110. Not just tea – although this comes in stylish silver pots – but inexpensive home-cooked lunches. Fruit crumbles are very popular.

# Cumbria

**AMBLESIDE** *Drunken Duck Inn* Barngates, (053 94) 36347. Much-beloved pub for

great bar meals – local trout, Cumberland sausages, fine desserts – and well-kept ales and wines.
*Sheila's Cottage* The Slack, (053 94) 33079. Restaurant that's also good for afternoon teas; popular options include potted shrimps, chicken tagliatelle, sticky toffee pudding.

**ARMATHWAITE** *Dukes Head* (069 74) 72226. Small country hotel-cum-inn with a reliable restaurant; good attention to detail and friendly service.

**BOWNESS-ON-WINDERMERE** *Linthwaite House Hotel* 1 Crook Road, (053 94) 88600. Stylishly decorated hotel in some acreage; a young chef with good ideas and an attractive menu. Reports, please.

**BROUGHTON IN FURNESS** *Beswicks* Langholm House, The Square, (0229) 716285. Relaxing, Georgian surroundings for careful home cooking.

**CARLISLE** *Crosby Lodge Hotel* Crosby-on-Eden, nr Carlisle, (0228) 573618. Family-run country-house hotel; pleasant spot, quality ingredients, charming service.

**CARTMEL FELL** *Masons Arms* Strawberry Bank, (053 95) 68486. Not the easiest pub to locate, but worth careful map scouring; wide choice of bar food, 200 international bottled beers and several on draught.

**MELMERBY** *Shepherds Inn* (0768) 881217. Slate-roofed pub in fine walking country; regional specialities a feature, also real ales and over 40 whiskies.

**WINDERMERE** *Holbeck Ghyll* Holbeck Lane, (053 94) 32375. Comfortable accommodation and four- or five-course menus in this Victorian hunting-lodge. Sauces and lukewarm food on occasion let the cooking down; however, ancillaries are better.

# Derbyshire

**ASHFORD** *Riverside Country House Hotel* Fennel Street, (062 981) 4275. Comfortable Georgian country house; some clumsy, sauce-laden cooking, although cheeseboard and desserts are much better.

**BASLOW** *Cavendish Hotel* (0246) 582311. Part of the Chatsworth estate; fair cooking in the Garden Room restaurant; also serves afternoon teas.

**CHARLESWORTH** *George & Dragon Hotel* Glossop Road, (0457) 852350. Decent pub cooking of straightforward things such as French onion soup and steaks.

**DARLEY ABBEY** *Darleys on the River* Darley Abbey Mill, (0332) 364987. Wonderful setting on the wooded banks of the River Derwent. Fair cooking of fresh ingredients; good-value set lunches.

**MELBOURNE** *Bay Tree* 4 Potters Street, (0332) 863358. Good attention to detail; terrines, mousses, estimable desserts and petits fours.

# Devon

**ASHPRINGTON** *Durant Arms* (0803) 732240. Friendly, spick and span place dispensing real ales and traditional food using local ingredients.

**DODDISCOMBSLEIGH** *Nobody Inn* (0647) 52394. Old beamed pub with many hundreds of wines – lots by the glass – and attached wine shop. Simple cooking and a big selection of farmhouse cheeses.

**EXETER** *Royal Clarence* Cathedral Yard, (0392) 58464. Comfortable, well-run hotel, elegantly presented food, good sauces, consistent.

**EXMOUTH** *Temple Winds* The Beacon, (0395) 222201. A graceful one-time shop; dedicated cooking which will improve with time. Good wine list.

**GITTISHAM** *Combe House* (0404) 42756. Beautiful Elizabethan manor set in parkland; respectable cooking embraces excellent incidentals. More reports, please.

**IDE** *Old Mill* 20 High Street, (0392) 59480. Converted mill in a peaceful location; classical ideas take in fresh fish, guinea-fowl and dark chocolate parfait.

**KINGSTEIGNTON** *Old Rydon Inn* Rydon Road, (0626) 54626. Listed farmhouse incongruously surrounded by housing estate; attractive conservatory dining area, an adventurous kitchen,

well-kept wines and ales.

**KNOWSTONE** *Masons Arms Inn* (039 84) 231. Unspoilt thatched cottage that's a good all-rounder for bar food, real ales and wines; soups, pâtés and ploughman's recommended.

**LYNTON** *Hewitt's Hotel* North Walk, (0598) 52293. Astonishing views from the terrace, comfortable bedrooms, steady cooking, plus clotted-cream teas.

**NORTH BOVEY** *Blackaller Hotel* (0647) 40322. Hotel and restaurant (non-residents welcome) in a pretty setting; fair English cooking encompasses crab salad, venison in blackcurrant sauce, chocolate torte.

**PLYMOUTH** *Barretts* 27 Princess Street, (0752) 221177. Wine bar that's open long hours for the theatre crowd; short menu, some seafood.

**ROCKBEARE** *Jack in the Green* (0404) 822240. Useful roadside spot run by a keen team; imaginative bar food, good puddings and wines.

**SALCOMBE** *Soar Mill Cove Hotel* nr Salcombe, (0548) 561566. It's a pity the décor of this one-storey hotel is no match for the beautiful location; food is ambitious, service is friendly.

*Spinnakers* Fore Street, (0548) 843408. High-quality fish and well-reduced sauces; puddings need some work. Good service and value.

**SHEEPWASH** *Half Moon Inn* (040 923) 376. Port of call that's popular with anglers (game fishing on the River Torridge). Straightforward bar meals, good choice of wines.

**TIVERTON** *Lowman* 45 Gold Street, (0884) 257311. Enthusiastically run restaurant using local supplies for a frequently changing menu; while home-made bread and petits fours have pleased, meats have on occasion been disappointing.

**TUCKENHAY** *Maltsters Arms* Bow Creek, (0803) 732350. Smart new chef (chefs change often here), who cooks more exciting but expensive food in the restaurant; pub food keeps Keith Floyd's profile high.

# Dorset

**BOURNEMOUTH** *Helvetia* 61 Charminster Road, (0202) 555447. Cheerful Swiss place that's part wine bar (fondues here), part restaurant. Lots of veal, rich sauces, ice-cream concoctions, decent cappuccino.

**CRANBORNE** *La Fosse* London House, The Square, (0725) 517604. Fair English cooking. Attractive bedrooms, substantial breakfasts.

**DORCHESTER** *Yalbury Cottage* Lower Bockhampton, nr Dorchester, (0305) 262382. Set dinners with just one sitting (booking recommended) in Hardy country; comfortable bedrooms.

**LODERS** *Loders Arms* (0308) 22431. Unpretentious village inn with a growing reputation; imaginative food on a short blackboard menu.

**MILTON ABBAS** *Hambro Arms* (0258) 880233. Attractive position; blackboard specials the best bet, also popular for four-course Sunday lunches.

**POOLE** *Allan's* 8 Bournemouth Road, Lower Parkstone, (0202) 741489. Seafood restaurant offering good value for straightforward cooking.

*Haven Hotel* 161 Banks Road, Sandbanks, (0202) 707333. Ambitious cooking in a conference-centre hotel; delicious puddings; expensive.

**SHAVE CROSS** *Shave Cross Inn* Marshwood Vale, (0308) 868358. Honey-coloured thatched inn dating back to the fourteenth century; lovely garden, real ales, bar food.

**SHERBORNE** *Pheasants* 24 Greenhill, (0935) 815252. Restaurant-with-rooms catering for modern English tastes; game is a feature, vegetables and desserts elicit praise.

**WAREHAM** *Jackson's Seafood Restaurant* 57 North Street, (0929) 551662. Fresh fish from Chesil Bay boats. More reports, please.

*Oliver's* 14A North Street, (0929) 556164. Small family place turning out simple French dishes and several choices of meringue.

# East Sussex

**BRIGHTON** *Al Duomo* 7 Pavilion Buildings, (0273) 326741. Reliable Italian offering more than just pasta; try the profiteroles.

*La Caperon* 113 St Georges Road, Kemp Town, (0273) 680317. Good-value lunch spot run by a husband and wife team; enjoyable cooking includes choice for vegetarians and indulgent desserts.

*Food for Friends* 17A–18 Prince Albert Street, The Lanes, (0273) 202310. Long-standing, committed enterprise; first-rate organic breads, cakes, organic wines and vegetarian cooking of the ethnic, world school.

*Latin in the Lane* 10 King's Road, (0273) 328672. Friendly Italian with an interesting menu; commendable baked sea bream and grilled baby chicken with rosemary.

**FIRLE** *Ram Inn* (0273) 858222. Estate village location for daily-changing menus, some free-range produce, hearty portions and choice draught beers.

**FLETCHING** *Griffin Inn* (082 572) 2890. Sixteenth-century inn serving restaurant and bar meals. The highpoints are the wine list and well-kept real ales.

**HOVE** *Chai Talay* 67 Church Road, (0273) 771170. Reliable and authentic Thai (try the steamed fish), but service can be slow.

**LEWES** *Pailin* 20 Station Street, (0273) 473906. Simple Thai food that although sometimes heavy on sugar and garlic is nevertheless a useful consideration.

**MAYFIELD** *Rose & Crown Inn* Fletching Street, (0435) 872200. Highly popular pub with beamed bars and pretty gardens. All types of meals, real ales, German wheat beer and fruit wines.

**MILTON STREET** *Sussex Ox* (0323) 870840. In fine South Downs walking country find reliable bar meals and complete facilities for families.

**THREE LEGGED CROSS** *Bull* Dunster Mill Lane, (0580) 200586. Ancient inn that's much frequented by hikers; garden and two petanque pitches, bar meals, decent wines.

## Essex

**CASTLE HEDINGHAM** *Old Moot House*
1 St James Street, (0787) 60342. Reliable
English cooking within an Elizabethan
house; this is farming country so expect
big portions, thick gravy and cream-laden
desserts.

**CLAVERING** *Cricketers* (0799) 550442.
Sixteenth-century whitewashed inn
producing first-rate, fresh bar meals; real
ales and well-chosen wines.

**COGGESHALL** *White Hart* Market End,
(0376) 561654. Atmospheric, ancient inn
also with smart accommodation. An
Italian chef producing a Continental
mixture – results are sometimes uneven,
but it all moves at a pleasant pace.

**GOSFIELD** *Green Man* The Street, (0787)
472746. Traditional hostelry attracting
the Essex hordes – particularly for its cold
table and seasonal cooking.

**HEYBRIDGE** *Chigborough Lodge*
1 Chigborough Road, (0621) 853590.
Charming country setting and
inexpensive, deceptively good food.

**LITTLEBURY** *Queens Head Inn* High Street,
(0799) 522251. Unspoilt Tudor pub for
impressive food (especially fish) and local
real ales.

**ROCHFORD** *Renoufs* Bradley Way, (0702)
544393. Long-standing, well-run French
restaurant and hotel.

**WESTCLIFF-ON-SEA** *Paris* 719 London
Road, (0702) 344077. Inventive cooking
of such things as pheasant and venison
terrine; eels in herb jelly; deep-fried
skate; Cointreau crème brûlée. More
reports, please.

**WITHAM** *Lian* High House, 5 Newland
Street, (0376) 510684. Chinese with a
good, local reputation.

## Gloucestershire

**BISHOP'S CLEEVE** *Cleeveway House* (0242)
672585. Lovely old house with three
bedrooms; old-fashioned cooking with a
few highlights.

**BLOCKLEY** *Crown Inn* High Street,
(0386) 700245. Upmarket pub with
accommodation, French-style restaurant

and snack menu; fish figures
prominently.

**CHELTENHAM** *Beaujolais* 15 Rotunda
Terrace, Montpelier, (0242) 525230. A
bistro that has improved, though, if all
the costs are added together, it may come
out quite dear.

*Finns* 143 Bath Road, (0242) 232109.
English bistro cooking with some frills;
fish is particularly recommended.

**GLOUCESTER** *College Green Eating House*
7 College Street, (0452) 520739. Fair
cooking includes creamy soups, ample
vegetables and decent coffee.

**LOWER ODDINGTON** *Fox Inn* (0451)
870888. Well-scrubbed Cotswold
character; good wine list, long menu.

**NAILSWORTH** *Stone Cottage* Old Market,
(0453) 832808. The ambitious ideas don't
always come off; however, plainer things
have pleased, especially desserts.

**PAINSWICK** *Painswick Hotel* Kemps Lane,
(0452) 812160. Elegantly decorated
Palladian house with a new chef this year
who is still finding his feet – more than a
few shortcuts and inconsistencies in the
cooking; lots of fish, shellfish from the
seawater tank, good breads, poor coffee.

**STOW-ON-THE-WOLD** *Grapevine Hotel*
Sheep Street, (0451) 830344. Attractive,
no-smoking dining-room dominated by a
nineteenth-century grapevine, covering
the glass roof. Straightforward things
work best; separate vegetarian menu.

**TETBURY** *Close Hotel* 8 Long Street,
(0666) 502272. Beautifully restored
house with elegant accommodation,
turning out well-sauced pheasant and
lamb and other English mainstays.

**TEWKESBURY** *Le Bistrot André* Church
Street, (0684) 290357. Small, intimate
bistro open in the evening. Short menu,
all fresh produce.

*New World* 61 High Street, (0684)
292225. Well-run Vietnamese restaurant;
piquant flavours, finish with pear and
apple fritters.

**WINCHCOMBE** *Pilgrims Bistro* 6 North
Street, (0242) 603544. Converted
shop that's a cheerful bistro; grilled
mussels in wine, bobotie, lemon
cheesecake.

## Greater London

**HARROW** *Percy's* 66–68 Station Road, North Harrow, 081-427 2021. Usefully placed restaurant with a no-smoking policy; interesting menu with healthy options highlighted; enjoyable cooking and good incidentals.

**PINNER** *La Giralda* 66 Rickmansworth Road, 081-868 3429. Old-fashioned cooking, not expensive, a treasure-trove Spanish wine list.

**TWICKENHAM** *Cézanne* 68 Richmond Road, 081-892 3526. Café-like restaurant, casual atmosphere, competent cooking.

## Greater Manchester

**ALTRINCHAM** *Franc's* 2 Goose Green, 061-941 3154. Informal French bistro for formulaic food and pleasant service.

**CHEADLE** *Brasserie 66* 66 High Street, 061-428 2474. Neighbourhood restaurant; fair cooking at fair prices, careful presentation.

**MANCHESTER** *Café Alto* Wilmslow Road, Rusholme, 061-225 7108. Noisy, popular, modish place offering equally modern Mediterranean menus; perfectly acceptable cooking.

*Café Istanbul* 79 Bridge Street, 061-833 9942. Popular Turkish restaurant that's often busy; fresh ingredients, much use of the chargrill, Turkish coffee, good value.

*Café Primavera* 48 Beech Road, Chorlton, 061-862 9934. Fashionably modern restaurant in both its atmosphere and menus; pleasing cooking, cheerful service, gets very busy.

**PRESTWICH** *Lagaccio* 1 Scholes Lane, 061-798 6805. Above-average Italian that's good for garlicky baked aubergine, seafood pancake and well-topped pizzas.

## Hampshire

**EMSWORTH** *36 on the Quay* The Quay, 47 South Street, (0243) 375592. Elegant and expensive (silver domes still in evidence) restaurant with harbour views; good

cuisine includes fine pastry and chocolate desserts.

**EVERSLEY** *New Mill* New Mill Road, (0734) 732277. Surrounded by water and weeping-willows on three sides, this is a fabulous location. High prices for ambitious cooking, best for desserts and petits fours.

**FORDINGBRIDGE** *Hour Glass* Burgate, (0425) 652348. Old beamed cottage offering English cooking that though variable may be useful for the area.

**GRATELEY** *Plough Inn* (0264) 889221. Pleasant pub by a spreading chestnut tree; blackboard menu – go for the fresh fish.

**LIPHOOK** *Old Thorns* Longmoor Road, Griggsgreen, (0428) 724555. Very incongruous place: smart, corporate-style country hotel with an 18-hole golf course and both English and Japanese restaurants.

**LYMINGTON** *Limpets* 9 Gosport Street, (0590) 675595. Congenial long-standing French restaurant; try the paupiette of sole and the crème brûlée.

*Provence* Gordleton Mill Hotel, Silver Street, Hordle, (0590) 682219. Luxurious restaurant but a change of chef as we went to press. More reports, please.

**MILFORD ON SEA** *Bridge Cottage* 10 High Street, (0590) 642070. Attractive town house; good reports of Scottish oysters, chocolate marquise and enthusiastic service.

**NEW ALRESFORD** *Old School House* 60 West Street, (0962) 732134. Attentive service and careful presentation but let down by uneven cooking.

**RINGWOOD** *Old Cottage* 14 West Street, (0425) 474283. Seventeenth-century riverside cottage run by husband and wife team; fair cooking and enjoyable desserts.

**ROCKBOURNE** *Rose and Thistle* (072 53) 236. Characterful thatched pub in a very pretty village; first-rate bar food with excellent incidentals and good wines.

**WINCHESTER** *Nine The Square* 9 Great Minster Street, (0962) 864004. Close to the cathedral find ambitious ideas not always carried through; sauces and pastry are less successful than vegetables and coffee.

## Hereford & Worcester

**EVESHAM** *Riverside* The Parks, Offenham Road, (0386) 446200. Small country-house hotel providing comfortable accommodation and daily-changing menus; very acceptable cooking includes fine puddings.

**OMBERSLEY** *Crown & Sandys Arms* (0905) 620252. Historic pub with a civilised atmosphere; menus with lots of choice including vegetarian specials. Drink well-kept draught beers, country wines and mead.

**ROSS-ON-WYE** *Chase Hotel* Gloucester Road, (0989) 763161. Attractive Georgian house, cheerful staff, sound cooking.

**RUCKHALL** *Ancient Camp Inn* (0981) 250449. Remote yet upmarket country inn enjoying spectacular views; fine ingredients result in fair cooking: pan-fried chicken, fresh pasta and no chips.

**STOURPORT-ON-SEVERN** *Severn Tandoori* 11 Bridge Street, (0299) 823090. Consistent Indian cooking, a good local reputation, pleasant service.

**UPTON BISHOP** *Moody Cow* (098 985) 470. Rustically decorated pub that's good for Sunday lunch.

**WHITNEY** *Rhydspence Inn* (0497) 831262. Ancient black and white timbered drovers' inn with beautiful views and regularly changing menus.

**WINFORTON** *Sun Inn* (0544) 327677. Wye Valley pub serving imaginative food: the Far East is raided for inspiration and there is some adaptation of Elizabethan dishes; choice draught beers.

**WOOLHOPE** *Butchers Arms* (0432) 860281. Half-timbered hillside pub with a long menu; Woolhope pie, which contains wild rabbit, bacon and cider, is the speciality.

## Hertfordshire

**BERKHAMSTED** *Regal* 157–159 High Street, (0442) 865940. Creditable Home Counties version of Pekinese/Szechuan cooking; high-points are still the crispy duck and fish. Noticeably friendly and chatty service.

**EAST BARNET** *Le Papillon* 236 East Barnet Road, 081-440 7897. Little French bistro that's useful for the area.

**HEMEL HEMPSTEAD** *Gallery Restaurant* Old Town Hall Arts Theatre, High Street, (0442) 232416. Theatre restaurant serving snacks to three-course meals.

**WATTON-AT-STONE** *George & Dragon* High Street, (0920) 830285. Gentrified pub turning out sound cooking with a strong emphasis on fish; decent house wines by the glass.

## Humberside

**BEVERLEY** *Cerruti 2* Beverley Station, Station Square, (0482) 866700. Former railway refreshment room, now a separate operation; fresh fish dishes, chocolate roulade.

**HORNSEA** *When the Boat Comes In* 34 Cliffe Road, (0964) 535173. Basic café-style place cooking almost entirely fish. This is all fresh but occasionally let down by the sauces. Finish with home-made meringue and fair coffee.

## Kent

**BARHAM** *Old Coach House* Dover Road (A2), (0227) 831218. French roadside restaurant that, although basic, might be useful; check opening hours before setting out.

**BROADSTAIRS** *Marchesi Bros.* 18 Albion Street, (0843) 862481. Family-run place with views of the sea; the menu caters for all tastes, cooking is consistent.

**CANTERBURY** *George's Brasserie* 71–72 Castle Street, (0227) 765658. Useful restaurant with sometimes loud Muzak and occasional high prices for adequate food.

*Tuo e Mio* 16 The Borough, (0227) 761471. Genuine, family-run Italian near the cathedral. Good antipasti, fresh pasta and fish, excellent espresso. Gets busy, so booking is wise.

**IVY HATCH** *Plough* Coach Road, (0732) 810268. Tile-hung roadside pub with

549

conservatory addition; cosmopolitan menu, good for Sunday lunch, gets exceptionally busy.

**LAMBERHURST** *Brown Trout* The Down, (0892) 890312. Pretty, highly popular village pub with a large garden; lovely food includes fresh fish bought daily from Billingsgate.

**TENTERDEN** *Il Classico* 75 High Street, (0580) 763624. Friendly, reliable Italian that's good for bruschetta, seafood salad, pasta and zabaglione.

**TUNBRIDGE WELLS** *Eglantine* 65 High Street, (0892) 524957. Informal restaurant, some have said untidy, that can deliver competent cooking: bouillabaisse and pasta, for example. *Royal Wells Inn* Mount Ephraim, (0892) 511188. Victorian hotel with a choice of restaurants; good cooking of such things as sweetbreads, roast beef and seasonal game.

# Lancashire

**BROUGHTON** *Broughton Park Hotel* Courtyard Restaurant, Garstang Road, (0772) 864087. Country house-cum-country business hotel with passable cooking.

**CLITHEROE** *Brown's Bistro* 10 York Street, (0200) 26928. Useful bistro, fair materials, some poor sauces.

**GOOSNARGH** *Bushell's Arms* Church Lane, (0772) 865235. Traditional North Country specialities – black pudding, Flookburgh shrimps – alongside more international offerings; wonderful choice of wines.
*Solo* Goosnargh Lane, (0772) 865206. Sound cooking and fine presentation; set-price meals have pleased.

**POULTON-LE-FYLDE** *Stocks* 2 Queens Square, (0253) 882294. European cooking and an extensive wine list.

**WHITEWELL** *Inn at Whitewell* Forest of Bowland, (0200) 448222. Splendid, isolated spot in the Forest of Bowland; good bar food takes in kippers, Cumberland sausage and Coniston trout.

# Leicestershire

**GLOOSTON** *Old Barn Inn* Andrews Lane, (085 884) 215. Cosy sixteenth-century inn with an interesting menu; well-kept beers and robust home cooking.

**HINCKLEY** *Royal China* Watling Street (A5), (0455) 632424. Large, elegant Chinese serving Peking and Cantonese dishes. More reports, please.

**LEICESTER** *Man Ho* 14–16 King Street, (0533) 557700. Smart Chinese; the menu lists sizzling dishes and a wide choice of seafood.
*The Case* 4–6 Hotel Street, St Martin's, (0533) 517675. City-centre restaurant for reliable cooking and varied menus; home-made ravioli in goats' cheese sauce, saddle of venison with redcurrants, prune and armagnac tart.

**MARKET HARBOROUGH** *Eliot's* 35 High Street, (0858) 466966. All-day café-style place for fair cuisine at reasonable prices.

**OAKHAM** *Barn at Furleys* 12 Burley Road, (0572) 770245. Attractive, interior-designed tea-room offering first-class snacks and lunches: fresh herb pancakes with scallops, rocket and fennel salad, club sandwiches with home-made mayonnaise, strawberry crème brûlée. More reports, please.

**REDMILE** *Peacock Inn* Church Corner, (0949) 42554. Smart pub with a pretty garden, close to Belvoir Castle. A French chef, decent draught beers and wines.

**STRETTON** *Ram Jam Inn* Great North Road, (0780) 410776. A1 roadside pit-stop that's above the average. Brasserie-style menus, a few interesting choices; a few ups and downs but it's certainly useful.

**UPPINGHAM** *Lake Isle* 16 High Street East, (0572) 822951. Eighteenth-century town house that has restaurant and rooms; fresh ingredients, good breads, lovely wines.

**WALCOTE** *Black Horse* Lutterworth Road, (0455) 552684. Traditional black and white pub serving all-Thai food; good range of real ales.

# Lincolnshire

**BURGH LE MARSH** *Windmill* 46 High Street, (0754) 810281. Great bread in this restaurant in the mill's back yard. Cooking has good points, though not always on display all at once.

**LOUTH** *Ferns* 40 Northgate, (0507) 603209. Friendly place for fair home cooking and generous portions.

**NEWTON** *Red Lion* (052 97) 256. Seventeenth-century pub with a warm welcome; an impressive cold table takes centre-stage.

# Merseyside

**BIRKENHEAD** *Pastime* 42 Hamilton Square, 051–647 8095. Basement restaurant in Victorian garden square; acceptable cooking with a few fancy details; good home-made bread and petits fours.

**BOOTLE** *Rui's* 13 Aintree Road, 051-922 1212. Valuable oasis in an otherwise culinary desert; try the sole véronique and chicken risotto.

**HESWALL** *Crispin's* 106 Telegraph Road, 051-342 8750. An unprepossessing location but useful for straightforward things such as savoury pancake, sirloin steak and duck breast with caramelised honey and ginger.

**LIVERPOOL** *La Grande Bouffe* 48A Castle Street, 051-236 3375. Well-established cellar bistro that's plainly decorated; eclectic cuisine includes strong vegetarian section; pleasant service.

# Norfolk

**COLTISHALL** *Norfolk Mead Hotel* Church Street, (0603) 737531. Comfortable country-house hotel close to the Broads; well-presented, nicely cooked food and high marks for puddings: try the banoffi pie or Grand Marnier soufflé.

**FOULSHAM** *Gamp* Claypit Lane, (036 284) 4114. Honest cooking in a cosy, beamed dining-room.

**GREAT YARMOUTH** *Red Herring* 24–25 Havelock Road, (0493) 853384. Basic street-corner pub but serving real ales and the satisfying staple bar lunch of Norfolk sausages in French bread.

**GUIST** *Tollbridge* Dereham Road, (036 284) 359. Fixed-price menus; fresh fish, Cromer crab, Ceasar salad, Gressingham duck. No smoking.

**LITTLE WALSINGHAM** *Old Bakehouse* 33–35 High Street, (0328) 820454. Enjoyable English cooking in an agreeable atmosphere; desserts have been praised.

**NORWICH** *Brasted's* 8–10 St Andrews Hill, (0603) 625949. Relaxing, tented dining-room and a new chef finding his feet; can work out expensive.

*Lloyd's* 66 London Street, (0603) 624978. Good ingredients, beautiful presentation, attentive service; try the Norfolk crab-cakes, dark chocolate soufflé and decent coffee.

**STIFFKEY** *Red Lion* 44 Wells Road, (0328) 830552. Coast-road cottage in north Norfolk hill country doing decent bar food, draught beers and regular live music.

**SWAFFHAM** *Strattons* Ash Close, (0760) 723845. Pretty Queen Anne hotel and restaurant with a very keen chef. Imaginative, well-reported cooking using lots of fresh herbs; very attractive desserts. Also a lovely place to stay. More reports, please.

**WARHAM ALL SAINTS** *Three Horseshoes* Bridge Street, (0328) 710547. Old, characterful pub offering traditional English dishes based on Norfolk produce; well-kept ales, home-made lemonade.

# Northamptonshire

**FOTHERINGHAY** *Falcon Inn* Main Street, (083 26) 254. Sit in lounge, dining-room or conservatory to eat from one menu; interesting soups, good English cooking, cold buffet at weekend lunch. Well-kept draught beers and wines.

**NORTHAMPTON** *Ristorante Ca'd'Oro* 334 Wellingborough Road, (0604) 32660. Reliable, unpretentious Italian for good-value fresh pasta, calf's liver, espresso.

# Northumberland

**BERWICK-UPON-TWEED** *Rob Roy* Dock Road, Tweedmouth, (0289) 306428. Fresh fish and seafood including superb Lindisfarne oysters and local lobster.

**MORPETH** *La Brasserie* 59 Bridge Street, (0670) 516200. Something for everyone on this cosmopolitan menu. Cooking has pleased; useful for the area.

**WARENFORD** *Warenford Lodge* (0668) 213453. Old stone inn with an interesting menu; find regional specialities alongside Pecorino pasta and Andalucian vegetable pot.

**WOOLER** *Ryecroft Hotel* 28 Ryecroft Way, (0668) 81459. Set-price menus of mostly British dishes; consistent standards, professional staff, also does afternoon teas.

# North Yorkshire

**ASKRIGG** *King's Arms Hotel* Market Place, (0969) 50258. Old coaching-inn with traditional bars. Simple bar food; full meals served in the Clubroom Restaurant have drawn praise.

**GOATHLAND** *Mallyan Spout Hotel* (0947) 86206. Hotel and pub in a remote moorland village; local produce on the menu includes cheeses and fish, competent cooking, interesting sauces.

**HARROGATE** *Bettys* 1 Parliament Street, (0423) 502746. Traditional tea-rooms with a formidable reputation; the place to be for coffee and cakes, which have proved a wiser bet than the light meals.

**HELMSLEY** *Black Swan* Market Place, (0439) 70466. Smart, seventeenth-century inn that's part of the Forte Heritage formula. Good for traditional Sunday lunch, although some have found the place expensive.

**MIDDLEHAM** *Waterford House* Kirkgate, (0969) 22090. Restaurant and accommodation on the edge of the Dales National Park; pleasing cooking, generous portions; for pudding try the Yorkshire curd tart.

**NORTHALLERTON** *Bettys* 188 High Street, (0609) 775154. Brunch, lunch and very good afternoon teas at this smaller branch of the famous chain.

**REETH** *Burgoyne Hotel* On the Green, (0748) 84292. Elegant stone house that's home to fair English cooking; good for Sunday lunch.

**SAXTON** *Plough Inn* (0937) 557242. Pub in pretty village producing fair food: fennel soup, seafood parcel, smoked fish.

**WHITBY** *Trenchers* New Quay Road, (0947) 603212. Huge, glitzy fish and chip restaurant on the quayside. Locally caught fish, children's menus, cheerful atmosphere.

**YORK** *Bettys* 6–8 St Helen's Square, (0904) 659142. Open until mid-evening for a pit-stop snack or light meal; cakes and pastries made to both Swiss and Yorkshire recipes.

*Grange Hotel, Ivy Restaurant* Clifton, (0904) 644744. Regency hotel with a formal dining-room. Several reports of uneven cooking this year.

*Partners* 13A Ousegate, (0904) 627929. Rather too wide a choice – stay with the blackboard offerings – and a few short-cuts taken. Puddings are good.

*Taj Mahal* 7 Kings Staith, Ouse Bridge, (0904) 653944. An old merchant's house close to the river, now home to first-rate Indian cuisine. Vegetable koftas, chicken jalfrezi and chapatis are all recommended.

# Nottinghamshire

**NETHER LANGWITH** *Goff's* Langwith Mill House, Langwith Road, (0623) 744538. Pleasing cooking in a well-decorated Georgian house; set-price meals and a regularly changing menu.

**NOTTINGHAM** *Mandarin* 23 Hockley, (0602) 586037. City-centre Chinese for fresh ingredients and good sauces.

# Oxfordshire

**BRIGHTWELL BALDWIN** *Lord Nelson Inn* (0491) 612497. Restaurant-style dining, French country wines by the glass, garden.

**CUMNOR** *Bear & Ragged Staff* Appleton Road, (0865) 862329. Country pub close to Oxford which has all-day opening. Interesting menu, sound cooking, lovely wines.

**DORCHESTER-ON-THAMES** *George Hotel* High Street, (0865) 340404. Old coaching-inn but a new chef as we went to press. Well-chosen wines.

**GREAT TEW** *Falkland Arms* (060 883) 653. Fifteenth-century partly thatched, creeper-clad inn; traditional English food, choice draught beers.

**HENLEY-ON-THAMES** *Francesco's* 8 Bell Street, (0491) 573706. Small, genuine Italian café selling freshly baked pizzas and croissants, proper cappuccino and espresso.

**OXFORD** *Gee's* 61A Banbury Road, (0865) 53540. Popular restaurant in handsome Victorian conservatory, but the food may sometimes slip.

*Heroes* 8 Ship Street, (0865) 723459. Crowded-out pit-stop for light lunches, made-to-order sandwiches, creamy hot chocolate; also does take-away.

*Ma Cuisine* 21 Cowley Road, The Plain, (0865) 201316. Unpretentious and authentic French cuisine despite some inconsistencies.

*Munchy Munchy* 6 Park End Street, (0865) 245710. Archetypal ethnic café working to a South-East Asian formula. Aromatic spicing, some uneven results.

**SHIPTON-UNDER-WYCHWOOD** *Lamb Inn* (0993) 830465. Centuries-old Cotswold inn; popular cold buffet and daily specials.

**STANDLAKE** *Bell* High Street, (0865) 300657. Quiet, civilised pub producing good shortcrust pies, salads, fruit crumbles. Sunday lunch is a roast.

**STOKE ROW** *Crooked Billet* Newlands Lane, (0491) 681048. Ancient pub in the heart of the Chilterns. Weekly-changing menus, no bar (beer is kept in the cellar) but excellent wines.

**WALLINGFORD** *Regatta* Wallingford Bridge, 103 High Street, (0491) 826126. Riverside restaurant in large boathouse; pleasing cooking at reasonable prices.

# Shropshire

**BRIDGNORTH** *Haywain* Hampton Loade, nr Bridgnorth, (0746) 780404. A riverside setting for evening meals and Sunday lunch; consistent cooking of a set menu formula.

**HILLTOP** *Wenlock Edge Inn* (074 636) 403. Friendly family-run place with fabulous views; home cooking and interesting wines.

**HOPTON CASTLE** *Park Cottage* (054 74) 351. Tiny cottage dining-room facing the ruin of a Norman keep. Lovely views, but ingredients and execution have sometimes faltered.

**HOPTON WAFERS** *Crown Inn* (0299) 270372. Upmarket hostelry for high-quality bar food, a comprehensive wine list and outdoor seating.

**LUDLOW** *Queen's House* Wigmore, nr Ludlow, (056 886) 451. Cellar restaurant, friendly atmosphere, imaginative food.

**NORTON** *Hundred House Hotel* (095 271) 353. The interior of this hostelry stops just short of kitsch, but delightful gardens provide visual relief. Interesting enough menus with lots of fresh herbs; service has not always pleased.

# Somerset

**CASTLE CARY** *Bonds* Ansford Hill, (0963) 350464. Small hotel and restaurant run by a friendly team. Consistent results from a regularly changing menu and an impressive cheeseboard.

**DULVERTON** *Ashwick House* nr Dulverton, (0398) 23868. Relaxing hotel with lots of personal touches. Imaginative meals, fresh materials, happy atmosphere.

**HENLADE** *Mount Somerset* (0823) 442500. Regency house on the Blackdown Hills, close to Taunton. Elegant bedrooms, opulent dining-room with conservatory addition, uninterrupted views. Chef Richard Smith is settling in well. More reports, please.

**KNAPP** *Rising Sun* (0823) 490436. Splendid Somerset inn where food is the main feature: lots of fresh fish from both local and exotic waters; also popular for Sunday roast lunch and decent wines.

**Luxborough** *Royal Oak of Luxborough* (0984) 40319. Fourteenth-century Exmoor pub with loads of character, real ales, local ciders, traditional bar food.

**Monksilver** *Notley Arms* (0984) 56217. Pub with garden in a pretty Quantocks village. Reliable home cooking; try the treacle tart with clotted cream.

**North Perrott** *Manor Arms* (0460) 72901. Well-known place that houses a good kitchen. Menus include vegetarian choices and Sunday lunch is always popular.

**Porlock** *Anchor and Ship Hotel* Porlock Weir, (0643) 862636. Victorian hotel in a quiet hamlet facing the harbour. Recommended dishes have included watercress soup, fresh salmon and strawberry charlotte.

*Oaks Hotel* (0643) 862265. High-up views of beach and sea. Straightforward cooking from daily-changing menus of such things as Exmoor venison and wild woodland mushroom pie.

## South Yorkshire

**Doncaster** *Woods' Tea Rooms* 3A Wood Street, (0302) 327126. Traditional tea-rooms also doing a good trade in lunches. Speciality teas and coffees, indulgent cakes, home cooking.

**Sheffield** *Mediterranean* 271 Sharrowvale Road, (0742) 661069. Bold but approximate versions of Spanish and North African dishes in popular neighbourhood restaurant. Tapas at tea-time Tuesday to Friday.

**Sprotbrough** *Boat Inn* Nursery Lane, (0302) 857188. Quiet, riverside pub, originally the farmhouse where Sir Walter Scott wrote much of *Ivanhoe*. Simple bar food, wines by the glass.

**Tickhill** *Forge* 1 Sunderland Street, (0302) 744122. Elaborate food that includes home-made breads, good fish dishes and abundant vegetables. Popular in the area.

## Staffordshire

**Eccleshall** *Old Parsonage* High Offley, Woodseaves, nr Eccleshall, (0785) 284446. Country house with conservatory-style dining-room; straightforward English cooking, attentive service.

**Lichfield** *Pig Barn* Swinfen, nr Lichfield, (0543) 480307. Converted barn with an interesting menu and pleasant service.

**Stoke-on-Trent** *Haydon House* Haydon Street, Basford, nr Stoke-on-Trent, (0782) 711311. Fair cooking; fresh ingredients, some home-grown and first-rate sauces.

## Surrey

**Bramley** *Le Berger* 4A High Street, (0483) 894037. French restaurant that's open only for dinner (lunch by arrangement).

**Croydon** *Siamese* 164 Cherry Orchard Road, East Croydon, 081-681 3402. Authentic, delicate Thai flavours, a good selection of starters, everything beautifully presented.

**Egham** *Bonne Franquette* 5 High Street, (0784) 439494. Pastel-painted restaurant serving dressed-up English food. Minus points for haphazard service, tired sauces and coffee; higher marks for meat and desserts.

**Epsom** *Le Raj* 211 Firtree Road, (0737) 371371. Slickly marketed Indian restaurant with above-average Bangladeshi food; nothing radical but perfectly pleasant.

**Ewhurst** *Windmill Inn* Pitch Hill, (0483) 277566. Perfect in summer – uninterrupted views, enormous terraced garden – but good all year round for decent bar food that's well thought out. Draught beers, drinkable wines.

**Guildford** *Manor at Newlands* Newlands Corner, (0483) 222624. Elegant place for fair cooking; monkfish recommended.

*Rumwong* 6–18 London Road, (0483) 36092. Fair Thai cooking and attractive service.

**KINGSTON UPON THAMES** *Restaurant Gravier* 9 Station Road, Norbiton, 081-549 5557. Family-run French that mostly pleases; expensive.

**LIMPSFIELD** *Old Lodge* High Street, (0883) 712996. Consistent Anglo-French cooking on the Surrey borders. More reports, please.

**RICHMOND** *Burnt Chair* 5 Duke Street, 081-940 9488. Concise menus with something for everyone. Delicate to bland flavours in such things as quail's egg salad, loin of lamb with garlic and rosemary, bread-and-butter pudding with a strawberry coulis.

*Cantina* 32 The Quadrant, 081-332 6262. Creditable Mexican (rather than the usual Tex-Mex). Relaxed atmosphere, free-range meat, chillies and tortillas aplenty; cool off with creamy desserts.

**WEYBRIDGE** *Casa Romana* 2 Temple Hall, Monument Hill, (0932) 843470. Well-established Italian with well-decorated surroundings. Good antipasti selection, nicely cooked fish, smooth service.

*Colony* 3 Balfour Road, (0932) 842766. Smart, suburban Chinese employing a variety of regional styles. Recommended satays, Cantonese shredded duck, Peking duck.

## Tyne & Wear

**NEWCASTLE UPON TYNE** *Café Procope* 35 The Side, Quayside, 091-232 3848. Informal operation that's a feature of the Newcastle scene; eclectic menus, large portions, casual service.

*Rupali* 6 Bigg Market, 091-232 8629. Well-marketed Indian restaurant with a good reputation for regional dishes and smooth service.

**NORTH SHIELDS** *Chainlocker* 50 Duke Street, New Quay, 091-258 0147. Basic, no-frills pub opposite the ferry; worth knowing about for good prawns, wild salmon and other fresh fish.

## Warwickshire

**ALDERMINSTER** *Bell* (0789) 450414. Converted coaching-inn that's rated for its imaginative food, impressive wine list and well-kept draught beers.

**RYTON-ON-DUNSMORE** *Ryton Gardens Café* National Centre for Organic Gardening, Wolston Lane, (0203) 303517. No longer just vegetarian – organic vegetables but also organic chicken and beef.

**STRATFORD-UPON-AVON** *Le Bonaparte* Caterham House Hotel, 58–59 Rother Street, (0789) 267309. Traditional French, used by members of the RSC. Likely dishes might be foie gras, sweetbreads and salmon steak.

*Opposition* 13 Sheep Street, (0789) 269980. Busy bistro that's a Godsend for theatre-goers. Consistent cooking, well-flavoured sauces, good pastry.

*Shepherd's* Stratford House Hotel, 18 Sheep Street, (0789) 268233. Conservatory restaurant at the rear of the hotel. Straightforward stuff but perfectly pleasing.

**WARWICK** *Fanshawe's* 22 Market Place, (0926) 410590. Very acceptable cooking and a warm welcome; puddings have been praised.

## West Midlands

**BIRMINGHAM** *Le Provençal* 1 Albany Road, Harborne, 021-426 2444. Cheerful French for straightforward dishes: snails, calf's liver with bacon, fresh fish.

*Punjab Paradise* 377 Ladypool Road, 021-449 4110. Indian balti-house; good use of fresh ingredients, pleasant service.

*Taipan* 2A Wrottesley Street, 021-622 3883. New Korean restaurant with a few Thai influences.

**HOCKLEY HEATH** *Nuthurst Grange* Nuthurst Grange Lane, (0564) 783972. Highly priced (except for a few basic menus) and elaborate country hotel and restaurant.

**OLDBURY** *Jonathans* 16–24 Wolverhampton Road, 021-429 3757. Interesting hotel and restaurant on

Birmingham's doorstep. Eclectic menus, some uneven cooking; traditional afternoon teas.

## West Sussex

**CHICHESTER** *Comme Ça* 67 Broyle Road, (0243) 788724. Reliable French with lots of choice, pre- and post-theatre menus available.

**CUCKFIELD** *Murrays* (0444) 455826. Husband and wife team; rather uneven but popular cooking that can on occasion be heavy-handed.

**EASEBOURNE** *Ye Olde White Horse* Easebourne Street, (0730) 813521. Upmarket inn that's close to Cowdray Park. Indeed, game is from that estate and all ingredients are local. Eclectic menus, sound cooking, great wines.

**FUNTINGTON** *Hallidays* Watery Lane, (0243) 575331. Roses round the door, low beams inside; pleasing enough food, very competent desserts, useful for Sunday lunch.

**HORSHAM** *Cole's* The Old Barn, Worthing Road, Southwater, nr Horsham, (0403) 730456. Family-run restaurant for competent cooking and a pleasant atmosphere.

**TILLINGTON** *Horseguards Inn* Upperton Road, (0798) 42332. Only a mile or so from Petworth House (National Trust), this is a good stopping-place for imaginative snacks and full meals. Drinkable wines and real ales.

**WEST HOATHLY** *Cat Inn* North Lane, (0342) 810369. Popular village pub with a regularly changing blackboard menu; everything freshly cooked.

## West Yorkshire

**BRADFORD** *Bharat* 502 Great Horton Road, (0274) 521200. Well-known Indian with lots on the menu, including interesting specials; hand-pulled Tetley Bitter.

*Hansa's* 44 Great Horton Road, (0274) 730433. Indian restaurant that's good for dhosas, chutneys and pooris.

**GRANGE MOOR** *Kaye Arms* 29 Wakefield Road, (0924) 848385. Busy pub doing a quick turnover in food. Brasserie-style menu, good results.

**GUISELEY** *Harry Ramsden's* White Cross, (0943) 874641. Prime fish and chips, cheerful service.

**HALIFAX** *Holdsworth House* Holdsworth, nr Halifax, (0422) 240024. Characterful hotel with some charm. Useful for Sunday lunch (a roast) and more unusual offerings.

**HUDDERSFIELD** *Ramsden's Landing* Aspley Wharf, Wakefield Road, (0484) 544250. Popular brasserie with lots of menu choice and happy customers.

**ILKLEY** *Bettys* 32–34 The Grove, (0943) 608029. Another branch of the famous tea-rooms; just the ticket for coffee and cake.

**LEEDS** *Salvo's* 115 Otley Road, Headingley, (0532) 755017. Queue for a table (no bookings) for Italian meals; bruschetta, pasta, chargrilled vegetables, tiramisù.

**ROYDHOUSE** *Three Acres Inn* (0484) 602606. Family-run inn with a good reputation; lunch-time bar meals, evening restaurant, B&B accommodation.

**SHELF** *Bentley's* 12 Wadehouse Road, (0274) 690992. Cosy, converted cellar restaurant with blackboard menus; homely cooking and interesting desserts. More reports, please.

**WENTBRIDGE** *Wentbridge House* (0977) 620444. Attractive old hotel in wooded acreage. Lunches here have been enjoyed.

## Wiltshire

**ALDBOURNE** *Raffles* 1 The Green, (0672) 40700. Congenial spot for fair cooking.

**BRADFORD-ON-AVON** *Dandy Lion* 35 Market Street, (0225) 863433. Upmarket inn with a brasserie feel to it; call in for morning coffee and pastries, or imaginative meals.

**HINDON** *Lamb at Hindon* (0747) 89573. Home cooking at reasonable prices. Sunday lunch is a roast.

**LACOCK** *At the Sign of the Angel* Church Street, (0249) 730230. Charming old house in a National Trust village. Inconsistent cooking but a lovely place to stay; good breakfasts and a well-stocked cellar.

**LITTLE BEDWYN** *Harrow Inn* High Street, (0672) 870871. Village pub run as a co-operative and well thought of locally. Eclectic choice of snacks and meals, regularly changing real ales and New World wines.

**SALISBURY** *Crustaceans* 2–4 Ivy Street, (0722) 333948. Seafood restaurant that's useful for Salesians. Reports, please.

# Scotland

map 8

## Faraday's

2–4 Kirk Brae, Cults, Aberdeen AB1 9QS
ABERDEEN (0224) 869666
on A93, 2m from city centre

COOKING 1
COST £17–£36

The building was once a hydro-electric sub-station, but for all that the place feels intimate, and tables are attractively laid with fresh flowers and candles, though space is at a premium. John Inches serves up modestly priced lunches and a short evening *carte* (Monday to Thursday), but on Friday and Saturday nights the kitchen moves into a higher gear with a four-course set dinner – 'a welcome addition to the Aberdeen scene,' according to visitors from Liverpool. The menu reads like a world tour, taking in Thai chicken satay, smoked salmon with 'fool's' caviare and blini, Moroccan tageen and osso buco as well as patriotic roast loin of pork with Bramley apple and mint sauce. Sweets range from marinated winter fruit salad with Muscavado yogurt cream to banana cake with sticky toffee sauce. The cooking is robust, although disappointments have been recorded: the soup course has been 'weak' and sweets have 'promised without ever fulfilling'. Coffee is plentiful and strong. Some reporters consider the 50-strong wine list quite expensive, but it offers plenty of variety across the range. House wine is £12.90 a litre.

CHEFS: John Inches and Roger Ross   PROPRIETOR: John Inches   OPEN: Mon to Sat, exc Mon L; 12 to 1.30, 7 to 9.30   CLOSED: 2 weeks from 26 Dec   MEALS: alc (main courses L £5 to £12, D £11 to £14). Set Fri and Sat D £23.50   SERVICE: net prices, card slips closed   CARDS: Access, Visa   DETAILS: 42 seats. 4 tables outside. Private parties: 32 main room. Car park. Vegetarian meals. Children's helpings. Smart dress preferred. Wheelchair access (also WC). Music. Air-conditioned

## Silver Darling

Pocra Quay, Footdee, Aberdeen AB2 1DQ
ABERDEEN (0224) 576229

COOKING 1*
COST £26–£44

The harbourside setting gives views of the spasmodically occupied fleet which supplies the fish, and the walk from car to restaurant can sometimes be breezy. The place seems invariably full, which may result in disorganised service. While there is praise for the fine raw materials such as in a Japanese sushi roll or imaginative use of Creole spices, most people look forward to something from the charcoal grill. Brochette of fish and prawns with grilled vegetables, fillet of sea trout with sorrel sauce and a trio of fish with three different sauces are examples. Halibut and mussels en papillote or a monkfish and langoustine stew with a garlic sauce are instances of a different style, and meat-lovers can be entertained happily with grilled rib of beef, or braised duck with a millet pancake. The provençal theme crops up regularly and when joined with fish may result in a soupe au pistou made with scallops, salmon and prawns. The pace and price of the restaurant do occasionally cause upsets. The notes and layout of the wine list disguise its brevity. House wines are £8.50.

CHEF: Didier Dejean   PROPRIETORS: Catherine Wood, Didier Dejean and Norman Faulks
OPEN: Mon to Sat, exc Sat L; 12 to 2, 7 to 10   CLOSED: 2 weeks from Christmas   MEALS: alc
D (main courses £14 to £16). Set L £14 to £16.95 (2 courses)   SERVICE: not inc   CARDS:
Access, Amex, Diners, Visa   DETAILS: 35 seats. Private parties: 35 main room. Vegetarian
meals with prior notice. Children welcome. Smart dress preferred. No pipes in dining-
room. Wheelchair access (also WC). Music. Fax: (0224) 626558

---

**ABERFOYLE Central**                                                          map 8

## Braeval Old Mill 🍷

By Aberfoyle FK8 3UY
ABERFOYLE (087 72) 711                                            COOKING 4
on A81, 1m from Aberfoyle                                        COST £27–£46

'We were expecting it to be good but it was rather better,' said someone who nearly found it too far from Glasgow for dinner, but not quite. The conversion of the mill – 'sparse but homely' – enlivened by bold colours, good taste and the warm features of the building itself, was the first mammoth task set the Nairns in their drive for a restaurant of their own. Then came the cooking, and learning, the expansion, the enforced contraction after an accident, and so to the current formula of a set-price four-course dinner, with no choice until sweets. One such dinner included carrot, honey and ginger soup; a salad of duck breast; and salmon on a bed of cucumber with a galaxy of vegetables. Lasagne of monkfish and mussels with coriander velouté, then chicken with wild mushroom sauce, each slice separated by a morel, then chocolate marquise with a cinnamon sauce were components of another. This cooking shows finesse, depth of flavour, a way with spices (and with wild mushrooms) and startling freshness. Fish – for instance, brill with scallops and champagne and chive sauce, or salmon with tomato and avocado compote and a basil butter sauce – benefits from this quality. The restrictions on choice do not meet everyone's needs, but Nick Nairn has distinguished colleagues in this policy (see La Potinière, Gullane). It has had an effect on his accuracy, his flavours, his seasoning. He is never one to gild the lily, but it is nice to see it perfectly formed. The 'House selection' of wines, starting at £12.50, takes in New World whites as well as a Tempranillo from Ochoa and Jaboulet's Côtes de Ventoux. Elsewhere the evidence of intelligent buying is reinforced with J.M. Boillot Puligny, CVNE Rioja Blanco and especially fine antipodeans. A nice balance of the modest and the expensive will satisfy most; half-bottles will repay study – they are very good indeed. CELLARMAN'S CHOICE: Bianco 1991, Avignonesi, £14.50; Rioja, Viña Real Gran Reserva 1973, CVNE, £25.

CHEF: Nick Nairn   PROPRIETORS: Nick and Fiona Nairn   OPEN: Tue to Sat, D only, and Sun L (weekday L by arrangement for 6 or more); 12.30 to 1.30, 7 to 9.30   CLOSED: 1 week Feb, 1 week June, 1 week Nov   MEALS: Set Sun L £18.50, Set D £27.50   SERVICE: not inc, card slips closed   CARDS: Access, Visa   DETAILS: 32 seats. Private parties: 30 main room. Car park. Vegetarian meals with prior notice. No children under 10. Smart dress preferred. No cigars/pipes in dining-room. Wheelchair access (1 step; also WC). No music

---

**ACHILTIBUIE  Highland**                                                     map 8

## ▲ *Summer Isles Hotel*  🍷 ✳

Achiltibuie IV26 2YG
ACHILTIBUIE (085 482) 282                                          COOKING 2*
off A835 at Drumrunie, 10m N of Ullapool                    COST £35–£45

The hotel rejoices in aspects of its isolation: modern communications are at a premium (but at least they exist), solar panels help self-sufficiency, and there is promise of peace and quiet, space and far horizons (fog permitting). At its core an old inn, the place has grown spasmodically to afford more rooms, kitchens and other impedimenta – grand it isn't. Achiltibuie itself has been described as 'a long ribbon of not very attractive buildings including a large new housing development and many abandoned structures'. Chris Firth-Bernard cooks a five-course dinner every night with increasing emphasis on fish from the bay in front of the hotel. This has meant a smidgeon more choice, hitherto restricted to the sweet course. Soup, perhaps broccoli and coriander with a loaf of home-made bread (a different sort each night), is the invariable beginning, followed by something like a scallop mousse or a carpaccio of venison with a tomato, pepper and anchovy relish, or even a hot Stilton soufflé. When meat forms the centrepiece, for instance in venison with a port and juniper gravy and crisp smoked bacon, fish, as in salmon with spinach, sorrel and shallots, is always offered as an alternative. Desserts and cheeses are substantial and satisfying and send most to bed happy. Service charge is not an issue here as none is added or expected. Petits châteaux and bourgeois clarets remain strongly represented on the wine list with almost as many in half-bottles as in full; this is canny buying combined with unrapacious mark-ups. The extravagant must resort to Burgundy or Italy for satisfaction. For most, the range and quality offered below £20 will be more than adequate; half-bottles, listed clearly, are a delight but the absence of Alsatian halves is a curiosity. CELLARMAN'S CHOICE: Pernand Vergelesses 1989, Chartron et Trebuchet, £22; St Joseph 'Le Grand Pompée' 1989, Jaboulet, £17.

---

CHEF: Chris Firth-Bernard   PROPRIETORS: Mark and Geraldine Irvine   OPEN: all week, D only; 8   CLOSED: mid-Oct to Easter   MEALS: Set D £31   DETAILS: 26 seats. Private parties: 8 main room. Car park. Vegetarian meals. Children's helpings. No children under 8. No smoking in dining-room. No music   ACCOMMODATION: 12 rooms, all with bath/shower. B&B £41 to £88. Deposit: £50. No children under 8. Pets welcome (not in public rooms). Afternoon teas (in adjoining café). Fishing. Doors close at 11. Confirm by 6. Fax: (085 482) 251 (*The Which? Hotel Guide*)

---

*The* Guide *relies on feedback from its readers. Especially welcome are reports on new restaurants appearing in the book for the first time.*

## ▲ *Cameron House Hotel, Georgian Room* §✳

COUNTY OF THE YEAR RESTAURANT

**NEW ENTRY**

Loch Lomond, Alexandria G83 8QZ
ALEXANDRIA (0389) 55565
off A82, ½m N of Balloch roundabout,
3½m N of Dumbarton

COOKING 3
COST £21–£62

This preternaturally Scottish baronial Lomond-side house is a further venture
for the Craigendarroch Group from Ballater. Expect, therefore, a glitzy health
and leisure facility, serious cooking at serious prices, and generally a degree of
commitment to quality. The Group has secured the services of Jeff Bland, one of
Scotland's more able grand-hotel chefs, and his output has not disappointed
those wanting to escape Glasgow for a country fling. Techniques are, of course,
borrowed from the hautest of haute cuisine, but materials and stylistic tilt are
often those of Scotland. Nowhere was this better exemplified than in a heather
honey charlotte of meltingly tender and light consistency, but with flavours
entirely Scottish. Food can be both light and flavoursome: a breast of chicken
comes on a bed of paper-thin, pale-green sage-infused noodles. A dish with
more gusto, such as duck with celeriac, cherries and port, shows again the
ability to balance flavours, to cook correctly, and to make sauces with real taste
('a good port had certainly contributed'). Discretion ensures no lapses, but skill
makes possible variety – for instance, into a dressing that hinted of cumin with
a fine terrine of chicken. Ancillaries, like bread, have also been approved, even
if the cheeseboard has not received quite the same praise. Though dishes may
at first sight seem precious, the intelligence of the cooking and apparent
devotion to flavour ensure success. Whether everyone will enjoy the over-
cosseted style of the operation depends on habits and wallets. The last will
need to be fat to cope with a house champagne at £34.95, but the rest of the
wine list can be combed for cheaper alternatives, from a choice developed by
Justerini & Brooks – reliable, therefore, even if not exciting. House wines are
from £11.65.

CHEF: Jeff Bland PROPRIETORS: Craigendarroch Group OPEN: all week, exc L Sat and
Sun; 12 to 2, 7 to 10 MEALS: alc (main courses £18 to £19). Set L £12.95 (2 courses) to £40,
Set D £29.95 to £40 SERVICE: net prices, card slips closed CARDS: Access, Amex, Diners,
Visa DETAILS: 44 seats. Private parties: 40, 125 and 275 private rooms. Car park.
Vegetarian meals. Children's helpings. No young children. Jacket and tie. No smoking in
Georgian Room. Wheelchair access (also WC). Music. Air-conditioned
ACCOMMODATION: 68 rooms, all with bath/shower. Rooms for disabled. Lift. B&B £125 to
£295. Children welcome. Baby facilities. Afternoon teas. Garden. Swimming-pool. Sauna.
Tennis. Fishing. Golf. Snooker. TV. Phone. Confirm by 6. Fax: (0389) 59522

---

*'The people running this restaurant are extraordinarily combative. Not only did the chef
run out of the kitchen to tell us off because we'd wanted to make sure that the jelly in the
terrine wasn't made from gelatine; the waitress was in dispute with people at two other
tables, and seemed to be aiming at rudeness.'*
On eating in Suffolk

---

## ALYTH Tayside

map 8

### ▲ Drumnacree House Hotel

NEW ENTRY

St Ninians Road, Alyth PH11 8AP
ALYTH (082 83) 2194
off A926, Blairgowrie to Kirriemuir road

COOKING 2
COST £22–£35

When Allan Cull was down home in Louisiana with the oil industry, he learnt some Cajun cooking. Paul Prudhomme was his hero. In the unlikely setting of this ancient market town, in a small house run as a hotel ('Guests feel so much at home, we sometimes have to wake them after dinner to say it's time for bed'), his efforts of re-creation may be sampled. Chicken and smoked-ham jambalaya, blackened pork chops, seafood dirty rice or smoked sausage and chicken gumbo are the thing, and 'sensitivity and discernment' are shown in their achievement. White-trash manners are not essential, however. A parallel menu delights as many, if not more, with deceptively simple fresh food running along well-planned lines. First courses such as chicken liver parfait with honey pickles, or smoked salmon, or asparagus in season may be followed by lamb with a herb crust, fresh wild salmon, chicken with apricots and a spiced cream sauce, or perhaps a plain steak. The deception is in the accuracy and the seasoning – these seem spot on. Ch. La Jaubertie from Nick Ryman, Ch. Tayac and a Dry Creek Fumé Blanc are three examples from a sound wine list, with house wines at £12 a litre.

CHEF: Allan Cull  PROPRIETORS: Allan and Eleanor Cull  OPEN: Tue to Sat, D only (D Mon and Sun residents only); 6.30 to 9  CLOSED: 22 Dec to 1 Jan  MEALS: alc (main courses £7.50 to £12)  SERVICE: not inc  CARDS: Access, Visa  DETAILS: 40 seats. Private parties: 50 main room, 12 private room. Car park. Vegetarian meals. Children's helpings. Smart dress preferred. No cigars/pipes in dining-room. Wheelchair access (also WC). Music  ACCOMMODATION: 6 rooms, all with bath/shower. B&B £31 to £60. Deposit: £10. Children welcome. Pets by arrangement. Garden. TV. Doors close at midnight. Confirm by 6

## ANSTRUTHER Fife

map 8

### Cellar ▮ ✱✹

24 East Green, Anstruther KY10 3AA
ANSTRUTHER (0333) 310378

COOKING 3*
COST £17–£44

The building that houses the Cellar was once a store for herring barrels. It has not been so prettified as to lose that original simplicity, and the same can be said of the cooking. With little exception, Peter Jukes cooks seafood and does it with consistency, to a stable, though not entirely predictable, repertoire. He sees this as his strength, and so do his customers – they return time after time. But it is quality they seek as well as predictable patterns. 'We were so impressed by our supper that we treated ourselves to a lunch and it was the most delightful we have had in years.' Delight is an important element in the Cellar's success: a pleasing and characterful welcome allied to very able cooking of dishes such as lobster and smoked-trout quiche (cooked as ordered), smoked haddock omelette, grilled halibut with hollandaise, turbot and scallops braised with Chablis and asparagus finished with cream, and bass beurre blanc. Finish with crème brûlée, and rest satisfied. A flurry of activity on the already excellent wine list has brought in a set of French country wines from £10.50 and eight wines are offered by the glass, including, at the time of writing, a terrific Riesling from Zind-Humbrecht. Alsace generally shows well with Rolly-Gassmann, Kuentz-Bas and Trimbach all represented, while white burgundies, including a page of Chablis, are very fine. Half-bottles could be augmented perhaps at the expense of the possibly over-generous range of clarets. Prices are fair, with much intelligent selection offered below £15. CELLARMAN'S CHOICE: Riesling, Cuvée Frédéric Emile 1985, Trimbach, £19.50; Rully Blanc premier cru Mont-Palais 1991, Oliver Leflaive, £18.95.

CHEF: Peter Jukes   PROPRIETORS: Peter and Vivien Jukes   OPEN: Mon to Sat, exc Mon L; 12.30 to 1.30, 7 to 9.30   CLOSED: Christmas, 1 week May   MEALS: alc (main courses £4.50 to £10.50). Set D £22.50 (2 courses) to £27.50   SERVICE: not inc, card slips closed   CARDS: Access, Amex, Visa   DETAILS: 32 seats. Private parties: 36 main room. Vegetarian meals with prior notice. Children's helpings L. No children under 8. Smart dress preferred. No smoking in dining-room. Music

---

## ARISAIG  Highland

map 8

## ▲ Arisaig House ✱

Beasdale, By Arisaig PH39 4NR
ARISAIG (068 75) 622
on A830, 3m E of Arisaig Village

COOKING 2
COST £29–£61

David Wilkinson has returned to the fold from the other side of Scotland after a stint at his own restaurant in Cromarty. This Philip Webb house – forbidding to the eye at first, but revelling in a fine interior partly refitted in the 1930s after a severe fire, and blessed with great gardens and location – has been the site of constant work and improvement by the Smithers family. It is simple, luxurious, country-house cooking that matches the incidentals and tone of the place. The simplicity is not without art – for instance, a warm salad of chicken livers with Indonesian dressing, or rouille croûtons pepping up the shellfish bisque, or a basket of wild mushrooms decently seasoned (for once) with lemon juice – but there is a wise avoidance of the over-complicated. Prices are not low, but trimmings help to heal the wound. The wine list is also pitched to the free-spending classes, in clarets particularly, though plenty of other regions represent very fair value. Little appears from beyond the French borders. House wines are £15 for a Beaujolais or £17.50 for a Chablis.

CHEF: David Wilkinson   PROPRIETORS: Ruth, John and Andrew Smither   OPEN: all week; 12.30 to 2, 7.30 to 8.30   CLOSED: Nov to end Mar   MEALS: alc L (main courses £10), Set D £29.50 to £35   SERVICE: not inc, card slips closed   CARDS: Access, Amex, Visa   DETAILS: 36 seats. 5 tables outside L. Private parties: 10 main room. Car park. Vegetarian meals. No children under 10. Smart dress preferred. No smoking in dining-room. Wheelchair access (1 step). No music   ACCOMMODATION: 13 rooms, all with bath/shower. B&B £70 to £195. Deposit: £100. No children under 10. Afternoon teas. Garden. Snooker. TV. Phone. Doors close at midnight. Confirm by 4.30. Fax: (068 75) 626 (The Which? Hotel Guide)

---

▲ This symbol means accommodation is available.

---

## AUCHENCAIRN Dumfries & Galloway

map 8

▲ *Collin House* ⅔✳

**NEW ENTRY**

Auchencairn, Castle Douglas DG7 1QN
AUCHENCAIRN (055 664) 292
off A711, ¼m E of Auchencairn

COOKING 2
COST £32–£40

John Wood was once a record producer whose oeuvre includes Pink Floyd's
first two singles. Now he produces hospitality – very successfully, reporters
say. Collin House is 'on one of the hills that lead gently down to the sublime
tranquillity of Auchencairn Bay': that's a visitor speaking, not a brochure.
Beyond, Cumbria rises. The house is plain Georgian, and the cedar of Lebanon
in the garden dates from the same period. A nightly menu pursues the Scottish
country-house line of relative plainness, yet offers enough sophistication and
care to give added value to the good materials. Strawberries in April seem a
mite unseasonal, but the venison, the trout, the scallops and the lamb were
exactly what was wanted. Seasoning and the use of herbs are sometimes over-
eager, but sauces such as a pepper sauce with venison or port with lamb are
excellent. Bread seems home-baked and includes a decent olive loaf. Tapénade
on toast was an appreciated appetiser. The wine list, which is not dear, has lots
of Yapp wines and some fun notes. The visitor on his or her own should be
happy with the halves provided. House wines are from £6.25.

CHEF: John Wood   PROPRIETORS: Pam Hall and John Wood   OPEN: all week, D only; 7.30
for 8.15   CLOSED: 4 Jan to 12 Mar   MEALS: Set D £26   SERVICE: not inc, card slips
closed   CARDS: Access, Visa   DETAILS: 20 seats. Private parties: 24 main room. Car park.
Vegetarian meals with prior notice. Children's high teas. Smart dress preferred. No
smoking in dining-room. No music   ACCOMMODATION: 6 rooms, all with bath/shower.
B&B £45 to £74. Deposit: 20%. Children welcome. Dogs by arrangement. Garden. TV.
Phone. Confirm by 5   (*The Which? Hotel Guide*)

## AUCHMITHIE Tayside

map 8

*But 'n' Ben* ⅔✳ £

Auchmithie DD11 5SQ
ARBROATH (0241) 77223
on coast, 3m NE of Arbroath, off A92

COOKING 1
COST £13–£29

'To find such an open and cheerful place on a grey Monday in October was
nothing short of miraculous,' enthused travellers from Yorkshire who thought
the front-of-house 'clockwork grannies' were excellent. You will find no
fanciness or fireworks here, just honest handling of fresh ingredients. The
restaurant is a cottage high on the clifftops in the village of Auchmithie, which
claims to be the birthplace of the Arbroath smokie. It is no surprise that this
local delicacy appears regularly – transformed into a soup, cooked with butter
and also included in 'very satisfying' pancakes. Fresh local fish – scallops,
monkfish, lobsters – is treated with due respect and game appears in season.
Margaret Horn starts baking at eight in the morning, producing scones, Border
tarts, Bakewell tarts, shortbread, gâteaux and fruit slices, which are served
right through the day. Elsewhere on the menu, you might find crab on toast,

poached salmon salad, pan-grilled Aberdeen Angus steaks and mince with tatties. High tea is a grand Scottish occasion. Most wines on the cheap and cheerful list will leave change from £10. House wine is £7.25.

CHEFS: Margaret and Angus Horn   PROPRIETORS: Margaret, Iain and Angus Horn   OPEN: Wed to Mon; 12 to 3, 4 to 5.30, 7 to 9.30   MEALS: alc (main courses £6.50 to £16)   SERVICE: not inc, card slips closed   CARDS: Access, Visa   DETAILS: 40 seats. Private parties: 40 main room. Vegetarian meals. Children's helpings. Smart dress preferred. No smoking in dining-room. Wheelchair access (also WC). No music

---

**BALLATER Grampian**                                                                   map 8

## ▲ *Craigendarroch Hotel, The Oaks* 🐟✳

Braemar Road, Ballater AB35 5XA
BALLATER (033 97) 55858                                                        COOKING 3
1m W of Ballater, on A93                                                      COST £23–£52

Not much is heard of this giant complex of time-share, hotel, restaurants and leisure facility, where history and tradition are a construct of the mind. There are two serious restaurants (The Oaks and The Lochnagar) within the core of the building, both offering elaborate versions of Scottish staples. In The Oaks, a much appreciated summer meal consisted of a poached lobster, chervil and tomato ravioli with baby vegetables in a brioche crust, followed by pan-fried rack of lamb with a spicy crust in a basil sauce with caramelised shallots and, to finish, a creamy blackcurrant cheesecake with a crispy basket of ice-cream. On a Scottish night – a staple event on Mondays – the cock-a-leekie lost its essential boldness of flavour and stirling virtues, and first-class beef in pastry got a smattering of Scottish oatmeal and a madeira sauce. Drambuie parfait with raspberries, blueberries and strawberries in a brandy-snap basket, served with shortbread and chocolate thistles, proved an excellent combination. Coffee was good as was the fine selection of home-made rolls at the beginning. Quality is high in this vein of production, just as service is elaborate (though too many trainees were spotted by one eagle-eyed reader) and dress is formal. House wine is £11.75.

CHEFS: Edward Cooney and Andrew Tanner   PROPRIETORS: Craigendarroch Group   OPEN: all week, D only, and Sun L; 12.30 to 2.30, 7 to 10   MEALS: alc (main courses £14 to £19.50). Set Sun L £17.50, Set D £24   SERVICE: net prices, card slips closed   CARDS: Access, Amex, Diners, Visa   DETAILS: 45 seats. Private parties: 12 main room, 90 and 100 private room. Car park. Vegetarian meals. Children's helpings. Jacket and tie. No smoking in dining-room. Wheelchair access (also WC). Music. Air-conditioned   ACCOMMODATION: 50 rooms, all with bath/shower. Lift. B&B £99 to £125. Children welcome. Baby facilities. Afternoon teas. Garden. Swimming-pool. Sauna. Tennis. Fishing. Snooker. TV. Phone. Fax: (033 97) 55447 (*The Which? Hotel Guide*)

---

*Prices quoted in the* Guide *are based on information supplied by restaurateurs. The prices quoted at the top of each entry represent a range, from the lowest meal price to the highest; the latter is inflated by 20 per cent to take account of likely price rises during the year of the* Guide.

---

## ▲ Green Inn

9 Victoria Road, Ballater AB35 5QQ
BALLATER (033 97) 55701

COOKING 2*
COST £15–£37

The inn has given way to restaurant; there is no bar, but there are bedrooms. The dining-room itself is a happy confection of chunky pine furniture set amidst fresh flowers, a colour scheme of pinks and greys, and tables spaced well enough for relaxation. The Purves have got off to a good start. Carol looks after the customers, with the minimum of help or fuss. Jeff does the cooking (witness to which are all the diplomas hung proudly on the walls), a fine compromise between local materials and a style alert to the wider world. One wholly satisfactory meal consisted of hot-and-sour beetroot soup with collops of smoked duck breast; sliced duck with creamy clapshot and a sweet-and-sour sauce made with kumquats; Scotch beef with a black pudding and chicken liver pâté on a herb sauce ('What seemed to be an unenterprising choice turned out to be a triumph,' a first-timer noted); vegetables, including red cabbage with a little mashed potato, a potato and celeriac tart, and sugar-snap peas; raspberries soaked in whisky that kept up the reputation of Scottish soft fruit; and treacle tart that endorsed the art of Scottish pastry-making. A love of the sweet and sour (beetroot, kumquats, red cabbage) was evident but did not distort too greatly the natural flavours. Cooking is accurate and generous. The Purves are enthusiasts for Scottish cheese and a pause at the board is recommended. The wine list is sensibly short, but the choices and prices are extra-sound. Leflaive burgundies, Jumilla Altos de Pio and Heydt Gewurztraminer show good suppliers. House wine is £7.95.

CHEF: Jeff Purves   PROPRIETORS: Carol and Jeff Purves   OPEN: all week D, and L Sat and Sun; 12 to 1.30, 7 to 9.30   CLOSED: Sun Oct to Mar   MEALS: alc D (main courses £12 to £14.50). Set L £9.25   SERVICE: not inc   CARDS: Access, Visa   DETAILS: 32 seats. Private parties: 36 main room. Vegetarian meals. Children's helpings. No smoking while others eat. Wheelchair access. Music. Air-conditioned   ACCOMMODATION: 3 double rooms, all with bath/shower. B&B £40. Deposit: £10. Children welcome. Pets welcome. Garden. TV. Doors close at midnight. Confirm by 6

## ▲ Tullich Lodge ✠

Ballater AB35 5SB
BALLATER (033 97) 55406
on A93, 1½m E of Ballater

COOKING 2
COST £13–£38

'Built in the Scottish baronial style, of pink granite, Tullich, a late-Victorian house of character, is all crenellations, crowsteps, turret and tower.' So says the literature, which could add that the owners are full of character too. This is a distinctive place – one that sometimes appeals more to regulars than first-timers. The house inside answers well to the external description: no character is lost in the furnishing, and it is a great and individual place to stay at. The cooking does not aim at being in a restaurant manner, rather it is what you would like to do at home, were you lucky enough to live in a place like this. The dinners are set, the methods are natural, the materials good. Mussels with white wine, parsley and shallots, then oyster mushrooms with garlic and croûtons, before pan-fried scallops with white wine, potatoes and broccoli, then raspberries and blueberries with crème fraîche or cheeses, before coffee was the running order on an evening when the shellfish was plentiful. Smoked salmon, beetroot soup, poached halibut or roast grouse (at a surcharge), before a raspberry cream torte was the enviable choice for a party in the autumn. The cycle of menus usually, though not always, avoids repetitiousness during a single sojourn. Light lunches are also available. The wine list has respect for age and quality. House wines are £8.50 or £11.50.

CHEF: Neil Bannister   PROPRIETORS: Hector Macdonald and Neil Bannister   OPEN: all week; 1, 7.30 to 9   CLOSED: end Nov to end Mar   MEALS: light L (around £7). Set D £23   SERVICE: not inc, card slips closed   CARDS: Access, Amex, Diners, Visa   DETAILS: 26 seats. Private parties: 24 main room. Car park. Vegetarian meals. Children's helpings (high tea for very young). Jacket and tie. No smoking in dining-room. Wheelchair access (2 steps; also WC). No music   ACCOMMODATION: 10 rooms, all with bath/shower. B&B £90 to £190. Children welcome. Baby facilities. Pets welcome (not in public rooms). Garden. Phone. Doors close at midnight. Confirm by 6. Fax: (033 97) 55397 (*The Which? Hotel Guide*)

---

**BLAIRGOWRIE Tayside**                                                      map 8

## ▲ *Kinloch House Hotel* 🍷 ⁘✳

By Blairgowrie PH10 6SG
BLAIRGOWRIE (0250) 884237                                    COOKING 2
on A923, 3m W of Blairgowrie                                  COST £19–£48

On a summer's evening – especially with a full moon – this imposing mansion takes on a romantic grandeur. The setting is beautiful, and if the exterior and proprietor are a little daunting, 'both were built to last and inspire confidence'. This is an establishment where unobtrusive professionalism and hard work count for a great deal (you do not have to worry about service charges here, as they are neither expected nor accepted). As one guest commented: 'David Shentall has perfected the art of being a country house host.' Bill McNicoll's cooking suits the style of the place admirably: 'good ingredients uncluttered by coulis clichés and strawberry garnishing.' The daily four-course menu is backed up by more exotic – and more expensive – supplements. Steaks and seafood loom large; otherwise you may find warm salad of pigeon breast and smoked bacon, pork fillet in Stilton sauce with garlic noodles, and breast of chicken with leeks and grain mustard sauce. One fine meal featured spinach roulade with cream cheese, timbale of fresh plaice with prawns and rack of lamb cooked pink. The sweets trolley is an awe-inspiring sight. A huge range of malts dominates the bar. Although clarets offer especially intelligent range, the Loire with Huet and Alsace with Rolly-Gassmann look equally appealing. The New World is strongly represented but Italy has yet to enthuse the wine-buyer. Much decent drinking can be had around and below £15, but at the higher levels prices push hard. House wines start at £9.40.

---

*All details are as accurate as possible at the time of going to press, but chefs and owners often change, and it is wise to check by telephone before making a special journey. Many readers have been disappointed when set-price bargain meals are no longer available. Ask when booking.*

CHEF: Bill McNicoll   PROPRIETORS: David and Sarah Shentall   OPEN: all week; 12.30 to 2,
7 to 9.15   CLOSED: 15 to 30 Dec   MEALS: Set L £13.95, Set D £22.90   SERVICE: card slips
closed   CARDS: Access, Amex, Diners, Visa   DETAILS: 60 seats. Private parties: 35 private
room. Car park. Vegetarian meals. Children's helpings L and high tea. No children under 7.
Jacket and tie. No smoking in dining-room. Wheelchair access (also WC). No music
ACCOMMODATION: 21 rooms, all with bath/shower. Rooms for disabled. D, B&B £73 to
£177.50. No children under 7. Children welcome. Baby facilities. Pets welcome (certain
rooms only). Afternoon teas. Garden. TV. Phone. Doors close at midnight. Fax: (0250)
884333

---

**CAIRNDOW** Strathclyde                                            map 8

## *Loch Fyne Oyster Bar* £

Clachan Farm, Cairndow PA26 8BH
CAIRNDOW (049 96) 236                                      COOKING 2
on A83, at head of Loch Fyne                               COST £14–£35

'The oysters are still the most delicious I know – small, sweet and fresh to the
taste-buds. I was strongly tempted to a second dozen. The hot smoked salmon
remains enormously successful, and the service on this occasion was excellent,
if informal. Of course, the view down Loch Fyne would seduce the hardest
heart.' So writes someone who is happy to be marooned hereabouts, to take pot
luck in fairly basic but clean and fresh surroundings, and to eat the best of raw
materials. Loch Fyne oysters are milder and less briny than many Pacifics, but
succulent and subtle, and best when not too cold. Some readers have thought
that if you have them hot with garlic butter, they are too mild for the garlic. The
smoked salmon is excellent as are lightly smoked steaks served hot with a
sauce containing a hint of horseradish and whisky. Other items appear on the
menu, but people agree less on the wisdom of straying from the main agenda of
the simply cooked or raw. The place gets busy, children are everywhere (as
they should be in a holiday zone), and this can affect the service. For value, it
cannot be beaten. The wine list is trimmed down to suit the proceedings, but
everything is the proper job, just like the oysters. House Gros Plant is £8.90.

---

CHEF: Greta Cameron   PROPRIETORS: Loch Fyne Oysters Ltd   OPEN: all week; 9am to
9pm   MEALS: alc (main courses £4 to £11)   SERVICE: not inc   CARDS: Access, Amex,
Visa   DETAILS: 80 seats. 10 tables outside. Private parties: 50 main room. Car park.
Vegetarian meals. Children's helpings. No-smoking area. Wheelchair access (also WC).
Music. Fax: (049 96) 234

---

**CANONBIE** Dumfries & Galloway                                   map 8

## ▲ *Riverside Inn* ♥ ⅚✳ £

Canonbie DG14 0UX
CANONBIE (038 73) 71512 and 71295                          COOKING 2
on A7, just over the border                                COST £15–£34

The old slate-roofed inn by the River Esk is a destination for a wide region. 'We
will happily drive the 70 miles in order to eat dinner (not to mention one of the
best breakfasts in Britain) here. The food is simply presented, but very good

and rarely disappointing – so much better than much "designer" cooking.'
Another visitor, from still further afield, makes the same point: 'It may be less
sophisticated than some of your other entries, but it is top-quality "home"
cooking and a great find.' Good materials and industrious housekeeping –
breadmaking has been added to the skills of producing jam, marmalade and
pickles – are the foundations of success in meals that may be composed of
dishes like potted salmon, chicken and bacon terrine, salmon fish-cakes with
hollandaise, lots of fresh fish cooked with beer batter, good chargrilled beef,
and roast duck with a herb pudding. The bar food is as much appreciated as the
menu in the dining-room. Adnams supplies the wines and its cheerful
idiosyncracy continues to reinforce the pleasures of the Riverside. Prices are
very reasonable and the few halves do at least offer real choice. House wine is
£7.95. CELLARMAN'S CHOICE: Vin de Pays d'Oc, Ozidoc, Sauvignon 1991,
£8.95; Graves, Dom. de Gaillat 1986, £14.95.

CHEFS/PROPRIETORS: Robert and Susan Phillips  OPEN: Mon to Sat; 12 to 2, 7.30 to 9
CLOSED: Feb, 2 weeks Nov, 25 and 26 Dec, 1 and 2 Jan  MEALS: bar alc L and D (main
courses £5 to £12). Set restaurant D £21  SERVICE: not inc, card slips closed  CARDS:
Access, Visa  DETAILS: 28 seats. 4 tables outside. Private parties: 28 main room. Car park.
Vegetarian meals. Children's helpings. No children under 5. Smart dress preferred
(restaurant). No smoking in dining-room. Wheelchair access (also WC). No music
ACCOMMODATION: 6 rooms, all with bath/shower. Rooms for disabled. B&B £27 to £84.
Deposit: £20. Children welcome. Pets by arrangement. Garden. TV. Doors close at
midnight. Confirm by 2 (*The Which? Hotel Guide*)

---

COLBOST Highland                                                        map 8

## Three Chimneys ♟ ✸

Colbost, nr Dunvegan,
Isle of Skye IV55 8ZT
GLENDALE (047 081) 258                                          COOKING 2*
on B884, 4m W of Dunvegan                                     COST £16–£46

'No more whisky shop, and there was no lobster available on this day, but all
else lived up to expectation.' This was the comment of someone who perceived
that Shirley Spear does everything in a thoroughgoing manner. The demise of
the shop is but prelude to more space and comfort for diners in this set of
cottages just back from the foreshore. The emphasis, of course, is on local
produce, whether it be seafood, meat or plants pulled from the soil. 'The hot
shellfish platter contained oysters, crab, scallops, mussels and langoustines.
Each species had its own topping,' purred one satisfied customer. Seafood may
seem the obvious draw: the partan pie at lunch, the lobster salad, or the hot
lobster medley that offers lobster, langoustines, mussels and scallops with a
brandy and sherry cream sauce. But there are also lamb with redcurrant and
rosemary gravy, venison with thyme and juniper, or smoked products such as
pheasant and venison, not to mention the soups. Shirley Spear is proud of her
invincible championing of Skye food and self-help. It has paid off in her lean
years as well as fat. The good-value wine list offers consistent quality across the
range, encompassing decent Riojas and Rhônes, the finest classics from good
years and sensible variety in halves. House selection wines are from £8.95.

CELLARMAN'S CHOICE: Vin de Pays Catalan, Dom. Gauby 1991, £15.95; Coteaux du Languedoc, Dom. les Embals, cépage Syrah 1992, £10.25.

CHEF: Shirley Spear  PROPRIETORS: Eddie and Shirley Spear  OPEN: Mon to Sat (Sun D 'major' bank hols and Aug); 12 to 2, 7 to 9  CLOSED: Nov to end Mar  MEALS: alc L (starters/main courses £2.50 to £20). Minimum £2.50 L. Set D £25 to £30  SERVICE: not inc  CARDS: Access, Visa  DETAILS: 30 seats. 2 tables outside. Private parties: 20 main room, 14 and 20 private rooms. Car park. Vegetarian meals. Children's helpings L. Smart dress preferred. No smoking in dining-room. Music

---

**CRINAN** Strathclyde                                                    map 8

## ▲ Crinan Hotel, Lock 16 Seafood Restaurant ♟

Crinan PA31 8SR
CRINAN (054 683) 261                                                COOKING 2
off A816, 6m NW of Lochgilphead                                     COST £44–£60

This hotel, hardly a specimen of great beauty, is perched by the lock at the north end of the Crinan canal, forming a bottleneck between Loch Fyne and the Atlantic. The location is glorious, the views are great and the restaurant on the rooftop that serves clams, oysters, prawns and lobster is a wonderful place at which to savour them. So fresh is the produce that a weather forecast is posted – storms mean no eating tonight. The meals are set, over five courses and coffee, and may run through mussels marinière followed by Loch Fyne clams on the half shell, before jumbo prawns 'Corryvrekan' – sizzling in pans with tropical fruit – then dessert, before cheese. The hotel has simple but pleasing rooms, all with a sea view. The Westward Restaurant on the ground floor offers a much wider range of dishes, but gets less consistent reports. The Crinan Bar is approved for its food as well. The Ryans are good at their job. The pity about the wine list is the unremitting application of a multiplier that puts a Sancerre at a highish £23 and non-vintage champagnes at over £35. No beef though about the quality, which shows strength in all areas. There is more than adequate drinking below £15, a few half-bottles and decent selections from south-west France. House wines are £9.95.

CHEF: Nicolas Ryan  PROPRIETORS: Nicolas and Frances Ryan  OPEN: Wed to Sun, D only (L by arrangement); 8  CLOSED: Oct to end Apr  MEALS: Set D £35 to £40  SERVICE: not inc, card slips closed  CARDS: Access, Amex, Visa  DETAILS: 20 seats. Private parties: 20 main room. Car park. Vegetarian meals. Children's helpings on request. Jacket and tie. No smoking during meals. Wheelchair access (also WC). No music  ACCOMMODATION: 22 rooms, all with bath/shower. Rooms for disabled. Lift. B&B £75 to £130. Deposit: 10%. Children welcome. Pets welcome. Afternoon teas. Garden. TV. Phone. Doors close at midnight. Confirm by 6. Fax: (054 683) 292 (*The Which? Hotel Guide*)

---

*'The general grubbiness and scruffiness of this restaurant made us dubious before we started, and the wanderings of three large dogs in and out of the dining-room while we were eating added to the impression. When we spotted a very large cockroach on my chair our distaste was complete. The proprietors were not unduly concerned and blamed the property next door.'*  On eating in Kent

---

---

CULLEN Grampian                                                    map 8

## ▲ *Bayview Hotel* £                          [NEW ENTRY]

57 Seafield Street, Cullen AB56 2SU
CULLEN (0542) 41031, changes to                          COOKING 1*
(0542) 841031 autumn 1993                                COST £16–£34

It is possible to dine in either bar or dining-room at this ideal small hotel
overlooking Cullen harbour. Choose between light and dark, view and no
view, the food is the same. There is a short regular menu, but the best thing to
do is to check the blackboard with daily offerings, mainly fish, by John Ferrier.
After eating fish soup, cornets of smoked salmon stuffed with lightly spiced
prawns, sole stuffed with crab, and grilled halibut with parsley sauce, one
couple could only say that the cassis bombe with blackcurrant coulis was the
perfect end to the meal. The food is simple, carefully cooked and naturally
served. The short wine list has house wines at £8.30.

---

CHEF: John Ferrier   PROPRIETOR: David Evans   OPEN: all week; 12 to 1.45, 6.30 to 9
MEALS: alc (main courses £6 to £12.50)   SERVICE: not inc, card slips closed   CARDS:
Access, Visa   DETAILS: 35 seats. Private parties: 20 main room. Vegetarian meals. No
children under 14 in bar. No music   ACCOMMODATION: 6 rooms, all with bath/shower.
B&B £35 to £60. Children welcome. TV. Phone. Doors close at 11. Confirm by 6

---

CUPAR Fife                                                         map 8

## *Ostlers Close* ♟

25 Bonnygate, Cupar KY15 4BU                             COOKING 3
CUPAR (0334) 55574                                       COST £19–£44

Bonnygate is a small lane off the main street, Ostlers Close is a small house –
'not cramped; how to put it politely? Compact and bijou,' speculated local
supporters. 'Few places this small', they added, 'can cope with relatively big
parties. Yet, despite murmurs about delay, we were happy to wait for cooking
of this quality and intelligence.' Seafood has to be the main attraction:
langoustines with a stir-fry of sea kale on a fresh herb butter sauce, a ragoût of
seafood with pesto, and monkfish with bacon and pesto are instances that have
drawn praise. 'Thank goodness for the *Guide*: we were able to lunch on wild
mushrooms in puff pastry, lamb with madeira sauce, venison with cranberries,
and vegetables – cabbage with saffron and orange, sweetened carrots and
potato cakes – that were different. The greengage tart with custard as dessert
was almost too much.' Amanda Graham does the honours with tact and charm
and the place has all the gear for proper eating. While the wine list may lack
heavyweight first growths, it has splendid and catholic range lower down the
scale. Particular strengths are antipodeans and Alsaces in whites, Spain and
clarets in reds. Half-bottles, modestly priced, show care in selection from
good merchants. House wine is £7.45. CELLARMAN'S CHOICE: Savennières,
Ch. de Chamboureau 1991, £14.25; Grand Cru St-Emilion, Ch. Yon-Figeac
1989, £15.30.

CHEF: James Graham   PROPRIETORS: Amanda and James Graham   OPEN: Tue to Sat; 12.15 to 2, 7 to 9.30 (10 Sat)   CLOSED: 2 weeks June   MEALS: alc (main courses L £7.50 to £10, D £14.50 to £15.50)   SERVICE: not inc, card slips closed   CARDS: Access, Visa   DETAILS: 28 seats. Private parties: 22 main room. Vegetarian meals with prior notice. Children's helpings. No children under 6 D. No smoking during meals. No music

---

## DRUMNADROCHIT Highland
map 8

## ▲ *Polmaily House* ⁵✳

Drumnadrochit IV3 6XT
DRUMNADROCHIT (0456) 450343
on A831 Cannich road, 2m W of Drumnadrochit

COOKING 2*
COST £31–£41

Reports on this civilised mansion set against the backdrop of the Highlands focus on the merits of the kitchen. 'We couldn't believe the standard,' noted a well-travelled couple from Yorkshire. Alison Parsons' four-course fixed-price dinners have their share of country-house stalwarts, although the cooking also displays a more modern edge and takes note of the seasons. A typical menu from September shows the style: fricassee of young grouse and guinea-fowl in puff pastry followed by chanterelle soup, then casseroled oxtail or matelote of Dover sole, monkfish and mussels, before home-made caramel ice-cream with cardamom cake and Scottish farmhouse cheeses. Occasionally the set-up fails – 'flabby' tasteless scallops, turbot unnecessarily embellished with tomato – but the overall impression is sound. Service and accommodation draw a mixed response, although guests have approved of the excellent breakfast kippers. The Highland location means that wine deliveries can be spasmodic and the cellar may be depleted by the end of the season. But the list offers a good selection, divided up into price bands from under £15 to over £25, backed up by some promising halves from reputable sources. House wine is £7.50.

---

CHEFS: Alison Parsons and Barbara Drury   PROPRIETORS: Alison and Nick Parsons   OPEN: all week, D only; 7.30 to 9   CLOSED: Nov to Mar   MEALS: Set D £25   SERVICE: not inc, card slips closed   CARDS: Access, Visa   DETAILS: 30 seats. Private parties: 15 main room. Car park. Vegetarian meals with prior notice. Children's helpings. Smart dress preferred. No smoking in dining-room. Wheelchair access (also WC). No music   ACCOMMODATION: 9 rooms, 7 with bath/shower. B&B £35 to £100. Deposit: £25. Chidren welcome. Baby facilities. Garden. Swimming-pool. Tennis. Phone. Doors close at midnight. Confirm by 4. Fax: (0456) 450813 (*The Which? Hotel Guide*)

---

## DRYBRIDGE Grampian
map 8

## *Old Monastery* ⁵✳

Drybridge AB56 2JB
BUCKIE (0542) 32660
2½m S of Buckie, junction of A98 and A942

COOKING 1
COST £26–£41

The monastery, which is just outside the village, was only built during the last century as a retreat, but the monks certainly knew where to find the best view. The Grays have worked on the comfort ever since, keeping the chill at bay with wood-burning stoves, and retaining some of the ecclesiastical atmosphere –

you eat in the chapel and drink in the cloisters – though their hospitality is anything but sepulchral. The cooking, though priced up, is at its best simple and unfussed: deep-fried whitebait, a couple of soups, filo rolls of leeks and smoked ham with a carrot sauce, a mushroom and coriander mousse with pimento sauce are some of the starters. The main courses are mostly meat, with a couple of fish dishes. The wine list covers a good range, generously supplied with halves. House wines start at £7.50.

CHEF: Douglas Gray   PROPRIETORS: Douglas and Maureen Gray   OPEN: Tue to Sat; 12.15 to 1.45, 7 to 9 (9.30 Sat)   CLOSED: first 2 weeks Nov, last 3 weeks Jan   MEALS: alc (main courses £11 to £14.50)   SERVICE: not inc, card slips closed   CARDS: Access, Amex, Visa
DETAILS: 40 seats. Private parties: 45 main room. Car park. Vegetarian meals. Children's helpings. No children under 8. Smart dress preferred. No smoking in dining-room. No music

---

DUNKELD Tayside                                                                             map 8

## ▲ *Kinnaird* ▼ ✳

Kinnaird Estate, By Dunkeld PH8 0LB
BALLINLUIG (0796) 482440
2m N of Dunkeld, take B898                                                    COOKING 4
signed Dalguise                                                               COST £31–£58

There is punctilious correctness here in matters of service: 'shades of the court at Versailles,' mused one. Kinnaird is grand, with grand prices and cooking to match. As with the best of such places, the grandeur does not get in the way of taste or 'flawless service'. The small Georgian house is decorated with flair as well as providing comfort, and guests will be unused to such luxury as their own open fires in the bedrooms. A periodic recidivist noticed that John Webber's preludes and postludes to the meal were less imaginative than they used to be, but none of the invention, or standards, of the nub of the affair have been lost. A carpaccio of turbot with a filo parcel of crabmeat, a fine piece of poached beef with vegetables, potatoes and horseradish dumplings, and an intensely flavoured caramel soufflé served with a caramel ice-cream made up his meal. Excellent, was his verdict, and this was echoed by a refugee from bad weather who felt the soufflé justified the entire trip. There is a short *carte*, at fixed price (inclusive of every trimming), that emphasises fish for the first course so as to concentrate on meat later. Reports applaud the balance of flavours, rarely mentioning over-reduction (an earlier failing) or blandness. Dishes such as a salad of scallops with carrots and Sauternes, monkfish and lobster tortellini with chive butter sauce, cassoulet of fish with a light cream sauce, vegetables and lentils, noisettes of lamb with coriander and onion, and smoked breast of duck with a jasmine tea sauce show a ready acceptance of recent developments together with a pleasing simplicity of composition. Come pudding time, always note the hot soufflé, or accept the very sound pastry-work. Coffee does not get a good press. A page of suggestions provides useful guidance for the wine-wary. Thereafter prices and quality escalate; the tendency is to favour the large and well-established makers so expect firm reliability; this is exemplified by the list of bourgeois clarets that takes in Cissac, Chasse-Spleen and St-Bonnet. Half-bottles are listed separately and very good they are too. The New World is not ignored, and decent French country wines are easier on the finances than some on the list. House wines are from £14. CELLARMAN'S CHOICE: Rongopai Wines, Te Kauwhata, Chardonnay 1990, £21; L'Ermitage de Chasse-Spleen, 1986, £18.

CHEF: John Webber  PROPRIETOR: Mrs Constance Ward  OPEN: all week; 12.30 to 1.45, 7 to 9.30  CLOSED: Feb  MEALS: Set L £19.50 (2 courses) to £24, Set D £34 to £38  SERVICE: net prices, card slips closed  CARDS: Access, Amex, Visa  DETAILS: 35 seats. Private parties: 25 private room. Car park. Vegetarian meals. No children under 12. Jacket and tie. No smoking in dining-room. Wheelchair access (also WC). No music  ACCOMMODATION: 9 rooms, all with bath/shower. Rooms for disabled. Lift. B&B £95 to £170. No children under 12. Pets in kennels only. Garden. Tennis. Fishing. Snooker. TV. Phone. Fax: (0796) 482289 (*The Which? Hotel Guide*)

---

## DUNVEGAN Highland

map 8

## ▲ *Harlosh House* ⁊✶

By Dunvegan, Isle of Skye IV55 8ZG
DUNVEGAN (047 022) 367
off A863, 3m S of Dunvegan

COOKING 2
COST £23–£54

To call this eighteenth-century house isolated is an understatement, but the welcome is friendly to a fault, as one couple who had broken down found to their relief. 'It must have one of the best views of the world' is compensation for the possibility that the 'rooms may feel a little small when the weather turns inclement', but the Elfords do everything to make you ignore what is going on outside. Downstairs is all old-fashioned comfort; upstairs are newly decorated bedrooms. Peter Elford does not make a great thing about being in Scotland. The cooking, therefore, has nothing strained about it, no false simplicity, but uses materials to create refined food very much in tune with current sensibilities. Squid stir-fried with ginger and red peppers, haggis baked on a flat mushroom, halibut with vegetables and a dill butter sauce, skate with black butter (given a twist by balsamic vinegar), and venison with a port and lemon sauce are some of the dishes that have impressed with their presentation as well as flavour. Desserts are short and simple – maybe two ices, a chocolate terrine or some cheese. Coffee is taken in the lounge afterwards. Peter Elford says that he has been blessed with a better supply of herbs this year, giving him a chance to lighten sauces and make more of flavour. Service can be slow but it should look up when Lindsey Elford returns to the fray after looking after baby. The wine list has shown extension this season, providing a very decent range at fair prices. House wines are £7.50.

CHEF: Peter Elford  PROPRIETORS: Peter and Lindsey Elford  OPEN: Tue to Sun, D only (Mon residents only); 7 to 9  CLOSED: mid-Oct to Easter  MEALS: alc (main courses £9.50 to £25)  SERVICE: not inc  CARDS: Access, Visa  DETAILS: 18 seats. Private parties: 18 main room. Car park. Vegetarian meals for residents with prior notice. Children's helpings. No smoking in dining-room. Wheelchair access (1 step). Music  ACCOMMODATION: 6 double rooms, 5 with bath/shower. B&B £79. Deposit: £40. Children welcome. Baby facilities. Afternoon teas. Garden. Doors close at midnight. Confirm by 5 (*The Which? Hotel Guide*)

## L'Auberge ♥

| | |
|---|---|
| 56 St Mary Street, EH1 1SX | COOKING 2 |
| 031-556 5888 | COST £15–£57 |

L'Auberge's setting between the Castle and Holyrood House, is pure Scottish, although the food and almost everything else are wholeheartedly French. The four-course table d'hôte has more than a hint of cuisine grandmère in dishes such as smooth chicken liver parfait, mussels in puff pastry with leek and cream sauce, noisettes of lamb, salmon with grain mustard sauce, and cold chocolate terrine. The seasonal *carte* attempts to kill off any memory of nouvelle cuisine by offering generous portions of bourgeois cooking with some modern overtones. Medallions of venison (not marinated) are sauté and served with a julienne of celeriac, juniper berries and gin; grilled salmon steak is served with cucumber and tomato butter cream. The kitchen is keen on Scottish produce, making use of everything from fresh chanterelles and Orkney cheese biscuits to rabbits bred by a policeman from East Lothian. Service draws mixed reports. Given the knowledge and enthusiasm required to compile the wine list, the persistent use of alternative vintages is a surprise. Alsace would benefit from a change or expansion of the sources; that apart, this virtually francophile list – New World bottles are on a single-page addendum – excels in Bordeaux and offers a good balance of petits châteaux (classed growths and good years) and a fair few in halves. Burgundy and the Rhône are not outdone but there is greater caution here. Prices are fair. House wine is £7.85. CELLARMAN'S CHOICE: Sauvignon Blanc, Dom. de la Chaignée 1991, £12.85; premier Côtes de Bordeaux, Ch. Ricaud 1988, £14.25.

CHEF: Fabrice Bresulier   PROPRIETOR: Daniel Wencker   OPEN: all week; 12.15 to 2, 6.30 to 9.30 (10 Sat)   CLOSED: 25 and 26 Dec, 1 and 2 Jan   MEALS: alc (main courses £12 to £19). Set L £6.95 (1 course) to £10, Set D £19.85   SERVICE: not inc   CARDS: Access, Amex, Diners, Visa   DETAILS: 50 seats. Private parties: 35 main room, 25 private room. Vegetarian meals. Children's helpings. Smart dress preferred. No smoking during meals. Wheelchair access (1 step). Music. Air-conditioned. Fax: 031-558 1691

## Denzler's 121

| | |
|---|---|
| 121 Constitution Street, Leith, EH6 7AE | COOKING 1 |
| 031-554 3268 | COST £20–£37 |

The location, just outside Leith Docks, is unpromising and the impressive stone façade of this former bank building strikes some as 'dour', but inside all is spacious and elegant. Contemporary Scottish pictures add to the relaxed atmosphere. Swiss veal specialities receive endorsements and are accompanied by 'excellent' pommes berrichonne or spätzli. Other enjoyable dishes have included deep-fried mushrooms, 'supreme' crab soup, and pheasant in a well-judged cream and orange sauce. Puddings are extravagant concoctions relying heavily on ice-cream. Generally the cooking succeeds, although gripes about tough venison and 'dry, tasteless' apple strudel have raised question marks about the regime. Service has mostly been friendly and efficient, but the occasional slip-up has been reported. Simple, cheap lunches take in air-dried

Grisons beef and ham, an elaborate version of Gruyère cheese on toast, lambs' sweetbreads and Black Forest gâteau. Dôle and Valais Swiss wines top the list, which runs to 100 fairly priced bins. House French is £10.35 a litre.

CHEFS: Sami Denzler and Ian Gordon   PROPRIETORS: Sami and Pat Denzler   OPEN: Tue to Sat, exc Sat L; 12 to 2, 6.30 to 10   CLOSED: 1 week beginning Jan, 2 weeks end July   MEALS: alc (main courses L £5.50 to £6.50, D £9 to £11)   SERVICE: net prices, card slips closed   CARDS: Access, Amex, Visa   DETAILS: 72 seats. Private parties: 72 main room. Vegetarian meals with prior notice. Children's helpings on request. Smart dress preferred. No music

## Indian Cavalry Club  £

| NEW ENTRY |

3 Atholl Place, EH3 8HP                                                   COOKING 1
031-228 3282 and 2974                                               COST £16–£47

The restaurant (five minutes' walk from the west end of Princes Street) really is a club which you can join, although open to all comers. A long cream room is sparsely decorated with prints and lances, although 'the only genuinely military feature is the over-staffing'. The menu makes interesting reading and suggested side dishes and wines are listed alongside most items: pineapple sambar and Chardonnay with Kathmandu chicken, aloo paneer and Côtes du Rhône with lamb pasanda. Chilli garlic chicken has just the right amount of fire without drowning out other flavours. Vegetable dishes such as bhindi bhaji, creamy-textured tandoori aubergine bharta ('a winner') and chickpea and mushroom biriani have impressed readers, although an excess of oil can mar the overall effect. The choice of sweets includes creamed vermicelli ('like kulfi left out in the rain') with dates and pistachios. Delicately spiced lemon tea is a good refresher; otherwise you can drink lassi or lager. The list of around two dozen wines has been thoughtfully chosen to match the food. House wine is £8.50. As we went to press the owners were about to launch their Spicy-Affairs bistro – reports, please.

CHEFS: Bilquis Chowdhury, Sultan Miah and Mohammed Zubair   PROPRIETORS: Shahidul Alam Chowdhury and Bilquis Chowdhury   OPEN: all week; 12 to 2.30, 5.30 to 11.30   MEALS: alc (main courses £6 to £12). Set L £6.95 (1 course) to £17.95, Set D £9.95 to £17.95. Minimum £7 D   SERVICE: not inc   CARDS: Access, Amex, Diners, Visa   DETAILS: 120 seats. Private parties: 80 main room, 40 private room. Vegetarian meals. Children's helpings on request. Smart dress preferred. No-smoking area. No music. Fax: 031-225 1911

## Kalpna  ⁕  £

2–3 St Patrick Square, EH8 9EZ                                      COOKING 2
031-667 9890                                                             COST £11–£31

'If anyone needs converting to vegetarian food, I'd take them here,' writes an Edinburgh lady. Kalpna serves, arguably, the best Indian food in the city. Service is still fast and efficient, and the food is as good as ever – although a vegan expert has noted a tilt towards more dairy products. The cooking is Gujarati and dishes are noted for their freshness and subtlety. Khumb masala (mushrooms in a creamy coconut sauce) is a perennial favourite; otherwise the menu offers superb light kachoris (lentil fritters) with tamarind sauce, aloo ghobi and massive birianis. The Annapurna thali is excellent value for a starter: three vegetable dishes, wholegrain rice, raita, pickles, a couple of light puffy puris and a chapati. Desserts, such as mango kulfi, seero and carrot and sesame halva, are regularly endorsed. Masala tea and lager are available, but it is worth considering the serious wine list, which is supplied by Wines of Paris. House wines are from £6.50.

CHEF/PROPRIETOR: Ajay Bhartdwaj   OPEN: Mon to Sat, exc Sat L; 12 to 2, 5.30 to 10.30   MEALS: alc (main courses £3.50 to £8.50). Buffet L £3.50 to £6   SERVICE: 10%, card slips closed   CARDS: Access, Visa   DETAILS: 65 seats. Private parties: 35 main room. Vegetarian meals. Children's helpings. No smoking. Wheelchair access (1 step). Music

## Kelly's

46 West Richmond Street, EH8 9DZ                                    COOKING 2
031-668 3847                                                          COST £16–£39

This diminutive restaurant, not far from the university, has stuck to its last and survived the dim period of recession, even reintroducing lunches. Jacquie Kelly is gaining skill and ability with time and reports this year have been better than ever for meals that beat many Edinburgh rivals for consistency and taste. She does not aim for complexity, but a meal that included tomato and orange soup, asparagus with a raspberry vinaigrette, boned saddle of lamb with shallots and redcurrant sauce, and medallions of venison with a bilberry sauce was spot-on for flavour. The room has always been a pleasant one to sit in, and service is extremely amiable, if sometimes slow. Next door to the restaurant is a small art gallery-cum-reception room also run by the Kellys. The wine list fits the bill here: many good growers, many unfamiliar as well, and not too much choice. Prices are kept sensibly low, and the house selections – all at £10 – cover tremendous range. Jeff Kelly has sampled them all and will advise. There is a cheaper house wine at £8.50.

CHEFS: Jacquie Kelly and Nicholas Carnegie   PROPRIETORS: Jacquie Kelly and Jeff Kelly   OPEN: Tue to Sun, exc L Tue and Sat and Sun D; 12 to 2, 6.30 to 9.30   CLOSED: first 3 weeks Oct, first week Jan   MEALS: alc L (main courses £4.50 to £7.50). Set D £19.50 to £23.50   SERVICE: not inc, card slips closed   CARDS: Access, Amex, Visa   DETAILS: 36 seats. Private parties: 36 main room. Vegetarian meals. Children's helpings. No children under 6. Smart dress preferred. No smoking before 9pm. Wheelchair access (also WC). Music

## Loon Fung £

NEW ENTRY

2 Warriston Place, EH3 5LE                                          COOKING 1
031-556 1781                                                          COST £15–£44

A long-standing fixture of the Edinburgh Chinese scene, this restaurant consists of two light and airy rooms with basic furnishings and well-spaced tables. As befits a Cantonese kitchen, fish is the strong suit and daily specials are worth exploring. A reasonable showing of dim-sum and one-plate rice and noodle dishes are in keeping and 'recommended specialities' such as mango chicken and Korean-style beef merit consideration. Otherwise the menu of around 120 dishes includes carefully executed items such as deep-fried salt and chilli prawns, crisp-skinned duck with ginger and pineapple, and juicy squid with black-bean sauce. Presentation relies heavily on flamboyant vegetable sculptures. Service is prompt and keeps pace with the trade. The minimal wine list is bolstered by lagers and liqueurs, although tea is probably the best option. House French is £8.50. Another outlet is at 32 Grindlay Street, Edinburgh, Tel: 031-229 5757.

CHEF: Tin Fat Siu  PROPRIETORS: Sammy Tam and Tin Fat Siu  OPEN: all week, exc L Sat and Sun; 12 (2 Sat and Sun) to 11.30 (12.30am Fri and Sat)  CLOSED: 25 Dec, Chinese New Year  MEALS: alc (main courses £4.50 to £15). Set L and D £11.50 (minimum 2) to £12.50 (minimum 8)  SERVICE: 10%  CARDS: Access, Amex, Visa  DETAILS: 100 seats. Private parties: 50 main room, 50 private room. Vegetarian meals. Children welcome. Smart dress preferred. Wheelchair access (also WC). Music

## Le Marché Noir

| 2–4 Eyre Place, EH3 5EP | COOKING 2 |
| 031-558 1608 | COST £13–£35 |

There is strength yet in the French-bistro concept of British eating out, but the cooking here is beyond bistro: popular theme nights, for instance Languedoc in the autumn, explore the byways of French country cooking – updated to include smoked goose with avocado. Service remains French, relaxed and amiable: 'We arrived to find it was the night of a theme evening, but our appetites were not up to that, so they were happy to offer us something simpler. So pleased were we that we returned the next night for another pleasant time.' Restaurants should restore, and this one does: the food satisfies the inner person, the ambience – resolutely French menus that require tableside translation, picture-laden walls, and Gallic-style drapes – soothe the outer. The menus are fixed-price, and two of them are available at any one time, offering a wide choice in all. Fast-cooked restaurant dishes such as escalope of pork with chestnuts and honey or quail stuffed with veal served with mushrooms and mustard differentiate Le Marché's style from the long-braised casseroles and sticky stews that made the bistro reputation. Desserts, however, are on the straightforward side, and are none the worse for it. Some of the old-style Doudet-Naudin burgundies remain on the wine list and will please many; the prices reflect quality closely. Half-bottles have yet to establish favour here. House wine is £8.50.

CHEFS: Neil Ross and David Connell  PROPRIETOR: Malcolm Duck  OPEN: all week D, Mon to Fri L (L Sat and Sun by arrangement); 12 to 2.30, 7 (6.30 Sun) to 10 (10.30 Fri and Sat, 9.30 Sun)  MEALS: Set L £7 to £16.50, Set D £18.50 to £22.50  SERVICE: not inc (10% for 6 or more)  CARDS: Access, Amex, Visa  DETAILS: 45 seats. Private parties: 35 main room. Vegetarian meals. Children's helpings. Smart dress preferred. No smoking during meals. Wheelchair access (1 step; also WC). Music. Fax: 031-556 0798

*See the inside of the front cover for an explanation of the 1 to 5 rating system for cooking standards.*

*The text of entries is based on unsolicited reports sent in by readers, backed up by inspections conducted anonymously. The factual details under the text are from questionnaires the Guide sends to all restaurants that feature in the book.*

# Martins ♀ ⅝⚹

| | |
|---|---|
| 70 Rose Street North Lane, EH2 3DX | COOKING 3 |
| 031-225 3106 | COST £23–£49 |

'Martin Irons plays the part of the enthusiastic amateur, but we soon caught that this was a hard-nosed professional operation.' This may seem a left-handed compliment, but it draws attention to the zeal of Martin Irons as host and to his wish to get things right. This year has seen more questioning as to his success, though the verdict is generally in his favour. Portion size and, in Edinburgh terms, cost have been the main grumbles, though few can query the value of the two-course set-lunch menu even if evenings reach nearer the economic heavens. The style of the kitchen has strong undertones of nouvelle cuisine in scale and arrangement though the recipes are more robustly modern, as seen, for example, in a warm salad of scallops with chorizo and diced pickled plums or sauté duck and chicken with spring onions, lentils and chillis. The restaurant is as light and modern as the food, and there is no denying the success of the Irons' presentation of cheese (almost always the highpoint of people's reports, which says a small something about the cooking), nor their attention to details such as the delicious bread. This is altogether one of the most successful of Edinburgh's smaller restaurants. It is located, Martin Irons informs us, 'between Frederick Street and Castle Street in the North Lane'. The wine list is exemplary, but why the Italians get the cold shoulder is unexplained. This apart, the wines are drawn from all quarters from fine and fashionable growers. Kistler Estate from Sonoma, J.M. Boillot's Puligny and Barge's Côte Rôtie stand out. Prices, albeit high, reflect quality but there is more than enough below £14. Half-bottles show care in range and quality. House wines are £9.20. CELLARMAN'S CHOICE: Bourgogne Aligoté 1990, Rouget, £19.70; Côtes du Rhône, cépage Syrah 1991, Laurent, £15.90.

CHEFS: Forbes Stott and Christopher Colverson   PROPRIETORS: Martin and Gay Irons
OPEN: Tue to Sat, exc Sat L; 12 to 2, 7 (6.30 during Festival) to 10   CLOSED: 24 Dec to 24 Jan, 1 week from 28 June, 1 week from 28 Sept   MEALS: alc (main courses £14 to £16). Set L £10.95 (2 courses) to £17   SERVICE: not inc (10% for 6 or more)   CARDS: Access, Amex, Diners, Visa   DETAILS: 28 seats. Private parties: 28 main room, 8 private room. Vegetarian meals. No children under 8. No smoking in dining-room. Wheelchair access (3 steps). No music. Fax: 031-220 4062

# Pierre Victoire £

| | |
|---|---|
| 10 Victoria Street, EH1 2HG | COOKING 1 |
| 031-225 1721 | COST £9–£24 |

The culinary juggernaut that Pierre Levicky set in motion has gathered momentum. Soon, Pierre Victoires will be opening all over Britain; often franchises, they will still subscribe to Pierre's founding principles of French food at low, low prices and the certain *je ne sais quoi* jumble-sale style of the fixtures and fittings. The Victoria Street venue is the first of the line, still operated by the man himself, as is the Grassmarket branch (38 Grassmarket, EH1 2TU, Tel: 031-226 2442) and the Leith operation (8 Union Street, EH8 9LU, Tel: 031-557 8451). It is readily admitted by friend and foe that comfort may sometimes be at a premium, that the pace may be fast and furious, and that not everything is brilliant. But the value...especially those set three-course lunches at under a fiver. À la carte prices at dinner may be higher than at lunch-time, but are still very low. The days when lobster and langoustine were as often on as off the menu seem to have passed but turbot and salmon are frequently served. The core of a dish is often very satisfactory; what may suffer is the trimming – meagre vegetables on one occasion, for example. People rarely comment adversely about attitude or service, though remarks have been made about the state of the semi-open kitchen. Everyone there seems to have or to give a good time. The wine list is now kept purposely short; many of the producers are unfamiliar because the restaurant buys direct rather than through the well-worn channels of wine merchants. House wines are £5.90.

CHEF/PROPRIETOR: Pierre Levicky   OPEN: Mon to Sat; 12 to 3, 6 to 11 (last orders 4pm and 1am during Festival)   CLOSED: 25 and 26 Dec, 1 Jan   MEALS: alc (main courses £6 to £9). Set L £4.90   SERVICE: not inc, card slips closed   CARDS: Access, Visa   DETAILS: 70 seats. Private parties: 30 main room. Vegetarian meals. Children's helpings. Wheelchair access (also women's WC). Music. Fax: 031-662 4708

## Shamiana ·* £

14 Brougham Street, Tollcross, EH3 9JH                                  COOKING 1*
031-229 5578 and 228 2265                                                COST £18–£36

The gaudy plastic menu, complete with pictures of dishes, displayed outside this restaurant close to the King's Theatre suggests a fast-food joint, whereas the interior is quite swish with its black and white tiled floors, pink linen and luxuriant greenery. Children and families contribute to the atmosphere of the place. The menu is sensibly short and has plenty of choice for vegetarians: smoky, garlicky dhal, aloo sag, baigan bhurta delicately seasoned with 'sour mango powder' and 'beautifully scented' sabzi pilau have pleased meatless diners. Carnivores have enjoyed Hyderabadi murgh (chicken with rich lemon, nut and poppy seed sauce) and tandoori mixed grill (although the quality of the meat was uneven on one occasion). Otherwise the north Indian and Kashmiri repertoire embraces saali boti khumbabi (a Parsee wedding dish of lamb with dried apricots), chicken tikka with sweet-and-sour sauce, and bhuna gosht. The roti and kulcha are high-quality breads. Pistachio kulfi makes a good finale. The wine list is far from run-of-the-mill, curry-house plonk; instead, it provides a thoughtfully selected choice of around 30 bottles that are appropriate to the food. House French is £6.95.

CHEFS: M.A. Butt and Mahmood Khan   PROPRIETORS: M.A. Butt and A.N. Butt   OPEN: all week, exc L Sat and Sun; 12 to 2, 6 to 11.30   CLOSED: 25 Dec, 1 Jan   MEALS: alc (main courses £6 to £8)   SERVICE: 12.5%, card slips closed   CARDS: Access, Amex, Diners, Visa DETAILS: 45 seats. Private parties: 36 main room, 12 private room. Vegetarian meals. Children's helpings. Smart dress preferred. No smoking in 1 dining-room. No cigars in dining-rooms. Wheelchair access (1 step). Music. Air-conditioned

£  indicates that it is possible to have a three-course meal, including coffee, a half-bottle of house wine and service, at any time the restaurant is open (i.e. at dinner as well as at lunch, unless a place is open only for dinner), for £20 or less per person.

## Shore ⅝✳ £

3–4 Shore, Leith, EH6 6QW
031-553 5080
off A199 on Firth of Forth,          COOKING 1*
2m E of city centre          COST £17–£33

One enters through the smoky and rough-edged atmosphere of the adjacent pub, but is soon charmed by the place's plain-spoken simplicity. Take a telescope to read the blackboard, but then note the concentration on fish (or game if the weather's really bad) and order turbot with leeks and a cream sauce, or lemon sole simply grilled with ginger and spring onions. Alternatively, try salmon baked with herbs or monkfish with asparagus and a saffron sauce which have been judged equally fresh, succulent and exactly cooked. Matters at either end of the meal (which might begin with, for instance, parsnip and lentil soup, plain langoustines or a salad of smoked trout with a lime dressing, and end with sticky toffee pudding, chocolate mousse or poached pears) are described as satisfactory, 'if unremarkable'. The coffee is good. Jazz or folk music in the bar bring in the crowds; cheap set-price lunches are also appreciated. The wine list saves your pennies and has a sound choice over a limited range. House wines are £7.80.

CHEFS: Kevin O'Connor, Philippa Crookshank and Dan Styles  PROPRIETORS: Philippa Crookshank and Simon Edington  OPEN: all week; 12 (12.30 Sun) to 2.30, 6.30 to 10.15  CLOSED: 25 and 26 Dec, 1 and 2 Jan  MEALS: alc (main courses £6 to £11). Set L £6.50 (2 courses)  SERVICE: not inc (10% for 8 or more)  CARDS: Access, Visa  DETAILS: 50 seats. 5 tables outside. Private parties: 36 main room. Vegetarian meals. Children's helpings. No smoking in dining-room. Wheelchair access. Music

## Spices ⅝✳ £            | NEW ENTRY |

110 West Bow, EH1 2HH          COOKING 1
031-225 5028          COST £14–£35

This restaurant, near the castle and picturesque Grassmarket, is the carnivorous sibling of Kalpna (see entry, Edinburgh) and is likewise totally no-smoking. On two floors, it has Charles Rennie Mackintosh-style chairs ('the most comfortable we have ever sat on'), brick-coloured tablecoths and Indian paintings on the walls. It sounds like an odd combination, but the result is casually comfortable in 'a vaguely plush sort of way'. The menu blurb makes great play about the history and use of spices, and the short repertoire is effusively described. Dishes come not only from regions of the Indian sub-continent, but also from Africa. The use of unusual flavourings is a noble experiment which does not always hit the mark but, as one reporter observed, 'clients are unlikely to be bored'. Kuku paka (a chicken speciality from Zanzibar) comes in a thick sauce 'the colour of blackberry yogurt', flavoured with coconut, ginger and lemon. Other recommendations have included tandoori paneer, an unusual fruit chaat, smoked chicken tikka, raarha rogan josh, dhal makhni, and aloo jeera with cumin seeds. Char chari (deep-fried bhindis or aubergines) is a dish 'to die for' and other vegetables are reckoned to be 'gorgeously fresh and punchy'. Wines are from Cockburns of Leith and the short list is sharp, well-chosen and fairly priced. House wine is £6.95.

CHEF: Ajay Bhartdwaj   PROPRIETORS: Ajay Bhartdwaj and Moussa Jogee   OPEN: Mon to Sat; 12 to 2, 5.30 to 11   MEALS: alc (main courses £7 to £8). Buffet L £5.50   SERVICE: 10%, card slips closed   CARDS: Access, Visa   DETAILS: 70 seats. Private parties: 40 main room, 35 private room. Vegetarian meals. Children's helpings. No smoking. Wheelchair access (also WC). Music

## Vintners Rooms 🍷 ⚡

87 Giles Street, Leith, EH6 6BZ                                     COOKING 3*
031-554 6767                                                        COST £18–£43

Behind a screening wall (to keep out malefactors) and gate that opens on to the street, the Rooms form part of an eighteenth-century bonded warehouse, cellar and wine auction house – a remarkable site. The main chamber, housing the bar, a fireplace and tables used for light meals and informal visits, is immensely atmospheric, especially in the flickering candlelight. Natural tones of wood and stone give way to elaborate plasterwork in the restaurant itself, which was once the auction room. Tim Cumming maintains his faith with good cooking, an enticing menu and excellent wines. 'I started with sauté scallops with rhubarb butter, the scallops cooked to give texture without roughness, the tart rhubarb cutting the richness. Then I had duck with plum cassis sauce, the fat little trimmed, but the sauce sharp and well flavoured. The real problem was making a choice from the menu, torn as I was between the duck, sea bass stuffed with scallops and salmon en croûte with ginger and currants.' Desserts for this reporter posed less of a problem, since the prune, almond and armagnac tart had pastry as good as he could make at home. From this account it might seem that everything comes with a fruit accompaniment, but sea trout with sorrel sauce, venison with port sauce, and fresh pasta with a hazelnut pesto soon convince otherwise. The natural and unaffected style of the cooking is wholly to be recommended. The same might be said of the manner in which the restaurant is run, making it one of the more civilised retreats in this city. An Alsatian house wine from the excellent Rolly-Gassmann, albeit an Edelzwicker, augurs well. Classics of some maturity are offered at modest mark-up, and the range of antipodeans and Californians is short but to the point. This list has begun to show excitement alongside a firm Edinburgh reserve. A careful selection of half-bottles completes the picture. House wines are from £8.50. CELLARMAN'S CHOICE: Margaret River, Sauvignon 1991, Leeuwin, £16.45; Givry, Clos Marceaux 1989, Pascale Juillot, £19.50.

CHEF: Tim Cumming   PROPRIETORS: Sue and Tim Cumming   OPEN: Mon to Sat; 12 to 2.30, 7 to 10.30   CLOSED: 2 weeks Christmas   MEALS: alc (main courses wine bar D £11.50 to £15, restaurant £12.50 to £16). Set wine bar L £8 (2 courses) to £10.75   SERVICE: not inc   CARDS: Access, Amex, Visa   DETAILS: restaurant 60 seats, wine bar 30 seats. Private parties: 36 main room. Car park. Vegetarian meals. Children's helpings. Smart dress preferred. No smoking in dining-room. Wheelchair access (2 steps). No music. Fax: 031-554 8423

⚡ *indicates that smoking is either banned altogether or that a dining-room is maintained for non-smokers. The symbol does not apply to restaurants that simply have no-smoking areas.*

## Waterfront Wine Bar £

1C Dock Place, Leith, EH6 6LU          COOKING 1*
031-554 7427          COST £16–£32

On the edge of an eighteenth-century lock-gate system, the wine bar occupies the lock-keeper's cottage, with extra seating in a conservatory. It is busy, informal, fair value and energetic. People mainly go for dishes such as hummus and pitta bread, smoked trout pâté with celery wheat wafers, beef and tomato soup and langoustines mayonnaise. Puddings such as gooey banana cake and soft fruit and fromage frais laced with liqueur make for a happy finish. 'We wondered however they could make a profit, so generous were they with the fillet steak' was a report that set the tone. Meat is often chargrilled and shellfish is serious. Wines are also generously priced, with a fixed-profit system rather than a percentage mark-up. Notwithstanding the claim by the owners to eschew 'big names', in Alsace Dopff et Irion predominates and you cannot get much bigger than that. As wine bars go this is well ahead of the bunch. The bin-end list is worth more than a glance and a range of decent rather than exceptional wines is now offered by the glass. French house wine is £7.80.

CHEFS: Robin Bowie, Jenny McCrea and Alana Harrower   PROPRIETORS: Robin Bowie, Sarah Reid, and Helen and Ian Ruthven   OPEN: all week; 12 (12.30 Sun) to 2.30 (3 Fri to Sun), 6 to 9.30 (10 Fri and Sat, 9 Sun)   CLOSED: 25 and 26 Dec, 1 and 2 Jan   MEALS: alc (main courses £6 to £12)   SERVICE: not inc (10% for 8 or more)   CARDS: Access, Visa DETAILS: 100 seats. 19 tables outside. Private parties: 60 main room. Vegetarian meals. No children under 5. No-smoking area. Wheelchair access (also WC). Music

## ▲ Witchery by the Castle 🍷          | NEW ENTRY |

Castlehill, Royal Mile, EH1 1NE          COOKING 2
031-225 5613          COST £21–£55

It is easy to walk straight past this place, as one flees the Scotch Whisky Heritage Centre next door. As its name suggests, however, the Witchery is indeed at the entrance to Edinburgh Castle. Its two dining-rooms give some taste of Edinburgh Old Town, where the austerity of the externals hides many a surprise within doors. 'It is like dining in an old castle, with an abundance of dark timber – elaborately painted on the ceiling – as well as loud baroque Muzak.' Scotticisms get as far as a whisky ice-cream with poached pears and a red berry sauce – 'I couldn't for the life of me work out why the chef had chosen this flavour,' a reporter commented ingenuously – but for the most part the repertoire is mainstream and unstartling. However, execution of dishes such as fresh mussels and crabmeat in a pastry shell, and venison with wild mushrooms and a game sauce, is passable; presentation is nicely achieved; and service is excellent. The cost of the meal, though, may raise certain reservations. The wine list is a weighty blockbuster packed with so much information that some pages list only three wines. It is strong on range, with many *grand cru* Bordeaux, and growers such as Ducru-Beaucaillou, Bonny Doon, Bodegas Amezola, Heitz and Rolly-Gassmann, to name but a few. The bottles are chosen intelligently and with a sharp eye for quality. Prices are fair and much is below £15; the offerings by the glass are notable and many diners will be content to stray no further. The selection of eight house wines starts at £9.95.

CHEF: Andrew Main    PROPRIETOR: James Thomson    OPEN: all week; 12 to 4, 6 to 11
CLOSED: 25 Dec    MEALS: alc (main courses £12 to £18.50). Set L £10.40 (2 courses) to
£12.95    SERVICE: not inc    CARDS: Access, Amex, Diners, Visa    DETAILS: 120 seats.
5 tables outside. Private parties: 60 main room, 60 private rooms. Vegetarian meals.
Children's helpings L and before 8pm. Smart dress preferred. Music    ACCOMMODATION:
1 suite with bath/shower. B&B £120. Deposit: £20. TV. Phone. Fax: 031-220 4392

---

**ELRICK Grampian**                                                    map 8

## Courtyard

Broadstraik Inn, Elrick AB32 6TL
ABERDEEN (0224) 742540                                      COOKING 1*
on A944, 6m W of Aberdeen                                    COST £16–£40

This 'slightly baronial' hall (formerly the stable) behind the Broadstraik Inn
has stuck to its guns of serving food of more character than steak and scampi.
Tony Heath is encouraged by support for the evening trade and the steady
growth of lunches (even in Aberdeen there is a substratum of 'ladies who
lunch'). Guinea-fowl braised with orange and green lentils, venison with
poached pear and a compote of cherry tomatoes, and John Dory stuffed with
asparagus and saffron are three dishes he would like to call his own, but others
would add a warm salad of duck with oyster mushrooms, a salad of pastrami
and avocado, fillet of venison with sun-dried tomatoes, tagliatelle and a rich
red-wine sauce, and warm fresh cherry and almond flan with a cherry sauce.
The inn next door may not be prepossessing, but the dining-room has been
described as 'understated, with well-spaced tables and elegant fixtures'. The
value of the place is appreciated by locals and visitors alike. Value is also the
leitmotif of the adequate wine list. House wines are from £9.50.

---

CHEFS: Katy Barr, Neil Simpson and Tony Heath    PROPRIETORS: Tony Heath and Shona
Drysdale    OPEN: Wed to Sun, exc Sat L (other days by arrangement); 12 to 2, 6.30 to 9.30
MEALS: alc (main courses L £4.50 to £8.50, D £11 to £14.50). Set Sun L £13.75    SERVICE:
not inc, card slips closed    CARDS: Access, Amex, Visa    DETAILS: 36 seats. Private parties:
40 main room. Car park. Vegetarian meals. Children's helpings. Smart dress preferred.
Wheelchair access (also WC). Music. Fax: (0224) 742976

---

**ERISKA Strathclyde**                                                 map 8

## ▲ Isle of Eriska Hotel

Eriska PA37 1SD
LEDAIG (063 172) 371                                         COOKING 2
off A828, 12m N of Oban                                      COST £43–£52

The Buchanan-Smiths have been in residence at this towered and turreted
Victorian mansion for two decades and still treat it as their home. After years of
practice, they have learned the art of good country hospitality: 'Robin
Buchanan-Smith really does all this terribly well,' observes one contented
visitor, and the family's efforts are backed up by well-trained staff. Sheena
Buchanan-Smith still works to a five-course dinner menu with restricted
choice. A typical March selection shows the style: deep-fried Brie with tomato

sauce or gravlax before cream of leek soup ('always excellent') or fillet of plaice with chive butter. The centrepiece is a roast carved from the trolley, although an alternative such as baked cod with herb cheese crust is always offered. To finish, you will find a trolley of sweets, a savoury canapé and some Scottish cheeses. Guests have noted that the hotel offers excellent high teas for children. The whole island is like an unofficial nature reserve; there are scores of different birds, otters, deer and badgers – feeding them after dark is a favourite pastime. The adequate, though cautious, wine list is strong in clarets and the Loire. Prices are very fair, with the benchmark Cloudy Bay Sauvignon coming out at a very modest £13.70. The halves are a limited but intelligent spread. Many of the house wines are New World at £8.50.

CHEF: Sheena Buchanan-Smith   PROPRIETORS: the Buchanan-Smith family   OPEN: all week, D only; 8 to 9   CLOSED: Dec to Mar   MEALS: Set D £35   SERVICE: not inc, card slips closed   CARDS: Access, Visa   DETAILS: 40 seats. Private parties: 12 main room. Car park. Vegetarian meals. Children under 10 high tea. Jacket and tie. No cigars/pipes in dining-room. Wheelchair access (also WC). No music   ACCOMMODATION: 17 rooms, all with bath/shower. Rooms for disabled. B&B £125 to £170. Deposit: £100. Children welcome. Baby facilities. Pets welcome (not in public rooms). Garden. Tennis. Fishing. TV. Phone. Doors close at 11. Confirm by 5. Fax: (063 172) 531 (*The Which? Hotel Guide*)

---

**FORT WILLIAM Highland**                                                    map 8

## Crannog 🎄✕

Town Pier, Fort William PH33 7NG                                   COOKING 1*
FORT WILLIAM (0397) 705589                                          COST £18–£38

'Book in advance' is one reporter's sound advice, 'and ask for a table by the windows, looking down Loch Linnhe at the sailing yachts and at the sun and the shadows on the distant hilltops.' Heady, romantic stuff, considering that the restaurant is a converted bait storehouse on the water-front near the town centre. The place was set up by local fishermen as a means of selling their own catch and it is based on a simple but crucial notion: the shorter the food chain, the more easily quality and consistency can be ensured. In practice, the co-operative succeeds admirably. The printed menu brings together the raw and the cooked: oysters, home-cured salmon, home-produced gravlax, pickled herrings, alongside fish terrine with a silky asparagus mayonnaise, thickly sliced salmon in crisp filo pastry and skate in black butter. Bouillabaisse is full of flavour, 'but the real stars of the show are huge helpings of langoustines grilled with garlic butter'. The quality of the seafood and the sheer commitment are never in doubt, although one reporter felt that 'the cooking lacks the courage of its convictions'. Desserts such as cranachan, vacherin and full-strength sorbets are 'divine'. Service is generally friendly, if a little slow. Three dozen wines are keenly priced and chosen with the food in mind. Justerini & Brooks house wines are from £7.50. The second branch at 28 Cheapside, Glasgow, Tel: 041-221 1727 is trying hard but may 'claim more skill in fish cuisine than it possesses', according to an inspector.

---

*See inside the front cover for an explanation of the symbols used at the tops of entries.*

CHEF: Susan Trowbridge   PROPRIETORS: Crannog Ltd   OPEN: all week; 12 to 2.30, 6 to 10 (9 Nov to Feb)   MEALS: alc (main courses £6.50 to £14)   CARDS: Access, Amex, Visa   SERVICE: not inc, card slips closed   DETAILS: 50 seats. Private parties: 25 main room. Car park. Vegetarian meals. Children's helpings. No smoking in 1 dining-room. Wheelchair access (also WC). Music. Fax: (0397) 705026

## ▲ Inverlochy Castle 🅃✴ | NEW ENTRY

Torlundy, Fort William PH33 6SN
FORT WILLIAM (0397) 702177                                         COOKING 3
3m N of Fort William, off A82                                     COST £34–£62

'When money is irrelevant, Inverlochy makes a good stopping place. In fact, on this occasion, so different was it to the last, I was persuaded that it would be worth a few sacrifices to have an evening there.' This was the conclusion of a Scot who keeps us posted on progress in this Victorian giant, with every possible attribute of a major-league mansion hotel, stuck in the middle of nowhere. Changes in the kitchen caused us to reassess the entry, though what has changed in truth is not the formula so much as the standard. A short menu, but with adequate range, investigates mainstream cooking calculated never to offend. It is extremely accurate this year, with few failures. As such it pleases perfectly its constituency, but would leave someone used to comparatively expressive cookery wondering why he need pay so much. Ballottine of foie gras with Sauternes jelly and apple purée precedes mushroom and rosemary soup which could be bolder. Best end of lamb with a herb crust is fine meat, exactly cooked, with well-balanced gravy. Beans, carrots and broccoli are cooked properly but could be more interesting. Strawberry sablé is textbook stuff, as are mango, passion-fruit and strawberry sorbets. Part of the payment is for the setting – grandiloquent to look at, but kept alive and buzzing by an unstuffy staff. This is a good place to stay at. The wine list has items that surprise by their value. This may be modified, however, when you realise the wine prices are listed without VAT. The reason for this quirk is not immediately apparent.

CHEF: Simon Haig   PROPRIETOR: Grete Hobbs   OPEN: all week; 12.30 to 1.45, 7.15 to 9.15   CLOSED: 1 Dec to 1 Mar   MEALS: Set L £24.50 to £27.50, Set D £40   SERVICE: not inc, card slips closed   CARDS: Access, Amex, Visa   DETAILS: 40 seats. Private parties: 30 main room. Car park. Vegetarian meals. No children under 12 (high tea 6.30). Jacket and tie. No smoking in dining-room. No music   ACCOMMODATION: 16 rooms, all with bath/ shower. B&B £145 to £240. Children welcome. Baby facilities. Afternoon teas. Garden. Tennis. Fishing. Snooker. TV. Phone. Fax: (0397) 702953 (*The Which? Hotel Guide*)

---

*Restaurateurs justifiably resent no-shows. If you quote a credit card number when booking, you may be liable for the restaurant's lost profit margin if you don't turn up. Always phone to cancel.*

*The 1995* Guide *will be published before Christmas 1994. Reports on meals are most welcome at any time of the year, but are extremely valuable in the spring. Send them to* The Good Food Guide, *FREEPOST, 2 Marylebone Road, London NW1 1YN. No stamp is needed if posted in the UK.*

## Amber Regent

| | |
|---|---|
| 50 West Regent Street, G2 2QZ | COOKING 1 |
| 041-331 1655 and 1677 | COST £16–£43 |

The Amber Regent, opposite the Odeon cinema, impresses for its comfort, speed of service and as a destination for celebrations and jollity, rather than for arcane Cantonese ingredients or particularly authentic combinations. Materials, however, are very fresh, and textures and flavours as they should be. Decorative presentation is a strong point; braised king prawns in red sauce, venison with mandarin sauce and duck with garlic and plum sauce have been approved. The wine list is wide-ranging and reasonably priced, although short on vintage detail. House wines cost £8.90.

CHEF: Tommy Ho  PROPRIETOR: Andy Chung  OPEN: Mon to Sat; 12 to 2.15, 6 to 11.30 (midnight Sat and Sun)  MEALS: alc (main courses £8.50 to £12). Set L £6.95 (2 courses), Set D £21 to £28  SERVICE: not inc  CARDS: Access, Amex, Diners, Visa  DETAILS: 90 seats. Private parties: 100 main room, 16 private room. Vegetarian meals. No children under 10. Smart dress preferred. Music. Air-conditioned. Fax: 041-353 3393

## Buttery

| | |
|---|---|
| 652 Argyle Street, G3 8UF | COOKING 3 |
| 041-221 8188 | COST £20–£48 |

'It has an interesting, exciting and intimate atmosphere,' reported a visitor from down south about this converted pub furnished with the output of several architectural antique dealers. The cooking, she went on, is almost as elaborate as the furnishings: 'There were too many stuffings, ingredients, sauces and accompanying parcels; even their vegetables were overdressed.' However, the flavour and texture of the turbot were superb, and the mousse parcel wrapped in spinach was also delicious; only the egg and onion sauce was superfluous. This theme of complexity can be seen in a menu that offers seafood and spinach on light and dark lobster sauces, chicken stuffed with haggis on a mustard cream sauce, and lemon sole on an apple, pear and raisin pancake with a lemon sauce. However, not everyone thinks Stephen Johnson overlards the joint, and nearly all reports agree that the staff are well motivated and competent, even if occasionally overstretched by the press of business. Prices are not low – a spend of close to £50 per head has been admitted by the management – though economy is not impossible, and the Belfry downstairs offers cheaper, quicker meals. The wine list runs through a decent, but unexciting and sometimes doubtful (look at the claret vintages) range; Jadot and Faiveley are to the fore in burgundies. Prices are not giveaway, but they rarely are in Glasgow. House wines are £10.95.

CHEF: Stephen Johnson  PROPRIETORS: Alloa Pubs and Restaurants Ltd  OPEN: Mon to Sat, exc Sat L; 12 to 2.30, 7 to 10.30  CLOSED: bank and local hols  MEALS: alc (main courses £12 to £14). Set L £14.75  SERVICE: 10% (net prices Set L), card slips closed  CARDS: Access, Amex, Diners, Visa  DETAILS: 55 seats. Private parties: 45 main room, 8 private room. Car park. Vegetarian meals. Children's helpings on request. Smart dress preferred. Wheelchair access (also WC). Music. Air-conditioned. Fax: 041-204 4639

## *Café Gandolfi* £

| | |
|---|---|
| 64 Albion Street, G1 1NY | COOKING 1 |
| 041-552 6813 | COST £15–£27 |

This well-frequented place sits on a spare wind-blown street on the eastern edge of the Merchant City, the interior filled with interestingly chunky wooden furniture, the windows framing stained-glass fishes, and a grand series of photographs of Glasgow cafés in one corner: it looks the part of an inspired, well-used long-runner on the city's scene. The cooking maintains its quality, the menu its main outlines. Daily dishes such as Mexican meatballs or scallops with garlic and lemon juice served with mange-tout and tagliatelle impart variety to the regulars of choux puffs filled with Dunsyre Blue, or smoked venison, pastrami, vegetarian koulibiac with red pepper sauce, or Italian sausage with peperonata. Good ice-creams, relaxed informed service, excellent beers and a short list of wines all available by the glass complete the picture. House wine is £8.30. As we went to press the proprietors were hoping to open on Sundays.

CHEFS: Maggie Clarence and Rona Tait  PROPRIETORS: Iain M. Mackenzie and Seumas MacInnes  OPEN: Mon to Sat; 9am to 11.30pm  CLOSED: bank hol Mons  MEALS: alc (main courses £5 to £7.50)  SERVICE: not inc (10% for bookings and 6 or more)  DETAILS: 60 seats. Private parties: 12 main room. Vegetarian meals. Children's helpings. No children under 14 after 8pm. Music

---

## ▲ *Forte Crest, Jules' Bar and American Grill* £  `NEW ENTRY`

| | |
|---|---|
| Bothwell Street, G2 7EN | COOKING 1 |
| 041-248 3010 | COST £19–£41 |

Anxious to smarten its image in downtown Glasgow – where competition among hotel groups is fierce – Forte went to Ken McCulloch of One Devonshire Gardens (see entry) and the city's restaurant guru to see how to repackage this operation. His solution may be tasted, back under the control of Forte. Impressions have been favourable for well-motivated service and for passable cooking of slightly spicy food. Not spicy enough was an opinion on the horseradish and tomato salsa with crab cakes, and those little patties did not have the zest expected 'when fresh crab is bouncing out of shops in the city'. But a chillified breast of duck was great, with shiitake mushrooms and water-chestnuts, and redfish Cajun-style with a saffron sauce and a good scallop for texture contrast earned its praise. Some vegetables have been better than others, and there are those who go for the banana cream pie – a biscuit base, banana, whipped cream and chocolate flakes. Wines are not impossibly priced, and house wines are £8.90.

---

£ *indicates that it is possible to have a three-course meal, including coffee, a half-bottle of house wine and service, at any time the restaurant is open (i.e. at dinner as well as at lunch, unless a place is open only for dinner), for £20 or less per person.*

---

CHEF: Frank Bogie  PROPRIETORS: Forte plc  OPEN: all week, exc L Sat and Sun; 12 to 2.30, 6 (6.30 Sun) to 11  CLOSED: 25 Dec, 1 Jan  MEALS: alc (main courses £5.50 to £12.50)  SERVICE: not inc  CARDS: Access, Amex, Diners, Visa  DETAILS: 60 seats. Private parties: 16 private room. Car park. Vegetarian meals. Children welcome. Wheelchair access (also WC). Music. Air-conditioned  ACCOMMODATION: 254 rooms, all with bath/shower. Rooms for disabled. Lift. B&B £69.50 to £119. Children welcome. Baby facilities. Pets welcome (bedrooms only). Afternoon teas. Air-conditioned. TV. Phone. Confirm by 4. Fax: 041-221 8986

## ▲ Glasgow Hilton, Camerons  `NEW ENTRY`

1 William Street, G3 8HT                                              COOKING 3
041-204 5555                                                        COST £28–£66

The nickelodeon tower block and peristyled hall are sure signs of modern hotel culture where theme is paramount. The hungry will seek out either Minsky's New York Deli-Diner or Camerons, the luxury restaurant. Both are under the control of Ferrier Richardson, once owner of October in Bearsden. Minsky's is done out in red gingham and yankee-doodle-dandy; Camerons gets the waiters in tartan trews and recreates a series of rooms that evoke some grandiose classical classical shooting lodge. It is all stage-set design, but fun when it does not take itself too seriously. To dispense with Minsky's: first reports say you get genuine Ferrier Richardson food. Carrot and coriander soup, studded vegetable terrine, roast lamb with first-class vegetables, and even roast turkey 'with some gusto' have been approved of and come at a fair price (wine excepted), though desserts were not so impressive. Camerons is completely full-dress, and very full-price. The menu appears as a book, page 11 being shellfish from Loch Fyne, the rest a careful listing of food that will not offend likely Hilton customers: short on offal, no hint of new-wave verve here. Even a filo parcel of mozzarella, tomato and basil, sun-dried tomatoes and olive vinaigrette managed to be boring. However, there is hope if Ferrier Richardson is allowed his wings. The venison consommé was very bold and clear, and sea bass with a tomato and courgette compote and red wine sauce had potential. Ancillaries, except for the Lebanese flat bread, were not distinguished by their flavour. Service is first-rate and committed. It is a pity that the management seems only committed to the balance sheet and timorous tastes. The wine list shows the first magnificently. The £26 charged for Sancerre is impressive, and the £21 for Guigal Côtes du Rhone 1989 even more so (when you can buy it from merchants for around a fiver). The arrangement by variety has much to recommend it, and the range is acceptable. House wines start at £12.50.

CHEF: Ferrier Richardson  PROPRIETORS: Ladbroke Group plc  OPEN: all week, exc L Sat and Sun; 12 to 2.30, 7 to 11  MEALS: alc (main courses £12 to £19). Set L £16.50 (2 courses) to £19, Set D £35  SERVICE: not inc  CARDS: Access, Amex, Diners, Visa  DETAILS: 58 seats. Private parties: 16 main room, 8 and 14 private rooms. Car park. Vegetarian meals. Children's helpings. Smart dress preferred. Wheelchair access (also WC). Music. Air-conditioned  ACCOMMODATION: 319 rooms, all with bath/shower. Rooms for disabled. Lift. B&B £130 to £155. Children welcome. Baby facilities. Pets welcome. Afternoon teas. Swimming-pool. Sauna. Air-conditioned. TV. Phone. Confirm by 6. Fax: 041-204 5004

The Good Food Guide *is a registered trade mark of Consumers' Association Ltd.*

## Killermont Polo Club  £ | NEW ENTRY |

2022 Maryhill Road, nr Bearsden, G20 0AB
041-946 5412

COOKING 1
COST £14–£45

This has had many recommendations, not only for the food but for the setting and atmosphere. Visits are good fun. The house might have been a manse but is now heavy with 'photographs of polo players and comfortable with lavish drapery'. Kal Dhaliwal does actually ride out with a team of players, which gives more than a base of reality to the restaurant's theme. The menu is shorter than that at many Indian places but this has not deterred recommendations for the tikka dishes (good chicken, proper marinade), chicken with cream and coconut with 'an unctuous texture, the fenugreek and coriander lingering on the tongue', and excellent pakora. Breads and rice have also been approved. Service may sometimes be up and down, but jollity will intervene before irritation. Desserts are European. Krug apart, the wine list is realistically priced and starts with house wines at £8.25.

CHEF: Jas Sagoo  PROPRIETORS: Kal Dhaliwal, Pami Dhaliwal and Jas Sagoo  OPEN: all week, exc Sun L; 12 to 2, 5 to 10.30  CLOSED: 25 Dec, 1 Jan  MEALS: alc (main courses £7 to £12). Set L £6.95 to £7.95, Set Sun and Mon D £9.95  SERVICE: not inc  CARDS: Access, Amex, Diners, Visa  DETAILS: 90 seats. Private parties: 50 main room, 20, 30 and 50 private rooms. Car park. Vegetarian meals. Children's helpings on request. Smart dress preferred. Music

## ▲ One Devonshire Gardens  ♥

1 Devonshire Gardens, G12 0UX
041-339 2001 and 334 9494

COOKING 3
COST £30–£57

At the end of a fine classical terrace stand three houses with the number 1. Ken McCulloch bought the original number 1, then leap-frogged to the third house before completing the hand with number 2. This gradual development, together with a desire to conserve and enhance rather than alter beyond recognition, explains the slightly aberrant tripling up of front doors and welcomes. No discreet passageway connects the properties, so with restaurant and reception in the first, residents of the others brave the elements to get their commons. The hotel is a masterpiece of dark-toned luxury. Rooms are large, comfortable and suitable for any image-conscious reader of glossy magazines. Service is inexhaustible, informed and very keen. The portals may seem a mite hallowed, the tone quiet and consolatory rather than full of beans, but this should not discourage use of the restaurant, where Andrew Fleming cooks quite lively food, even if it is to be eaten with a smile rather than a guffaw. Well-mannered dishes such as steak and kidney pudding at lunch-time, or a saddle of venison with spiced shallots and a game sauce at night, put him through his paces. Standards, for instance gravlax or a game terrine with sweet pickled grapes, are capably interpreted, and vegetables are treated properly. Bread and coffee have been less satisfactory. Service in the restaurant is of a piece with the rest of the hotel. The range and quality of the wine list, with the inclusion of an especially careful selection of half-bottles, are undeniable. But all this is to be balanced with prices bordering on the outrageous, driven by the systematic application of a multiplier that we hesitate even to guess at. House wines are £16. CELLARMAN'S CHOICE: Rully Rabourcé, premier cru 1991, Olivier Leflaive, £25.35; Marqués de Griñon, Cabernet Sauvignon 1986, £27.90.

CHEF: Andrew Fleming   PROPRIETOR: Ken McCulloch   OPEN: all week, exc Sat L; 12 to 2, 7 to 10.30   MEALS: Set L £19, Set D £35   SERVICE: not inc, card slips closed   CARDS: Access, Amex, Diners, Visa   DETAILS: 40 seats. Private parties: 8 main room, 8, 16 and 40 private rooms. Car park. Vegetarian meals. Children's helpings on request. Smart dress preferred. Music   ACCOMMODATION: 27 rooms, all with bath/shower. B&B £115 to £155. Children welcome. Baby facilities. Pets welcome (not in public areas). Afternoon teas. TV. Phone. Confirm 1 day ahead. Fax: 041-337 1663 (*The Which? Hotel Guide*)

## La Parmigiana                                        NEW ENTRY

447 Great Western Road, G12 8HH                        COOKING 1
041-334 0686                                           COST £13–£37

'Must book; it is very well known and heavily used by regulars,' advises a Glaswegian about this popular Italian venue near Kelvinbridge underground. Newcomers may miss the unobtrusive entrance hidden behind curtains; the place is at the end of the bridge, just past the fish and chip shop. An old wooden dresser with cornucopia mouldings is the most striking feature of the narrow dining-room, and beautifully draped curtains hang in the windows. The atmosphere is buoyant. Very correct, extremely professional staff are overseen by the hawk-eyed owner. Pasta is made on the premises, although spot-on tagliatelle with pesto has been better than 'hard, insipid' ravioli with spinach and ricotta. Fish shows up strongly in the shape of poached salmon with balsamic vinegar sauce, and frittata of different species grilled and seared over charcoal – a dramatic-looking selection of squid, tuna, a lightly flashed scallop, fleshy monkfish and a splayed langoustine. Quail is served with a 'competent' sauce of grappa and white wine or paired with venison, polenta and port sauce. To finish, blackcurrant tart with blackcurrant coulis and a light alcoholic sponge layered with mascarpone and chocolate have been given the seal of approval. The wine list has a strong Italian contingent, with plenty of reasonable drinking for around £15. House wines are from £8.90 a litre.

CHEF: Sandro Giovanazzi   PROPRIETORS: Angelo and Sandro Giovanazzi   OPEN: Mon to Sat; 12 to 2.30, 6 to 11   MEALS: alc (main courses £8.50 to £10.50). Set L £6.80   SERVICE: not inc   CARDS: Access, Amex, Diners, Visa   DETAILS: 55 seats. Private parties: 60 main room. Vegetarian meals. Children's helpings. Smart dress preferred. Music. Air-conditioned

## Rogano

11 Exchange Place, G1 3AN                              COOKING 1
041-248 4055                                           COST £23–£65

The restaurant is at the hub of shopping Glasgow. Its entrance in a short alley off Buchanan Street may be unassuming, but push the doors ajar to enjoy the art deco of the ground-floor restaurant and basement café. It is not exactly as it was; the restoration of 1985 changed shapes and fittings, but the carpet, maple panelling, curving screens and atmospheric (though shortened) bar are period pieces. The place fairly hums, helped by a very willing staff and a menu that is best known for seafood which is generally cooked according to fairly modern lights. Some visitors this year have felt that the place does not always live up to its promise, or its prices. Even the seafood was in one instance less than brilliant – down to the oysters, which were lean and poorly prepared. Standards at the café, where prices are lower, have been equally mixed. Dishes such as scallops with Chinese noodles, king prawns and lemon grass have on occasion lacked balance, flavour and seasoning, vegetables have not been to standard. The ambience of comfortable enjoyment and the enthusiasm of the staff reconcile many to these faults. The wine list is best for white Loires and burgundies.

CHEF: James Kerr  PROPRIETORS: Alloa Pubs and Restaurants Ltd  OPEN: all week, exc Sun L; 12 to 2.30, 7 to 10.30  CLOSED: bank hols  MEALS: alc (main courses café £8.50 to £10, restaurant £15 to £27.50). Set L £15  SERVICE: 10%, card slips closed  CARDS: Access, Amex, Diners, Visa  DETAILS: 55 seats. Private parties: 70 main room, 16 and 16 private rooms. Vegetarian meals. Children welcome. Wheelchair access (also WC). Music. Air-conditioned. Fax: 041-248 2608

---

## Ubiquitous Chip ▮ £

| 12 Ashton Lane, G12 8SJ | COOKING 2* |
| 041-334 5007 | COST £14–£49 |

No matter how long a place has been running – and Ron Clydesdale has been pulling people into the Chip for more than 20 years – things go up and down. If last year was not a great vintage, this year seems better. One old hand reflects that over time 'the lane outside has gone from being a mysterious semi-derelict dark alley to a trendy food ghetto, presumably as a result of the Chip's success'. Another, who thought she had not been for nearly a lifetime, remembered how 'I couldn't believe then that such a place could exist in grey Glasgow, and to walk in today remains a startling and dramatic experience with such proliferating greenery in the courtyard.' 'Sit near the pool in the jungle of foliage' is the advice of a third, 'on busy nights one can be relegated to the nether regions.' A dinner of Finnan haddies, oak-smoked with no further cooking, was 'splendid, simple Scottish'; the vegetarian haggis, unlikely as it sounds, was equally successful. Vegans have enthused about the success of their meals here – 'the best I have eaten in a long, long time' – but meat- and fish-eaters seem content with the fish soup, scallops on roasted potato with garlic and a vermouth sauce, mutton stuffed with mussels (some have found the white wine and shellfish reduction less flavoursome than expected) or a dish of roast hare. Fish, game, mutton and beef are strong points. Local cheeses are properly listed and desserts – with fair variation of ice-creams, oatmeal, shortbread and bulk – get steady endorsement. Failures have occurred at peak times and service, though usually exceptionally cheerful, can fret or forget. Upstairs at the Chip offers a cheaper all-day menu. The wine list has long been the high-spot; it has tremendous range matched by fair prices and an eye for quality that embraces the modest as much as the grand. The knowledgeable should be even more pleased, especially with bin-ends. House wine is from £7.75.

CHEF/PROPRIETOR: Ron Clydesdale   OPEN: all week; downstairs 12 to 2.30, 5.30 to 11; upstairs noon to 11   CLOSED: 25 Dec, 1 and 2 Jan   MEALS: alc (main courses downstairs £10 to £15, upstairs £4 to £8). Set L downstairs £10 (2 courses)   SERVICE: not inc   CARDS: Access, Amex, Diners, Visa   DETAILS: 130 seats. 12 tables outside. Private parties: 60 main room. Vegetarian meals. Children's helpings. Wheelchair access (also WC). No music. Fax: 041-337 1302

---

**GULLANE** Lothian                                                                                       map 8

## *La Potinière*

Main Street, Gullane EH31 2AA
GULLANE (0620) 843214
on A198, 4m SW of North Berwick

COOKING 4
COST £22–£39

Our mild criticisms of this diminutive school-house restaurant but a mashie's or a niblick's length from Muirfield golf course were unhesitatingly disputed in the course of the last year. People have fervidly defended Hilary Brown's sensitive cooking and David Brown's tight-rope performance of juggling wine list and waiting single-handed among a score and more of lunchers (dinner Friday and Saturday only) happy to be treated to food that tastes and a bill that does not shock. 'I thought she was in a rut,' said one, 'but after my last meal, I take it all back.' There is a formula: a set meal that follows a familiar pattern. However, if you return, David Brown's card index of guests ensures that the dishes themselves are not repeated. One spring day saw tomato and mint soup; salmon with lentils and a morel sauce; guinea-fowl stuffed with unsulphured apricots and mint, with a gratin dauphinois and salad; and a lemon surprise pudding. 'The primary tastes were all there, clean and clear, balanced and subtle.' Details, as they should be, are carefully thought out: a salad of mange-tout, leaves and pimentos in a walnut dressing; walnut and sultana bread. Some people react badly to others' routines and patterns; for them, perhaps, La Potinière is not nirvana, but for a surprising number it is. The wine list must number among the most elegant, although clarity is occasionally hostage to style. The wines themselves are wonderful; a strong section from the south-west of France precedes a range of clarets at fair prices. In Burgundy the big houses predominate but mature Chablis are notable. Halves are most pleasing. A tendency to eschew small growers, most apparent in Alsace where the pickings can be rich, may indicate a degree of self-satisfaction. But then, there is much here to satisfy. House wine is £9.25.

---

CHEF: Hilary Brown   PROPRIETORS: David and Hilary Brown   OPEN: L Mon, Tue, Thur and Sun, D Fri and Sat; 1, 8   CLOSED: 1 week June, Oct   MEALS: Set L £17.50 to £18.50, Set D £27.50   SERVICE: net prices   DETAILS: 30 seats. Private parties: 30 main room. Car park. Children welcome. No smoking in dining-room. Wheelchair access (1 step). No music

---

*'When the waiter brought the bill, he said, ''The carpet cleaners are arriving at any moment.'' We departed before we were covered in foam!'* On eating in London

*'Waiter at a seaside hotel explaining a rather precious (and poor) menu: ''And the fisherman's catch today is salmon fish-cakes.'''* On eating in Suffolk

---

**HADDINGTON** Lothian                                                                    map 8

## ▲ *Browns Hotel* ᛉ⋇

1 West Road, Haddington EH41 3RD
HADDINGTON (0620) 822254                                              COOKING 2
off A1, 16m E of Edinburgh                                            COST £23–£38

Either side of the small Ionic portico, bright-eyed flowers glow a positive riot.
The small late-Georgian house is a pleasure from the outside and enjoyed for its
domestic feel – classical music most of the day, good Scottish art on the walls,
bold colours and comfortable furnishings. Colin Brown cooks a set-price
dinner that has choice for the main dish, but none for the entrée or soup course
and, surprisingly, none for the dessert. But no objections are heard to chicken
quenelles, followed by nettle soup, succeeded by fillet of veal with wild
mushrooms and cream before an almond basket filled with fruit. Quantities are
not stinted. Appetites should be sharpened. The wine list has a socially aware
stretch of cheaper clarets and some very sound choices across the range from
other regions and other countries. Prices are very fair indeed. House wines are
from £7.75.

CHEF: Colin Brown   PROPRIETORS: Colin Brown and Alexander McCallum   OPEN: all
week, D only, and Sun L (Mon to Sat L parties only); 12.30 for 1, 7.30 for 8   MEALS: Set
Sun L £17.25, Set D £24.50   SERVICE: not inc, card slips closed   CARDS: Access, Amex,
Diners, Visa   DETAILS: 30 seats. Private parties: 30 main room, 30 private room. Car park.
Vegetarian meals with prior notice. No children under 12. Smart dress preferred. No
smoking in dining-room. Wheelchair access (2 steps; also WC). Music   ACCOMMODATION:
5 rooms, all with bath/shower. B&B £59.50 to £78. Deposit: £20. Children welcome. Baby
facilities. Garden. TV. Phone. Doors close at midnight. Confirm by 6. Fax: (0620) 822254

---

**INVERNESS** Highland                                                                    map 8

## ▲ *Culloden House*

Inverness IV1 2NZ
INVERNESS (0463) 790461                                               COOKING 2
off A96, 3m E of Inverness                                            COST £25–£48

This must be one of the grandest hotels in northern Scotland: an imposing
Georgian building with two flanking service wings and an Adamesque interior
that never wavers in its commitment to ornament and cut glass. The full
Scottish experience is provided by kilted proprietor and staff, and as such
places have to be treated as part theatre and theme park, Culloden House must
rate as one of the more successful. The cooking is designed to buttress the
image. It does not take the route of Scots domestic, but provides elaborate
compositions in the manner of fillet of beef coated with a spinach sauce,
sprinkled with chestnuts, bacon and onion, or lamb cutlets topped with
mushrooms, glazed with hollandaise and served with a Bordelaise sauce. The
complexity does not make the cooking necessarily more memorable, but nor is
it out of step with the standards of the hotel itself. Service is always praised.
The wine list has some thoroughbreds to amuse the rich or connoisseur, but the
range and choice among less expensive bottles are not to be sneezed at either.
House wines start at £9.25.

CHEF: Michael Simpson  PROPRIETORS: Ian and Marjory McKenzie  OPEN: all week;
12.30 to 2, 7 to 9  MEALS: alc L (main courses £8.50 to £13.50). Set D £29.50  SERVICE: not
inc, card slips closed  CARDS: Access, Amex, Diners, Visa  DETAILS: 45 seats. Private
parties: 51 main room, 34 private room. Car park. Vegetarian meals. Children's helpings.
No children under 10. Jacket and tie. No music  ACCOMMODATION: 24 rooms, all with
bath/shower. B&B £110 to £190. Deposit: £150. No children under 10. Afternoon teas.
Garden. Sauna. Tennis. Snooker. TV. Phone. Doors close at midnight. Fax: (0463) 792181

---

## ▲ Dunain Park ✸✸

Inverness IV3 6JN
INVERNESS (0463) 230512                                         COOKING 1*
on A82, 1m out of Inverness                                    COST £31–£37

A reader commented that the most enjoyable feature of a stay here was Ann
Nicoll's tour around the tables after each meal. The personal touch is important
in places on this scale: not a palace, but more than just a house. A small
Italianate tower keeps the draught off the entrance, just as the house and
gardens are themselves sheltered beneath forested hills. The interior is
understated, with good furniture allied to comfort and warmth. Dinner has a
short and oft-changing choice – 'We stayed for four days and never needed to
repeat any dish.' A set of steaks for the beef-minded is also on permanent offer.
Ann Nicoll experiments, as with a dinner of curried carrot soup, sun-dried
tomato soufflé with grain-mustard cream sauce, loin of lamb in pastry with a
nutmeg-flavoured duxelle and a mint béarnaise, and seriously traditional
puddings off the buffet. Chutneys and spices figure often, so do wild
mushrooms and seasonal specials from the Highlands. Small wonder,
therefore, that the list of malts, enthusiastically run through by Edward Nicoll,
is as long as his arm. The wine list is decent too, with growers like Robert
Ampeau, Mme Joly, Christian Salmon, Penfolds and Trimbach assuring
quality as well as spread at fair prices. House wines are £10.

CHEF: Ann Nicoll  PROPRIETORS: Ann and Edward Nicoll  OPEN: all week, D only; 7 to 9
CLOSED: 3 weeks Jan to Feb  MEALS: alc (main courses £12.95)  SERVICE: not inc, card
slips closed  CARDS: Access, Amex, Diners, Visa  DETAILS: 36 seats. Private parties: 10
main room. Car park. Vegetarian meals. Children's helpings with prior notice. Smart dress
preferred. No smoking in dining-room. Wheelchair access. No music  ACCOMMODATION:
14 rooms, all with bath/shower. Rooms for disabled. B&B £45 to £140. Deposit: £50.
Children welcome. Baby facilities. Pets welcome (not in public rooms). Afternoon teas.
Garden. Swimming-pool. Sauna. TV. Phone. Doors close at midnight. Fax: (0463) 224532
(The Which? Hotel Guide)

---

## Whitecross ✸✸                                    [NEW ENTRY]

Ivy Cottage, Muirtown Locks,
Inverness IV3 6LS
INVERNESS (0463) 240386                                        COOKING 2
½m from centre, on old Beauly Road (A852)                     COST £15–£43

'This gem of a restaurant is a small house on the bank of the canal. Ring the bell
for admission, start with a drink downstairs then up you go for the meal to an
attic floor, skylights only, where two rooms have been knocked into one,

though the central fireplace remains.' These were the instructions of a northern traveller impressed by his first sampling of some fresh and inventive cooking. A simple lunch of asparagus, meatloaf with mashed potatoes, then baked lemon cream with fruit purée indicated much talent. This is given a longer work out at dinner, which has also been confirmed as satisfactory. A winter meal of venison tart with apple and celeriac, sole wrapped in cabbage and served with a chive butter sauce, and mallard basted with honey, with a port and juniper sauce and some roast parsnips, showed Paul Whitecross can also strut the high stage. It bodes well. The Justerini wine list is very sound. House wines are from £9.

CHEF: Paul Whitecross   PROPRIETORS: Paul and Glynis Whitecross   OPEN: Tue to Sun, exc Sat L and Sun D; 12.30 to 2.30, 7 to 9.30   MEALS: alc D (main courses £11 to £14). Set L £6.75 (2 courses) to £8.75, Set D £19.95   SERVICE: not inc, card slips closed   CARDS: Access, Diners, Visa   DETAILS: 24 seats. Private parties: 10 and 15 private rooms. Car park. Vegetarian meals. Children's helpings. Smart dress preferred. No smoking in dining-room. Music

---

**KENTALLEN** Highland                                                  map 8

## ▲ *Ardsheal House* ♀ ⅝✳

Kentallen PA38 4BX
DUROR (063 174) 227                                          COOKING 2
on A828, 4m S of Ballachulish Bridge                 COST £24–£49

'A guest told us that we were the last country-house hotel in the region, as opposed to hotel in the country. We took it as a compliment,' write the Taylors about their white Georgian house, complete with log fires and panelling aplenty, by the shores of Loch Linnhe. The place is reached by a long and rambling track, but digestions are left intact to tackle a dinner that reaches five courses, and costs nearly twice as much in high season as in winter. Tea in the garden was 'a magical experience', wrote one who then dined on calf's liver with a shallot and apple confit and a port sauce, sweet potato and bacon soup, pavé of lamb with braised lentils, redcurrant and rosemary sauce, a mixed salad with celery and pears, with a dessert of sticky toffee pudding. He slept well too. George Kelso has been keeping up with the culinary Joneses at this far-flung outpost of British hospitality with grit and determination for more than five years. Approval has been registered for general standards in the kitchen, and particularly for the overall atmosphere of protected ease. At lunch-time, snacks can be taken rather than the set lunch. The tendency of the wine list to rely on big names, albeit good ones and especially those from Burgundy, discourages unmitigated praise. However, the range of clarets maintains interest, and elsewhere buying is always soundly reliable. Prices are very fair and effort goes into finding halves. House wines are £9.

---

*Prices quoted in the Guide are based on information supplied by restaurateurs. The prices quoted at the top of each entry represent a range, from the lowest meal price to the highest; the latter is inflated by 20 per cent to take account of likely price rises during the year of the Guide.*

---

CHEF: George Kelso   PROPRIETORS: Jane and Robert Taylor   OPEN: all week; 12 to 1.45, 8.30   CLOSED: 3 weeks Jan   MEALS: Set L £17.50, Set D £32.50 (£18.50 Nov to Apr)   SERVICE: not inc   CARDS: Access, Amex, Visa   DETAILS: 35 seats. Private parties: 40 main room. Car park. Vegetarian meals with prior notice. Children's helpings L and high tea. Smart dress preferred. No smoking in dining-room. Wheelchair access (3 steps; also WC). Music   ACCOMMODATION: 13 rooms, all with bath/shower. D,B&B £85 to £180 (reduced rates in winter). Deposit: variable. Children welcome. Baby facilities. Pets welcome. Afternoon teas. Garden. Tennis. Snooker. Phone. Fax: (063 174) 342 (*The Which? Hotel Guide*)

---

## KILLIECRANKIE Tayside                                    map 8

### ▲ *Killiecrankie Hotel* 🍴✳ £

Killiecrankie PH16 5LG
PITLOCHRY (0796) 473220                                   COOKING 1
off A9, 3m N of Pitlochry                                 COST £15–£38

The Killiecrankie Pass has this resting place for lunch and dinner. The splendour of the surroundings assures it a living, though the hospitality may take a day or two to warm. Cooking, which can be tried in bar or restaurant, is better for plain dishes than fancy ones; the beef is regularly mentioned. Should faults arise, the Andersons seem very willing to correct them. Though the menu is quite long, desserts are but two choices: a tart and one other. The tarts are great, we are assured by those who have tried them. The wine list is a quick world tour courtesy of Justerini & Brooks. House wines are from £8.25.

CHEF: Paul Booth   PROPRIETORS: Colin and Carole Anderson   OPEN: all week; 12.30 to 2, 7 to 8.30   CLOSED: Jan and Feb   MEALS: alc bar L (main courses £5 to £7). Bar supper menu (main courses £7 to £11.50). Set D £24   SERVICE: not inc, card slips closed   CARDS: Access, Visa   DETAILS: 34 seats. Private parties: 12 main room. Car park. Vegetarian meals. Children's helpings. No children under 5 in dining-room. Smart dress preferred. No smoking in dining-room. Wheelchair access (1 step). No music   ACCOMMODATION: 11 rooms, all with bath/shower. Rooms for disabled. B&B £39 to £92. Deposit: £30. Children welcome. Baby facilities. Pets welcome (not in public rooms). Afternoon teas. Garden. TV. Phone. Doors close at midnight. Fax: (0796) 472451 (*The Which? Hotel Guide*)

---

## KINCLAVEN Tayside                                       map 8

### ▲ *Ballathie House* 🍴✳                    **NEW ENTRY**

Kinclaven, By Stanley PH1 4QN
MEIKLEOUR (0250) 883268                                   COOKING 2
off B9099, take right fork 1m N of Stanley               COST £16–£43

There are mandatory turrets at each end of this relaxed Victorian country house set in a 1,500-acre estate, and the interiors are positively cheerful (and classical) by contrast with some in the region. Serious sportsmen, who might stay in the adjacent lodge, still come here for fishing and shooting, but the idle traveller will not be disappointed. The cooking demonstrates the shift away from 'over-gilding, the belief that two sauces are better than one, or that the guest prefers congealed, garnished masterpieces to hot plain food.' Yet not all is plain – as one reader found when he bit into a miniature Scotch egg served with his aperitif and found it was black pudding – nor does it lack skill. A galantine of guinea-fowl with pistachios pinpointed the exact texture and taste required. The mango mousse in a brandy-snap basket trembled as it should. Set-price menus are arranged with a limited choice, but a longer list of alternatives is offered to the chef's selection for that night (at no extra cost). People have spoken well of the soups – 'no nonsense, fresh tips, good stock, no frills' was the comment about an asparagus soup – the pigeon breasts with beetroot and celeriac, the duck with red onion and thyme, the halibut with vermouth and dill, and the scallops, shellfish and salmon. Service is highly proficient. The wine list ranges the world, with an eye to value as well as quality. The house selection starts at around £8.

CHEF: Kevin MacGillivray  PROPRIETORS: Ballathie House Hotel Ltd  OPEN: all week; 12 to 2, 7 to 9  MEALS: alc L (main courses £4.50 to £5.50). Set L £10, Set Sun L £14.75, Set D £25  SERVICE: not inc  CARDS: Access, Amex, Diners, Visa  DETAILS: 60 seats. Private parties: 22 private room. Car park. Vegetarian meals. Children's helpings. Smart dress preferred. No smoking in dining-room. Wheelchair access (also WC). No music ACCOMMODATION: 27 rooms, all with bath/shower. Rooms for disabled. B&B £60 to £130. Children welcome. Baby facilities. Pets by arrangement. Afternoon teas. Garden. Tennis. Fishing. TV. Phone. Fax: (0250) 883396

---

**KINGUSSIE Highland**                                                    map 8

## ▲ The Cross

Tweed Mill Brae, Ardbroilach Road,
Kingussie PH21 1TC                                                COOKING 3*
KINGUSSIE (0540) 661166                                            COST £20–£56

'The transition from a small restaurant-with-rooms to a hotel with significantly larger restaurant could have been traumatic. The Hadleys have managed it with aplomb.' This was the verdict of one reader who heard about the departure from the village centre to a converted tweed mill by a rippling stream (uphill from the traffic lights on Main Street, and 200 metres on the left). Ruth Hadley has not changed the formula or the style of her nightly dinner menus (extra length and cost on Saturday). Her repertoire is familiar to regulars, but does not pall with time. Gressingham duck with cranberries and ginger, fillet of beef with shallots and red wine, and salmon on a bed of spring greens are simple offerings made memorable by distinct and alert flavours. Soups likewise do not disappoint for taste. A vegetarian extolled the virtues of the alternative menus, running through goats' cheese soufflé, red pepper soup, aubergine with pesto and Parmesan, and mushroom goulash. These things brought into high profile the ability to manipulate flavour without lurching into false ambitions. 'Lemon curd ice-cream is a wow,' enthused one – so are the cheeses, others have chimed in. The new restaurant is more spacious and lacks pretension. Tony Hadley is still the attentive host, willing to debate a bottle, discuss a cheese or devote minutes of time to a single point. Residential accommodation is 'developing', a euphemism that might go. The wine list has had no need to change, and it would be hard to better such a cheerful, well-informed and reasonably priced bunch of wines. Marqués de Murrieta white in three vintages and well-chosen halves catch the eye, but Cloudy Bay should perhaps

599

not have the monopoly on New Zealand whites. House wines are from £6.95.
CELLARMAN'S CHOICE: Cloudy Bay Sauvignon Blanc 1993, £15.85; Côtes-du-Rhône-Villages, Ch. de la Gardine 1984, £13.80.

CHEF: Ruth Hadley   PROPRIETORS: Tony and Ruth Hadley   OPEN: Wed to Mon, exc Wed
L; 12.30 to 2, 7 to 9   CLOSED: Dec, Jan and Feb   MEALS: Set L £12.50 (2 courses) to £15,
Set D £25 to £35   SERVICE: not inc, card slips closed   CARDS: Access, Visa   DETAILS: 30
seats. 9 tables outside. Private parties: 30 main room. Car park. Vegetarian meals with prior
notice. No children under 12. No smoking in dining-room. Wheelchair access (also WC).
No music   ACCOMMODATION: 9 rooms, all with bath/shower. D,B&B £65 to £150. Deposit:
£50. No children under 12. Afternoon teas. Garden. Phone. Confirm by 5. Fax: (0540)
661080

---

**KINLOCHMOIDART Highland**                                                          map 8

## Kinacarra £

Kinlochmoidart, Lochailort PH38 4ND
SALEN (096 785) 238                                                          COOKING 2
on A861, at head of Loch Moidart                                            COST £19–£32

'As you drive around and beyond Loch Shiel, past the site where the seven men
of Moidart landed, a long stone cottage stands by the side of the road. The
restaurant is bright and simply decorated with sponged green walls, pine
tables and a view through to the kitchen.' So ran a confirmation of the quality
of this small restaurant in a building that was once a school and before that a
police station. Angus MacLean does not just serve the food, he catches or shoots
it, which enhances the immediacy of it all – and probably improves the taste.
To eat profiteroles stuffed with fresh langoustines and served with a Newburg
sauce, turbot with a lime butter sauce, venison in a rich stock reduction and
cream sauce, followed by a coffee and cream meringue and a pear sponge cake
was an experience to be savoured. Value is self-evident here, and the direct
rendering of tastes and flavours is enviable. The menu changes gradually, day
by day, and seafood and game are naturally the materials best explored. The
wine list may be extremely brief, but at least the prices are sensible. House
wines are £7.85.

CHEF: Frances MacLean   PROPRIETORS: Angus and Frances MacLean   OPEN: Tue to Sun;
12 to 2, 7 to 9   CLOSED: Christmas, Mar   MEALS: alc (main courses £7.50 to £12)
SERVICE: not inc   DETAILS: 24 seats. 1 table outside. Private parties: 28 main room. Car
park. Vegetarian meals. Children's helpings. Smart dress preferred. Wheelchair access (also
WC). No music. Air-conditioned

---

'"Was everything to your liking?" asked the waitress. "To be honest, we would have liked
to have had the gravy offered separately," said I. "Best to be honest," said the
disappearing waitress.'  On eating in Oxfordshire

'In due time my tandoori chicken appeared. I wonder whether in your early teens you
made model aeroplanes as I did and whether you remember the balsa wood from which we
used to make the fuselage and wings. I ask because the chicken had much the same
consistency and certainly not significantly more flavour.'  On eating in London

---

KYLESKU **Highland** map 8

## ▲ *Kylesku Hotel* ✠ £ | NEW ENTRY |

Kylesku, By Lairg IV27 4HW
SCOURIE (0971) 502231 and 502200
on A894, at S side of old ferry crossing,      COOKING **2\***
by new bridge linking Unapool and Kylestrome      COST **£14–£36**

'This is an oasis of good-quality food in the vast gastronomic desert between
Ullapool and the North Pole,' remarked one who showed utter relief at
discovering this fairly ordinary-looking pub with a boxy modern extension on
the front overlooking the loch from where the ferry once ran – there is now a
bridge. Marcel Klein seems to run a social service for the walkers, tourists and
other people who light upon his place. The value is remarkable, and the quality
of the raw materials (the hotel has its own boat) is as high as could be expected:
home-smoked salmon, giant mussels, grilled langoustines, great fish such as
haddock simply pan-fried. Meat cookery is of the type of beef Stroganov,
chicken tikka, chicken with mushrooms and tarragon, and grilled rump steak.
Desserts are laid out on the table and no cavil was heard against a meringue
with home-made strawberry ice-cream. The wine list is basic and house wines
are £6.95.

CHEFS: Marcel Klein and Miss S. O'Sulliven   PROPRIETOR: Marcel Klein   OPEN: all week
(restaurant D only); 12.15 (12 bar) to 2.15, 7 to 9 (6 to 9.30 bar)   CLOSED: 5 Nov to 16 Mar
MEALS: alc restaurant D (main courses £10 to £14). Bar menu (main courses £2 to £8)
SERVICE: not inc, card slips closed   CARDS: Access, Visa   DETAILS: restaurant 24 seats,
bar 30 seats. 4 tables outside. Private parties: 20 main room. Car park. Vegetarian meals.
Children's helpings. Smart dress preferred restaurant. No smoking in 1 dining-room.
Wheelchair access (also WC). Music   ACCOMMODATION: 7 rooms, 6 with bath/shower.
Rooms for disabled. B&B £25 to £38. Deposit: 10%. Children welcome. Baby facilities.
Small dogs welcome. Afternoon teas. Garden. Fishing. Snooker. Doors close at 11.30.
Confirm by 8

LINLITHGOW **Lothian** map 8

## *Champany Inn* ▮

Champany, Linlithgow EH49 7LU
PHILPSTOUN (050 683) 4532 and 4388
2m NE of Linlithgow at junction of      COOKING **3\***
A904 and A803      COST **£28–£63**

The original inn is now the Chop & Ale House, where something of the
flavours of the Champany can be tried at lower prices in a more pubby
atmosphere. The restaurant itself is no pub at all. It is a remarkable shape, with
a custom-made carpet, heavy wooden tables ('the shine overlaid by scorch
marks,' one person reported), all natural finishes and considerable weight and
presence to the trimmings – down to a cage for the wine cellar and tank for the
lobsters. Pick your meal, literally, from displays; have your steak cut for you.
The meat is aged on site, nothing is cut until ordered and the taste of the beef is
incredibly sweet and subtle. Meals here tend to follow certain patterns: it is a
speciality house with variations on defined themes. Beef, salmon and lobster

are the main notes, with subsidiary harmonies coming from the smoke house (the salmon is much liked) and the charcoal grill. Lamb and chicken, foie gras and turbot are other possible ingredients. Salads or vegetables are available on the side; Stilton and sweet things are also there for the choosing. Standards, the cry is almost unanimous, are high indeed. If simple cooking is the thing, this is the place at which to try it. Big and expensive are the key words for the wine list; our disparaging comments of previous years about the inaccessible and encyclopaedic character of the list still stand. We have never disputed the quality, although there is a tendency to reach for the safe big name; Alsace, if you can find it, is a case in point – Hugel and Trimbach, excellent though they are, could reasonably be expected to be in the company of smaller but equally prestigious names. A short-cut can be found through this massive tome: half-bottles, albeit few, are well chosen and modestly priced. House wine is £9.50.

CHEF: Clive Davidson   PROPRIETORS: Clive and Anne Davidson   OPEN: Mon to Sat, exc Sat L; 12.30 to 2, 7 to 10   CLOSED: 1 week from 24 Dec   MEALS: alc (main courses £14.50 to £20.50). Set L £13.75 (2 courses), Set D £27.50 to £35   SERVICE: 10%, card slips closed CARDS: Access, Amex, Diners, Visa   DETAILS: 50 seats. Private parties: 50 main room. Car park. Vegetarian meals. No children under 8. Smart dress preferred. Wheelchair access (1 step). No music. Fax: (050 683) 4302

---

MILNGAVIE Strathclyde                                                    map 8

## Gingerhill £                                                  | NEW ENTRY |

1 Hillhead Street, Milngavie G62 8AS
041-956 6515                                                      COOKING 1
6m N of Glasgow, off A81                                        COST £13–£41

'Join us for an afternoon at Gingerhill, sample the canapés by Gingerhill, taste the wine by Oddbins, enjoy the jazz in the garden, and have a private viewing of the wildflower and landscape paintings by Pam Carter.' It sounds seductive, this minute restaurant in Milngavie, which is unlicensed and offers very fresh fish (mainly from Gigha) cooked accurately and appealingly. It has converted many, for curdy turbot or crisp pan-fried hake, and for excellent plain squat lobster. There is a vegetarian tilt to the menu if fish is not your thing, or steaks for the carnivores. But reporters have stayed with the marine life and like it. Ancillaries, desserts and coffee, for instance, are not quite so successful.

CHEF: Heather Andrew   PROPRIETOR: Carol Thomson   OPEN: Mon to Sat L, Thur to Sat D (other evenings by arrangement for 6 or more); 11 to 3, 7.30   MEALS: alc D (main courses £7.50 to £17). Light L (£2 to £8.50). Unlicensed, but bring your own: no corkage   SERVICE: not inc, card slips closed   CARDS: Access, Diners, Visa   DETAILS: 26 seats. 4 tables outside. Private parties: 16 main room. Vegetarian meals. Children's helpings. No smoking while others eat. Music

---

*The* Guide *office can quickly spot when a restaurateur is encouraging customers to write recommending inclusion – and sadly, several restaurants have been doing this in 1993. Such reports do not further a restaurant's cause. Please tell us if a restaurateur invites you to write to the* Guide.

---

**MOFFAT Dumfries & Galloway** map 8

## ▲ *Beechwood Country House Hotel*

Harthope Place, Moffat DG10 9RS | COOKING 1
MOFFAT (0683) 20210 | COST £16–£30

'Many in the town did not know what they were missing,' observed one visitor who had made the winding journey from the north end of the high street, turning off between the church and the school and continuing just beyond the limits of the town. Some potential customers have been disappointed when lunch is abandoned through there being no bookings (be warned), but most who stay the night report enthusiastically on the open welcome, the good food and the opportunity to chat with Carl Shaw at the end of the meal when he delivers the puddings to each table. 'He always had a special surprise' on his menus was another note; perhaps because he is no enemy of experiment, with dishes as various as king prawns stuffed with minced beef and served with pimentos, or grilled aubergine with chilli and green coriander. Desserts meet the bill exactly when they consist of pancakes flamed with rice wine, a feuilleté of cream cheese, currants and strawberries, apple tart and chocolate layer cake. Lunches are simpler and cheaper. The wine list is more than adequate for the task, and includes some very decent properties. House wines are £6.95 or £7.85.

CHEF: Carl Shaw PROPRIETORS: Jeffrey and Lynda Rogers OPEN: all week; 12 to 2, 7.30 to 9 MEALS: Set L £11.50, Set D £19 SERVICE: not inc, card slips closed CARDS: Access, Amex, Visa DETAILS: 26 seats. 2 tables outside. Private parties: 26 main room, 12 private room. Car park. Vegetarian meals. Children's helpings. Smart dress preferred. No smoking in dining-room. Wheelchair access. Music ACCOMMODATION: 7 rooms, all with bath/shower. D,B&B £61 to £102. Children welcome. Baby facilities. Pets welcome. Afternoon teas. Garden. TV. Phone. Scenic. Doors close at midnight. Fax: (0683) 20889 (*The Which? Hotel Guide*)

## ▲ *Well View*

Ballplay Road, Moffat DG10 9JU | COOKING 2
MOFFAT (0683) 20184 | COST £14–£33

The directions to Well View – past the fire station, up a suburban street with old houses on one side and a modern housing estate on the other – are hardly inspiring, but this sturdy Victorian house is surrounded by well-screened gardens, with delightful views of the hills from the back bedrooms. Janet Schuckardt cooks to a fixed-price menu of variety and balance, but little choice apart from starters and sweets. Presentation is immaculate. One typically fine meal began with sauté scallops and wild mushrooms in filo pastry with dill sauce and a sprig of chervil, followed by a palate-refreshing orange and Grand Marnier sorbet. On this occasion the pair of centrepiece dishes featured butterfly fillet of Galloway beef with whisky and mustard sauce garnished with lovage, and guinea-fowl with madeira and pink peppercorn sauce, plus a festive assortment of vegetables. Cheeses had a strong Scottish presence and sweets included cold orange soufflé with thyme garnish (herb flourishes are a

trademark of the kitchen) served with orange cream and marmalade sauce. Other reports have mentioned sole mousseline in Chardonnay sauce, pork fillet in mushroom sauce, and a tuile of fresh autumn berries with chestnut ice-cream and intermingled vanilla and raspberry sauces that was of 'magazine photograph standard'. Meals begin with a canapé 'taster' and finish with coffee and sweetmeats in the comfortable lounge. Wine-buying is careful, intelligent and unflashy. A seemingly unremitting application of a multiplier results in bottles at the lower end of the list offered almost cheaply – for example, the reliable Médoc Ch. La Tour St-Bonnet 1986 at £11.95 – but does no favours further up the scale. However, range is good, half-bottles are available and fine, if sometimes cautious and names like Hugel, Faiveley and Jaboulet abound. Much satisfying drinking can be had for well below £15. House wine is £7.50.
CELLARMAN'S CHOICE: Bourgogne, Chardonnay 1990, Dom. Prieur-Brunet £13; Brouilly, Ch. de Chapitre 1991, Rodet, £14.20.

CHEF: Janet Schuckardt  PROPRIETORS: Janet and John Schuckardt  OPEN: all week, exc Sat L; 12.15 to 1.15 (24 hours' notice required L), 6.30 to 8.30  CLOSED: first week Jan, 1 week Nov  MEALS: Set L £9 to £10, Set D £19 to £21  SERVICE: not inc, card slips closed  CARDS: Access, Visa  DETAILS: 24 seats. Private parties: 12 main room, 6 private room. Car park. Vegetarian meals with prior notice. Children welcome. Smart dress preferred. No smoking in dining-room. Wheelchair access (2 steps). No music  ACCOMMODATION: 6 rooms, all with bath/shower. B&B £30 to £74. Deposit: £20. Children welcome. Baby facilities. Garden. TV. Doors close at 11.30. Confirm by 5 (*The Which? Hotel Guide*)

---

## MUIR OF ORD  Highland
map 8

## ▲ *Dower House* ▆ ▟✳

Highfield, Muir of Ord IV6 7XN
MUIR OF ORD (0463) 870090
on A862, 1m N of Muir of Ord

COOKING 2*
COST £37–£45

The house is an eighteenth-century piece of eccentricity with glorious gardens. 'We were assigned a luxurious and charming suite complete with fireplace, harmonium (not functioning), big armchairs and bathroom fixtures Queen Victoria would have recognised. But everything worked, and the Aitchisons were thoughtful hosts.' So wrote a couple who had been touring the Highlands and who considered the cooking uneven, though acceptable. First courses, for them, were the most successful – they did not enjoy the stodgy toffee pudding at the end, though desserts are often said to be the strongest suit. The couple's meals were plagued by unbalanced seasoning, whether of lemon or of salt. Others, however, have had more success with menus that offer a pair of choices for each principal course, with a soup after the first. Robyn Aitchison is not afraid to spice things up, be it a breast of duck with piquant sauce, Angus beef with a herb relish, or pears with a ginger sabayon. This gives liveliness to an otherwise steady repertoire. Soups, such as rosemary and courgette or avocado and mint or simple celeriac, are often enjoyed. The owners impress by their calm hospitality, though service can be 'ridiculously slow', even on quiet nights. The handsome wine list in chunky script may sound off alarm bells signalling a danger of pretentiousness, but although it may be a little unwieldy, the contents show intelligent and canny selection. A reduction in length has not diminished quality. The bin-ends will repay study as the relics of the older, fatter list make their way there. Prices are not unreasonable. House wine is £12. CELLARMAN'S CHOICE: Chittering Estate, Chardonnay 1990, £17; Menetou-Salon Rouge, Le Petit Clos 1988, £15.

---

CHEF: Robyn Aitchison   PROPRIETORS: Robyn and Mena Aitchison   OPEN: all week, D only (L by arrangement); 7.30 to 9   CLOSED: 25 Dec, 1 week Oct, 1 week Mar   MEALS: Set D £28   SERVICE: not inc, card slips closed   CARDS: Access, Visa   DETAILS: 26 seats. 2 tables outside. Private parties: 26 main room. Car park. Vegetarian meals with prior notice. Children's helpings 6.30 to 9. No children under 5 after 7.30. Smart dress preferred. No smoking in dining-room. Wheelchair access (also WC). No music   ACCOMMODATION: 5 rooms, all with bath/shower. Rooms for disabled. B&B £35 to £90. Deposit: 25%. Children welcome. Baby facilities. Pets by arrangement. Garden. TV. Phone. Doors close at 11.30. Confirm by 4. Fax: (0463) 870090

---

**NAIRN Highland**                                                       map 8

## ▲ Clifton House  🍷 ⅛✳                              | NEW ENTRY |

Nairn IV12 4HW
NAIRN (0667) 53119                                              COOKING 2*
W of town roundabout on A96                                  COST £24–£39

Although J. Gordon Macintyre has lived and breathed this house for over 60 years, change and development are still within his grasp. A reader who had not visited for a couple of years was struck by the improvement in the food and its consistency over a five-day period. The Victorian house is remarkable, particularly for the lavish brio of the Macintyres' decoration and furnishing: fine pictures, hand-blocked wallpapers, good antique pieces, colour and dash, lots of books and fresh flowers (and hot water, the hotel's brochure adds) make this a very individual place to stay at. Come winter, the atmosphere is kept alive by theatrical nights and concerts, and theatre is the term most often invoked for the overall effect of the place. This is nowhere more so than in the giant dining-room where a classically expressed menu works out a vein of French bourgeois cooking with variations, hence terrine de pintade aux noix, Stilton mousse with tabouleh and an aubergine charlotte or carré d'agneau à la touraine, saumon au beurre blanc and rognons de porc Henri IV. It is more than matched by the wine list and those other pillars of good living and collecting – the cheeseboard and the whiskies. The wines are a rare amalgam of magnificence and good sense; first growths of fine years at commensurate prices are neatly balanced with bourgeois clarets, carefully chosen Beaujolais and Rhônes and a fine range from Italy and the antipodes. Dessert wines apart, half-bottles are disparaged, but that lack is partly compensated by a dozen decent offerings by the glass. Prices start at £8. CELLARMAN'S CHOICE: Sancerre 1991, Riffault, £18; Chiddingstone, Pinot 1989, £17.

---

*The 1995* Guide *will be published before Christmas 1994. Reports on meals are most welcome at any time of the year, but are extremely valuable in the spring. Send them to* The Good Food Guide, *FREEPOST, 2 Marylebone Road, London NW1 1YN. No stamp is needed if posted in the UK.*

---

CHEFS: J. Gordon Macintyre and Charles Gordon Macintyre   PROPRIETOR: J. Gordon
Macintyre   OPEN: all week; 12.30 for 1, 7.30 to 9.30   MEALS: alc (main courses £10.50 to
£14)   SERVICE: net prices, card slips closed   CARDS: Access, Amex, Diners, Visa
DETAILS: main room 35 seats, Green Room 12 seats. Private parties: 35 main room, 12 Green
Room. Car park. Vegetarian meals with prior notice. Children's helpings on request. Smart
dress preferred. No smoking in Green Room. Music   ACCOMMODATION: 12 rooms, all with
bath/shower. B&B £54 to £96. Deposit: 10%. Children welcome. Pets welcome. Afternoon
teas. Garden. Doors close at midnight. Fax: (0667) 52836. (*Which? Hotel Guide*)

---

## NEWTONMORE Highland — map 8

## ▲ Ard-Na-Coille ▮ ⁝✳

Kingussie Road, Newtonmore PH20 1AY
NEWTONMORE (0540) 673214                                        COOKING 3
on A86, at N end of Newtonmore                                  COST £37–£46

'We drank like Rothschilds, on a budget far more modest than the Baron's' is a
comment to underline a principal attraction of this understated ('but the master
bedroom, large, airy and elegant, was worth the extra') hotel well away from
the world. Barry Cottam and Nancy Ferrier are considerate hosts, but
contemplative more than rumbustious. There is agreement that the formula of a
five-course no-choice dinner has not stifled Barry Cottam's sense of adventure,
even if at times the effort is not repaid by enhanced flavours: 'A breast of
guinea-fowl and a leg that had been stuffed then roasted separately required
enormous pains, but the result lacked character.' The usual remark, however, is
that there are flavours, but that the accumulation may overwhelm, and meals
can be too much, even for frames bolstered by vigorous walks. A sequence thus
described was cheese soufflé, then prawn bisque, then venison with
dauphinois potatoes. Cooking is more than Scottish simple, and the repertoire
wider than that of many a country house. Barry Cottam knows his wines but
one reader noted that 'advice has to be pursued with some determination and is
diffidently offered'. The alternative – choosing for oneself – presents little risk
as the quality is second to none; a Riesling by Rolly-Gassmann featuring as a
house wine is clear evidence that we are in capable hands. Prices do not start
low, with little below £15, but beyond this the mark-up system is fair. Halves
are especially fine. This is the place to consider a malt whisky-tasting for very
modest outlay. House wines are from £13. CELLARMAN'S CHOICE: California,
Mount Eden, Chardonnay 1989, £26; Côte Rôtie 1987, Gentaz-Dervieux, £24.

---

CHEF: Barry Cottam   PROPRIETORS: Barry Cottam and Nancy Ferrier   OPEN: all week,
D only; 7.45   CLOSED: mid-Nov to end Dec, 1 week Apr, 1 week Sept   MEALS: Set D
£27.50   SERVICE: not inc, card slips closed   CARDS: Access, Visa   DETAILS: 24 seats.
Private parties: 18 main room, 6 private room. Car park. Vegetarian meals with prior notice.
Children's helpings. No smoking in dining-room. No music   ACCOMMODATION: 7 rooms,
all with bath/shower. D,B&B £60 to £140. Deposit: £30 (new customers only). Children
welcome. Baby facilities. Pets welcome (not in public rooms). Garden. Phone. Doors close
at 11.30. Confirm by 4. Fax: (0540) 673453 (*The Which? Hotel Guide*)

---

CELLARMAN'S CHOICE: *Wines recommended by the restaurateur, normally more
expensive than house wine.*

---

## Harding's ♥ ✳

2 Station Road, North Berwick EH39 4AU
NORTH BERWICK (0620) 4737

COOKING 2
COST £15–£33

This was once a tea-room conveniently next to the railway station, slate-roofed and white-painted outside, simply furnished with an eye to space and light, and given colour by kilims hung on the walls. Added focus is lent by the sight of Chris Harding himself at work in the kitchen on the other side of the hatch. 'The aim is to provide a welcoming, informal atmosphere where someone enjoying a candlelit dinner will feel just as at ease as someone who has been in for warm scones with home-made jam,' states the menu. Australian origins are worn lightly on the wine list and sometimes infuse the cooking with an enjoyment of spices – carrot and ginger soup, turbot with coriander, ginger and lime – though wilder gestures are moderated in view of the location. Chris Harding cooks naturally, offering soundly based food such as duck with red wine and shallots, sole with dill and a saffron sauce, or a salad of goats' cheese with grapefruit and a hazelnut dressing. It is a place at ease with itself, that melds into the surroundings. Fickle wine journalists who no longer care for the antipodean should avoid North Berwick. Mr Harding rightly stands by his country's winemakers and selects from the best, joined by a handful of New Zealanders. Prices are fair, with decently aged bottles such as Vasse Felix Cabernet 1982 from Margaret River at £20. An addendum of carefully chosen French bottles shows judgement unclouded by chauvinistic pride. House wine is £8. CELLARMAN'S CHOICE: Balgownie, Chardonnay 1989, £19.40; Mosswood, Pinot Noir 1989, £20.75.

CHEF/PROPRIETOR: Christopher Harding   OPEN: Wed to Sat; 12.15 to 2, 7.30 to 9   CLOSED: 1 week Oct, 4 weeks Jan/Feb   MEALS: alc L (main courses £5 to £6). Set D £21   SERVICE: not inc   DETAILS: 24 seats. Private parties: 24 main room (Wed and Thur pm only). Car park. Vegetarian meals with prior notice. Children's helpings on request. No smoking. Wheelchair access (also WC). No music

## ▲ Knipoch Hotel ▮

Oban PA34 4QT
KILNINVER (085 26) 251
on A816, 6m S of Oban

COOKING 2
COST £35–£56

The long butter-coloured house is the filling of a sandwich of wooded hills behind and the water that laps the foreshore of Loch Feochan. The Craig family have long been in residence and their formula remains essentially as before. A set meal of varying length is of that Scottish sort that ennobles home cooking. It comes, however, at a very undomestic price. When all the flavours and materials are exact, it satisfies. When they are not, it leaves people wondering why they ever left their homes. Materials are important: the Craigs spend much time gathering them (wood mushrooms), processing them (home-smoked scallops and salmon, home-roasted coffee beans), and talking about them.

Seafood is therefore recommended; so, too, are the meat and game. Methods are reticent and simple; hence a meal that began with a vigorous kale soup and took in a salad of duck breast with clementines, mango, mayonnaise and crisp lettuce, before some halibut simply poached and served on a foaming mousseline sauce with a great tang of lemon and wine to it. The vegetables were exact and fresh, the Camembert that followed was ripe, and the meringue filled with cream and raspberries sitting on a reduced Beaujolais syrup made a perfect end. The place wins when the attention to detail is unremitting. Everyone agrees, however, that the wine list is exemplary. The relief is that high price is not the main criterion for selection; almost the reverse is the case, with unbeatable range and interest of wines well below £15. This fine selection stretches from Huet Vouvrays and magnificent well-aged Mosels and clarets, to the brief but canny choice from Italy and Spain. Half-bottles are not abundant but the range offered affords real choice. House wines are from £7.90.

CELLARMAN'S CHOICE: South Australia, Aroona Valley, Chardonnay 1990, £9.90; Côtes du Rhône 1988, Dom. du Vieux Chêne, £9.90.

---

CHEFS: Colin and Jenny Craig   PROPRIETORS: the Craig family   OPEN: all week, D only (L by arrangement); 7.30 to 9   CLOSED: mid-Nov to mid-Feb   MEALS: Set D £27.50 to £37.50   SERVICE: not inc, card slips closed   CARDS: Access, Amex, Diners, Visa   DETAILS: 44 seats. Private parties: 24 main room. Car park. Vegetarian meals with prior notice. Children's helpings. Smart dress preferred. No music   ACCOMMODATION: 17 rooms, all with bath/ shower. B&B £59 to £118. Children welcome. Baby facilities. Afternoon teas. Garden. TV. Phone. Doors close at midnight. Confirm by 6. Fax: (085 26) 249. (*Which? Hotel Guide*)

---

PEAT INN  Fife                                                                                          map 8

---

## ▲ *Peat Inn* 🍾

---

Peat Inn KY15 5LH
PEAT INN (033 484) 206
at junction of B940 and B941,
6m SW of St Andrews

COOKING **4**
COST £24–£57

Peat Inn is on the map: the former halting-place gave its name to the cottages that dot the crossroads. The inn is not much more than a cottage itself, yet over the years it has expanded by accretion, not only of buildings (the Residence behind with its luxury rooms) but also of layers of elaboration and forceful decoration. By the time the dining-room – very French with its tapestry high-backed chairs – is reached all thought of 'cottage' has sped. David Wilson's cooking could be said to have followed the same course: there is a firm foundation of Scottish materials and a sense of season, but an evolving appreciation of modern French practice has taken Peat Inn's reputation into the international stratosphere. Links with the past persist in a fair-deal lunch; links with French habits are revealed on two set-price dinner menus that supplement the *carte* (one of these is a 'tasting' menu for the whole table only). Modernity is seen in dishes such as monkfish with potato and onion and a light meat sauce, or smoked salmon dressed with olive oil. These can offend traditionalists but please the many who like a bit of imagination. The underlying approach here is both simple and conservative, evinced by main courses such as venison with red wine and port, pigeon with wild mushrooms and juniper, duck with honey and orange, and lobster with vegetables and herbs in a broth. They form the vehicle for a presentation that some find too tricky and a style of restauration that occasionally comes over as mildly ponderous. This, most Wilson-watchers agree, is not at all what was intended, and for them Peat Inn remains the epicentre of culinary enthusiasm. Gratuities are not expected. A no-fuss approach to wine-buying and service is declared at the head of the list: this is refreshing and true. The list is clear, not overlong and draws its supplies from some of the best merchants in the land. Pricing is fair throughout, with decently mature classics not costing an arm and a leg. The absence of a house wine we regard as no particular loss, but some help could be afforded to the less informed with a selection or page of recommendations; meanwhile, take up David Wilson's offer to provide advice.

CHEF: David Wilson PROPRIETORS: David and Patricia Wilson OPEN: Tue to Sat; 12.30 for 1, 7 to 9.30 MEALS: alc (main courses £16 to £19). Set L £18.50, Set D £28 to £42 SERVICE: card slips closed CARDS: Access, Amex, Diners, Visa DETAILS: 48 seats. Private parties: 24 main room, 10 and 12 private rooms. Car park. Vegetarian meals with prior notice. Children's helpings. No smoking during meals. Wheelchair access (also WC). No music ACCOMMODATION: 8 rooms, all with bath/shower. Rooms for disabled. B&B £95 to £130. Children welcome. Dogs welcome. Garden. TV. Phone. Confirm by 4. Fax: (033 484) 530. (*Which? Hotel Guide*)

**PEEBLES Borders** map 8

## ▲ *Cringletie House*

Eddleston, Peebles EH45 8PL
EDDLESTON (0721) 730233 COOKING 2
on A703, 2½m N of Peebles COST £18–£38

'We still say "Wow!" when we emerge through the trees and look up at this magnificent pile of a place' is the conclusion of a report that urges the qualities of Aileen Maguire's cooking (breakfasts included) as well as the sense of occasion imparted by dinner, impressive public rooms and a parkland setting that gives meaning to the term 'Scottish baronial'. The Maguires do not behave in a baronial fashion, however, which helps. There has always been a line of invention in the dinner menus – five courses and coffee with a choice of four or five things at most stages – that sets the kitchen apart from the dressed-up simplicity of much Scottish country cooking. This is witnessed in dishes like parsley pie with wild mushroom sauce or stuffed aubergine with mushrooms, celery and fresh coriander for starters, or salmon with lemon and cardamom, sole with a parsley and oatmeal crust and onion and sun-dried tomato sauce, or fillet of pork with Gruyère and leeks served as main dishes. Desserts have deserted the trolley or sideboard and have perhaps gained in quality thereby. Simple caramel custards, raspberry compotes and lemon tarts have given much pleasure. Steady support is maintained for the accuracy of the cooking here, including that of vegetables, and its consistency. The wine list sets its sights on bottles that do not cost an arm and a leg. The choices are still wide, none the less, and the bourgeois clarets, and antipodean and Rhône sections should attract the attention. House Duboeufs are £10 a litre.

CHEFS: Sheila McKellar, Paul Maguire and Aileen Maguire PROPRIETORS: Stanley and Aileen Maguire OPEN: all week; 1 to 1.45, 7.30 to 8.30 CLOSED: 2 Jan to 5 March MEALS: alc L Mon to Sat (main courses £5 to £6). Set Sun L £14, Set D £23.50. Minimum £5.50 weekday L SERVICE: not inc, card slips closed CARDS: Access, Visa DETAILS: 56 seats. Private parties: 27 main room. Car park. Vegetarian meals. Children's helpings. No smoking in dining-room. No music ACCOMMODATION: 13 rooms, all with bath/shower. Lift. B&B £47.50 to £86. Children welcome. Pets welcome. Afternoon teas. Garden. Tennis. TV. Phone. Doors close at 11. Confirm by 5. Fax: (0721) 730244. (*Which? Hotel Guide*)

---

**PERTH Tayside**                                                        map 8

## Number Thirty Three  £                          | NEW ENTRY |

33 George Street, Perth PH1 5LA                          COOKING 1
PERTH (0738) 33771                                    COST £18–£40

The place is 'surprisingly opulent', thought one who had enjoyed his seafood dinner. The opulence is expressed in art deco style, across an oyster bar and restaurant that offer the customer two routes to satisfaction – light or heavy, short or long. Travellers who happened on Perth at festival time were impressed by the bourride's chunky sufficiency and enticed by its aroma. Others have found scallop mousse within smoked salmon delicate and well made, oysters fresh, and a platter of fish exactly the ticket for lunch. Service has at times been thought disconcerting, but only once or twice, and perhaps refuge from any worries may be found in the wine list – as fair a collection of whites as could be needed. House wines are £9.60.

CHEFS: Mary Billinghurst and Craig Davidson PROPRIETORS: Gavin and Mary Billinghurst OPEN: Tue to Sat; 12.30 to 2.30, 6.30 to 9.30 CLOSED: 10 days Christmas and New Year MEALS: alc (main courses Oyster Bar £5 to £7, restaurant £8 to £13) SERVICE: not inc CARDS: Access, Amex, Visa DETAILS: restaurant 24 seats, Oyster Bar 18 seats. Private parties: 24 main room. Vegetarian meals. No children under 5. Smart dress preferred. No cigars in dining-room. Wheelchair access. Music

---

## Timothy's  £

24 St John Street, Perth PH1 5SP                         COOKING 1
PERTH (0738) 26641                                    COST £12–£26

'Not a lot changes – even our staff do not change much; out of 30 we employ, three have been with us since we started, and 15 for over five years. We were all young to start with,' writes Athole Laing of this club-like institution where the choice runs through the whole gamut of Danish open sandwiches and various cold platters. Hot food is restricted to soup and fondue, but do not think this is a British Rail buffet – the salmon, beef, ham, chutneys and jams for the trifle and scones are all local or home-made. People respond well to the Laings' willingness to help people delayed by weather or traffic, and the restaurant also acts as a meeting-place and social centre. Wines chop and change but their value is palpable, and the choice is careful. House wines are £7.50.

---

*A report form is at the back of the book; write a letter if you prefer.*

---

CHEF: Caroline Laing   PROPRIETORS: Caroline and Athole Laing   OPEN: Tue to Sat; 12 to 2.30, 7 to 10 (post-theatre D by arrangement)   MEALS: alc (main courses £4 to £8.50). Minimum £6 after 9.30pm   SERVICE: not inc, card slips closed   CARDS: Access, Visa DETAILS: 70 seats. Private parties: 70 main room, 30 private room. Vegetarian and vegan meals. Children's helpings on request. Wheelchair access. Music. Air-conditioned

---

**PORT APPIN Strathclyde**                                                                map 8

## ▲ *Airds Hotel* ▮ ⁵✗

Port Appin PA38 4DF
APPIN (063 173) 236                                                    COOKING 4
2m off A828, on E shore of Loch Linnhe                                 COST £43–£56

The building itself has position – by the shore of Loch Linnhe – but no great style (it was once the ferry inn). Thus the interior's vibrant colours, deep and prevailing drapes, wonderful flower displays and overall comfort, even luxury, are all the more arresting. A minority of visitors find the décor out of keeping with the unpretentious exterior: in the main, however, most people swoon over the view, enjoy the high level of housekeeping, and clamour to return. Betty Allen's cooking – or that of her son Graeme, for this is truly a two-generation affair – has none of the 'over-this' or 'over-that' about it. 'How does she achieve such simplicity allied with such intensity of flavour?' asks one. 'Our third meal was every bit as enjoyed as our first,' commented another. A very true judgement is at work, both composing menus and fixing the level of complexity that should be permitted in the kitchen. 'The fish was in the peak of condition, but somehow it always does seem to peak on the plate' was the admiring remark of one who had enjoyed halibut with spinach and a chive sauce on the first evening, and turbot on a bed of honeyed aubergine with a tarragon cream sauce on the second. The dishes on offer are not simple, as those at a dinner party or home-cooked might be, but they are not overworked. Salads of scallops with coriander, ginger and olive oil, and of quail with truffle oil show the light touch. Yet Loch Linnhe prawns with a herb mayonnaise indicate that the really simple, yet near perfect, approach is also espoused. 'Grown-up' vegetables (no infanticide here) are properly cooked and have flavour. Desserts continue the line of studied understatement, with single notes dominating when justifiable. The standards of welcome from a kilted crew are generous. The dark hours of the night can be spent with the wine list, which might win a Booker Prize for length and content; the number and range of half-bottles gets special mention. We have long drawn people's attention to this as one of the most intelligent and fair-minded lists in the *Guide*: the balance of mature wines from well-established names and decent New World bottles reveals a lovely approach, which is supported by some of the best merchants in the business. Italy, Germany and the Rhône provide strong competition for some magnificent classics. House wines are from around £10.

---

*The text of entries is based on unsolicited reports sent in by readers, backed up by inspections conducted anonymously. The factual details under the text are from questionnaires the* Guide *sends to all restaurants that feature in the book.*

---

CHEFS: Betty Allen and Graeme Allen  PROPRIETORS: Eric, Betty and Graeme Allen
OPEN: all week; 12.30 to 2 (snacks only), 8 for 8.30  CLOSED: early Jan to end Feb  MEALS:
Set D £34  SERVICE: not inc, card slips closed  CARDS: Access, Visa  DETAILS: 36 seats.
Private parties: 10 main room. Car park. Vegetarian meals with prior notice. Children's
helpings. Smart dress preferred. No smoking in dining-room. Wheelchair access. No
music  ACCOMMODATION: 12 rooms, all with bath/shower. D,B&B £98 to £237. Deposit:
£100. Children welcome. Pets by arrangement. Afternoon teas. Garden. TV. Phone. Doors
close at 11.30. Confirm by 4. Fax: (063 173) 535 (*The Which? Hotel Guide*)

---

**PORTPATRICK** Dumfries & Galloway                                        map 8

## ▲ *Knockinaam Lodge* 🛏✳

Portpatrick DG9 9AD
PORTPATRICK (077 681) 471                                        COOKING 2
off A77, 3m S of Portpatrick                                     COST £30–£47

The location, well away from other people, with the sea hogging the horizon, is
tip-top and the hotel accommodation comfortable, even if some rooms are
small: 'a little poky and narrow' was the franker description of a couple who
paid £100 a night for a room with a single small armchair 'stuck in the
fireplace'. The latterday reputation of Knockinaam has been founded on the
fiercely Gallic nouvelle cuisine of Daniel Galmiche. He has now been replaced
by a Scot, but the menu sails on in French – 'if you are the sixth couple, the
complete translation and explanation of the meal by M. Frichot gets rather
boring', the portions remain nouvelle dainty, and the cooking is very
acceptable. Dinner is still at a set (high) price – three courses, with a choice of
two at each stage. Mushroom ravioli with vegetable tagliatelle and a madeira
sauce, followed by noisette of lamb with tarragon before a hot chocolate soufflé
(needing the bulk), is a meal that sets the character of the place. Fish, no longer
so obviously Seychellois, is fresh and good. The wine list has a fine set of
clarets and burgundies mainly from Chanson. House wines start at £9.75.

CHEF: Stuart Muir  PROPRIETORS: Marcel and Corinna Frichot  OPEN: all week; 12.30 to 2,
7.30 to 9  CLOSED: 4 Jan to 20 Mar  MEALS: Set L £22, Set D £30  SERVICE: not inc, card
slips closed  CARDS: Access, Amex, Diners, Visa  DETAILS: 28 seats. Private parties: 32
main room. Car park. Vegetarian meals with prior notice. Children's high teas. No children
under 8. Smart dress preferred. No smoking in dining-room. Wheelchair access (1 step; also
WC). No music  ACCOMMODATION: 10 rooms, all with bath/shower. B&B £68 to £136.
Deposit: £100. Children welcome. Baby facilities. Pets welcome. Afternoon teas. Garden.
TV. Phone. Doors close at midnight. Fax: (077 681) 435 (*The Which? Hotel Guide*)

---

*'In the middle of my crab-meat was a label reading ''Frozen White Pasteurized
Crabmeat''; I suppose I should be grateful it was thoroughly defrosted.'*
On eating in Bristol

*'The main courses were disappointing. Guinea-fowl arrived pink to almost rare, lamb
cutlets had had none of the fat removed – and could convincingly claim to have had
additional quantities added – and Dover sole was served in portions more appropriate for a
Sindy doll on a diet.'*  On eating in London

---

## QUOTHQUAN Strathclyde map 8

## ▲ *Shieldhill Hotel* ✴

Quothquan, nr Biggar ML12 6NA
BIGGAR (0899) 20035                               COOKING 1
off B7016, 4m NW of Biggar           COST £22–£48

'The only member of staff we saw was the owner, Jack Greenwald. He answered the telephone, opened the door, carried the bags, served the drinks, took the orders, cooked the meals, and did the gardening.' This report of herculean effort might be modified this year, for there are new chefs in the kitchen and Jack Greenwald can relax in his ancient mansion – though old in structure, it is as modern as can be in its fabrics and boldly coloured furnishings. The cooking has received more recommendations than of late, which bodes well for the new regime. The style is sophisticated Scottish country house: timbale of smoked finnan haddock with cabbage and pine-nuts and a fennel and dill dressing, beef with an onion marmalade 'nestling' on a pink and green peppercorn sauce and duck with orange sauce are some of the examples quoted. Cheeses have been recommended, as have the home-made chocolates. The wine list has a useful Californian bias (the owner hails from there). House wines are £8.95.

CHEFS: Keith and Nicola Braidwood   PROPRIETORS: Jack Greenwald and Christine Dunstan   OPEN: all week, D only, and Sun L; 12 to 2, 7 to 9   MEALS: Set Sun L £13.50, Set D £24 to £29.50   SERVICE: not inc, card slips closed   CARDS: Access, Amex, Diners, Visa
DETAILS: 26 seats. Private parties: 26 main room, 12 private room. Car park. Children's helpings on request. No children under 12. Smart dress preferred. No smoking in dining-room. Wheelchair access. Music   ACCOMMODATION: 11 rooms, all with bath/shower. B&B £88 to £155. Deposit: 50%. No children under 12. Baby facilities. Afternoon teas. Garden. TV. Phone. Fax: (0899) 21092 (*The Which? Hotel Guide*)

## ST MARGARET'S HOPE Orkney map 8

## ▲ *The Creel*

Front Road, St Margaret's Hope KW17 2SL
ST MARGARET'S HOPE (085 683) 311                     COOKING 3
off A961, on South Ronaldsay island          COST £23–£33

'Sadly, for islands surrounded by seas yielding fantastic shellfish, boasting lochs teeming with wild brown trout and with fields full of prime beef, Orkney is a culinary desert, with only a few oases,' observes a reader who travels from Edinburgh to enjoy this admirable restaurant. The setting, by the harbour front, is a bonus. Alan and Joyce Craigie are Orcadians and know what to do with the fresh local produce. The menu is short, simple and steers clear of over-elaboration. Mussels are cooked with onions, garlic and tomatoes; 'unassuming' house pâté is a delicious coarse terrine accompanied by a rowanberry and whisky sauce; scallops are seared on the chargrill and served with a sauce of ginger and lentils; saddle of lamb comes with a mint and green peppercorn crust. Also look for the leg of South Ronaldsay lamb, marinated and smoked over oak chips, and try the bere bannocks (local barley bread). Vegetables and cheeses are from the island. Desserts often include some traditional specialities such as cloutie dumplings with home-made custard and 'brides cog' pears (roasted and arranged round a brandy-snap basket filled with ice-cream and served with a sauce made from an Orcadian recipe). The 'chef's special' – layers of chocolate mousse, brandy-snaps, meringue and cream caramel with butterscotch sauce – gets regular endorsements. Service is informal and attentive. The wine list is not encyclopaedic, but it has been chosen with care and mark-ups are realistic. Argentinian house wine is £8.30.

CHEF: Alan Craigie  PROPRIETORS: Joyce and Alan Craigie  OPEN: all week D June to Aug, Wed to Sun D Apr, May and Sept, Fri and Sat D Oct to Mar (L by arrangement); 7 to 9 CLOSED: Jan  MEALS: alc (main courses £10.50 to £13)  SERVICE: not inc, card slips closed  CARDS: Access, Visa  DETAILS: 38 seats. Private parties: 38 main room. Vegetarian meals with prior notice. Children's helpings. No children under 5. Smart dress preferred. Wheelchair access (2 steps; also WC). No music  ACCOMMODATION: 3 rooms, all with bath/shower. B&B £25 to £40. Deposit: 10%. Children welcome. Baby facilities. Garden. TV. Doors close at 12.30am. Confirm by 4

---

**STEWARTON** Strathclyde                                                   map 8

## ▲ *Chapeltoun House* ▼ ✳

Irving Road, Stewarton KA3 3ED
STEWARTON (0560) 482696                                          COOKING 1
2m from Stewarton, on B769 towards Irvine                  COST £22–£42

This turn-of-the-century country house, 20 miles south-west of Glasgow and near the coast, was built by a city merchant. The exterior is imposingly symmetrical, the interior heavily Edwardian classical, though now lightened by the decorative work of the McKenzies. It is comfortable, with a certain formality, in the cooking as well as in the service and ambience. Some of the emphasis on mousses and fillings has shifted to more modern accents, as in a dish of guinea-fowl with green lentils; but elaboration persists, not without its qualities, in something like a saddle of venison with a duo of sauces – calvados and apple cream, and a deep-brown Grand Marnier sauce. The wine list shows good sense and allows for thrift, with decent New World and bourgeois clarets in the reds and adequate Alsaces and Loires. Age and top quality are equally available in 1979 Côte Rôtie from Guigal at £39.90 and Condrieu 1986 at £35.90. House wine is £9.50. CELLARMAN'S CHOICE: Marlborough, Sauvignon Blanc 1991, Hunters, £16.90; Barolo Riserva 1985, S. Orsola, £21.30.

CHEF: Tom O'Donnell  PROPRIETORS: Colin and Graeme McKenzie  OPEN: all week; 12 to 2, 7 to 9.15  MEALS: Set L £15.50, Set D £23.90  SERVICE: not inc, card slips closed CARDS: Access, Amex, Visa  DETAILS: 50 seats. Private parties: 50 main room, 50 private room. Car park. Vegetarian meals. No children under 12. Smart dress preferred. No smoking in dining-room. Wheelchair access (also WC). No music  ACCOMMODATION: 8 rooms, all with bath/shower. B&B £65 to £129. No children under 12. Pets by arrangement. Afternoon teas. Garden. Fishing. TV. Phone. Doors close at midnight. Confirm by 1. Fax: (0560) 85100 (*The Which? Hotel Guide*)

---

*The* Guide *is totally independent, accepts no free hospitality, and survives on the number of copies sold each year.*

---

**STRONTIAN Highland** map 8

## ▲ *Kilcamb Lodge* 🎄✳

Strontian PH36 4HY
STRONTIAN (0967) 2257        COOKING 3
on A861, by N shore of Loch Sunart        COST £31–£37

Mother Ann and father Gordon Blakeway used to run a market garden (useful
for vegetables); son Peter has trained at Gidleigh, Airds and Claridges; postie
Wendy hurtles round the lanes in the morning and helps confect puddings
later: Kilcamb Lodge is a 'delightful, friendly and efficiently run place'. This
old Scottish manor house, a miracle of isolation set on the shores of Loch
Sunart, is as clean as a new pin – so new are the Blakeways to the hotel scene
that there is no time yet for ennui – and inspections comment on the 'superb'
position, 'wonderful views', cosy interior complete with log fire, and
comfortable dining-room. The food cooked here is good enough to cheer
the Highlands and offers better value than many eateries to boot. A short
fixed-price menu gives new choices every evening; the style is one of
understatement, making the consumption the more pleasurable. Dishes have
included chicken and spinach pancakes; a salmon fish-cake with tomato and
dill sauce; an intermediate course of pea and mint sauce; breast of duck with
enough flavour to be gamey, with a plum purée and a sage cream sauce; then
real dinner-party puddings like 'tipsy' trifle, heavily laced with brandy, and
raspberry meringue. Plain food is good food, when it is properly prepared,
when the sauces have flavour and the materials are fresh: the cooking here
bodes well to being of that sort. The wine list list is adequate but abbreviated.
House wines from Moreau are £7.75.

CHEFS: Ann Blakeway and Peter Blakeway   PROPRIETORS: the Blakeway family   OPEN:
all week, D only; 7.30   CLOSED: 1 Nov to 31 Mar   MEALS: Set D £24   SERVICE: not inc,
card slips closed   CARDS: Access, Visa   DETAILS: 26 seats. Private parties: 30 main room.
Car park. Vegetarian meals with prior notice. Children's helpings 6.30pm on request.
Smart dress preferred. No smoking in dining-room. Wheelchair access (2 steps; also men's
WC). No music   ACCOMMODATION: 10 rooms, all with bath/shower. B&B £40 to £80.
Deposit: £35. Children welcome. Baby facilities. Pets in 2 rooms. Afternoon teas. Garden.
Fishing. Fax: (0967) 2041 (*The Which? Hotel Guide*)

---

**SWINTON Borders** map 8

## ▲ *Wheatsheaf Hotel,*
## *Four Seasons* 🎄✳ £

Swinton TD11 3JJ
SWINTON (0890) 860257        COOKING 2
on A6112, Coldstream to Duns road        COST £15–£34

This traditional village pub/hotel may be small, but there is a variety of ways to
eat here: in the bar, with a blackboard menu of daily specials, or in the
restaurant, where you may choose between a sun-lounge extension or
enclosure within solid walls. What they have in common is that they are busy
– all the time. Fish, be it shellfish, salmon or flat fish, is a main support of the

enterprise: whitebait impressed, pan-fried Dover sole with lemon and butter delighted, and local smoked salmon made a journey worthwhile. Hungry people also enjoy the substantial meats – the sirloins, the Gressingham duck with caramelised plums, and the braised oxtail. Cooking can be 'saucy' and for one repeat visitor it was this that let down otherwise very fine ingredients. The wine list goes for wide range in a small compass and does not overload the choice with high prices. House wines are from £7.25.

CHEF: Alan Reid   PROPRIETORS: Alan and Julie Reid   OPEN: Tue to Sun; 11.45 to 2, 6 to 9.30   CLOSED: 2 weeks mid-Feb   MEALS: alc (main courses £4.50 to £11)   SERVICE: not inc, card slips closed   CARDS: Access, Visa   DETAILS: 56 seats. 6 tables outside. Private parties: 26 main room, 18 and 26 private rooms. Vegetarian meals. Children's helpings. Smart dress preferred. No smoking in 1 dining-room. Wheelchair access (1 step). No music   ACCOMMODATION: 4 rooms, 1 with bath/shower. B&B £25 to £54. Deposit: 50%. Children welcome. Baby facilities. Pets welcome (not in public areas). Garden. Snooker. TV. Doors close at midnight. Confirm by 6

---

**TIRORAN** Strathclyde                                                              map 8

## ▲ *Tiroran House* ░✳

Tiroran, Isle of Mull PA69 6ES
TIRORAN (068 15) 232                                                      COOKING 2*
off B8035, 6m S of Gruline                                              COST £21–£46

Sit in the panelled, candle-lit dining-room, the woodwork of which glows with beeswax and elbow grease, and feel protected from all the weather the Isle of Mull can muster; or take to the conservatory, where a vine grows overhead and there are views of garden, rhododendrons and loch to lull the mind. The Blockeys cater principally for residents, so book ahead to see if there is room for those in search of dinner only. 'You wouldn't know it was a hotel; it is like someone's home with genuine antique furniture,' wrote one admiring visitor. The house party is the theme tune to which Tiroran dances, but the group discipline implicit in the form is applied gently and pleasantly structures the day. The dinner-card is ready after tea; order before changing – the race starts at 7.45 prompt, so come down early for a drink. Any house that can provide cooking like this would be high on most people's lists. Sauce-making is pukka, tastes are self-evident and materials are good. Lettuce and cucumber soup with lovage, artichoke hearts with a mushroom soubise and local prawns with garlic mayonnaise constituted the first-course choices one night in May. Then came a no-choice fillet of beef with simple fresh vegetables (they always seem to do something interesting with potatoes here), followed by a dessert of perfect Britishness (fool, tart or bread-and-butter), then cheese and coffee. All is quiet good taste, delivered without unneeded fanfare. The wines are as thoroughbred as the methods shown throughout the house. House wines are £12.95 but as they are either an Oliver Leflaive or a Ch. Lamarque, who could complain?

---

*All entries in the* Guide *are rewritten every year, not least because restaurant standards fluctuate. Don't trust an out-of-date* Guide.

---

CHEF: Sue Blockey  PROPRIETORS: Robin and Sue Blockey  OPEN: all week, D only (L residents only); 7.45  CLOSED: Oct to mid-May  MEALS: Set L £12.50, Set D £28.50 SERVICE: not inc  DETAILS: 22 seats. Private parties: 8 main room. Car park. Vegetarian meals with prior notice. No children under 10. Smart dress preferred. No smoking in dining-room. No music  ACCOMMODATION: 9 rooms, all with bath/shower. D,B&B £125 to £210. Deposit: £50. No children under 10. Dogs welcome (in annexe). Garden. Confirm by noon. Fax: (068 15) 232. (*Which? Hotel Guide*)

---

## TROON Strathclyde                                                    map 8

## ▲ *Highgrove House*

Old Loans Road, Troon KA10 7HL                                    COOKING 1
TROON (0292) 312511                                               COST £16–£40

This white-painted house, close to the village of Loans and the town of Troon, overlooks the Firth of Clyde and Arran. Bill Costley's menus are all things to all men, from a long catalogue of lunch dishes, to an evening brasserie menu that does some simple things like lamb cutlets with tomatoes and fresh basil, to something rather more elaborate on the *carte*, which may delve into the contrast of sweet and sour with a vengeance, as in chicken stuffed with banana, rolled in coconut, served with a curry and mango sauce. The wine list is a quick general tour, with claret showing best. House wines are £9.75.

---

CHEF: James Allison  PROPRIETORS: William and Catherine Costley  OPEN: all week; 12 to 2.30, 6 to 9.30  MEALS: alc (main courses L £5 to £6.50, D £8.50 to £13.50). Set D £15.95  SERVICE: not inc, card slips closed  CARDS: Access, Amex, Visa  DETAILS: 110 seats. 6 tables outside. Private parties: 100 main room, 18 and 35 private rooms. Car park. Vegetarian meals. Children's helpings. Smart dress preferred. Wheelchair access. Music. Air-conditioned  ACCOMMODATION: 9 rooms, all with bath/shower. B&B £55 to £69. Children welcome. Small dogs welcome. Afternoon teas. Garden. Air-conditioned. TV. Phone. Fax: (0292) 318228

---

## UIG Highland                                                         map 8

## ▲ *Baile-na-Cille* 🍴✕

Timsgarry, Uig, Isle of Lewis PA86 9JD
TIMSGARRY (085 175) 242                                           COOKING 1*
B8011 to Uig, then right down track on to shore                   COST £22–£27

'Dinner-party cooking for those who happen to have discovered and reached the edge of Great Britain' is Richard Gollin's description of eating at his white house at the edge of Uig sands, well beyond the Pillars of Hercules. The dinner party caters for children too, and Joanna Gollin's cooking encompasses rather more adventure than high tea in Hornsea: Russian vegetable soup with pine-nut dumplings, local mussels or smoked salmon, duck stuffed with apricots, walnuts and black pudding (the black pudding on its own at breakfast), lamb cooked with rowanberries, good venison and fresh lobsters – the list continues, and is a reminder of the self-sufficiency of the Western Isles, as long as you do not want tropical fruit. The cheerfulness here breaks through most storm clouds. The wine list is good fun too, thanks to supplies of Rhônes and

Loires from Yapp Brothers; there is even Breaky Bottom, the best of British. House wines are £8.50, the rest go from £12.50.

CHEF: Joanna Gollin    PROPRIETORS: Baile-na-Cille Ltd    OPEN: all week, D only (snack L all week, exc Sun); 7.30    CLOSED: Oct to end Apr    MEALS: daytime snacks. Set D £18 SERVICE: net prices, card slips closed    CARDS: Access, Visa    DETAILS: 30 seats. Private parties: 30 main room. Car park. Vegetarian meals with prior notice. Children's helpings. No smoking in dining-room. No music    ACCOMMODATION: 12 rooms, 8 with bath/shower. B&B £19 to £60. Deposit: £20 to £50. Children welcome. Baby facilities. Pets welcome. Afternoon teas. Garden. Fishing. Fax: (085 175) 241. (*Which? Hotel Guide*)

---

**ULLAPOOL** Highland                                                              map 8

## ▲ *Altnaharrie Inn*

Ullapool IV26 2SS                                                    COOKING 5
DUNDONNELL (085 483) 230                                      COST £56–£70

There cannot be many restaurants in Great Britain where the bill notes 'Dinner including ferry and VAT'. Altnaharrie, a former drovers' inn, is isolated by water from the quay at Ullapool, which is where you park the car, ring for transport and clamber aboard the MV *Mother Goose*. It is a trip for the physically competent, wellingtons may sometimes be in order, or if not, insect repellent against the midges. Space is available only for residents, so outsiders can dine only when the rooms are not all taken: ring ahead. The owners have not destroyed the original feel of the place by importing luxury, though cosseting is the order of the day. 'Bric-à-brac and clever tinkering' is how one person saw the intelligent and characterful conversion that will never extend so far as to provide TVs or telephones. Gunn Eriksen cooks a set menu, choice occurring only the last, sweet lap. Its consistent level of performance is what gives the place so high a rating in people's opinions. True, there is less of a trick to cooking a set meal than to balancing the various demands of a whole menu, but if the food on the plate is so good, who is going to measure? Also, people who return do not get the same food twice, so more than one menu may be cooked on a single night. The style of the food is beyond simplicity, yet the elaboration never strays into art for art's sake, and the presentation, although of a high order, is not stupidly fussy. One 1993 menu consisted of a warm salad of scallops and summer truffles beefed up with a sweet wine sauce infused by the scallop juices and veal stock; courgette-flower soup with the flowers themselves stuffed with a mousseline of shellfish; roast saddle of lamb with a herb gravy, the elaboration coming from a leek-wrapped fillet of lamb with stuffing of foie gras, herbs and garlic; cheese, but not just Scottish; then a choice of thin apple tart, a confection of pear and chocolate, or cherry tart. Service is steady and non-intrusive (note that credit cards are not accepted); wines are discussed and got ready beforehand. The list is not simply a constellation of good names from a wide net that trawls wines from around the world. It also has the good sense to include a house selection, some fine half-bottles and decent wines by the glass. Prices at the higher end appear driven by a substantial multiplier but more than enough is affordable. House selections are from £11.70.

CHEF: Gunn Eriksen  PROPRIETORS: Fred Brown and Gunn Eriksen  OPEN: all week, D only; 8  CLOSED: early Nov to late Mar  MEALS: Set D £50  SERVICE: net prices  DETAILS: 18 seats. Private parties: 14 main room. Car park. Vegetarian meals with prior notice. Children's helpings. No children under 8. Smart dress preferred. No smoking. No music ACCOMMODATION: 8 rooms, all with bath/shower. D,B&B £100 to £270. Deposit: £75. Pets by arrangement. Confirm by 4 (*The Which? Hotel Guide*)

---

## WALLS Shetland map 8

## ▲ Burrastow House ¼✳

Burrastow, Walls ZE2 9PB
WALLS (059 571) 307
at Walls drive to top of hill,                                                    COOKING 1
turn left then 2m to Burrastow                                              COST £15–£35

'This must be the most isolated decent restaurant in the UK,' exclaimed one wondering visitor – all the way from Edinburgh, indeed – who went on to extol the vision of seals gambolling in the water almost on the doorstep. Bo Simmons is at great pains to keep up standards and the variety of imported produce. The natural resources, particularly the shellfish, will be the chief attraction for many on the short daily menu, but mango and papaya ice-cream, or tomato and mozzarella salad, are supplied for those who hanker after big-city markets. Salmon and lobster mousse, salmon and turbot in saffron sauce, upstanding soups, and indulgent puddings are particularly recommended. The place has a slightly zany feel to it which contributes to the happy informality. The decent wine list includes makers such as Bossard (Muscadet), Sorin (Burgundy), Terres Blanches (Provence) and Billecart-Salmon (Champagne). Many of the bottles are organic. House wines are £7.20.

---

CHEF/PROPRIETOR: Bo Simmons  OPEN: Tue to Sun, exc Sun D; 12.30 to 2.30, 7.30 to 9 CLOSED: 24 Dec to 21 March  MEALS: alc (main courses £6 to £7). Set D £22.50  SERVICE: not inc  DETAILS: 30 seats. Private parties: 22 main room. Car park. Vegetarian meals. Children's helpings. No smoking in dining-room. No music  ACCOMMODATION: 5 rooms, all with bath/shower. Rooms for disabled. D,B&B £56 to £122. Children welcome. Baby facilities. Pets welcome. Afternoon teas. Garden. Fishing. Doors close at midnight. Confirm by 4. Fax: (059 571) 213. (*Which? Hotel Guide*)

# Scotland round-ups

All the eating-places listed below have been recommended by readers but for one reason or another have not graduated to the main listing. They are not places that simply failed at inspection. All reports on these places would be most welcome.

ABERLOUR (Grampian) *Archiestown Hotel* (034 06) 218. Small, comfortable hotel on Speyside; fresh soups, seafood and fish.

ARBROATH (Tayside) *Gordon's* 32 Main Road, Inverkeilor, nr Arbroath, (024 13) 364. Husband-and-wife team cooking imaginative French dishes; also do B&B.

ARDVASAR (Highland) *Ardvasar Hotel* Sleat, Isle of Skye, (047 14) 223. Old coaching-inn with a homely atmosphere; fair bar food and good, traditional desserts.

AYR (Strathclyde) *Fouter's Bistro* 2A Academy Street, (0292) 261391. Reliable bistro with a relaxing atmosphere and well-chosen wines.

BIGGAR (Strathclyde) *Culter Mill* Coulter, nr Biggar, (0899) 20950. Bistro bar and à la carte dining-room next to an old water-mill.

BRODICK (Strathclyde) *Auchrannie Country House* Isle of Arran, (0770) 302234. New hotel with attractive dining-room; fair cooking includes venison, spaghetti, strawberry cheesecake and profiteroles.

CALLANDER (Central) *Roman Camp Hotel* off Main Street, (0877) 30003, changes to (0877) 330003 December 1993. Jacobean hunting-lodge complete with turret, acreage and atmosphere. Excellent ingredients, classic ideas, occasional over-rich combinations.

CARNOUSTIE (Tayside) *Park Avenue* 11 Park Avenue, (0241) 53336. Quality materials competently cooked and well presented.

EDINBURGH (Lothian) *Ann Purna* 45 St Patrick's Square, 031-662 1807. Edinburgh's newest Indian vegetarian restaurant, offering Gujarati cuisine. Lovely breads, delicate saucing.

*Atrium* 10 Cambridge Street, 031-228 8882. New restaurant/brasserie for chef/proprietor Andrew Radford.

*La Bagatelle* 22A Brougham Place, Tollcross, 031-229 0869. Pleasing French cooking that's well presented; good service.

*Balmoral Hotel* Bridges Restaurant, 1 Princes Street, 031-556 2414. Convenient, comfortable brasserie open all day. Ambitious cooking; decent wines.

*Chez Jules* 1 Craig's Close, 29 Cockburn Street, 031-225 7007. Basic, basement bistro for keenly priced French food.

*Chinese Home Cooking* 21 Argyle Street, 031-229 4404. Cheap – not that cheerful – and basic Cantonese in bedsit-land. Unlicensed, but bring your own.

*Cosmo Ristorante* 58A North Castle Street, 031-226 6743. Despite slow service this is home to fair cooking: fresh fish –

especially Dover sole – has been praised, also decent lasagne, tiramisù and chocolate fudge cake.

*Doric Tavern* 15 Market Street, 031-225 1084. Busy, friendly, inexpensive place with an adventurous menu; recommended are crayfish bisque, monkfish and cassoulet parisienne with crusty bread.

*Grain Store* 30 Victoria Street, 031-225 7635. Stripped-pine place above shops; straightforward food, good wines.

*India Gate* 23 Brougham Place, 031-229 1537. Pleasant Indian cooking, sometimes explosive chillis.

*Marrakech Hotel* 30 London Street, 031-556 7293. Moroccan cooking of couscous and tageens; basement dining-room, bring your own wine.

*Pierre Lapin* 32 West Nicholson Street, 031-668 4332. Pierre Levicky's vegetarian (but not vegan) place: inexpensive, fair cooking – try toasted brioche with brazil nuts and corainder pâté, fricassee of mushrooms, and fruit tart.

*Suruchi* 14A Nicolson Street, 031-556 6583. Some south Indian dishes in addition to a conventional sub-continent listing; decent dosas and halva; inexpensive.

*Szechuan House* 12 Leamington Terrace, 031-229 4655. Moved to a new address but still home to reliable Chinese cooking: bang-bang chicken, deep-fried shredded beef in chilli sauce, rice noodles Singapore-style.

*Tubtim* 148 Nicolson Street, 031-556 9351. Pleasant Thai restaurant producing good sweet-and-sour flavours, incorporating coconut milk and kaffir lime leaves.

GLASGOW (Strathclyde) *October Café* The Rooftop, Princes Square, Buchanan Street, 041-221 0303. Smart shopping-centre spot for an interesting lunch (evenings it's now solely a drinking bar). Short, weekly-changing menus.

*Two Fat Ladies* 88 Dumbarton Road, 041-339 1944. Basic décor that's low on comfort and space, but fish is the pride and joy, and can be good.

**GLENELG** (Highland) *Glenelg Inn* By Kyle of Lochalsh, (059 982) 273. Ancient inn overlooking the Isle of Skye; home cooking, facilities for children, accommodation.

**INVERNESS** (Highland) *Pierre Victoire* 75 Castle Street, (0463) 225662. Another successful addition to the chain: a proven formula of sound French cooking, cheaply priced, in a fun atmosphere. More reports, please.

**JEDBURGH** (Borders) *Glenfriars Hotel* The Friars, (0835) 62000. Comfortable accommodation, first-rate materials simply cooked.

**KELSO** (Borders) *Sunlaws House Hotel* Heiton, nr Kelso, (0573) 450331. Attractive country-house hotel in huntin', shootin' and fishin' territory. Nice place to stay at, competent (if conservative) cooking; fresh salads, wild salmon, pear clafoutis.

**KILFINAN** (Strathclyde) *Kilfinan Hotel* Tighnabruaich, nr Kilfinan, (070 082) 201. Old coaching-inn surrounded by beautiful scenery. Elegant four-course dinners; seafood ragoût in langoustine butter, pheasant in port wine and grape sauce, brandy-snap basket of fruits.

**KINROSS** (Tayside) *Grouse & Claret* Heatheryford, (0577) 864212. Skilfully converted farmstead that's now a restaurant with accommodation; seafood, seasonal game and winning sweets. More reports, please.

**KIRKCUDBRIGHT** (Dumfries & Galloway) *Auld Alliance* 5 Castle Street, (0557) 30569. Husband-and-wife team cooking consistently; locally caught fish and shellfish and Galloway beef are features.

**KIRKWALL** (Orkney) *Foveran* St Ola, Mainland, (0856) 872389. Hotel with large acreage, overlooking Scapa Flow (binoculars provided at window tables for otter viewing); local produce used to good effect includes terrific scallops.

**LAMLASH** (Strathclyde) *Carraig Mhor* Isle of Arran, (0770) 600453. Small stone cottage with views over Holy Island; specialises in fresh sea food and is useful for the area.

**LOCHINVER** (Highland) *Lochinver Larder* Main Street, (057 14) 356. Interesting-sounding restaurant-cum-coffee-shop-cum-delicatessen; lots of local produce, things for vegetarians.

**MARKINCH** (Fife) *Balbirnie House* Balbirnie Park, (0592) 610066. Grade I listed Georgian mansion in several hundred acres, complete with golf course; a new chef, fine looking materials. More reports, please.

**MELROSE** (Borders) *Burt's Hotel* Market Square, (089 682) 2285. Well-reported bar meals of straightforward items: sirloin steak, salads, crisp chips.

**NEWTON STEWART** (Dumfries & Galloway) *Kirroughtree Hotel* (0671) 2141. Imposing country-house hotel with two dining-rooms (smokers and non-smokers) and variable Anglo-French cooking.

**SHIELDAIG** (Highland) *Tigh an Eilean* nr Strathcarron, (052 05) 251. Well-maintained hotel in a wonderful location, on Loch Torridon. Local produce; lovely hosts.

**SPEAN BRIDGE** (Highland) *Old Pines* Gairlochy Road, (0397) 712324. Comfortable accommodation and a conservatory dining-room that's open to non-residents. First-rate meals include fresh fish and seafood and indulgent desserts. Very friendly hosts; unlicensed, but bring your own.

**STEIN** (Highland) *Loch Bay* Vaternich, Isle of Skye, (047 083) 235. Seafood restaurant in an old fishing village; worth travelling to for fresh fish, chowders, seafood platters and decent chips.

**STONEHAVEN** (Grampian) *Tolbooth* Old Pier, (0569) 62287. Specialises in seafood, all freshly caught; several good wines.

**TURNBERRY** (Strathclyde) *Turnberry Hotel* (0655) 31000. Refurbished, much golf and leisure. Good reports for luxury dining-room in more comfort than for miles around, with some high prices.

**ULLAPOOL** (Highland) *Morefield Motel* (0854) 612161. Basic décor but fresh seafood; eat in the bar or the restaurant in summer.

# Wales

---

**ABERAERON Dyfed**                                    map 4

## *Hive on the Quay* £

| Cadwgan Place, Aberaeron SA46 0BU | COOKING 1 |
| ABERAERON (0545) 570445 | COST £10–£30 |

Since 1975 the Holgate family (of honey fame) have run this enterprise on the old coal wharf between Aberaeron's two harbours and show no signs of flagging. The honey-bee exhibition and the honey ice-creams continue to attract the crowds. Dyfed is one of the bastions of organic production and the Holgates are true supporters of the cause. Superb, rough-textured bread and farmhouse cheeses are highlights. Through the day the café deals in sandwiches and robust home-made cakes plus teas and coffees. Lunch is a cold buffet. The slightly more formal evening restaurant offers a choice of traditional Welsh dishes with a few international ideas tossed in for good measure. The Holgates have their own fishing boat and a new retail shop within the courtyard, so local fish shows up in dishes such as provençal fish soup, lobster Newburg and lemon sole grilled with fennel. Welsh lamb also stakes its claim. Sweets are dominated by the home-made honey ice-cream menu. The organic philosophy extends to the mini wine list; otherwise the range of drinks takes in Wadworth 6X, Weston's cider and mead. House wines are £7.

CHEFS: Sarah Holgate, John Bromley and Margaret Morgan  PROPRIETORS: Margaret and Sarah Holgate  OPEN: all week (D 8 Jul to 5 Sept only); 12 to 2, 6 to 9.30  CLOSED: end Sept to 29 May  MEALS: alc D (main courses £6 to £11). Buffet L  SERVICE: not inc L, 10% D, card slips closed  CARDS: Access, Visa  DETAILS: 60 seats. 2 tables outside. Private parties: 35 main room. Vegetarian meals. Children's helpings. Wheelchair access. Music

---

**ABERDOVEY Gwynedd**                                  map 4

## ▲ *Penhelig Arms Hotel* 🍾

| Aberdovey LL35 0LT | COOKING 2 |
| ABERDOVEY (0654) 767215 | COST £13–£32 |

This black and white building, built in the eighteenth century, stands next to Penhelig harbour, and many of the bedrooms overlook the Dyfi estuary (and the road that runs in front of the hotel). 'Small wonder that hungry golfers descend in numbers to play the splendid course nearby and eat the ample food,' remarks one who did just that, noting in passing that the Hughes are careful not to accept too large and too rowdy a group who might disturb the genial buzz of individuals who have come to enjoy this pub-hotel. Yet there can be so many bargain-seekers, for instance at Sunday lunch-time, that the meal gets a little rushed and edges slightly rough. But longer-term visitors report sound cooking of meals of the order of chicken terrine with green peppercorns and a Cumberland sauce, wild duck with redcurrant and juniper sauce, served with ample vegetables and dauphinois potatoes, a good choice of Welsh cheese, and desserts such as bread-and-butter pudding (which was dull by contrast with what had come before). The clever balance between the pub (the real ales are regularly changed) and the hotel side is often praised. So too are the good value of the cooking and its decent attempt to offer local materials (try the fish). Tips are neither expected nor encouraged. 'Wine of the month' puts you in touch with the Hughes' current enthusiasms. The list is brief and packed with good names, with a bias towards mid-price excellence rather than top-flight extravagance. Halves are provided generously, and all for prices that demand extended experiment. House wine is £8. CELLARMAN'S CHOICE: St-Véran, Dom. des Valanges 1990, Paquet, £12.50; Rioja Reserva, Contino 1982, £19.75.

CHEF: Jane Howkins   PROPRIETORS: Robert and Sally Hughes   OPEN: all week; 12 to 2, 7 to 9   CLOSED: 25 and 26 Dec, exc bar   MEALS: alc bar L (main courses £4 to £6). Set Sun L £10.50, Set D £16.50   SERVICE: card slips closed   CARDS: Access, Visa   DETAILS: 36 seats. Private parties: 20 main room. Car park. Vegetarian meals with prior notice. Children's helpings. No music   ACCOMMODATION: 10 rooms, all with bath/shower. B&B £38 to £98. Deposit: £30. Pets welcome. Afternoon teas. TV. Phone. Doors close at midnight. Confirm by 6. Fax: (0654) 767690 (*The Which? Hotel Guide*)

---

ABERSOCH Gwynedd                                                    map 4

## ▲ *Porth Tocyn Hotel*

Abersoch LL53 7BU
ABERSOCH (0758) 713303                                       COOKING 2*
on minor road 2½m S of Abersoch                            COST £21–£38

Nick Fletcher-Brewer sent us some menus from 1981 to compare with the current output at this popular seaside hotel where the view reconciles most people to a holiday in Britain, and the cooking and general happy clubbiness make the rest of the family suggest a return visit next year. What price the Algarve? The formula – a five-course meal with a short choice for three of them – has not changed, but the cooking has developed beyond 'dinner party' style. Prue Leith of Leith's (see entry, London) and Myrtle Allen at Ballymaloe (see entry under Shanagarry, Republic of Ireland) are named as two current mentors, even if dishes like veal with a Benedictine cream sauce have stayed the course from the beginning. At any rate, it is sound cooking, generously served, using local materials when suitable, enjoying some elaboration from the plain and simple – for instance, salmon is filled with watercress and served with lime hollandaise, beef is wrapped in pastry for a Wellingtonian classic – and finishing with a flourish at dessert which will probably include at least one sponge pudding and a thoroughly alcoholic meringue. The wine list is as sound as the rest of the operation. Villa Montes from Chile, Vacheron's

Sancerre and Mas de Gourgonnier from Provence show that good-value quality is not ignored in favour of famous names. House wines start at £10.45.

CHEF: E.L. Fletcher-Brewer  PROPRIETORS: the Fletcher-Brewer family  OPEN: all week; 12.30 to 2, 7.30 to 9.30  CLOSED: mid-Nov to week before Easter  MEALS: Set Sun L £14, Set D £17.50 (2 courses) to £23. Light L weekdays  SERVICE: not inc, card slips closed  CARD: Access  DETAILS: 50 seats. Vegetarian meals with prior notice. No children under 7 at D. Smart dress preferred. No pipes in dining-room. Wheelchair access (1 step; also WC). No music  ACCOMMODATION: 17 rooms, all with bath/shower. 3 rooms for disabled. B&B £36.50 to £105. Deposit: £40. Children welcome. Baby facilities. Pets welcome. Afternoon teas. Garden. Swimming-pool. Tennis. TV. Phone. Doors close at midnight. Fax: (0758) 713538 (*The Which? Hotel Guide*)

## ▲ Riverside Hotel

Abersoch LL53 7HW
ABERSOCH (075 871) 2419                                          COOKING 1*
on A499, 6m SW of Pwllheli                                       COST £18–£34

The extensions to this hotel on the harbour bridge might have been designed by a graduate from the Lego school of architecture, but the place has pretty views over harbour and river and an acre of landscaped gardens. If the sun plays along, you can have a cheaper bar lunch on the lawn; for dinner, you descend down spiral stairs to the bright basement, which has raffia-backed chairs and pine tables. The owners share the cooking, which has grown from Welsh farmhouse to embrace the likes of Réunion Island chicken in a coconut and saffron sauce, but which is now wending its way back towards farmhouse again. Crisp pastry tartlets might be filled with scallops and leeks or (less Welshly but no less tastily) spinach and Parmesan; pork with orange and watercress displayed zest to good effect. Chestnut-stuffed fillet steak wrapped in smoked bacon and lemon sole with a mussel and chervil custard are two dishes which regularly appear on the menu, and Welsh lamb is a lodestar. Home-made puddings like walnut and honey tart or apple and cinnamon strudel are a strength (yogurt is summoned from Anglesey), and Wales comes cheesily into its own with Pencarreg and Caerphilly. Service is quick, efficient and cheerful, and the wine list, which begins at £7.75, has taken a step forward this year with a transfusion from Haughton Fine Wines (including David Wynn's delicious unoaked Shiraz at £11.50). All wines, usefully, are annotated.

CHEFS/PROPRIETORS: John and Wendy Bakewell  OPEN: all week; 12 to 2, 7.30 to 9 CLOSED: Nov to 1 Mar  MEALS: bar meals. Set D £15.95 (2 courses) to £21  SERVICE: not inc, card slips closed  CARDS: Access, Amex, Diners, Visa  DETAILS: 36 seats. Private parties: 36 main room. Car park. Vegetarian meals. Children's helpings. No children under 5 D. Smart dress preferred. Music  ACCOMMODATION: 12 rooms, all with bath/shower. B&B £40 to £80. Deposit: £40. Children welcome. Baby facilities. Afternoon teas. Garden. Swimming-pool. Fishing. TV. Phone. Doors close at 11.30. Confirm by 4. Fax: (075 871) 2671

'This is the first occasion on which I can remember eggs being off at breakfast time.'
On eating in Yorkshire

BEAUMARIS Gwynedd                                                            map 4

## ▲ Ye Olde Bulls Head Inn ▼ ✳

Castle Street, Beaumaris,
Anglesey LL58 8AP                                                  COOKING 2*
BEAUMARIS (0248) 810329                                            COST £16–£41

This ancient inn – a stone's throw from the castle – was built in 1472 and
updated in 1617. Since 1987, David Robertson and Keith Rothwell have
steadily transformed the place into one of the best establishments in the area. It
still works as a pub (turn left into the bar), but is also one of the smarter dining
sites in Gwynedd (turn right into the lounge with its big sofas and crackling
log fire). The cooking is based around a *carte* and fixed-price three-course
dinner menus. As one reporter observed, 'The competition between nouvelle
cuisine and modern British cookery has resolved itself into a collage based on a
foundation of solid, French principles, with flair and surprises drawn in from
wherever in the world provides inspiration.' Witness slices of lightly grilled
black pudding with a 'dressed collation' of finely chopped peach, red chilli,
and yellow and green peppers on a bed of frisée. Or, again, consider pan-fried
strips of chicken with water-chestnuts, artichokes and lemon balm. More
robust ideas, such as a 'raucous dish' of crisp bacon and lambs' kidneys with
rich wine sauce and lamb en croûte with leeks and Welsh mustard, have also
impressed. Occasionally diners have detected a 'lack of subtlety' (a well-
dressed salad marred by chopped raw onion, or cassolette of seafood masked
by its powerful sauce), but there is no doubting the quality of the ingredients
or the skilful execution. Desserts such as strawberry and passion-fruit crème
brûlée and chocolate and orange mousse are 'loud in taste and contrast'. Service
is businesslike, rather than 'smiley'. A well-enjoyed Californian Chardonnay
house wine sets the tone for the unfussy, but nevertheless excellent wine list. It
is a refreshing intelligence that offers a soundly enjoyable Barbera d'Asti from
dell'Acquese for £8.50 four lines away from a properly aged Antinori
Tignanello at £28.50. All pockets are catered for; even at the top end the mark-
ups are only a fair reflection of cost. There is a good range of half-bottles. House
wines are £11.50. CELLARMAN'S CHOICE: New Zealand, Cabernet Sauvignon/
Franc 1990, Vavasour, £13.95; Crozes-Hermitage 1991, Graillot, £17.95.

CHEFS: Keith Rothwell and Anthony Murphy   PROPRIETORS: Rothwell and Robertson
Ltd   OPEN: all week; bar Mon to Sat L 12 to 2.30; restaurant Sun L 12 to 1.30, D 7.30 to 9.30
(9 Sun)   CLOSED: 25 and 26 Dec, 1 Jan   MEALS: alc (main courses bar £3.50 to £5,
restaurant £11.50 to £14.50). Set Sun L £13.75, Set Mon to Fri D £17.95   SERVICE: not inc
CARDS: Access, Visa   DETAILS: 70 seats. Private parties: 70 main room. Car park.
Vegetarian meals. Children's helpings. No children under 7 restaurant. No smoking in
dining-room. No music   ACCOMMODATION: 11 rooms, all with bath/shower. B&B £42 to
£72. Children welcome. Baby facilities. TV. Phone. Doors close at midnight. Confirm by 6.
Fax: (0248) 811294 (*The Which? Hotel Guide*)

---

*An asterisk (\*) after the 1 to 5 cooking mark at the top of an entry signifies that the* Guide
*and its readers think that the restaurant is a particularly fine example within its rating.*

---

---

BRECHFA Dyfed                                                                                                map 4

## ▲ Tŷ Mawr

| NEW ENTRY |

Brechfa SA32 7RA
BRECHFA (0267) 202332                                                    COOKING 2
on B4310, 6m N of A40 at Nantgaredig                          COST £17–£31

The name may mean 'big house' in English, but the place is in fact small.
Beams, natural stone and 'medieval mortar' guarantee peace and calm and
country atmosphere, and compensate for lack of grandeur. The Tudhopes have
brought this small hotel back into the *Guide* with their enthusiasm (Dick
Tudhope will even tell you the day the lamb you are eating was born) and skill.
'The twice-baked soufflé was light, wobbly and aromatic' – for some reason
undisclosed to the public, this recipe is ascribed to the Dominicans. 'The
Tudhopes' skill in baking, whether it be bread or the cheese puffs, or the
chocolate pudding, is evident.' Although not everything is so exact, readers
complimented the 'almost Japanese style of saucing with a precisely cooked
fillet of Arctic char'. The kitchen is switched in to the local supply lines,
benefiting everyone, yet Beryl Tudhope does not flinch from straying far afield
for recipes and ideas. Jasmine tea ice-cream with poached apricots is hardly
typical west Wales, nor is lamb with a robust ratatouille, even if the lamb
popped out but a field away. It is good value and good fun. Prior bookings are
essential. The wine list is as full of comments and advice as Dick Tudhope and
the range is a well-chosen inexpensive set of bottles from around the world,
stemming mainly from Haughton Fine Wines. House Côtes de Gascogne from
Plaimont is £8.25.

CHEF: Beryl Tudhope   PROPRIETORS: Beryl and Dick Tudhope   OPEN: Thur to Sun L, Wed
to Sat and Mon D; 12 to 1.30, 7 to 9.30   CLOSED: last week Nov, last 2 weeks Jan   MEALS:
Set L £9.95, Set D £15.95 to £18.75   SERVICE: not inc, card slips closed   CARDS: Access,
Amex, Visa   DETAILS: 35 seats. Private parties: 50 main room. Car park. Vegetarian meals.
Children's helpings L. Smart dress preferred. Music   ACCOMMODATION: 5 rooms, all with
bath/shower. B&B £44 to £68. Deposit: £10. Children welcome. Baby facilities. Pets
welcome. Afternoon teas. Garden. Fax: (0267) 202437 (*The Which? Hotel Guide*)

---

BROAD HAVEN Dyfed                                                                                    map 4

## ▲ Druidstone Hotel  £

Broad Haven SA62 3NE
BROAD HAVEN (0437) 781221
from B4341 at Broad Haven turn
right at sea, after 1½m turn left to                                  COOKING 1
Druidstone Haven, hotel ¾m on right                          COST £16–£33

'We are a traditional beach-house with very few rules, almost no technology –
really a million miles from city life,' writes Jane Bell of her childhood home,
which she has been running as a very personal hotel for more than 20 years. It
stands high on the wild clifftops overlooking the Atlantic, and the views are
out of this world. The set-up is endlessly fascinating; the place is full of clutter
and runs on tolerance, freedom and good humour. Dogs and children are

everywhere. Visitors are invariably hooked after one trip: 'We have been for years and our children and grandchildren go now,' write long-time followers. The Bells are full-time in the kitchen; Jane works with fresh fish and local produce, husband Rod draws spicy inspiration from around the world. The cooking is honest and generous with bags of flavour. Squid with Greek sauce, lemon chicken soup, watercress and cream-cheese pâté, curry, steamed sea bass with herbs, and wild sewin cooked with orange and lemon peel are examples from this year's reports. Puddings are unadorned country creations: rosemary torte with plum compote, apple tart, alcoholic home-made ice-creams. The wine list contains around 30 inexpensive offerings, and Rod Bell knows his stuff. House wine is £6.

CHEFS/PROPRIETORS: Rod and Jane Bell OPEN: all week, D only, and Sun L; 12.30 to 2.30, 7.30 to 9.30 CLOSED: Mon to Wed 6 Nov to 15 Dec, Mon to Wed 6 Jan to 12 Feb MEALS: alc (main courses £6 to £12) SERVICE: not inc, card slips closed CARDS: Access, Amex, Diners, Visa DETAILS: 40 seats. 6 tables outside. Private parties: 40 main room, 8 private room (winter only). Car park. Vegetarian meals. Children's helpings. No smoking while others eat. Wheelchair access (also WC). Music (some nights) ACCOMMODATION: 9 rooms and 5 cottages. 2 cottages for disabled. B&B £23 to £57. Deposit: £20. Children welcome. Baby facilities. Pets welcome. Afternoon teas. Garden (*The Which? Hotel Guide*)

---

## CAPEL COCH Gwynedd

map 4

## ▲ Tre-Ysgawen Hall

Capel Coch, Llangefni, Anglesey LL77 7UR
LLANGEFNI (0248) 750750
on B5111, between Llangefni and Amlwch

COOKING 1
COST £21–£50

Life is sometimes difficult on Anglesey ('We rattled about like peas in a pod'), but this hotel sails on and gathers supporters in its wake. There is no giving up the attempt to luxury and comfort in this large late-Victorian house, nor is Steven Morris abandoning his attempt to cook good food. 'My consommé was deeply gamey, my steak exactly cooked, and the trio of chocolate finished me off,' reported a lover of plain food, even if the coffee was poor. Meat cookery, for instance duck with five-spice and a courgette chutney, or a roast saddle of hare, seems the strongest suit; more complex items, for example a terrine of salmon, may register on the blandness scale. The wine list is broadly based enough for most requirements. House wines are £9.80.

CHEF: Steven Morris PROPRIETORS: Mr and Mrs Ray Craighead OPEN: all week; 12 to 2.30, 7 to 9.30 MEALS: alc (main courses £14.50 to £18). Set L £14, Set D £19.95 SERVICE: not inc CARDS: Access, Amex, Diners, Visa DETAILS: 64 seats. Private parties: 120 main room, 24 and 48 private rooms. Car park. Vegetarian meals. Children's helpings. Jacket and tie. Wheelchair access (2 steps; also WC). Music ACCOMMODATION: 20 rooms, all with bath/shower. Rooms for disabled. B&B £79.50 to £109.50. Deposit: 10%. Children welcome. Baby facilities. Pets by arrangement. Afternoon teas. Garden. TV. Phone. Doors close at midnight. Fax: (0248) 750035 (*The Which? Hotel Guide*)

---

*The text of entries is based on unsolicited reports sent in by readers, backed up by inspections conducted anonymously. The factual details under the text are from questionnaires the* Guide *sends to all restaurants that feature in the book.*

---

## Armless Dragon

97 Wyeverne Road, Cathays,
Cardiff CF2 4BG                                          COOKING 2
CARDIFF (0222) 382357                                    COST £15–£35

'The profusion of menus is rather confusing,' observed a reporter. 'One in your hand, one on the wall, and one on a white board erected near your table. None match!' David Richards' bistro close to the university and the theatres is nothing if not idiosyncratic. This is a place that works to its own rules; the décor is dominated by striking original oil paintings and a window full of luxuriant plants. The cooking is idiomatic, adventurous, personal and spicy, with influences from Thailand, China, Mexico and the USA Deep South – although many of the ingredients are local. A new feature is the excellent-value fixed-price lunch menu (including a drink) offering the likes of escabèche of smelts, stir-fried samphire with noodles, shrimps and laverballs, then strawberries Romanoff. Otherwise the ever-changing repertoire might include crab soup with lemon grass, mushroom and almond toast with fiery Thai sauce, steaks, and specials such as rillettes of duck with pickled samphire, cassoulet and all manner of fresh fish cooked in a variety of ways. Sweets such as hunza apricots and cashew cream or chocolate and raisin ganache are equally original. Coffee from the espresso machine is appreciated. The wine list displays the same personal touch; it roams far and wide, but prices are eminently affordable. House wines are £7.90.

CHEFS: David Richards and Deborah Coleman   PROPRIETOR: David Richards   OPEN: Tue to Sat, exc Sat L; 12.15 to 2.15, 7.15 to 10.30 (11 Sat)   MEALS: alc (main courses £8.50 to £12.50). Set L £7.90 (2 courses) to £9.90   SERVICE: not inc   CARDS: Access, Amex, Diners, Visa   DETAILS: 50 seats. Private parties: 50 main room. Vegetarian meals. Children's helpings on request. No cigars/pipes in dining-room. Wheelchair access. Music

## La Brasserie/Champers/ Le Monde  £

60–61 St Mary Street, Cardiff CF1 1FE                    COOKING 1*
CARDIFF (0222) 372164/373363/387376                      COST £14–£37

A giant of a complex: three restaurants together in neighbouring buildings – not forgetting the banqueting suite – absorbing over 300 people. The cooking, even with three kitchens, is fast and furious, with chargrilling, spit-roasting and grilling ruling the culinary roost. Service can be fairly prompt, too, the customer helping it along in Champers by choosing the raw material from a display beyond the bar. Champers is predominantly Spanish, with a good slate of Riojas, grills, 'picante' sauces and meat. At La Brasserie the line is more French with fish and game taking centre-stage, supplemented by spit-roasted sucking pig, racks of lamb and roast duck. At Le Monde, fish and seafood – cold and warm water – occupy most of the menu. People accept the smart pace (the last course at Champers is essentially crêpes suzette or cheese) for the quality of material. House wines are £6.95.

CHEFS: Kurt Fleming and Carmen Laventure (La Brasserie); Genaro Sandonato and Denis
Louis (Champers); Andrew Jones, Chris Kovkaras and Paul Griffiths (Le Monde)
PROPRIETOR: Benigno Martinez   OPEN: Mon to Sat (and Sun D Champers); 12 to 2.30, 7 to
12.15   MEALS: alc (main courses La Brasserie £5 to £11.50, Champers £4 to £11, Le Monde
£5 to £15)   SERVICE: not inc, card slips closed   CARDS: Access, Amex, Diners, Visa
DETAILS: La Brasserie 75 seats, Champers 70 seats, Le Monde 180 seats. Private parties: 70,
75 and 100 main rooms, 40 and 120 private rooms. Vegetarian meals (Le Monde only with
prior notice). Smart dress preferred. Wheelchair access in all (La Brasserie 2 steps; also
WC). Music. Air-conditioned Le Monde. Fax: (0222) 668092

## Chikako's £

| | |
|---|---|
| 10–11 Mill Lane, Cardiff | COOKING 1 |
| CARDIFF (0222) 665279 | COST £18–£32 |

Chikako Cameron has been something of a pioneer of Japanese cooking in
southern Britain over the years. She reminds us that she began with a
restaurant in High Barnet, before opening in Melksham then Bath and now
Cardiff, opposite the Holiday Inn. The cooking remains creditable, with an
unusual concern for organics, local producers and the usual preoccupation with
freshness. Smoked salted tuna and silken tofu with bonito flakes are still
recommended, as is ositashi. Sushi can be prepared with advance warning, and
sashimi is usually available, but there is quite a lot of teppanyaki and sukiyaki
goin' on. The crème caramel is healthy and good, as is the azuki bean ice-cream.
A single main dish can be had at a reduced cost if required. Drink saké at £2.60
for a small jug. House wine is £6.90.

CHEF/PROPRIETOR: Chikako Cameron   OPEN: all week, D only (L by arrangement); 6 to 11
CLOSED: 25 Dec   MEALS: Set L and D £11.80 to £19.50   SERVICE: 10%, card slips closed
CARDS: Access, Visa   DETAILS: 70 seats. Private parties: 50 main room, 10 and 10 private
rooms. Vegetarian meals. Children welcome. Smart dress preferred. Music.
Air-conditioned. Fax: (0222) 665279

## Quayles

| | |
|---|---|
| 6–8 Romilly Crescent, Canton, | |
| Cardiff CF1 9NR | COOKING 2 |
| CARDIFF (0222) 341264 | COST £19–£42 |

The Cannings say that Quayles has become a haven for the Cardiff-based media
(perhaps they are drawn by the raised bar at one end of the long room).
Certainly the restaurant's cool – some might say clinical – Mediterranean
ambience, derived from a whole-hearted embrace of the colour white, signals
that Quayles is different from its more classically inclined predecessor,
Gibsons. Other signals are the food and music evenings and the informative
guest appearances by chefs like Marco Pierre White, Antony Worrall-
Thompson, et al. Materials, methods and recipes all receive the modernising
treatment, with chargrilling, pastas, spices from around the world and novel
breads spearheading the change. Success has not gone unnoted, though there
have been instances where the intensity of flavour demanded has been missed,
or where balance of strong and weak (smoked salmon with red onion salad) is

completely out of kilter. None the less, shoppers report on the restoring capabilities of Tuscan bean soup and old hands comment on the excellence of coffee and walnut roulade. Service may be of the 'student' school, but it is willing and cheerful. The wine list is abbreviated, save for notes of half a dozen fine wines from small parcel purchases. House wines are £7.50.

CHEFS: Irene Canning, Matthew Canning and John Khalid  PROPRIETORS: Canning and Co (Cardiff) Ltd  OPEN: Wed to Mon, exc Sun D; 12 to 2.30, 7 (7.30 Sat) to 10.30 (post-theatre D by arrangement)  CLOSED: 26 Dec, Easter Mon, bank hols  MEALS: alc (main courses £7.50 to £13.50). Set L £5.25 (2 courses) to £11.95, Set Sun L £11.50, Set D before 8 £7.75 (2 courses)  SERVICE: not inc, card slips closed  CARDS: Access, Amex, Visa DETAILS: 50 seats. Private parties: 50 main room. Car park. Vegetarian meals. Children's helpings. No-smoking area. Wheelchair access (also WC). Music. Air-conditioned

---

**CHIRK Clwyd**                                                                                        map 4

## ▲ *Starlings Castle*

Bronygarth, nr Chirk SY10 7NU
OSWESTRY (0691) 718464
take Weston Rhyn turn from A5 N
of Oswestry to Selattyn, turn right
through village, climb for 2½m, turn                                    COOKING 3
right at top of hill, then follow signs                                 COST £24–£42

Advice on how to locate this slightly castellated farmhouse high on a hill surrounded by sheep and scudding clouds is hard to come by. The telephone directions are invariably clear, whereas location by address will reveal that the place is sited between every element in the written details. However, find it, fall through the large front door, relax before a stove and CD player, enjoy the company of animals and humans and think yourself lucky to run across a haven of sensible humanity so far from civilisation. The Pitts exude a sense of hospitality; the farmhouse is nicely set up for entertaining; and the food is determinedly fresh. The style of cooking has links back to the great leap forward of Elizabeth David, French provincialism and Britain in the early '70s. This itself is an attraction. Substantial is one word for it. Dishes such as pork and game terrine with a red onion marmalade, or fresh crab with avocado, followed by rib steak with green peppercorn sauce, loin of pork with mushrooms, or salmon in pastry with sultanas and ginger are examples of the tendency. Hot chocolate soufflé or prune and armagnac tart may bring up the rear. People enjoy the vigorous approach. The wine list is a cheerful affair; it may lack expensive heavyweights, but from decent house wines at £8 upwards through Menetou-Salon from Pellé, good antipodeans and some notable red burgundies most people will be well enough pleased. Prices are fair, but even the few half-bottles of a year ago seem to have disappeared.

---

*Restaurateurs justifiably resent no-shows. If you quote a credit card number when booking, you may be liable for the restaurant's lost profit margin if you don't turn up. Always phone to cancel.*

CHEFS/PROPRIETORS: Antony and Jools Pitt   OPEN: all week, D only, and Sun L; 12.30 to 2.30, 7.30 to 9.30   MEALS: alc (main courses £9.50 to £14.50)   SERVICE: not inc   CARDS: Access, Visa   DETAILS: 28 seats. Private parties: 28 main room. Car park. Vegetarian meals with prior notice. Children's helpings. Wheelchair access (1 step; also WC). No music   ACCOMMODATION: 8 rooms. B&B £20 to £40. Deposit: £30. Children welcome. Baby facilities. Pets welcome (not in public rooms). Afternoon teas. Garden. TV (*The Which? Hotel Guide*)

---

**CLYTHA Gwent** map 4

## ▲ *Clytha Arms* ⁵⁄✳ £ | NEW ENTRY

Clytha, nr Abergavenny NP7 9BW
ABERGAVENNY (0873) 840206
off old Abergavenny to Raglan road,                          COOKING 1
S of A40, 6m E of Abergavenny                               COST £14–£33

The Canning family has a long association with restaurants in this part of South Wales. Irene Canning runs Quayles in Cardiff (see entry) and her son Andrew moved from the Beaufort Arms, Monkswood, to open this new venture in a converted dower house surrounded by green lawns not far from the River Usk. The place still functions as an informal pub, with five real ales and snacks in the public bar, but most interest now centres on the food in the restaurant. Dishes are written up on an illuminated French beer sign and the menu focuses on France and Wales, with inspiration also gleaned from other parts of the globe. Cawl, laverbread and pungently flavoured meatless Glamorgan sausages are up front, along with consommé with quail's eggs, oysters, and blue cheese and port soufflé. Main dishes are equally eclectic: for example, excellent Malaysian fruit curry served in a hollowed-out pineapple, salmon in filo pastry, crab with spring onion and ginger, and tagliatelle with wild mushrooms. The cheeseboard is impressive and sweets such as steamed treacle pudding are first-rate. Occasionally there are erratic moments, but the set-up is committed to good ingredients handled with manifest skill, and prices are modest. The wine list offers a sensible choice at sensible prices. House wines are £7.25.

---

CHEF: Andrew Canning   PROPRIETORS: Andrew and Beverley Canning   OPEN: all week, exc Sun D and Mon L (also L bank hol Mons); 12.30 to 2.30, 7.30 to 9.30   MEALS: alc (main courses £6.50 to £12). Set Sun L £8.25   SERVICE: not inc, card slips closed   CARDS: Access, Visa   DETAILS: 60 seats. 12 tables outside. Private parties: 50 main room, 16 private room. Car park. Vegetarian meals. Children's helpings. No smoking in dining-room. Wheelchair access (2 steps). No music   ACCOMMODATION: 3 rooms, all with bath/shower. B&B £30 to £60. Children welcome. Baby facilities. Afternoon teas. Garden. TV. Doors close at midnight. Confirm by 5

---

⁵⁄✳ *indicates that smoking is either banned altogether or that a dining-room is maintained for non-smokers. The symbol does not apply to restaurants that simply have no-smoking areas.*

£ *indicates that it is possible to have a three-course meal, including coffee, a half-bottle of house wine and service, at any time the restaurant is open (i.e. at dinner as well as at lunch, unless a place is open only for dinner), for £20 or less per person.*

COLWYN BAY Clwyd                                           map 4

## Café Niçoise

124 Abergele Road, Colwyn Bay LL29 7PS          COOKING 2
COLWYN BAY (0492) 531555                         COST £19–£39

The restaurant is a converted Victorian shop on the main road running through Colwyn Bay and, as the name suggests, it draws its inspiration mainly from Provence. Carl Swift's short menus take in home-made gnocchi with saucisson, baked cod with a tapénade and red pepper coulis, and daube of lamb with baby vegetables. More intriguing, personal ideas include smoked halibut with horseradish mousse. Desserts are in the classical mould of apple tart in puff pastry with caramel sauce, and mille-feuille of strawberries and raspberries with crème anglaise. Service has been pleasant and 'relatively unflustered' according to reporters who reckoned the place was 'a good find'. Wine loyalties are not confined to France, with care and interest shown in Italy and Spain and a page of decent New World bottles. Prices are very fair. House wines are from £6.95.

CHEF: Carl Swift   PROPRIETORS: Carl Swift and Lynne Curtis   OPEN: Mon to Sat, exc Mon L; 12 to 2, 7 to 10   MEALS: alc (main courses £7 to £12.50). Set Mon to Thur D £12.95   SERVICE: not inc, card slips closed   CARDS: Access, Visa   DETAILS: 32 seats. Private parties: 30 main room. Vegetarian meals. Children's helpings. Smart dress preferred. Music

---

CRICKHOWELL Powys                                          map 4

## Nantyffin Cider Mill Inn  £     | NEW ENTRY |

Brecon Road, Crickhowell NP8 1SG
CRICKHOWELL (0873) 810775
on junction of A40 and A479,                       COOKING 1
1½m W of Crickhowell                               COST £16–£33

'This is a great set-up, just right for this part of the world' was the enthusiastic comment of a first-time visitor to this split-level barn conversion – all beams, dark slate and stone, and plain, sensible furnishings. Yet it remains a drinking pub for the drinker – and cricket enthusiast (it sponsors Crickhowell CC) – as well as offering a full range of food, from ploughman's lunch (good) to duck breast with kumquats. The freshness of the materials is impressive – 'I could descant for hours on the vegetables,' wrote one – and the flavours are robust. The technique depends on honesty rather than finesse, but this is entirely fitting. The wide range is demonstrated by filo parcels of crab, prawns and samphire with a dill sauce; huevos à la flamenca; mushroom risotto; liver and bacon; and Thai-style pork kebab with a peanut dipping sauce. Desserts, on a shorter slate, may need greater attention to detail. 'Coffee for one was enough for eight.' Wine prices are very sensible, but the bottles are not bought without thought. Robert Chevillon's Nuits-St-Georges or the house Resplandy Cabernet Sauvignon are instances of good choice. House wines are from £7.95.

---

CHEFS: S. Gerrard and P. Davies  PROPRIETORS: S. Gerrard and G. Bridgeman  OPEN: all week; 12 to 2.30, 6.30 (7 Oct to Mar) to 10  CLOSED: Mon Oct to Nov and Jan to Mar  MEALS: alc (main courses £5 to £12). Set Sun L £9.95  SERVICE: not inc  CARDS: Access, Visa  DETAILS: 65 seats. 8 tables outside. Private parties: 70 main room. Car park. Vegetarian meals. Children's helpings. Smart dress preferred. No cigars/pipes in dining-room. Wheelchair access (also WC). No music

---

## DEGANWY Gwynedd                                          map 4

## *Paysanne* £                                         | NEW ENTRY |

Station Road, Deganwy LL31 9EJ
ABERCONWY (0492) 582079                                    COOKING 2
off A55, 2m S of Llandudno                                 COST £14–£32

You know it is going to be French when you are told of the 75- or 95-franc menus. But the currency conversion is done for you and Barbara Ross' skill at converting French cooking into something sourced from Wales is impressive. Bob Ross plays the double bass and picks the wines. These, too, are impressive: a set of unfamiliar but obviously carefully researched French growers at admirable prices. The pitch of the place is exact: bistro-style, busy and buzzy, good direct cooking of fresh food. Avocado with prawns and a curry mayonnaise, Bury black pudding with mustard sauce and apples, cassoulet and a fish casserole flamed with Pernod and finished with cream could hardly be bettered for generosity and accurate cooking. Desserts sound run-of-the-mill, but the pastry for the walnut tart showed you should not underestimate the cook just because a dish sounds boring. Small wonder the place has been picking up prizes. House wines are £7.90.

CHEF: Barbara Ross  PROPRIETORS: Bob and Barbara Ross  OPEN: Tue to Sat, D only; 7 to 9.30  CLOSED: first 3 weeks Jan  MEALS: alc (main courses £8 to £11). Set D £7.50 to £15  SERVICE: not inc, card slips closed (10% for 8 or more)  CARDS: Access, Visa  DETAILS: 36 seats. Private parties: 40 main room. Vegetarian meals with prior notice. No children under 7. Smart dress preferred. No smoking before 9.30. No pipes in dining-room. Wheelchair access (1 step; also WC). Music. Fax: (0492) 583848

---

## DOLGELLAU Gwynedd                                        map 4

## *Dylanwad Da* ⁵⁺ £

2 Ffôs-y-Felin, Dolgellau LL40 1BS                         COOKING 1*
DOLGELLAU (0341) 422870                                    COST £18–£30

The outside may be drab, and the bar area may be likened to a smart take-away, but the main dining-room is none of those things, and visitors from Skegness were struck by how many of the customers were speaking in Welsh about sheep. Dylan Rowlands has succeeded in creating a neighbourhood restaurant in these parts that lasts and does not depend utterly on incomers. His cooking does not admit mistakes. A meal that included smoked trout mousse from a mould lined with smoked salmon served with a lightly pungent horseradish cream before roast loin of lamb with dill – unlikely, but it worked magnificently – ended with a very good apricot ice-cream. Local cheeses were by contrast disappointing in their lack of variation. Puddings like a mango cheesecake or a cherry sponge have been endorsed for their lightness yet fulfillingness. All this costs very little money. The same might be said of the wine list. Margins are low, value is high, quality is very acceptable. House wines are £7.80.

CHEF/PROPRIETOR: Dylan Rowlands   OPEN: D only; all week Easter and Whitsun, July to Sept; Thur to Sat winter; 7 to 9.30   CLOSED: Feb   MEALS: alc (main courses £7 to £11) SERVICE: not inc   DETAILS: 30 seats. Private parties: 30 main room. Vegetarian meals. Children's helpings. No smoking in dining-room. Wheelchair access (1 step; also WC). Music

---

**EGLWYSFACH Powys**                                                      map 4

## ▲ *Ynyshir Hall* ✻

Eglwysfach SY20 8TA
GLANDYFI (0654) 781209                                          COOKING 2
on A487, 6m SW of Machynlleth                              COST £21–£48

The long, white house – its façade balanced by a flanking greenhouse/ conservatory – seems to sit in a world of its own, in an amphitheatre delineated by rhododendrons and foliage, protecting it from rude day-to-day buffetings. The bold colours of the decoration and bolder paintings (by Rob Reen himself) that hang throughout the house are thrown into relief by this happy isolation. David Dressler maintains his enthusiasm for sometimes quite elaborate food, with layers of mousses or fillings to spice up the main ingredient in dishes such as sole with a salmon mousse served with a sorrel and Hermitage sauce, or roast lamb with faggots and a red onion and orange sauce. There is some adventurous flavouring, too, for instance in a vegetarian dish such as chickpeas with coriander, ginger and garlic served with gnocchi in a red pepper sauce. He does not stint on the labour, for each main dish has its own vegetable accompaniment. Whereas the cooking was sometimes a victim of country-house fussiness, it has got bolder – perhaps in response to the move in customers' tastes. The wine list is graced by drawings done by Rob Reen when on a trip to Cyprus; they should not distract the drinker from a very sound list of solid quality with none-too-high prices. House wines are from £10, but have a look at the Australian selection for value and range of taste.

CHEF: David Dressler   PROPRIETORS: Rob and Joan Reen   OPEN: all week; 12.30 to 1.30, 7 to 8.30   MEALS: Set L £15, Set D £23   SERVICE: not inc, card slips closed   CARDS: Access, Amex, Visa   DETAILS: 26 seats. Private parties: 25 main room, 16 private room. Car park. Vegetarian meals. No children under 9. Smart dress preferred. No smoking in dining-room. Music   ACCOMMODATION: 8 rooms, all with bath/shower. B&B £65 to £125. Deposit: 20%. No children under 9. Pets welcome by arrangement. Afternoon teas. Garden. TV. Phone. Doors close at midnight. Fax: (0654) 781366 (*The Which? Hotel Guide*)

---

'*I tried this restaurant on two occasions. On the first visit I had fish in a cream sauce served on an unheated plate; on the second visit, when I left the table for a short time I returned to find that my meal had been taken back to the kitchen and kept warm – salad and all!*'   On eating in Gloucestershire

---

FISHGUARD Dyfed                                                              map 4

## Tate's Brasserie 🌟 £

Main Street, Goodwick,
Fishguard SA64 0BN
FISHGUARD (0348) 874190                                              COOKING 2
off A40, NW of Fishguard                                           COST £14–£36

The sparse village of Goodwick is the site of the Fishguard Ferry Terminal, and
Diana Richards' Victorian house attracts a regular crew of travellers looking for
genuine food and sustenance. Consequently, the place is open all day and all
kinds of options are available, from snacks and bistro dishes to full à la carte
dinners. From the street, you walk into a tiny bar area (generally used for
informal meals); down steep stairs is the modest dining-room, which reminded
one visitor of a Victorian antique shop. Diana Richards uses local produce with
a vengeance. Mussels with wild garlic and spinach topped with Caerphilly
cheese are typical of her style. She gathers laver and uses it as a stuffing, in a
sauce with brill or sea bass, and in a gratin with Pen-clawdd cockles. She also
relishes the challenge of spider crab ('hell to clean and dress, but such a good
flavour'). Her thoughts also stray further afield for inspiration, drawing in
mulligatawny soup, gnocchi alla Romana, Malaysian-style duck with a 'Euro/
Asian' risotto, and oxtail with olives. Desserts often look to the past, as in
'medieval' bread-and-butter pudding and lemon posset. The desire to please
extends to the wines; knowledge of mid-priced, immensely enjoyable bottles
is here very wide. Rioja from the single vineyard Contino Estate, Janodet's
Morgon and Mitchelton Marsanne all characterise the approach. House
wine is £7.

CHEF/PROPRIETOR: Diana Richards   OPEN: all week, exc Tue (Tue D Whitsun to Oct and
winter by arrangement); noon (11am for snacks) to 9.30 (12 to 2, 7 to 9.30 Sun)   MEALS: alc
D (main courses £9 to £14.50). Set bistro L and D £10.50 (inc wine) to £13.50, Set Sun L
£8.75   SERVICE: not inc   DETAILS: 34 seats. Private parties: 26 main room. Vegetarian
meals. Children's helpings. No smoking in main dining-room. Wheelchair access. Music

---

## ▲ Three Main Street 🌟

3 Main Street, Fishguard SA65 9HG                                   COOKING 1*
FISHGUARD (0348) 874275                                            COST £16–£35

What was once the Great Western Hotel is now an informal guesthouse,
restaurant and daytime coffee-shop (where light lunches are also served) rolled
into one. The Georgian town house stands a few minutes' drive from the ferry
terminal. The interior is all old pine furniture, polished floorboards, rich
colours and fresh flowers. Informality rules; charm and good humour abound.
In the evenings the restaurant – white starched linen and candlelight –
provides the *carte*. Marion Evans is a staunch supporter of local produce and
buys with care: Cardigan Bay scallops, Welsh black beef, regional farmhouse
cheeses and organic flour ('it is worth a trip just to eat the bread rolls, which are
cooked fresh each day,' raved one loyal fan). Sewin with chive and hollandaise
sauce and roast loin of lamb with wild garlic show one side of the repertoire.
Elsewhere colourful exoticism and a keenness to soak up influences appear:

chicken Simla ('a sort of apotheosis of the Anglo curry'), medallions of venison with redcurrant and port, and sea bass with herb crust and shellfish sauce have been mentioned in reports. Vegetarian dishes, such as glazed shallot and onion tart with coriander, are far from the clichéd world of nut cutlets. Sweets earn their share of praise: hazelnut meringues with plum compote, frangipane with apricot coulis, and Earl Grey parfait have been highly commended. Credit cards are not accepted. The short, sharp wine list has a sprinkling of organics; local non-alcoholic Elderflower Spritz Cariad is also available. House wine is £8.95.

CHEFS: Marion Evans and Andrew Griffith  PROPRIETORS: Marion Evans and Inez Ford
OPEN: Mon to Sat; 12 to 2.30, 7 to 9.30  CLOSED: Feb  MEALS: alc (main courses L £4 to £5,
D £8.50 to £13)  SERVICE: not inc  DETAILS: 36 seats. Private parties: 24 main room.
Vegetarian meals. Children's helpings. No smoking in dining-room. Wheelchair access
(1 step). No music  ACCOMMODATION: 3 double rooms, all with bath/shower. B&B £30 to
£45. Children welcome. Afternoon teas (*The Which? Hotel Guide*)

---

FORDEN Powys                                                                          map 4

## ▲ *Edderton Hall*

Forden SY21 8RZ
FORDEN (0938) 580339                                                    COOKING 1*
off A490, 4m S of Welshpool                                          COST £18–£31

All agree that the views are superb, and so is the location. The house is a fine bit of Georgian, done up by the Hawksleys themselves, and neither overblown nor sterile. 'We were greeted by the owner when we arrived. She then did the cooking, the waiting and the after-dinner chat, removing her shoes while sitting on the sofa, but the meal was superb and one of those evenings long remembered,' reads a report that confirms this is by no means an impersonal, stiff-necked operation. While Warren Hawksley MP is away at Westminster representing the people, Evelyn Hawksley does the cooking and son Bevan bakes the bread and looks after front-of-house. It is the firm opinion of people who have been eating here since opening day that the cooking has improved and that the longueurs that were once a feature have well-nigh disappeared. Bevan's bread is outstanding, and he changes the flavours every month – sunflower- and pumpkin-seed wholemeal and dill and lemon white made one tasty pairing. The style of cooking is creative – 'a little too ambitious for a cook who doesn't follow recipes' was the comment of one visitor – but the flavours come through even if meats are left too long in the heat. Smoked chicken meatballs with lemon, garlic and parsley sauce, or chargrilled wild boar with damson and juniper sauce and pickled damsons are two instances of gutsy tastes working well. A pear tarte Tatin was 'definitely rustic'. The good, sound wine list starts with house wines at £7.75 a litre.

---

*The* Guide *is totally independent, accepts no free hospitality, and survives on the number of copies sold each year.*

*Several sharp operators have tried to extort money from restaurateurs on the promise of an entry in a guidebook that has never appeared. The Good Food Guide makes no charge for inclusion and does not offer certificates of any kind.*

---

CHEF: Evelyn Hawksley PROPRIETORS: Warren and Evelyn Hawksley OPEN: all week; 12.30 to 2, 7.30 to 9.30 (later bookings by arrangement) MEALS: Set L £10.95, Set D £18.95 SERVICE: not inc, card slips closed CARDS: Access, Amex, Diners, Visa DETAILS: 30 seats. 3 tables outside. Private parties: 20 main room, 45 private room. Car park. Vegetarian meals. Children's helpings. Smart dress preferred. Wheelchair access (also WC). Music ACCOMMODATION: 8 rooms, all with bath/shower. B&B £22 to £85. Deposit: 10%. Children welcome. Pets welcome. Afternoon teas. Garden. TV. Phone. Confirm by 2. Fax: (0938) 76452 (*The Which? Hotel Guide*)

---

**FREYSTROP Dyfed** map 4

## Jemima's ░✸

Freystrop, nr Haverfordwest SA62 4HB
JOHNSTON (0437) 891109 COOKING 2
on Burton road, 2m SW of Haverfordwest COST £17–£33

'Ann Owston is an original' (observes a reporter) and continues to go her own way. She is normally to be found beavering away in the kitchen, or taking orders, writing out menus and serving – not to mention tending the garden behind her pink cottage restaurant. One party which arrived for lunch at 1pm and did not leave till 3.45pm thought the whole experience was 'extraordinary value for money, but all done with style, balance and agreeable conversation'. On that occasion the delights included spicy carrot and chive soup with excellent home-made brown rolls, salmon trout with hollandaise, superb boiled potatoes and salad with a fine dressing, as well as home-made gooseberry ice-cream. Ann keeps faith with local and home-grown produce, but the world is her culinary oyster: Szechuan prawns, ragoût of seafood with home-made pasta, chicken with oregano in filo pastry, and roast lamb with rosemary have all been enjoyed. Equally delightful desserts are often adorned with herbs or flowers from the garden: pavlova decorated with crystallised primroses, meringue nest with mint-flavoured crème anglaise and mint leaves, nectarines and cream with raspberry coulis and borage flowers. The short wine list encompasses remarkable range and reliable quality. Half-bottles are selected intelligently and Australian house wines are £7.

CHEF: Ann Owston PROPRIETORS: Ann Owston, Wendy Connelly and April Connelly OPEN: Tue to Sun, exc Sat L and Sun D; 12 to 2, 7 to 9 CLOSED: Tue and Wed winter MEALS: alc (main courses £8.50 to £10.50). Set L £6 (2 courses) to £10, Set D £13.50 SERVICE: not inc, card slips closed CARDS: Access, Amex, Visa DETAILS: 24 seats. Private parties: 24 main room. Car park. Vegetarian meals. Children's helpings. No smoking in dining-room. No music

---

*'We sat next to the semi-open kitchen, which resembled a bomb site. The chef was opening oysters one minute then piling veg from plastic buckets on to plates ready for the microwave – without washing or wiping his hands. At one stage there was a used frying-pan in the middle of the kitchen floor next to a cooked new potato which was duly squashed by one of the waitresses under her foot. Later the chef opened the fridge door, grabbed a pile of something in his hand (meat I think) and duly smelt it to see if it was OK.'*
On eating in Scotland

---

GANLLWYD Gwynedd                                                    map 4

## ▲ *Dolmelynllyn Hall* ♚ ✿

Ganllwyd, nr Dolgellau LL40 2HP
DOLGELLAU (0341) 40273                                         COOKING 2
on A470, 5m N of Dolgellau                                     COST £29–£36

The feel and atmosphere of an Edwardian country house is how some people
describe the ambience at this hall which in fact dates back to 1550 – the oldest
stones are now part of the dining-room. Joanna Reddicliffe (née Barkwith), no
longer working solo, has not deviated from her daily menu of five courses with
a small but balanced choice at each stage. This is bolder than normal country-
house food, trying for an effect far removed from 'plain but good', yet not
burdened by fuss or presentational bother. The recipes have a slight edge to
them – for instance, a first course choice of scallop and sweetcorn soup or
smoked goose on a salad of grapes with sour cream and chive dressing, or wild
mushroom risotto. Main dishes, always with one vegetarian option, may
include pigeon breast on a chinese-style cabbage 'seaweed', or monkfish in
sesame seeds with crab sauce. Adjustments on the supply side seem so far to
have maintained the quality of the wine list. Range is wide, with Italy and
Beaujolais and fine Australians notable. Prices remain very fair. House wines
are from £8.25. CELLARMAN'S CHOICE: Rioja, Ygay 1985, Marqués de Murrieta,
£15.25; Montagny, premier cru 1990, Roy, £15.25.

CHEFS: Joanna Reddicliffe and Andrew Bruin   PROPRIETORS: Jon Barkwith and Joanna
Reddicliffe   OPEN: all week, D only; 7 to 8.30   CLOSED: Dec to end Feb   MEALS: Set D
£22.50   SERVICE: not inc, card slips closed   CARDS: Access, Amex, Visa   DETAILS: 20
seats. Private parties: 40 main room, 20 private room. Car park. Vegetarian meals. No
children under 10. Smart dress preferred. No smoking in dining-room. Wheelchair access
(1 step). Music   ACCOMMODATION: 11 rooms, all with bath/shower. B&B £37.50 to £95.
Deposit: £25. No children under 10. Dogs welcome (not in public rooms). Afternoon teas.
Garden. Fishing. TV. Phone. Doors close at midnight. Confirm by 6. Fax: (0341) 40273

GLANWYDDEN Gwynedd                                                  map 4

## *Queen's Head* £

Glanwydden LL31 9JP
ABERCONWY (0492) 546570                                        COOKING 1
just off B5115 Colwyn Bay to Llandudno road                   COST £14–£35

Formerly a village wheelwright's cottage, the Queen's Head now co-exists
happily as successful country pub and restaurant. Some have found it hard to
locate (it is just off the Llanrhos Road between Llandudno Junction and
Colwyn Bay) but it has a loyal following of regulars who often drive many
miles for the village ambience and the food, which never seems to disappoint.
Fish from the nearby village of Conwy is the mainstay, and the owners can lay
their hands on anything from lobsters and scallops to monkfish and salmon.
Mussels and crab are specialities. Smoked produce is from a local smokehouse:
goose breast might be served with kiwi fruit, salmon may be transformed into a
pâté. One highly enjoyable lunch included spinach and mushroom soup,
salmon and pasta bake packed with large chunks of fresh fish, lamb cutlets

with honey, 'excellent' treacle tart with custard, and chocolate and brandy trifle. More ambitious items – such as chicken breast wrapped in smoked bacon with blue cheese and tarragon sauce and noodles – appear in the evening and snacks are served in the bar. The short list of around 30 wines has plenty of catholic drinking for around £10. House wine is from £7.95.

CHEFS: Neil MacKenzie and Andrew Hadfield  PROPRIETORS: Robert and Sally Cureton
OPEN: all week; 12 to 2, 6.30 to 9  CLOSED: 25 Dec  MEALS: alc (main courses L £5 to £6.50,
D £6.50 to £13). Bar snack menu (£2 to £6.50)  SERVICE: not inc, card slips closed
CARDS: Access, Visa  DETAILS: 120 seats. 12 tables outside. Private parties: 26 main room.
Car park. Vegetarian meals. No children under 7. Wheelchair access (1 step). Music.
Fax: (0492) 546487

---

HARLECH Gwynedd                                                          map 4

## ▲ Castle Cottage 🐝✳

| Pen Llech, Harlech LL46 2YL | COOKING 1* |
| HARLECH (0766) 780479 | COST £15–£28 |

Set near the castle in one of the oldest houses in historic Harlech, Castle Cottage is going from strength to strength under the stewardship of Glyn and Jacqueline Roberts. Visitors always receive a warm welcome and are ushered into the cheerful log-fired sitting-room for drinks and tiny canapés. The décor in the dining-room could do with a face-lift, but tables are well spaced, service is friendly and, above all, the food is good. Glyn Roberts cooks with a light touch and an eye for appealing presentation. Meals are fixed-price for two or three courses: during the summer expect about five choices at each stage, fewer in winter. A host of dishes have pleased visitors: curried parsnip soup, baked green-lipped mussels, Stilton and walnut tartlet with tomato sauce, duo of lambs' kidneys and noisettes in port wine sauce, feuilleté of seafood with dill and wine sauce, and hake in cream and cockle sauce. Vegetables are crisp, fresh and served in manageable amounts. Among the sweets, an individual treacle tart with a separate jug of Drambuie cream stands out as a 'tour de force'. Pots of coffee are served with 'charming' petits fours. The wine list now has a stronger showing of half-bottles and representatives from the New World. House French is £7.95.

CHEF: Glyn Roberts  PROPRIETORS: Glyn and Jacqueline Roberts  OPEN: all week, D only,
and Sun L; 12.30 to 2.30, 7 to 9.30  MEALS: Set Sun L £10, Set D £14 (2 courses) to £16.50
SERVICE: not inc  CARDS: Access, Amex, Visa  DETAILS: 50 seats. Private parties: 50 main
room. Vegetarian meals. Children's helpings. Smart dress preferred. No smoking in dining-
room. Wheelchair access (3 steps). Music  ACCOMMODATION: 6 rooms, 4 with bath/
shower. B&B £20 to £44. Deposit: £10. Children welcome. Baby facilities. Pets welcome.
Doors close at midnight. Confirm by 6

---

*All entries in the* Guide *are rewritten every year, not least because restaurant standards fluctuate. Don't trust an out-of-date* Guide.

*All letters to the* Guide *are acknowledged with an update on latest sales, closures, chef changes and so on.*

---

## ▲ Cemlyn ♛ ⁛✳

High Street, Harlech LL46 2YA                                          COOKING 3
HARLECH (0766) 780425                                                 COST £16–£32

'The dearth of customers was matched by one of sea trout and lobsters,'
reflected Ken Goody on last autumn's business, 'but visitors were still able to
enjoy the scallops, and the free-range pork and chicken.' This house with
stunning views of the castle ('We didn't stay for coffee as we wanted to admire
the view before dark') is Ken Goody's kingdom: pictures abound, frogs of
every sort save live appear on ledge and niche, and the place oozes
individualism. His approach to cooking is his own too: robust, sometimes bold,
occasionally rough, and always aiming at pushing the natural flavour. Dishes
such as turkey escalope stuffed with ham and baked with cheese and tomato
have an old-fashioned 'restaurant' ring to them, but braised tongue with caper
and mustard sauce is the highest form of nostalgia. There are novelties, too, like
the lemon sorbet brûlée – 'It tasted like lemon ice-cream melting fast under the
burnt topping'. The value, as in so many of the smaller Welsh restaurants, is a
great inducement, even if it were not for the character of the place. To keep a
tight rein on business, on the wine front Mr Goody has resorted to the sale of
his 'award list of 1991 and 1992'. The Goody eye for quality and his very
modest mark-ups remain, however. There may be fewer heavyweights, but the
concentration on more limited range is on the whole no bad thing – all very
intelligent and considerate to the customer. House wines are from £7.
CELLARMAN'S CHOICE: Bianco 1991, Avignonesi, £11; Madiran, Dom.
Meinjarre 1989, Brumont, £9.50.

CHEF/PROPRIETOR: Ken Goody   OPEN: all week, D only, and Sun L (Mon to Sat L by
arrangement); 12.15 to 2, 7 to 9.30   CLOSED: Nov to mid-Mar   MEALS: Set Sun L £10, Set
D £14.50 (2 courses) to £17.50   SERVICE: not inc, card slips closed   CARDS: Access, Visa
DETAILS: 52 seats. 3 tables outside. Private parties: 12 main room, 10 private room.
Vegetarian meals with prior notice. No children under 8. No smoking in 1 dining-room.
Wheelchair access. No music   ACCOMMODATION: 1 room, with bath/shower. B&B £30 to
£40. Babies welcome. TV. Doors close at midnight. Confirm by 6

---

HAWARDEN Clwyd                                                              map 4

## Swiss Restaurant Imfeld ⁛✳

NEW ENTRY

68 The Highway, Hawarden CH5 3DH
HAWARDEN (0244) 534523                                               COOKING 2
on B5125, 6m W of Chester                                            COST £14–£43

Markus Imfeld is Swiss and says that when he first opened his restaurant in
this small village, once the home of Mr Gladstone and convenient for the
Cheshire business classes, he soft-pedalled his culinary origins. Not that there
was much chance of forgetting them when seated in a room surrounded with
Swiss music, pictures and knick-knacks – real *gemütlichkeit* here – but cooking
too has gradually become more evidently Swiss. There is a page of fondu
specialities (available on Friday and Saturday evenings), and the menu is
peppered with Swiss names, even if many of the dishes they describe will be
familiar to English eaters. Öpfel Nierli is actually kidneys cooked with apple

and onion, the sauce finished with calvados, and Rauchlachs is smoked salmon with avocado and a curried mousseline. However, Knöpfli there are, and Raclette valaisanne, and the occasional Swiss speciality night. The Swiss enjoy a German love of cabbage in many forms, and they like to mix fruit and meat in an Anglo-German way. Markus Imfeld's cooking has therefore struck a chord of sympathy in Cheshire and Clwyd. This extends to the major desserts: of course there is strudel, but also walnut tart with kirsch cream and an elderberry sauce. Every second Wednesday of the month sees a 'gourmet evening', with a seven-course menu at £22. The wine list does not offer much choice; far more sensible to stick to the handful of Swiss wines such as Calamin from the Vaud or Auvernier, made with the Chasselas grape, from Neuchâtel. House wines are from £7.50.

CHEF: Markus Imfeld   PROPRIETORS: Yvonne and Markus Imfeld   OPEN: Tue to Sun D, Sun L; 12 to 2, 7 to 9 (10 Sat)   CLOSED: 2 weeks Feb, 2 weeks Oct   MEALS: alc (main courses £8 to £17). Set L £8.95 to £9.95, Set D £14.50 to £19.50   SERVICE: not inc, card slips closed   CARDS: Access, Visa   DETAILS: 40 seats. Private parties: 50 main room. Car park. Vegetarian meals. Children's helpings. Smart dress preferred. No smoking in 1 dining-room. Wheelchair access. Music

---

**LLANBERIS Gwynedd**                                                    map 4

## Y Bistro ⁵✳

43–45 High Street, Llanberis LL55 4EU
LLANBERIS (0286) 871278                                            COOKING 1
off A4086, at foot of Mount Snowdon                         COST £24–£38

Nerys Roberts writes that she has been cooking here for a lifetime. Life sentence, perhaps, but not such durance vile that springtime visitors did not find a gentle welcome, a bilingual menu, and dishes such as leg of lamb steak with leeks and a port wine sauce, or rib of beef with a chasseur sauce, fresh, crisp vegetables on the side, and desserts such as hazelnut meringue or rice pudding with pineapple. The language may be Welsh, but the culinary vernacular is pure bistro. A warm-hearted place that offers good value. The wine list has beefed up its halves and has an Australian Anglesey Chardonnay. House Hungarians are £8.25.

CHEF: Nerys Roberts   PROPRIETORS: Danny and Nerys Roberts   OPEN: all week, D only, exc D winter Mon and Sun (L by arrangement); 7.30 to 9.45   MEALS: Set D £18 to £24   SERVICE: not inc, card slips closed   CARDS: Access, Visa   DETAILS: 50 seats. Private parties: 60 main room, 24 private room. Vegetarian meals. Children's helpings. Smart dress preferred. No smoking in dining-room. Wheelchair access (2 steps). Music

---

Card slips closed *in the details at the end of an entry indicates that the total on the slips of credit cards is closed when handed over for signature.*

*The 1995 Guide will be published before Christmas 1994. Reports on meals are most welcome at any time of the year, but are extremely valuable in the spring. Send them to* The Good Food Guide, *FREEPOST, 2 Marylebone Road, London NW1 1YN. No stamp is needed if posted in the UK.*

---

# Walnut Tree Inn 🍾

Llandewi Skirrid NP7 8AW
ABERGAVENNY (0873) 852797                                    COOKING 4
on B4521, 3m NE of Abergavenny                              COST £27–£68

A reader who had boned up on Ancient Greece took issue with our description
of the conditions in this pub-turned-restaurant-extraordinaire – we called
them spartan. The tiny entrance bar may be that, he admitted (and there you
can eat every item offered on the general menu), but he would describe the
bistro beyond (which contains fairly tight-packed and bare tables) as Doric,
and the dining-room (one room beyond that where there are tablecloths and
Apicella pictures) as positively Corinthian. Others would say that the outside
tables on a hot summer's day are paradise. The Taruschios' pub has grown over
the years – 30 of them, to be exact – but the cooking stays much the same
(though vegetables are now charged separately). There is a beguiling mixture
of Italian (Franco comes from the Marches) and home-grown, with a touch of
Eastern exoticism for good measure. One man who has celebrated many New
Year's Days at the Walnut Tree reflected that the free drink on the last occasion
was not champagne, but that his crispy crab pancakes (an oriental touch), the
abundant and varied supplies of bread, the panaché of fish with a balsamic
vinaigrette, roast partridge on a crust served with lentils, followed by a
compote of fruit with cardamom ice-cream and a slightly heavy *dolce torinese*
were as good as ever. The menu is vast (16 main courses, 8 vegetables, 23
desserts), yet manages to be 'resplendently fresh' – as witnessed in lunch-time
dishes of seafood bruschetta, Italian sausage, the polenta with Parma ham and
tomato sauce, roast monkfish with laverbread and orange sauce, skate with
olives and orange, and the definitive version of Lady Llanover's salt duck. The
creativity of the kitchen does not often flag, and the list of dishes would be long
were the best ones to be singled out. Service is characterful, natural and usually
efficient, though lots of customers may slow the process down or cause
forgetfulness. Inevitably, over the years, as many people take issue with the
Walnut Tree recipe as applaud it long and loud. For people in the former camp,
the informality and discomfort, coupled with the admittedly firm prices, cause
distress. Our usual reservations about wine lists sourced from a single
merchant have to be revised when Reid Wines are the suppliers. However,
notwithstanding a range as good as any which majors in Italians, there are a
few niggles: half-bottles are sparse, prices start low but seem to be based on an
unremittingly applied formula which does no favours for the top bottles, and
comments continue about wines that arrive at the table at the wrong
temperature (some too warm, others too cold). House wine is £9.75.

CHEF: Franco Taruschio   PROPRIETORS: Franco and Ann Taruschio   OPEN: Tue to Sat;
12.15 to 3, 7.15 to 10   CLOSED: 2 weeks Feb   MEALS: alc (main courses £7 to £16). Cover
£1 dining-room   SERVICE: not inc   DETAILS: bistro 55 seats, dining-room 40 seats. 5 tables
outside. Private parties: 36 main room. Car park. Vegetarian meals. Children's helpings.
Wheelchair access (also WC). No music. Air-conditioned

| LLANDRILLO Clwyd | map 4 |
|---|---|

## ▲ *Tyddyn Llan*

Llandrillo LL21 0ST
LLANDRILLO (049 084) 264                                    COOKING **3**
on B4401, 4½m S of Corwen                                  COST £19–£38

Peter Kindred designed sets for the first series of *Fawlty Towers*, 'but there's nothing Fawlty about Tyddyn Llan,' added our informant hastily. Nothing at all, and this jewel of a house set among the most glorious walking country has a satisfactorily calming effect. The new dining-room (well, three years old) shows off his skills to a T. The fortunate arrival of Dominic Gilbert has steadied the kitchen after a period of change. He cooks exactly and generously – almost too generous, or rich or sweet, for some – from a repertoire that is mainstream but still lively. A meal that took in filo parcels of scallops and leeks with a simple white wine sauce, rack of lamb with tomato and basil concassé and olive oil, duck with oranges and a beetroot and blackcurrant sauce, finishing with a fine flourish on fresh orange mousse with a mango coulis, and pear Belle Hélène with a poppy seed ice-cream seemed to satisfy many constituencies. A stay of a week elicited the comment that the menu may not change enough to ensure lots of variety and that, unexpectedly, the hotel ran better when it was busy than when quiet. A selection of snacks is usually available at lunch-time. The wine list seems a model of spread, selection and price. Note the Spanish range, enjoy the sensible prices, and try the organics from Burgundy. House wines start at £9.75.

CHEFS: Dominic Gilbert and Wendy Phillips   PROPRIETORS: Peter and Bridget Kindred
OPEN: all week; 12.30 to 2, 7 to 9.30   CLOSED: first week Feb   MEALS: Set L £12.50 to £13.50, Set D £19.50 to £21.50   SERVICE: not inc, card slips closed   CARDS: Access, Visa
DETAILS: 60 seats. Private parties: 90 main room, 30 private room. Car park. Vegetarian meals. Children's helpings. No cigars/pipes in dining-room. Wheelchair access (also WC). Music   ACCOMMODATION: 10 rooms, all with bath/shower. B&B £54 to £92. Deposit: 15%. Children welcome. Baby facilities. Pets welcome (not in public areas). Afternoon teas. Garden. Fishing. Phone. Doors close at midnight. Confirm by 6. Fax: (049 084) 264
(*The Which? Hotel Guide*)

| LLANDUDNO Gwynedd | map 4 |
|---|---|

## ▲ *Bodysgallen Hall* ♥

Llandudno LL30 1RS
ABERCONWY (0492) 584466                                    COOKING **2\***
off A470, 1m S of Llandudno                                COST £22–£53

The skilfully renovated and reworked Hall is ancient, atmospheric and enjoyed for its amalgam of building periods, amazing views and the gardens – worth a visit for themselves. The service gives an impression of country-house living – another magic of restoration, enhanced, for some, by the pianist of an evening. Mair Lewis cooks competently. The style is subdued, or correct, not breaking the bounds of its setting. This makes for a steady experience in a meal that may include gravlax with honey and mustard mayonnaise or smoked trout tartare with a lemon and cucumber salad, collop of veal on a tomato basil coulis or lamb with an onion marmalade, before a final course of chocolate and banana parfait on a hazelnut cream. Such was one evening's well-executed consumption – even if the staff knew little about the cheeses. On the quality wine list, a house selection is supplemented by a cellarman's choice – a dozen-plus decent wines from around the globe all at £14. Genuine effort is made to provide halves, but with a modest Alsace at £12 and a Jaboulet Crozes-Hermitage at £15, there is a hefty premium. Bin-ends also merit a glance. House wine is £11.25. CELLARMAN'S CHOICE: Portugal, Moscato 1991, João Pires, £14; Tinto da Anfora 1988, Novo, £14.

CHEF: Mair Lewis   PROPRIETORS: Historic House Hotels Ltd   OPEN: all week; 12.30 to 2, 7.30 to 9.45   MEALS: Set L £11 (1 course, inc wine) to £15.90, Set D £28 to £32   SERVICE: net prices, card slips closed   CARDS: Access, Amex, Diners, Visa   DETAILS: 70 seats. Private parties: 45 main room, 25 private room. Car park. Vegetarian meals. No children under 8. Jacket and tie. No cigars/pipes in dining-room. Wheelchair access (also WC). Music   ACCOMMODATION: 28 rooms, all with bath/shower. Rooms for disabled. D,B&B £122 to £250. No children under 8. Pets welcome in some rooms. Afternoon teas. Garden. Tennis. TV. Phone. Doors close at midnight. Confirm by 6. Fax: (0492) 582519 (*The Which? Hotel Guide*)

---

## Richard's £

| 7 Church Walks, Llandudno LL30 2HD | COOKING 1 |
|---|---|
| LLANDUDNO (0492) 877924 and 875315 | COST £16–£29 |

Richard Hendey has dropped the affix 'Lanterns' and has made several changes to his much-liked restaurant near the western end of the promenade. The place still has two eating areas – upstairs and downstairs – each with its own kitchen, although one menu now runs throughout. There are great keenness and enthusiasm behind this set-up and the cooking is pleasurable without seeking novelty for its own sake. Starters might feature 'intriguing' salmon and halibut mousse with spinach, dressed crab and ham-wrapped celery with Mornay sauce. Main courses – anything from game pie or lamb cutlets with mint and garlic to salmon fillet with lemon butter to chargrilled pigeon with plum sauce – come with appropriate seasonal vegetables (swede mousse in February was a treat for one visitor). Medallions of fillet steak have been exceptionally well cooked and presented, while desserts such as treacle tart, lemon ice-cream and hot toffee pudding earn full marks. Sally Templeman is a pleasant hostess who knows how to serve wine. The wine list offers plenty of choice, fair mark-ups and some interesting bottles, especially among the Spanish reds. House wine is £6.45.

CHEFS: Richard Hendey and William Johnson-Newbold   PROPRIETOR: Richard Hendey OPEN: all week, D only; 6.30 (6 summer) to 10   MEALS: alc (main courses £8 to £12) SERVICE: net prices, card slips closed   CARDS: Access, Visa   DETAILS: 48 seats. Private parties: 20 main room, 10 and 20 private rooms. Vegetarian meals. Children's helpings. No-smoking area. Music

---

Net prices *in the details at the end of an entry indicates that the prices given on a menu and on a bill are inclusive of VAT and service charge, and that this practice is clearly stated on menu and bill.*

---

## ▲ St Tudno Hotel 🍴

| | |
|---|---|
| Promenade, Llandudno LL30 2LP | COOKING 2 |
| LLANDUDNO (0492) 874411 | COST £18–£38 |

The traditional Victorian façade can 'fool the unknowing into passing what is the finest hotel in the resort,' remarked a visitor who returned to the place after a 10-year absence. Owners Martin and Janette Bland have created a charming establishment that manages to stay the right side of good taste, despite its 'fancy' decoration. Their constant presence is much appreciated, while staff are knowledgeable and genuinely helpful. Most visitors are keen to praise the efforts of chefs David Harding and Ian Watson, and reporters have been generous with their superlatives: 'simply magnificent' soups, 'imaginative' sauces, and 'superb' desserts. The fixed-price menus have their share of hotel classics, such as sirloin steak with wild mushrooms, but there is much more besides. Fine pastry-work is a feature – witness jalousie gâteau of brandy-soaked mincemeat with honey and chocolate sauce. Other star dishes have included collops of veal with orange and lemon in a 'gentle' herb and wine sauce. There is a local flavour to dishes such as poached fillet of sole with laverbread sauce and the selection of organic cheeses is loyal to Welsh producers. Light meals are served in the comfortable coffee lounge. Haughton Fine Wines is responsible for the list, which has plenty of interesting drinking at fair prices, a good showing of halves and several organics. House Australian is £10.95.

CHEFS: David Harding and Ian Watson   PROPRIETORS: Martin and Janette Bland   OPEN: all week; 12.30 to 2, 7 to 9.30 (9 Sun)   MEALS: Set L £13.50, Set D £25   SERVICE: not inc, card slips closed   CARDS: Access, Amex, Visa   DETAILS: 60 seats. Private parties: 30 main room. Car park. Vegetarian meals. Children's helpings. No children on high chairs D. Smart dress preferred. No smoking in dining-room. Wheelchair access (3 steps). No music. Air-conditioned   ACCOMMODATION: 21 rooms, all with bath/shower. Lift. B&B £55 to £120. Deposit: £25. Children welcome. Baby facilities. Pets by arrangement. Afternoon teas. Swimming-pool. TV. Phone. Doors close at 11.30. Fax: (0492) 860407 (*The Which? Hotel Guide*)

---

LLANGAMMARCH WELLS Powys                                     map 4

## ▲ Lake Country House Hotel 🍴

| | |
|---|---|
| Llangammarch Wells LD4 4BS | |
| LLANGAMMARCH WELLS (059 12) 202 | COOKING 1* |
| off B4519, 4m E of Llanwrtyd Wells | COST £22–£41 |

Half-timbering aplenty adorns this Edwardian house behind a defensive perimeter of rhododendrons. A lake – for serious fishing – is part of its charms. No matter how rugged the outdoor pursuits – riding, fishing, walking or golf – residents are assured enough chintz and curtaining to cosset every night-time hour. Richard Arnold's cooking has ambitious intentions. Honeyed guinea-fowl sits on a bed of stir-fried vegetables, and is sauced by ginger and tomato provençale; lamb is stuffed with apricots, mint and walnuts, with a red wine and shallot sauce; soups may manage to combine courgette, sweet peppers and rosemary; even cheesecake is more than lemon, with a boost from elderflower to give it character. This works often but sometimes misfires when advertised flavours do not make their expected contribution. Bar snacks and light lunches are served in the lounge on weekdays. The wine list is very good, with all the signs of Tanners of Shrewsbury bearing much of the credit. Good growers across the board provide revitalised reds from Chapoutier, Rolly-Gassmann Alsaces and decent French regional wines. A column for half-bottles, however, is barely utilised and there is little evidence, dessert wines apart, of anything by the glass to compensate for this. House wines are £9.75.

CHEF: Richard Arnold  PROPRIETORS: Jean-Pierre and Jan Mifsud  OPEN: all week, D only, and Sun L (Mon to Sat L by arrangement); 12.30 to 2, 7.30 to 8.45  MEALS: Set Sun L £15.50, Set D £24.50  SERVICE: not inc, card slips closed  CARDS: Access, Amex, Visa DETAILS: 60 seats. Private parties: 60 main room. Car park. Vegetarian meals. Children's helpings. No children under 8 D. Jacket and tie. No smoking in dining-room. Wheelchair access (also WC). No music  ACCOMMODATION: 19 rooms, all with bath/shower. Rooms for disabled. D,B&B £88.50 to £157. Deposit: £40. Children welcome. Baby facilities. Pets welcome. Afternoon teas. Garden. Tennis. Fishing. Snooker. TV. Phone. Fax: (059 12) 457 (*The Which? Hotel Guide*)

---

**LLANGOLLEN Clwyd**                                                           map 4

## ▲ *Gales* ♣ £

18 Bridge Street, Llangollen LL20 8PF                              COOKING 1
LLANGOLLEN (0978) 860089                                          COST £12–£19

This is a 'wine bar with rooms', not a restaurant, not a hotel. The distinction needs to be made to capture the informality, the warmth of welcome and the lack of pretension. It is a centre for walking: 'We went off to walk on Sunday morning and, though we had not booked a room for that night, they offered us the use of bath and shower when we returned at lunch-time.' The character of the place was described as 'pews and tables, cleaned often' – to be translated as neither grand, nor tremendously comfortable, but with every sort of wood furnishing, and kept up to the mark. Sometimes the cooking is simple to a fault, but materials like the home-cured ham, or robust casseroles such as seafood pie, have gained support, especially after all that tramping. All this may be seen as prelude to the wine list. The main list offers good range, makers and properties from all over, like Oxford Landing in Australia and Umani Ronchi in Italy, and fair prices. Then there is the fine wine list which offers from the cellar a remarkable slate of clarets, burgundies and ports with a growing New World section as well. Prices – for instance, of 1970 clarets – are no greater than would be paid in a wine merchant. House wines are £6.95.

CHEFS: Jenny Johnston, Joanne Thomas and John Gosling  PROPRIETORS: Richard and Gillie Gale  OPEN: Mon to Sat; 12 to 2, 6 to 10  MEALS: alc (main courses £4.50 to £6) SERVICE: not inc  CARDS: Access, Visa  DETAILS: 70 seats. 4 tables outside. Private parties: 20 private room. Car park. Vegetarian meals. Children welcome. Music ACCOMMODATION: 13 rooms, all with bath/shower. B&B £30 to £49. Children welcome. Pets by arrangement. TV. Phone. Doors close at 11.30. Confirm by 6. Fax: (0978) 861313

---

*Dining-rooms where live and recorded music are never played are signalled by* No music *in the details at the end of an entry.*

---

## LLANSANFFRAID GLAN CONWY  Gwynedd                    map 4

### ▲ *Old Rectory* ❦ ✻

Llansanffraid, Glan Conwy LL28 5LF
ABERCONWY (0492) 580611                                   COOKING 3
on A470, ½m S of junction with A55                        COST £37–£45

A star-spangled brigade of American visitors has discovered the pleasures
of this fine country house, judging by this year's healthy clutch of
recommendations. The setting and the views across the valley to Conwy Castle
are clearly an attraction, but most reports centre on the place itself and, in
particular, on Wendy Vaughan's cooking. The old house – tenderly
transformed into a country-house hotel – was originally a Georgian rectory.
The welcome is invariably warm, and smoking and music are banned in the
dining-room, which now offers separate tables for those who do not want the
communal eating experience. Offering a set menu with no choice until cheese
and desserts can be a drawback, but ideas are well thought out and the choice
of ingredients is impeccable. Welsh black beef and mountain lamb are from
local sources, fish is landed in Conwy, and ice-creams are made on the
premises using milk and double cream courtesy of a herd grazing in the nearby
Vale of Clwyd. A dinner on a June night began with smoked salmon tartare
with walnut vinaigrette and pickled samphire, before roast loin of lamb stuffed
with laverbread mousse, accompanied by a leek and laverbread timbale and
red wine sauce. Roast and sauté guinea-fowl with a farce of its own leg has also
been recommended and 'clever, fresh' desserts might feature chocolate cream in
a featherlight filo case with pear ice-cream. The cheese course rotates on a
three-day cycle, offering the possibility of grilled goats' cheese or cheese soufflé
as well as eye-opening Celtic varieties in the raw; as an alternative there is a
green salad or a fruit sorbet. An enthusiasm for good sherry is always a pointer
to a fine wine list, and pertains here. Sensible range of half-bottles included,
this is a delightful and earthy selection; prices are really quite modest, with
much on offer below £15 and top-notch classics such as Ch. Montrose 1979
generally kept under £30. House wine is £11.90. CELLARMAN'S CHOICE:
Bourgogne Chardonnay 1990, Henri Clerc, £18.90; Mexico Baja, La Cetto,
Petite Syrah 1988, £11.90.

CHEF: Wendy Vaughan  PROPRIETORS: Michael and Wendy Vaughan  OPEN: all week,
D only; 7.30 for 8  MEALS: Set D £26  SERVICE: not inc, card slips closed  CARDS: Access,
Amex, Diners, Visa  DETAILS: 16 seats. Private parties: 12 main room. Car park. Vegetarian
meals with prior notice. No children under 5. Smart dress preferred. No smoking in dining-
room. No music  ACCOMMODATION: 6 rooms, all with bath/shower. B&B £53 to £97. No
children under 5. Pets in coach-house bedrooms only. Afternoon teas. Garden. TV. Phone.
Doors close at 11.45. Fax: (0492) 584555 (*The Which? Hotel Guide*)

---

'As it was Valentine's Day the restaurant was decorated with gas-filled, red heart-shaped
balloons. We asked if we could take a couple for our children, and the owner curtly replied
that we could have one. This was surprising as most people were leaving and very few had
taken any balloons. The owner also rather unceremoniously handed out a rose to each
lady.'  On eating in Kent

## ▲ Lake Vyrnwy Hotel ⚹✳

Lake Vyrnwy, Llanwddyn SY10 0LY
LLANWDDYN (069 173) 692                                COOKING 1
on B4393, at SE end of Lake Vyrnwy                     COST £16–£34

The Victorian hotel stands in a 24,000-acre sporting estate that is also an RSPB Reserve, and makes much of its memorable views. Game is in plentiful supply, the waters are stocked with trout, while the hedgerows and lakeside are plundered for free food. This is an industrious kitchen, and chef Andrew Wood manages to maintain variety in his daily-changing menus. Asparagus and Roquefort soup is served with savoury apple scone; duck liver pâté comes with leek bread, and port and wild plum sauce. Main courses might range from roast loin of pork to guinea-fowl with sweetbread stuffing and honey and lemon sauce. The two-acre kitchen garden provides plentiful supplies and inspiration: witness vegetarian options such as emphatically green fricassee of spinach, onions and baby leeks with lovage and white wine sauce. Vegetables themselves receive imaginative treatment, as in potato and rhubarb gratin or parsnip and poppy seed mousse. Desserts are as good as they sound: chocolate and pear tart with pear and brandy sauce, orange and Welsh whisky sponge pudding, and home-made 'hokey pokey' ice-cream. Tanners supply the long wine list, halves are well represented and plenty of affordable drinking is available across the range. House wine is £8.90.

CHEF: Andrew Wood   PROPRIETORS: Market Glen Ltd   OPEN: all week; 12.30 to 1.45, 7.30 to 9.30   MEALS: Set L £10.45, Set Sun L £11.95, Set D £21.50   SERVICE: not inc, card slips closed   CARDS: Access, Amex, Diners, Visa   DETAILS: 120 seats. Private parties: 120 main room, 150 private room. Car park. Vegetarian meals. Children's helpings. Smart dress preferred. No smoking in conservatory. No music   ACCOMMODATION: 38 rooms, all with bath/shower. B&B £55.50 to £118.50. Children welcome. Baby facilities. Pets welcome (not in public rooms). Afternoon teas. Garden. Tennis. Fishing. TV. Phone. Doors close at 11.30. Fax: (069 173) 259 (*The Which? Hotel Guide*)

## *Seguendo di Stagioni* ▼ £

Harford, nr Pumpsaint,
Llanwrda SA19 8DT
PUMPSAINT (055 85) 671
on A482 between Llanwrda and                           COOKING 1
Lampeter, 1½m NW of Pumpsaint                          COST £14–£32

Aldo Steccanella is a glorious host: you may end up singing arias as the climax to an evening in this country restaurant that began life as the Pigs'n'Piglets transport café (watch out for its large sign opposite the Shell garage), grafted its Italian cooking on to the back of the building, then suspended cups of tea for a wine shop that handles some very good Italian vintages. Cooking here has risen beyond 'three hundred ways with veal and dover sole'; it may offer bruschetta, pasta with porcini, or rabbit stew with white wine, mushrooms and juniper. Yet not everything has the bravura and depth of flavour of the farmhouse original. None the less, applaud Aldo for trying; essay yourself the verdure miste and a fillet of beef with black peppers and smoked ham; and try the good-value 'pasta special' menu available Tuesday to Thursday (there are set meals for parties). Look very carefully at the all-Italian wine list. This has bottles of top quality such as the Barolo Monprivato from Mascarello and the Chianti of Isole e Olena. Prices are fair, with house wine from Italy at £7.50. CELLARMAN'S CHOICE: Moscato d'Asti 1992, Cantina Araldica, £9.25; Barbera d'Asti 1990, Ceppi Storici, £12.95.

---

CHEF: Aldo Steccanella  PROPRIETOR: Jennifer Taylor  OPEN: Tue to Sun D, Sat and Sun L (weekday L by arrangement); 12 to 3, 7 to 10.30  MEALS: alc (main courses £8 to £12). Set L £8.75 to £10.75, Set D Tue to Fri £7.95 (2 courses) to £15  SERVICE: not inc, card slips closed  CARDS: Access, Visa  DETAILS: 35 seats. 4 tables outside. Private parties: 30 main room. Car park. Vegetarian meals with prior notice. Children's helpings. Smart dress preferred. No music. Fax: (055 85) 671

---

**LLYSWEN Powys**  map 4

## ▲ Griffin Inn  ⁵✳ £

Llyswen LD3 0UR
LLYSWEN (0874) 754241  COOKING 1
on A470 Builth Wells to Brecon road  COST £15–£33

It helps when a village pub has its own river and shoot, at least it does if the chef is then going to cook the produce. The Griffin takes full advantage of its country location, to attract guests to its bedrooms and diners to its restaurant for food that is excellent value and best appreciated for dishes such as wild rabbit ragoût, pigeon braised in cider, fresh wild salmon, and venison and feathered game in season. A list of desserts kicks off with chocolate squidgy cake and apple and blackberry crumble – music to appetites set up by brisk country walks, and gluttons who need no such stimulus. House Bulgarian wine is £4.95.

---

CHEF: Eileen Havard  PROPRIETORS: the Stockton family  OPEN: all week, exc Sun D; 12 to 2, 7 to 9  MEALS: alc (main courses L £4.25 to £7.50, D £7.50 to £15). Set Sun L £11.50 SERVICE: not inc, card slips closed  CARDS: Access, Amex, Diners, Visa  DETAILS: 50 seats. 4 tables outside. Private parties: 30 main room, 10 and 30 private rooms. Car park. Vegetarian meals. Children's helpings. Smart dress preferred. No smoking in dining-room. Wheelchair access (1 step). No music  ACCOMMODATION: 8 rooms, 7 with bath/shower. B&B £28.50 to £50. Deposit: 10%. Children welcome. Baby facilities. Pets welcome. Garden. Fishing. Phone. Fax: (0874) 754592

---

## ▲ Llangoed Hall  ▮ ⁵✳

Llyswen LD3 0YP
LLYSWEN (0874) 754525  COOKING 3
on A470, 1m NW of Llyswen  COST £24–£70

'We regard this as definitely the best of the bunch,' wrote one seasoned connoisseur of the country-house hotel. The Hall is on the edge of the valley of the nascent Wye. Although some early bits remain, the predominantly Edwardian tone was set by architect Clough Williams-Ellis' reconstruction of

1912, which incorporated the original Jacobean porch. Williams-Ellis was a master of mood and atmosphere and, a few rather boring corridors apart, Sir Bernard Ashley has been able to create an enlivening, comfortable, well furnished and handsome hotel. Sir Bernard has enjoyed himself with British (especially Scottish) paintings from the turn of the century. Some of the best are in the yellow and blue neo-classical dining-room where Mark Salter has proved his staying power, consistency and invention since the hotel first opened. 'Restricted by the fact that his guests are eating his rich food for more than one night, he strikes the balance between heights one does not often reach and not so overfeeding the victim that the second night's dinner loses its charm' was one verdict. While the cooking does not avoid the 'country house' classification, it does not fall into the pits of overcomplication or insipidity. Materials are of the best: seafood such as wild salmon, lobster, sea bass and red mullet have been praised; and local lamb, venison and a mixed bag of game singled out among meats. The style is not so new-wave as to ignore mousses and timbales (spinach with a gazpacho sauce, or cauliflower with Stilton), but meat now tends to be cooked fairly simply, with all the work focusing on vegetables. Desserts show that familiar country-house affection for the cooked pudding, as well as demonstrating the fluffier instances of grande cuisine like a Grand Marnier crêpe soufflé or champagne mousse with peach sauce. The staff, from the management down, are almost beyond reproach. In a few short years the Hall has become one of the most pleasant spots to stay at. With barely a bottle below £15 and the bulk of interest centred on wines that cost well over £30 the final bill is likely to be considerably augmented. Quality is very good and rarities such as a 1962 Prunotto Barolo and 1966 Gigondas appear. Burgundy and Alsace resort to safe but good names; excitement is reserved for the New World. The half-bottle section has been strengthened and there is a helpful wide-ranging short list of recommendations. House wines are from £11.50. CELLARMAN'S CHOICE: Mâcon-Lugny 1991, £19.50; Sonona County, Cabernet Sauvignon 1985, Simi, £19.50.

CHEF: Mark Salter  PROPRIETOR: Sir Bernard Ashley  OPEN: all week; 12.15 to 2.15, 7.15 to 9.30  MEALS: alc (main courses £16.50 to £25). Set L £16, Set Sun L £17.50, Set D £35.50  SERVICE: not inc, card slips closed  CARDS: Access, Amex, Diners, Visa  DETAILS: 46 seats. Private parties: 32 main room, 14 and 36 private rooms. Car park. Vegetarian meals. Children's helpings. No children under 8. Jacket and tie. No smoking in dining-room. Wheelchair access (2 steps; also WC). No music  ACCOMMODATION: 23 rooms, all with bath/shower. B&B £95 to £285. Deposit: £50. No children under 8. Pets welcome (in kennels). Afternoon teas. Garden. Tennis. Fishing. Snooker. TV. Phone. Fax: (0874) 754545 (*The Which? Hotel Guide*)

*All details are as accurate as possible at the time of going to press, but chefs and owners often change, and it is wise to check by telephone before making a special journey. Many readers have been disappointed when set-price bargain meals are no longer available. Ask when booking.*

*The* Guide *office can quickly spot when a restaurateur is encouraging customers to write recommending inclusion – and sadly, several restaurants have been doing this in 1993. Such reports do not further a restaurant's cause. Please tell us if a restaurateur invites you to write to the* Guide.

# Ann FitzGerald's
# Farmhouse Kitchen ♈

Mabws Fawr, Mathry SA62 5JB
CROESGOCH (0348) 831347                                COOKING 2
off A487, 6m SW of Fishguard                          COST £20–£42

Ignore any signs to other farmhouses or kitchens dotted round Mathry; make
only for Ann FitzGerald's. It is on the south side of the main road that now
bypasses the village, but once you have conquered misgivings about the state
of the surface, you will fetch up in a farmyard. To one side are derelict
buildings (nothing to do with the restaurant), to the other is a farmhouse. Its
age is revealed in ceiling and walls, while the restless curiosity of its cook is
revealed in the menu. (There cannot be many places this far west that offer
sushi rolls or tempura.) The menu itself is long, though choice can be hastened
by working through the set-price abbreviation that calls on the *carte* for its
ingredients. Be ready to eat copiously, for nothing is stinted, either in quantity
or in the substantial character of the cooking. Sauces are big, dishes may have
several components, sweets will be sweet. Rabbit is served with the leg
braised and the loin stuffed with black pudding and apple and then roasted,
with a red wine, port and mustard sauce; lobster thermidor is in the old style;
curried crab pancake is giant, though not always hot enough (in both senses).
People enjoy the appetisers at the outset and the crusty white rolls. They also
find the service endlessly willing and the wine list a conspicuous set of
bargains that needs careful reading. The wine expertise is apparent here so
advice may well be sought; the accent is on robust no-fuss wines characterised
by a range of bourgeois clarets and some particularly fine Italians, such as
Cepparello, the super-Tuscan from Isole e Olena, and decently aged Barolo.
The absence of halves is compensated by some very moderate prices. House
wine is £8.50. CELLARMAN'S CHOICE: Côtes du Rhône, Blanc, Dom. Pelaquie
1989, Laudun, £12; La Poja 1983, Allegrini, £25.

CHEFS/PROPRIETORS: Ann and Lionel FitzGerald   OPEN: all week; 12 to 2, 7 to 9.30
CLOSED: L Jan to Easter   MEALS: alc (main courses £11.50 to £15). Set Sun L £14, Set D
£21.50   SERVICE: not inc   CARDS: Access, Visa   DETAILS: 40 seats. 3 tables outside.
Private parties: 40 main room. Car park. Vegetarian meals. Children's helpings L and D
before 7.30. Wheelchair access (also WC). No music

*Prices quoted in the* Guide *are based on information supplied by restaurateurs. The prices
quoted at the top of each entry represent a range, from the lowest meal price to the highest;
the latter is inflated by 20 per cent to take account of likely price rises during the year of
the* Guide.

*The 1995* Guide *will be published before Christmas 1994. Reports on meals are most
welcome at any time of the year, but are extremely valuable in the spring. Send them to
The Good Food Guide, FREEPOST, 2 Marylebone Road, London NW1 1YN. No stamp
is needed if posted in the UK.*

NANTGAREDIG Dyfed                                                          map 4

## ▲ *Cwmtwrch Farmhouse Hotel, Four Seasons*

**NEW ENTRY**

Nantgaredig SA32 7NY
CARMARTHEN (0267) 290238                                    COOKING 1
on B4310, 1m N of Nantgaredig                               COST £18–£33

'An absolute haven in fairly hostile territory,' writes a Welsh lady who values this authentic farm hotel for its charm, peace and quiet comfort – not to mention its heated swimming-pool. The converted Georgian building stands in 30 acres of farmland with the Four Seasons restaurant in outbuildings. 'Country kitchen' sums up the décor of the dining-room, with its white-painted stone walls, slate floor and pine furniture. Farm implements hang from the beams. The owners' three daughters run the kitchen and offer a lunch-time *carte* and a fixed-price dinner menu of around eight choices at each stage (some dishes carry supplements). Local Welsh produce (some procured by family and relations) finds its way into dishes such as Brechfa smoked salmon salad with dill sauce, Carmarthen cured ham with bruschetta, baked mullet with bacon and sage, and leg of lamb roasted with honey. The food is appreciated for its freshness and quality: witness dishes such as onion and Stilton soup, excellent osso buco, Creole fish casserole with red peppers, and strawberry pavlova. The reasonably priced list of around 60 wines has been put together with care from three different merchants. House wine is £8.50. Live jazz evenings are a regular attraction.

CHEFS/PROPRIETORS: Emma Willmott, Charlotte Pasetti, and Maryann and Simon Wright OPEN: all week, exc Sat L; 12.30 to 2.30, 7.30 to 9.30   MEALS: alc L (main courses £5.50 to £12). Set D £15.50   SERVICE: not inc   DETAILS: 55 seats. Private parties: 55 main room. Car park. Vegetarian meals. Children's helpings. No smoking while others eat. Wheelchair access (also WC). Music   ACCOMMODATION: 6 rooms, all with bath/shower. Rooms for disabled. B&B £32 to £46. Deposit: £10. Children welcome. Baby facilities. Pets welcome (certain bedrooms). Garden. Swimming-pool. Golf. TV

---

NEWPORT Dyfed                                                             map 4

## ▲ *Cnapan* 

East Street, Newport SA42 0SY                               COOKING 1
NEWPORT (0239) 820575                                       COST £12–£35

'Highly commended for its extremely friendly (not zany) atmosphere and good, genuine food. The menu did not change during our visit, but there were always extras on the blackboard. Obviously they were very busy, but such was their pleasantness that we moved from one table to the next between our main course and our pudding so that they could accommodate more diners.' This is success indeed, to persuade the normally immobile to take up their chairs and walk. There is no wish to stay stick-in-the-mud in the kitchen: whole continents are ransacked for ideas. This may be expressed in dishes like warm avocado stuffed with seafood in a cream sauce, pancakes stuffed with mushrooms and given a toasted-cheese topping, or chicken breast with a blue-cheese stuffing and a bacon-flavoured sauce, and pork fillet with a Chinese-style plum and ginger sauce. It is wholly in character that the desserts should put hairs on the chest of wilting diners: lemon and ginger log, bread-and-butter pudding, sticky apple shortbread. The wine list is a measured set of bottles that are not overpriced, yet take in as wide a range as possible. House wines are £7.25.

CHEFS: Eluned Lloyd and Judith Cooper   PROPRIETORS: Eluned and John Lloyd, Judith and Michael Cooper   OPEN: Wed to Mon, exc Sun D; 12 to 2, 7 to 9   CLOSED: Feb, midweek Nov to Mar   MEALS: alc D (main courses £9 to £15). Set Sun L £8.50. Light L Mon and Wed to Sat   SERVICE: not inc, card slips closed   CARDS: Access, Visa   DETAILS: 36 seats. 6 tables outside. Private parties: 36 main room. Car park. Vegetarian meals. Children's helpings. Smart dress preferred. No smoking in dining-room. Wheelchair access (2 steps; also WC). Music   ACCOMMODATION: 5 rooms, all with bath/shower. B&B £24 to £48. Deposit: 20%. Children welcome. Baby facilities. Garden. TV. Doors close at 11.30. Confirm by 5. Fax: (0239) 820878 (*The Which? Hotel Guide*)

---

NORTHOP Clwyd                                                                          map 4

## ▲ *Soughton Hall* ⁵⁺✶

Northop CH7 6AB
NORTHOP (0352) 840811                                                         COOKING 2
off A5119, 1m S of Northop                                                    COST £26–£56

The palatial Hall, surrounded by avenues and good gardens, has some remarkable rooms with Victorian detail. The cooking has to be of a very high standard to keep up with the gestures of satin-robed waitresses and full-scale progress round each public room of the mansion, and Thomas Ludecke does his best. The *carte*, though new price-cutting measures are in force at weekends, is dear indeed, but the set-meal and 'weekend special' deals are better value. Simplicity, as in a lunch of carrot soup, melon marinated with citrus fruits, 'thick slices of exquisite beef, nearly any vegetable we wanted, then fresh strawberries and home-made ice-cream', was virtue rewarded. But dishes such as a ballottine of chicken with a ham, truffle and pistachio mousseline, or noisettes of lamb on a bed of mint couscous garnished with raspberries, show a spirit longing to be unleashed into the realms of the highest style. The wine list displays a sensible open-mindedness about examples from beyond France, though its clarets are in the main a sound bunch. House wines are £10.95.

CHEF: Thomas Ludecke   PROPRIETORS: John and Rosemary Rodenhurst   OPEN: Mon to Sat, exc L Mon and Sat; 12 to 2.30, 7 to 10   CLOSED: first 2 weeks Jan   MEALS: alc (main courses £10 to £20, 'weekend special' £8 to £12.50). Set D £24.50   SERVICE: not inc, card slips closed   CARDS: Access, Amex, Visa   DETAILS: 50 seats. Private parties: 60 main room, 100 and 100 private rooms. Car park. Vegetarian meals. No children under 12. Smart dress preferred. No smoking in dining-room. Music   ACCOMMODATION: 12 rooms, all with bath/shower. B&B £65 to £100. Deposit: £50. No children under 12. Afternoon teas. Garden. Tennis. TV. Phone. Fax: (0352) 840382 (*The Which? Hotel Guide*)

---

Not inc *in the details at the end of an entry indicates that no service charge is made and any tipping is at the discretion of the customer.*

## PENMAENPOOL Gwynedd map 4

## ▲ *Penmaenuchaf Hall* ❦ ❧

Penmaenpool, nr Dolgellau LL40 1YB
DOLGELLAU (0341) 422129       COOKING 2
off A493, 2m W of Dolgellau       COST £22–£36

Originally the home of a Bolton cotton magnate, this impressive Victorian
mansion now functions as a luxurious small country-house hotel. It stands
above the Mawddach estuary only five miles from the sea, and chef Nic Walton
makes good use of fish from the local boats in his regularly changing fixed-
price menus. Light modern cooking presents guests with such dishes as
vegetable risotto in chilli and tomato sauce, Creole fish-cakes, and fillet of beef
with bean sprouts and black-bean gravy. The repertoire also embraces simple
roast beef as well as elaborate grenadine of veal roasted in a basil oil, filled
with chicken forcemeat and set on a wild mushroom sauce. Many vegetables
come from the hotel's ever-growing kitchen garden. Desserts, such as amaretto
cheesecake with a Tia Maria glaze and guava purée, are equally imaginative,
although the 'Anton Mosimann' bread-and-butter pudding has not lived up to
its reputation. Welsh cheeses are served with savoury biscuits and sesame
bread produced in-house. If the mark-up presses a little hard over £20, the six
house wines (from £9.85) offer decent compensation. The list, supplied by
Tanners, is nicely balanced and reliable, with many good names to ponder.
The alternative vintage habit should be discouraged. CELLARMAN'S CHOICE:
Marlborough, Chardonnay 1992, Stoneleigh, £17.90; Beaujolais-Villages, Ch.
Chassantour 1992, Perroud, £15.20.

CHEF: Nic Walton   PROPRIETOR: Mark Watson   OPEN: all week; 12 to 2.30, 7 to 9.30
(9 Sun)   MEALS: Set L £13.50, Set D £19.95   SERVICE: not inc, card slips closed
CARDS: Access, Visa   DETAILS: 30 seats. Private parties: 18 and 80 private rooms. Car park.
Vegetarian meals. Children's helpings. Smart dress preferred. No smoking in dining-room.
Wheelchair access (also WC). Music   ACCOMMODATION: 14 rooms, all with bath/shower.
B&B £65 to £140. Deposit: £15. Children welcome. Baby facilities. Afternoon teas. Garden.
Fishing. Snooker. TV. Phone. Doors close at 11.30. Confirm by 6. Fax: (0341) 422129 (*The
Which? Hotel Guide*)

## PONTFAEN Dyfed map 4

## ▲ *Tregynon Country Farmhouse Hotel* ❦ ❧

Gwaun Valley, Pontfaen SA65 9TU
NEWPORT (0239) 820531
B4313 towards Fishguard, first right,       COOKING 1
and right again for ½m       COST £20–£31

The Gwaun Valley, deep in the Pembrokeshire National Park, is a 'Site of
Special Scientific Interest', which is a bonus for wildlife buffs staying at this
remote sixteenth-century farmhouse. Inside is stone-walled and comfortable
rusticity. Peter and Jane Heard make almost everything themselves and even
oak-smoke their own bacon and hams. The food is slanted towards

vegetarianism, 'but not aggressively so', and freshness is the key word. The short fixed-price menus change daily and dishes are cooked to guests' requirements. Residents place their orders at breakfast; others have to telephone in advance. One frustrated reporter thought this was 'an awful fuss for a restricted choice', but there have been many enjoyable meals, taking in sweetcorn soup, avocado with Stilton and grapes, rack of local lamb, gammon in pastry, and trout with almonds. The farm-grown vegetables are impressively good. Sweets such as sticky toffee pudding, lemon tart and home-made ices have also met with approval, and the Welsh cheeseboard is worth exploring. The wine list is brief in content but long on description. For its 40-odd bins the range is remarkable; small can be beautiful. House wine is £7.25.

CELLARMAN'S CHOICE: Hawkes Bay Chardonnay 1990, Babich, £15.50; Brouilly, Ch. de la Perrière 1988, £11.60.

CHEFS: Peter and Jane Heard, and Sian Phillips  PROPRIETORS: Peter and Jane Heard
OPEN: all week, D only; 7.30 to 8.30  MEALS: Set D £14.75 (£14 residents)  SERVICE: not inc, card slips closed  CARDS: Access, Visa (3% charge)  DETAILS: 28 seats. Private parties: 16 main room. Car park. Vegetarian meals. Children's teas (residents). Smart dress preferred. No smoking in dining-room. Music  ACCOMMODATION: 8 double rooms, all with bath/shower. B&B £45 to £59.50 per room. Deposit: 25%. Children welcome. Baby facilities. Afternoon teas. Garden. TV. Phone. Fax: (0239) 820808 (*The Which? Hotel Guide*)

---

PORTHGAIN Dyfed                                                          map 4

## *Harbour Lights*

Porthgain SA62 5BW
CROESGOCH (0348) 831549                                        COOKING 2*
off A487 at Croesgoch, 4m W of Mathry                         COST £15–£39

'Despite the fact that we were soaked through and were accompanied by a soggy lurcher, they let us have their last table later that evening' is the tale of a reader whose day started with a rainstorm – hardly unexpected in west Wales – but ended with mussels with Pernod and cream, crab Mornay, sticky toffee pudding and meringue with raspberry coulis. 'Don't be fooled by the exterior of the little gem of a restaurant,' she admonished. People are at one in liking the style of the welcome, the simple domestic feel of the place, the unmatched antique crockery and, above all, Anne Marie Davies' cooking. She may be self-taught, but she has learned well. The obvious thing to seek out is the shellfish bolstered by rich and gloupy sauce, as in lobster thermidor, or simple mayonnaise. There is a strong following, too, for the vegetable cookery: the vegetable-filled pancakes with Pencarreg cheese, or maybe a timbale of leek, pepper and mushrooms as a main course. A fondness for cheese shows in the make-up of the savoury dishes. Desserts are satisfying: sticky toffee pudding with bananas gets rave reviews. The wine list is a model of its type. The bottles are not the usual run-of-the-mill from the merchants, the notes are genuinely informative and short, and the prices are very fair. House wines are £8.50.

---

CELLARMAN'S CHOICE: *Wines recommended by the restaurateur, normally more expensive than house wine.*

---

CHEF/PROPRIETOR: Anne Marie Davies OPEN: Mon to Sat, exc Mon L; 12 to 2, 7 to 9 MEALS: light L (courses £3 to £6.50). Set D £16.50 (2 courses) to £19.50 SERVICE: not inc CARDS: Access, Visa DETAILS: 35 seats. 6 tables outside. Private parties: 20 main room, 20 private room. Car park. Vegetarian meals. Children's helpings with prior notice. No smoking during D. Wheelchair access. Music

**PORTMEIRION Gwynedd** map 4

## ▲ *Hotel Portmeirion* 🍷 ✱ NEW ENTRY

Portmeirion LL48 6ET
PENRHYNDEUDRAETH (0766) 770228 COOKING 1*
off A487, between Penrhyndeudraeth and Porthmadog COST £20–£40

The village is a legend in its own lifetime. The architect Clough Williams-Ellis created a paradise that even now is not spoiled by crowds, and is a rapturous place to stay at (either in the hotel or in cottages in the village itself). The hotel building is at the bottom of the site, by the water's edge. The inside, after a disastrous fire, was restored with panache and ingenuity that preserves the original 'light opera' view of architecture. The setting and admitted enthusiasm of the hotel staff might be enough to reconcile most people to food that goes up and down in standard. This year, however, there has been a definite up with the arrival of Craig Hindley. A set-price menu gives ample choice, though sometimes a stable accompaniment matches a varying centrepiece. Thus duck with candied orange, raisins and jasmine tea sauce, a combination which balanced well, is on another day guinea-fowl done ditto. Fillet of beef with spring vegetables and grain mustard sauce is converted into breast of chicken ditto. This approach works better than it might because the cooking is fairly light-handed and flavours are muted rather than hefty. None the less, delicacy suited a timbale of crab with crème fraîche as well as an onion and mushroom soup, as it did a main dish of halibut with cucumber and lemon butter sauce. Techniques are decent and materials well sourced. Service can be slow, people have remarked, but the atmosphere is without doubt convivial. Two pages of 'House selection' wines under £13, including Gran Colegiata from Toro and a more than decent Chianti, are both helpful and encouraging. Quality and fair price are maintained through the main list with good range and fine names scattered liberally. House wine is £9.50. CELLARMAN'S CHOICE: Pant Teg, Cyfuniad Sych, Llysfaen 1992, £12.50; Mexico, La Cetto, Cabernet Sauvignon 1987, £12.

CHEF: Craig Hindley PROPRIETORS: Portmeirion Ltd OPEN: all week, exc Mon L; 12.30 to 2, 7 to 9.30 CLOSED: 10 Jan to 4 Feb MEALS: Set L £13.50, Set Sun L £16, Set D £20 (2 courses) to £25 SERVICE: not inc, card slips closed CARDS: Access, Amex, Diners, Visa DETAILS: 90 seats. 3 tables outside. Private parties: 100 main room, 12 and 30 private rooms. Car park. Vegetarian meals. Children's helpings. Smart dress preferred. No smoking in dining-room. No music ACCOMMODATION: 34 rooms, all with bath/shower. B&B £54.50 to £129. Deposit: £25. Children welcome. Baby facilities. Garden. Swimming-pool. Tennis. Fishing. TV. Phone. Confirm by 6. Fax: (0766) 771331 (*The Which? Hotel Guide*)

*🍾 denotes an outstanding wine cellar; 🍷 denotes a good wine list, worth travelling for.*

PWLLHELI Gwynedd                                                    map 4

## ▲ *Plas Bodegroes* ❦ ✳

Pwllheli LL53 5TH
PWLLHELI (0758) 612363 and 612510                      COOKING 4
on A497, 1m W of Pwllheli                               COST £35–£43

The name refers to the woodland glade that surrounds this pretty white house
with a verandah that sits just beyond Pwllheli. It began life as a restaurant, but
over the years Christopher and Gunna Chown have beavered away, improved,
expanded into their own dwelling and developed the rooms to the extent
where it is nearly a hotel. Food, however, is still centre-stage. Dinner is a five-
course extravaganza, carefully constructed to avoid the dreaded 'restaurant
bloat', that constitutes very fair value for money. A summer meal of lobster
fish-cake with tartare sauce, with tagliatelle and venison sauce as a garlic-laden
second stage, went on to braised fillet of brill with vermouth and asparagus
before cheese and a finale of cinnamon biscuit, rhubarb and apple with
elderflower custard. The balance of expectation and surprise is especially well
handled when it comes to ingredients – this is cool, neo-classical cooking, but
not afraid to try things out. The setting of the dining-room, with Venetian
masks and Welsh art for decoration, and the sitting-rooms of homely elegance,
is seductive – the more so because of the hospitality of the Chowns themselves.
They steer a fine course between the correct and the informal. No need for
comment on the wine list save to remind readers of its excellence and
remarkable, fair prices. Many half-bottles are on offer, so sit back, enjoy and
experiment. The house selection alone puts many restaurants to shame. They
know what they are about here and are keen to share their enjoyment with a
nice lack of ostentation and absence of greed. House wine is £10. CELLARMAN'S
CHOICE: Gewurztraminer 1989, Rolly-Gassmann, £16.50; Les Baux, Mas de
Gourgonnier 1989, £15.

CHEF: Christopher Chown  PROPRIETORS: Christopher and Gunna Chown  OPEN: Tue to
Sun, D only; 7 to 9.30 (9 out of season)  MEALS: Set D £30  SERVICE: net prices, card slips
closed  CARDS: Access, Amex, Visa  DETAILS: 45 seats. Private parties: 45 main room.
Car park. Vegetarian meals with prior notice. Children's helpings with prior notice. No
smoking in dining-room. Wheelchair access (1 step; also WC). Music  ACCOMMODATION:
8 rooms, all with bath/shower. B&B £40 to £110. Deposit: £50. Children welcome. Baby
facilities. Pets by arrangement. Garden. TV. Phone. Confirm by 6. Fax: (0758) 701247 (*The
Which? Hotel Guide*)

ROSSETT Clwyd                                                      map 4

## *Churtons* £                                          | NEW ENTRY |

Machine House, Chester Road,
Rossett LL12 0HW
ROSSETT (0244) 570163                                   COOKING 1
on B5445, off A483, between Chester and Wrexham        COST £19–£35

One of a pair of wine bars or bistros run by the Churton family (the other is in
Tarporley, Cheshire), this place has the advantage of continuity. 'Our
neighbours said they came here once a month,' reported a first-time visitor,

'and although the menu changed, their favourites (kidneys and trout) remained.' Nick Churton manages the trick of maintaining interest without destroying loyalty. The place itself is an atmospheric miscellany of antique fixtures and fittings, some linked to the wine trade. 'Every table has its own character, many of them seat at least six, so you are in for a sharing time' was a half-warning half-celebration of the fact that you may end up talking to your neighbour. The food, from the fairly wide menu chalked up on a blackboard, is in bistro mode, but shows some nice touches. Deep-fried Brie with a coating of nuts and a cranberry sauce is still slaying them in Clwyd, but there are devilled kidneys on toast, Stilton and walnut mousse, thick steaks of ham with port and raisin sauce, excellently simple vegetables and a pineapple cheesecake that was thought to rescue the reputation of that dish. The wine list is many times better than your average wine bar's. The range is generous, the prices are sensible and the makers sound. Marcilly Frères is the source of much of the burgundy, Salavert of the Rhônes. House wines start at £7.20.

CHEFS: Ade Garratt, Jackie Lloyd, Louise MacDougall and Eve Bletcher PROPRIETORS: Nick Churton, James Churton and Richard Bowen-Jones OPEN: Mon to Sat; 12 to 2.15, 7 to 10 CLOSED: 24 Dec to 3 Jan, bank hol Mons MEALS: alc (main courses £7 to £14) SERVICE: not inc CARDS: Access, Amex, Visa DETAILS: 55 seats. 2 tables outside. Private parties: 20 main room, 12 private room. Car park. Vegetarian meals. Children's helpings Sat L. No children under 12 (exc Sat L). Wheelchair access (1 step). Music. Air-conditioned. Fax: (0244) 570099

---

**SWANSEA West Glamorgan** map 4

## Annie's £

56 St Helen's Road, Swansea SA1 4BE COOKING 1
SWANSEA (0792) 655603 COST £20–£28

Reporters have endorsed this converted schoolhouse and have made much of Ann Gwilym's cooking. She is now in sole charge of the kitchen, preparing everything from starters to sweets, with a staunch Gallic flavour to her menu, as well as seasonal appropriateness. In winter she offers traditional cassoulets, rillettes, confits and dishes such as shanks of Welsh lamb braised with red wine, garlic, thyme and celery hearts. Venison has been pleasantly pointed up with redcurrant sauce, while the ceps in boeuf à l'ancienne 'were an instant transportation to my first visit to Les Landes,' according to one visitor. During the summer, lighter and more modern specialities come into their own: warm prawn salad chinoise, poached fillet of sole on a bed of sorrel with tomatoes and chives, for example. Desserts are the likes of fruit flan and a chocolate mousse that generated 'waves of pleasure' in one delighted diner. Liqueur coffees are much liked and the short list of two dozen wines from Lay & Wheeler provides enjoyable drinking at keen prices. House wine is £7.90.

CHEF/PROPRIETOR: Ann Gwilym OPEN: Tue to Sat, D only (and Mon D summer); 7 to 9.30 (10.30 Fri and Sat) MEALS: Set D £15.80 SERVICE: net prices, card slips closed CARDS: Access, Visa DETAILS: 60 seats. Private parties: 34 main room, 26 private room. Vegetarian meals. Children's helpings. Music

## *La Braseria* £

28 Wind Street, Swansea SA1 1DZ                          COOKING 1
SWANSEA (0792) 469683                                    COST £15–£32

This Spanish bodega-style operation on two floors is part of the group that includes La Brasserie in Cardiff (see entry). 'Spain in Swansea! Select your own meat for cooking. Noisy but enjoyable' were the notes of someone who looked on its existence with some relief. It runs on the same principles as the Cardiff show: a certain amount of pick-your-own, a lot of simple but direct cooking, good materials, salads rather than vegetables, and a fair wine list. Fish is the main business upstairs, meat down below. Chargrilling is almost universal, though sea bass in rock salt is baked and very, very popular. The wine list is serious on Riojas and has some fine clarets too: plain food, high drinking. House wines are from £6.95

CHEF: M. Tercero   PROPRIETORS: Iceimp Ltd   OPEN: Mon to Sat; 12 to 2.30, 7 to 12
MEALS: alc (main courses £4 to £11.50)   SERVICE: not inc, card slips closed   CARDS:
Access, Amex, Diners, Visa   DETAILS: 162 seats. No children under 8. Smart dress
preferred. Wheelchair access (1 step; also WC). Music

## *Happy Wok* £

22A St Helen's Road, Swansea SA1 4AP                     COOKING 1
SWANSEA (0792) 466702 and 460063                         COST £10–£35

'Do not be put off by the plain and unimaginative external frontage,' pleads a loyal follower of this restaurant in the town centre. He adds: 'The dim green light of which I once complained has thankfully been exchanged for warmer colours and increased brightness.' If the setting sounds prosaic, the cooking makes amends. Peking duck and crispy, fragrant Szechuan duck are centrepieces on a menu that holds few surprises but offers creditable versions of familiar dishes, including spring rolls, hot-and-sour soup, chicken and beef in a bird's-nest, and Szechuan-style prawns. Sizzling specialities are favourites and rice is eagerly endorsed. Matching the food is a sharp little wine list from Celtic Vintner of Swansea. House French is £6.50.

CHEF: K.W. Yuen   PROPRIETORS: I.M. Diu and K.W. Yuen   OPEN: Tue to Sun; 12 to 2, 6.30
to 11.15   CLOSED: 1 week summer   MEALS: alc (main courses £5 to £8). Set L £4.50, Set L
and D £12 to £15 (minimum 2)   SERVICE: not inc   CARDS: Access, Amex, Visa   DETAILS:
55 seats. Private parties: 50 main room. Vegetarian meals. Children welcome. Smart dress
preferred. Music. Air-conditioned

## *Number One Wind Street*

1 Wind Street, Swansea SA1 1DE                           COOKING 2
SWANSEA (0792) 456996                                    COST £17–£34

A local inhabitant recalls that this was one of the few buildings in the central area to escape blitz damage, and adds that it was for years regarded as a 'mecca for consumers of tobacco'. Since then, the place has been taken over by Kate Taylor (formerly of the Green Dragon bistro) and transformed into a light modern restaurant. The interior is elegantly furnished in pine, with grey ceilings and cream walls covered with abstract paintings and photographs of old Swansea. The mood is cheerful. The cooking depends on local produce, prepared in the French manner. Colourful warm terrine of crab and hake, salad of smoked duck and hazelnuts, loin of Welsh lamb with potato and garlic purée, noisettes of venison with oyster mushrooms, and poached fillet of brill with dill and mustard sauce have received enthusiastic endorsements. Desserts, such as crème brûlée and chocolate and chestnut pavé, are in similar vein. Welsh and French cheeses stand shoulder to shoulder. The set-price lunch menu offers unbeatable value for simpler dishes such as rillettes of pork, veal and mushroom pie, and lemon syllabub. The fairly priced French wine list is backed by a small contingent from Spain and Germany. Half-bottles show up well. House wine is £6.95.

CHEF: Kate Taylor   PROPRIETORS: Peter Gillen and Kate Taylor   OPEN: Mon to Sat L, Wed to Sat D; 12 to 2.30, 7 to 9.30   CLOSED: 25 Dec to 2 Jan   MEALS: alc (main courses £8.50 to £12.50). Set L £8.95 (2 courses) to £10.95   SERVICE: not inc, card slips closed   CARDS: Access, Amex, Visa   DETAILS: 40 seats. Private parties: 45 main room. Vegetarian meals. Children's helpings. Wheelchair access. Music

---

TALSARNAU Gwynedd                                                              map 4

## ▲ *Maes-y-Neuadd* ⁵✳

Talsarnau LL47 6YA
HARLECH (0766) 780200                                                    COOKING 2*
off B4573, 1m S of Talsarnau                                            COST £16–£40

This handsome Welsh slate and granite house set under hills, with its 'stunning' views across Snowdonia towards the sea (best at sunset), was, in medieval times, the scene of bardic musings. Today, corporeal diversion is the priority – there are walks aplenty for the adventurous – initiated by an enthusiastic welcome and the comfort of flowers and fabrics. Peter Jackson has taken over the kitchen: he relishes raiding Wales' 'natural larder' for lamb, laverbread, lobster and leek. The three-course dinner has been reduced in price, and the lunch format has been changed to allow those with smaller appetites or purses to opt for just one or two courses, such as professionally crafted fish terrine (inlaid with mussel fragments, lumpfish caviare and green peppercorns), served with a refreshing yogurt sauce, followed (on a Sunday) by Welsh beef with a Yorkshire pudding or poached salmon with a warm butter sauce. Evening dishes are more artful: loin of Welsh lamb might be wrapped in laverbread; a stew of mussels, oysters and cockles is served with a leek essence; and medallions of Anglesey venison are partnered with mustard seed and barley. Vegetables, and portions, have sometimes left serious walkers with lingering appetites, but desserts of the banana fritter or bread-and-butter pudding order resolve matters; pretty sorbets and ice-creams tempt less ravenous strollers. A profusion of soft breads – eight varieties are baked daily – consoles further. Service is attentive, almost courtly. The wine list is unannotated, house wines (at £8.45) aside, with prices a league nearer London than men of Harlech might expect. The list's heart belongs to France. Halves are good.

661

CHEFS: Peter Jackson and Christopher Dawson  PROPRIETORS: Michael and June Slatter,
Malcolm and Olive Horsfall  OPEN: all week; 12.15 to 1.45, 7 to 9.15  MEALS: Set L £6.75
(1 course) to £13.50, Set D £19.50 to £26  SERVICE: not inc, card slips closed  CARDS:
Access, Amex, Diners, Visa  DETAILS: 50 seats. Private parties: 44 main room, 12 and 14
private rooms. Car park. Vegetarian meals. Children's helpings. No children under 8 D.
Smart dress preferred. No smoking in dining-room. Wheelchair access (2 steps; also WC).
No music  ACCOMMODATION: 16 rooms, all with bath/shower. Rooms for disabled. B&B
£47 to £97. Deposit: £25. Children welcome. Baby facilities. Pets welcome. Afternoon teas.
Garden. TV. Phone. Doors close at midnight. Confirm by 4. Fax: (0766) 780211 (*The Which?
Hotel Guide*)

---

## TALYLLYN Gwynedd

map 4

## ▲ *Minffordd Hotel* 🍴✕

Talyllyn LL36 9AJ
CORRIS (0654) 761665
at junction of A487 and B4405, 8m SW of Dolgellau

COOKING 1
COST £21–£25

'A blueprint of what we think a small hotel should be' is a fitting description of
this house run by the Pickles family, nestling (for once that is the apposite
term) beneath the rearing slopes of Cader Idris. People will be very sorry to
hear of the death of Bernard Pickles. Jonathan Pickles does not charge a lot for
his cooking and provides thoroughly genuine, fresh food of the sort (the odd
strawberry garnishing the chilled cucumber soup apart) that used to be
available in those fondly remembered country lunches we all wish we had had,
but never really did. Meat or fish is quite plainly cooked – though pork may be
wrapped in bacon and served with a direct cream sauce. Vegetables are plain
and copious, and desserts will probably include a pudding – spotted dick,
perhaps. The decently priced wine list is from a good merchant and offers
reliable choice. House wines are £7.75.

CHEF: Jonathan Pickles  PROPRIETOR: Jessica Pickles  OPEN: Mon to Sat, D only; 7.30 to
8.30  CLOSED: Nov to Mar  MEALS: Set D £17  SERVICE: net prices, card slips closed
CARDS: Access, Diners, Visa  DETAILS: 28 seats. Car park. Vegetarian meals. Children's
high tea. No children between 3 and 12. No smoking in dining-room. Wheelchair access.
No music  ACCOMMODATION: 6 rooms, all with bath/shower. B&B £59 to £98. Deposit:
10%. No children between 3 and 12. Garden. Phone. Doors close at 11. Confirm by 6. Fax:
(0654) 761517 (*The Which? Hotel Guide*)

---

## THREE COCKS Powys

map 4

## ▲ *Three Cocks Hotel*

Three Cocks LD3 0SL
GLASBURY (0497) 847215
on A438, between Brecon and Hay-on-Wye

COOKING 2
COST £27–£40

This creeper-clad inn near the main road doubles as a hotel and restaurant and
visitors agree that it 'really does have those old-fashioned qualities of service
and friendliness'. A roaring fire warms the sitting-room, while the dining-
room reminded one guest of a French country auberge, offering honest, simple

and effective food. The Winstones used to have a restaurant in Belgium, and their menus are dotted with ideas from across the water. Tureens of shellfish soup have an authentic tang, helpings of Ardennes ham are served with onions pickled in honey, pork gets a mustard sauce, duck is paired with apricots, and loin of Welsh lamb is cooked with ginger. All these dishes have been praised, but the highlight for one couple was a subtle terrine of guinea-fowl with sauce verte. Fish specials are from the market. The cooking is overtly generous (expect up to eight different vegetables) and second helpings are de rigueur. Excellent coffee and petits fours round off the meal. The short wine list has a Welsh representative and prices are fair. Also look for the novel range of unusual Belgian beers. House wine is £7.50.

CHEF: Michael Winstone   PROPRIETORS: Mr and Mrs Michael Winstone   OPEN: Wed to Mon, exc Sun L; 12 to 1.30, 7 to 9   MEALS: alc (main courses £12 to £15). Set L and D £23 SERVICE: net prices   DETAILS: 30 seats. Private parties: 25 main room. Car park. Vegetarian meals. Children's light suppers. Smart dress preferred. Music   ACCOMMODATION: 7 double rooms, all with bath/shower. B&B £60. Children welcome. Baby facilities. Garden. Doors close at midnight. Confirm by 5 (*The Which? Hotel Guide*)

---

**TREFRIW Gwynedd**                                                                map 4

## Chandler's ⅝✳

Trefriw LL27 0JH
LLANRWST (0492) 640991                                                      COOKING 2
on B5106, NW of Llanrwst                                                   COST £21–£36

The casual atmosphere of this no-nonsense brasserie in the middle of the village is matched by an idiosyncratic modicum of comfort. Tables are old school desks with bare benches attached, the floors are slate slabs polished with wear, and the white walls are adorned with pictures of cockerels. The mood is very relaxed and service is down-to-earth. Adam Rattenbury's menu is in keeping with the style of the place: a handwritten card is bolstered by a regularly changing board of specials reflecting local and seasonal supplies. The result is a bonanza of ideas with fish as a strong suit: deep-fried monkfish with apple butter, steamed sea bass fillet with spring onion and soy sauce, brill with vermouth and cream sauce, Conwy salmon and much more. Vegetarians do well with apricot and coriander stew, kebabs with almond pilaff or buckwheat pancakes filled with mushrooms. Reporters have praised lambs' sweetbreads with crispy bacon in madeira sauce, warm goats' cheese salad, loin of veal with creamy ginger sauce, generous helpings of excellent vegetables and sweets such as crème fraîche brûlée with blueberries and nectarines. 'Weird and wonderful wines at reasonable prices' is a fair description of the short list, which has plenty from the New World, as well as halves and bin-ends worth exploring. House wines are around £8.25.

CHEFS/PROPRIETORS: Adam and Penny Rattenbury, and Tim Kirton   OPEN: Tue to Sat, D only; 7 to 10   CLOSED: 26 to 30 Dec, 4 weeks from end Jan, 1 to 2 weeks Oct   MEALS: alc (main courses £8 to £14)   SERVICE: not inc, card slips closed   CARDS: Access, Visa DETAILS: 36 seats. Private parties: 30 main room. Car park. Vegetarian meals. Children welcome. No smoking in dining-room. Music

map 4

## ▲ Crown at Whitebrook

Whitebrook NP5 4TX
MONMOUTH (0600) 860254
5m S of Monmouth, between A466 and B4293

COOKING 1*
COST £20–£38

The Bates have converted the village inn, set on a steep hill in a wild and woody part of Wales, into their vision of a French auberge. Roger Bates is a touch more enthusiastic than most aubergistes, especially if you are there to sample his wife's cooking. This rejoices in full French titles and a fair share of pastry – tarts of goats' cheese or of mushrooms and onions, filo pastry wrapping to a chicken and morel 'sausage', loin of venison wrapped in puff, and then mille-feuille made with potato galettes. There is no lack of effort here, and people enjoy that aspect, the liberal use of wild mushrooms and the wealth of vegetables that are ushered out with the main dish. The attitude towards service is clear: 'We do not mention service, we do not charge for service, and we do not expect service.' The wine list displays an over-readiness to go for the big-name producers – not always a bad thing when the quality is decent as in this case. Spain is especially strong and a good run of bourgeois clarets lends encouragement. Prices are fair and halves are well stocked. House wine is £7.50.

CHEF: Sandra Bates   PROPRIETORS: Roger and Sandra Bates   OPEN: all week, exc Mon L and Sun D (residents only); 12 to 2, 7 to 9 (9.30 Fri and Sat)   CLOSED: 25 and 26 Dec
MEALS: Set L £14.50, Set D £24.50   SERVICE: card slips closed   CARDS: Access, Amex, Diners, Visa   DETAILS: 30 seats. 6 tables outside. Private parties: 30 main room, 10 and 12 private rooms. Car park. Vegetarian meals. Children's helpings. Smart dress preferred. No-smoking area. No cigars/pipes in dining-room. Wheelchair access (1 step). No music
ACCOMMODATION: 12 rooms, all with bath/shower. D,B&B £70 to £120. Children welcome. Pets welcome (not in public areas). Garden. TV. Phone. Fax: (0600) 860607 (*The Which? Hotel Guide*)

---

 map 4

## ▲ Stone Hall

Welsh Hook, Wolf's Castle SA62 5NS
LETTERSTON (0348) 840212
1½m off A40, between Letterston and
Wolf's Castle, beyond Welsh Hook

COOKING 1
COST £22–£33

The core of Stone Hall dates back to the fourteenth century, although only a few traces of the original structure remain, in the slate-flagged floors, rough oak beams and huge inglenook fireplace. The building has evolved over the years and now functions as a quality restaurant with homely accommodation. Owners Alan and Martine Watson both appear out front, although Alan tends the cellar and Martine oversees the kitchen, supervising a stream of visiting French colleagues. Chefs come and go here and it is sometimes difficult to ascertain exactly whose hands are at the stove. The short *carte* is backed up by a four-course table d'hôte, and – like the décor – the style is 'French bourgeois' with regional overtones. Reporters have been impressed by the thick, grainy fish soup, salad of sauté chicken livers and grapes, confit of duck with a fan of poached pear, John Dory with chervil butter sauce, and chocolate gâteau. The mainly Gallic wine list is modestly priced given vintages and descriptions, and organics are given an outing. House wine is £8.20.

CHEFS: Christoph Caron and Martine Watson   PROPRIETORS: Alan and Martine Watson   OPEN: Tue to Sun, D only; 7 to 9.30   MEALS: alc (main courses £9.50 to £11.50). Set D £14.50 to £15   SERVICE: not inc   CARDS: Access, Amex, Visa   DETAILS: 34 seats. Private parties: 45 main room, 30 private room. Car park. Vegetarian meals. Children's helpings. Smart dress preferred. No cigars/pipes in dining-room. Music   ACCOMMODATION: 5 rooms, all with bath/shower. B&B £43 to £58. Deposit: £20. Children welcome. Baby facilities. Garden. TV. Doors close at 12.30am. Confirm by 6. Fax: (0348) 840815

# Wales round-ups

All the eating-places listed below have been recommended by readers but for one reason or another have not graduated to the main listing. They are not places that simply failed at inspection. All reports on these places would be most welcome.

**ABERDOVEY** (Gwynedd) *Old Coffee Shop* 13 New Street, (0654) 767652. Not just coffee, but quality cakes and lunches and a friendly welcome.
*Maybank Hotel* 4 Penhelig Road, (0654) 767500. Compact hotel and restaurant with estuary views. Some quality ingredients – asparagus, crab, smoked salmon, halibut – and, despite some uneven execution, well-made desserts.
**CAERNARFON** (Gwynedd) *Bakestone* 26 Hole in the Wall Street, (0286) 675846. Inexpensive and charming spot by the castle; fair cooking, good vegetables.
**CLYDACH** (Gwent) *Drum & Monkey* Blackrock, (0873) 831980. Whitewashed inn now operating as a brasserie; an enterprising menu, but the place is still finding its feet.
**DINAS MAWDDWY** (Gwynedd) *Old Station Coffee Shop* (0650) 531338. Pleasing home cooking in a self-service set-up.
**ERBISTOCK** (Clwyd) *Boat Inn* (0978) 780143. Quiet, pastoral setting by the River Dee. Stay with the bar food; although some things have disappointed, the fish cooking and apple strudel have pleased.
**HAY-ON-WYE** (Powys) *Old Black Lion* 26 Lion Street, (0497) 820841. Thirteenth-century inn with fishing rights on the Wye; good atmosphere and cooking that draws the crowds.
**LALESTON** (Mid Glamorgan) *Great House* High Street, (0656) 657644. Fifteenth-century in origin, now a well-appointed restaurant. Fresh ingredients, varied menus, charming service.
**LETTERSTON** (Dyfed) *Something's Cooking* The Square, (0348) 840621. Seriously good fish and chips.
**LLANBEDR** (Gwynedd) *Llew Glas* (034 123) 555. Trevor Pharoah's new venture; some good ideas and lots of enthusiasm, but the menu sometimes tries too hard to capture all ends of the market.
**LLANDUDNO** (Gwynedd) *Martin's* Craig-y-Don, (0492) 870070. Pleasing cooking, right down to the home-made chocolates served with coffee. More reports, please.
*Number One Food and Wine Bar* 1 Old Road, (0492) 875424. Wine bar that's valuable for the area.
**MOLD** (Clwyd) *Chez Colette* 56 High Street, (0352) 759225. French bistro good for simple dishes, friendly service and low prices.
**NEWCHAPEL** (Dyfed) *Ffynone Arms* Newchapel, nr Boncath, (0239) 841235. Old drovers' inn with bar and bistro menus. Nice garden, real ales.

**PONTFAEN** (Dyfed) *Gelli Fawr Country House* (0239) 820343. Stone farmhouse in an unspoilt setting. Plus points for bread (an individual, home-baked loaf of different doughs), also good vegetables, Welsh cheeses.

**PWLLHELI** (Gwynedd) *Glynllifon Country House* Llanbedrog, (0758) 740147. Indian restaurant incongruously placed in country house with 10 acres. Authentic cooking usually served buffet-style, delicate flavours, good breads.

**RHYL** (Clwyd) *Splash Point* Hilton Drive, (0745) 353783. Hotel that may be useful for its food: fresh fish, straightforward stuff, barbecues in summer.

**ST CLEARS** (Dyfed) *Butchers Arms* High Street, (0994) 231069. Tiny, cottagey pub with pretty restaurant; also does bar meals.

**SWANSEA** (West Glamorgan) *P.A.'s* 95 Newton Road, Mumbles, (0792) 367723. Well-run wine bar with an enterprising kitchen; decent ingredients, good selection of wines.

**TENBY** (Dyfed) *Penally Abbey* Penally, nr Tenby, (0834) 843033. Atmospheric Gothic country-house hotel in abbey grounds. Fair cooking with a few French influences, delightful desserts.

**WREXHAM** (Clwyd) *Llwyn Onn Hall Hotel* Cefn Road, (0978) 261225. Comfortable place with pleasant bedrooms and atmosphere, good variety of dishes, well thought of locally.

# Isle of Man

## La Rosette

Main Road, Ballasalla                                                        COOKING **2**
CASTLETOWN (0624) 822940                                          COST £21–£42

The apparent simplicity of Bob Phillips' menu masks, according to some, his true capacity as a chef. The diminutive, but redecorated, rooms that make up the restaurant have taken on a bistro function this year, but Rosa Phillips still offers a grand welcome. If local fish and shellfish are not your medicine, then beef steak is the most likely alternative. Methods are straightforward, but the food benefits from able handling and a plethora of vegetables. The adequate wine list begins with house wines at £9.50.

CHEFS/PROPRIETORS: Bob and Rosa Phillips   OPEN: Tue to Sun, exc Sun D; 12 to 3, 7 to 10   MEALS: Set L £12.50, Set D £25   SERVICE: not inc, card slips closed   CARDS: Access, Visa   DETAILS: 40 seats. Private parties: 8, 10 and 16 private rooms. Vegetarian meals with prior notice. Children's helpings. Smart dress preferred. Fax: (0624) 822702

## Silverburn Lodge                                              | NEW ENTRY |

Bridge Road, Ballasalla                                                      COOKING **2**
CASTLETOWN (0624) 822343                                          COST £18–£42

Though the island may have a minimal history of hunting, this lodge houses a red and gilt dining-room with just these overtones in the décor and a bistro addition (with lower prices) in the 'Saddle Room'. Perhaps the equation promotes the idea of tradition, for the menus in both rooms are certainly that, with a bit more zip coming from the daily specials. Agreement is general, however, about the precise and consistent cooking. First courses – a Spanish plate of tomato, chorizo, Serrano ham, anchovies and Manchego cheese, or scampi with asparagus (a huge helping) – are ample preludes to Dover sole stuffed with a salmon soufflé, served on crab and prawns, which may leave little room for something from the trolley of sweet dishes – sticky toffee meringue, for example. 'Bernie's Bins' supplement the general wine list. House wines from Pierre Ponnelle cost £9.

*If a restaurant is new to the* Guide *this year (did not appear as a main entry in the last edition)* NEW ENTRY *appears opposite its name.*

CHEF: David Kennish    PROPRIETORS: Bernie and Jo Hamer    OPEN: Tue to Sun, exc Sat L (Bistro open) and sun D; 12 to 2, 7.30 to 9.30    MEALS: alc (main courses Bistro £4 to £10, restaurant £11 to £16.50). Set L £11.50 to £20, Set D £20    SERVICE: not inc    CARDS: Access, Visa    DETAILS: 75 seats. Private parties: 80 main room. Car park. Vegetarian meals. Children welcome. Smart dress preferred. Wheelchair access (also WC). Music

---

**DOUGLAS  Isle of Man**                                                                 map 4

## ▲ Boncompte's

Admiral House, Loch Promenade, Douglas                              COOKING **2**
DOUGLAS (0624) 629551                                                     COST £17–£45

Locals reckon that Jaime and Jill Boncompte's restaurant is 'one of the most prestigious' eating places on the island. It is part of a Victorian hotel by the promenade, with high-ceilinged rooms and bay windows overlooking the sea. The gracious dining-room makes an immaculate setting for a four-page, handwritten menu that clings to the past, while tentatively acknowledging current fashion. Avocado with smoked salmon and prawns sits alongside marinated roast peppers with olive oil; steak Diane and duckling with orange sauce share the stage with sole and scallops with saffron sauce. One highly successful meal also yielded perfectly cooked rendezvous of seafood and spot-on tournedos with two different glazes. Sweets, which are generally displayed on a trolley, rely heavily on fresh fruit and rich cakes, although a memorable crème brûlée was the highlight for one reporter. Service rarely falters. The wine list offers plenty of creditable drinking in the £10 to £15 bracket. House wine is £9.50.

CHEFS: Jaime Boncompte and Michael Ashe    PROPRIETORS: Jaime and Jill Boncompte    OPEN: Mon to Sat, exc Sat L; 12.30 to 2, 7.30 to 10    MEALS: alc (main courses £9.50 to £15.50). Set L £10.50, Set D £15.95    SERVICE: not inc (12.5% for 10 or more)    CARDS: Access, Diners, Visa    DETAILS: 80 seats. Private parties: 95 main room, 26 and 30 private rooms. Car park. Vegetarian meals. Children's helpings. Smart dress preferred. Wheelchair access (also WC). Music. Air-conditioned    ACCOMMODATION: 12 rooms, all with bath/ shower. Rooms for disabled. Lift. B&B £50 to £120. Children welcome. Baby facilities on request. TV. Phone. Confirm 1 day ahead. Fax: (0624) 675021

---

**LAXEY  Isle of Man**                                                                   map 4

## Riverside Studio

Glen Gardens Pavilion, Laxey                                         COOKING **1**
LAXEY (0624) 862121                                                     COST £21–£38

Above the main road in the village are the Laxey Glen gardens, which are pleasure gardens along Victorian lines. This is where holidaymakers would stroll, take tea, and entertain themselves before the days of cinema, television and bingo. Nowadays, they come to the Riverside Studio and feast on fondues and grills. These are described, then cooked by Peter Ellenberger on his charcoal grill behind the cocktail bar. Dinner over, customers can vacate the tables and dance. Peter Ellenberger plays the baritone saxophone, so when he has finished cooking he can pick up the instrument and blow 'Making

Whoopee'. It's a relaxed place, with good raw ingredients simply treated, and makes for a good night out. On holiday what else do you want? There is a short but acceptable wine list and house wines from Corney & Barrow are £8.95.

CHEF/PROPRIETOR: Peter R. Ellenberger    OPEN: Tue to Sun, exc Sun D; 12 to 2, 7 to 10
MEALS: alc (main courses £8.50 to £14)    SERVICE: not inc    CARDS: Access, Visa    DETAILS:
60 seats. 8 tables outside. Private parties: 60 main room, 200 private room. Car park.
Vegetarian meals. Children's helpings. Wheelchair access (also WC). Music

---

**RAMSEY  Isle of Man**                                                    map 4

## Harbour Bistro

5 East Street, Ramsey                                              COOKING 1
RAMSEY (0624) 814182                                          COST £21–£40

The decoration of nets, anchors and *trouvailles* from old boats gives this place opposite the swing bridge a chance to live up to each element in its name: you can't forget the harbour at its doors, and this is indeed a bistro. Shellfish and seafood are its major currencies – specialities include Manx queenies cooked any way you want, and lobster and Dover soles are on daily delivery. The printed menu is given a boost each meal with specials chalked on boards and the place hums along in a friendly and happy manner. The wine list is in keeping with the style of the place. House wines are £8.85.

CHEFS: Karen Wong and Patrick Devaney    PROPRIETORS: Karl Meier, Karen Wong and
Ken Devaney    OPEN: all week, exc Sun D; 12 to 2.15, 6.30 to 10.30    CLOSED: 2 weeks
Oct    MEALS: alc (main courses £6.50 to £14)    SERVICE: not inc, card slips closed
CARDS: Access, Visa    DETAILS: 50 seats. Private parties: 60 main room. Vegetarian meals.
Children's helpings. Wheelchair access (1 step; also WC). Music.

# Isle of Man round-ups

The eating-places below have been recommended by readers but for one reason or another have not graduated to the main listing. They are not places that simply failed at inspection. All reports on these plates would be most welcome.

DOUGLAS  *L'Experience*  Summerhill, (0624) 623103. French bistro with a relaxed, informal atmosphere. Set menus of such things as salad niçoise, cassoulet and crème caramel; good bread and coffee.

PORT ST MARY  *Chateaux Lawro*  5 High Street, (0624) 833087. Primarily fresh fish – and a wine list dominated by interesting whites to match. Early-bird set dinners in the week offer excellent value.

# Channel Islands

---

**ROZEL** Jersey map 1

## *Apple Cottage* £

La Brecque du Sud, Rozel Bay
COOKING 1
JERSEY (0534) 861002
COST £16–£42

The restaurant, a little eighteenth-century granite cottage by the bay with a quaint tea-room attached, is as pretty as its name. Local seafood is the undoubted star of the show – monster crabs and lobsters, mussels, scallops and oysters – as well as luxury fish such as red mullet and turbot. Baked sea bass with garlic and fennel is a speciality. Elsewhere there is a full contingent of steaks, grills and dishes such as veal marsala and calf's liver and bacon. Salads are also served at lunch-time. Reporters have praised the fresh asparagus, pâté, Dover sole and Black Forest gâteau, although they regretted the presence of background music in the dining-room. It is wise to book. The wine list is extensive and wide ranging, with clarets and burgundies showing up strongly. House wine is £6.

CHEF: S.C. Pozzi   PROPRIETORS: Mr and Mrs S.C. Pozzi   OPEN: Tue to Sun, exc Sun D; 12 to 2.15, 7 to 9.30   CLOSED: end Dec to end Jan   MEALS: alc (main courses £6 to £17). Set L £9.50 to £10.50   SERVICE: not inc, card slips closed   CARDS: Access, Visa   DETAILS: 65 seats. 15 tables outside. Private parties: 60 main room. Car park. Vegetarian meals. Children's helpings. Smart dress preferred. No cigars/pipes in dining-room. Wheelchair access (1 step; also WC). Music

---

**ST PETERS** Guernsey map 1

## *Café du Moulin*

Rue de Quanteraine, St Peters
COOKING 1
GUERNSEY (0481) 65944
COST £18–£37

Unlike most of Guernsey's restaurants, this large stone house is neither tucked away in a town street nor sitting primly by the sea. Instead it lies in a 'hidden valley in what little country Guernsey has left'. Reflecting this otherness is a determined attempt by David and Gina Mann to avoid the time-warped, silver-service platitudes of island competitors. It is a queer world when French produce, sold less than 50 miles away, has to reach the island via London and Southampton, yet this is what the Manns report; local ingredients are used where they exist, so scallops, crabs, herbs, lamb and eggs are among those habitually Guernsey-fresh. Dishes are not complex in construction, but contrasts are firmly drawn: for example, a Brie beignet with a port-and-date sauce, roast loin of lamb with tabbouleh, and brill fillets with spinach mousse and a tomato and basil concassée and fresh tagliatelle (everything is home-made, bread, pasta and ice-cream included). Desserts are a touch homelier. A light lunch menu is available. The wine list is short but up to date: Cousino Macul's 1987 Cabernet Sauvignon (£11.50), David Wynn's 1991 Shiraz and Riesling (£10 each), and St Hallett's 1992 Poachers Blend (£10.95) are some of the better alternatives to the straightforward house wines at £6.95.

CHEF: David Mann   PROPRIETORS: David and Gina Mann   OPEN: Wed to Sun, exc Sun D (also Tue June to Oct); 12.15 to 1.15 (1.45 summer), 7.15 to 9.30   CLOSED: 2 weeks Nov, 2 weeks Feb   MEALS: alc (main courses £12 to £13). Light L menu. Set L £12.50   SERVICE: not inc   CARDS: Access, Visa   DETAILS: 45 seats. 10 tables outside. Private parties: 45 main room. Car park. Vegetarian meals. Children's helpings. No children under 7 D. Smart dress preferred. No smoking while others eat. Wheelchair access (also WC). Music

---

ST SAVIOUR  Jersey                                                            map 1

▲ *Longueville Manor*  ⁑

St Saviour                                                          COOKING 2*
JERSEY (0534) 25501                                                COST £19–£50

'Peaceful and pleasant' surroundings soothe, and the immaculate gardens, which furnish vegetables for the tables and flowers for the rooms, find their echo in the house's antiques and paintings. The menus continue to entice, couching French delicacy in the more straightforward idiom of English; and when the dishes are good, they excel. A puff-pastry pillow filled with asparagus and scallops was 'excellent', as was fillet of beef with woodland mushrooms and red wine sauce; assorted sorbets with tropical fruits were 'absolutely magic – looked too good to eat'. One vegetarian reporter, staying for two weeks, enjoyed 'wonderful and varied dinners every evening'. Yet there is often surprising inconsistency, even within the confines of a single meal: along with fine beef came roast veal with madeira sauce described as 'hunks of tasteless meat in a very ordinary sauce' and on yet another occasion suckling pig was 'soggy skin and uncooked layers of fat under that'. Mainlanders tend to find portions too large. Service, from pleasant and very polite staff, is generally good, and the wine list is grand and rather expensive. There is choice below £20, but it could do with bolstering. House wines at £7 are dull: red Chinon at £10.75 or white Alsace Pinot Blanc at £11 offer much better value.

CHEF: Andrew Baird   PROPRIETORS: the Lewis family and the Dufty family   OPEN: all week; 12.30 to 2, 7.30 to 9.30   MEALS: alc (main courses £17.50 to £19.50). Set L £15.50 (2 courses Mon to Sat) to £17.50, Set D £28.50   SERVICE: net prices, card slips closed   CARDS: Access, Amex, Diners, Visa   DETAILS: 65 seats. 8 tables outside. Private parties: 65 main room, 16 and 20 private rooms. Car park. Vegetarian meals. Children welcome. Smart dress preferred. No smoking in 1 dining-room. Wheelchair access (also WC). Air-conditioned   ACCOMMODATION: 32 rooms, all with bath/shower. Rooms for disabled. Lift. B&B £100 to £285. Deposit: £55. No children under 7. Dogs welcome. Afternoon teas. Garden. Swimming-pool. Tennis. TV. Phone. Confirm by 6. Fax: (0534) 31613 (*The Which? Hotel Guide*)

# Channel Islands round-ups

All the eating-places listed below have been recommended by readers but for one reason or another have not graduated to the main listing. They are not places that simply failed at inspection. All reports on these places would be most welcome.

GOREY (Jersey) *Jersey Pottery Restaurant* (0534) 851119. Tourist landmark; restaurant around leafy courtyard, only open for lunch in the week (pottery opening hours). Every kind of seafood imaginable, fresh fish, salads, excellent pastry-based desserts.

ROZEL (Jersey) *Château la Chaire* Rozel Bay, (0534) 863354. Smart hotel with an able chef. Nouvelle presentation of roulade of salmon and sole, mango sorbet, steamed panaché of local seafish in hazelnut and lemon butter, iced nougat parfait.

ST AUBIN (Jersey) *Old Court House Inn* (0534) 46433. Seafront spot that can get very busy (sometimes smoky). Mostly fish in various guises but some steaks too.

ST BRELADE (Jersey) *Sea Crest Hotel* Petit Port, (0534) 46353. Small modern hotel serving fair-value Anglo-French food. A useful place for lunch when exploring the south-west side of the island. More reports, please.

ST HELIER (Jersey) *Gio's* 58 Halkett Place, (0534) 36733. Friendly Italian; blackboard specials supplement the *carte* – simple but enjoyable stuff.

ST PETER PORT (Guernsey) *La Frégate* Les Cotils, (0481) 724624. Beautiful views – ask for a window table – and French cooking of a good standard. Polished service.

*La Grande Mare* Vazon Bay, (0481) 56576. Modern hotel complex with a reliable restaurant. Typical things are smoked salmon, unusual sorbets, venison, tarte au chocolat; decent coffee and petit fours.

*Le Nautique* Quay Steps, (0481) 721714. An old-fashioned warehouse with pretty harbour views. Curried oysters, straightforward fish and cups of espresso have been enjoyed.

*San Lorenzo* 42–44 Fountain Street, (0481) 722660. Genuine Italian for seafood, pasta, marinated vegetables, good selection of all-Italian wines.

SARK (Sark) *Dixcart Hotel* (0481) 832015. The island's oldest hotel has a woodland setting and comfortable rooms. Local fish and shellfish, good vegetables, all nicely cooked.

# Northern Ireland

---

**BALLYCLARE  Co Antrim**  map 9

## Ginger Tree

| NEW ENTRY |

29 Ballyrobert Road, Ballyclare BT39 9RY  COOKING 1
BELFAST (0232) 848176  COST £12–£39

'It is nowhere near Ballyclare,' warns a travelling reporter. In fact, the
restaurant is a converted bay-windowed farmhouse set in an acre of land a
couple of miles out of the town. The owner claims that it is Northern Ireland's
first Japanese establishment. 'Minimalist' sums up the décor, although the
monochrome effect is relieved by stunning abstract paintings; outside is a 'dear
little Japanese garden'. In this setting, the sound of the Carpenters' greatest hits
coming through the loudspeakers struck an odd chord for one party. The menu
is an accessible introduction to Japanese food – nothing too esoteric, but a
neatly balanced selection of dishes showing off the classic flavours, cooking
techniques and artistry of the cuisine. Set meals are a good bet and provide a
pleasurable way of sampling the repertoire: clear fragrant suimono soup with
shreds of feathery omelette, piquant morsels of sushi, skewers of yakitori with
a subtle delicate sauce, huge tempura prawns, and chicken teriyaki. Butamaki
(French beans rolled in very thin flattened slices of pork) have been revelatory.
Drink tea or saké; house wine is £7.95.

---

CHEFS: Shotapo Obana and Elizabeth English  PROPRIETOR: P. Donaldson  OPEN: Mon
to Sat, exc Sat L; 12 to 2.30, 7 to 9.30 (10 Sat)  CLOSED: 25 to 27 Dec, 12 and 13 July
MEALS: alc (main courses £7.50 to £11.50). Set L £5.95 to £10.50, Set D £7.50 to £24.50
SERVICE: not inc (10% for 8 or more)  CARDS: Access, Amex, Diners, Visa  DETAILS: 70
seats. Private parties: 70 main room, 35 private room. Car park. Vegetarian meals.
Children's helpings. Smart dress preferred. Wheelchair access (1 step; also WC). Music.
Air-conditioned

---

**BALLYNAHINCH  Co Down**  map 9

## Woodlands

29 Spa Road, Ballynahinch BT24 8PT  COOKING 1
BALLYNAHINCH (0238) 562650  COST £25–£30

'Such a pleasant haven,' reported one visitor from across the water who was
taken by the peaceful, rural setting of this renovated house built in 1740.
Alison Sandford serves a meal that reflects the locality in its materials, yet, to
this same visitor, the style was far more reminiscent of England (in the '70s)

than of Ireland today. Hence dishes such as pancakes with smoked haddock and a gratin topping, fillets of plaice with a celery and tomato stuffing, topped with melted cheese, and pigeon breasts with port and juniper sauce will satisfy all generations and all comers. House Duboeuf is £8.95.

CHEF: Alison Sandford   PROPRIETORS: Alison and David Sandford   OPEN: Thur to Sat, D only; 7.15 to 9.30   MEALS: Set D £19.95   SERVICE: net prices, card slips closed CARDS: Access, Visa   DETAILS: 45 seats. Private parties: 30 main room, 12 and 30 private rooms. Car park. Vegetarian meals with prior notice. Children's helpings. Smart dress preferred. No music

---

BELFAST  Co Antrim                                                                    map 9

## La Belle Epoque

61–63 Dublin Road, Belfast BT2 7RS                                     COOKING 2*
BELFAST (0232) 323244                                                    COST £13–£34

The house lives up to its name with lashings of mirrors, tiles and pictures of ladies all recreating that *belle époque* of languid afternoons and saucy evenings. The welcome and the atmosphere are anything but languid, however, and this remains one of Belfast's most bubbling places. The long menu is still couched in French, though there is nothing particularly Gallic about prawn cocktail with pineapple or deep-fried salmon trout croquettes with asparagus sauce. Meat cookery is often enjoyed here, as are the vegetables that range from lentils to stir-fry, and from risotto to full-blown bouquetière. The wine list stays mainly in France and has little truck with details about makers or shippers. House wines are £7.50.

CHEFS: Alan Rousse and Chris Fitzgerald   PROPRIETORS: Alan Rousse, Chris Fitzgerald, G. Sanchez, J. Delbart and J. Lindsay   OPEN: Mon to Sat, exc Sat L; noon to 11 (6 to 11 Sat)   MEALS: alc (main courses £8.50 to £11). Set L £5 (2 courses)   SERVICE: not inc CARDS: Access, Amex, Diners, Visa   DETAILS: 82 seats. Private parties: 16 main room. Vegetarian meals. Children welcome. Smart dress preferred. Wheelchair access (also WC). Music. Fax: (0232) 238138

## Nick's Warehouse

35–39 Hill Street, Belfast BT1 2LB                                     COOKING 1
BELFAST (0232) 439690                                                    COST £14–£32

Nick and Kathy Price's converted warehouse at the back of St Anne's Cathedral is back in full swing after an accidental fire in 1992. Finding the place – at the end of one of the last cobbled streets in Belfast – was a real surprise for one party, although they were less enthusiastic about the 'masses of fake foliage' and the lack of a no-smoking area in the dining-room. Daily menus inhabit the modern bistro world of avocado salad with Parmesan shavings and blackened monkfish with chilli relish, as well as offering game terrine with rhubarb chutney, sirloin steak and pasta with aubergines. The cooks care about supplies: some vegetables are organically grown, lamb is from a herd of Texel sheep reared near the Irish Sea, and game is well hung. Diners have particularly liked warm pigeon breast salad with balsamic dressing and duck breast with five-spice sauce, although tortillas and nut galettes have been 'disappointing'. Good-value light lunches are served in the downstairs wine bar. A decent list of around 40 wines has some racy youthful bottles. House wines start at £5.95.

CHEFS: Nick Price, Simon Toye and Sean Jones   PROPRIETORS: Nick and Kathy Price
OPEN: Mon to Sat, exc Mon D and Sat L; 12 to 3, 6 to 9   CLOSED: 25 and 26 Dec, Easter
Mon, 12 Jul   MEALS: alc (main courses restaurant £8.50 to £12, wine bar £4 to £6.50)
SERVICE: not inc   CARDS: Access, Diners, Visa   DETAILS: restaurant 45 seats, wine bar
45 seats. Private parties: 45 main room. Vegetarian meals. Children's helpings restaurant.
No children wine bar. Wheelchair access wine bar (also WC). Music. Air-conditioned

## Roscoff ▾

7 Lesley House, Shaftesbury Square,
Belfast BT2 7DB                                                          COOKING 3*
BELFAST (0232) 331532                                                   COST £20–£52

'For all that it is one of the friendliest places in the world, Belfast is physically a grotty city, and the length of street on which Roscoff stands is as grotty a city-centre area as you'll find.' Even the restaurant itself, from the outside, may fail to entice: the 'apparently over-white hard-edged steel and glass interior' reminded one diner of a surgery. Yet once you are inside, all is 'welcoming sparkle': spotlights wash the colour of modern paintings on to the walls, and the sense of bright, clean busyness 'is reflected in the attitude of the staff who are friendly, attentive and helpful to just the right degree'. Italy seems to be winning the struggle for Paul Rankin's heart and palate, as indicated by the *carte*'s highlights, such as wild herb risotto, chicken bruschetta, squab chicken with fresh pasta and chargrilled mushrooms or chargrilled fillet of beef with a salad of bacon and Roquefort; dishes in the set-price menus, being slightly simpler, wear their ethnic inspiration less emphatically. The cooking is precise and vivid: two pieces of pork in a bruschetta 'had been cooked to just the right element of moistness, and rested on a roundel of crisped bread on which were piled wild mushrooms, very finely chopped. The mushrooms had absorbed some of the sauce and the combined taste of pork, mushrooms and sauce was exquisite.' A starter of roast scallops was 'cooked to perfection', and the hazelnut and basil pesto proved ideally complementary. 'Beautifully cooked fish' is local, save in stormy weather; summer organic vegetables, too, are local. Desserts are the only stage of the meal where the kitchen nods: fresh fruit mille-feuille 'was overcooked and rather heavy', though apricot soufflé and crème brûlée have both been memorable. The wine list makes a serious attempt to do the whole world justice: familiar names provide its classic core, but better value is to be had on the periphery, with good selections from New Zealand (including Montana and Hunters), Australia (including Taltarni and Petaluma) and America (including Fetzer and Dom. Drouhin). House wines are from £8.95.

CHEFS/PROPRIETORS: Paul and Jeanne Rankin   OPEN: Mon to Sat, exc Sat L; 12.30 to 2.30,
6.30 to 10.30   MEALS: alc (main courses £10.50 to £14.50). Set L £13.50, Set D £18.50
SERVICE: not inc   CARDS: Access, Amex, Diners, Visa   DETAILS: 80 seats. Private parties:
20 main room. Vegetarian meals. Children's helpings. No-smoking area. Wheelchair access
(also WC). Music. Air-conditioned

## Strand £

| 12 Stranmillis Road, Belfast BT9 5AA | COOKING 1 |
|---|---|
| BELFAST (0232) 682266 and 663189 | COST £11–£23 |

This lively 'wine bar/restaurant' is handily placed close to Queens University and does brisk business with students and people from the city. 'It seems a million miles away from the much publicised troubles,' noted one visitor from the mainland. The place is pure bistro: all noise, bustle and conversation, with small booths, dark green walls, art deco wall-lamps and loud music. The set-up runs right through the day and a cut-price menu of single dishes such as pasta carbonara and steak and kidney pie with Guinness is served from noon to 7pm. The main menu also offers remarkably good value with monkfish in apple butter, asparagus crêpes, liver Stroganov and cod fillet with a subtle ginger and peppercorn sauce. A clutch of desserts might include poached pears 'plugged' with marzipan, raspberry brûlée and brandied fig ice-cream. Despite a few rough edges and inconsistencies in the cooking, the Strand remains an asset to the locality. Sixty wines cover the globe and some reliable names appear among the suppliers, although a few half-bottles would be welcome. House wine is £5.95.

CHEFS: Michael McAuley and Donna Donaldson PROPRIETOR: Anne Turkington OPEN: all week; noon to 11pm MEALS: alc (main courses £3 to £8) SERVICE: not inc CARDS: Access, Amex, Diners, Visa DETAILS: 76 seats. 2 tables outside. Private parties: 30 main room, 30 private room. Vegetarian meals. Children's helpings. Smart dress preferred. Wheelchair access (3 steps). Music. Air-conditioned

---

**BELLANALECK Co Fermanagh** map 9

## Sheelin £

| Bellanaleck BT92 2BA | COOKING 1 |
|---|---|
| ENNISKILLEN (0365) 348232 | COST £16–£30 |

This thatched building has been a village store, a tailor's shop and a shebeen since 1810; it is full of the atmosphere such age imparts, and is a landmark for those who come to look as well as those who come to eat. The dinner formula is a set price for a five-course meal, the components of which are much loved and little varying. Trencherpersons will not be disappointed by the likes of duck with redcurrant and orange, or sole stuffed with prawns and finished with wine and cream. House wines are £6.45.

CHEFS: Marion Maxwell and Jacqueline Owens PROPRIETOR: Arthur Cathcart OPEN: all week L, Wed to Sat D (Tue to Sun D June to Aug); 12.30 to 2.30, 7 to 9.30 MEALS: alc (main courses £7.50 to £11.50). Set D £11 to £19 SERVICE: not inc, card slips closed CARDS: Access, Amex, Visa DETAILS: 30 seats. Private parties: 24 main room. Car park. Vegetarian meals. Children's helpings. Smart dress preferred. Wheelchair access (also WC). Music. Fax: (0365) 348190

---

'Seemingly good except for the parsley garnish full of grit, and tormented looking.'
On eating in Northants

---

**BUSHMILLS  Co Antrim**                                      map 9

## ▲ *Auberge de Seneirl* ⚡✳

28 Ballyclogh Road, Bushmills BT57 8UZ
DERVOCK (026 57) 41536                                   COOKING 2
off B17 Coleraine road                                   COST £25–£40

This old school-house stands three miles from the Giant's Causeway and has
been lovingly restored by the Defres into a characterful restaurant-with-rooms,
where Madame offers French cooking with a Provençal and Gascon slant. This
does not stop her experimenting, British-style, with sweetness and fruit in
dishes such as turbot with lime sauce, quail stuffed with cherries, and fillet of
beef with ginger and armagnac. Portions are very generous, and the standard is
maintained right through to the sweet and succulent end of the meal with ice-
creams, pancakes, or a charlotte of white and dark chocolate. M. Defres imparts
his particular style to the service and to the production of bottles from the
cellar. There are sound materials in the wine list, and fair prices. M. Defres
offers a half-dozen bottles as preferred selections; prices start at £9.35.

CHEF: B.E. Defres  PROPRIETORS: J.L. and B.E. Defres  OPEN: Tue to Sat, D only; 7 to 9.30
CLOSED: Christmas, summer school hols (telephone to check)  MEALS: Set D £17 to £24
SERVICE: not inc, card slips closed  CARDS: Amex, Diners  DETAILS: 35 seats. Private
parties: 30 main room, 10 private room. Car park. Vegetarian meals with prior notice.
Children's helpings with prior notice. Smart dress preferred. No smoking in dining-room.
Wheelchair access (1 step). Music  ACCOMMODATION: 5 rooms, all with bath/shower. B&B
£37 to £74. Deposit: £20. Children welcome. Baby facilities. Garden. Swimming-pool.
Sauna. TV

---

**COLERAINE  Co Derry**                                      map 9

## ▲ *Macduff's* ⚡✳

Blackheath House, 112 Killeague Road,
Blackhill, Coleraine BT51 4HH
AGHADOWEY (0265) 868433                                  COOKING 1
off A29, 7m S of Coleraine                               COST £21–£34

The dining-room is housed in the cellars of this rather grand Georgian rectory a
few miles inland from the Causeway coast. It was once the home of the writer
of the hymn 'All things bright and beautiful' and is set in a stunning landscape.
Visitors will enjoy the comfort of the place and the calm welcome of the
Erwins. Margaret Erwin cooks country-house style, taking advantage of the
local soft fruit, the game (lots of woodcock) and the fine lamb in the early
summer. Variety is tipped into the balance with things like chicken tikka
masala and steak with a sauce of onions and hazelnuts. House wines are £7.20.

CHEF: Margaret Erwin  PROPRIETORS: Joe and Margaret Erwin  OPEN: Tue to Sat, D only;
7 to 9.30  MEALS: alc (main courses £8.50 to £10.50)  SERVICE: not inc, card slips closed
CARDS: Access, Visa  DETAILS: 36 seats. Private parties: 36 main room, 14 private room.
Car park. Vegetarian meals. No children under 12. Smart dress preferred. No smoking in
dining-room. No music  ACCOMMODATION: 5 rooms, all with bath/shower. B&B £30 to
£60. No children under 12. Dogs by arrangement. Afternoon teas. Garden. TV. Fax:
(0265) 868433

## LONDONDERRY  Co Londonderry

map 9

# ▲ Beech Hill
# Country House Hotel

32 Ardmore Road, Londonderry BT47 3QP
LONDONDERRY (0504) 49279
off A6 Londonderry to Belfast road at
Faughan Bridge, opposite Ardmore Chapel

COOKING 2
COST £15–£39

Thirty-two acres of ground, gardens, waterfalls and ponds are a magnificent setting for this restored eighteenth-century country house that offers the grand manner to Londonderry. On display in the dining-room, which overlooks a waterfall, is a set of eighteenth-century china in mint condition that had remained hidden away for years. Noel McMeel cooks, in a fashion that is informed by the best chefs in the region, dishes such as escalopes of salmon and monkfish with tagliatelle of vegetables and a mustard sauce, and breast of duck with pickled cabbage and a red wine and blackcurrant sauce. Ancillaries, local cheeses and materials are in keeping with the modern ambitions – for example, fresh scallops with home-made pasta and pesto. House wine is £7.95.

CHEF: Noel McMeel   PROPRIETORS: Leo and Seamus Donnelly   OPEN: all week; 12 to 2.30, 6 to 9.45   CLOSED: 24 Dec D, 25 Dec   MEALS: alc (main courses £11 to £13). Set L £9.95 to £14, Set D £16.95   SERVICE: not inc, card slips closed   CARDS: Access, Amex, Visa   DETAILS: 35 seats. Private parties: 80 main room, 12 and 20 private rooms. Car park. Vegetarian meals. Children's helpings. Smart dress preferred. Wheelchair access (also WC). Music   ACCOMMODATION: 17 rooms, all with bath/shower. B&B £50 to £100. Children welcome. Baby facilities. Afternoon teas. Garden. Fishing. TV. Phone. Doors close at midnight. Confirm by 1pm. Fax: (0504) 45366

## PORTRUSH  Co Antrim

map 9

# Ramore  £

The Harbour, Portrush BT56 8BN
PORTRUSH (0265) 824313

COOKING 3
COST £17–£40

'It was a revelation and a pleasure to find somewhere so smart and lively on two nights (Monday wine bar, Wednesday restaurant) in a deserted, out-of-season resort, in grim weather. The place was great, the service good, the food very fine in the restaurant, more rough and ready, but outstanding value, in the wine bar.' This reporter's meal took in Thai crab salad with lime and coriander – 'the coriander was none too evident, but the vinaigrette was nice' – pork fillet with Emmental and Parma ham in a mustard cream sauce, a paella which was thought better than many in Barcelona, though it had a smoked haddock sauce to bring it straight home to Northern Ireland, and a lemon soufflé to finish. Others have agreed with these findings. 'I felt complete amazement at the stylishness of the restaurant,' (the exterior is hardly preparation for it) observed one who enjoyed the jazz, the Helmut Newton posters, the open kitchen and the overall effect of buzz and society. Presentation is a watchword, though not at the expense of quantity, or of flavour. Salmon fish-cake was dauntingly large, but turned out light with good texture. The wine list gives plenty of New World value. The French section is steady; go for clarets first. House wines start at £6.75.

CHEF: George McAlpin  PROPRIETORS: John and Joy Caithness, and George and Jane McAlpin  OPEN: restaurant Tue to Sat, D only; 6.30 to 10.30. Wine bar Mon to Sat; 12 to 2, 5 to 9  MEALS: alc (main courses restaurant £6.50 to £11, wine bar £3 to £6.50)  SERVICE: not inc, card slips closed  CARDS: Access, Visa  DETAILS: 80 seats. Private parties: 80 main room. Car park. Vegetarian meals. Children's helpings. No pipes in dining-room. Wheelchair access (1 step). Music. Air-conditioned.

# Northern Ireland round-ups

All the eating-places below have been recommended by readers but for one reason or another have not graduated to the main listing. They are not places that simply failed at inspection. All reports on these places would be most welcome.

**BELFAST** (Co Antrim) *Antica Roma* 67–69 Botanic Avenue, (0232) 311121. Bustling Italian that's dramatically decorated with columns, statues, frescoes and a central atrium. Reasonable execution of a typical Italian menu; enjoy the upbeat atmosphere.
*La Boheme Restaurant and Art Gallery* 103 Great Victoria Street, (0232) 240666. French-run restaurant offering competitively priced set meals. Decent bistro cooking.
*Bishops* Bradbury Place, (0232) 313547. Quite simply a fish and chip shop with a sit-in area open till early evening (open till very late for take-away). High-quality ingredients beautifully fried.

**DONAGHMORE** (Co Tyrone) *Top Bar* 73 Castlecaulfield Road, (086 87) 61448. Converted terrace cottage now a restaurant useful for the area. Straightforward menus, comprehensive wine list.
**HELEN'S BAY** (Co Down) *Deans on the Square* 7 Station Square, (0247) 852841. Tastefully refurbished old railway building. Imaginative menus incorporating some Irish traditions; light and filling desserts – try the steamed chocolate pudding.

# Republic of Ireland

If you should visit the Republic, please let us have reports on your meals. We are grateful to those who have done so this year. Owing to the shortage of reports, however, we still feel unable to give marks for cooking.

Prices are quoted in Irish punts. To telephone the Republic from mainland Britain, dial 010 353, followed by the area code and number we have listed, but dropping the initial zero (0).

---

ADARE Limerick                                                                    map 9

## ▲ *Adare Manor*

Adare
LIMERICK (061) 396566                                              COST £26–£65

Walk for 11 minutes from the village gate through parkland to this Tudor-Gothic mansion with decoration and furnishings 'as magnificent as we have seen'. So ran our instructions from a reader who was impressed by the international cooking, the prices in the giant wine list and the tilt towards international tourism that may be inevitable in a place like this. That said, standards are high and the place itself is an experience. House wine is £15.

CHEF: Gerard Costelloe   PROPRIETORS: Tom and Judi Kane   OPEN: all week; 12.30 to 2.30, 7 to 10   MEALS: alc (main courses £16 to £22). Set Sun L £14.95, Set D £28   SERVICE: 15%, card slips closed   CARDS: Access, Amex, Diners, Visa   DETAILS: 74 seats. Private parties: 90 main room, 30 and 220 private rooms. Car park. Vegetarian meals. Children's helpings. No children under 4 after 7pm. Jacket and tie. No-smoking area. Wheelchair access (1 step; also WC). Music   ACCOMMODATION: 64 rooms, all with bath/shower. Rooms for disabled. Lift. B&B £112 to £298. Children welcome. Afternoon teas. Garden. Swimming-pool. Sauna. Fishing. Golf. Snooker. TV. Phone. Confirm by 4. Fax: (061) 396124

---

AHAKISTA Co Cork                                                                  map 9

## *Shiro* 🍴✳

Ahakista
BANTRY (027) 67030
on coast road from Durrus towards Sheep's Head            COST £39–£50

In a remote former priest's house overlooking Dunmanus Bay, Kei and Werner Pilz run a Japanese dinner house which offers a daily-changing five-course menu of exquisite craftsmanship that begins with ume-shu (sweet plum aperitif with saké), goes on to zensai before suimono (seasonal soup), then lays out a choice between some Japanese standards like teriyaki or sashimi or tempura, or particular dishes that may not be met elsewhere such as roasted sea trout which is then boiled in ginger and lemon, or chicken and sheep's liver grilled in garlic butter and served with a ginger sauce. The restaurant is very small, very select, and booking is essential. Wines cost from £11.

CHEF: Kei Pilz  PROPRIETORS: Kei and Werner Pilz  OPEN: all week, D only; 7 to 9
MEALS: Set D £32  SERVICE: net prices, card slips closed  CARDS: Access, Amex, Diners,
Visa (5% surcharge)  DETAILS: 12 seats. Private parties: 7 main room, 5 and 7 private
rooms. Car park. Vegetarian meals. No children under 12. No smoking in 1 dining-room.
Music. Fax: (027) 67206

---

**BALLINA Co Mayo**                                                          map 9

## ▲ *Mount Falcon Castle*

Ballina
BALLINA (096) 21172                                                 COST £24–£29

This neo-Gothic stone house set in woodland offers dinner round a single giant
table to its residents – who are likely to be tired out by a day's fishing. The
cooking avoids elaboration, but when you can draw on the farm for daily
supplies, who needs elaboration? House wine is £8.50.

CHEF/PROPRIETOR: Constance Aldridge  OPEN: all week, D only; 8  CLOSED: 3 days
Christmas, Feb, Mar, Oct  MEALS: Set D £17.50  SERVICE: 10%, card slips closed  CARDS:
Access, Amex, Diners, Visa  DETAILS: 22 seats. Private parties: 22 main room. Car park.
Vegetarian meals with prior notice. Children's helpings. Smart dress preferred. No music
ACCOMMODATION: 10 rooms, all with bath/shower. B&B £40 to £80. Deposit: 30%.
Children welcome. Baby facilities. Pets welcome. Garden. Tennis. Fishing. Doors close at
11. Confirm by noon. Fax: (096) 21172

---

**BALLYDEHOB Co Cork**                                                       map 9

## *Annie's*

Main Street, Ballydehob
BALLYDEHOB (028) 37292                                               COST £14–£35

Diners at Annie's may first go across the road (clutching a menu) for a drink at
the pub opposite and choose their meal. Annie crosses over and takes the order.
'It is something else,' claims one regular visitor, describing the restaurant's
close reliance on what has come off the boats that hour or day. The menu might
as well be thrown away and Annie's recommendations acted upon without
question. Find not just fish, but also 'the best steak in Ireland, and equal to the
best in service,' according to one happy man. All this praise comes for
somewhere with very few pretensions, offering just good food. A snack menu
appears at lunch. House wines are from £10.

CHEFS/PROPRIETORS: Anne and Dano Barry  OPEN: Tue to Sat, exc Sat L (open Sun and
Mon Jul and Aug); 12.30 to 2.30, 6.30 (7 winter) to 9.30 (times may differ in winter)
CLOSED: first 3 weeks Oct  MEALS: alc (main courses light L £4 to £7, D £11 to £14), Set D
£20  SERVICE: not inc  CARDS: Access, Visa  DETAILS: 24 seats. Private parties: 25 main
room. Vegetarian meals. Children's helpings. No cigars/pipes in dining-room. Wheelchair
access. No music

---

*'The head waitress person is a pain in the arse (we got a lecture about the strength of the
wine with our seventh bottle).'*  On eating in Tyne & Wear

---

## BALLYLICKEY  Co Cork                                    map 9

# ▲ *Sea View House Hotel*

Ballylickey
BANTRY (027) 50073 and 50462
on N71 Bantry to Glengarriff road                          COST £17–£33

Cheese, including the wonderful Milleens, comes from the emporium at the
bottom of the driveway. Other materials are direct from farm or boat. Hake,
John Dory or halibut may be served with creamy sauces and generously
buttered vegetables, and desserts will share the same profligate disregard of the
waistline. The place enjoys a great position above Bantry Bay and a country-
house atmosphere. Wines cost from around £11.

CHEF/PROPRIETOR: Kathleen O'Sullivan  OPEN: all week, D only, and Sun L; 12.30 to 1.30,
7 to 9.30  CLOSED: mid-Nov to mid-Mar  MEALS: Set Sun L £10, Set D £19.50  SERVICE:
10%, card slips closed  CARDS: Access, Amex, Diners, Visa  DETAILS: 50 seats. Private
parties: 15 main room. Car park. Vegetarian meals. Children's helpings on request.
Wheelchair access (also WC). No music  ACCOMMODATION: 16 rooms, all with bath/
shower. Rooms for disabled. B&B £40 to £100. Deposit: 1 night. Children welcome. Baby
facilities. Pets welcome (not in public rooms). Afternoon teas. Garden. Phone. Doors close
at midnight. Fax: (027) 51555

## BALLYVAUGHAN  Co Clare                                  map 9

# ▲ *Gregans Castle*

Ballyvaughan
ENNIS (065) 77005
on N67, 3m S of Ballyvaughan                               COST £19–£63

Galway Bay is the source of the fish, vegetables are organically grown, fine
meat such as venison with blackberry sauce, or beef with a mustard and herb
crust, are local too. Gregans Castle exemplifies the Irish ability for self-
sufficiency, while giving the materials an interesting twist. Home-made ice-
creams are 'the best I've ever had', reported one traveller who warmed to the
lived-in feel to the house, the happy isolation ('no other buildings within a
mile'), and the impressive gardens that are 'not overdone, but yet must
swallow hours of hard work'. House wine is £11.75.

CHEFS: Peter Haden and Margaret Cronin  PROPRIETORS: Peter, Moira and Simon Haden
OPEN: all week; 12 to 3, 7 to 8.30  CLOSED: end Oct to end Mar  MEALS: alc (main courses
£10 to £26). Set D £26. Bar L (main courses £5 to £18). Minimum £10 D  SERVICE: 12.5%,
card slips closed  CARDS: Access, Visa  DETAILS: 50 seats. Private parties: 80 main room.
Car park. Vegetarian meals. Children's helpings. Smart dress preferred. No-smoking area.
No cigars/pipes in dining-room. Wheelchair access (also WC). No music
ACCOMMODATION: 22 rooms, all with bath/shower. Rooms for disabled. B&B £69 to £154.
Deposit: £40. Children welcome. Baby facilities. Afternoon teas. Garden. Phone. Doors
close at 11.30. Fax: (065) 77111

▲ *This symbol means accommodation is available.*

---

**BRAY  Co Wicklow**                                              map 9

## *Tree of Idleness*

---

Seafront, Bray
DUBLIN (01) 2863498 and 2828183                          COST £23–£47

They are not idle at all in Bray, and this sea-front Greek restaurant with a
remarkable wine cellar again receives applause this year for excellent service
and fresh, well-presented food. Typically praised dishes include tomatoes
yemista stuffed with bacon, mushrooms and shallots, plain rack of lamb with
shallot and mushroom sauce, and quails mavrodaphne if you prefer the Greek
culinary line. House wines are £10.

---

CHEF: Ismail Basaran  PROPRIETOR: Susan Courtellas  OPEN: Tue to Sun, D only; 7.30 to
11 (10 Sun)  CLOSED: Christmas, first 2 weeks Sept  MEALS: alc (main courses £9.50 to
£17). Set D £15.50 to £19.50  SERVICE: 10%, card slips closed  CARDS: Access, Diners,
Visa  DETAILS: 50 seats. Private parties: 18 main room. Vegetarian meals. Children's
helpings. No-smoking area. Wheelchair access (1 step; also WC). Music

---

**CASHEL  Co Galway**                                             map 9

## ▲ *Cashel House Hotel*

---

Cashel
CLIFDEN (095) 31001
on N59 from Galway                                        COST £36–£50

The nineteenth-century house has gradually been extended with new bedroom
wings set in the midst of manicured gardens – rhododendrons and azaleas are a
feature. There is a hint of hotel to the proceedings – rather than relaxed country
house which is so often the specific of Irish hospitality – and that goes for the
cooking style as well. House wine is £11.50.

---

CHEF: Dermot McEvilly  PROPRIETORS: Dermot and Kay McEvilly  OPEN: all week; 1 to 2,
7.30 to 9  MEALS: alc (main courses £13 to £17). Set D £26 to £27  SERVICE: 12.5%, card
slips closed  CARDS: Access, Amex, Visa  DETAILS: 70 seats. 3 tables outside L. Car park.
Vegetarian meals. Children's tea 6.15pm. No children under 5. Smart dress preferred.
No-smoking area. Wheelchair access (also WC). No music  ACCOMMODATION: 32 rooms,
all with bath/shower. Rooms for disabled. B&B £46 to £150. Deposit: £100. No children
under 5. Dogs in bedrooms only. Afternoon teas. Garden. Tennis. TV. Phone. Fax:
(095) 31077

---

**CASHEL  Co Tipperary**                                          map 9

## *Chez Hans*

---

Rockside, Cashel
CASHEL (062) 61177
at foot of Rock of Cashel                                COST £31–£47

This attractively converted chapel does not mess about with understatement,
either decorative or culinary. The style is classically plentiful and might
include dishes like a gratin of Rossmore oysters, warm salad of chicken and

duck livers, cassolette of seafood and pineapple served plain but for once with enough kirsch. House wines are from £10.50.

CHEF/PROPRIETOR: Hans-Peter Matthia   OPEN: Tue to Sat, D only; 6.30 to 10   CLOSED: 3 weeks Jan   MEALS: alc (main courses £14.50 to £19.50)   SERVICE: not inc, card slips closed   CARDS: Access, Visa   DETAILS: 80 seats. Private parties: 100 main room. Car park. Vegetarian meals with prior notice. Children's helpings. Smart dress preferred. No-smoking area. Wheelchair access (also WC). Music

---

## CLIFDEN  Co Galway                                                    map 9

# O'Grady's

Market Street, Clifden
CLIFDEN (095) 21450                                                  COST £15–£40

The restaurant owns its own trawler, thus guaranteeing that the fish is of the best. The plush interior is now supplemented by a bistro addition – less money, less comfort – but the fish remains the chief draw. Reports of mussels stuffed with garlic and breadcrumbs, seafood terrine with a béarnaise sauce, boiled lobster with garlic butter and fried monkfish and scallops with garlic, mushrooms and bacon reveal not only a chef in love with garlic (and customers liking it too) but a wholly satisfactory kitchen working with excellent materials. House wines are from £9.

CHEF: P.J. Heffernan   PROPRIETOR: Michael O'Grady   OPEN: Tue to Sun; 12.30 to 2.30, 6.30 to 10   CLOSED: Nov to end Feb   MEALS: alc (main courses £7.50 to £12.50). Set L £8.95 to £12.95, Set D £18.95. Minimum £7.50   SERVICE: not inc, card slips closed   CARDS: Access, Amex, Visa   DETAILS: 65 seats. Private parties: 15 main room, 10 private room. Vegetarian meals. No children under 5. Smart dress preferred. Wheelchair access (2 steps). Music

---

## CLONAKILTY  Co Cork                                                    map 9

# Dunworley Cottage ⁵✸ £

Butlerstown, Clonakilty
BANDON (023) 40314
on coast between Clonakilty and Bandon                               COST £19–£41

The Nordic tilt to the cooking and service at this remote homestead none the less mirrors the region's emphasis on fresh raw materials and direct, expressive recipes. Try the nettle soup, the black and white puddings, the excellent fish, or the unexpected stir-fried chicken and vegetables with sweet-and-sour sauce. Special diets are catered for and all dishes are signposted for the epicure anxious to avoid cholesterol, dairy produce, meat or gluten. Lobster and crayfish can be bought in if ordered a few days in advance. House wines are from £9.75.

CHEF: Asa Helmersson   PROPRIETOR: Katherine Noren   OPEN: Wed to Sun; 1 to 3, 6.30 to 9   CLOSED: 6 Jan to mid-Mar, Nov   MEALS: alc (main courses £6 to £13)   SERVICE: not inc   CARDS: Access, Amex, Diners, Visa   DETAILS: 50 seats. Private parties: 25 main room. Car park. Vegetarian meals. Healthy eating options. Children's helpings. No smoking in 1 dining-room. Wheelchair access (also WC)

## ▲ *Arbutus Lodge*

Montenotte, Cork
CORK (021) 501237                                              COST £18–£49

Declan Ryan and the Ryan family make this nineteenth-century mayoral
residence an essential stop for the travelling epicure. It combines grandeur
with an unforced and unpatronising gregariousness while producing food –
and stunning wines – that was once firmly based on a Franco-Irish tradition
but now pays more than lip-service to Italy and the New World. The '90s see
polenta and grilled Mediterranean vegetables on the streets of Cork, but no
matter what the source or inspiration the quintessential loyalty to place and
producer remains. House wines are £9.30.

CHEFS: Declan Ryan and Helen Ward    PROPRIETORS: the Ryan family    OPEN: Mon to Sat;
12.30 to 2, 7 to 9.30    MEALS: alc (main courses £15). Set L £12.50, Set D £21.50 to £27.75.
Bar L (main courses £5.50 to £6.50)    SERVICE: not inc    CARDS: Access, Amex, Diners,
Visa    DETAILS: 50 seats. 8 tables outside (bar food). Private parties: 10 main room. Car
park. Vegetarian meals. Children welcome. No cigars/pipes in dining-room. No music.
Air-conditioned    ACCOMMODATION: 20 rooms, all with bath/shower. B&B £42 to £110.
Children welcome. Garden. Tennis. TV. Phone. Doors close at 12.30am. Fax: (021) 502893

## *Clifford's*

18 Dyke Parade, Cork
MARDYKE (021) 275333                                          COST £21--£44

'One of the best in Ireland and one of the top in Europe' goes an account that
continues. 'All too often people get to a certain level of quality and stay at that
plateau. Clifford's always strives to be better.' The panache in the decoration
and conversion of the Georgian building that once housed the City Library,
the exemplary service, the sensitive deployment of local produce (spring
lamb is offered, but as fitfully according to supplies as the rarest and hardest-
caught fish): these are the elements of a stunning recipe. House wine
is £12.50.

CHEF/PROPRIETOR: Michael Clifford    OPEN: Mon to Sat, exc L Mon and Sat; 12.30 to 2.30,
7.30 to 10.30    CLOSED: 1 week Christmas, last 2 weeks Aug    MEALS: Set L £12.75, Set D
£27    SERVICE: not inc    CARDS: Access, Amex, Diners, Visa    DETAILS: 45 seats. Private
parties: 50 main room, 35 private room. Vegetarian meals. No children under 4. Jacket and
tie. No-smoking area. No music. Air-conditioned

## *Crawford Gallery Café*  £

Emmet Place, Cork
CORK (021) 274415                                              COST £17–£34

This delightful art gallery café is run by the owners of Ballymaloe House (see
entry, Shanagarry). The people are generous, warm-hearted and sociable and
the place can get busy at lunch-time. However, there are plenty of tables and a
short menu is offered at a reasonable price, which might take in a good soup,

fresh plaice landed the night before at Ballydehob, and traditional puddings like treacle tart, or rhubarb and ginger pie. House Duboeuf is £10.

CHEFS: Myrtle and Fern Allen, Rosie Mcleod and Don Cullinane PROPRIETORS: Myrtle and Fern Allen OPEN: Mon to Sat L, Wed to Fri D; 12 to 2.30, D 6 to 9.30 CLOSED: 2 weeks after Christmas, bank hols MEALS: alc (main courses £6 to £11). Set D £15. Light L menu. Minimum £2.50 L SERVICE: not inc CARDS: Access, Visa DETAILS: 70 seats. Private parties: 70 main room. Vegetarian meals. Children's helpings. No-smoking area. Wheelchair access (also WC). Music. Air-conditioned. Fax: (021) 652021

---

**DINGLE Co Kerry** map 9

## ▲ Doyle's

4 John Street, Dingle
TRALEE (066) 51174 COST £24–£42

This is the more established of the two seafood restaurants in the town. Some reporters go for one, some for the other; some say this trades on its reputation, others that it is brilliant, and that's that. It's great for lobster, it's also full of character. But it can be busy and that may be the cause of the occasional hiccup. House wines are from £10.50.

CHEF: Stella Doyle PROPRIETORS: John and Stella Doyle OPEN: Mon to Sat, D only; 6 to 9 CLOSED: mid-Nov to mid-Mar MEALS: alc (main courses £10.50 to £16) SERVICE: 10%, card slips closed CARDS: Access, Diners, Visa DETAILS: 48 seats. Private parties: 12 main room. Vegetarian meals with prior notice. Children's helpings. No-smoking area. Wheelchair access (also WC). No music ACCOMMODATION: 8 rooms, all with bath/shower. Rooms for disabled. B&B £38 to £62. Deposit: £50. Children welcome. TV. Phone. Fax: (066) 51816

## Half Door

John Street, Dingle
TRALEE (066) 51600 COST £17–£47

One reporter was struck mightily by the warmth of the O'Connors' welcome, no matter how late her arrival for lunch at this second seafood restaurant in the town. The fresh fish is admirable, so is the atmosphere, and so have been the made-up dishes such as seafood pancake, baked crab in white wine, served on a croissant, and even the pavlova – 'the best ever'. House wine is £10.75.

CHEF: Denis O'Connor PROPRIETORS: Denis and Teresa O'Connor OPEN: Wed to Mon; 12.30 to 3, 6 to 10 CLOSED: Jan to Easter MEALS: alc (main courses L £4.50 to £20, D £11 to £20) SERVICE: not inc, card slips closed CARDS: Access, Amex, Diners, Visa DETAILS: 52 seats. Private parties: 30 main room. Vegetarian meals. Children's helpings 6 to 7.30pm. No children under 3 D. Wheelchair access (also WC). Air-conditioned

---

Card slips closed *in the details at the end of an entry indicates that the total on the slips of credit cards is closed when handed over for signature.*

Not inc *in the details at the end of an entry indicates that no service charge is made and any tipping is at the discretion of the customer.*

---

## DOUGLAS  Co Cork
map 9

# ▲ Lovetts

Churchyard Lane, Well Road, Douglas
CORK (021) 294909 and 362204
COST £22–£47

The ground floor of this pleasant late-Georgian house is home to the restaurant and bar. There is a short and rapidly changing fixed-price menu that leaves its options open for the fish which constitutes its first love, ceding perhaps some affection in winter months to game. While first courses may be adventurous, such as spicy pork meat in filo parcels with sweet pepper and onion confit, or black pudding mousse with mustard sauce, main dishes toe a more direct line of (good) meat and sauce, or, of course, good fish. House wine is £11.

CHEF: Margaret Lovett  PROPRIETORS: Dermod and Margaret Lovett  OPEN: Mon to Sat, exc Sat L; 12.15 to 2, 7 to 9.45  CLOSED: 24 to 26 Dec, Good Fri, bank hols  MEALS: alc (main courses £10.50 to £16). Set L £14.50, Set D £22  SERVICE: not inc, card slips closed  CARDS: Access, Amex, Diners, Visa  DETAILS: 35 seats. Private parties: 50 main room, 24 private room. Car park. Vegetarian meals. Healthy eating options. Children's helpings. Smart dress preferred. No-smoking area. No cigars/pipes in dining-room. Wheelchair access (also WC). Music  ACCOMMODATION: 18 rooms (in 9 self-catering houses), all with bath/shower. £80 per house. Deposit: 10%. Children welcome. Baby facilities. Garden. TV. Phone

## DUBLIN  Co Dublin
map 9

# Commons
NEW ENTRY

Newman House,
85–86 St Stephen's Green, Dublin 2
DUBLIN (01) 4752597 and 4780530
COST £25–£60

The restaurant is in one of the glorious houses around St Stephen's Green and is nearly as sub-fusc as the University College which was also born here. The prices, the setting and the style of service are all geared for somewhere extremely fancy indeed, and the food shares the same ideals. Dishes like oriental fish nage, or courgette flowers stuffed with sweetbreads, or baked hake with an almond crust and a red wine and bone-marrow sauce show an affection for modernity. The prices are very steep and an inspector was not sure that they were entirely merited by the performance. House wine is £11.

CHEF: Gerry Kirwan  PROPRIETOR: Michael Fitzgerald  OPEN: Mon to Sat, exc Sat L; 12.30 to 2.15, 7 to 10  CLOSED: bank hols  MEALS: alc (main courses £16.50 to £19). Set L £16, Set D £27.50  SERVICE: 15%  CARDS: Access, Amex, Diners, Visa  DETAILS: 60 seats. Private parties: 60 main room, 30 and 60 private rooms. Vegetarian meals. Children welcome. Smart dress preferred. No-smoking area. Music. Air-conditioned. Fax: (01) 4780551

Healthy eating options *in the details at the end of an entry signifies that a restaurant marks on its menu, in words and/or using symbols, low-fat dishes or other healthy eating choices.*

## Le Coq Hardi

35 Pembroke Road, Ballsbridge, Dublin 4
DUBLIN (01) 6689070 and 6684130                    COST £24–£73

This is a place with a very serious wine list and a mega-cellar. It is one of
Dublin's grand restaurants in the European tradition, exploring classic cooking
as well as classic drinking. The lunch menus perhaps take a more innovative
line than the grande cuisine traditions of formal dinner, offering more robust
dishes like black and white puddings, beef bourguignonne, fish-cakes, veal
sausage with Puy lentils, and wing of skate with black butter, ginger and soy.
The surroundings are equally impressive: the building is Georgian, and 'fine'
paintings, mirrors and brass point up the club-like atmosphere. House wines
start at £14.

CHEFS: John Howard and James O'Sullivan   PROPRIETORS: John and Catherine Howard
OPEN: Mon to Sat, exc Sat L; 12.30 to 3, 7 to 11   CLOSED: bank hols, 2 weeks Aug   MEALS:
alc (main courses £12.50 to £24). Set L £14.50 to £16, Set D £24.50   SERVICE: 12.5%, card
slips closed   CARDS: Access, Amex, Diners, Visa   DETAILS: 50 seats. Private parties: 50
main room, 4, 10 and 30 private rooms. Car park. Vegetarian meals. Children's helpings.
Smart dress preferred. No-smoking area. Music. Air-conditioned. Fax: (01) 6689887

## Eastern Tandoori

34–35 South William Street, Dublin 2
DUBLIN (01) 6710428 and 6710506                    COST £15–£53

This thoroughly Indian restaurant has two other branches in Dublin and
Blackrock. The setting is authentic, from the hand-made furniture to the
uniforms of the staff. The cooking is upper-crust conventional Indian, with
dishes from both north and south and from Bangladesh. Various special set
menus are available. House wine is £11.50.

CHEFS: Henry Paul, Oli Ullah, Iqbal Ahmed and B.H. Molon   PROPRIETORS: Mr and Mrs
Feroze Khan   OPEN: all week, exc Sun L; 12 to 2.30, 6 to 11.30   CLOSED: 25 Dec L, Good
Fri, bank hols L   MEALS: alc (main courses £7 to £13.50). Set L £7.50, Set D £14.95 to
£18.50. Minimum £9.50   SERVICE: 12.5%, card slips closed   CARDS: Access, Amex,
Diners, Visa   DETAILS: 64 seats. Private parties: 80 main room. Vegetarian meals.
Children's helpings. Smart dress preferred. No-smoking area. Wheelchair access. Music.
Air-conditioned.

## Les Frères Jacques ⁑✳

74 Dame Street, Dublin 2
DUBLIN (01) 6794555                    COST £21–£52

This long and narrow restaurant to one side of the Olympia Theatre rejoices in
its French character, yet manages interesting variations on classic dishes to
produce items like a rendezvous of seafood that contained an almost oriental
steamed pastry filled with prawn meat. The style in general, however, is light
and Gallic – modern French rather than that of grandmother. Seafood is worth
looking at, especially the lobsters from the tank or the oysters. House wine
is £10.50.

CHEF: Eric Tydgadt   PROPRIETORS: Jean-Jacques and Suzy Caillabet   OPEN: Mon to Sat, exc Sat L; 12.30 to 2.30, 7.30 to 10.30 (11 Fri and Sat)   MEALS: alc (main courses £15.50 to £17). Set L £13, Set D £20   SERVICE: 12.5%, card slips closed   CARDS: Access, Amex, Visa   DETAILS: 65 seats. Private parties: 40 main room, 12 and 40 private rooms. Vegetarian meals. Children's helpings. Smart dress preferred. No smoking in 1 dining-room. Music. Fax: (01) 6794725

## Kapriol

45 Lower Camden Street,
Dublin 2
DUBLIN (01) 4751235 and 2985496                                    COST £26–£56

This is an Italian restaurant of unforced charm where, in addition to a set of standards known to most trattoria-goers both sides of St George's Channel, there is an emphasis on dishes from the Veneto. Much of the pasta is home-made, tastes are pronounced, and the family-run atmosphere promotes jollity and well-being. House wine is £10.50 per carafe.

CHEF: Egidia Peruzzi   PROPRIETORS: Giuseppe and Egidia Peruzzi   OPEN: Mon to Sat, D only (L by arrangement for 10 or more); 7.30 to 12   MEALS: alc (main courses £8.50 to £18). Minimum £8.40   SERVICE: 12.5%   CARDS: Access, Amex, Diners, Visa   DETAILS: 30 seats. Private parties: 36 main room. Vegetarian meals. Children's helpings. Smart dress preferred. No-smoking area. Wheelchair access (1 step). Music

## Locks

1 Windsor Terrace,
Portobello, Dublin 8
DUBLIN (01) 543391 and 538352                                    COST £20–£53

The canalside setting has piquant charm, and the service is beguiling. The menu gives as much space to fish as to meat, and there is a widening of horizons in recipes such as monkfish and prawns with a Thai curry sauce, and duck with a pineapple sauce, served with coriander, chilli and grapefruit. Suckling pig with apple and horseradish makes an appearance here, as it has done this year on other Irish menus. House wines are from £9.50.

CHEF: Brian Buckley   PROPRIETOR: Claire Douglas   OPEN: Mon to Sat, exc Sat L; 12.30 to 2, 7.15 to 11   CLOSED: 1 week Christmas, bank hols   MEALS: alc (main courses £13 to £18). Set L £12.95, Set D £18.95   SERVICE: 12.5%   CARDS: Access, Amex, Diners, Visa DETAILS: 50 seats. Private parties: 50 main room, 35 private room. Vegetarian meals with prior notice. Children's helpings on request. Smart dress preferred. No cigars/pipes in dining-room. Wheelchair access. No music. Fax: (01) 538352

*The* Guide *is totally independent, accepts no free hospitality, and survives on the number of copies sold each year.*

*The text of entries is based on unsolicited reports sent in by readers, backed up by inspections conducted anonymously. The factual details under the text are from questionnaires the* Guide *sends to all restaurants that feature in the book.*

## Patrick Guilbaud

46 James Place, Dublin 2
DUBLIN (01) 6764192                                    COST £26–£66

This is another restaurant in the grand tradition, or *grande tradition* if you want
to be pedantic. It combines an illustrious menu with full houses and a fine
setting of hanging plants, good paintings and a vision of the kitchen in full
flow. Any reflections on the cost may be tempered by the knowledge that the
set lunch is excellent value. Guillaume Lebrun works with classics like the
cannette de Challans en deux services or lobster with a light orange sauce, and
with their modern derivatives in dishes such as foie gras with a compote of figs,
or rack of lamb with a parsley purée and a light, herbed salad dressed with a
pimento oil. House wines cost from £15.

CHEF: Guillaume Lebrun   PROPRIETOR: Patrick Guilbaud   OPEN: Tue to Sat; 12.30 to 2,
7.30 to 10.15   MEALS: alc (main courses £16 to £19). Set L £15.50, Set D £25. 'Menu
Surprise' £45   SERVICE: 15%   CARDS: Access, Amex, Diners, Visa   DETAILS: 70 seats.
Private parties: 80 main room, 30 private room. Car park. Vegetarian meals. Children
welcome. Smart dress preferred. No-smoking tables. Wheelchair access (2 steps). No music.
Fax: (01) 601546

---

**DUN LAOGHAIRE  Co Dublin**                          map 9

## Restaurant Na Mara

1 Harbour Road, Dun Laoghaire
DUBLIN (01) 2806767 and 2800509                        COST £20–£60

The building was part of the original railway terminal – would that all
suburban railway stations were built like this. A traveller on his way back to
England by ferry decided to stay in a bed and breakfast and spend the
difference between that and hotel fees on a slap-up dinner. He did not regret
the decision, though noting that prices were high and that some of the head
waiters were slightly more snooty than used to be the case. Eat fish – crab
mousse, seafood sausage, seafood chowder, fresh turbot, salmon en feuilleté
and a blanquette of seafood. Some of the ambitious dishes have a slight hiccup
in technique, but materials are very good, and the experience is really dandy.
House wine is £10.

CHEF: Derek Dunne   PROPRIETORS: Irish Rail Catering Services   OPEN: Mon to Sat; 12.30
to 2.30, 7 to 10.30   CLOSED: bank hols   MEALS: alc (main courses £11 to £22.50). Set L
£12.50 to £15.50, Set D £23   SERVICE: 15%, card slips closed   CARDS: Access, Amex,
Diners, Visa   DETAILS: 80 seats. Private parties: 80 main room, 35 private room. Vegetarian
meals. Children welcome. Smart dress preferred. No-smoking area. Wheelchair access
(2 steps; also WC). Music. Air-conditioned. Fax: (01) 2844649

---

*All letters to the* Guide *are acknowledged with an update on latest sales, closures,
chef changes and so on.*

*All entries in the* Guide *are rewritten every year, not least because restaurant standards
fluctuate. Don't trust an out-of-date* Guide.

---

**DURRUS  Co Cork**                                                    map 9

## *Blair's Cove House*

Durrus
BANTRY (027) 61127
1m out of Durrus on Barleycove to Goleen road          COST £34–£41

On the one hand there is the buffet laid out with various starters and, later, desserts; on the other – and in full view – there is the wood-fired grill on which main dishes such as rib of beef, confit of duck, chicken yakitori, and rack of lamb are produced. Then there is the fish. All in all, simplicity here is a virtue rewarded. Wines are from £12.

CHEFS/PROPRIETORS: Philippe and Sabine de Mey   OPEN: Tue to Sat, D only; 7.30 to 9.30
CLOSED: Nov to end Mar   MEALS: Set D £23   SERVICE: 10%, card slips closed   CARDS:
Access, Amex, Diners, Visa   DETAILS: 60 seats. Private parties: 35 main room. Car park.
Vegetarian meals with prior notice. Children's helpings. Smart dress preferred. Music

---

**GOREY  Co Wexford**                                                  map 9

## ▲ *Marlfield House*

Courtown Road, Gorey
GOREY (055) 21124                                            COST £24–£46

'The standard improves each year,' claims someone who has been 10 seasons on the trot. 'The bar meals are vastly superior to those available anywhere else', but the conservatory is for proper dining. The cooking is of the sort favoured by English country houses – light, quite elaborate, avoiding anything too obvious – and the service and setting are remarkable. So too is the wine list. House wine is £13.

CHEFS: Rose Brannock and Mary Bowe   PROPRIETORS: Mary and Ray Bowe   OPEN: all
week; 12.30 to 1.45, 7.15 to 9.30   MEALS: Set L £17.50, Set D £28. Bar meals L   SERVICE:
10%, card slips closed   CARDS: Access, Amex, Visa   DETAILS: 60 seats. Private parties: 60
main room, 25 private room. Car park. Vegetarian meals. Children's helpings. Smart dress
preferred. No cigars/pipes in dining-room. Wheelchair access (also WC). No music
ACCOMMODATION: 19 rooms, all with bath/shower. Rooms for disabled. B&B £70 to £365.
Deposit: £80. Children welcome. Baby facilities. Afternoon teas. Garden. Sauna. Tennis.
TV. Phone. Doors close at 11.30. Confirm by 5. Fax: (055) 21572

---

**HOWTH  Co Dublin**                                                   map 9

## *King Sitric*

East Pier, Howth
DUBLIN (01) 325235 and 326729                               COST £20–£56

A meal of mussels marinière, oysters, lobster, turbot and a bottle of Meursault revealed that this is a tip-top spot for fish as fresh as can be. The wine list is good too, with special reference to Chablis and white burgundies. The setting may surprise those who expect something more discreet, but when faced with such produce, taste in the mouth becomes paramount. House wine is £11.

CHEF: Aidan MacManus   PROPRIETORS: Aidan and Joan MacManus   OPEN: Mon to Sat (L May to Sept only); 12 to 3 (seafood and oyster bar), 6.30 to 11   CLOSED: first week Jan, Easter, bank hols   MEALS: alc (main courses L £6.50 to £15.50, D £12.50 to £18.50). Set D £22   SERVICE: not inc, card slips closed   CARDS: Access, Amex, Diners, Visa   DETAILS: 60 seats. Private parties: 45 main room, 22 private room. Vegetarian meals. Children's helpings. Smart dress preferred. No-smoking area. Wheelchair access (also WC). Music. Fax: (01) 392442

---

**KANTURK  Co Cork**                                                                                   map 9

## ▲ Assolas Country House

Kanturk
KANTURK (029) 50015
signposted from N72, NE of Kanturk                                              COST £33–£40

The term country house is for once absolutely accurate. Situation, sense of place, atmosphere and reality combine to a single creation that avoids as far as possible the taint of commercialism. Hazel Bourke cooks a dinner of studied simplicity with roast meats as the centrepiece. Reports have sometimes hinted that the attitude is not always matched by performance. The attitude towards service is admirable: 'We do not apply a service charge and tipping is not expected.' House wine is £13.

CHEF: Hazel Bourke   PROPRIETORS: the Bourke family   OPEN: all week, D only; 7 to 8.30 (8 Sun)   CLOSED: 1 Nov to 1 Apr   MEALS: Set D £26   SERVICE: card slips closed   CARDS: Access, Amex, Visa   DETAILS: 30 seats. Private parties: 34 main room, 18 private room. Car park. Vegetarian meals. Children's helpings. No children under 7 after 7pm. Smart dress preferred. No music   ACCOMMODATION: 9 rooms, all with bath/shower. B&B £50 to £140. Deposit: £100. Children welcome. Garden. Tennis. Fishing. Phone. Doors close at 11.30. Fax: (029) 50795

---

**KENMARE  Co Kerry**                                                                                  map 9

## ▲ Park Hotel

Kenmare
KILLARNEY (064) 41200                                                               COST £27–£67

This is one of the grandest of the new generation of Ireland's hotels, pursuing European excellence and elaboration in a magnificent setting, with antiques everywhere, smooth and hitch-free service, and every form of hotel diversion available. The food is similarly ornamental. One reader commented that he had feared it was all too fuddy-duddy – fit for 50-year-olds – but a visit with three under-10s had proved him wrong. The welcome was faultless, and the sheen of sophistication fell away to reveal unforced and natural hospitality. House wine is £14.95.

---

*Several sharp operators have tried to extort money from restaurateurs on the promise of an entry in a guidebook that has never appeared. The Good Food Guide makes no charge for inclusion and does not offer certificates of any kind.*

---

CHEF: Brian Cleere   PROPRIETOR: Francis Brennan   OPEN: all week; 1 to 1.45, 7 to 8.45
CLOSED: 1 Nov to 23 Dec, 2 Jan to 3 Apr   MEALS: alc (main courses £18 to £25). Set L
£17.50, Set D £35   SERVICE: not inc   CARDS: Access, Amex, Diners, Visa   DETAILS: 90
seats. Private parties: 60 main room, 45 private room. Car park. Vegetarian meals.
Children's helpings 6 to 6.30pm. No children under 8 D. Smart dress preferred. No cigars/
pipes in dining-room. Wheelchair access (also WC). Music   ACCOMMODATION: 50 rooms,
all with bath/shower. Rooms for disabled. Lift. B&B £123 to £252. Deposit: 50%. Children
welcome. Baby facilities. Afternoon teas. Garden. Tennis. Golf. TV. Phone. Doors close at
midnight. Confirm 3 weeks ahead. Fax: (064) 41402

## ▲ Sheen Falls Lodge, La Cascade

NEW ENTRY

Kenmare
KILLARNEY (064) 41600                                                    COST £28–£84

Dine in La Cascade, looking at the falls in this new hotel that one tourist called
'the best in Ireland and equal to any top-class hotel anywhere'. He was
impressed by the sense of permanence in an enterprise so young, by the well-
stocked cellar, and by the cooking that runs to Thai-style sweetcorn soup as
well as oysters from the west coast, to cardamom ice-cream with fruits scented
with allspice and mirabelle as well as Irish farmhouse cheeses. House wine
is £15.95.

CHEF: Fergus Moore   PROPRIETOR: Bent Hoyer   OPEN: all week, D only, and Sun L; 1 to 2,
7.30 to 9.30   CLOSED: 4 Jan to 4 Feb   MEALS: alc D (main courses £16.50 to £25.50). Set
Sun L £17.50, Set D £35   SERVICE: not inc, card slips closed   CARDS: Access, Amex,
Diners, Visa   DETAILS: 120 seats. Private parties: 120 main room, 24 private room. Car
park. Vegetarian meals. Children's helpings. Smart dress preferred. Wheelchair access (also
WC). Music. Air-conditioned   ACCOMMODATION: 40 rooms, all with bath/shower. Rooms
for disabled. Lift. B&B £155 to £220. Deposit: £100. Children welcome. Baby facilities.
Afternoon teas. Garden. Sauna. Tennis. Fishing. Snooker. TV. Phone. Fax: (064) 41386

## KILKENNY  Co Kilkenny                                                    map 9

## ▲ Lacken House

Dublin Road, Kilkenny
KILKENNY (056) 61085                                                    COST £28–£42

Eugene McSweeney remarks that 'Irish food is being redefined at this time,
and I'm proud to be part of it'. His short menu is product-led; the hospitality is
direct and individual; the cooking is direct and immediate, putting as little
gloss as possible on the daisy-fresh materials. House wine is £12.

CHEF: Eugene McSweeney   PROPRIETORS: Eugene and Breda McSweeney   OPEN: Tue to
Sat, D only; 7 to 9.30   CLOSED: 1 week Christmas   MEALS: alc (main courses £12 to £16.50).
Set D £22   SERVICE: net prices, card slips closed   CARDS: Access, Amex, Diners, Visa
DETAILS: 35 seats. Private parties: 45 main room, 20 private room. Car park. Vegetarian
meals. Children's helpings. Smart dress preferred. No-smoking area. No music
ACCOMMODATION: 8 rooms, all with bath/shower. B&B £25 to £56. Deposit: £10. Children
welcome. Baby facilities. Garden. TV. Phone. Doors close at midnight. Confirm by 6.
Fax: (056) 62435

## KINSALE  Co Cork

map 9

## ▲ *Blue Haven*  £

3 Pearse Street, Kinsale
CORK (021) 772209

COST £15–£44

Chef Stanley Matthews has been transferred from Oxford City to Kinsale
United and here he cooks in the restaurant part of this busy town-centre hotel.
The bar food 'was so good that we tarried in the town in order to try a meal in
the restaurant,' reported one couple who then found the restaurant was not
open on a November Sunday evening. It is clear that this place manages to
combine the plentiful seafood with some quite alert modern cooking. House
wine is £10.50.

CHEF: Stanley Matthews  PROPRIETORS: Brian and Anne Cronin  OPEN: all week; 12.30 to
3, 7 to 10.30  CLOSED: 25 Dec  MEALS: alc (main courses £8 to £16.5). Bar menu L and D
(main courses £4 to £10)  SERVICE: 10% restaurant, not inc bar, card slips closed  CARDS:
Access, Amex, Diners, Visa  DETAILS: restaurant 50 seats, bar 160 seats. 9 tables outside L.
Private parties: 50 main room. Vegetarian meals. Children's helpings. No-smoking area.
Wheelchair access (also WC). Music. Air-conditioned  ACCOMMODATION: 10 rooms, 7
with bath/shower. Rooms for disabled. B&B £25 to £84. Children welcome. Baby facilities.
Afternoon teas. TV. Phone. Doors close at 11.30. Confirm by 6. Fax: (021) 774268

## LETTERFRACK  Co Galway

map 9

## ▲ *Rosleague Manor*  ⅜✳

Letterfrack
CLIFDEN (095) 41101
on N59 to Westport, 7m from Clifden

COST £22–£41

Visitors to this isolated manor house with stunning views have noted
continuing quality in the supplies to the restaurant kitchen and a slight
updating of the style of cooking – and an improvement in puddings and
desserts. Fond memories have been rehearsed of fillet of beef with parsley
purée or, better, with shallots and cloves of garlic, or of lamb noisettes with a
mousse of sweetbreads, or calf's liver with orange and vermouth sauce. House
wine is £10.50.

CHEF: Nigel Rush  PROPRIETORS: Anne Foyle and Patrick Foyle  OPEN: all week; 1 to 2.30,
8 to 9.30 (10 Sat)  CLOSED: Nov to Easter  MEALS: alc (main courses £8 to £13). Set L £6
(2 courses) to £15, Set D £20 to £24  SERVICE: not inc, card slips closed  CARDS: Access,
Amex, Visa  DETAILS: 60 seats. Private parties: 9 main room. Car park. Vegetarian meals.
Children's helpings 6 to 8pm. Smart dress preferred. No smoking in dining-room.
Wheelchair access (2 steps). No music  ACCOMMODATION: 20 rooms, all with bath/
shower. Rooms for disabled. B&B £35 to £100. Deposit: £40. Children welcome. Pets by
arrangement (bedrooms only). Afternoon teas. Garden. Sauna. Tennis. Snooker. Phone.
Doors close at 11.30. Fax: (095) 41168

⅜✳ *indicates that smoking is either banned altogether or that a dining-room is maintained
for non-smokers. The symbol does not apply to restaurants that simply have no-smoking
areas.*

## MALLOW  Co Cork                                                        map 9

### ▲ *Longueville House* ⅜✳

Mallow
MALLOW (022) 47156
4m from Mallow on Killarney road                                    COST £22–£59

The stately house and glorious conservatory are well matched by an aristocratic
wine list and very sound cooking by William O'Callaghan, who trained among
the starred heads of Europe before setting up his ladle in the family pot.
Luxuries are deployed readily in dishes like ballottine of quail and foie gras,
and the estate is plundered for lamb, or maybe sucking pig to make the main
course memorable. Don't forget to leave space for dessert, be it a lemon
pudding baked to order or a hot feuilleté of garden rhubarb and apples.
House wine is £11.

CHEF: William O'Callaghan  PROPRIETORS: Michael and Jane O'Callaghan, and William
and Aisling O'Callaghan  OPEN: all week (L bookings only); 12.30 to 2, 7 to 9.15
CLOSED: 20 Dec to 15 March  MEALS: alc (main courses £13 to £18). Set L £14 to £16, Set D
£24 to £36  SERVICE: not inc, card slips closed  CARDS: Access, Amex, Diners, Visa
DETAILS: 50 seats. Private parties: 30 main room, 20 private room. Car park. Vegetarian
meals with prior notice. Children's helpings with prior notice. No children under 10.
Jacket and tie. No smoking in 1 dining-room. No music  ACCOMMODATION: 16 rooms,
all with bath/shower. B&B £40 to £150. No children under 10. Afternoon teas. Garden.
Fishing. Snooker. TV. Phone. Doors close at midnight. Confirm by 6. Fax: (022) 47459

## MAYNOOTH  Kildare                                                     map 9

### ▲ *Moyglare Manor* ⅜✳

Moyglare, Maynooth
DUBLIN (01) 6286351
on N4, 2km W of Maynooth                                            COST £18–£49

The tall manor house is replete with antiques and offers a menu that includes
dishes such as salmon wrapped in puff pastry with a white wine sauce, or quail
stuffed with chestnuts and a burgundy sauce, or poached monkfish with red
pepper sauce. The lines of inspiration, therefore, are Irish-French restaurant
cooking rather than any evangelical approach to Irish ethnicity. The wine list is
impressive, with clarets and Rhônes to match the best, and other worthwhile
sections. House wine is £11.95.

CHEF: Jim Cullinane  PROPRIETOR: Nora Devlin  OPEN: all week, exc Sat L; 12.30 to 2.30,
7 to 9  MEALS: alc (main courses £13.50 to £17.50). Set L £9.95 to £15.50, Set D £18.50
SERVICE: 12.5%, card slips closed  CARDS: Access, Amex, Diners, Visa  DETAILS: 80 seats.
Private parties: 50 main room, 50 and 50 private rooms. Car park. Vegetarian meals.
Children's helpings. No children under 12. Smart dress preferred. No smoking in 1 dining-
room. Wheelchair access (also WC). Music  ACCOMMODATION: 17 rooms, all with bath/
shower. Rooms for disabled. B&B £75 to £110. Deposit: £50. No children under 12.
Afternoon teas. Garden. Tennis. Phone. Doors close at 11.30. Confirm by 4. Fax:
(01) 6286351

**MIDLETON  Co Cork**                                                 map 9

## Farm Gate  £

The Coolbawn, Midleton
MIDLETON (021) 632771                                    COST £15–£35

A local correspondent urges that this restaurant, housed in a delicatessen, is 'a splendid example of what can be produced at most reasonable cost and puts to shame other restaurants in the county who charge the earth for inferior products'. People stress the value for money and the excellence of the raw materials, which are not overworked but interpreted in British style, when they eat dinner here on the two nights a week when the restaurant is functioning. Duck is often said to be their speciality. Eyes should not be closed to the surrounding paintings and sculpture. Lunches are light and modestly priced.

CHEFS: Máróg O'Brien and Angela Collins  PROPRIETOR: Máróg O'Brien  OPEN: Mon to Sat L, Fri and Sat D; 12 to 3.30, 7.30 to 9.45  MEALS: alc (main courses light L £4 to £9, D £9.50 to £14)  SERVICE: not inc  CARDS: Access, Visa  DETAILS: 60 seats. 5 tables outside. Private parties: 60 main room, 20 private room. Vegetarian meals. Children's helpings. No-smoking area. Wheelchair access (1 step; also unisex WC). Music. Air-conditioned

**MOYCULLEN  Co Galway**                                              map 9

## Drimcong House

Moycullen
GALWAY (091) 85115 and 85585                             COST £23–£42

'The Drimcong Food and Wine Experience' is a cookery course held in the winter months at this lakeland house not far from Galway. Gerry Galvin knows enough to teach an army of enthusiasts. His style borrows both from Irish tradition and modern habits. Reporters are struck by the boldness and immediacy of the food here. Vegetarian and children's menus are also available. House wine is £9.50.

CHEF: Gerry Galvin  PROPRIETORS: Gerry and Marie Galvin  OPEN: Tue to Sat, D only; 7 (6.30 summer) to 10.30  CLOSED: Christmas to Mar  MEALS: alc (main courses £10 to £16). Set D £14.95 to £17.95  SERVICE: 10%, card slips closed  CARDS: Access, Amex, Diners, Visa  DETAILS: 50 seats. Private parties: 50 main room, 10, 25 and 32 private rooms. Car park. Vegetarian meals. Children welcome. Wheelchair access (3 steps; also WC). Music

**NEWMARKET-ON-FERGUS  Co Clare**                                     map 9

## ▲ Dromoland Castle

Newmarket-on-Fergus
LIMERICK (061) 368144                                    COST £31–£73

This giant neo-Gothic pile was the seat of the clan O'Brien. Its refurbishment makes it glow almost as brightly as when it was first gilded and decorated in peacock colours and ornament. Today the clientele is drawn often from abroad, particularly the USA, who enjoy the golf as well as the grand-luxe setting. The cooking is resolutely international, now the responsiblity of a chef hot from the

Hotel de Paris in Monte-Carlo who has superimposed his style on the Irish location. There is a Taste of Ireland menu, which shows certain similarities to the international modern on the other pages. House wines are from £15.

CHEF: Jean-Baptiste Molinari   PROPRIETORS: Dromoland Castle Owners Association OPEN: all week; 12.30 to 2.15, 7 to 10   MEALS: alc (main courses £17 to £21). Set L £19, Set D £32 to £45   SERVICE: 15%, card slips closed   CARDS: Access, Amex, Diners, Visa DETAILS: 96 seats. Private parties: 20 main room, 20 to 450 in private rooms. Car park. Vegetarian meals. Children's L and tea. No children under 8 D. Jacket and tie D. No cigars/ pipes in dining-room. Wheelchair access (also WC). Music   ACCOMMODATION: 73 rooms, all with bath/shower. Rooms for disabled. B&B £204 to £418. Deposit: 1 night. Children welcome. Baby facilities. Afternoon teas. Garden. Tennis. Fishing. Golf. Snooker. TV. Phone. Doors close at 1am. Confirm 1 week ahead. Fax: (061) 363355

---

**NEWPORT  Co Mayo**                                                          map 9

## ▲ *Newport House* 🍴✳

Newport
NEWPORT (098) 41222                                             COST £32–£41

The house may not be large, but it is endlessly comfortable, has its own stretch of salmon water and thus attracts 'middle-aged salmon fishermen' like flies. The menu puts an emphasis on local produce, indeed vegetables and herbs are grown in the hotel's garden. The kitchen aims to enhance, rather than mask natural flavours. Kieran Thompson calls his wine list 'pretentious for a house of this size', but it would be more accurate to call it 'good'. House wine costs from £10.

CHEF: John Gavin   PROPRIETORS: Kieran and Thelma Thompson   OPEN: all week; 7 to 9.30 (light L by arrangement)   CLOSED: 30 Sept to 20 Mar   MEALS: Set D £27   SERVICE: net prices, card slips closed   CARDS: Access, Amex, Visa   DETAILS: 36 seats. Private parties: 12 main room. Car park. Vegetarian meals. Children's helpings on request. Smart dress preferred. No smoking in dining-room. Wheelchair access. No music ACCOMMODATION: 18 rooms, all with bath/shower. Rooms for disabled. B&B £44 to £116. Deposit: 10%. Children welcome. Baby facilities. Afternoon teas. Garden. Snooker. Phone. Fax: (098) 41613

---

**OUGHTERARD  Co Galway**                                                    map 9

## ▲ *Currarevagh House* 🍴✳

Oughterard, Connemara
GALWAY (091) 82312 and 82313
4 miles NW of Oughterard on Hill of
Doon Lakeshore road                                            COST £24–£30

This is really only a place for residents, although people who are not staying the night can arrange a booking if there is room. Currarevagh is very much a country house, set in 150 acres on Lough Corrib, with its 365 islands and lots of fishing. The style is simple yet fresh, the atmosphere one of a house party, though tables are separate in the dining-room. Breakfast will cast you back a few decades as well. House wines cost from £7.90.

CHEF: June Hodgson   PROPRIETORS: Harry and June Hodgson   OPEN: all week, D only; 8
CLOSED: Nov to Mar   MEALS: Set D £17.50   SERVICE: 10%   DETAILS: 30 seats. Private
parties: 10 main room. Car park. Vegetarian meals with prior notice. Children's helpings
with prior notice. Smart dress preferred. No smoking in dining-room. No music
ACCOMMODATION: 15 rooms, all with bath/shower. B&B £39 to £78. Deposit: £25. Children
by arrangement. Pets by arrangement. Garden. Tennis. Fishing. Doors close at midnight.
Confirm by noon. Fax: (091) 82731

---

## SHANAGARRY  Co Cork

map 9

## ▲ *Ballymaloe House* ⁛✳

Shanagarry, Midleton
CORK (021) 652531
2m outside Cloyne on Ballycotton road                                    COST £23–£46

News came into the *Guide* office of people being invited to observe an experiment in stone-age cookery at Ballymaloe – the home, farm and impressive hotel of the Allen family. This willingness to break new ground is a mark of the bubbling enthusiasm that still motivates every part of the family and team, making Ballymaloe one of the most infectiously engaging places to eat and stay at in the Republic. Somehow Myrtle Allen has succeeded in combining professionalism with an unforced and natural approach. This means that the place can cope with popularity and number without becoming sloppy, retaining a smile for all comers. The cooking also manages to combine the ambitions of a proper chef with the palatability of something produced over home fires. A remarkable place. House Duboeuf is £13.

CHEF: Myrtle Allen   PROPRIETORS: Ivan and Myrtle Allen   OPEN: all week; 1 to 1.30, 7.30
to 9.30   CLOSED: 24 to 26 Dec   MEALS: Set buffet L £14.50, Set D £28   SERVICE: not inc,
card slips closed   CARDS: Access, Amex, Diners, Visa   DETAILS: 120 seats. Private parties:
60 main room, 20 and 40 private rooms. Car park. Vegetarian meals. Children's helpings on
request. Children's tea 5.30pm. Jacket and tie D. No smoking in 1 dining-room. Wheelchair
access (1 step). No music   ACCOMMODATION: 30 rooms, all with bath/shower. Rooms for
disabled. B&B £56 to £98. Deposit: £30. Pets by arrangement. Garden. Swimming-pool.
Tennis. Golf. Phone. Doors close at midnight. Fax: (021) 652531

---

## WATERFORD  Co Waterford

map 9

## *Dwyers*

8 Mary Street, Waterford
WATERFORD (051) 77478 and 71183                                        COST £19–£36

The restaurant is strong on fish, and very strong on Muzak, reported one reader who found this former police barracks adequate though not as demonstrative of flavour as it might have been. The owners say the emphasis is on local produce served simply. House wines cost from £10.90.

CHEF: Martin Dwyer  PROPRIETORS: Martin Dwyer and Síle Dwyer  OPEN: Mon to Sat,
D only; 6 to 10  CLOSED: 1 week Christmas, 2 weeks July, bank hols  MEALS: alc (main
courses £10.50 to £12.50). Set D £12 (6 to 7.30pm)  SERVICE: not inc, card slips closed
CARDS: Access, Amex, Diners, Visa  DETAILS: 32 seats. Private parties: 24 main room, 10
private room. Vegetarian meals. Children's helpings on request. No-smoking area.
Wheelchair access (also WC). Music

## WEXFORD  Co Wexford                                           map 9

# Granary

Westgate, Wexford
WEXFORD (053) 23935                                         COST £25–£40

'Adventurous, painstaking, tasty and attractive' were epithets crammed into a
report on this converted grain store with museum displays to prove it. The
cooking is also 'cheerful', sometimes slightly missing the mark of flavour or
immediacy, but compensating for this with undimmed enthusiasm and
generosity. House wine is £9.75.

CHEFS: Mary Hatton and Vincent Whitmore  PROPRIETORS: Paddy and Mary Hatton
OPEN: Mon to Sat, D only (bank hol Sun and post-opera D during Wexford Festival);
6 to 10  CLOSED: 3 days Christmas  MEALS: alc (main courses £10 to £13). Set D £18.95
SERVICE: not inc  CARDS: Access, Amex, Diners, Visa  DETAILS: 45 seats. Private parties:
16 main room, 20 private room. Vegetarian meals. Healthy eating options. Children's
helpings 6 to 7. No-smoking area. Wheelchair access. Music

## WICKLOW  Co Wicklow                                          map 9

# ▲ Old Rectory ⅝✳

Wicklow Town
WICKLOW (0404) 67048                                        COST £32–£50

Paul Saunders' collection of firemen's helmets gives a certain angle to the
decoration of this Georgian rectory with a garden, where you choose from a
'floral menu' featuring edible flowers during the Wicklow Gardens Festival.
Linda Saunders is a talented and expressive cook who rarely lacks for
invention in dishes such as nasturtium flowers stuffed with Cashel blue cream
and cucumber or pansy pancakes. The house is small enough for visits to feel
like a house party, the jollity of which is maintained from start to finish by the
hosts. House wines are from £11.

CHEF: Linda Saunders  PROPRIETORS: Paul and Linda Saunders  OPEN: all week, D only;
8  CLOSED: 1 Nov to Easter  MEALS: alc (main courses £15 to £18). Set D £24  SERVICE:
not inc, card slips closed  CARDS: Access, Amex, Diners, Visa  DETAILS: 16 seats. Private
parties: 20 main room. Car park. Vegetarian meals. Children's helpings. Smart dress
preferred. No smoking in dining-room. Wheelchair access (3 steps). Music
ACCOMMODATION: 5 rooms, all with bath/shower. B&B £59 to £84. Deposit: £15. Children
welcome. Baby facilities. Garden. TV. Phone. Doors close at 1am. Confirm by 6. Fax:
(0404) 69181.

# Your rights in restaurants

This is the nasty bit of the *Guide*. No one wants to go out for a meal only to end up in court. No one wants to start a soufflé, then progress to a bout of fisticuffs with the waiting staff. That sort of behaviour ruins an appetite, and is certainly fatal to digestion. However, we should not be coy about money, or the goods and services that money buys. If restaurants manifestly fail to deliver, we should expect reasonable recompense. But it's not all one way. A restaurant has rights too. When you make a booking or you start to order food in a restaurant, you enter into a legally binding contract with the restaurant.

A restaurant is in the business of providing food to customers who consume it on the premises. It must therefore offer satisfactory food, safe practices of cooking and preparation, the equipment and hardware with which to eat it, and a place in which to eat it. The restaurant must also generally deliver things from the spot where they were prepared to the customer who is going to eat it. For food, read also wine and beverages. There is a lot of potential trouble in that short definition.

Satisfactory food means broadly that the dishes are as described on the menu and are prepared with reasonable skill and care. Food must be prepared in a way that does not endanger health and conforms to whatever standards are generally accepted. If a chef says that a bullet-hard potato is 'cooked', he may be expressing a new-wave theory about potatoes. It would be difficult to get him for endangering health, but you can easily claim the food has not been prepared properly.

Satisfactory equipment and furnishings for preparation and eating are rather easier to assess. This is not a matter of taste, more a question of potential injury. You can call on any number of experts to help determine whether these aspects of the restaurant's obligations conform to the law. If you can't abide eating in a blue room, and the owner has painted it cerulean – hard chips. That's just likes and dislikes.

Serving the food is integral to the restaurant's function. Bad service is often a cause of complaint, perhaps dispute. While the restaurant should always provide reasonable service, it is never easy to determine when it passes from adequate to bad. This depends on the type of restaurant and the price you are asked to pay for the meal. If the service is not of a reasonable standard you are entitled to withold a charge for service.

But hold hard! You, the customer, have to conform to certain standards as well. A customer must behave reasonably, and may have to dress in an acceptable fashion (the rules for this are made up by the management); he or she must turn up to a reserved table at the time agreed; he or she must pay the bill if the meal and service are satisfactory. The restaurateur does have rights and these are often ignored by the public at large who think that restaurants are there to serve them 24 hours a day every day of the year: 'What, you don't open on bank holiday?' was an expostulation often encountered when the Editor of this guide used to run a restaurant. 'No,' he would answer, 'you're on holiday, so are we.' A restaurant can open and close when it chooses. A restaurant can refuse admission to whomever it wishes, unless it be on grounds of gender, colour or race. A restaurant can charge what it likes, provided it tells you first. And finally, a restaurant may cook what it chooses, so long as it has a menu displaying details in the correct places. If it wants to have a 'potato day' it can do an utterly tuberous menu.

All these rights can collide with wishes; all these obligations can turn to trouble if not performed. A superstructure of regulation has arisen to set out rights. Hence criminal laws such as the Consumer Protection Act 1987 (to prevent misleading price indications), the Trades Descriptions Act 1968 (to ensure that statements in menus and other promotional literature are accurate), the Food Safety Act 1990 (covering hygiene in places where the public eats).

# A chapter of accidents

*Rodney and Samantha are celebrating their fifth wedding anniversary and decide the Pasty Diamond is the place at which to retie the knot. It has an entry in* The Good Food Guide; *their friends speak highly of the food; everyone, it seems, has a good time there. Samantha says she will book a table for Wednesday night and rings up accordingly.*

A booking made is a contract between two parties. The intending customer must turn up at the time agreed. Any delay (for instance, because the car breaks down), should be notified to the restaurant. It is within its rights to refuse to re-arrange the time, and to re-let the table. If Rodney and Samantha don't turn up at all, then they are liable for the restaurant's loss of profit (not the entire cost) if the table cannot be re-let. It sometimes happens that people arrive at the Pasty Diamond and George the manager has no record of their booking. This can be very embarrassing. If George cannot give them a table and they really did make that booking, they can claim recompense for travel expenses, possibly even for inconvenience. If the transaction was not in writing, it can be difficult to prove your case. Many's the restaurateur who has people lying through their teeth that they made a booking; just as many's the customer who has found his or her reservation lost when in fact the place is a shambles that could never keep a diary straight. So keep a record of when you telephoned and to whom you spoke.

*Actually, Rodney and Samantha make it on time and George's welcome is impeccable. Sitting on plump sofas with a glass of sherry each, they are handed the menu. Rodney's face falls. His friend Bill had assured him, '£30 a head'. But it is plain as a pikestaff that it's going to be more than that. 'Wonderful French food,' Samantha's workmate had told her. In fact, what she is reading is a menu full of Italian specialities.*

The proper display of menus and charges is a pool of clarity in the fog surrounding 'trouble at table'. A restaurant must show a menu at or near its entrance. The prices should include VAT. Any extra costs should be displayed in as equally prominent type as the rest of the contents. Hence any cover charge, charge for bread and butter or additional levy for service should be clearly mentioned. A Code of Practice under the Consumer Protection Act 1987 suggests various ways of including 'extras' as inclusive prices with the food. The Code is very influential when deciding if a restaurant has broken the law with misleading prices, but it is neither compulsory, nor has everyone heeded it. 'Discretionary' service charges, for instance, exist in many places even though the Code frowns on them. If the restaurant has conformed to regulations pertaining to display, there is nothing Rodney or Samantha can do about their misapprehensions. They can leave straight away but are breaking their contract. Otherwise, they are liable for what they should have found out about in the first place.

*Another problem is that Samantha is none too hungry. What she really fancies are two light first courses, not a substantial meat or fish main course. George the manager slides up to take the order and points out that the chef will not enjoy doing this. His attitude is 'I've bought all this food, now I'm going to sell it.' Actually, what he says is 'I fear there is a minimum charge, madam, you will have to order a main course.'*

A minimum charge must be stated prominently on the menu. However, no customer is under any obligation to eat either prescribed dishes or in a prescribed order so long as he or she is willing to pay what is requested. Chef must curb any urge to say what the customer should eat. Similarly, if a customer asks for his or her meat well done, chef has to do it – unless something is declared on the menu along the lines of 'our meat is cooked medium or rare'.

*That little problem over, George leaves the wine list to Samantha as he pops off to the kitchen. She chooses a Sancerre 1990. This comes from a maker other than the one who makes the wine she gets at the off-licence, for which she pays about £7. The Pasty Diamond has it on the list at £25. No sooner is the order taken than George leads Rodney and Samanatha to their table. He returns with the wine and offers it to Rodney for tasting – typical! Rodney passes it to*

*Samantha, who gives it a good nose and careful tasting. It's off! George rushes round as if his tail's on fire, slurps some out of a glass and firmly disagrees.*

The wine list is governed by the same rules as the menu. However, a restaurant need not display the whole list at its door, just a few representative entries. If the cellar is in chaos and 1989 is served instead of 1990, or the maker is different, then the customer is entitled to demand the correct vintage, or a replacement bottle (which doesn't mean it comes free). If you feel, as the customer, that £25 is much too much to pay, choose something cheaper. George can charge whatever he likes. Remember, however, that when you make these simplistic comparisons with supermarket prices the producer may make a considerable difference, so may the year, so may any variation between your benchmark and what is actually offered for sale. There is much difficulty about disputes over a wine's condition. How do you canvass opinion against George's denial? Do you approach other tables? You must hope to settle amicably. It is in George's interest to agree with you. The one sanction would be to pay for the wine under protest, put it in your shopping bag and take it to an accepted expert: a vivid illustration of how uneasily legal disputes sit with the experience of dining out.

*Our couple's dinner is fraught with disaster at every turn. Waits between courses are interminable, and the staff cannot even get the order right. When the waitress arrives with Samantha's monkfish and Rodney's medium-to-well-done entrecôte it turns out that George has told chef best end of lamb, not steak. Rodney sends the lamb back. The waitress doesn't know what to do. She leaves Samantha with her fish dish and rushes off to ask for a steak. By the time it appears, Samantha's fish and vegetables are cold. Starting to tremble every time she comes near the table, the waitress spills wine over Rodney's shirt. Already, the first courses have been fairly poor: the warm salad of calf's liver that Samantha had ordered was stone cold, and the liver like leather; she is convinced that Rodney's prawns were off-colour well before they were bathed in sauce.*

Rodney is getting a case for 'bad service', even though it may not have been the waitress' fault, but due entirely to delays and confusions in the kitchen. However, it's still bad service in the eyes of the customer. The cold salad when the menu said 'warm' is a case of misrepresentation; the shoe-like liver is a matter of opinion, clear though it may seem to the hapless eater. If the prawns really do seem off, it is suicidal to eat them. This is the time to complain. Don't let things slide just because you wish to avoid a fuss. Actually, disregarding the trouble with the wine, Rodney and Samantha wanted to have a good time. Unfortunately, if you want to get your rights, you may have to sacrifice enjoyment. The wrong order is another self-evident fault that has to be rectified for the customer to be satisfied. However, the waitress went about it in the wrong way.

People really do like to eat together. The only answer is to start the whole main course again. Spilling wine down Rodney's front will entitle him to be paid for dry cleaning or laundry, or even a replacement.

*It's pudding time and the couple order brown sugar meringues with bananas and cream. What turns up? Peaches instead of bananas. (Bananas were forgotten from the greengrocer's order.)*

A restaurant may not vary the menu without warning. Mistakes can and do happen, but they need to be admitted before, not after, the dish arrives at table. Our man can't insist on bananas if there are none, but he could refuse the dish and try something else.

*The consequences of real incompetence can sometimes be greater than restaurants realise. Rodney asks for the bill and notices that there is a 15 per cent service charge. He removes this from the total and suggests to George, the manager, that he should pay only a proportion of the bill. For George, this is the last straw. He reckons they have been fussing on purpose. He loses his temper and threatens to call the police. He also shows signs of becoming violent. So Rodney pays, but under protest. George won't take his cheque, and insists on cash.*

A restaurant can refuse payment by cheque. Similarly, restaurants only have to accept credit cards if they agree before you order, or there is a sign on the door indicating acceptance. Rodney is within his rights to deduct service, whether it be 'discretionary' or not, if he thinks the service has been truly bad. If service is included in the prices displayed on the menu, then he may deduct a proportion. He is also entitled to refuse payment for any dishes that are not what he ordered, or do not meet the description on the menu, or do not seem to be of a reasonable standard. However, if George cuts up rough, he may think it politic to leave the money. To protect any future action, he should make it clear that he is paying under protest – either write a note there and then, or write later (but not too late) and keep a copy. The police will not usually involve themselves in such disputes unless a breach of the peace, say, is in question. If George thinks the whole affair was engineered, for some reason, he may be right to insist on payment. It is not easy to enforce this, but if he decides not to pay, Rodney has to leave his name and address.

*When the couple are about to leave, Samantha's coat can't be found.*

A restaurant must take reasonable care of your belongings, yet most places have notices disclaiming liability. These are valid if your clothes are not left in a cloakroom and the notices are displayed prominently, and the loss is not caused by the restaurant's negligence. If there is no cloakroom, you need to ask staff to put your coat in a safe place, otherwise you may lose your right to compensation.

*During the night, Rodney falls ill. It's those prawns.*

Well, is it? Not every case of sickness after a meal in a restaurant is down to food poisoning. It may be drunkenness, unfamiliarity with rich cooking, coincidental illness. It is never easy to prove food poisoning, or to point with confidence at the source. The only answer is to see a doctor, who will identify the symptoms and their possible cause. Then you need to call the Environmental Health Officer so that he or she may visit the restaurant and perhaps identify the source of danger – either in kitchen practice or in unsound foodstuffs. The ideal is that you should have samples of the foods consumed, but that is another development of the surreal premise that every meal in a restaurant is a case for lawyers, not a reason for enjoyment.

Rodney's and Samantha's anniversary celebration has been disastrous. What could they do about it? In the beginning, they need to complain. No anger necessary, merely a quiet word about what they were expecting. Restaurants prefer that complaints come on the spot, not in letters three weeks later. If it gets beyond this, then tinkering with the bill is one way to solve the problem – small comfort though this usually gives. All parties should work towards compromise from the word go. When Rodney rushes home vowing legal action, he would have to go to a solicitor, or get advice free from a Citizens Advice Bureau, Law Centre or Consumer Advice Centre. The Trading Standards departments or the Environmental Health Officers of the local council may be able to help him without his having recourse to legal advice. Or he could join *Which? Personal Service*, which gives help to individuals – ring (0992) 587773 for details.

Rodney could then, probably, write to the restaurant itself, stating his reasons for complaint and claiming a refund of his bill. If no satisfactory result is achieved, then a solicitor's letter could be the next step, or action under the small claims procedure in the county court (sheriff court in Scotland) – which can be undertaken without a solicitor. The financial limits to small claims cases (£1,000 in England, Wales and Northern Ireland; £750 in Scotland) are rarely going to be exceeded in a dispute with a restaurant.

# General lists

## London restaurants by cuisine

### AFGHAN
Buzkash, SW15

### ARAB & MID-EASTERN
Adams Café, W12
Al Bustan, SW1
Al Hamra, W1
Efes Kebab House, W1
Iznik, N5
Laurent, NW2
Maroush/Maroush III, W2/W1
Tageen, WC2

### BRITISH
Bentley's, W1
Beth's, NW3
Brady's, SW18
Buchan's, SW11
Connaught, W1
Dorchester, W1
English Garden, SW3
Faulkner's, E8
Grahame's Seafare, W1
Greenhouse, W1
Ivy, WC2
Lanesborough, SW1
Quaglino's, SW1
Quality Chop House, EC1
Rules, WC2
Savoy Grill, WC2
Two Brothers, N3
Upper Street Fish Shop, N1
Wiltons, SW1

### CHINESE
Cheng-du, NW1
Dorchester, Oriental, W1
Four Seasons, W2
Fung Shing, WC2
Green Cottage, NW3
Imperial City, EC3

Jade Garden, W1
Mandarin Kitchen, W2
Mayflower, W1
Mr Kong, WC2
New Loon Fung, W1
New World, W1
Now & Zen, WC2
Panda Si Chuen, W1
Pearl, SW1
Poons, WC2
Royal China, W2
Vegetarian Cottage, NW3
Zen Central, W1

### FRENCH/BELGIAN
Alexandra, SW20
Les Associés, N8
Au Jardin des Gourmets, W1
L'Aventure, NW8
Belgo, NW1
Bibendum, SW3
Bistrot Bruno, W1
Brasserie Faubourg, SW8
Le Cadre, N8
Chez Nico at Ninety Park Lane, W1
La Dordogne, W4
L'Estaminet, WC2
Four Seasons Hotel, W1
Le Gavroche, W1
Gavvers, SW1
Lobster Pot, SE11
Lou Pescadou, SW5
Magno's Brasserie, WC2
Le Meridien Hotel, Oak Room, W1
Mon Plaisir, WC2
Le P'tit Normand, SW18
St James's Court Hotel, Auberge de Provence, SW1
Les Saveurs, W1

Le Suquet, SW3
La Tante Claire, SW3
La Truffe Noire, SE1

### GREEK
Daphne, NW1
Greek Valley, NW8
Kalamaras, W2

### HUNGARIAN
Gay Hussar, W1

### INDIAN
Bombay Brasserie, SW7
Gopal's of Soho, W1
Great Nepalese, NW1
Malabar, W8
Ragam, W1
Salloos, SW1

### INDIAN VEGETARIAN
Kastoori, SW17
Rani, N3
Sabras, NW10
Sree Krishna, SW17
Surya, NW6

### INDONESIAN/STRAITS
Melati, W1
Singapore Garden Restaurant, NW6

### ITALIAN
Alba, EC1
Al San Vincenzo, W2
Bertorelli's, WC2
Cantina del Ponte, SE1
Casale Franco, N1

Daphne's, SW3
Florians, N8
The Halkin, SW1
L'Incontro, SW1
Mezzaluna New York, WC2
Neal Street Restaurant,
  WC2
Olivo, SW1
Orso, WC2
Osteria Antica Bologna,
  SW11
Osteria Basilico, W11
Il Passetto, WC2
Pizzeria Castello, SE1
Pizzeria Condotti, W1
Regent Hotel, NW1
Riva, SW13
River Café, W6

## JAPANESE
Ajimura, WC2
Arisugawa, W1

Ikkyu, W1
Inaho, W2
Mitsukoshi, SW1
Miyama, W1
Neshiko, N1
Shogun, W1
Suntory, SW1
Wagamama, WC1
Wakaba, NW3

## KOREAN
Bu San, N7
Jin, W1

## MAURITIAN
Chez Liline, N4
La Gaulette, W1

## SPANISH
Albero & Grano, SW3

## SWEDISH
Anna's Place, N1

## THAI
Bahn Thai, W1
Bedlington Café, W4
Blue Elephant, SW6
Phuket, SW11
Sri Siam, W1
Sri Siam City, EC2
Thai Garden, E2
Thailand, SE14

# Restaurants-with-rooms (6 bedrooms or fewer)

## England
Abingdon, Thame Lane
  House
Barnstaple, Lynwood House
Barwick, Little Barwick
  House
Baslow, Fischer's at Baslow
  Hall
Birdlip, Kingshead House
Blandford Forum, La Belle
  Alliance
Bradfield Combust,
  Bradfield House
Bradford, Restaurant
  Nineteen
Bray, Waterside Inn
Brimfield, Poppies
Bruton, Claire de Lune
Calstock, Danescombe
  Valley Hotel
Carterway Heads, Manor
  House Inn
Cartmel, Uplands
Cleeve Hill, Redmond's
Croyde, Whiteleaf at Croyde
Dartmouth, Billy Budd's
Dedham, Fountain House
Dent, Stone Close
Diss, Salisbury House
Dorrington, Country
  Friends

Drewsteignton, Hunts Tor
  House
East Buckland, Lower Pitt
Erpingham, Ark
Eyton, Marsh
Glastonbury, No.3
Grasmere, White Moss
  House
Harwich, Pier at Harwich
Haworth, Weavers
Hayfield, Bridge End
Holdenby, Lynton House
Kintbury, Dundas Arms
Lavenham, Great House
Leck, Cobwebs
Long Crendon, Angel Inn
Lower Brailes, Feldon
  House
Lympstone, River House
Manchester, Moss Nook
Manchester, Woodlands
Mary Tavy, Stannary
Melksham, Toxique
Montacute, Milk House
Morston, Morston Hall
New Alresford, Hunters
Paulerspury, Vine House
Pool in Wharfedale, Pool
  Court
Poulton-le-Fylde, River
  House

Powerstock, Three
  Horseshoes
Redlynch, Langley Wood
Richmond, Howe Villa
Ripon, Old Deanery
Ross-on-Wye, Pheasants
Shepton Mallet, Bowlish
  House
Shipton Gorge, Innsacre
Spark Bridge, Bridgefield
  House
Staddlebridge, McCoy's
Staithes, Endeavour
Stoke-by-Nayland, Angel
  Inn
Storrington, Manleys
Thornton Cleveleys,
  Victorian House
Torquay, Mulberry Room
Ulverston, Bay Horse Inn
Waterhouses, Old Beams
Whimple, Woodhayes
Whitstable, Whitstable
  Oyster Fishery Co
Winchcombe, Wesley
  House
Winkleigh, London House
Wye, Wife of Bath
Wylam, Laburnum House

# Scotland

Alyth, Drumnacree House, Hotel
Auchencairn, Collin House
Ballater, Green Inn
Canonbie, Riverside Inn
Cullen, Bayview Hotel
Dunvegan, Harlosh House
Edinburgh, Witchery by the Castle
Haddington, Browns Hotel
Moffat, Well View
Muir of Ord, Dower House
St Margaret's Hope, The Creel

Swinton, Wheatsheaf Hotel
Walls, Burrastow House

# Wales

Brechfa, Tŷ Mawr
Clytha, Clytha Arms
Fishguard, Three Main Street
Harlech, Castle Cottage
Harlech, Cemlyn
Llansanffraid Glan Conwy, Old Rectory
Nantgaredig, Cwmtwrch Farmhouse Hotel

Newport (Dyfed), Cnapan
Talyllyn, Minffordd Hotel
Wolf's Castle, Stone Hall

# Northern Ireland

Bushmills, Auberge de Seneirl
Coleraine, Macduff's

# Republic of Ireland

Wicklow, Old Rectory

# The Good Food Club 1993

Many thanks to all the following people who contributed to this
year's *Guide* ...

Lady Aberdare
Dr A.H. Abrahams
Dr Sidney
 Abrahams
A.D. Abrams
J. Abramsky
Dr and Mrs F.
 Abramson
Sir John Acland
Ms Heather Acton
Martin Adams
Robert Adams
Peter Adcock
R.C.S. Adey
John Adrian
Sir David
 Ainsworth
Mrs M.D.
 Ainsworth
John R. Aird
R.C. Albert
Mrs S. Albinson
Ms Helen Alcock
N.S. Alcock
Hugh Aldersey-
 Williams
John and Judith
 Aldersey-
 Williams
Mrs M.D. Alderson
Stephen Aldis
Minda and Stanley
 Alexander
Jane and Alisdair
 Alexander-Orr
Mrs F. Alford
Dr and Mrs A.A.
 Alibhai
Ms Susan Allard
G.B. Allen
R.G. Allen
W.J. and D. Allen
Richard Allisette

Sir Anthony
 Alment
Lionel P. Altman
Mrs Dorothy
 Ambrose
T. Amos
R.S. Amsden
Mrs J.H. Anderson
John R. Anderson
Keith Anderson
M.H. Anderson
Mrs Margaret
 Anderson
R. Anderson
Mrs Gladys
 Andrews
Gwen and Peter
 Andrews
John Andrews
Lee Andrews
Miss S.M. Andrews
Steve Angel
Mr and Mrs Kurt
 Angelrath
Mark Antoine
Sean C. Appleton
Mrs John
 Arbuthnott
Mrs Cynthia Archer
Stephen and Ruth
 Archer
Jean Arnold
Hugo Arnold
Mrs Mary Arnold
E.A. Arthur
Brian Ashby
D.P. Ashew
Mrs E. Ashford
Maurice Ashley
G. Ashworth
Mrs J. Aslan
N. Astin
Gordon Astley
Mrs Hazel Astley

Mrs R. Aston
Reginald Atkin
Alison and Michael
 Atkinson
John Atkinson
Julian Atkinson
R.J.S. Atkinson
David Attwood
Frank and Doreen
 Attwood
Sir Bernard Audley
Mr and Mrs D.
 Auerbach
Mr and Mrs D.G.
 Austin
Mrs Heather Auton
Andrew Averill
Ms Kate Avery
J.L. Awty
Mrs Valerie Ayling
John and Sue
 Aylward
Mrs J. Baber
Mr and Mrs V. Bach
F. Bacon
Michael G. Bader
John and Edna Baer
Mr and Mrs R.
 Baggallay
Jane and Martin
 Bailey
Mrs Joyce Bailey
Mary Bailey
Ian C. Baillie
Steve Bainbridge
Alan and Margot
 Baker
Mrs E. Baker
John Baker
Mrs Julia Baker
M.G. Baker
R.J. Baker
Mr and Mrs I.
 Balaam

Dr I. Balfour
Ms Amanda Ball
Mrs M. Ball
Robin Ballance
Kate Banfield
Ms Diana Bannister
K. Barber
H.F.H. Barclay
Carl Barker
Helen Barker
Mrs J.A. Barker
John A. Barker
Tim Barlow
Antony Barnes
C.A. Barnes
David Barnes
Dr R.D. Barnes
H.A. Barraclough
Geoff Barratt
Mrs P. Barratt
Lionel Barrow
Mrs B.J. Barry
Matthew Bartlett
F.E. Bartholomew
Mrs R.A. Bartlett
W.J. Bartlett
Mrs E.A. Barwood
M.G. Batchelor
John and Beryl
 Bateman
Timothy Battle
Mrs P.A.V. Batts
Dr John R. Batty
D.N. Baty
K. Baxter
Conrad Bayliss
S. Bazley
Tony and Theo
 Beamish
Andrew C. Bean
Ms Sarah Beattie
Mrs C.E. Beaumont
Stephen Beaumont
F.R. Beckett

H.H. Beckingsale
Mrs L. Beckley
M.J. Beech
Dr W.E. Beer
Pauline Beever
Mrs J. Beggs
C. Bell
Gail Bell
Ken Bell
Mrs D. Bellerby
Mrs P. Bellfield
Ronald Benjamin
Dr A.N. Bennett
Hilary Bennett
Ian Bennett
Mrs N.P. Bennett
Mrs P.A. Bennett
R.K. Bennett
Stephen Bennion
Suzanne and Philip
  Bentley
M.F.M. Benton
William Bentsen
Stephen Beresford
Mr and Mrs H.I.
  Berkeley
J.L. Bernstein
Richard Bernstein
David Berry
Mr and Mrs T.R.
  Berry
Ms Trish Bertram
W.J. Best
G. Betts
Dr D.R. Bickerton
Mrs B. Bicknell
J.D. Bidwell
Mike Bieber
G.W.R. Biggs
Miss A. Billings
E.R. Birch
Sir Roger Birch
Michael J. Bird
Benedict Birnberg
James K. Bishop
Julian Bishop
Mrs M.B. Bisser
Andy Black
Dr D. Black
Mrs M.S. Black
Mrs Sue Black
A.W. Blackburn
Mr and Mrs B.J.
  Blackburn
Mrs V. Blackburn
Mr and Mrs C.
  Blackman
J.R. Blain
Diana Blake
Fiona M. Blake
R.W. Blamey
Marilyn Blank

Mrs J.A. Blanks
Mrs Barbara
  Blatchley
Edward Blincoe
Mr and Mrs S. Bliss
F.N. Bloor
Mrs Marina
  Bluemel
Dr S.M. Blunden
K.W. Bogle
A.M. Bolton
C.T. Bolton
Roy Bond
John R. Bone
Mia Bone
Ms Vanessa Bone
George J. Bonwick
Catherine Boon
Mr and Mrs D.J.
  Booth
Dr P.M.J. Borland
John W. Borland
Mrs Borthwick
John W.
  Bosomworth
Ms Gillian Bouttell
G.H. Bowden
Paul Bowden
Richard Bowden
A.J. Bowen
W.M. Bowen
Eva Bower
Mr and Mrs D.
  Bowman
L. Box
J.A. Boyd-Smith
Prof Roy Boyne
J. Brace
J.L. Bracey
Miss D. Bradfield
Alan Bradley
C.J. Bradley
Drs David and Elsa
  Bradshaw
Mr and Mrs J.G.
  Bradshaw
Peter Bradshaw
Dr and Mrs John
  Braithwaite
J.L. Bramwell
Anthony Brandon-
  Bravo
Nial Brannigan
Nicholas Bray
Maurice Bready
Mr and Mrs G.W.
  Breeze
Mr and Mrs R.S.B.
  Brewer
A. Brian
Ms Clare L.
  Bridgman

J.B. Brierley
A.V. Briers
Mrs J. Briggs
P. and A. Briggs
M. Brightwell
W.J.M. Brightwell
Nicholas
  Brimblecombe
S. Brindle
Mr and Mrs D.J.
  Brine
K.H. Brining
B.J. Britton
Mona and Julian
  Britton
Philip Broadley
P.J. Brocklehurst
Roy Y. Bromell
C. and E. Brooke
Mr and Mrs John
  Brookes
Prof M.C.T. Brookes
R.C.P. Brookhouse
Harry Brooks
Mrs Marian Brooks
Dr Andrew Brown
Chris Brown
Colin and Shirley
  Brown
David P. Brown
Dr and Mrs D.G.
  Brown
Graham Brown
Peter B. Brown
R.V. Brown
Rachel Brown
Rev Richard Brown
W.M. Brown
Dr William N.
  Brown
Mr and Mrs L.
  Bruck
Mrs J. Brushfield
David E.H. Bryan
Mrs Karen Bryan
M. Bryan
Mrs Rachel Bryan
Ian Bryant
John and Lynda
  Bryant
Mrs K. Bryden
R.F. Bryn-Davies
P.A. Buckley
Mrs A.E. Budd
John Bugler
Mrs Daphne
  Bullock
D.J. Bunter
R. Buresh
B.P. Burgess
Dr J.G. Burgess
Bob Burke

William A. Burkett
Paul R. Burn
R.D. Burnell
A.S. Burns
M.H. Burr
Mrs O.G. Burrell
S.K. Burrell
Ernest Burrington
Timothy Burt
Chris Burton
Peter Burton
Khan Busby
Rev G.R. Bush
A. Bushell
Mrs K.B. Bushen
Lindsay Butcher
Paul and Christine
  Butler
P.J. Butler
S. Butler-Madden
D. Butterfield
Joe Bux
R.C. Buyers
Amanda
  Cadwallader
Prof Robert Cahn
Brian and June
  Cairns
Mrs M.W. Calderon
Capt D.S. Caldwell
J. Camb
Avis Caminez
David Campbell
Simon Campbell-
  Smith
Dr T.J. Cantor
Ms Julia Carling
Mr and Mrs Carlisle
Richard Carpenter
J. Carr
P.A. Carraro
Mrs J. Carrera
E. Carte
Ms Alyson Carter
N. Carter
P.E. Carter
Ms Corinne Cartier
Mrs S. Cartlidge
David Cartwright
R. Carty
H.J. Case
John B. Cass
Mr Cassidy
C.J. Castledine
Mrs P. Cate
R.E. Catlow
Dr R.A. Cavanagh
Lyn Cecil
George C. Cernoch
P.D. Cetti
Sir Bernard
  Chacksfield

713

Miss E.J. Chadwick
Peter Chadwick
Ms Veronica
  Chamberlain
Mrs Liz Chambers
Robert Chandler
Mrs Kathleen
  Chaplin
G.B. Chapman
Mungo Chapman
W.M. Chapman
J.M. Chappell
D.T. Chard
S. Charles
Michael J.
  Charlesworth
Jane Charlton
S. Chatha
Mrs Y.K. Cheng
W.J. Chesneau
Brian J. Chignell
Miss B.
  Chmurzynska
Mr and Mrs Andy
  Christie
Mrs S.G. Christie
P.H. Chronnell
Norman Civval
Ms Jane Clacy
Miss M.E. Clamp
Lesley Clare
Rev Lionel Clare
B.M. Clark
Ms Isabell Clark
Mrs Mary Clark
Dr R.M. Clark
Ms D. Clarke
E. and A. Clarke
Mr and Mrs V.
  Clarke
Tim Claxton
Hilary Claydon
Henry Clayton
R.S. Clayton
M. Clements
W.C. Clements
Kenneth Cleveland
Jennifer Clickner
P. Clifford
S.P. Clipston
Mr P.J. Clymer
Mr and Mrs K.
  Coates-Jones
M. Cobbold
Adam Cochrane
Mrs A. Cock
Robert Cockcroft
Ms T. Cockroft
D.J. Cocksedge
W.F. Coghill
S. Cohen
Prof V. Cohen

Dr J.R. Coke
Mrs Barbara M.
  Cole
Mrs Elizabeth Cole
Mr and Mrs. G.G.
  Coleman
Mrs D. Coles
Simon Coles
N.P. Coley
W. Colfer
J.L. and M.A.
  Collen
Janet Collett
Mr and Mrs
  Collings
Paul and Ann
  Collins
Susie and Paul
  Collins
Peter Collis
M. Colton
Graham Comfort
Ms S.G. Comins
Michael Comninos
P. Conneely
Sean Connolly
Peter Constable
J.P.F. Cooke
M.W.H. Cooksley
Mrs P. Coolahan
D.R. Cooper
Mrs J.M. Cooper
P.J. Cooper
Dr and Mrs J.C.W.
  Cope
J.P. Corbett
R.C. Corbett
Ron Corbett
J. Corbluth
M.G. Corkill
Mrs Julia
  Cornborough
Mrs C. Cornes
Mrs Hannah Cotton
John Cotton
Mrs Rosemary
  Counsell
I.D. Courtnage
N.A. Coussmaker
Archie Coutts
T. Simon Couzens
Ms Janet Coward
Mr and Mrs A.
  Cowell
J.L. Cox
M.J. Cox
Jim Craddock
Mrs C.E. Cramb
David Cramb
Mr and Mrs Ian
  Crammond

Mr and Mrs S.
  Crampton
Mr and Mrs Peter
  Crane
Ms Eleanor
  Cranmer
J.D. Cranston
T.J. Craven
C.W.D. Creasey
Andrew M.
  Critchley
Dr G.S. Crockett
Mrs A.C. Croft
Ron Crompton
T.E. Crompton
Irene Cromwell
Ms Helen
  Crookston
Mrs Erica Cropley
J.D. Crosland
John and Judy
  Cross
Mrs Mary Cross
Rodney Cross
Barbara Crossley
Mrs J.B. Crowe
John E. Crowe
T. Crowther
Mr and Mrs A.
  Cruickshank
Dr S.N. Crutchley
Ms Joanna Culver
James Cumming
Frank Cummins
J.M. Cummins
Dr and Mrs P N
  Cunliffe
G.L. Cunningham
Steve Currid
John Curtis
Dr John Cuthbert
Mrs E. Cutler
Robert Dale
L. Dalzell-Piper
T.D. Dampney
Mrs Joseph K. Dana
M. Dance
Dr V.J. Daniel
Peter Danny
Dr Jean Dar
L. and P. Darby
David V. Davey
Kate Davey
Mr and Mrs P.
  Davey
Ms Kate Davidson
W.H. Davidson
A.G. Davies
D.C.G. Davies
Hon Edward D.G.
  Davies
J. Davies

Mrs June Davies
Mrs M. Davies
Mrs Molly Davies
Mrs N.J. Davies
P.E. Davies
Peter Davies
Mrs S. Davies
Andrew Davis
Roger and Jan
  Davis
Mrs S.C. Davis
T.R. Davis
Dr William Davison
R.M. Davison
Dr and Mrs R.P.R.
  Dawber
K. Dawson
Mr and Mrs Keith
  Dawson
Mrs June Day
Mr and Mrs Hans
  de Vos
Dr M.A. de Vries
Nigel Deacon
N.C. Dee
Mr and Mrs A.E.
  Demby
Mr and Mrs
  Jonathan Denby
C. Devereux
Richard Devey
Louise Devine
I.C. Dewey
R.E. Dickie
Mrs J.C. Dickinson
Ms Mertel
  Dickinson
Mrs C.M. Dickson
K.G. Dietz
Mrs Diane Dillon
A. A. Dines
Colin Divall
M. and Mrs A.
  Dixon
George Dobbie
Colin Donald
Dr R.G. Donald
Ms Jayne Donnelly
G.M. Doobie
Mrs J.A. Dore-
  Berman
D.H. Dossett
Gabrielle Downes
Mrs J.M. Downes
S.N. Downie
Aly Dracup
John A. Drew
Garth Drinkwater
Jeff Driver
F.B. Drummond
Richard Duggleby
A. Duncan

N.B. Duncan
David H. Durbin
Denis Durno
Mrs S.F. Durrell-Walsh
Ms Clare Durward
Dr and Mrs Robert F. Duvall
Mark Dyer
Mrs Judith Earl
Colin Eastaugh
Don Easton
Mr and Mrs J.A. Easton
Dr and Mrs L.M. Easton
Mr and Mrs K. Eckett
Dr S. Eden
Helen Edge
Miss E. Edgell
B.J.S. Edmond
J.C. Edmondson
Mrs Edwards
Anton Edwards
Caroline Edwards
D.E. Edwards
Ms Kathryn Edwards
M.J. Edwards
Mark Edwards
Dr R. Edwards
Dr John Eggleton
Dr and Mrs P.D. Elderfield
Steven V. Elief
Joan B. Elkins
C.M. Elland
Ms C.J. Elliot
George Elliott
J. Elliott
L.C. Elliott
Mrs A. Ellis
Arthur G. Ellis
A.N. Ellis
A.R.M. Ellis
D.R. Ellis
Gerry and Joy Ellis
Martin Ellis
Mrs N.M. Ellis
R. Ellis
D.C. Elmer
J. Elmes
C.W. Elston
Ms Jan Elston
Nicholas and Victoria Elton
Prof and Mrs C.E.Engel
Matthew Engel
Robert Entwistle
David Erskine

Mrs H. Etherington
Mr and Mrs J. Ette
J.S. Evans
Ramon G. Evans
Mrs S. Evans
David R. Everett
J.A. Everson
Mrs J. Every
Michael Fabricant
Jed Falby
Mrs A. Fardell
Ms Karen Farley
M. Farmer
Capt C.A. Farquharson
Mr R.A. Farrand
Paul Farrant
Ms Ann Farrow
Ms Helen Faulkner
Mrs T.J. Faulkner
R. Fausset
Dr D. Fawkner-Corbett
Elizabeth Fay
Simon Feast
David G. Felce
K.L. Fenner
N.E.H. Ferguson
M.C. Ferrier
L. Ferrone
S.J. Few
Ms H. Fielding
George Filbey
Dr N. Finer
Robert A. Fiorentino
Mr and Mrs Fisher
Chris Fisher
J.E. Fisher
Mr and Mrs J.R. Fisher
Mr and Mrs J. Fitton
Dr P.J. Flanagan
T.C. Flanagan
Petter Flatter
F.B. Fleet
J.G. Fleming
Clare Fletcher
Dr R.F. Fletcher
Ron Fletcher
Paul Flintoff
Andrew Flower
Eric Foex
Mrs P.M. Foll
David Foot
M.R.D. Foot
R.J. Foote
P. Forbes
Miss B.I. Forbes-Adam
G. Ford

P.J. Forrest
Prof J.M. Forsythe
Mr and Mrs Roger Forward
Mrs Alethea Foster
J.M. Foster
John P. Foster
Mrs Colwyn Foulkes
Miss Nicola Foulston
Mrs G. Fowler
R.J.N. Fowler
Mrs V. Fowler
Miss J.A. Fox
Mr and Mrs S. Fox
J.B. Foxall
Mrs Dorothy Foy
Mohammed Foysol
Derek and Marilyn Frampton
Dr Norman France
Mr Francis
Richard Francis
Christopher and Lisa Francis-Lang
G.V. Frank-Keyes
P.J. Frankis
Mrs Pauline Frankland
H.C. Franks
Dr Fraser
C. Fraser
Mr and Mrs C. Fraser
Donald H. Fraser
R.H. Fraval
G.M. Freakes
Elaine Freeman
B. Freemantle
Robert Freidus
Mr and Mrs P.J. Frogley
H. and D.T. Frontin
Dr P.K.D. Froome
Dr R. Fry
Mr and Mrs D. Fryer
Mrs M.J. Fuller
Lt Col S.J. Furness
Dr and Mrs R. Gadsby
John Gagg
Mrs Wenna Galbraith
Mrs Ruth Gale
Ashleigh Gallagher
Mrs M.P. Gardner
Dr S. Gardner
Stephen Garford
S. Garner
Jenny Garrett

Michael H. Garrison
Miss M. Garrod
C.E. Garside
Robert Garstang
Bernard Garston
Mrs P.J. Garvey
Dr R.A.P. Gaubert
Mr and Mrs D.M. Gavin
J. Gazdak
Mrs D. Genders
Mr and Mrs Steven George
Anthea and David Gerrie
John Getty
John Gibbins
Mr and Mrs Austin Gibbons
C.F. Gibbs
P. Gibbs
Paul S. Gibbs
Richard J. Gibson
D. Gifford
Mr and Mrs N. Gilbert
R. Gilchrist
Mrs L. Giles
Phillip Gill
Mr and Mrs D.M. Gillard
Mr and Mrs Peter Gillett
Mr and Mrs C.D.D. Gilmour
Mrs Helen Gilmour
Wg Cdr and Mrs J.I. Gilson
Dr Alan Gilston
Ms Sarah Girling
David Gitton
P.J. Glenister
John Glover
D. and Mrs S. Glover
Mrs Joy Glover
Graham C. Goddard
Mr and Mrs N.R.B. Godden
Mr and Mrs C. Godfrey
Mrs J. Godfrey
Mrs Lois Godfrey
N. and P.A. Godley
M. Goffsmill
Ms. Maria Goldberg
Joy and Raymond Goldman
Mrs V.S. Goldston
B.J. Goldthorpe
J.D. Gomm
Tom Gondris

Norman Goodchild
D. Goodger
Dr P.D. Goodstein
Mrs B. Gordon
David Gordon
D.V. Gordon
Mrs Gloria Gordon
John Gordon
Mr and Mrs J.W. Gordon-Smith
Dr J.R. Gosden
N.S. Goss
Mrs J.B. Gould
L. Gould
S. Gould
Mrs Rita Goy
Margaret Grady
Mrs Graham
A. Graham
Hugh Graham
Mrs O.E. Granger
Mr and Mrs P.J. Granger
Brian Grant
Ian G. Grant
Mr and Mrs L.J. Grant
R.L. Grant
R.S. Grant
Mr and Mrs B. Gray
J.S. Gray
Michael Gray
Miss Green
A. Green
Alan Green
Carey and Kier Green
Hylton Green
C. Greenhow
J. Greenslade
N.D.A. Greenstone
Dr A.J. Greenwood
Mr and Mrs K. Greenwood
Sally Greenwood
Prof K.J. Gregory
Mr and Mrs J. Grenfell
R.F. Grieve
E.J. Griew
E. Griffin
Edward F. Griffin
Geoffrey and Barbara Griffin
J.R. Griffin
Mrs S.A. Griffin
Mrs J. Griffiths
Harry Griffiths
Moira Griffiths
Christine A. Grimes
J.W. Grimes
Don Grisbrook

John Grossman
Oscar Grut
Mrs S. Gueuning
Sally Gugen
Alexander Gunning
Rosalind Gunning
Alistair Guyan
J.D. Hackett
Tove Haga
M.E. Hague
Mrs P.E.M. Halford
C.J. Hall
I. Hall
Mr and Mrs P.J. Hall
W.O. Hall
A.R. Hallett
W.J. Hallett
Peter and Pamela Hallinan
Jack D. Halliwall
Mr and Mrs G. Hallsworth
Tom Halsall
S.H. Hambrook
Mr and Mrs M. Hambury
A. Hamilton
J.R.L. Hamilton
L. Hamilton
Mrs Meg Hamilton
G.B.T. Hammond
D.H.C. Hampshire
Mr and Mrs Nicholas Hancock
P.L. Hands
Philip J. Hanna
B. Hannam
Mrs G. Hansford
Mr and Mrs Hanson
Ms Yvonne Hanson
R. Harding
P.L. Hardy
Mrs Harkes
A. Harley
R. Harper
Mr and Mrs Derek Harpur
R.W. Harries
Alan and Sue Harris
Clifford Harris
Mrs H.M. Harris
Katy Harris
Naomi Harris
Noel and Janet Harris
Raymond Harris
F.T. and M.G. Harrison
G.W. Harrison
Paul B. Harriss

Mr and Mrs D.J. Harrold
C.T. Hart
Miss W. Hart
Donald Hartog
V. Hartwell
Mr and Mrs C. Harvey
Dr D. Harvey
Mr and Mrs J. Harvey
Dr Kenneth Harvey
Dr Peter Harvey
Mrs Jan Harvie-Clark
C.R. Haskins
J.R. Haslam
Mr Hasson
Ms Suzannah Hastie
S.J.D. Hatch
Mr and Mrs Hatton
Marc Hauer
Count Richard Haugwitz-Reventlow
Frank Hawkins
R.G.P. Hawkins
A.E. Haynes
Philip A. Haynes
E.F. Hayward
Ms Kathryn Hayward
R.K. Haywood
Roger Heading
S.E. Hearne
Rev N.C. Heavisides
Mrs Sue Hedge
Michael Heeley
Ms Julie Heetas
A.D. Hein
J.F. Hembury
Roger Hemingway
Alexandra Henderson
Ms Gillian Henderson
J.R. Henderson
T. Hennessy
N.F. Henshaw
Cyril Hepplewhite
D. Herbert
Mrs G.K. Herbert
Michael Herbert
Philip Herlihy
J. Hermans
Ms Eleanor Hermon
Dr A. Herxheimer
Mrs V. Heseltine
John Heskell
Gad Heuman

Malcolm C. Hibberd
Mr and Mrs T.J.O. Hickey
Leon Hickman
Ms M.M. Hicks
Michael Higgins
S.C. Higgs
J.M.M. Hill
Ms Joanna Hill
Wendy Hillary
Mr and Mrs Hillier
Dr Janet Hillier
Mr and Mrs D.W. Hills
J. Hills
Janet Hilton
Ronald and Maureen Hinde
Dr K.L. Hindle
Mr and Mrs Hird
Mrs B.M. Hirst
Elizabeth and Michael Hjort
Dr Stephen Hoare
Manosi J.A. and M. Hoban
Dr P.R. Hobson
Peter Hockley
Mrs J.E. Hodgson
Stephen G. Hodgson
F. Hodkinson
Dr Michael Hoey
Mrs U. Hofheinz
Mrs S.D. Hogg
Robin Hoggard
David Holbrook
Mary B.T. Holden
Mrs P. Holder
A.M. Holland
Mrs J.K. Holland
G. Hollas
Mrs A.E. Hollingworth
David J. Holloway
Paul G. Holloway
Mrs C.M. Holmes
Mr and Mrs R. Holmes
Dr Roger E. Homan
S.H. Honeyman
Ruth and David Honour
Ms J.A. Hood
R.A. Hood
R. Hooper
Capt John D. Hope
Sally and Tony Hope
Mrs B.M. Hopewell
Mrs M. Horgan

R.T. Horn
Giovanna Horowitz
Robert Horsford
Mrs C.L. Horsley
Mr and Mrs M.
  Horton Ledger
Dr Keith Hotten
Mrs Norma L.
  Hough
Peter Houlton-
  Jones
Mr and Mrs B.
  House
Mrs K. Houslay
Mr Howard
G.R.L. Howard
R. Howard
Mrs S.J. Howard
Michael Howarth
J.N. Howe
Dr D. and Mrs
  Howell
Geoffrey Howell
Mr and Mrs H.
  Howell
R.W.F. Howell
R. Howgego
Mrs Dianne
  Howlett
Dr Trevor A.
  Howlett
Robert Hubble
David G.T. Hudd
S. Huddin
Mr and Mrs. G.A.
  Hudson
Joan and Peter
  Hudson
Max and Cordelia
  Hudson
C. Hughes
Mr and Mrs J.R.
  Hughes
Mrs Joyce Hughes
Dr M.A. Hughes
Mrs Susan Hughes
N. and M. Hull
David Humphrey
Roland Humphreys
Mr and Mrs R.A.
  Humphries
Rona Hunnisett
Ms A.J. Hunt
Dr and Mrs D. Hunt
Mrs M. Hunt
D.M. Hunter
C.J. Hurd
J.D.W. Hurd
Mrs Razia B.
  Hussain
Mr Hutcheon
Paul Hutley

Mike Hutton
Colin T. Hyde
Dr M.T. Hyde
Mr and Mrs David
  Hyman
Mrs Ann Hynes
T.J. Hypher
Rosie Inge
Mrs Brenda Innes
Dr D.S. and Mrs
  L.M.C. Irvine
Dr S.D. Iversen
Dr Bruce Jackson
Mrs J.J. Jackson
James McG.
  Jackson
Keith Jackson
S. Jackson
Stephen D. Jackson
David Jacobs
Eric Jaffé
C. Jago
Mrs C. James
Mrs Sandra James
J.R. Jameson
Alastair Jamieson
Miss N. Jarratt
Ms Caroline Jarrett
Moira Jarrett
Michael W. Jarvis
Mrs V. Jarvis
A.J. Jeavons
Roland Jeffery
Richard M. Jenkins
Flt Lt M.D. Jenvey
Michael J. Jervis
David Jervois
Stephen Jessel
Mr and Mrs David
  M. Jinks
M.J.F. Jobbins
B.M. Joce
Gareth Johns
Alison Johnson
Mr and Mrs H.M.
  Johnson
Iris Johnson
Mrs J.K. Johnson
L.S. Johnson
Ms Maureen
  Johnson
V.H. Johnson
Dr and Mrs
  Johnston
Andrew Johnston
Mr and Mrs Bob
  Johnston
Dr I.H.D. Johnston
John Johnston
S.H. Johnston
Audrey Jones
Dr D.M. Jones

David V. Jones
G. and P.R. Jones
Mr and Mrs H.D.
  Jones
Ian Jones
Mrs M.C. Jones
Dr T.E.G. Jones
Mrs V.L. Jones
Charles Joseph
Nathan and Sarah
  Joseph
Mr and Mrs M.
  Joyce
Richard Joyce
M.R. Judd
Jeffrey L. Kalp
A.K. Kameen
Dr Dawn Kanelleas
Drs Leon and Dina
  Kaufman
Mrs J.A. Kay
Jenny Keegan
D. Keel
Francis J. Keenan
Sheila Keene
Mrs Ann Kefalas
Mrs Karen Keil
Peter and Maria
  Kellner
Dr C. Kelly
Frances Kelly
John Kelly
Peter Kelsey
S. Kember
Mr and Mrs J.
  Kempsell
David Kennett-
  Brown
Mr and Mrs J.T.
  Kent
Mrs Jean Kent
C.D. Keogh
Dr Robert Ker
N.R. Kermack
M.P. Kershaw
Mrs D. Kertesz
Mrs I.F. Ketch
H.D. Kettle
Mrs S. Kewley
Sally Kibble
Adam Kightley
Ms P.A. Kilbride
J.H. Kilby
Matthew Kile
H.C. Kimber
Mr and Mrs Peter
  Kimble
Rev A.B.King
Derek King
Lesley King
Mrs N. King
R.S. King

James Kingston-
  Stewart
Mr and Mrs W.A.
  Kinsman
Dr N.J.W. Kippax
Dr I.S. Kiss
Ruth Kitching
P. Klein
Albert Klyne
Mrs Judy Knapp
Dr Anthony
  Knudsen
Norman N. Komar
H.W. Kootstra
Ms H. Kroll
P.D. Kudelka
C.J. Kuhl
Steve and Carole
  Kuhlmann
D.S. Kyle
Ms Dorothy Kyne
I. Laidlaw-Dickson
J.C.E. Laing
R.A. Lakeman
Mrs A.L. Lambert
Ms Joanna Lamiri
L. Landau
C.H. Landon
John Landon
R.D. Lane
Dr C.A. Lang
Mrs P. Lang
Tony and Christine
  Langrick
N. Lank
C.B. Lanyon
Mr and Mrs A.
  Lanzl
Raymond Laren
Dr R.D. Last
Dr David Latto
Mrs R. Lauffer
P.D.N. Laurie
M.J. Lavering
J. and M. Lawrence
M.E. Lawrence
Susanne Lawrence
Ms Sandra Lawson
Norman Lazenby
Mrs Agnes Leach
F.W.B. Leadbetter
Christopher J. Leak
F.J. Lee
Mrs Judy Lee
L. Lee
M.P. Lee
R. Lee
M.J. Leese
Chris H. Lehmann
David Leibling
Lord Leigh
B. Leigh

Mrs S. Miles
L.C. Miller-
Williams
Mrs Catherine Mills
O. S. Mills
Sue Mills
Mrs A. Miln
A.J. Milton
Ms Anthea
Minchom
David Mintz
Alison Mitchell
I.W. Mitchell
Arthur Mole
A. Moliver
Mrs Jean Monks
Ms B.S. di
Monteluce
Miss E. Moody
Vic Moody
Mrs C.M. Moore
D.C. Moore
Mr and Mrs J.
Moore
Mr and Mrs M.
Moore
P. Moore
Patricia Moore
Sheila and Dennis
Moore
Mrs B. Morgan
Kate Morgan
Mrs Lorette Morgan
Rhian Morgan
Mrs Carole Morris
Mrs Deborah
Morris
Mr and Mrs M.J.
Morris
Mr and Mrs
Michael Morris
R.P. Morris
Richard I. Morris
Ms Sian Morris
Dr M.G Moulder
Guy de Moubray
Mr and Mrs W.A.
Moxon
Ian G. Mucklejohn
Stewart Muir
G.T.R. Muir
A. Mumford
Ms Debra Mumford
David Murdoch
J.A. Murphy
Francis Murray
Mrs G.M. Murray
G.R. Murray
Mr and Mrs J.A.
Murray
Mrs M.L. Murray
Smith

D.H. Murrell
A.G. Mursell
Joseph Napolitano
Conrad and
Georgina Natzio
M.H.W. Neal
T. Neate
Mr and Mrs Elden
Neddeau
A.K.H. Nelson
W.L. Nelson
Mrs D.M. Nelstrop
Mr and Mrs. R.V.
Netherclift
C. Netting
Julia Neuberger
Mrs Sylvia
Neumann
Dr T.S. Neumann
Dr Richard Neville
Dr J.M. Newbery
Mrs Maureen
Newey
Charles S. Newman
Emma Newman
Ernest Newton
D. Nicholas
Linda Nicholas
David Nicholls
Ms P.A. Nicholls
R.A. and P.N.
Nicholls
R.G. Nicholls
R. and C. Nisbet
Mrs P. Nixon
J.J. Noble
Mrs Alice Noras
M.C. Norman
J.G. Norris
Graham Norwood
Richard Nourse
Mrs W. Nowell
David Nutt
Mrs E. Nuttall
Graham F. Nutter
G. O'Bryan-Tear
Maurice O'Connor
A.B. O'Dowd
E.W. O'Grady
Dermot O'Hara
N. O'Keefe
Jane and Kevin
O'Mahoney
Les O'Neil
M.J. O'Neil
Paul O'Neill
W.B. O'Neill
Mrs Ashling
O'Reilly
H.D. O'Reilly
B.A. O'Sullivan
A.P. Oakley

Nigel D.J. Oakley
John Oddey
Charles Odenweller
Nicholas Offen
A. Offer
David C.N. Ogilvie
R.A.L. Ogston
A.I. Ogus
H.N. Olden
Dr B. Olding
Mrs Julia Ordford
S.J. Orford
Mrs E. Orme
A.G. Orr
Mrs Patricia Orwell
Jonathan Osborne
Mr and Mrs R.E.
Osborne
George Ottley
B.T. Overall
A.J. Owen
C.M. Owen
Sian Owen
Mark Owen-Ward
Ms Ann Owston
Mrs Dorothea Pace
Mr and Mrs M
Pacitti
B.W. Page
Mrs C.M. Page
Diana Page
Nadia Pallatt
Mr and Mrs T.J.
Pallatt
Mrs K. Palmer
Andrew Parffrey
R. Paris
Dr Richard Parish
Barbara and George
Parker
J.J. Parker
J.M. Parker
Mrs M. Parker
T.R. Parker
J.B. Parkinson
J.D. Parkinson
Michael Parri-
Hughes
Corinne Parry
Mrs Muriel Parsons
D.A. Passey
Miss E. Passon
M.A. Pateman
Mrs I. Paterson
M.H.O. Paterson
R.G. Paterson
Mrs C.J. Paton
Mr and Mrs J.
Patrick
James Patrick
Mrs Brenda
Pattison

Michael Pattison
Dr R.L. Patuck
F.D. de Paula
Miss C. Payne
Michael Payton
A. and R. Peace
E.D.M. Peacock
A.J. Pearce
H.R. Pearce
Mrs P.J. Pearce
C.J. Pearson
D.S. Pearson
John Pearson
Mrs N.C. Pearson
David and Tina
Pease
Mr and Mrs Julian
Peck
G.A. Peel
John Pegler
Stephen Pegler
Charles Pelham
Miss H. Pennant-
Williams
H.F. Pennington
Drs D.B. and D.S.
Pepper
D. Peppercorn
A.J. Periquet
David Pert
P. Peterson
Bruce D. Pettie
Miss Cynthia
Pettiward
Peter Petts
Michael Phelan
Drs Anne and
Andrew Phellas
Alicia Gregg
Phillips
B.J.E. Phillips
C.E. Phillips
Mrs C.N. Phillips
Chris Phillips
Robert and Susan
Phillips
Ms S. Phillips
S.L. Phillips
T.M. Phillips
Mrs I.L. Phillipson
A.M. Pickup
Dr A.D. Picton
Mrs M. Piers-Hall
Gerald and Erica
Pillow
Gerald S. Pitchforth
M.D.W. Pitel
Hugh Pitt
Dr David Pittam
Joann Pitz
Mrs J. Plante Cleall
Mrs Lois J. Plascott

G.J. Platts
P.L. Pleasance
Prof Peter H. Plesch
J. Pliener
Catherine Plummer
A.J.G. and M.L.
Pollard
Brian J. Pollard
Janet Pope
Mrs John Pope
P.S.M. Pope
K. Porteous Wood
J.A. Porter
K.F. Porter
Kathleen J. Porter
David Potter
Dr J.M. Potter
B.M. Powell
Joan A. Powell
Michael Power
Helen and Anthony
Powers
Mrs P.J. Powis
Dr and Mrs S.R. Da
Prato
Mrs Carol Pratt
Mrs Gillian Pratt
D.B. Prell
M.J. Prendergast
Mrs R. Pressberg
Mrs M. Prettejohns
Dr and Mrs D.B.
Price
G.V. Price
Mrs V. Prifti
Peter J. Prior
J.F. Pritchard
A. Procter
M.A. Proctor
Mrs E. Prosser
Andrew Proud
W.R. Proudfoot
C.L. Pugh
Mrs A. Pulfer
Pippa Purcell
Chris Purchase
C. Purslow
Mrs Linda Pyne
Dr Anthony Quastel
J.J. Quinn
Dudley Quirk
Mrs B. Quirke
H. Rabinowitz
Mrs Gillian Radford
Ms Ingrid Radford
Mrs J.C. Radice
Ms Jean Rainey
Luke and Anne
Rainey
A. Rampton
Dr and Mrs D.G.S.
Randall

Mr and Mrs G.P.
Ransome
Mrs Caroline
Raphael
Peter Ratzer
Simon Raven
Marc Rawcliffe
Mrs Mary Rayner
Christopher
McCartney Read
M. Ready
Mrs Jane Reddish
Dr A.R. Reece
D. Reed
Dr J. Reed
Miss P.H. Reed
A.I. Rees
Mr and Mrs M.C.
Rees
Mrs R.I. Reeves
Christopher R.M.
Reeves
John Reid
Mrs Sarah Reid
Dr and Mrs W.
Reith
M.W. Reynolds
Mrs Siobhan
Reynolds
D.B. Richards
J.M. Richards
Simon Richards
C.J. Richardson
David Richardson
Mrs Katharine
Richardson
P.D.I. Richardson
W.T. Richardson
Dr David Rickards
G.K. Rickett
Carol Riddick
Lloyd C. Ridgwell
P.P. Riggs
Gordon Ringrose
Dr B. Ritson
Bruce Roberts
Ms Claire Roberts
Mrs Elaine Roberts
Ms Jane Roberts
Muriel Roberts
Mrs P.A. Roberts
Mrs A.M.
Robertson
Mrs Bronwyn
Robertson
J.C. Robertson
Mr and Mrs John
Robertson
Mr and Mrs Nigel
Robertson
A.E. Robinson
Ian Robinson

L.T. Robinson
Derek Robson
J. Rochelle
Mrs J. Roddy
Charles N. Rogers
Mrs Nina Roland
Mrs N. Rooks
Arthur Rooms
Ms F. Rooney
Mrs Clare Rose
Daniel Rose
Dr Eric Rose
Iain Rose
Mr and Mrs Jeffery
Rose
Mrs A. Rosenfeld
Mrs Cicely M. Ross
Gillian Ross
Nicholas Ross
W.H. Ross
P.E. Rosser
Veronica Rossignol
K. Rossiter
P.I. Rossiter
Mr Rothwell
E.I. Rout
Mrs Virginia Routh
David and Diana
Rowlands
G. Rowley
Jill Rowley
Mr and Mrs
Rowlinson
R.C. Rowson
B.B. Roy
Angela M. Royle
Ian Royle
Peter Rozee
A.J. Rugg
J.A. Rumble
M. Rushton
J.S. Russ
Alexander B.
Russell
Mrs Clare Russell
David Russell
H. Russell
Prof J.K. Russell
Mr and Mrs R.E.P.
Russell
Andrew Rutherford
Mrs R. Rutter
J.M. Ryan
R.S. Ryder
Miss B. Ryrie
C.R. Samms
Mrs Samuel
M. Samuel
O.W. Samuel
J.E.A. Samuels
P. Sanders
Margaret Sandra

Miss Louise Sargent
C.J.P. Saunders
D.M.St.G. Saunders
Peter Saunders
P.L. Saunders-
Griffiths,
P. Sauzier
John W. Savery
George Sayer
Peter Sayers
Ms Sally Saysell
W.D. Scantlebury
Mrs J. Schafer
Prof P.J. Scheuer
Tony Schneider
Michael Schofield
H. Scholes
Alexander
Schouvaloff
Mrs Corinne
Schuler
R. Schwarz
Lady Scott
Mrs Alison Scott
Mrs Ann Scott
Dr Ian G. Scott
J.G.J. Scott
Dr J.M. Scott
Prof J.S. Scott
Dr N. Scott
P.D. Scott
R.J. Scott
Stella Scott
Dr T. Scott
Mr and Mrs W.P.
Scott
Mr and Mrs B.
Scragg
Mrs J.S. Scragg
B. Scrutton
Marc J. Seale
Ms Eithne Scallan
Philip Seaman
Mrs S.A. Searles
J.R.E. Sedgwick
Ms Ursula
Sedgwick
B.A. Segal
Peter Seglow
R.A.N. Segrave
Mrs Henri Selmer
Ms A. Sennett
J.M. Sennett
Ms Philippa Sethi
Dr M. Severn
Mrs D.M. Shalit
Brian Shallom
James Shanks
Dr C.W. Sharp
Mr and Mrs R.
Sharp
Robin Sharp

Stephen Sharp
D. and S. Shaw
Hilary Shaw
Mrs Veronica Shaw
The Very Rev D.J.
Shearlock
Barry Sheerman
Mrs Gillian Sheffer
Mrs A.V. Shelley
Mrs H.J. Shepperd
Louise Sheppard
Howard Sherman
S. Sherwood
K. Shield
Miss H.J. Shields
Mr James
Shorrocks
Paul J. Short
Mr and Mrs G.
Short
Ellis D. Shortt
S.P.Shrimpton
Dr and Mrs T.E.
Sicks
Jo Silburn
N.F. Silby
Michael J. Silver
P.H. Simon
A.B. and C.
Simpson
Mrs O. Simpson
R.J. Sims
Ms Anne Sinclair
R. Sinclair-Taylor
Arlette and Brian
Singleton
A.M. Sinnott
P.M. Sivell
Mrs D.M.
Sivewright
Ms Francesca
Skelton
Peter Skinnard
Mrs Wendy Skones
D.A. Slade
Mr and Mrs. R.F.
Slade
Mrs C.S. Slaski
Mrs K. Slay
J.T. Slevin
Simon Small
N.S.L. Smart
Roz Smart
Charles Smedley
Mrs C. Smith
Craig Smith
Dr D.A. Smith
D.C. Smith
David Smith
F.M.K. Smith
Ian and Sheila
Smith

John R. Smith
Kay Smith
Kenneth E. Smith
Lance Smith
Margaret Smith
Pamela Smith
Philip Smith
R.A. Smith
Robin Smith
Mrs S.C. Smith
T.A. Smith
W.M. Smith
Martha Smith-
Spencer
A.J.M. Smithson
Mr and Mrs J.
Smyth
Miss P.M. Snell
Mr and Mrs T.
Snowball
Ms Zak Solomon
Dr B. Solomons
G. Solomons
E.V. Somers
Ms Suzanne Sontar
Mrs E.M. Southey
Mrs V.M. Sowle
Dr C.V. Sowter
Mr and Mrs P.W.
Spacey
Mrs Monika
Sparham
Alan Spedding
Dr M.E. Speechly-
Dick
Mrs G. Spencer
Martha Smith
Spencer
Dr Chris Spencer-
Jones
J.F. Spinlove
B. and C. Spratt
L. Squire
Mrs Felicity Stanak
H.J. Standen
J.R.P. Staniforth
Sybella Stanley
J. Stanley-Smith
T.J.G. Stannus
Mrs F.J. Stasiak
Mrs Daphne
Statham
A.J. Stead
John Stead
Dr G. Steadman
P.J. Stedman
Mrs G.M. Stein,
F.M. Steiner
Dr J. Steinert
P. Stephens
A.M. Stephenson
R.F. Stephenson

D.R. Stevens
Malcolm Stevens
Richard Stevens
John Stevenson
Sylvia Stevenson
Dr and Mrs J.
Stewart
Capt and Mrs J.S.
Stewart
Dr R.H.M. Stewart
R.J. Stewart
S. Stewart
Stephen Stockton
A.C. Stoker
Mr and Mrs A L
Stone
Mr and Mrs C.M.
Stooke
D.W. Stooke
Mary Stow
J. Stratton
J.W. Straw
Mrs J.M. Streat
Hilary and Malcom
Strong
Prof and Mrs A.E.
Stuart
Douglas Stuart
Dr Clive Stubbings
Hugh Stubbs
R.F. Stupples
Allan Sturmer
H. Style
C.J. Styles-Power
Michael Sullivan
A. Sutton
Geoffrey Sutton
Mr and Mrs R.A.
Sutton
S.P. Swaby
Charles H.
Swartwout
M. Swingler
Ms Brenda Symes
Cdr Patrick
Tailyour
Ms Anne Tait
Thomas T. Tait
Mr and Mrs John
Talbot
J.A. Tarrant
Drs M.J. and E.J.
Tarsh
D.W. Tate
Mr and Mrs M.B.
Tate
Dr P.H. Tattersall
Mrs J.A. Taylar
A. Taylor
Mrs A.C. Taylor
D.J. Taylor
Mrs J. Taylor

Mrs J.A. Taylor
Ms Jean Taylor
John and Eileen
Taylor
Mrs Julia Taylor
M.G.M. Taylor
Mr and Mrs P.
Taylor
S. Taylor
Mr and Mrs Steven
Taylor
T.W. Taylor
Richard C. Teasel
John Teenan
Mrs D.C. Terrell
T.C. Thackray
D.A. and H.V. Thain
J. Thellusson
Russell Thersby
A.I. Thomas
Alan Thomas
D. Thomas
Prof E.J. Thomas
Fred Thomas
J.W. Thomas
James Thomas
James M. and
Jenny Thomas
R. Thomas
R.E. Thomas
Rebecca Thomas
Mrs V.E. Thomas
David Thompson
Dawn Thompson
Mrs H. Thompson
Ms Jacqueline
Thompson
Mrs L.C. Thompson
Miles M. Thompson
Mrs D.M. Thomson
Mr and Mrs R.S.
Thomson
Mrs C. Thorne
Ms Sue Thorne
D. Thornton
G.N. Thornton
Sir Peter Thornton
Michael Thursfield
G. Thwaites
Louise Thynne
Rory Tierney
Harold Tillek
Mrs Marigold Tilly
Margaret Tillyard
H. Tint
Mrs Marjorie
Tipton
Prof M.S. Tite
Julian Tobin
Mrs Jan Todd
Julian M. Tollast
F. Tomlin

Dr D.R. Tomlinson
Michael Tomlinson
Mrs Jean Toper-Gray
J.P.S. Tottman
A. Towler
A.T. Townley
Dr Peter J. Travis
E. Tre-Vett
Mrs S. Trench
Chris and Karen Trinder
Victoria Trombetta
Nick Tsatsas
D. Robert Tucker
James H. Tucker
Mr and Mrs Andrew Tugwell
Ian Tunnacliffe
Mrs R.W.C. Tunnicliffe
Adrian Turner
Mrs Barbara Turner
Mrs Brenda Turner
Mr and Mrs G. Turner
M.A. Turner
Marion Turner
P.E. Turner
Mrs Pauline Turner
Stuart Turner
J.S. Turpin
Eric Turrell
Ms Debbie Tyler
N.O. Tyler
I. Tysh
Adrian Underwood
M.R. Underwood
Dr G. Undrill
I.M.W. Ure
D.B. Uren
Susan and Laurence Usiskin
K.A. Uttley
Thomas Vacara
Patricia Valentine
B. Van Gulik
Jaako Vanhatalo
Gloria Varley
M.A. Varley
Mrs L. Veitch
G.S. Venables
W.R. Venner
A.C. Verdie
Dirk Vermeulen
P.M. Village
Ms Suzanne Viner
Sidney Vines
Mr and Mrs. R.N. Vingoe
R.J.S. and D.M. Vobe

Diana Vowles
Dr M.H.G. Waddington
D.G. Wadsworth
Mr and Mrs E. Walker
Mrs K. Walker
Mark Walker
Mrs Val Walker-Dendle
M. Wall
Mrs P. Wallace
Dr M.V. Wallbank
Mr and Mrs Waller
James A. Waller
Dr Robert Waller
E.G. Walsh
Thomas Walsh
W.J. Walter
Alan Walter
N.R. Walton
Barbara Want
Mr and Mrs David Ward
G.A.B. Ward
K.G. Ward
T.E. and D.J. Ward-Hall
A.J. Wardrop
Mr and Mrs Peter Ware
Miss S. Warne
Mrs K. Warner
Mrs G.M. Warren
Mrs S.L. Warren
G.M. Warrington
Mrs Pat Warrington
Ms Jane Warrington-Smith
Mrs C.N. Warrington-Smyth
Toshio Watanabe
J.J. Waters
Susan Watkin
J.H. Watkins
Annabel Watson
Brian Watson
Hilary Watson
Mrs J.R. Watson
John S.L.Watson
Stephen Watson
Jessie L. Watters
Mr and Mrs E.K. Watts
Mr and Mrs N.M. Watts
Mrs Jayne Weaver
Allen J. Webb
John F. N. Wedge
Mrs G. Weir

Dr B.H. Wells
D.R. Wells
Dr Frank Wells
R.A. Wells
Mrs Jennie Wendon
Ms Barbara Wensworth
Mrs D.I.H. West
I.E. West
J.F.M. West
M.J. West
Sarah Weston
Mrs M. Wettern
Mr and Mrs M.J. Wevill
Dr K. Whale
Robert Wharton
S.T. Wharton
Kate Wheeldon
John Wheeler
Ben Whitaker
E.H. Whitaker
G.T. Whitaker
Dr David R. Whitbread
E. Clifford White
Mr and Mrs Colin White
James White
Mrs Jean White
N.H. White
Mrs R.G. Whitham
Mr and Mrs Whiting
D.P. Whittaker
Paul Whittaker
J. Whittick
D. A Whitworth
John Whyte
S.W. Whytehead
P.R. Widgery
Lord Wigoder
Arthur Wilbraham
R.N. Wilby
A.R. Wild
D. Wileman
Shani Wileman
Derek A. Wiley
M. Wilkie
John B. Wilkin
Anthony Wilkinson
Hugh Wilkinson
Prof Shelagh Wilkinson
Prof Yorick Wilks
P. Willer
K. William-Powlett
A.N. Williams
Alan E. Williams
B.J.Williams
C.D. Williams
Dr E. Williams

J.R. Williams
Mr and Mrs John Williams
Dr and Mrs R. Williams
R.H. Wiliams
Mr and Mrs R.W. Williams
Siriol Williams
Steven D. Williams
Mr and Mrs.J.R. Williamson
Liz Williamson
Mr and Mrs M. J. Williets
Mrs Jean Willson
A.R. Wilson
Mrs Anita Wilson
Anna C. Wilson
Nicholas J. Wilson
M. Wilson
Prof P.N. Wilson
Peter and Shirley Wilson
Jenny Wilson-Jones
Mrs Willy
Janet Wilston
Wouter L. Wilton
Peter Wimbush
Jane J. Windsong
F.J. Winkley
Dr Windsor
Mrs Anna Witham
John Withers
D.E. Witts
Mrs Jean Wix
Mrs Jill Wolfe
Kevin Wong
G.S. Wood
Mr and Mrs M.G. Wood
Mr and Mrs N.A. Wood
Sharon and Nicolas Wood
M. Woodgate
Mrs M. Woodhead
Mrs A.D. Woodhouse
David Woods
Barbara M. Wooldridge
R.C. Woolgrove
Mrs Anne Woolhouse
Thomas Woolrych
Alan Worsdale
J.A. Worsfold
Nicholas Wraight
Mr and Mrs P. Wraight

Mary V. Wraith
John Wratten
Andrew Wright
Mrs Carolyn Wright
G.L. Wright
Dr Harold Wright
Mrs Irene Wright

Mr and Mrs
 Stephen Wright
Alan Wyatt
Mr and Mrs L.P.
 Wyatt
R.A. Wyld
Sally Wyllie

Mrs S.J. Wynn
Dr D.P. Yates
Geoffrey Yates
John Yates
Patricia York
P.T. Young
Nan Youngman

Dr J.S. Yudkin
Dr D.P. Yules
Ms Yasmeen Zafar
B. Zimm

# Alphabetical list of main entries

Abbey Green, Chester, Cheshire
Adams Café, London W12
Adare Manor, Adare, Co Limerick
Adlard's, Norwich, Norfolk
Airds Hotel, Port Appin, Strathclyde
Ajimura, London WC2
Alastair Little, London W1
Alba, London EC1
Albero & Grana, London SW3
Al Bustan, London SW1
Alexandra, London SW20
Alfonso's, Cookham, Berkshire
Alfred's, Louth, Lincolnshire
Al Hamra, London W1
All Saints, London W11
Al San Vincenzo, London W2
Al-Shami, Oxford, Oxfordshire
Altnaharrie Inn, Ullapool, Highland
Amber Regent, Glasgow, Strathclyde
Amberley Castle, Queen's Room, Amberley, West Sussex
Angel Inn, Hetton, North Yorkshire
Angel Hotel, Midhurst, West Sussex
Angel Inn, Stoke-by-Nayland, Suffolk
Angel Inn, Long Crendon, Buckinghamshire
Ann FitzGerald's Farmhouse Kitchen, Mathry, Dyfed
Anna's Place, London N1
Annie's, Ballydehob, Co Cork

Annie's, Moreton-in-Marsh, Gloucestershire
Annie's, Swansea, West Glamorgan
Apple Cottage, Rozel, Jersey
Arbutus Lodge, Cork, Co Cork
Ard-Na-Coille, Newtonmore, Highland
Ardsheal House, Kentallen, Highland
Argyll, London SW3
Arisaig House, Arisaig, Highland
Arisugawa, London W1
Ark, Erpingham, Norfolk
Arkle, Chester Grosvenor Hotel, Chester, Cheshire
Armadillo, Liverpool, Merseyside
Armenian, Granada Hotel, Manchester, Greater Manchester
Armless Dragon, Cardiff, South Glamorgan
Armstrongs, Barnsley, South Yorkshire
Arundell Arms, Lifton, Devon
Les Associés, London N8
Assolas Country House, Kanturk, Co Cork
Au Jardin des Gourmets, London W1
L'Auberge, Edinburgh, Lothian
Auberge de Provence, St James's Court Hotel, London SW1
Auberge de Seneirl, Bushmills, Co Antrim
Auctioneer, Clitheroe, Lancashire
Austins, Aldeburgh, Suffolk
L'Aventure, London NW8

Aynsome Manor, Cartmel, Cumbria
Ayudhya, Kingston upon Thames, Surrey
Bahn Thai, London W1
Baile-Na-Cille, Uig, Highland
Ballathie House, Kinclaven, Tayside
Ballymaloe House, Shanagarry, Co Cork
La Barbe Encore, Cranleigh, Surrey
Barnaby's Restaurant, Exmouth, Devon
Barnards, Cosham, Hampshire
Barton Cross, Huxham, Devon
Bath Place Hotel, Oxford, Oxfordshire
Bath Spa Hotel, Vellore Restaurant, Bath, Avon
Baumann's Brasserie, Coggeshall, Essex
Bay Horse, Ulverston, Cumbria
Bayview Hotel, Cullen, Grampian
Beadles, Birkenhead, Merseyside
Beaujolais, Bath, Avon
Bedlington Café, London W4
Beech Hill Country House Hotel, Londonderry, Co Londonderry
Beechwood Country House Hotel, Moffat, Dumfries & Galloway
Beetle & Wedge, Moulsford, Oxfordshire
Belgo, London NW1
Bell, Aston Clinton, Buckinghamshire
Bell's Diner, Bristol, Avon

La Belle Alliance, Blandford Forum, Dorset

La Belle Epoque, Belfast, Co Antrim

Bentley's, London W1

La Bergerie, Harrogate, North Yorkshire

Bertorelli's, London WC2

Beth's, London NW3

Bibendum, London SW3

Bilbrough Manor, Bilbrough, North Yorkshire

Billboard Café, London NW6

Billesley Manor, Billesley, Warwickshire

Billy Budd's, Dartmouth, Devon

Bishopstrow House, Warminster, Wiltshire

Y Bistro, Llanberis, Gwynedd

Bistro Montparnasse, Southsea, Hampshire

Bistrot Bruno, London W1

Bistrot 190, London SW7

Black Bull Inn, Moulton, North Yorkshire

Black Chapati, Brighton, East Sussex

Black House, Hexham, Northumberland

Black Swan, Beckingham, Lincolnshire

Blackwater Hotel, Le Champenois, West Mersea, Essex

Blair's Cove House, Durrus, Co Cork

Blostin's, Shepton Mallet, Somerset

Blue Elephant, London SW6

Blue Goose, Settle, North Yorkshire

Blue Haven, Kinsale, Co Cork

Blueprint Café, London SE1

Boar's Head, Ripley, North Yorkshire

Bobby's, Leicester, Leicestershire

Bodysgallen Hall, Llandudno, Gwynedd

Bombay Brasserie, London SW7

Boncompte's, Douglas, Isle of Man

Bonnets Bistro, Cheltenham, Gloucestershire

Les Bouviers, Merley, Dorset

Bowlish House, Shepton Mallet, Somerset

Box Tree, Ilkley, West Yorkshire

Boyd's, London W8

Brackenbury, London W6

Bradfield House, Bradfield Combust, Suffolk

Brady's, London SW18

Braeval Old Mill, Aberfoyle, Central

La Braseria, Swansea, West Glamorgan

La Brasserie, Cardiff, South Glamorgan

Brasserie du Marché aux Puces, London W10

Brasserie Faubourg, London SW8

Brasserie Forty Four, Leeds, West Yorkshire

Breamish House, Fowburn, Northumberland

Bridge End, Hayfield, Derbyshire

Bridgefield House, Spark Bridge, Cumbria

Bridge House, Beaminster, Dorset

Brockencote Hall, Chaddesley Corbett, Hereford & Worcester

Brook's, Brighouse, West Yorkshire

Brown's, Worcester, Hereford & Worcester

Browns Brasserie, Southampton, Hampshire

Browns Hotel, Haddington, Lothian

Bruernes Lock, Stoke Bruerne, Northamptonshire

Buchan's, London SW11

Buckland Manor, Buckland, Gloucestershire

Buckland-Tout-Saints Hotel, Queen Anne, Kingsbridge, Devon

Burlington Restaurant, Devonshire Arms, Bolton Abbey, North Yorkshire

Burrastow House, Walls, Shetland

Bu San, London N7

But'n'Ben, Auchmithie, Tayside

Buttery, Glasgow, Strathclyde

Buzkash, London SW15

By Appointment, Norwich, Norfolk

Le Cadre, London N8

Café des Arts, London NW3

Café du Moulin, St Peter's, Guernsey

Café Fish, London SW1

Café Gandolfi, Glasgow, Strathclyde

Café Niçoise, Colwyn Bay, Clwyd

Café Royal, London W1

Café Volnay, Porthoustock, Cornwall

Calcot Manor, Tetbury, Gloucestershire

Callow Hall, Ashbourne, Derbyshire

Cameron House Hotel, Alexandria, Strathclyde

Camerons, Glasgow Hilton, Glasgow, Strathclyde

Canteen, London SW10

Cantina del Ponte, London SE1

Capers, Torquay, Devon

The Capital, London SW3

Capriccio, Taunton, Somerset

Le Caprice, London SW1

Carved Angel, Dartmouth, Devon

Casale Franco, London N1

Cashel House Hotel, Cashel, Co Galway

Castle Cottage, Harlech, Gwynedd

Castle Hotel, Taunton, Somerset

Cedar Restaurant, Evesham Hotel, Evesham, Hereford & Worcester

Cellar, Anstruther, Fife

Cemlyn, Harlech, Gwynedd

Champany Inn, Linlithgow, Lothian

Le Champenois, Blackwater Hotel, West Mersea, Essex

Champers, Cardiff, South Glamorgan (see entry for La Brasserie)

Droveway, Chichester, West Sussex

Druidstone Hotel, Broad Haven, Dyfed

Drum and Monkey, Harrogate, North Yorkshire

Drumnacree House Hotel, Alyth, Tayside

Duffin's, Kendal, Cumbria

Dunain Park, Inverness, Highland

Dundas Arms, Kintbury, Berkshire

Dunworley Cottage, Clonakilty, Co Cork

Dusty Miller, Low Laithe, North Yorkshire

Dwyers, Waterford, Co Waterford

Dylanwad Da, Dolgellau, Gwynedd

Eagle, London EC1

Eastern Promise, Grampound, Cornwall

Eastern Tandoori, Dublin, Co Dublin

Eastwell Manor, Boughton Lees, Kent

L'Ecluse, New Haw, Surrey

Edderton Hall, Forden, Powys

Ees Wyke, Near Sawrey, Cumbria

Efes Kebab House, London W1

El Nido, Forton, Lancashire

Elio's, Barton-on-Humber, Humberside

The Elms, Abberley, Hereford & Worcester

Endeavour, Staithes, North Yorkshire

English Garden, London SW3

Epicurean, Cheltenham, Gloucestershire

Epworth Tap, Epworth, Humberside

L'Escargot, London W1

Eslington Villa Hotel, Gateshead, Tyne & Wear

Esseborne Manor, Hurstbourne Tarrant, Hampshire

L'Estaminet, London WC2

Evesham Hotel, Cedar Restaurant, Evesham, Hereford & Worcester

The Exchange, Dartmouth, Devon

Exeter Arms, Easton on the Hill, Northamptonshire

Fantails, Wetheral, Cumbria

Faraday's, Aberdeen, Grampian

Farlam Hall, Brampton, Cumbria

Farm Gate, Midleton, Co Cork

Faulkner's, London E8

Feathers Hotel, Woodstock, Oxfordshire

Feldon House, Lower Brailes, Warwickshire

Fifehead Manor, Middle Wallop, Hampshire

Fifteen North Parade, Oxford, Oxfordshire

Fifth Floor, London SW1

First Floor, London W11

Fischer's at Baslow Hall, Baslow, Derbyshire

Fish at Sutton Courtenay, Sutton Courtenay, Oxfordshire

Fisherman's Lodge, Newcastle upon Tyne, Tyne & Wear

Fishes', Burnham Market, Norfolk

La Fleur de Lys, Shaftesbury, Dorset

Flitwick Manor, Flitwick, Bedfordshire

Floodlite Restaurant, Masham, North Yorkshire

Florians, London N8

Food for Thought, Fowey, Cornwall

Forsters, East Boldon, Tyne & Wear

Forte Crest, Jules' Bar and American Grill, Glasgow, Strathclyde

Fountain House, Dedham, Essex

Four Seasons, London W2

Four Seasons, Wheatsheaf Hotel, Swinton, Borders

Four Seasons Hotel, London W1

Fox and Goose, Fressingfield, Suffolk

French House, London W1

French Partridge, Horton, Northamptonshire

Frères Jacques, Dublin, Co Dublin

Fumi, Gateshead, Tyne & Wear

Fung Shing, London WC2

Funnywayt'mekalivin, Berwick-upon-Tweed, Northumberland

Gales, Llangollen, Clwyd

Galley, Swanage, Dorset

Gannets Bistrot, Newark, Nottinghamshire

Garlands, Bath, Avon

La Gaulette, London W1

Le Gavroche, London W1

Gavvers, London SW1

Gay Hussar, London W1

Gaylord, Manchester, Greater Manchester

Gemini, Tadworth, Surrey

General Havelock Inn, Haydon Bridge, Northumberland

George Hotel, Stamford, Lincolnshire

George and Dragon, Burpham, West Sussex

George & Dragon, Rowde, Wiltshire

Gidleigh Park, Chagford, Devon

Gilbert's, London SW7

Gilpin Lodge, Windermere, Cumbria

Ginger Hill, Milngavie, Strathclyde

Ginger Tree, Ballyclare, Co Antrim

Glasgow Hilton, Camerons, Glasgow, Strathclyde

Gopal's of Soho, London W1

Le Gourmet, Newark, Nottinghamshire

Grafton Manor, Bromsgrove, Hereford & Worcester

Grahame's Seafare, London W1

Granada Hotel, Armenian, Manchester, Greater Manchester

Granary, Wexford, Co Wexford

Granita, London N1

Gravetye Manor, East Grinstead, West Sussex

Great House, Lavenham, Suffolk

LIST OF MAIN ENTRIES

Le Meridien Hotel, Oak Room, London W1
Le Mesurier, London EC1
Mezzaluna New York, London WC2
Michael's, Bristol, Avon
Michael's Nook, Grasmere, Cumbria
Michels', Ripley, Surrey
Middlethorpe Hall, York, North Yorkshire
Midsummer House, Cambridge, Cambridgeshire
Mijanou, London SW1
Milk House, Montacute, Somerset
Mill at Harvington, Harvington, Hereford & Worcester
Miller Howe, Windermere, Cumbria
Miller Howe Café, Windermere, Cumbria
Millers, The Bistro, Harrogate, North Yorkshire
Mims, Barnet, Hertfordshire
Minffordd Hotel, Talyllyn, Gwynedd
Mirabelle, Grand Hotel, Eastbourne, East Sussex
Mr Kong, London WC2
Mr Underhill's, Stonham, Suffolk
Mitsukoshi, London SW1
Miyama, London W1
Mock Turtle, Dorchester, Dorset
Le Monde, Cardiff, South Glamorgan (see entry for La Brasserie)
Monkeys, London SW3
Mon Plaisir, London WC2
Moon, Kendal, Cumbria
Moonacre, Alderholt, Dorset
Moorings, Wells-next-the-Sea, Norfolk
Morels, Haslemere, Surrey
Moreteyne Manor, Marston Moretaine, Bedfordshire
Morston Hall, Morston, Norfolk
Mortimer's, Bury St Edmunds, Suffolk
Mortimer's on the Quay, Ipswich, Suffolk

Moss Nook, Manchester, Greater Manchester
Mount Falcon Castle, Ballina, Co Mayo
Moyglare Manor, Maynooth, Co Kildare
Mulberry Room, Torquay, Devon
Muset, Bristol, Avon
Museum Street Café, London WC1
Nansidwell Country House, Mawnan Smith, Cornwall
Nantyffin Cider Mill Inn, Crickhowell, Powys
Neal Street Restaurant, London WC2
Neil's, Tavistock, Devon
Le Neptune, Sheffield, South Yorkshire
Neshiko, London N1
Netherfield Place, Netherfield, East Sussex
New Hall, Sutton Coldfield, West Midlands
New Loon Fung, London W1
Newport House, Newport, Co Mayo
New Regatta, Aldeburgh, Suffolk
New World, London W1
Nick's Warehouse, Belfast, Co Antrim
Nico Central, London W1
Nightingales, Petersham Hotel, Richmond, Surrey
19 Grape Lane, York, North Yorkshire
Normandie, Birtle, Greater Manchester
Northcote Manor, Langho, Lancashire
Noughts'n'Crosses, London W5
Now & Zen, London WC2
Number One Wind Street, Swansea, West Glamorgan
Number Thirty Three, Perth, Tayside
No.3, Glastonbury, Somerset
Nunsmere Hall, Sandiway, Cheshire
O'Grady's, Clifden, Co Galway

Oak Room, Le Meridien Hotel, London W1
Oakes, Stroud, Gloucestershire
The Oaks, Craigendarroch Hotel, Ballater, Grampian
Ockenden Manor, Cuckfield, West Sussex
Odette's, London NW1
O'Keefe's, London W1
Old Beams, Waterhouses, Staffordshire
Old Boot House, Shotley, Suffolk
Old Deanery, Ripon, North Yorkshire
Ye Olde Bulls Head, Beaumaris, Gwynedd
Old Fire Engine House, Ely, Cambridgeshire
Old Forge, Storrington, West Sussex
Old Hoops, Saffron Walden, Essex
Old House, Wickham, Hampshire
Old Manor House, Romsey, Hampshire
Old Monastery, Drybridge, Grampian
Old Parsonage, Oxford, Oxfordshire
Old Rectory, Campsea Ash, Suffolk
Old Rectory, Llansanffraid Glan Conwy, Gwynedd
Old Rectory, Wicklow, Co Wicklow
Old Vicarage, Ridgeway, Derbyshire
Old Vicarage, Witherslack, Cumbria
Old Vicarage Hotel, Worfield, Shropshire
Old Woolhouse, Northleach, Gloucestershire
Olive Tree, Leeds, West Yorkshire
Olive Tree, Queensberry Hotel, Bath, Avon
Olivo, London SW1
One Devonshire Gardens, Glasgow, Strathclyde
192, London W11
Orangery, Chiseldon House Hotel, Chiseldon, Wiltshire
Orso, London WC2

L'Ortolan, Shinfield, Berkshire

Osborne Hotel, Langtry's, Torquay, Devon

Osteria Antica Bologna, London SW11

Osteria Basilico, London W11

Ostlers Close, Cupar, Fife

Panda Si Chuen, London W1

Paris, Leeds, West Yorkshire

Paris House, Woburn, Bedfordshire

Park Hotel, Kenmare, Co Kerry

La Parmigiana, Glasgow, Strathclyde

Partners Brasserie, North Cheam, Surrey

Partners West Street, Dorking, Surrey

Il Passetto, London WC2

Patrick Guilbaud, Dublin, Co Dublin

Paul's, Folkestone, Kent

Pavilion, Consett, Co Durham

Paysanne, Deganwy, Gwynedd

Pearl, London SW1

Pearl City, Manchester, Greater Manchester

Peat Inn, Peat Inn, Fife

Peat Spade Inn, Longstock, Hampshire

Le Pêcheur at the Anglers, Walton-on-Thames, Surrey

Penhelig Arms Hotel, Aberdovey, Gwynedd

Penmaenuchaf Hall, Penmaenpool, Gwynedd

Pennypots, Blackwater, Cornwall

Penrhos Court, Kington, Hereford & Worcester

Perkins Bar Bistro, Plumtree, Nottinghamshire

Perry's, Weymouth, Dorset

Il Pescatore, Worcester, Hereford & Worcester

Petersham Hotel, Nightingales, Richmond, Surrey

Le Petit Canard, Maiden Newton, Dorset

Le Petit Max, Hampton Wick, Greater London

Le P'tit Normand, London SW18

Le Petit Pierrot, Claygate, Surrey

La Petite Auberge, Great Missenden, Buckinghamshire

La Petite Maison, Bottesford, Leicestershire

Pheasant Inn, Keyston, Cambridgeshire

Pheasants, Ross-on-Wye, Hereford & Worcester

Phuket, London SW11

Pied-à-Terre, London W1

Pier at Harwich, Harwich, Essex

Pierre Victoire, Edinburgh, Lothian

Pierre Victoire, London SW15

Pig'n'Fish, St Ives, Cornwall

Pink Geranium, Melbourn, Cambridgeshire

Pizzeria Castello, London SE1

Pizzeria Condotti, London W1

Les Plantagenêts, Leamington Spa, Warwickshire

Planters, Malvern Wells, Hereford & Worcester

Plas Bodegroes, Pwllheli, Gwynedd

Plumber Manor, Sturminster Newton, Dorset

Polmaily House Hotel, Drumnadrochit, Highland

Le Pont de la Tour, London SE1

Pool Court, Pool in Wharfedale, West Yorkshire

Poons, London WC2

Pophams, Winkleigh, Devon

Poppies, The Roebuck, Brimfield, Hereford & Worcester

Porth Tocyn Hotel, Abersoch, Gwynedd

Porthole Eating House, Bowness-on-Windermere, Cumbria

Portmeirion Hotel, Portmeirion, Gwynedd

Poston Mill, Vowchurch, Hereford & Worcester

La Potinière, Gullane, Lothian

Le Poussin, Brockenhurst, Hampshire

Priory Hotel, Bath, Avon

Priory Hotel, Wareham, Dorset

Le Provençale, Whitley Bay, Tyne & Wear

Quaglino's, London SW1

Quails, Chobham, Surrey

Quality Chop House, London EC1

Quan Ju De, Manchester, Greater Manchester

Quayles, Cardiff, South Glamorgan

Queen Anne, Buckland-Tout-Saints Hotel, Kingsbridge, Devon

Queensberry Hotel, Olive Tree, Bath, Avon

Queen's Head, Glanwydden, Gwynedd

Queen's Room, Amberley Castle, Amberley, West Sussex

Quince & Medlar, Cockermouth, Cumbria

Quincy's, Seaford, East Sussex

Ragam, London W1

Ramore, Portrush, Co Antrim

Ramsbottom Victuallers Company Ltd, Village Restaurant, Ramsbottom, Greater Manchester

Rampsbeck Country House Hotel, Watermillock, Cumbria

Randells, Launceston, Cornwall

Rani, London N3

Rankins', Sissinghurst, Kent

Ransome's Dock, London SW11

Read's, Faversham, Kent

Redmond's, Cleeve Hill, Gloucestershire